LF

The Handbook For
No-Load
FUND
INVESTORS

Fifteenth Annual Edition

By Sheldon Jacobs and the editors of
The No-Load Fund Investor—the complete
no-load mutual fund advisory service.

Editor-in-chief/**Sheldon Jacobs**
Statistical editor/**Marc Nugent**
Directory editor/**Earle Marsh**

Fifteenth Edition. Printed in the United States of America

The No-Load Fund Investor, Inc. is not associated with the management or sale of any mutual fund, nor with any mutual fund association. The *Investor's* sole objective is to present unbiased information about funds. The data contained herein have been obtained from the mutual funds themselves and from other sources believed reliable. Although carefully verified, data and compilations are not guaranteed. Readers desiring information about a particular fund should examine the fund's prospectus. Performance results do not take into account any tax consequences and are not, in or of themselves, predictive of future performance. *The Handbook For No-Load Fund Investors* is designed to provide accurate and authoritative information in regard to the subject matter covered. It is sold with the understanding that neither the author nor the publisher renders legal or accounting advice. If legal advice or other expert assistance is required, the services of a competent professional person should be sought.

If you have any suggestions for future editions of this *Handbook,* or have spotted any mistakes, we would be glad to hear from you. Important corrections will be made in our monthly *No-Load Fund Investor* newsletter.

Library of Congress Catalog Card No. 85—645285
ISSN: 0736-6264

Acknowledgments

Numerous people and organizations gave their assistance and support in the preparation of this Handbook. In particular we would like to thank the Investment Company Institute, the mutual funds' industry association, and all the no-load mutual funds which provided us with prospectuses, annual reports and directory information.

Additional copies of the *Handbook* can be obtained from *The No-Load Fund Investor* at $45 each. The *Handbook* with twelve monthly *No-Load Fund Investor* newsletter supplements is $129. Monthly *Investor* supplements are $90 per year additional for *Handbook* subscribers; a sample issue of the *Investor* newsletter can be obtained free by writing *The No-Load Fund Investor.*

The No-Load Fund Investor also publishes *Sheldon Jacobs' Guide to Successful No-Load Fund Investing* at $25.

THE NO-LOAD FUND INVESTOR, INC., Post Office Box 318, Irvington-on-Hudson, NY 10533, Telephone: 914-693-7420

Contents

Covering the wide world of no-load mutual funds

Just exactly, what is a no-load? Very simple, it's a type of mutual fund sold without a sales commission (which in the jargon of the industry is called a "load"). Selling funds without a sales charge is possible when no salespeople are involved in the purchase. By going directly to no-load fund companies, you can save substantial sums of money while still enjoying outstanding returns. That's because, on average, no-load funds perform as well as the more expensive load funds.

Years' ago, the difference between loads and no-loads was clear cut. That's no longer the case. Seeing the increasing popularity of no-loads, load fund companies have blurred the line. There are now load funds without front-end loads. Instead, they have back-end loads and ongoing sales charges (called 12b-1 fees.) More recently load fund companies have developed "level-load" funds. They don't have either front- or back-end loads. They still have high continuing fees. Load funds, by whatever name, are more costly, and thus inferior, to no-loads.

This book, *The Handbook For No-Load Fund Investors*, is designed to provide meaningful coverage of virtually all no-load stock and bond funds available to the public, as well as coverage of the important money market funds. In various chapters you will find detailed performance data and rankings, going back ten years, as well as a complete directory that gives you all the purchase information you need. This edition of the *Handbook* reports on 2,045 funds ranging from speculative aggressive growth funds to conservative money-market funds—and includes international funds, domestic funds, bond funds, and stocks funds.

The *Handbook* also has separate sections that cover load funds that are available no-load through certain discount stock brokers, and low-load funds that are marketed directly to the public, meaning that you buy without the help of a broker or financial adviser. Fidelity Magellan is an example of a low-load marketed directly to the public. We exclude low-load funds that are distributed through brokers, salesmen or financial advisers. We provide data on these direct marketed low-loads because we perform a vital information function in the absence of a salesmen. We do not recommend these funds.

While virtually all money market funds are no-load, the *Handbook* focuses on money funds that are part of no-load groups or allow you to switch into or out of no-load stock funds. We also include most of the large independent and stockbroker affiliated funds. We've generally excluded those money funds that are part of load fund families.

The *Handbook*, which has been published annually since 1981, complements two other publications published by *The No-Load Fund Investor*. In addition, there is *Sheldon Jacobs' Guide to Successful No-Load Fund Investing* (the "*Guide*"), which provides in-depth strategic information on how to select the best performing funds that suit your own needs. Until 1994, the *Guide* was part of this volume. Finally, there is our monthly newsletter, *The No-Load Fund Investor*, which updates the performance data in this book and issues continuing recommendations. The *Investor* newsletter, which has been published since 1979, covers 794 of the most popular funds each month.

How to use the Handbook

With its wealth of statistical and directory data, the *Handbook* can satisfy all your no-load mutual fund investing needs with concise to-the-point information.

How do I look up a fund to see how it has done?

Chapter 4 has all funds in alphabetical order. The left hand pages allow you to see how consistent a fund's performance has been over the last ten years. The right hand pages report on the fund's size, prices, dividends, risk and portfolio composition.

If you want to see a fund's performance over a three- or five-year period, you have two choices. We provide it on an annualized basis, which is an easy number to grasp, and also in terms of how much an investment would have grown over those years.

One of the most important criteria in determining the right fund for you is the fund's objective. It's listed in Chapter 4. In addition, the Directory provides a short extract of the objective as stated in each fund's prospectus. Here are capsule explanations of the meaning of each objective category. For a more definitive discussion of this important topic see the *Guide*.

Aggressive growth funds aim at maximum capital appreciation, and may take great risks to achieve this goal. They frequently invest in small company and less seasoned stocks. They may have high turnover of portfolio securities, leverage, or hold large amounts of cash. They are for investors willing to take a substantial amount of risk.

Growth funds are less risky and less volatile than aggressive growth funds. They typically invest in the growth stocks of larger companies and are suitable for a wide range of growth-oriented investors.

Growth-income funds combine a growth of earnings orientation with level or rising dividends. They offer more stable performance than either the aggressive growth or growth categories. Growth-income funds frequently hold a small portion of their portfolios in fixed-income securities.

Income funds seek stocks paying generous dividends, but may also hold fixed-income securities. It is the policy of the *Handbook* to use the Income category as a catch-all for a number of different types of mutual funds that have the common attributes of relatively low volatility and reasonable dividend income. These include the equity income funds, income funds (which may have up to 40% of their portfolios in fixed-income securities), balanced funds, domestic asset allocation funds and convertible securities funds.

Sector funds are non-diversified funds investing in specific industries. We include in this category the Fidelity, Invesco, and Vanguard sector portfolios as well as stand-alone funds investing in real estate, utilities and other industries.

Precious metals funds invest primarily in gold bullion or gold mining shares. While, technically, they could be included with the sector funds, we give them their own category because of their large numbers and the fact they frequently perform differently than other industry funds.

Global funds invest in both foreign and U.S. equity securities.

International funds invest in securities whose primary trading markets are outside the U.S. International funds can invest in any foreign country, regionally, or in specific countries.

Fixed-income funds hold taxable long-term fixed-income investments. International bond funds are included in this category.

Tax-free bond funds own municipal securities. Both fixed-income and tax-free bond funds have variable prices.

Money market funds hold short-term money market instruments. They have a fixed price, almost always $1. We sub-divide this category into general, government and muni money market funds. Money market funds with variable prices are put in the fixed-income category.

How do I compare a fund to other funds?

The best way to select top-performing funds is to go by our unique quintile ranking system. The *Handbook* uses superscript numbers (exponents) above each performance figure to show the fund's rank *within its objective category*. For example, an aggressive growth fund with a "1" above its performance figure is in the top 20% of all aggressive growth funds for the indicated period. A "2" indicates the fund was in the second 20% (or top 40%) of all funds that have the same investment objective. A "3" indicates the third or middle quintile. These are average funds. Funds ranked "4" or "5" are below average. Funds that have quintiles in the top two ranks are best.

In addition, Chapters 5 and 6 show fund performance in rank order for direct comparison.

How do I identify "pure" no-loads?

Pure no-load funds are identified in the Directory by a diamond after the fund's name. They have no front-end, back-end or 12b-1 fees. Funds without a diamond may still be called no-loads under current federal regulations if there 12b-1 fees are .25% or less.

How do I contact a fund?

The Directory section has the phone numbers, both 800 and local, and the funds' addresses.

Where do I get purchase information?

The Directory tells you minimum investments, if the fund is available in your state, whether it will accept telephone or wire orders.

How do I sell a fund?

Directory section provides some information, but see the prospectus.

Who manages the fund?

The Directory section lists each fund's manager or co-managers. Chapter 14 has an alphabetical listing of portfolio managers so you can see how many funds they manage, or simply match the manager to the fund.

Sheldon Jacobs, Editor
Irvington-on-Hudson, NY

SECTION I

1994
In
Review

CHAPTER 1

There was just no place to make money

You can sum up the investment climate for 1994 in very few words: there was no place to run, nowhere to hide—and almost no place to make any money.

For the first time in two decades, the stock and bond markets had treacherous years at the same time. And the markets overseas were just as troubled, if not in greater disarray.

In the U.S., the stock market had a so-so year. But the bond market was down more than in any year since the 1920s; by some measures, it was the worst year in history for bonds. The Federal Reserve fueled the conflagration by raising short-term interest rates six times in the 12 months of 1994 (actually, from February to November, so six times in less than 10 months). A seventh took place in January 1995, and at publication time, investors were hoping that it was the last.

In such an environment, how could mutual fund shareholders have hoped to enjoy the year? Most didn't, of course.

Investors gave the fund industry a vote of confidence

The fund industry finished 1994 with total net assets of $2.164 trillion. That was up just 4% from December 1993, when assets were $2.075 trillion. It was the smallest annual growth in the industry in 17 years, since 1977.

Interestingly, mutual fund investors were not intimidated by the stock market. Net sales of stock funds were the second best ever, exceeded only in 1993. The last time there was a net outflow from stock funds was September 1990, though net sales in November slumped to their lowest point since August 1991.

Bond investors bailed out, though, and who could blame them. Beginning in March, bond funds experienced net redemptions each month, fueled by all those interest rate hikes.

The small increase in fund assets did not imply that funds have become less popular investment vehicles. On the contrary, the number of new mutual funds increased a surprising 18%. By year-end, there were 5,375 mutual funds, 817 more than at the end of 1993. That is an astounding figure when you realize that as recently as January 1, 1983 the entire fund industry totaled just 857 funds.

It seems odd that mutual fund proprietors were so bullish in such a bearish year. Because, not only was the average fund's performance off anywhere from a little to a lot, but other mutual fund news also caused consternation. Nothing serious, but seriously annoying in such a grouchy year.

Some examples:

■ Insider trading became an issue briefly when the manager of Invesco Industrial Income, a hallmark no-load fund, was discovered to have used shareholders' money ill-advisedly. John Kaweski, a well-respected manager, was accused of propping up shares of a company in which he had a personal interest by purchasing them for his fund. Invesco summarily fired him, and the issue never really caught fire. Other large fund companies were quick to institute rules or point to existing restrictions that prevent managers from engaging in any shenanigans.

■ The word of the year was "derivatives." The concept is not a bad one—merely the notion that financial instruments would have a value linked to some underlying asset, such as a stock, bond or index. Unfortunately, some naive knuckleheads got carried away, and lost theirs (heads, that is). No less than the chief financial officer of Procter & Gamble and the controller of Orange County, Calif. lost their respective institutions millions of dollars by imprudently speculating in derivatives. As interest rates rose, their derivative investments took a pounding. Nor was the mutual fund industry immune. Although most funds claimed to have little or no activity in derivatives, at least one got into difficulty. Piper Jaffray Institutional Government Income lost 28.3% by investing heavily in very volatile securities derived from mortgages.

■ Leonine Fidelity, king of the mutual fund jungle, became uncharacteristically sheepish after several gaffs. At one point, the fund family failed to report accurate prices for its funds. At year-end, it was embarrassed in, of all places, its regal Magellan fund, at $36 billion and counting the undisputed all-time gorilla of the mutual fund world. The red faces at Magellan stemmed from a year-end miscalculation of the expected capital-gains distribution.

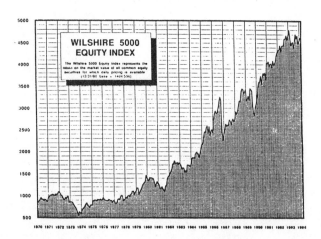

WILSHIRE 5000 EQUITY INDEX

The Wilshire 5000 Equity Index represents the return on the market value of all common equity securities for which daily pricing is available (12/31/80 base = 1404.596)

■ A small money market fund, Community Bankers of Denver, was the first modern money fund to "break the buck." Its share value dropped below $1. Although individual investors were not involved, and the fund was quickly folded by its owners, several large institutions, still it gave pause to mutual fund investors, who have become accustomed to the security of money market funds.

Put your money in a sock

Interestingly, money funds would have been nearly the best place to invest in 1994. When the year began, the typical money market fund was yielding about 3.25%. By year-end, the yield had risen to over 5%, and was still climbing. In no other broad fund category would investors have been treated so kindly, though two very specialized categories did provide hearty returns. The Technology funds followed by the *Handbook* were up 8.5% as a group. These funds were also the three- and five-year winners, averaging a 19.5% annual gain for the three-year period, and were up 21% a year for the past five years. Another excellent group during that period: the Financial funds, up 14.4% for three years, 15.1% for five.

Health/Biotech funds were up 6.7% in 1994. Much of the credit had to go to the demise of the Clinton Administration's extravagant health reform proposal. The health care industry breathed a sigh of relief when the plan keeled over and died.

And The Winner Is

The top funds for each of those time periods reflect the reality that most often a higher-risk specialized fund will be the big winner.

Last year's best performing fund was DFA Japanese Small Company, which was up 29.5%. Talk about volatility! It rose more than 28% during the first quarter of last year, but then plunged by 9% and 2.6% in the third and fourth quarters. The fund, which attempts to index the smaller one-half of the First Section of the Tokyo Stock Exchange, is erratic because the stocks themselves are highly speculative.

The top performers for the three- and five-year periods are similarly focused. Fidelity Select Home Finance, which averaged 27.3% for the three years, was the best fund during that time, and came in a close second to sister fund Fidelity Select Computers for the five-year period. Home Finance averaged 23.5% per year for the five years, while Computers was up 24.0% annually.

As with DFA Japanese Small Company, the two Select funds are volatile. In 1994, for example, Home Finance was up 12% in the second quarter, but off 10.5% in the fourth quarter. The fund invests almost entirely in smaller savings institutions, a strong group since 1990, when the thrift industry hit bottom. (Home

Finance was off 24.9% during the third quarter of 1990!) The course of interest rates has a major impact on the profitability of savings institutions. So the fund is an appropriate investment only for the most sophisticated—and nimble—investors.

That is nearly as true for Fidelity Select Computers, the five-year winner, as well. The fund is an almost pure play in computer hardware manufacturers. IBM, Texas Instruments, Intel, Compaq and Advanced Micro Devices are major holdings in the portfolio at any given time. Because it is product-sensitive, the hardware business can be cyclical. Despite that tendency, Select Computers has accomplished quite a feat over the past five years: it provided steady high performance. During the five years, its annual total return varied from 18.4% to 30.7%. But starry-eyed potential investors should beware. Clearly, such consistently high returns are not inevitable. After all, the preceding five years—1985 to 1989— contained two losing years, and two more with single-digit gains.

Stocks

In 1994, the average domestic stock fund posted a loss of 1.5%. While that is scarcely cause for precipitous action, though plenty of investors found it an occasion for wringing of hands and gnashing of teeth.

They would probably have found 1994 a still more ulcerous year had they been buying and selling individual stocks instead of investing in funds. Of 7,363 actively traded stocks, more than 80% were down more than 10% from their 52-week highs; more than 58% of them were down more than 20%; and more than 40% were down 30% or more. If you take a peak-to-trough view of the broad market indexes, the picture isn't very pretty, either. The Dow Jones Industrial Average and the S&P 500 declined 3.6% and 4.7% from their 1994 high points. That's a far cry from the highly publicized 2.1% year-over-year gain for the Dow in 1994, and the S&P's 1.5% decline.

Internationally, where you invested made quite a difference, even within regions of the world. In Asia, many of the markets that did so well in 1993 gave money back last year. Japan, meanwhile, did not have a great year, but it was the place to make money abroad, as the success of the DFA Japanese Small Company fund indicates.

Here at home, what type of stock fund you were in made a huge difference. One of the great ironies of 1994 was that investments previously thought to be quite conservative took the most ruthless hammering. Consider this: among stock funds, high flying science and technology funds scored by far the largest gains, while at the opposite end of the spectrum utilities, traditionally the widows' and orphans' safe haven, lost 8.8% of their value. Some of that was due to the rise in interest rates, of course. But analysts also felt that the fundamental economics of the utility industry were suspect.

Top Ten Fund Rankings

1 Year Performance Rankings by 1994 Performance	1994		3 Year Performance Rankings by 1992-1994 Performance	Annualized 3 yrs		5 Year Performance Rankings by 1990-1994 Performance-	Annualized 5 yrs		10 Year Performance Rankings by 1985-1994 Performance	Annualized 10 yrs
1 DFA Japan Sm Co	29.5		Fidelity Sel Home Finc	27.3		Fidelity Sel Computer.	24.0		Twentieth Cent Giftrust	25.6
2 PBHG Emg Growth SC	23.8		Oakmark	26.1		Fidelity Sel Home Fincl	23.5		Fidelity Sel Health	21.5
3 Robrtsn Stph Val Gro	23.1		Crabbe Huson Special SC	26.1		Fidelity Sel Electronics	23.1		Invesco Strat Health	20.6
4 Fidelity Sel Health	21.4		Fidelity Sel Electronics	25.4		Invesco Strat Tech	22.5		Vangd Spec-Health	20.0
5 Montgomery Growth	20.9		PBHG Growth	25.4		Fidelity Sel Technology	22.3		Invesco Strat Leisure	19.8
6 Fidelity Sel Computer	20.5		Fidelity Sel Computer	23.7		Twentieth Cent Giftrust	22.0		CGM Capital Dev	19.7
7 Fidelity Sel Medical Del	19.8		Fidelity Sel Software	21.7		Price, Rowe Sci/Tech	22.0		Berger 100	19.1
8 Strong Growth	17.3		Fidelity Sel Devl Comm	21.1		PBHG Growth	22.0		Fidelity Overseas	19.1
9 Fidelity Sel Electronics	17.2		Twentieth Cent Giftrust	20.7		Fidelity Sel Software	21.5		Invesco Strat Tech	18.9
10 Fidelity Japan	16.5		Fidelity Sel Multimedia	20.3		Crabbe Huson Special SC	19.5		Twentieth Cent Ultra	18.8

Across the board, stock funds lost in greater or lesser degree. While the average no-load general equity fund was off just 1.5%, many specific mutual fund categories fared considerably worse. On average, for instance, aggressive growth funds were down 2.5%; income funds, -2.6%; real estate funds, -4.5%; growth funds, -0.7%; and small cap funds, -0.8%.

Interestingly, the poor 1994 performance is being thought of in hindsight as perhaps inevitable, for several reasons. The second year of a President's term has historically been bad for stocks. Moreover, it's hard to see how stocks could withstand the battering of six interest rate hikes in less than 10 months. And, as the following table shows, over the past eight years stocks seem to have slid into a pattern or alternating good and mediocre to bad years.

No-Load Equity Funds

Year	Total Return %
1994	- 1.8
1993	+18.2
1992	+ 7.5
1991	+31.2
1990	- 6.6
1989	+23.4
1988	+15.1
1987	+ 2.0

No matter how forgettable a year might be, inevitably heros will emerge with memorable records. Winners in 1994 included some longtime champs as well as some excellent newcomers.

One of the most notable in 1994 was Twentieth Century Giftrust, which had a strong enough year—up 13.5%— to allow it to claim the title for best 10-year record. During the decade, the fund piled up an 875% gain, averaging an incredible 25.6% per year over the period. The idiosyncratic fund requires investors to give Giftrust shares irrevocably to an organization or a person, usually a child. And the investment has to stay with the fund for at least 10 years (or until a child reaches 18). Thus, the fund doesn't have to worry much about cash outflows. Twentieth Century Giftrust invests in the stocks of small, rapidly growing companies.

Other funds that were big winners in 1994: Robertson Stephens Value and Growth, which says it buys undervalued growth stocks, was up 23.1%; Montgomery Growth, which invests in medium-sized companies, had a total return of 20.9%; and PBHG Emerging Growth, up 23.8%. None of those funds has been around even three years.

Among no-loads with narrow-focus specialties, T. Rowe Price Science and Technology was up 15.8% for the year. And among health care funds, Fidelity Select Health Care was up 21.4% and Fidelity Select Medical Delivery, up 19.8%.

Needless to say, it was not such a winsome year for every category—or every fund. Among the markets and sectors that got clobbered last year, the worst beating came in the international arena. Latin American funds were down 16.9%; broad-based emerging market funds lost 11.6%. Some domestic market segments stumbled. Most notably, utility funds suffered an 8.8% loss, environmental funds were down 10.5% and gold funds were off 12.7%.

In each of these categories, some weathered the problems better than others. For instance, in the Far East, Price New Asia was off 19.2% for the year, Fidelity Southeast Asia was down 21.8%. But Fidelity Pacific Basin was off just 2.8%, and Vanguard Index Pacific was *up* 12.9%. The difference was whether the fund owned Japan. Fidelity Latin America was off 23.2%, Price Latin America 15.9%, but Scudder Latin America was down just 9.4% for the year. Among gold funds, Invesco Strategic Gold was off a thumping 27.9%, while Fidelity Select Precious Metals was down just 1.2%.

All of which argues for several investing strategies. Know your fund, and the potential risk that it poses. And, know the differences between funds that are in the same category but have radically different investment styles. Vanguard Index Pacific, for instance, maintains a much heavier weighting in Japan than other Pacific funds (many of which don't invest in Japan at all). That's because Japan is the dominant force in Asia—if not the world—with world's largest stock market. Price New Asia, meanwhile, avoids Japan altogether, concentrating on stock markets in Malaysia, Hong Kong, Singapore and Australia. Last year, many of those markets, Hong Kong in particular, got battered.

Among gold funds, Invesco Strategic Gold invests almost entirely in Canada and the U.S., avoiding the more volatile South African mining stocks. That proved a disadvantage last summer and fall when South African shares rocketed. A fund like Fidelity Select Precious Metals was well positioned to take advantage of the rise, with half its assets in South Africa. (On the other hand, one year's advantage can be another's heartbreak; Select Precious Metals lost 23.8% in 1988, 21% in 1990 and 21.8% in 1992.) Country distributions for all gold funds are detailed in Appendix B.

And then there are funds that take you to the moon, only to bring you crashing back to earth. The most vivid example in years: American Heritage. Taken over by manager Heiko Thieme in 1991, the fund was up 96% in 1991, 18.9% in 1992 and 41.4% in 1993—a cumulative gain of 229%. Then came last year. A shareholder who stayed with Thieme for the entire year lost a sickening 35.4% of his investment. Mainly, that was because Thieme made a large bet on Spectrum Information Technologies, then increased his stake when the stock plummeted.

No question Thieme is a gunslinger. He actively proclaims his high-risk approach in speeches and shareholder communications. He typically invests in restricted securities, which can be as much as 15% of his portfolio, and the illiquid stocks of companies with very small market capitalization. Adding insult to injury, Thieme was on the receiving end of a shareholder lawsuit that claimed among other things that some of the portfolio's holdings were carried at incorrect values, falsely inflating the value of shares in earlier years.

Bonds

Never as sexy as stocks, bonds are at least supposed to have the virtue of sobriety. Yet, as if the market had suddenly contracted a disease, bonds began performing like manic-depressives.

Who would ever have thought that Benham's Target 2020 fund would be down 17.7%, or that Fidelity Spartan Long-Term Government fund would be off 12.2%? You're just not supposed to witness drama in the bond market—especially the municipal market. Yet, the Fundamental New York Municipal fund was off 19.8%, attributable largely to the fact that the fund held derivatives. A more characteristic bond fund loss was the 4% drop that Loomis Sayles Bond suffered. Manager Dan Fuss told Barron's that

his fund's drop, while better than either the bond market or the average bond fund, was "something that he hadn't experienced before, although 'I've been doing this since 1958.'"

Of course the culprit was Uncle Alan. Chairman Greenspan led the Federal Reserve through six hikes in interest rates during the year, causing more chaos in the bond market, by some estimates, than at any time since systematic records began right after World War II.

The turbulence all but blind-sided investors— though it probably shouldn't have. Granted, interest rates dropped in 1993 to near-Depression era levels. Still, When the *Wall Street Journal* polled 52 economists at the beginning of 1994 on what they expected the 30-year Treasury bond to yield by Dec. 31st, most guessed 6% to 6.5%. The average was 6.39%. None thought that it would be as high as 8%, which is where the long bond hung through much of the fall, and only 6 of the 52 felt that the bond would yield more than 7%. Although most of the economists believed that the Fed would be raising rates, not a single one forecast the magnitude of the increase.

In hindsight, they probably should have. Because, the events of 1994 were a logical—if exaggerated— reaction to the longest bull market in the history of bonds. Interest rates dropped on an almost uninterrupted trajectory from 1982—with a spike up in 1987— until late in 1993, when rates began edging up.

The obvious strategy for dealing with last year's relentless rise in rates was to stay short-term. Money funds, of course, always have a positive rate or return. But ultra-short- and short-term bonds were the next best thing last year.

Among the 22 short-term tax-free funds that the *Handbook* follows, for instance, the range in performance went from plus 2.4% for the year (Twentieth Century Tax-Exempt Short-Term) to minus 1.7% (Babson Tax-Free Short-Term). The average for the group was a positive 0.2%.

Short-term taxable funds had a broader range, especially if international funds are included. The worst performer was Manager's Short-Term Government fund, down 6.2%; the best was Hotchkiss & Wiley Low Duration, up 5.1%.

The averages for all no-load funds that we track in the *Handbook* in various bond, as well as stock, categories can be found on page 30. Top 50 rankings are in Chapter 6.

As 1995 began, the inevitable counterswing of the pendulum began. In the early going, despite still another Federal Reserve rate hike late in January, the stock and bond markets both rallied. Would investors' optimism be sustained? No one could say. But there is great hope that 1995 will prove to be a far better year than 1994.

THE WINNERS

Top ranked no- or low-load each year

Year	Fund	Objective	% Gain	What happened
1994	DFA Japan Small Co.	international	29.5	In a generally down year, Japanese small stocks recover some of their bear market losses.
1993	United Services Gold Shares	precious metals	123.9	U.S. Gold wins for the fourth time.
1992	Fidelity Home Finance	sector	57.8	S&L stocks recover from the scandals of the 80s.
1991	CGM Capital Development	aggressive growth	99.1	Ken Heebner, one of the all-time pro's, turned in the best performance for a diversified fund since 1975. Unfortunately, the fund is closed.
1990	Fidelity Select Biotechnology	sector	44.3	Fidelity's youngest manager, 26 year old Michael Gordon, rode the crest of 1990s only equity group to show gains
1989	United Services Gold Shares	precious metals	64.7	Investing in risky South African shares pays off; U. S. Gold won for the third time.
1988	Kaufmann	aggressive growth	58.6	A small-cap fund, heavy in medical stocks, benefitted from takeover situations.
1987	DFA Japan Small Co.	international	87.6	Dimensional Fund Advisors' institutional fund, that required purchases be made in yen, achieved the biggest gain of the decade.
1986	Nomura Pacific Basin	international	74.5	For the second straight year, internationals benefit from a declining dollar and strong overseas markets.
1985	Fidelity Overseas	international	78.7	A bull market in foreign stocks and a declining dollar propelled this new fund, managed by a 29 year old Yale economics graduate, to the top.
1984	Vanguard Qual Div Port I	income	25.2	A fund designed to provide tax-sheltered income won; its gain was the smallest for a #1 fund since 1974.
1983	Fidelity Select Technology	aggressive growth	52.4	Rode the crest of the 1982-83 bull market in technology stocks.
1982	United Services Gold Shares	precious metals	64.1	In a year when stocks finished strong, U. S. Gold won out for the second time.
1981	Lindner Fund	growth	34.0	Money funds were the big winners in a down market, but a portfolio half in cash and a sizeable position in utilities brought Lindner honors.
1980	Hartwell Leverage	aggressive growth	93.9	A great year for equities; the most aggressive funds really shined.
1979	United Services Gold Shares	precious metals	172.9	Gold wins during an inflationary year.
1978	G. T. Pacific	international	50.9	A roller coaster year for U. S. stocks, the Far East was the place to invest.
1977	Value Line Leverage Growth	aggressive growth	51.1	Blue chips were battered, but secondaries and special situations had a great year.
1976	Sequoia	aggressive growth	70.8	Aggressive growth funds dominated in the second year of a powerful bull market. Sequoia achieved its best annual gain ever.
1975	44 Wall Street	aggressive growth	184.1	Leverage made for top performance in the year that began the great bull run.
1974	Sherman, Dean	aggressive growth	24.8	While money funds were the place to be, a non-diversified fund with 12 stocks gained an easy win by zooming to a 79% gain in the first quarter before succumbing to the bear.
1973	Wade Fund	growth	17.6	In a terrible year, Maury Wade got lucky by adding some gold stocks to his portfolio.
1972	Twentieth Century Growth	aggressive growth	42.4	The steady winner from Kansas City began its streak.
1971	Nicholas Strong Fund	aggressive growth	85.5	Both Nicholas and Strong have done very well managing their own funds since the split-up.

CHAPTER 2

Highlights from *The No-Load Fund Investor*

■ Our monthly publication, *The No-Load Fund Investor* newsletter publishes articles of lasting interest. In this chapter, we reprise those articles published since the 1994 Edition of the *Handbook* that we believe are particularly noteworthy.

Single family investing

(Published in three parts in the April, May, and June 1994 *Investors*.)

It can be advantageous to confine your investing to a single fund family. It is certainly more convenient, both in terms of switching and paperwork, and you have better control. It's particularly convenient to keep your IRA account at one fund group. You can split your IRA among several fund families, of course. But by keeping it in one place, you can switch by phone among the various funds in the group without having any time-consuming paperwork. And one additional benefit: you can save on those irritating little IRA fees since many funds waive them when your investments reach certain amounts.

IRAs are still a must

IRA's are still a wonderful deal if you can invest fully or partially on a pre-tax basis. If you have to make your contributions on an after-tax basis because you are already enrolled in a pension plan, it can still pay to contribute if you have a number of years to go before starting withdrawals. In this case, the still tax-deferred dividends and capital gains will enable you to achieve far greater growth than is possible without the shelter. If you are only a few years from retirement, a non-deductible IRA probably isn't worth the bother.

Anyone with working children should make certain that the kids contribute as much as they can to an IRA. *It's highly worthwhile, even if you have to put the money in for them.* Time is on their side. Don't let your children miss this easiest of all roads to long-term riches: the magic of compounding.

Fund groups most suitable for concentrating your money

We reviewed all the no-load groups that the *Investor* follows to determine which could best provide for all or most of your investing needs. We particularly considered tax-sheltered investing.

We used two criteria in evaluating the groups. 1)

Adequate diversification. A group had to have sufficient representation in both conservative and speculative no-load equity funds, international funds, and taxable bond funds in order to implement our recommended risk pyramids. 2) A family had to have individual funds that were worth recommending.

Not surprisingly, the largest groups fared best. If you want to keep all of your investments with one fund family, stick with those listed below. We ruled out a few groups that are quite good because they didn't have enough funds on our recommended list; however, they may still be okay for many investors. Even with the large groups listed below, we found it necessary to include a few funds not currently recommended by us. While the following recommendations bear some similarity to our Best Buys, in some cases we deviated to show you the range of possibilities.

Fidelity. The largest fund complex has a wealth of no-loads in all groups, except possibly internationals. We recommend enough Fidelity funds in the tables that a young person could easily put together a fine *Wealth Builder* portfolio, and gradually convert it into *Pre-Retirement* and *Retirement* Portfolios.

Wealth Builder		Port. Dist. %
Retirement Growth	agg gr	5
Value	growth	25
Europe Capital Appr	int'l	10
Emerging Markets	int'l	10
SE Asia	int'l	10
Equity Income II	gr-inc	20
Convertible Securities	income	20

Pre-Retirement		
Stock Selector	growth	10
Value	growth	20
Emerging Markets	int'l	5
Europe Capital Appr	int'l	10
Asset Mgr Growth	gr-inc	15
Convertible Securities	income	15
Capital & Income	fix-inc	15
Short-term bond	fix-inc	10

Retirement		
Equity Income II	gr-inc	15
International Growth & Inc	int'l	15
Emerging Markets	int'l	5
Puritan	income	15
Convertible Securities	income	15
Asset Manager	income	15
Mortgage Securities	fix-inc	20

Vanguard. Again, a wide variety of funds to meet all objectives. Very good strength in conservative equity and international areas. Tops among taxable fixed-income funds. Vanguard also has Star, a multi-fund specifically oriented to IRAs.

Wealth Builder		Port. Dist. %
Small Cap Stock	agg gr	5
Total market	growth	30
Primecap	growth	15
Index Europe	int'l	10
Int'l Growth	int'l	10
Windsor II	gr-inc	15
Convertible Securities	income	15

Pre-Retirement		
Primecap	growth	15
Index Europe	int'l	10
Int'l Growth	int'l	5
Index Value	gr-inc	20
Star	gr-inc	20
Wellington	income	10
GNMA	fix-inc	20

Retirement		
Index Value	gr-inc	15
Index Europe	int'l	10
Int'l Growth	int'l	10
Star	gr-inc	10
Convertible Securities	income	10
Index Balanced	income	15
GNMA	fix-inc	20
Vangd Hi Yld Corp	fix-inc	10

T. Rowe Price. Another top choice. Good strength among the growth funds and fixed-income funds; top choice for the internationals.

Wealth Builder		% Dist.
Science and Technology	sector	5%
New Era	growth	10%
Capital Appreciation	growth	10%
Spectrum Growth	growth	10%
New Asia	int'l	5%
Latin America	int'l	10%
European	int'l	10%
Growth & Income	gr-inc	20%
Equity Income	income	20%

Pre-Retirement		
Spectrum Growth	growth	10%
Capital Appreciation	growth	5%
New Asia	int'l	5%
European	int'l	10%
Latin America	int'l	10%
Dividend Growth	gr-inc	10%
Growth & Income	gr-inc	10%
Equity Income	income	20%
Spectrum Income	fix-inc	20%

Retirement		
Capital Appreciation	growth	5%
Spectrum Growth	growth	5%
European	int'l	10%
New Asia	int'l	5%
Latin America	int'l	5%
Dividend Growth	gr-inc	15%
Equity Income	income	20%
Spectrum Income	fix-inc	35%

Invesco. We recommend funds in all the essential categories. We prefer the older European and Pacific portfolios, although Invesco now has a general international fund. In order to achieve sufficient diversification, we show two funds that are not recommended in the tables. They have NR next to their names.

Wealth Builder		Port. Dist. %
Dynamics	agg gr	5
Emerging Growth	agg gr	5
Growth	growth	20
Value Equity (NR)	growth	20
Europe	int'l	10
Pacific Basin	int'l	10
Industrial Income	gr-inc	30

Pre-Retirement		
Value Equity	growth	15
Growth	growth	20
Europe	int'l	10
Pacific Basin	int'l	10
Industrial Income	gr-inc	20
Intermediate Gov Bond	fix-inc	15
High Yield	fix-inc	10

Retirement		
Growth	growth	10
Europe	int'l	10
Pacific Basin	int'l	5
Industrial Income	gr-inc	20
Total Return (NR)	income	15
Intermediate Gov Bond	fix-inc	25
High Yield	fix-inc	15

Scudder. While they have enough funds for sufficient diversification, we found it impossible to select recommended funds in all the essential categories. Scudder's best strength is in internationals and fixed-income.

Wealth Builder		Port. Dist.%
Capital Growth (NR)	agg gr	5
Quality Growth (NR)	growth	10
Value (NR)	growth	20
Growth & Income	gr-inc	25
Balanced (NR)	gr-inc	10
Global	global	5
Int'l Stock	int'l	10
Pacific Opportunities (NR)	int'l	10
Latin America	int'l	5

Pre-Retirement		
Value (NR)	growth	20
Global	global	10
Int'l Stock	int'l	10
Pacific Opportunities (NR)	int'l	5
Latin America	int'l	5
Growth & Income	gr-inc	15
Balanced (NR)	gr-inc	10
Sht Term Glob Income	fix-inc	5
Income	fix-inc	20

Retirement		
Value (NR)	growth	15
Growth & Income	gr-inc	20
Balanced (NR)	gr-inc	5
Global	global	5
Int'l Stock	int'l	15
Sht Term Glob Income	fix-inc	5
Income	fix-inc	35

Strong. This medium-sized group has most of the essentials for good diversified investing.

Wealth Builder	Port. Dist.%	
Discovery (NR)	agg gr	5
Opportunity	growth	20
Int'l Stock	int'l	15
Asia Pacific (NR)	int'l	10
Total Return	gr-inc	25
Investment	gr-inc	25

Pre-Retirement		
Opportunity	growth	20
Int'l Stock	int'l	10
Asia Pacific (NR)	int'l	10
Total Return	gr-inc	20
Investment	gr-inc	20
Government Securities	bond	10
Short-term bond	bond	10

Retirement		
Total Return	gr-inc	20
Int'l Stock	int'l	10
Asia Pacific (NR)	int'l	10
Investment	gr-inc	25
Government Securities	bond	20
Short-term bond	bond	15

While it's possible to do single family investing in other, smaller groups, we don't recommend it for investors who need good diversification in no-loads.

What's the outlook?

(May 1994 *Investor*; only excerpts are reprinted)

A significant correction has taken place in the stock and bond markets in recent months. In that light, let's review our basic investing strategy. Called flexible funding, this approach keeps us comparatively fully invested throughout the market cycle, while varying our risk levels as the market moves higher or lower. The strategy does not prohibit the use of cash in adverse times. But we have not resorted to that tactic in 1994, principally, because we do not feel that the market is overvalued when you take inflation and interest rate levels into account.

Flexible funding has been very successful, keeping us in the market since the Fall of 1990. That enabled us to enjoy the full benefits of gains through 1993. Our losses in the first quarter of 1994 were modest, except for the sizeable correction that we suffered in the emerging markets. (On the other hand, these markets provided us with enormous profits in 1993, so, we are still well ahead.)

An alternative to Flexible Funding would be market timing. Some timers have done very well this year. But another group waited until late March and early April before selling. By then, stocks had already declined about 10%. For this group to profit, not only will the market have to decline another 10%-15%, but also the timers will have to leap back into stocks almost exactly when the market reaches bottom. We don't know too many investment advisors with such exquisitely perfect timing. If they don't have it, though, the timers risk buying back into the market at higher prices than when they exited (not even considering the tax implications of selling at a profit, and thereby giving away some assets to the tax man next April). The timers have set themselves a difficult task. The Dow hit its 1994 low on April 19th at 3598.71, and has since recovered somewhat. It will be months before we will know whether or not that point was absolute ground zero.

The downside of being fully invested in a declining market is that temporarily you have paper losses. How long should it take to recoup these losses? The following table provides you with some parameters, showing all major declines in the last 40 years. On average, it took seven months for the S&P 500 to retrace 75% of its decline, and 13 months to completely recoup all its losses. The major exception to the pattern of speedy recovery was the 1973-74 crash, when inflation was accelerating at an unprecedented rate.

Stock market declines of 15%+

	Decline		Months to recover	
			75% of	100% of
Year (s)	%	Months	decline	decline
1953	15	9	4	6
1956-57	16	6	3	5
1957	20	3	11	12
1961-62	29	6	10	14
1966	22	9	5	6
1968-70	37	18	9	22
1973-74	48	21	20*	64
1975	15	2	2	4
1977-78	18	14	1	6
1978	17	2	7	10
1980	22	2	3	4
1981-82	22	13	2	3
1987	34	2	18	23
1990	20	3	5	5
Average	28%	8	7	13

*50% of decline recovered in 5 months
Source: David L. Babson & Co (based on the S&P 500)

What's a salesmen worth?

(June 1994 *Investor*)

Even though we firmly advocate no-load investing, we've never devoted a lot of space to bashing salesmen. We've always thought that they had a place for uninformed investors who had no desire to learn. However, we recently read an article which so completely epitomizes the problems of dealing with mutual fund salesmen and brokers that we thought it worthwhile to reprint. The article was a "point" and "counter point" debate on the subject. It originally appeared in *Mutual Fund Market News*, a trade publication for the industry. The load fund representative extolled the contribution of the salesmen. The no-load advocate demurred.

We reprint only the latter.

Was that "personalized, professional advice" worth paying for?
By Jason Zweig
(mutual funds editor of *Forbes* magazine.)

You'd have investors believe they pay a sales load not to buy a fund, but to get a broker's advice. If that's how brokers want to define the terms of the load-versus-no-load debate, fine. But I predict you'll be sorry.

Do you really want to remind investors of the roughly $100 billion in limited partnerships that were rammed down their throats in the 1980s? Investors paid several billion dollars in commissions for "securities" that are worth $15 billion at best, today—one of the worst catastrophes in the history of investing. Was that "personalized, professional advice" worth paying for?

Do you really want to remind investors of another product from the 1980s, option-income funds? They turned into such an embarrassment that the ICI no longer even recognizes them as an asset class. Was that "personalized, professional advice" worth paying for?

And do you really want to remind investors of short-term world income funds, a perfectly legitimate product that some irresponsible brokers insisted on selling as a CD equivalent? Was that "personalized, professional advice" worth paying for?

What about the municipal bond funds that some brokers put into their clients IRA accounts? Was that "personalized, professional advice" worth paying for?

When a broker told a prospect that "CDs are not insured," was that "personalized, professional advice" worth paying for? When a friend of mine wanted growth funds for a college savings plan and her broker tried to put a third of her money in municipal bonds maturing in 2021—12 years after her son will graduate from college—was that "personalized, professional advice" worth paying for?

I don't mean to pick on my good friends at Putnam, but their current ad campaign makes me scratch my head a bit. "You think you understand the situation," said one of Putnam's ads, "but what you don't understand is that the situation just changed."

Why then, was Putnam Health Sciences Trust one of the few health-care sector funds to experience net cash inflows in 1992? While brokers blindly heaved millions of dollars of their clients' money into the Putnam fund at a most inopportune time, lots of no-load buyers seemed to understand clearly that the situation had just changed.

The Putnam fund is a good one, but people who bought it in 1992 may wonder why their brokers could not understand what Hillary Clinton was saying on every evening newscast.

If brokers always give good advice, why are so many of the best load funds so darn tiny?

Hakan Castegren, the fine international manager, runs more than $2 billion in no-load Harbor International. But his Ivy International, a load fund, is struggling to get past $200 million. As a load fund, PBHG Growth couldn't get past $8 million, despite a stellar record. Last July it shed its sales charge and assets have shot past $300 million.

Switching the other way doesn't work very well. Marty Whitman's Third Ave Value amassed only $21 million in a year-and-a-quarter as a no-load, but after more than two years in the brokerage channel, it's still only around $140 million. Obviously brokers would rather send their clients' money elsewhere, often into funds with higher risk, mediocre performance and excessive expenses.

Among no-loads, however, money tends to flow into funds that provide reliable risk-adjusted performance at low cost. In other words, here the free market works. The Mutual Series Funds have never run a single advertisement since they were founded in 1949, yet assets have steadily grown past $7 billion.

The bottom line: No investor can be sure that paying a sales load will get him "personalized, professional advice." Most brokers' advice is good, but much of it is bad. All the investor can be sure of is that several hundred basis points of his hard-earned money will disappear into his broker's pocket.

I am endlessly fascinated by the brokerage industry's refusal to acknowledge the importance of costs. Why is it so hard for you to face the obvious question: Aren't we charging to much?

I wonder: When you shop for a mortgage, do you seek out a warm and fuzzy mortgage banker who gives "personalized, professional advice" but charges exorbitant points and interest rates?

Of course not. Yet that's exactly what you expect your clients to do. While performance is quite unpredictable, costs are almost perfectly predictable. Every basis point of expenses comes straight out of total return. That's why, in a bear market, most high-cost funds are doomed to underperform most low-cost funds. Many no-load bond funds charge well under 1% in annual expenses (to be fair, so do some good load funds). But many load bond funds charge close to 2%.

That excess simply indefensible. I think the day is coming when securities lawyers will contend that a broker who sells a bond fund with a 2% expense ratio is breaching his fiduciary duty to the client.

In the mid-1970s, when no self-respecting broker would touch mutual funds with a 10-foot pole, *Forbes* continued to urge readers to buy them. If the markets tank again, the fund industry will find out who its real friends are.

In the meantime, fancy semantic footwork with the connotation of the word "load" will not solve the image problem. Until the brokerage community has the intellectual honesty to admit that the cost of any mutual fund is a critical component of its value, no-loads will keep you from being eaten alive.

Should you go with the crowd?

(June 1994 *Investor*)

Mutual funds, like most investments, go in and out of vogue. Some funds languish for years with little public attention; others are recommended by a host of advisers. In most cases, funds receive multiple recommendations because they currently lead in one or more ranking. In a few cases, public relations plays a part.

Here's the question: should you buy what everybody is recommending? We ask because investors frequently tell us that they subscribe to a number of different publications, then feel comfortable purchasing funds that have been recommended by several of them.

To find the answer, we analyzed a summary of recommendations that appears regularly in the Hulbert Financial Digest. This newsletter lists funds that are recommended by three-to-nine newsletters in a given month (out of a base of about 50 fund newsletters). Our methodology was to track those funds recommended the most in January of the last three years, and then determine their quintile rank at year-end For example, in January, 1993, four funds had been recommended by nine different newsletters. For all of 1993, these four funds had an average quintile of 3.0; in this case, just average. In the same year, 27 funds had been recommended by three different newsletters. These 27 funds also had an average quintile of 3.0. A quintile of 3.0 is exactly average. "1"s are, of course, the best, "5"s the worst.

In 1991, funds that received the most recommendations did the best, and funds with only 3 or 4 recommendations did the worst. In 1992, the reverse was true. In 1993, the funds with the most and least recommendations did the worst. Averaging the three years we find that funds recommended by 5-7 newsletters did the best, while funds recommended by nine newsletters did the worst. Over the entire three-year period, all funds recommended by three or more newsletters did fractionally better than average (2.9 quintile).

Equity funds recommended by three or more newsletters

# nl's recommending funds	1991-1993 # funds recommended	Avg quintile
9	11	3.9
8	7	2.7
7	8	2.3
6	15	2.7
5	27	2.4
4	39	3.0
3	72	2.9
Total	179	2.9

We also took a look at the performance of all funds recommended by three or more newsletters to see how their performance compared to other funds that were recommended by two or fewer newsletters. We found that over the three years, 48% of the recommendations were in the first or second quintiles while only 33% were in the fourth and fifth quintiles.

Quintile distribution for all recommendations

Quintile	1993	1992	1991	3 years
1	33%	15%	34%	27%
2	25%	18%	13%	20%
3	17%	25%	26%	22%
4	7%	17%	17%	13%
5	18%	25%	11%	18%

In conclusion, it seems beneficial to pick a fund that has been recommended by at least a few services, but it doesn't really matter how many. Nine recommendations won't make a fund a surer bet. If you're getting your recommendations from newsletters, pick a publication you have confidence in, and whose style of investing suits you. Then stick with it.

ICI proposes new standards for series funds

(June 1994 *Investor*)

The Investment Company Institute has proposed new standard definitions for the various classes of shares now being sold by load funds. Under their suggested guidelines, here is how the various loads would be categorized:

Class A shares — front-end load
Class B shares — spread load
Class C shares — level load
Class D shares — hybrid level load

In addition, load funds could have two no-load categories for favored groups.

Class Y shares — for institutional investors
Class Z shares — for their own employees.

We're not going to explain the differences because you shouldn't buy any of these classes in any event.

Derivatives

(July 1994 *Investor*)

Investors have expressed concern lately regarding the use of derivatives by mutual funds. Most fund investors don't understand what derivatives are, don't understand the potential risks involved, and find it nearly impossible to determine the extent to which derivatives are being used by mutual funds. Let's demystify this issue.

Derivatives are a broad array of financial instruments whose true value is derived from other benchmarks, such as stocks, bonds, currencies, commodities and home mortgages. Generally, the term is being used to cover *options*, *forward contracts*, *futures*, *swaps*, and *structured notes*, but there are over 1200 different types of derivatives.

A *forward contract* is the actual purchase or sale of a commodity, government security, foreign currency or other financial instrument at a price specified now, with delivery and settlement at a specified future date. It is a completed contract (although it may not be completed by the original purchaser, since the contract can be and often is resold), unlike an options contract, where the owner has a choice of completing or not completing.

Futures are similar to forward contracts, but differ in that they are standardized and traded on futures exchanges. Unlike forward contracts, the counterparty to a futures contract is the clearing corporation for the appropriate exchange. Futures are typically settled in cash by selling the contract to a third party, rather than requiring actual delivery of the instrument or commodity that is being traded. One well known futures contract involves the S&P 500.

Swaps are another forward based derivative that involve two parties exchanging a series of cash flows at specific intervals known as payment or settlement dates. In a basic interest rate swap, one party exchanges a fixed-rate for a floating rate. Swaps can now involve cross-market payments (e.g. short-term rates in the U.S. vs. the U.K.) and cross-currency payments (dollars vs. yen). Mutual funds do very little with swaps.

Options provide the right (but not the obligation) to buy or sell a security at a specified time for a specified price in exchange for an agreed upon sum. If the right is not exercised during the specified period, the option expires and the option buyer forfeits the money that he paid for the right. A *call option* is a right to purchase a security; a *put option* is the right to sell one. It is also possible to write options on futures.

Caps, floors and collars. Much as forwards can be bundled to create swaps, options can be bundled to create other option-based contracts. The above are generally medium-to long-term transactions.

Structured notes (also called indexed securities) are debt instruments where the interest rate and/or the principal are indexed to an unrelated indicator (such as the price of oil). Sometimes they are inversely related (for instance, inverse floaters where the coupon rate goes down as an index goes up).

In the money markets, the term derivatives refers to notes with *floating or variable interest rates*, and not to instruments like futures or options.

How funds use derivatives

Broadly speaking, mutual funds invest in derivatives in three ways: 1) to hedge risks, 2) as a substitute for investments in traditional securities, and 3) to enhance yields.

Hedging, a strategy to reduce risks, is used by mutual funds to minimize losses due to changing currency rates.

Mutual funds that invest overseas may hedge the risks of currency fluctuations by entering into forward currency contracts which lock in an exchange rate. The funds not only hedge against the currency of the country they are invested in, but also in other currencies that behave in a similar fashion. This is known as a cross-hedge and is frequently more profitable than a direct hedge. Funds also hedge interest rate risks by using futures on Treasury securities.

Mutual funds may use derivative instruments as a substitute for investing in traditional securities when it is advantageous to do so. For example, when an S&P 500 index fund receives additional cash from investor purchases, it may be much cheaper to buy S&P futures on a temporary basis than to invest small amounts in 500 different stocks.

At other times, a derivative product may be the only investment that meets a desired need. For example, a fund that wishes to invest in securities denominated in Malaysian currency may not be able to find any such "natural" securities that meet its credit and liquidity standards. However, a structured note could be purchased that's indexed to the Malaysian currency.

Bond funds can enhance yields by receiving a cash premium from the sale of call options. They can leverage their returns by taking a large futures position on margin.

Derivatives began their rapid growth ten years ago in response to genuine needs of different categories of borrowers and investors. The CMO market, which began in 1983, was developed to meet investor needs for mortgage related products. Life insurance companies, for example, with typically long liabilities, could not easily buy mortgage pass throughs, with their attendant prepayment risk. Wall Street originators met their needs by segregating and prioritizing the distribution of cash flows to create shorter and longer issues.

By meeting genuine needs, the derivatives business exploded. But as a result, it became necessary to create and sell "byproduct" bonds, whose inherent characteristics did not suit the natural needs of any particular investor. In the zero sum game of dividing a series of cash flows, if nine out of ten slices of the pie, or tranches of the CMO, are made disproportionately attractive, then the remaining slice or tranche naturally will be disproportionally unattractive—and difficult to sell. One way to sell the "byproduct" bond is to offer a tremendous yield in order to tempt hungry investors into overlooking its fundamental structural weakness.

Derivatives come in such profusion and have so many uses, that they are going to be a permanent fixture on the investment scene. We have contacted several of the larger mutual fund groups and found that all were using some forms of derivatives. Furthermore, the Investment Company Institute recently did a study covering 52 fund groups with 1,728 funds accounting for over half of all long-term assets. The ICI found that 475 of these funds invested in derivatives. The majority of the funds using derivatives (318) had fixed-income objectives. The derivatives accounted for only 2.13% of the assets of the funds reporting some derivative holdings. However, the study went on to say that the maximum theoretical exposure—which was called the notional value—is actually 15.5% of assets.

The groups we talked to all insisted they are closely monitoring their use of derivatives and basically using them conservatively. Nevertheless, there have been some well publicized cases of funds taking large losses because of the use of derivatives, including losses in supposedly safe short-term bond funds. And in several other cases, money fund and bond fund sponsors made cash contributions to their funds, purchased securities from, or purchased shares in their funds in order not to penalize shareholders for the excessive risks they had undertaken.

These problems have developed in large part because derivatives are still new, and even the experts don't know how they will perform in a broad range of economic climates. Some of the byproduct derivatives are so complicated, no one knows just how they will perform.

What can shareholders do?

Mutual funds are going to continue to use derivatives. SEC Chairman Arthur Levitt has sent a letter to the industry asking for better ways to evaluate and address derivatives. There have been reports that regulatory authorities are going to pressure money funds to dump their holdings in derivative securities. If that happens, it would be an improvement. There have been some close calls in the money fund area.

In theory, the use of derivatives should be disclosed in the quarterly and annual reports. As a practical matter we don't think this disclosure is of much help. First of all, it's hard to find. In some cases, the pertinent information is buried in footnotes. Second, even if derivatives are identified, that doesn't give you much of a handle on the possible risks. Third, these reports are historical documents; it's quite possible that the portfolio will have changed materially by the time an investor reads the report. For example, nothing would prevent a fund manager from selling derivatives the day before the end of the report period, and buying them back the day after. In the case of money funds, the portfolios turn over every 50 or so days in any case.

Incidentally, we have it on good authority that one fund manager, whose fund suffered large losses, lied to a reporter who asked if the fund held any derivatives. This was just a few days before the losses occurred.

Fidelity has a new booklet out called "An Overview of Derivatives." The last two pages show how to find the derivatives in the Fidelity funds' portfolios. It can be obtained free from the fund group.

Here are some common sense steps you can take to protect yourself in this strange, new world:

1. Don't be in any rush to try new concepts. Many derivatives have not been tested through an entire market cycle. Remember how the cross-hedges failed the world money funds when the ERM (European Rate Mechanism) faltered.

2. There is no free lunch. If a fund is offering substantially higher yields than competitors with similar portfolios, and the differences can't be explained by fund size or a temporary waiver of expense charges, then you should conclude that you are being asked to take greater risks.

3. Favor simple investments over complex ones. A few years ago, the government plus funds sold by load fund groups seemed like better investments than the plain vanilla government funds. They weren't.

4. Don't expect the fund companies to disclose all the risks of investing. Try to check outside sources.

5. Favor fund groups that are known for their conservative approach.

Press 1 for profits
by Harvey Jacobs
(July 1994 *Investor*)

You've reached the Slush Family of Funds, a people company interested in up-close and personal service.

If you're interested in Aggressive Capital Appreciation, press 1 now. If you'd like Passive Depreciation, press 2. If you want Growth, press 3. For Shrinkage, press 4. If you are Mr. Sludge's tailor, press his blue pants.

If your interest is in Interest, press 5. If you're worried about Inflation, call Weight Watchers. If you're interested in Precious Metals, press 6. If you're interested in Worthless Paper, press 7. If your focus is Global, press 8. If you pressed 8, please specify First, Second, or Third world countries by pressing rapidly.

If your interest is in Futures, press 9. If your interest is the past, call Jurassic Park. If you are interested in building a portfolio for a comfortable retirement, press 10. If it's too late for that, press your prostate.

If you wish to speak to a Representative, press the cute little *. All our representatives are busy now, especially the Cute Little *. Until someone breaks loose, you'll be put on hold. If you'd like to hear

Music, press 11. If you prefer Classical, press 12. If you groove to Pop, press 13. If your bag is Rap, tap, slap or zap, 14.

If you press the little # sign, we'll send you a prospectus on our exciting new Aggressive Depletion Fund. Please read it carefully—but not too carefully—before investing.

The Surgeon General requires us to warn you that excessive pressing can be dangerous to your health, not to mention your wealth. If you sprained your fingertip, contact Sludge Legal Services. If you're pressing with any other body part, call Geraldo Rivera. If you're depressed, join the club. If you're using a rotary phone, forget it. You're just not our kind of people.

Harvey Jacobs (no relation) is a novelist residing in New York's Greenwich Village. His latest book is Beautiful Soup, published by Celadon Press, 101 W. 12th St., Suite 8G, New York, NY 10011 at $12.95.

Duration

(August 1994 *Investor*)

The *Investor* has long used average maturity as a rough measure of bond fund risk. The longer the average maturity, the greater the risk as measured by volatility; the shorter the average maturity, the less the risk. The following table, reproduced from the 1994 *Handbook*, shows how average maturity affected volatility last year.

Bond funds
How Average Maturity Affects Yield and Volatility

	Average Maturity 12/31/93	1993 Yield	1993 Net Asset Value High	Low	Volatility
Vanguard					
Treas. MM	59 days	2.9%	$1.00	$1.00	0.0%
Treasury Short	2.5 yrs	4.7	10.54	10.30	2.3
Treasury Inter	6.7 yrs	5.6	11.44	10.53	8.6
Treasury Long	23.5 yrs	6.4	11.34	9.74	16.4
Fidelity Spartan					
US Gov. MM	63 days	2.8	1.00	1.00	0.0
Limited Mat. Gov.	4.9 yrs	5.7	10.35	9.96	3.9
Gov. Income	15.2 yrs	5.7	11.12	10.66	4.3
Long-Term Gov.	22.7 yrs	6.5	13.87	11.77	17.8
Rowe Price					
Tx Expt MM	61 days	2.0	1.00	1.00	0.0
TF Short-Inter	3.2 yrs	4.2	5.38	5.28	1.9
Tax-Free Inc	18.9 yrs	5.4	10.23	9.39	8.9
TF High-Yield	21.3 yrs	5.9	12.76	11.88	7.4

While average maturity is useful, there's a better measure—called duration. It differs from average maturity in that it takes into account a bond's cash flows from current interest payments. Average maturity doesn't. Here's an example to show the difference. The Babson Bond-Portfolio L and the Benham Target 2005 Fund both had the same average maturity, about 11.4 years at the end of June. But the Babson Fund

has a far shorter duration, approximately 4.8 years vs. 11.4 years for the Benham Target Fund.

The reason for the difference is that the Babson Fund makes regular interest payments, which shorten the time needed to receive the sum total of interest and principal due you over the life of the bond. The Benham Fund is a zero coupon bond fund that doesn't make any distributions until its zero coupon bonds mature. With lower duration, the Babson Fund lost less in this year's rising interest rate environment. In the first six months, its total return declined 4.1%, while the Benham 2005 Fund declined 9.6%—more than twice as much.

Duration vs. average maturity

Fund	Avg. maturity	Duration	Jan-Jun performance
Babson Bond-Port L	11.3	4.8	-4.1
Benham Target 2005	11.4	11.4	-9.6
Babson diff.		-57.9%	-57.3%

Duration is a far more accurate measure of volatility due to interest rate changes. You can multiply a fund's duration by a change in interest rates and get a fund's price movement. A fund with a duration of five will lose 5% of its value with a 1% increase in interest rates. A fund with a duration of 10 would lose 10% of its value. Conversely, a 1% decline in interest rates would result in 5% and 10% gains in total value, respectively. If interest rates change by 2%, double the figures. You can't use average maturity to make these determinations.

The subtleties of duration

Generally speaking longer-term bonds have higher yields and thus have higher durations. Experience will tell you they are riskier. However, let's take the case of two bonds both maturing at the same time—say in 20 years. The bond with the higher yield will have a shorter duration, and thus be less volatile. That's because more interest is paid along the way. By the same token, changes in interest rates and yields will shorten or lengthen durations.

Like maturity, there is more than one way to calculate duration. In addition to calculating to maturity, it can also be calculated to call—that is, when a bond may be redeemed early by the issuer.

There are a number of factors that can reduce the accuracy of duration figures. If a fund holds convertible bonds, they may be excluded from the calculations. Similarly, foreign bonds, which may not track domestic interest rates, can throw the figures off. Derivatives are another problem. They may have different volatilities and, as happened earlier this year, a lack of liquidity can affect their prices, regardless of their theoretical value (i.e. nobody will buy them at a fair price, or sometimes, at any price).

Duration is less meaningful for junk bonds. Interest rate changes are only a small part of the risk of holding them. (That's why we list hi-yield bond funds in the long-term section, even though they may have intermediate-term maturities.)

Availability of the data

We contacted the service reps at 20 large no-load fund groups; 16 had data, but not all of it was timely. Four—Dreyfus, SAFECO, USAA and Evergreen—were unable to provide duration figures.

If or when we can get general industry cooperation to supply current duration figures, we will substitute them for average maturity. We don't know when this will be, but the mutual fund industry is moving in this direction. In the meantime, you should inquire about duration when you call a fund group. It's the best measure of interest rate sensitivity for bond funds.

NTF portfolios
(August 1994 *Investor*)

In the last three issues, we dealt with single family investing. While there were great advantages, particularly in terms of telephone switching and record keeping, the compensating disadvantage was a more limited selection of funds. A number of groups were strong in some areas, weaker in others.

With the advent of no transaction fee (NTF) investing through discount brokers such as Charles Schwab and Fidelity Brokerage, it is possible to have the simplicity of pure no-load, single family investing while choosing from among a far greater variety of top performing no-loads. With this in mind, we have created sample portfolios using each broker firm's no-transaction-fee funds only. These portfolios are modeled after our Best Buys, as were the single family portfolios we previously showed. We think using NTF funds at a discount broker makes a great deal of sense for all investors.

The **Fidelity FundsNetwork** currently offers about 315 funds from 31 outside fund families as well as all of Fidelity's no-loads on an NTF basis. The great advantage of the Fidelity FundsNetwork is the availability of many Fidelity funds on a no transaction fee basis. None of these funds are available at no fee from Charles Schwab's OneSource program. In the following recommended portfolios, we leaned toward non-Fidelity funds so as to examine more possibilities. We, of course, could have easily put together an all-Fidelity portfolio, as we did last April, but that wasn't our goal. If you're going to use the Fidelity FundsNetwork, you must open an account at Fidelity Brokerage; the Network is not available through a regular Fidelity mutual fund account. Once the account is opened, though, you can pay for your purchases with money from any of the Fidelity money funds.

Wealth Builder		Port. Dist. %
Dynamics	agg gr	5
Emerging Growth	agg gr	5
Growth	growth	20
Janus Mercury	agg-gr	5
Janus	growth	10
Montgomery Emerg Mkts	int'l	10
Fidelity Europe Cap App	int'l	10
Fidelity SE Asia	int'l	10
Dreyfus Gro & Inc	gr-inc	15
Fidelity Eq Inc II	gr-inc	15
Fidelity Convertible Sec	income	15
Founders Balanced	income	10

Pre-Retirement		
Montgomery Growth	growth	15
Fidelity Value	growth	10
Lexington Emerg Mkts	int'l	5
Fidelity Europe Cap App	int'l	10
Strong Intl Stk	int'l	10
Warburg Pincus Gro & Inc	gr-inc	15
Evergreen Foundation	income	15
Janus Flex	bond	10
Fidelity Mortgage Sec	bond	10

Retirement		
Fidelity Asst Mgr Growth	gr-inc	15
Strong Total Return	gr-inc	10
Montgomery Emerg Mkts	int'l	5
Fidelity Europe Cap App	int'l	10
Warburg Pincus Intl Eq	int'l	5
Fidelity Asset Mgr	income	10
Fidelity Puritan	income	10
Janus Flex	bond	20
Lexington GNMA	bond	15

Charles Schwab's OneSource offers 269 funds from 27 families on a no transaction fee basis (plus another 90 only through financial advisers). Most of these funds are also offered NTF at Fidelity, but there are two notable exceptions: Twentieth Century and Invesco. If you use the Schwab service, you must use Schwab's money funds. While Schwab has fewer NTF funds than Fidelity, it does have more funds overall. For example, it is possible to buy Fidelity funds at Schwab by paying their transaction fees.

Wealth Builder		Port. Dist.%
Berger Small Co	agg-gr	5
Montgomery Growth	growth	10
Lexington Emerg Mkts	int'l	10
Invesco Europe	int'l	10
Invesco Pac Basin	int'l	10
Warburg Pincus Gro & Inc	gr-inc	15
Dreyfus Gro & Inc	gr-inc	15
Twentieth Value	gr-inc	10
Dreyfus Balanced	income	15

Pre-Retirement		
N-B Guardian	growth	15
Strong Oppty	growth	10
Montgomery Emerg Mkts	int'l	5
Invesco Europe	int'l	10

Pre-Retirement		Port. Dist.%
Warburg Pincus Intl	int'l	10
Berger 101	gr-inc	15
Invesco Total Return	income	15
Janus Flex	bond	10
Lexington GNMA	bond	10

Retirement		
Strong Total Return	gr-inc	10
Founders Blue Chip	gr-inc	15
Montgomery Emerg Mkts	int'l	5
Strong Int'l Stk	int'l	15
Invesco Industrial Inc	gr-inc	10
Founders Balanced	income	10
Janus Flex	bond	20
Lexington GNMA	bond	15

In addition at least three other discount brokers offer NTF funds: Jack White, Waterhouse Securities, and Muriel Siebert. If we were to develop Best Buys portfolios for these brokers, they would be similar to the above.

Are there too many funds?

(September 1994 *Investor*)

With mutual funds popping up like spring dandelions, it's hard to keep track of them all. The latest count: nearly 5,000, an increase of nearly 650 funds in a year. Naysayers are now complaining there are too many funds. Some of their complaints:

■ So many funds are unnecessary and redundant;

■ the profusion can't help but hopelessly confuse investors;

■ and it all signifies a major bear market in the offing (since frantic investment activity generally signals the top of a market).

We disagree on all counts!

How many funds are just right, and how many unnecessary? It's like asking how many different automobile models are necessary? How many stocks? How many flavors of ice cream?

As a concept, "necessary" is irrelevant. The tremendous increase in the number of funds has been propelled by investor demand and by a desire on the part of fund groups to offer their investors a complete array of different types of funds. Today, every large fund group and many of the medium-sized families can provide shareholders with a complete selection of stock, bond and money market funds. That's good for them—and convenient for you.

About confusion: first of all, we seriously doubt that any significant number of investors are confused. To say that 4,940 funds are too many is like saying having over 10,000 actively-traded stocks makes it too difficult to choose one. We never met a broker who thought so.

In the case of mutual funds, about 950 are money market funds, to begin with. You obviously don't need to look at more than one or two of them. Next

about 1,500 are general equity funds, another 700 specialized and world funds, some 1,000 taxable bond funds and 900 tax-free bond funds. More than half of the long-term funds are load funds or no-loads that for one reason or another are not available to the general public; these can be eliminated immediately. In any case, funds then need to be subdivided into objective categories. At that point, you simply compare like funds. In the case of the *Investor*, you have a choice of 96 aggressive growth funds, 120 growth funds, 79 growth-income funds, 62 international funds, 139 tax-free funds, etc. Then you will want to know how many of these are successful. Those few that are become your real choices. You've now narrowed the universe down and made the task of selecting the best funds easily manageable.

Does growth foretell a bust?

Whether the vast expansion in funds—and cash inflows into them—foretells the end of a major up cycle is hard to say. In 1986 a similar pattern existed,

WHAT WE NOTED IN MARCH 1992
Total Sales Of Stocks & Bond Funds
(billions of dollars)

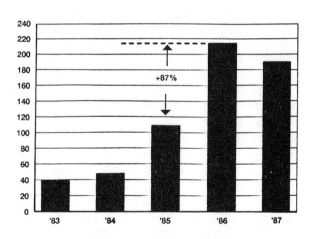

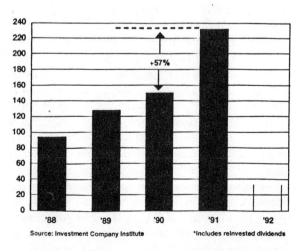

Source: Investment Company Institute   *Includes reinvested dividends

particularly in terms of mutual fund purchases. They had exploded over the three previous years, 1983-1985. The following year, 1987, of course saw a major break in the market and a decline in fund purchases. A few years later, in our March 1992 issue, we commented on this pattern, using the chart reproduced below. In the accompanying copy we said we thought 1992 would be a year of modest gains; we turned out to be right. However, we implied that we thought mutual fund purchases would go down in 1992. That turned out to be wildly wrong. Mutual fund purchases in 1992 jumped 55% above the 1991 level, and then leaped another 41% in '93 over '92.

So far in 1994, purchases are up 8% over the same months in '93. (All the above figures and the chart are gross sales, including reinvestments.) Net new sales, which exclude reinvestments and subtract redemptions, while still positive at $90 billion, are down 35%. However, 1994 net new sales have been severely impacted by net redemptions in bond funds. Excluding bond fund sales, net equity sales, at $78 billion, are actually up 17% over 1993.

Another, perhaps more relevant factor, is simply that the current popularity of mutual funds is due to the aging of the baby boom generation.

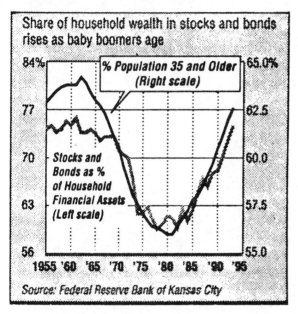

Source: Federal Reserve Bank of Kansas City

The point is that major bull markets end and bear markets begin for many reasons. Beware of overly simplistic cause and effect reasoning.

Protect us from the crises mongers

Now that the mutual fund industry has become a giant, it's become fair game for writers looking to profit by attacking the fund industry. One new book, "Surviving the Coming Mutual Fund Crisis," likens the growth of the fund industry to the South Sea Bubble mania of 275 years ago. Somebody should explain to the author that he's comparing an investment *vehicle* to an investment.

Other articles have more valid criticisms. That's not surprising. Any industry that has grown as gargantuan as this one is bound to have some warts. The problem is that the critics' charges lack perspective. The fund industry is well regulated, and is virtually unique among profit-making enterprises in that it seeks still more regulation. A substantial degree of industry self-regulation also exists. We can think of no better investment alternative. If not in funds, where else are you going to get respectable returns for the risks you take?

No-bond portfolios
(October 1994 *Investor*)

We want to report to you the results of some particularly thought-provoking research that concerns the allocation of your financial assets. The research was done by Peter L. Bernstein, an economist and securities analyst, whom we have quoted in the past. Originally, he did his work in 1988; recently, he updated it.

Bernstein's research leads him to argue against the common asset allocation strategy of 60% equities and 40% bonds. That's the approach many balanced funds take, including Dodge & Cox's, Founders', IAI's, Price's and Vanguard's Wellington. Bernstein argues that a portfolio consisting of 75% equities and 25% cash is at least as good, and may well be superior to the conventional allocation, depending on the market climate.

Here are some of the details of his research.

The his 1988 work, Bernstein used the S&P 500 as a proxy for stocks, the long-term Treasury bond to represent bonds, and 90-day Treasury bills for cash. Bernstein found that from 1954 until the middle of 1988, a portfolio comprised of 60% stocks and 40% bonds had an annual compound yield of 9.17% with a standard deviation (a measure of risk) of 5.78. Over the same period, a portfolio 75% stocks and 25% cash generated a 10.24% total return—12% greater. Meanwhile, the standard deviation rose only 4%, to 5.99%. Thus the stocks/cash portfolio delivered a substantially larger gain with only slightly more risk.

However, most stock market research is maddeningly time-period sensitive. A strategy that appears to work during one specific period of time, may not work at all in some other period. And you only have to vary the time slightly. In this case, The 1954-1988 period covered many years when bonds were in a bear market. This biased the results toward the stocks/cash strategy.

The study was recently redone using a 1974 to mid-1994 base. That's a period that includes the great bond bull market of the 80s. Not surprisingly, the advantage of the stocks/cash plan almost disappears. Over the last 20 years, the stock/bond portfolio averaged 11.40% per year, while the stock/cash portfolio averaged 11.18%. The standard deviations were 6.51% versus 6.29%. Thus, the stock/bond portfolio had a 2% advantage in performance at the cost of a 3.5% higher standard deviation.

Bernstein also replicated his study using other asset classes. Instead of using the S&P 500 as a representation of stocks, he substituted a mix of 70% S&P stocks and 30% small company stocks. Second, he substituted an intermediate-term bond for the long bond. The addition of small company stocks raises both the risk level and returns of the portfolio. Shortening bond fund maturities has the opposite effect. Making these changes improves the risk/reward relationship of both portfolios. The new mixed-stock portfolio and cash outperforms the new stock/bond portfolio at greater risk, but it is not as statistically significant as it appears in the accompanying chart.

Since these latest readings don't show one strategy clearly dominant over the other, why should you consider such a radical departure from conventional asset allocation?

Here are three reasons for substituting cash for bonds in your portfolio:

■ Bonds can suffer negative returns, cash cannot.

■ The original reason for balancing a stock portfolio with bonds is that, historically, the two asset classes did not move in tandem. This has been less true in recent years. Stocks and bonds now decline simultaneously much of the time. Since 1974, the S&P 500 has declined during 24 quarters out of 82. Long bonds also declined in 18 of these 24 quarters including, of course, the first quarter of 1994.

■ We believe the great, decade-long bull market in bonds is over. Thus the original study may be more relevant than the update.

When bonds are in a bear market, the stocks-and-cash plan is clearly superior. When bonds are in a bull market, the two strategies are roughly comparable. If that's the case, we feel you are better off with the stocks-and-cash approach. However, if you feel strongly about the direction of interest rates—and stocks, for that matter—this could change the equation. A substantial decline in interest rates in the remaining years of this century, for example, would enhance the appeal of the stocks/bonds strategy. On the other hand, if there is a resurgence of inflation, then it's a different story.

Looking down the road a few years, Alan Greenspan's term as the Federal Reserve chairman expires in March 1996. Already, there's speculation that a Clinton appointee, Vice Chairman Alan Blinder, may be the next Fed Chairman. In all likelihood, Blinder will not be as tough in controlling inflation as Greenspan has been! We're speculating, of course. But this possibility, along with such endemic factors as the current high price of gold and our government's continuing deficit financing makes us seriously consider gradually shifting from a conventional stock/bond portfolio to an emphasis on

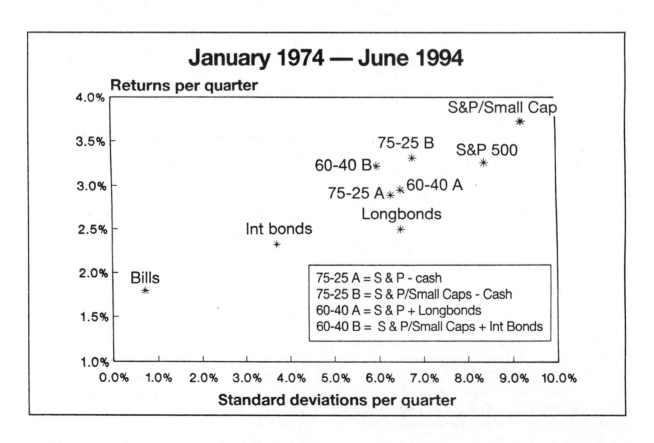

stocks and cash. We say gradually since current long-term bond yields are fairly high right now and, in the near term, might trend lower.

Again, taking the longer-term point of view, if you believe that the long-term bull market in bonds is essentially over, we suggest one way to gradually switch to a stock/cash allocation is to stop reinvesting distributions from your bond funds. Either have the fund send you a check each month, or, if you're with one of the larger groups, tell them to direct the distributions to a money or stock fund.

We also suggest you consider direct investments in Treasury bonds when fixed-income yields are low. As we pointed out, the problem with bonds is you can lose money. That's always true in bond funds, which have no maturity. However, if you buy individual bonds in the short- to intermediate-term range you have the option of holding to maturity and receiving the face value of the bonds. We suggest U.S. Treasuries because you have no worry about the credit risk.

Following the stocks-and-cash strategy doesn't necessarily mean you never hold bonds. It means that stocks and cash are your permanent investments. Cash becomes your diversifier and risk-reducer. Bonds are only bought opportunistically, that is, when you believe interest rates are about to decline. Then bonds can produce attractive returns. This is similar to our view of gold. We don't believe gold should be a permanent part of your portfolio. However, you can invest in gold when you think an opportunity is presenting itself. On the other hand, if you employ a traditional stock/bond allocation, the reverse is true. Cash becomes your opportunistic purchase.

First month performance
(November 1994 *Investor*)

The conventional wisdom, which we continue to espouse in the *Guide*, is not to buy brand new funds. Our logic: it doesn't pay to take a chance when so many outstanding funds already exist. This has always been our general recommendation, even though we've known some new funds that had excellent performances right out of the box.

However, in the current avalanche of new funds, more and more infants are doing quite well right from their cradle days. Since we suspect that some large fund groups might be favoring their new offerings in some way, we decided to do some statistical analysis to see if our suspicion had any foundation. Our methodology was to take each new fund's first calendar month performance and compare it to the average fund in its objective category. (If a fund begins in the middle of the month, we don't add it to our data base until the first of the next month.) To simplify our study, we restricted our research to actively-managed, diversified, domestic equity

funds. (It would have been pointless to include new index funds.) Since 1989, 105 funds met our criteria.

Our first finding was that the new funds did slightly better than average in their initial month. They posted an average 1.1% gain for the month, as compared to a 0.3% gain for the benchmarks. However, this 0.8% differential drops to 0.3% if we compute the median new fund, perhaps a fairer measure, since two new funds posted extreme performances their first month. For example, Monetta Mid-Cap Equity was up a stunning 16.7% in its first full month, 13.2% better than the average growth fund that month.

Best first month's performance

	New fund	Adv. over benchmark
Monetta Mid-Cap Eqty	16.7	13.2
Janus Enterprise	13.9	12.1
Fidelity Emerging Gr	14.8	6.6
Robrtsn Steph Contrarian	6.9	6.4
Janus Balanced	6.4	6.0
PBHG Emerg Gro	10.9	5.8

We next looked to see if we could develop any pattern according to specific fund family. To be blunt: are some of the larger groups favoring their new funds? For example, are the new funds allowed to load up on IPO's? Are other funds in the group buying the new fund's stocks to drive up prices? Are the families throwing their finest investment management minds into the new funds? And if any or all of this were true, could you profit from the knowledge?

We took an average of each family's new funds to see if we could discern any pattern. Families with only one new fund are excluded from the following table.

Average difference in total return
New funds versus their benchmarks

Family	# funds	Avg diff
Janus	4	5.5
Robertson Stephens	2	4.4
Lindner	3	2.6
Strong	3	2.0
Fidelity	10	1.9
Price, Rowe	4	1.6
Evergreen	3	1.4
Crabbe Huson	2	1.3
Mean		0.8
IAI	4	0.6
Royce	3	0.3
Median		0.3
Benham	3	0.2
Columbia	2	0.1
Dreyfus	5	0.0
Merriman	4	-0.2
Invesco	4	-0.3
USAA	2	-0.4
Montgomery	3	-0.5
Loomis Sayles	3	-0.8
Portico	3	-1.0
Scudder	3	-1.1
Capiello Rushmore	3	-2.1

While the groups at the top of the chart did substantially better than average, we want to emphasize that this evidence is all statistical. The results may be due to chance or simply fortuitous timing. (That was certainly the case when the Robertson Stephens Contrarian Fund was launched in a down month.) Nevertheless, if you like the concept of a new fund or a particular manager's record and want to take a flyer on it, we think you would have a better chance with a new fund from Janus, Fidelity, Strong, Price or Lindner. The odds on Fidelity look particularly good; eight out of ten of their new funds surpassed their benchmarks, and its latest fund, Export, available for sale on Oct. 10th, was up 7.1% in its first 24 days. The S&P 500 gained 0.6% during the same period.

Growth funds shine

(December 1994 *Investor*)

After several years when value funds outperformed growth funds, the cycle appears to have turned. Since June, growth funds have done better than their value-oriented cousins.

S&P/BARRA returns

Year	Growth	Value
1990	0.2	6.8
1991	38.4	22.6
1992	5.1	10.5
1993	1.7	18.6
1Q 1994	-4.3	-3.3
2Q 1994	-0.1	0.9
3Q 1994	7.2	2.6
Oct '94	6.3	1.4
Nov '94	-3.3	-4.1

The main reason for the switch appears to be that the better performance of the value stocks in 1992, 1993 and the first part of 1994 drove their valuations above those of the growth funds. Normally, growth stocks have higher ratios of price to earnings and market price to book value. This is shown graphically in the following table, provided by T. Rowe Price. It shows price/earnings ratios of S&P/BARRA Growth and Value indexes over the years. (These are the indexes tracked by the Vanguard Growth and Value Index Funds.)

As of September the five largest companies in the Value Index are Exxon, Royal Dutch Petroleum, General Motors, IBM and Mobil. These and other value stocks benefitted from the cyclical expansion in the economy in recent years. The five largest companies in the Growth Index are Wal-Mart, General Electric, Philip Morris, AT&T and Coca Cola. Now,

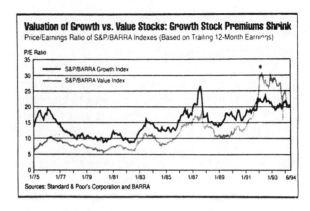

Valuation of Growth vs. Value Stocks: Growth Stock Premiums Shrink
Price/Earnings Ratio of S&P/BARRA Indexes (Based on Trailing 12-Month Earnings)
Sources: Standard & Poor's Corporation and BARRA

as the economy slows, companies with the ability to steadily grow earnings over the years have become relatively more attractive.

Persistency of performance study

(January, 1995 *Investor*)

Everyone knows that past results do not guarantee future performance. Still, buying on past performance remains the primary way to pick a fund. However, which past performance to consider remains a hotly debated topic. Our general advice is to look for good performance over the varying periods we show in the Investor's tables.

In the fall of 1991 we decided to track the results of a strategy based on a one-year hold in each year's top-ranked diversified no-load. We called it our Persistency of Performance study. The strategy calls for buying each year's top-ranked diversified no-load at the beginning of the following year. It is imperative that only diversified funds are considered. Diversified funds will generally continue to be above-average performers because of management continuity and portfolio momentum. On the other hand, the performance of non-diversified funds, such as sector or gold funds, is much more erratic if for no other reason than that the portfolio manager is less important. We find that if this strategy is followed for a long period of time, you can obtain returns considerably better than those of the average fund.

If you had adopted this strategy 19 years ago, you would have done more than four times as well as if you had invested in the average equity fund. One thousand dollars invested in the top-performers grew to $52,633,, an average annual gain of 23.2%. In comparison, the average diversified no-load grew to only $12,083 for a 14.0% average annual gain. (Data prior to 1992 were "back-tested." Since the beginning of 1992, we have followed the strategy "real-time.") Over the 19 years our top-rated selections have outperformed the average diversified no-load 14 times. One year was a tie. Notwithstanding the fact that most of our selections were high-volatility, aggressive funds, there were only two years with losses.

Last year at this time we recommended that followers of the Persistency of Performance strategy buy PBHG Growth, 1993's leading diversified no-load. In a tough year, PBHG Growth gained 4.8%, while the benchmark lost 1.5%.

How the top diversified domestic no-load equity funds fared

Year	No-load fund	Gain in record year	Gain following year	Average diversified no-load fund
1975	44 Wall Street	184.1	46.5	27.6
1976	Sequoia	70.8	19.9	3.5
1977	Value Line Leveraged Growth	51.1	27.6	11.6
1978	Twentieth Century Gr (3)	47.2	74.2	28.6
1979	Able Associates (3)	79.1	56.7	33.6
1980	Hartwell Leverage	93.9	-13.2	-1.0
1981	Lindner	34.8	27.1	23.7
1982	Tudor (6)	44.5	28.0	21.2
1983	Strong Investment (2)	44.7	9.7	-0.6
1984	Vanguard High Yield Stock	25.2	30.1	27.1
1985	Fidelity OTC (2)	69.0	11.4	13.9
1986	Strong Opportunity (7)	59.9	11.8	0.4
1987	Mathers (11)	26.9	13.7	15.6
1988	Kaufmann	58.6	46.8	22.9
1989	Twentieth Century Vista (5)	52.2	-15.7	-5.8
1990	Founders Discovery (11)	13.1	62.5	33.2
1991	Montgomery Small Cap (3)	98.7	9.6	9.6
1992	Oakmark (2)	48.9	30.5	14.7
1993	PBHG Growth (26)	46.5	4.8	-1.5
1994	PBHG Emerging Growth (2)	23.8	—	—
	Average gain	57.1	23.2	14.0
	What $1,000 grew to:		$52,633	$11,986

Excluded from the study were specialized (sector and precious metals) and international funds. The numbers in parentheses show the rank among all funds.

For those of you who are following the strategy, you should now switch out of PBHG Growth and into PBHG Emerging Growth Fund. With a 23.8% gain in 1994, it was the top-ranked diversified no-load. This is truly remarkable. It's the first time that a fund group has won in two consecutive years, so it will just take a phone call to implement the strategy. (There was only one other duplication—Twentieth Century Growth and Vista—but that occurred 12 years apart.)

PBHG Emerging Growth, is run on a day to day basis by Christine Baxter, the daughter of partner Harold Baxter. Gary Pilgrim, manager of Growth, is co-manager and has oversight responsibility.

PBHG Emerging Growth has the same philosophy as Growth: it owns stocks with earnings per share growing at an exceptional rate. The weighted average EPS growth of the fund's portfolio stocks the last 12 months was 68%. The basic difference between the two funds is that Emerging Growth buys stocks with smaller market caps—$250 million maximum at the time of purchase. They will continue to hold when the cap size exceeds the threshold. Median cap size of the fund as of Nov 30th was $249MM. As is true of virtually all of 1994's winners, the fund had a huge holding in technology stocks, 40% of assets. However, this position was arrived at using a bottoms up process, so this will likely change over time. The fund currently has 75 issues in the portfolio—all U.S. stocks, and keeps the number of issues in a 70-85 range. It will not allow its largest position to exceed 3%. Total net assets are currently $176 million. It's a volatile fund that stays fully invested. We think it will do well this year.

Retirement portfolios
(February, 1995 *Investor*)

The *Investor*'s three model portfolios, which each month we publish on the back page of the newsletter, take three approaches to planning. They differ in the amount of risk they assume, and are based on the premise that age is the primary determinant of the amount of risk.

We presume that younger, working investors can afford more risk and construct our *Wealth Builder* portfolio accordingly. As people get older, they tend to become more conservative. Our *Pre-Retirement* portfolio is aimed at this sort of investor. Finally, in retirement, people usually become income oriented; for them, we have the *Retirement* portfolio.

In the last few years this type of asset allocation—almost always shown graphically as a pie chart—has become commonplace in magazines and fund literature.

The problem with our Best Buys portfolios—and everyone else's model portfolios, for that matter—is that they are "one size fits all." Or, in our case, three sizes fit all. They assume that everybody who is working or in a similar age bracket has similar asset allocation needs. And the same for everyone who is retired. That's not necessarily true, of course. Other factors differentiate people. One of the most important, even among people the same age, is their wealth. Face it, the wealthy can afford to take greater risks without the concern that a serious loss would change their lifestyle.

In this article, we'd like to discuss the importance of wealth in constructing your portfolio. We especially emphasize the wealth factor for retirees, who are most dependent on their financial nest eggs.

To illustrate how wealth makes a difference we have constructed portfolios for retired couples with $3 million, $1 million, and $300,000 in financial assets. In order to make them as broadly applicable as possible we have made a number of generalized assumptions.

The assumptions

First, we assumed rates of return for stocks, bonds, and CDs based on long-term averages. Over the last 50 years, the S&P 500 has averaged 11.9% per year; the average small cap stock, 13.6% per year. In the case of fixed-income, we made an effort to take into account today's high rates. We assumed the million-dollar couples invested in tax-free bonds, while the $300,000 couple invested in taxables. In calculating income taxes, we assumed that both members of the household are over 65 years of age. To make it simple, we assumed no earned income or corporate pension, only investment income and Social Security. And, we ignored state income taxes. We based Social Security for the wealthiest couple on the maximum currently obtainable for someone who always earned at the Social Security wage-base maximum, plus an additional one-half for a spouse. Social Security for the $300,000 couple was based on the average sum currently paid. We split the difference for the $1 million portfolio. As you read on, keep in mind that different assumptions will give significantly different results. *Stocks may not achieve their long-term average the next five-to-ten years.*

Needs

Next we estimated how much each couple would need to maintain their style of living in the New York area and in Phoenix. New York, of course, is representative of a high cost part of the country. Phoenix is more typical of lower cost retirement areas in the South. While the differences may seem huge, they are loosely based on the cost of living index computed in the American Cost of Living Survey, constructed by the American Chamber of Commerce Research Association. The current index reading for the New York area is 206.3. For Phoenix, the comparable number is 101.2. As for any particular person's absolute level of need, everyone is different. So we just took a stab at it.

We then calculated the difference between each couple's income and their need in two ways. The first assumes that their respective portfolios will maintain their value. The second assumes a maximum loss of value that would take a number of years to recoup.

The results

As the table shows, the family with $3 million doesn't have anything to worry about. It doesn't matter whether their portfolios are invested in stocks or bonds. They will get a higher total return from stocks. Even with a worst case scenario, given sufficient time, the stocks will produce a greater return than a portfolio invested in municipal bonds. Thus, this lucky couple can live anywhere they want.

Illustrating this flexibility, a colleague of ours once told us of a wealthy doctor client for whom he was managing investments. The doctor had $600,000 in a pension plan, and instructed the manager to invest the dollars in the riskiest possible way. The money manager protested that since it was for retirement, the pension money should be invested as conservatively as possible. The doctor's response: he didn't need the money, so if it was lost there would be no impact on his lifestyle. On the other hand, if he achieved super gains, he would have enough to endow a wing of the hospital where he practiced. He had the wherewithal to make that his choice.

For the couple with $1 million in financial assets, we designed a portfolio comprised of 65% stocks and 35% bonds (the same as our *Retirement* portfolio). Under normal conditions it should provide a comfortable living either in New York or in a Southern retirement area. In a worst case situation, the couple would have to reduce their living expenses 11% in order to stay in New York. But they'd have more than enough to live elsewhere.

We prepared four different portfolios for the couple with only $300,000 in financial assets. In terms of risk, they ranged from a portfolio that was invested two-thirds in stocks and one-third in bonds to one invested entirely in bank CDs. Before we ran the numbers we thought that fixed-income would win out on a worst case basis. But this didn't turn out to be the case. Assuming that stocks can return their historical postwar average of 12% a year, they produce the winning strategy. Mix in some bonds, and volatility goes down. This makes us feel good about our Best Buys *Retirement* Portfolio with its weighting of 65% stocks, 35% bonds.

We decided to do the New York City vs. Phoenix comparison. It was partly inspired by potential managed account clients we've had who live in the New York area. Some with modest portfolios in the $300,000 range have questioned whether retirement in such a high-cost area would be viable.

After consulting with them about their lifestyles and cash flow, it became apparent that they would have difficulty retiring around New York. Frequently we told these people that if they wished to remain, they would need some sort of part-time job. Alternately, they should consider moving to a less expensive part of the country. Our figures bear this out. Only Option 1, the portfolio with 65% stocks, covered living needs in New York. The other three portfolios fell short. The super-safe CDs had an $11,566 deficit. On the other hand, the throw-off from all four portfolios would cover the lower living expenses in Phoenix.

In preparing these examples, we did not take inflation into account. Projecting these results out ten years would give an even greater advantage to stocks over fixed-income. Furthermore, we didn't consider eating into capital to meet living expenses, which could be a viable alternative for some people. But what we have proved once again, is just what we have always preached: the way to get true growth is to invest in equities, not lend your money at some rate of interest.

The point of this little exercise is to get you thinking about your own needs. These tables are a starting point to help you develop your own retirement strategy—which will be unique to you.

SECTION II

No-Load Fund Performance Tables

CHAPTER 3

Explanation of tables

Alphabetical tables of no-load funds

The statistical tables that follow show all no-loads in existence since the beginning of 1994 plus some begun during the year. Other funds started in 1994 and early 1995 are listed in the *Handbook's* Directory Sections.

Explanation of symbols: A † sign to the right of a fund names indicates the fund has a low load or sales charge applicable to some purchases. A ‡ sign next to the fund name indicates the fund is in some way limiting sales—it may be closed to new shareholders, restricting share ownership to certain classes such as corporations, institutions, clients of a brokerage house or purchasers of variable annuities. See the Directory Section for specifics. An asterisk beside a fund in Chapter 7 indicates there is switching between a fund group and an unaffiliated money fund. In Chapter 4, the right pages, percent distribution of portfolio columns: Parenthesis around a cash percentage figure indicates the fund is leveraged. The asterisk beside the column titled "bond" indicates that preferred stocks are also included in this category.

Performance computations: The *Handbook* shows performance on a total return basis. This is the percent gain or loss for a fund, including distributions, over the stated period. For example, for the AARP Capital Growth Fund we show a total return in 1994 of -10.0, meaning that including distributions, AARP Capital Growth lost 10.0% from Jan. 1 through Dec. 31, 1994. It is important to note that the *Handbook's* figures rate the funds' performance—not the investors' experience. The calculations do not take into account front-end low loads or redemption fees, nor taxes you might have to pay on distributions.

Three, five and ten year performance figures are compounded. This means you cannot average the individual years arithmetically to get the compounded results.

Quintile ranking system: The *Handbook* uses superscript numbers (exponents) above each performance figure to show the fund's rank *within its objective category*. For example, an aggressive growth fund with a "1" above its performance figure is in the top 20% of all aggressive growth funds for the indicated period. A "2" indicates the fund was in the second 20% (or top 40%) of all funds that have the same investment objective. A "3" indicates the third or middle quintile. These are average funds. Funds ranked "4" or "5" are below average. If you don't know a fund's objective, check the right hand pages of Chapter 4, which lists all stock and bond funds in alphabetical order.

Yield and Distributions: Are based on the income distributions for the latest twelve months divided by

ending NAV. An adjustment is made for capital gains distributions by adding them back into the ending NAV. For investment analysis, long and short-term capital gains distributions are totaled in the capital gains column.

In the case of the Benham Zero Coupon Bond Funds, we show a yield-to-maturity figure even though no actual interest is paid. It's the yield you would receive if you held the fund until it was liquidated at maturity.

Portfolio distribution: Shows the percent of each fund's year-end total assets invested in stocks, bonds and preferreds, and cash or cash equivalents. This information can be used in conjunction with the investing principles described in the *Guide*, and with the cash position data published in *The No-Load Fund Investor* newsletter.

NAVs and total assets are shown for two years. If a fund's assets have grown at a faster rate than its per share NAV, the fund has had net sales. If the asset growth was less than the per share growth, the fund is in net redemptions. See the *Guide* for investment implications.

Betas are computed using least squares correlation and regression analysis. Monthly percentage returns (adjusted for reinvestment of all distributions) are computed for both the funds and the Wilshire 5000, a broad market index reflecting fund portfolios for the latest 36 months. Second, these returns are expressed in "risk premium" form by subtracting from each the return on risk-free Treasury bills, thus reducing the observations to data reflective of the rewards attained for bearing risk. Betas, the funds' objectives, year-to-year variations in prices and the yield are all factors to consider in determining the amount of risk you wish to take.

As a benchmark, following are the average betas by objective for funds in this edition of the *Handbook*.

Betas ranked by objective
3 yrs ending 1994

Aggressive growth	1.16
Sector	1.07
Small company growth	1.04
Growth	.93
Growth-income	.86
Global	.76
International	.74
Income	.62
Tax-free	.39
Precious metals	.37
Fixed-income	.21
Avg stock	.91
Avg diversified stock	.94

Beta has two companions: the *coefficient of determination* and the *alpha*. The coefficient of determination, notated as "r²," measures the percentage of variability due to the market. Index funds have r²'s approaching 100. All their variability is due to the market. Gold funds have low r²'s. Their variability is only slightly related to the overall stock market. The other measure, alpha, which measures non-market-related variability, is considered by some to be an indicator of management ability.

The *Handbook* shows the beta and r², but not the alpha. Instead we include the *Sharpe* ratio, which measures the reward per unit of risk, with risk being defined as variability. It is the fund's performance, minus a risk free constant, divided by the fund's standard deviation. The Sharpe ratio, developed by Nobel prize winning economist William F. Sharpe, attempts to reduce all portfolio results to the same risk level in order to assess management's ability, i.e. a management which produces a mediocre return while taking a large risk with your capital is inferior to one which can produce that same return with much lower risk. In order to simplify the resulting ratings they are shown with letter grades—from A to F. Funds with an "A" have posted the best gains with the least risk within their objective category.

Chapter 4 also includes a fourth measure of risk, *standard deviation*, which measures a security's periodic variations from its own average performance. This differs from beta which measures the variation in relation to a separate index. The standard deviations are particularly useful for evaluating the risk of bond funds, because regressing their performance to a stock market index has limited value. We show betas for bond funds basically for consistency's sake. The greater the standard deviation, the greater the volatility and therefore the greater the risk. As a benchmark, the standard deviation for the latest three year period is 1.27 for the average fixed-income fund and 1.64 for the average tax-free fund.

The *Handbook's* alphabetical listing enables you to easily locate your fund and determine its performance, objective, risk, price, size and yield. Expense and turnover ratios can be found in the Directory section.

Additional stock and bond funds available no-load through discount brokers

Chapter 12 lists funds available through discount brokerage firms that are normally not available to individual investors. They include the following:
- Institutional funds that either have minimum initial investments of $100,000 or more, or are not available to individual investors, that can be purchased through discount brokerage firms at lower ($10,000 or less) initial minimums. Some are available to all brokerage customers and some are available only through financial advisers.
- Load funds that are available through discount brokerage firms at NAV. Some are available to all customers and some are available only through financial advisers.

Ranking tables

To pinpoint a fund's performance with other funds of the same objective consult the ranking tables which immediately follow the alphabetical tables. There, separate tables rank all no-loads by percent change within objective category for 1994, and for the three and five year periods ending in 1994. Next the *Handbook* shows the top 50 no-loads for the one, three, five, and ten-year periods. These tables enable you to spot the best performers without regard to their objective category.

Funds by fund group

The *Handbook* has a special statistical chapter designed to help you select the family best suited to your needs. The performance data in Chapter 7 are arrayed by fund group. No-load and low-load funds are arrayed from the most speculative to the most conservative. Each fund is listed with its objective, assets, one-, three- and five-year returns, as well as quintile rankings. We then give you space in adjacent columns to post the quintile ranks of funds that interest you. You can conveniently average the rankings and compare fund groups. For example, let's say you anticipate investing in an aggressive growth fund, an income fund and a municipal bond fund during the course of a full market cycle. In addition you plan to use the group's money market fund for "parking lot" purposes. You decide that in the Strong group you are interested in Strong Opportunity, Growth, International and Money Market. In the 1994 performance column, you post Opportunity's quintile ranking of "2," Growth's "1" and International's ranking of "3." Average the three numbers (2, 1, 3) to get a 2.0. Repeat this process for the other periods where data is available. Then do the same for other fund groups. The lower the average number, obviously, the better the family is for you. If you plan to use a group's money fund as a significant part of your investment strategy in a meaningful way for yield, then it too should be averaged in. In this case Money Market has a quintile ranking of "1."

As you evaluate these funds' quintile rankings, bear in mind that there are a limited number of no-load gold funds. In this case the actual performances are more relevant than their quintile rankings. Similarly, not all internationals are the same. The top European fund might be only average among all international funds.

Money Market Funds

Annual yields are given in compounded, not simple, interest. They show the total return an investor would receive for shares held a full calendar year. Annual compounded yields are higher than an average of weekly or monthly yields.

Valuation methods: The *Handbook's* valuation codes are 1) *Constant net asset value, mark-to-market.* The price of these funds never varies but their dividends may fluctuate wildly since they factor realized and unrealized appreciation and depreciation into their daily yields. 2) *Variable net asset value, mark-to-market.* No longer in use for money funds. 3) *Constant net asset value, 90 day maximum average maturity, penny rounding.* They technically mark-to-market, but their price doesn't change unless it varies by more than one-half of one percent. They can value any of their average maturities with less than 60 days maturity at cost rather than at market value. To use this method their average maturities must be less than 90 days and no instrument can have a maturity of more than 365 days. Their dividend reflects price appreciation and depreciation. 4) *Amortized cost, straight line accrual.* Shares are priced on the basis of historical cost. There is no marking-to-market but they must keep track of market value and like penny rounders if their price deviates by more than 0.5% the price will flip. The average portfolio maturity must also be less than 90 days.

Portfolio holdings show the percent distribution of each money fund's portfolio, with the most conservative holdings on the left. For taxable funds, foreign bank obligations include Eurodollar CDs, Yankee CDs and bankers acceptances. Second tier commercial paper: as defined by the SEC including letters of credit, medium term notes and short corporates. FRNs are floating rate and variable rate notes. For tax-free funds, rated demand and general market notes can be MIG-1 or MIG-2. Unrated paper generally is of the same quality as rated. See Glossary for other definitions.

The *Handbook* provides data for money market funds that are part of groups having no-load mutual funds, for money market funds that have switching arrangements with no-load mutual funds, and for the major independent and stockbroker affiliated money market funds. Yields are shown for funds that have been in existence for a full year. The Directory Section provides further information on these money market funds and other money market funds first offered during 1994.

Funds covered

The No-Load Fund Investor, Inc. uses a two-tiered structure in covering mutual funds. The annual *Handbook* covers virtually all no-load stock and bond funds available to the individual investor, and many money market funds.

The No-Load Fund Investor newsletter covers 794 funds in each monthly issue. Funds are selected for the newsletter on the basis of investor interest (sometimes evidenced by size), performance, availability, uniqueness, newsworthiness and how they cooperate with us in providing data on a timely basis.

Using the Investor newsletter tables

The monthly *No-Load Fund Investor* updates provide important timely information not in the *Handbook*. In addition, the data differ from the *Handbook* in some minor respects. Since the number of funds differs, quintile ranks, top fund ranks and fund averages can vary between the two publications. The top 20s are for funds reported in the *Investor* only. Other no-loads might have made the top rankings lists had they met our criteria for inclusion in the newsletter.

Performances, quintile ranks and yields are computed the same way in the *Investor* as in the *Handbook*. Because funds report total net assets slowly, the total net assets shown in the updates lag a month. Note also, that there are three separate sets of quintile rankings for the fixed-income and tax-free bond funds: Short maturity funds, intermediate maturity, and long maturity each have their own rankings. If they were lumped together, most short maturity funds would be in the bottom quintile during times of falling interest rates, and most long maturity funds would be at the bottom during times of rising interest rates. Speculative high-yield and zero coupon bond funds are ranked in the long-term section no matter what their maturities.

Cash % is the percentage of an equity fund's portfolio in cash or cash equivalents. Parentheses indicate fund is leveraged. Data is generally for the last day of the month but may be up to 5 days earlier. In the case of bond funds, the *average maturity* in years is shown. This is a more meaningful measure which includes the impact of cash.

Betas for equity funds and *standard deviations* for bond funds are included in the newsletter every third issue. They are computed on a one month's lag. Also in the newsletter is the *Sharpe* ratio, which measures the reward per unit of risk. For convenience they are shown next to the betas in the newsletter, but have nothing to do with them. They are a completely separate measure.

Performance Summary

Fund averages by objective and indices

No-Load Fund averages	Total # of Funds	1985	1986	1987	1988	1989	1990	1991	1992	1993	1994	Annualized 3 years	Annualized 5 years	Yield %
Total return percent														
All Stock Funds	881	27.6	17.2	2.0	15.1	23.4	-6.6	31.2	7.5	18.2	-1.8	7.3	8.3	1.4
All Diversified Stock*	649	27.8	14.3	0.5	16.0	22.9	-5.8	34.1	9.6	13.1	-1.5	6.8	8.6	1.6
Aggressive Growth	163	29.7	11.2	-1.5	16.2	25.7	-9.8	47.8	10.4	15.6	-2.5	7.3	9.8	0.5
Growth	215	27.5	14.6	2.4	15.8	23.5	-4.4	32.5	10.0	12.2	-0.7	6.9	8.7	1.1
Growth-Income	177	26.9	16.6	1.5	16.7	21.0	-4.7	26.6	8.7	11.7	-1.0	6.3	7.5	2.1
Income	94	25.4	16.3	-2.2	14.7	19.0	-2.7	25.4	9.0	13.0	-2.6	6.3	8.0	3.6
Asset Allocation	34	19.4	14.6	3.6	7.2	14.1	-1.6	23.5	7.4	13.5	-1.5	6.1	7.4	2.2
Asset Allocation, Global	9	13.5	27.2	11.7	7.8	15.6	-3.4	14.2	2.7	19.6	-5.4	5.6	5.3	1.5
Balanced	59	27.7	16.0	5.2	13.5	18.9	-0.2	25.3	7.0	11.4	-1.3	5.7	8.0	3.1
Convertible Funds	6	—	16.7	-7.2	15.8	15.1	-4.9	33.8	14.6	14.8	-4.3	7.9	9.8	4.2
Financial	7	42.6	13.9	-13.7	17.9	26.5	-14.5	59.4	32.9	18.8	-4.0	14.4	15.1	1.1
Health/Biotech	5	45.5	19.1	-1.9	14.6	47.4	25.5	79.7	-11.3	2.4	6.7	-1.3	16.4	0.5
Global Stock	35	13.5	27.2	10.0	10.3	19.2	-5.3	16.6	2.7	25.3	-4.6	7.9	6.2	0.8
International	125	46.4	58.6	17.6	15.8	22.4	-12.1	11.4	-6.3	38.5	-1.8	8.0	4.2	0.5
Natural Resources	8	13.7	14.9	11.6	7.2	33.2	-9.8	4.5	-1.1	14.6	-5.4	2.3	0.2	1.8
Precious Metals	15	-7.5	37.6	32.0	-19.0	24.8	-22.7	-4.9	-15.8	87.0	-12.7	10.9	0.0	1.7
Real Estate	10	—	—	-7.7	15.6	10.6	-17.5	32.7	14.3	20.2	-4.5	10.1	6.8	3.5
Small Company Growth	102	32.6	8.8	-4.3	20.9	22.2	-9.8	47.6	13.4	15.3	-0.8	8.8	10.7	0.5
Technology	10	17.4	5.4	-2.1	6.9	23.5	3.8	50.1	20.5	27.9	8.5	19.5	21.0	0.2
Utilities	13	25.6	16.7	-7.4	14.4	30.6	-4.0	23.8	9.7	13.2	-8.9	4.1	6.4	4.7
Fixed Income - Total	336	19.5	14.4	1.4	7.8	11.3	7.0	15.6	6.9	9.8	-3.0	4.4	7.1	5.9
Fixed Income - Corp Short	54	13.1	10.5	4.5	6.8	10.1	8.1	11.9	5.8	6.3	0.1	4.0	6.3	5.6
Fixed Income - Corp Inter	42	19.5	12.9	2.0	8.3	11.3	6.5	16.3	7.2	9.9	-2.8	4.7	7.2	6.0
Fixed Income - Corp Long	61	20.6	14.9	1.2	8.0	11.8	6.9	15.5	7.5	11.0	-3.9	4.6	7.1	6.3
Fixed Income - High Yld	14	23.4	15.0	1.0	12.9	1.1	-6.3	29.7	15.8	18.9	-2.2	10.3	9.9	9.6
Fixed Income - Gov Short	40	14.9	10.5	2.2	6.0	10.7	9.1	12.6	5.9	6.3	-1.2	3.5	6.5	5.3
Fixed Income - Gov Inter	42	19.8	11.3	1.9	6.9	13.1	9.0	15.0	6.7	8.5	-3.4	3.7	6.8	6.5
Fixed Income - Gov Long	40	21.4	13.2	0.3	7.3	13.4	7.2	15.2	6.5	10.4	-6.0	3.7	6.5	6.2
Fixed Income - World	32	20.6	6.0	13.4	2.5	2.2	11.6	15.4	5.2	13.3	-5.7	3.7	8.6	5.4
Tax-Free - Total	209	17.3	16.1	-1.2	9.9	9.0	6.3	11.3	8.3	11.6	-5.3	4.4	6.1	5.4
Tax-Free - Short	22	9.7	8.4	2.5	5.4	6.9	6.4	7.9	6.0	5.9	0.2	3.9	5.2	4.1
Tax-Free - Intermediate	31	14.6	13.8	1.3	7.5	8.2	6.7	10.7	7.7	11.0	-3.6	4.7	6.3	4.9
Tax-Free - Long	87	18.9	17.5	-1.4	10.9	9.5	6.5	11.6	8.6	12.3	-6.1	4.7	6.3	5.5
Tax-Free - High Yld	11	20.1	18.2	-0.7	11.3	9.6	5.5	11.7	8.4	11.5	-6.5	3.9	5.7	6.4
Tax-Free - NY	20	19.5	16.5	-3.2	10.2	8.8	5.2	12.9	9.2	12.4	-7.2	4.4	6.2	5.7
Tax-Free - CA	31	17.6	17.0	-3.5	10.8	9.2	6.8	11.0	8.3	12.4	-5.9	4.1	6.0	5.5
Tax-Free - MA	6	19.6	17.4	-2.5	11.1	8.9	6.6	12.1	9.2	13.1	-6.0	5.1	6.8	5.8
Money Market - General	103	7.8	6.3	6.1	7.1	8.9	7.9	5.8	3.4	2.7	3.7	3.2	4.6	3.7
Money Market - Government	83	7.6	6.1	5.7	6.8	8.6	7.6	5.6	3.3	2.6	3.6	3.2	4.5	3.6
Money Market - Tax-Free	126	4.9	4.3	4.1	4.8	5.9	5.5	4.2	2.6	2.0	2.4	2.3	3.3	2.4
Stock market indices														**Close**
S&P 500 w/reinvestment	—	31.8	18.6	4.9	16.6	32.2	-3.1	30.4	7.6	10.1	1.3	6.3	8.7	459.3
Dow Jones Industrials**	—	27.7	22.6	2.3	11.8	27.0	-4.3	20.3	4.2	13.7	2.1	6.6	6.8	3834.4
S&P 500**	—	26.3	14.6	2.0	12.4	27.3	-6.6	26.3	4.5	7.1	-1.5	3.3	5.4	459.3
NYSE Composite	—	26.1	14.0	-0.3	13.0	24.8	-7.5	27.1	4.7	7.9	-3.1	3.0	5.2	250.9
AMEX Index**	—	20.5	7.0	-1.1	17.5	23.5	-18.5	28.2	1.1	19.5	-9.1	3.2	2.8	433.7
Value Line Composite**	—	20.7	5.0	-10.6	15.4	11.2	-24.3	27.2	7.0	10.7	-6.0	3.6	1.4	277.5
NASDAQ Composite**	—	31.4	7.4	5.3	15.4	19.3	-17.8	56.8	15.5	14.7	-3.2	8.6	10.6	752.0
Russell 2000**	—	28.0	4.0	-10.2	22.5	14.2	-21.3	43.4	16.5	17.3	-3.2	9.8	8.3	250.4
Wilshire 5000**	—	27.2	12.5	-0.7	13.3	24.9	-9.3	30.3	6.2	8.6	-2.5	4.0	5.8	4540.6
Morgan Stanley EAFE**	—	53.0	66.8	23.2	26.7	9.2	-24.7	10.1	-13.9	30.4	6.4	6.1	-0.2	1037.9
Morgan Stanley Gold Mines**	—	-22.2	13.4	42.5	-33.5	49.6	-25.9	-8.1	-27.5	130.4	-11.2	14.1	0.2	714.7
Consumer Price Index	—	3.8	1.1	4.4	4.1	4.7	6.1	3.1	2.9	2.8	2.7	2.8	3.5	—

*Average of aggressive growth, growth, growth-income, and income funds.
**Without dividends reinvested

29

CHAPTER 4

Stock and bond funds — comprehensive summary

Arranged in alphabetical order

No-Load Fund	Total return percent with quintile ranks by objective										Annualized 3 yrs	5 yrs	What $10,000 grew to after 3 yrs	5 yrs
	1985	1986	1987	1988	1989	1990	1991	1992	1993	1994	3 yrs	5 yrs	3 yrs	5 yrs
AARP Blncd Stk & Bd...	—	—	—	—	—	—	—	—	—	—	—	—	—	—
AARP Capital Growth...	28.8[3]	15.9[2]	0.2[3]	27.3[1]	33.5[2]	-15.8[4]	40.5[4]	4.7[4]	16.0[3]	-10.0[5]	3.0[4]	5.3[5]	10,925	12,928
AARP GNMA & Trsy...	17.9[1]	10.9[3]	2.0[4]	7.1[2]	11.7[1]	9.8[1]	14.4[1]	6.6[2]	6.0[3]	-1.7[4]	3.6[4]	6.9[2]	11,102	13,946
AARP Growth & Inc...	30.2[2]	16.6[3]	0.8[4]	10.9[5]	26.5[2]	-2.0[2]	26.4[3]	9.2[2]	15.7[2]	3.1[1]	9.2[1]	10.0[1]	13,021	16,133
AARP Hi Qual Bd...	15.8[5]	10.7[4]	1.2[2]	8.1[3]	12.3[3]	7.7[3]	15.4[3]	6.2[4]	11.0[3]	-4.5[3]	4.0[4]	7.0[3]	11,260	13,992
AARP Insur TF Gen...	10.3[5]	16.8[4]	-1.5[3]	12.2[2]	10.8[1]	6.4[3]	12.3[2]	8.6[3]	12.7[3]	-6.2[3]	4.7[3]	6.5[3]	11,472	13,707
Acorn Int'l‡...	—	—	—	—	—	—	—	—	49.1[1]	-3.8[4]	—	—	—	—
Acorn SC‡...	31.5[2]	16.8[2]	4.3[3]	24.7[1]	24.9[2]	-17.5[5]	47.3[1]	24.2[1]	32.3[1]	-7.5[5]	15.0[1]	13.1[1]	15,209	18,477
Advance Cap Blncd...	—	—	—	17.6[2]	18.6[3]	-1.1[3]	18.3[5]	3.0[5]	5.0[5]	-2.7[4]	1.7[5]	4.2[5]	10,521	12,310
Advance Cap Bond...	—	—	—	5.1[5]	12.7[3]	8.5[2]	14.4[4]	7.0[3]	11.5[3]	-4.7[3]	4.4[3]	7.1[3]	11,373	14,116
Advance Cap Eqty Univ...	—	—	—	22.6[1]	23.8[2]	-7.5[4]	21.0[4]	2.2[5]	2.1[5]	-4.0[5]	0.1[5]	2.3[5]	10,021	11,216
Advance Cap LT Inc...	—	—	—	—	—	—	—	—	14.4[2]	-6.5[4]	—	—	—	—
Advance Cap Ret Inc...	—	—	—	—	—	—	—	—	13.9[2]	-5.3[4]	—	—	—	—
AIC: Clvr Cap Eq...	—	—	—	—	—	—	—	7.3[4]	12.5[3]	16.0[1]	11.9[1]	—	14,013	—
AIC: Clvr Cap Fix...	—	—	—	—	—	—	—	6.4[4]	11.4[3]	-2.8[2]	4.8[3]	—	11,516	—
AIC: Pin Oak SC...	—	—	—	—	—	—	—	—	1.8[5]	0.0[2]	—	—	—	—
AIC: Rlstn Gov Sec...	—	—	—	—	—	—	—	—	—	-6.5[4]	—	—	—	—
AIC: Rlstn Gr & Inc...	—	—	—	—	—	—	—	—	—	1.7[2]	—	—	—	—
AIC: Rlstn Midwest Gr...	—	—	—	—	—	—	—	—	—	7.2[1]	—	—	—	—
AIC: White Oak...	—	—	—	—	—	—	—	—	-0.3[5]	7.2[1]	—	—	—	—
Alliance World Inc...	—	—	—	—	—	—	—	—	4.1[5]	-4.2[3]	—	—	—	—
Amana Growth...	—	—	—	—	—	—	—	—	—	—	—	—	—	—
Amana Income...	—	—	-8.6[5]	13.6[3]	18.1[3]	-3.4[3]	23.7[3]	1.9[5]	11.6[4]	-6.5[5]	2.1[5]	4.9[5]	10,638	12,706
Amcor Vntg Eqty...	—	—	—	—	—	—	—	—	5.4[4]	2.0[2]	—	—	—	—
Amcor Vntg Fix Inc...	—	—	—	—	—	—	—	—	9.0[4]	-3.1[2]	—	—	—	—
Amcor Vntg Inter TF...	—	—	—	—	—	—	—	—	—	-5.4[5]	—	—	—	—
Amer AAdv Balncd...	—	—	—	13.8[3]	18.4[3]	0.6[2]	21.9[4]	9.3[3]	14.8[2]	-1.7[3]	7.3[2]	8.6[2]	12,336	15,126
Amer AAdv Gro & Inc...	—	—	—	23.0[1]	24.3[2]	-5.7[4]	26.3[3]	12.3[2]	16.1[2]	-1.0[3]	8.9[1]	9.0[2]	12,910	15,372
Amer AAdv Int'l...	—	—	—	—	—	—	—	-10.8[4]	42.8[2]	1.2[2]	8.8[3]	—	12,887	—
Amer AAdv Ltd Inc...	—	—	—	6.8[2]	8.3[5]	8.9[3]	13.2[3]	5.5[3]	6.9[3]	1.3[2]	4.5[1]	7.1[2]	11,422	14,079
Amer Heritage Gro...	—	—	—	—	—	—	—	—	—	—	—	—	—	—
American Heritage...	—	-25.6[5]	-19.0[5]	1.9[5]	-2.8[5]	-30.8[5]	96.9[1]	18.6[1]	41.3[1]	-35.4[5]	2.7[5]	8.1[4]	10,822	14,755
America's Utility...	—	—	—	—	—	—	—	—	13.3[3]	-13.1[5]	—	—	—	—
Amtrust Value...	—	—	—	—	—	—	—	—	—	1.8[2]	—	—	—	—
Analysts Inv Fix...	—	—	—	—	—	—	—	—	—	-6.4[4]	—	—	—	—
Analysts Inv Stk...	—	—	—	—	—	—	—	—	—	-2.7[4]	—	—	—	—
Analytic Enhncd Eqty...	—	—	—	—	—	—	—	—	—	-0.4[3]	—	—	—	—
Analytic Master Fix...	—	—	—	—	—	—	—	—	—	-1.1[1]	—	—	—	—
Analytic Option Eqty...	16.6[5]	10.5[5]	4.2[2]	15.6[3]	17.7[4]	1.4[1]	13.3[5]	6.2[4]	6.7[4]	2.5[1]	5.1[4]	5.9[4]	11,615	13,347
Analytic ST Gov...	—	—	—	—	—	—	—	—	—	0.0[3]	—	—	—	—
Anthem Agg Gro...	—	—	—	—	—	—	—	—	—	—	—	—	—	—
Anthem Balanced...	—	—	—	—	—	—	—	—	—	-3.0[4]	—	—	—	—
Anthem Eqty Inc...	—	—	—	—	—	—	—	—	—	—	—	—	—	—
Anthem Gov Sec...	—	—	—	—	—	—	—	—	—	-7.5[5]	—	—	—	—
Anthem Gro & Inc...	—	—	—	—	—	—	—	—	—	-2.7[4]	—	—	—	—
Anthem Income...	—	—	—	—	—	—	—	—	—	—	—	—	—	—
Anthem Inter Gov...	—	—	—	—	—	—	—	—	—	—	—	—	—	—
Anthem Muni...	—	—	—	—	—	—	—	—	—	—	—	—	—	—
Anthem Value...	—	—	—	—	—	—	—	—	—	—	—	—	—	—
API Cap Inc...	—	—	—	—	0.6[5]	-5.0[4]	24.1[3]	4.5[5]	9.9[4]	-0.4[2]	4.6[4]	6.2[5]	11,443	13,491
API Growth...	—	13.1[3]	-7.6[4]	26.0[1]	15.7[5]	-12.7[4]	46.0[3]	3.0[4]	18.3[2]	-3.4[4]	5.6[4]	8.4[4]	11,765	14,997
API Spec Mkts...	—	—	—	—	8.0[5]	-8.4[4]	0.9[5]	-1.3[5]	6.2[5]	-7.4[5]	-1.0[5]	-2.2[5]	9,702	8,967
API Total Ret...	—	—	—	—	11.1[5]	-16.0[5]	24.6[3]	4.2[5]	14.0[3]	-6.8[5]	3.5[5]	3.0[5]	11,077	11,593
Aquinas Balanced...	—	—	—	—	—	—	—	—	—	-3.1[4]	—	—	—	—
Aquinas Eqty Gro...	—	—	—	—	—	—	—	—	—	-6.8[5]	—	—	—	—
Aquinas Eqty Inc...	—	—	—	—	—	—	—	—	—	-2.9[4]	—	—	—	—
Aquinas Fix Inc...	—	—	—	—	—	—	—	—	—	-3.1[2]	—	—	—	—
Arbor OVB Cap App...	—	—	—	—	—	—	—	—	—	-5.5[5]	—	—	—	—
Arbor OVB Emg Gro...	—	—	—	—	—	—	—	—	—	-18.4[5]	—	—	—	—
Arbor OVB Gov...	—	—	—	—	—	—	—	—	—	-5.1[3]	—	—	—	—

See Chapter 3 for explanation of symbols

Total Net Assets $Million December 31 1993	1994	NAV per share December 31 1993	1994	1994 per share distributions Income	Capital gains	Yield % 12/31/94	beta	R²	Std. Dev.	Sharpe Ratio	Stocks	Bonds	Cash	Objective	No-Load Fund
—	177.9	—	14.32	—	—	—	—	—	—	—	—	—	—	income	AARP Blncd Stk & Bd
682.5	631.6	34.24	30.15	0.01	0.64	0.0	1.27	0.76	3.40	D	92	2	6	agg gr	AARP Capital Growth
6,629.9	5,248.9	15.77	14.56	0.94	0.00	6.5	0.18	0.22	0.89	D	0	59	41	fix-inc	AARP GNMA & Trsy
1,752.1	2,298.7	32.94	31.74	0.97	1.23	2.9	0.88	0.82	2.27	A	88	7	5	gr-inc	AARP Growth & Inc
622.2	529.1	16.51	14.92	0.86	0.00	5.7	0.30	0.25	1.40	C	0	85	15	fix-inc	AARP Hi Qual Bd
2,128.5	1,748.6	18.54	16.54	0.86	0.00	5.2	0.47	0.31	1.96	D	0	95	5	tax-free	AARP Insur TF Gen
906.9	1,364.8	15.94	15.24	0.09	0.01	0.6	—	—	—	—	85	5	10	int'l	Acorn Int'l
2,034.5	1,982.8	13.95	12.24	0.11	0.56	0.9	1.14	0.62	3.38	A	91	2	7	growth	Acorn SC
46.7	44.2	10.58	9.97	0.33	0.00	3.3	—	—	—	—	—	—	—	income	Advance Cap Blncd
4.7	4.0	10.82	9.61	0.71	0.00	7.4	—	—	—	—	—	—	—	fix-inc	Advance Cap Bond
7.6	12.6	9.46	9.08	0.00	0.00	0.0	—	—	—	—	—	—	—	gr-inc	Advance Cap Eqty Univ
1.1	1.2	10.60	9.20	0.72	0.00	7.8	—	—	—	—	—	—	—	fix-inc	Advance Cap LT Inc
47.3	84.2	10.54	9.22	0.77	0.00	8.3	—	—	—	—	—	—	—	fix-inc	Advance Cap Ret Inc
16.0	27.6	12.30	13.19	0.11	0.00	0.8	—	—	—	—	—	—	—	growth	AIC: Clvr Cap Eq
7.9	9.8	9.92	9.06	0.56	0.00	6.2	—	—	—	—	—	—	—	fix-inc	AIC: Clvr Cap Fix
8.8	10.2	12.17	12.17	0.00	0.00	0.0	—	—	—	—	—	—	—	agg gr	AIC: Pin Oak SC
5.6	7.4	9.98	8.90	0.44	0.00	4.9	—	—	—	—	—	—	—	fix-inc	AIC: Rlstn Gov Sec
9.8	17.4	10.42	10.40	0.16	0.00	1.5	—	—	—	—	—	—	—	gr-inc	AIC: Rlstn Gr & Inc
12.2	31.4	11.32	11.60	0.02	0.00	0.2	—	—	—	—	—	—	—	growth	AIC: Rlstn Midwest Gr
5.6	5.8	11.08	11.75	0.13	0.00	1.1	—	—	—	—	—	—	—	growth	AIC: White Oak
137.2	84.1	1.90	1.74	0.08	0.00	4.8	0.01	0.00	1.33	F	0	22	78	fix-inc	Alliance World Inc
—	1.7	—	4.68	—	—	—	—	—	—	—	90	0	10	growth	Amana Growth
10.8	10.0	13.19	11.81	0.35	0.19	2.9	0.87	0.73	2.36	F	91	9	0	income	Amana Income
119.1	131.1	10.41	10.44	0.15	0.02	1.5	—	—	—	—	100	0	0	growth	Amcor Vntg Eqty
88.0	79.5	10.27	9.43	0.52	0.00	5.5	—	—	—	—	0	98	2	fix-inc	Amcor Vntg Fix Inc
32.2	28.9	10.46	9.47	0.42	0.01	4.4	—	—	—	—	0	98	2	tax-free	Amcor Vntg Inter TF
544.5	212.5	12.36	11.49	0.52	0.00	4.5	0.65	0.73	1.76	B	57	36	7	income	Amer AAdv Balncd
492.0	21.3	13.88	12.77	0.42	0.00	3.3	0.96	0.84	2.44	B	98	1	1	gr-inc	Amer AAdv Gro & Inc
79.5	21.6	12.23	11.84	0.20	0.00	1.7	0.76	0.20	3.94	C	88	2	10	int'l	Amer AAdv Int'l
237.8	73.6	10.04	9.63	0.54	0.00	5.6	0.08	0.10	0.54	A	0	70	30	fix-inc	Amer AAdv Ltd Inc
—	3.7	—	3.43	—	—	—	—	—	—	—	10	0	90	growth	Amer Heritage Gro
149.8	56.9	1.53	0.85	0.14	0.00	—	1.22	0.30	5.31	F	84	0	16	agg gr	American Heritage
133.5	125.0	23.54	19.50	0.96	0.00	4.9	—	—	—	—	88	1	11	income	America's Utility
0.3	0.7	10.04	10.22	0.00	0.00	0.0	—	—	—	—	—	—	—	growth	Amtrust Value
1.1	1.2	14.07	12.48	0.75	0.00	6.0	—	—	—	—	—	—	—	fix-inc	Analysts Inv Fix
1.3	1.9	16.27	15.66	0.17	0.00	1.1	—	—	—	—	—	—	—	growth	Analysts Inv Stk
0.9	1.5	10.15	9.83	0.28	0.00	2.9	—	—	—	—	96	0	4	growth	Analytic Enhncd Eqty
8.1	6.2	10.26	9.50	0.64	0.00	6.8	—	—	—	—	26	73	1	fix-inc	Analytic Master Fix
64.7	48.2	11.96	11.12	0.31	0.82	2.6	0.55	0.84	1.38	B	98	0	2	gr-inc	Analytic Option Eqty
26.1	24.5	10.03	9.55	0.48	0.00	5.0	—	—	—	—	0	99	1	fix-inc	Analytic ST Gov
—	5.6	—	10.47	—	—	—	—	—	—	—	—	—	—	agg gr	Anthem Agg Gro
11.5	8.0	11.32	10.50	0.43	0.05	4.1	0.65	0.77	1.71	F	56	44	0	income	Anthem Balanced
—	5.6	—	9.96	—	—	—	—	—	—	—	—	—	—	gr-inc	Anthem Eqty Inc
4.7	2.9	11.23	9.74	0.66	0.00	6.9	0.33	0.21	1.64	F	0	93	7	fix-inc	Anthem Gov Sec
15.0	10.0	11.30	10.84	0.15	0.00	1.5	0.88	0.72	2.40	F	97	0	3	gr-inc	Anthem Gro & Inc
—	5.0	—	9.58	—	—	—	—	—	—	—	—	—	—	fix-inc	Anthem Income
—	5.4	—	9.62	—	—	—	—	—	—	—	—	—	—	fix-inc	Anthem Inter Gov
—	4.8	—	9.60	—	—	—	—	—	—	—	—	—	—	tax-free	Anthem Muni
—	5.8	—	9.68	—	—	—	—	—	—	—	—	—	—	growth	Anthem Value
2.9	3.0	16.00	15.21	0.36	0.76	2.4	0.82	0.93	1.96	D	97	0	3	income	API Cap Inc
49.7	50.4	12.83	11.28	0.00	1.11	0.0	1.13	0.69	3.17	D	96	0	4	agg gr	API Growth
1.6	2.0	6.90	6.47	0.00	0.00	0.0	—	—	—	—	—	—	—	gr-inc	API Spec Mkts
5.0	4.5	23.48	20.39	0.06	0.00	0.3	1.03	0.64	3.02	F	98	0	2	income	API Total Ret
—	30.1	10.00	9.43	0.26	0.00	—	—	—	—	—	—	—	—	income	Aquinas Balanced
—	10.1	10.00	9.31	0.01	0.00	—	—	—	—	—	—	—	—	growth	Aquinas Eqty Gro
—	32.2	10.00	9.39	0.32	0.00	—	—	—	—	—	—	—	—	gr-inc	Aquinas Eqty Inc
—	28.2	10.00	9.24	0.45	0.00	—	—	—	—	—	—	—	—	fix-inc	Aquinas Fix Inc
50.4	71.4	10.30	9.73	0.03	0.00	0.3	—	—	—	—	—	—	—	growth	Arbor OVB Cap App
33.9	36.4	10.15	8.28	0.00	0.00	0.0	—	—	—	—	—	—	—	agg gr	Arbor OVB Emg Gro
33.0	51.2	9.46	8.99	0.51	0.00	5.7	—	—	—	—	—	—	—	fix-inc	Arbor OVB Gov

No-Load Fund	1985	1986	1987	1988	1989	1990	1991	1992	1993	1994	Annualized 3 yrs.	Annualized 5 yrs.	What $10,000 grew to after 3 yrs.	5 yrs.
Arbor OVB WV TE	—	—	—	—	—	—	—	—	—	-5.0^1	—	—	—	—
Ariel Apprec	—	—	—	—	—	—	33.2^3	13.2^2	7.9^4	-8.4^5	3.8^4	—	11,190	—
Ariel Growth SC	—	—	11.4^1	39.9^1	25.1^3	-15.5^4	32.7^5	11.7^3	8.7^4	-4.2^4	5.2^4	5.5^5	11,629	13,040
Armstrong Assoc	21.0^5	11.5^4	-0.1^4	15.6^3	14.2^5	-6.7^4	18.5^5	6.7^4	15.1^2	5.4^1	9.0^2	7.4^4	12,937	14,306
ASM	—	—	—	—	—	—	—	5.7^4	13.3^2	1.1^2	6.6^2	—	12,107	—
Asset Mgmt ARM	—	—	—	—	—	—	—	4.4^5	4.7^5	1.9^1	3.7^4	—	11,144	—
Asset Mgmt Inter Mrtg	—	—	—	-0.6^5	12.7^3	6.2^4	16.2^2	7.9^1	6.8^5	-1.6^1	4.3^3	6.9^3	11,330	13,978
Asset Mgmt Mrtg Sec	20.7^2	10.0^5	1.7^4	8.6^1	11.7^4	9.6^2	14.8^3	6.4^4	6.8^4	-2.4^2	3.5^4	6.9^3	11,100	13,974
Asset Mgmt ST Gov	13.9^3	11.1^3	5.1^2	6.2^3	11.8^1	9.3^2	11.8^4	6.5^2	5.8^4	0.4^2	4.2^2	6.7^3	11,309	13,815
Austin Global Eqty	—	—	—	—	—	—	—	—	—	2.1^1	—	—	—	—
Avondale Total Ret	—	—	—	—	14.5^4	-0.1^2	26.9^2	-1.4^5	7.2^5	2.3^1	2.6^5	6.5^4	10,806	13,696
Babson Bond-Port L	20.7^4	13.8^4	1.9^2	7.2^4	13.1^3	7.8^3	15.0^4	8.6^2	11.1^3	-3.3^2	5.3^2	7.7^3	11,674	14,471
Babson Bond-Port S	—	—	—	—	10.8^4	8.1^3	14.5^4	7.0^3	8.4^4	-2.1^2	4.3^3	7.0^3	11,357	14,054
Babson Buffalo Blncd	—	—	—	—	—	—	—	—	—	—	—	—	—	—
Babson Enterprise II SC	—	—	—	—	—	—	—	17.2^1	19.8^2	-7.4^5	9.2^2	—	13,004	—
Babson Enterprise SC‡	38.6^2	9.0^4	-9.2^5	32.5^1	22.5^4	-15.9^4	43.0^3	24.6^1	16.3^3	2.5^2	14.1^1	12.3^2	14,838	17,849
Babson Growth	29.6^3	18.8^2	2.7^3	15.9^3	22.1^3	-9.4^4	26.0^4	9.1^3	10.3^3	-0.6^3	6.2^3	6.4^5	11,962	13,649
Babson Shadow Stk SC	—	—	—	22.5^2	11.2^5	-19.3^5	40.0^2	17.4^1	15.3^2	-4.3^4	9.0^2	7.9^4	12,953	14,629
Babson Stew Ivry Int'l	—	—	—	—	27.0^2	-9.4^2	15.1^2	-1.7^2	33.5^3	1.3^2	10.0^2	6.8^1	13,292	13,863
Babson TF Long	20.4^2	21.3^1	-1.9^3	11.6^3	8.8^4	6.3^4	11.8^3	8.4^4	12.3^4	-7.4^4	4.1^4	6.0^4	11,266	13,382
Babson TF Short	11.1^3	10.4^1	3.5^2	5.1^4	7.0^3	6.8^2	9.5^1	6.3^3	6.7^2	-1.7^5	3.7^4	5.4^3	11,144	13,032
Babson UMB Bond	16.1^5	12.3^4	2.9^1	5.9^5	11.3^4	8.0^2	13.2^5	6.6^4	8.3^4	-3.1^2	3.8^4	6.5^4	11,187	13,679
Babson UMB Heartland SC	—	—	4.9^2	-5.1^5	3.0^5	-1.0^1	9.1^5	11.0^3	6.0^5	0.7^2	5.8^4	5.0^5	11,842	12,790
Babson UMB Stock	23.1^4	12.3^3	5.4^2	13.9^4	19.0^4	-2.4^2	24.7^4	7.1^4	10.6^3	2.8^2	6.8^3	8.2^3	12,176	14,820
Babson UMB Worldwide	—	—	—	—	—	—	—	—	—	3.8^1	—	—	—	—
Babson Value	26.5^4	20.7^1	3.3^3	19.0^2	18.2^4	-11.4^5	28.6^4	15.4^2	22.9^1	2.5^2	13.3^1	10.6^2	14,535	16,572
Baron Asset SC	—	—	—	34.4^1	25.0^3	-18.6^5	34.0^4	13.9^2	23.5^1	7.4^1	14.7^1	10.5^3	15,106	16,486
Baron Growth & Inc	—	—	—	—	—	—	—	—	—	—	—	—	—	—
Bartlett Basic Value	25.3^4	13.7^4	-3.8^5	26.3^1	11.7^5	-9.6^5	26.0^3	10.2^2	11.7^3	0.4^2	7.3^2	7.1^3	12,359	14,072
Bartlett Fix Inc	—	—	2.8^2	7.7^2	12.6^3	6.0^5	14.4^4	6.9^3	6.9^4	-2.9^3	3.5^4	6.1^5	11,101	13,460
Bartlett ST Bond	—	—	—	—	—	—	—	—	—	—	—	—	—	—
Bartlett Value Int'l	—	—	—	—	—	-14.5^4	21.5^1	-1.8^2	31.4^4	-0.5^3	8.7^3	5.9^2	12,827	13,321
Bascom Hill Blncd	—	—	3.7^1	7.7^5	12.2^4	-7.3^4	25.0^3	8.4^3	4.3^5	1.1^1	4.6^4	5.8^5	11,429	13,243
Bascom Hill Invest	31.5^1	16.3^3	1.3^3	12.4^4	16.0^4	-14.3^5	32.1^2	11.6^2	2.5^5	3.9^1	5.9^3	6.1^4	11,885	13,461
BBK Diversa	—	—	8.5^4	6.6^5	12.7^4	-9.5^5	16.0^3	4.4^3	21.6^4	-9.4^4	4.8^4	3.8^4	11,504	12,071
BBK Int'l Equity	58.6^1	62.2^2	-7.7^5	11.8^3	14.0^5	-19.2^5	1.8^5	-11.4^4	37.8^3	-12.6^5	2.2^5	-2.6^5	10,677	8,782
BBK Int'l Fix Inc	—	—	—	—	—	—	14.0^4	7.0^3	14.8^2	-19.2^5	-0.3^5	—	9,924	—
Beacon Hill Mutual	33.5^2	6.0^5	5.3^2	4.3^5	20.9^4	5.9^1	26.4^4	-1.8^5	-5.2^5	0.3^3	-2.3^5	4.6^5	9,334	12,495
Benham Adj Rate Gov	—	—	—	—	—	—	—	5.2^4	3.6^5	-1.0^4	2.6^5	—	10,788	—
Benham AZ Inter	—	—	—	—	—	—	—	—	—	—	—	—	—	—
Benham CA Hi Yld	—	—	-11.1^5	12.5^2	9.7^3	5.7^5	10.9^4	9.2^2	13.2^2	-5.3^2	5.4^1	6.5^3	11,696	13,706
Benham CA Insur	—	—	-6.1^5	10.2^4	10.3^2	6.8^3	11.3^4	9.2^2	13.4^2	-6.5^3	5.0^2	6.6^2	11,580	13,756
Benham CA Inter	14.0^3	12.6^4	0.8^4	5.9^5	7.9^4	7.0^1	10.4^3	7.1^4	10.7^3	-3.7^3	4.5^3	6.2^3	11,417	13,483
Benham CA Long	17.9^4	19.2^2	-4.6^5	10.4^4	9.8^3	6.6^3	11.8^3	8.2^4	13.7^1	-6.5^3	4.8^3	6.5^3	11,507	13,713
Benham CA Short	—	—	—	—	—	—	—	—	5.9^4	-0.6^4	—	—	—	—
Benham Capital Mgr	—	—	—	—	—	—	—	—	—	—	—	—	—	—
Benham Equity Growth	—	—	—	—	—	—	—	4.1^5	11.4^3	-0.2^3	5.0^4	—	11,575	—
Benham Europ Gov	—	—	—	—	—	—	—	—	11.8^2	1.5^1	—	—	—	—
Benham FL Inter	—	—	—	—	—	—	—	—	—	—	—	—	—	—
Benham Glob Nat Res	—	—	—	—	—	—	—	—	—	—	—	—	—	—
Benham GNMA Inc	—	11.3^3	2.7^2	8.5^2	13.9^2	10.2^1	15.6^3	7.7^2	6.6^3	-1.5^1	4.2^3	7.6^2	11,304	14,390
Benham Gold Eqty	—	—	—	—	29.9^2	-19.5^2	-11.3^5	-8.7^2	81.2^4	-16.8^4	11.3^3	-0.3^4	13,780	9,849
Benham Income & Gro	—	—	—	—	—	—	39.1^1	7.9^3	11.3^3	-0.6^3	6.1^3	—	11,938	—
Benham LT Trsy/Agcy	—	—	—	—	—	—	—	—	17.0^1	-9.1^5	—	—	—	—
Benham Nat TF Inter	12.6^4	14.2^3	2.3^1	6.6^3	8.3^2	6.9^2	11.7^1	7.2^4	10.2^3	-3.4^3	4.5^3	6.4^3	11,406	13,609
Benham Nat TF Long	19.1^4	18.5^3	-6.8^5	11.2^3	9.7^3	6.7^3	12.9^1	9.2^2	14.3^1	-6.2^3	5.4^1	7.1^1	11,706	14,099
Benham ST Trsy/Agcy	—	—	—	—	—	—	—	—	5.0^4	0.3^2	—	—	—	—
Benham Target 1995	—	26.4^1	-3.1^5	7.9^3	15.3^2	9.2^1	16.2^3	7.3^3	6.9^5	0.8^1	5.0^2	8.0^2	11,564	14,669
Benham Target 2000	—	32.4^1	-6.0^5	11.5^2	19.8^1	6.3^3	20.7^2	8.5^2	15.5^2	-6.9^4	5.3^2	8.4^2	11,662	14,960
Benham Target 2005	—	42.2^1	-9.9^5	14.5^1	23.9^1	3.6^4	21.5^1	9.6^2	21.6^1	-8.9^5	6.7^2	8.8^1	12,133	15,265

See Chapter 3 for explanation of symbols

Stock and bond funds — comprehensive summary *continued*
Arranged in alphabetical order

Total Net Assets $Million		NAV per share		1994 per share distributions			Risk Analysis				% Distribution of Portfolio				
December 31		December 31			Capital	Yield %			Std.	Sharpe	12/31/94				
1993	1994	1993	1994	Income	gains	12/31/94	beta	R²	Dev.	Ratio	Stocks	Bonds	Cash	Objective	No-Load Fund
1.0	2.0	9.74	9.16	0.45	0.00	4.9	—	—	—	—	—	—	—	tax-free	Arbor OVB WV TE
219.3	128.5	20.11	19.51	0.06	1.27	0.3	—	—	—	—	—	—	—	growth	Ariel Apprec
225.8	130.8	27.39	26.98	0.23	1.70	0.8	0.83	0.50	2.75	C	100	0	0	agg gr	Ariel Growth SC
10.1	10.0	8.69	8.52	0.03	0.00	0.4	1.05	0.80	2.75	B	83	0	17	growth	Armstrong Assoc
14.0	6.5	9.91	9.59	0.25	0.17	2.6	0.87	0.68	2.46	D	97	0	3	gr-inc	ASM
1,419.9	863.0	9.99	9.72	0.46	0.00	4.7	—	—	—	—	0	93	7	fix-inc	Asset Mgmt ARM
234.3	211.0	9.92	9.21	0.55	0.00	6.0	0.12	—	—	—	0	94	6	fix-inc	Asset Mgmt Inter Mrtg
82.4	59.0	11.09	10.10	0.73	0.00	7.2	0.16	—	—	—	0	90	10	fix-inc	Asset Mgmt Mrtg Sec
237.4	165.0	10.84	10.31	0.57	0.00	5.5	—	—	—	—	0	88	12	fix-inc	Asset Mgmt ST Gov
—	1.0	—	10.21	—	—	—	—	—	—	—	0	—	—	global	Austin Global Eqty
7.8	6.6	23.64	23.10	0.18	0.00	0.8	0.88	0.70	2.45	F	73	24	3	income	Avondale Total Ret
160.4	137.0	1.63	1.47	0.11	0.00	7.3	0.22	0.17	1.22	B	0	97	3	fix-inc	Babson Bond-Port L
37.2	29.0	10.33	9.42	0.70	0.00	7.4	0.17	0.17	0.93	A	0	101	-1	fix-inc	Babson Bond-Port S
—	32.9	—	9.61	—	—	—	—	—	—	—	32	60	8	income	Babson Buffalo Blncd
31.0	36.8	17.60	16.19	0.02	0.09	0.1	0.97	0.56	3.01	B	98	0	2	agg gr	Babson Enterprise II SC
197.3	190.5	16.51	15.15	0.04	1.69	0.2	0.79	0.41	2.88	A	96	0	4	agg gr	Babson Enterprise SC
245.3	226.5	13.08	11.97	0.20	0.81	1.7	0.89	0.89	2.18	C	96	0	4	growth	Babson Growth
37.7	33.5	12.32	9.52	0.09	2.15	0.9	0.66	0.36	2.55	B	96	0	4	growth	Babson Shadow Stk SC
43.3	55.2	16.20	15.45	0.04	0.92	0.2	0.46	0.14	3.50	B	98	0	2	int'l	Babson Stew Ivry Int'l
33.5	26.6	9.28	8.16	0.42	0.02	5.2	0.46	0.33	1.83	D	0	99	1	tax-free	Babson TF Long
31.2	28.4	11.05	10.40	0.45	0.01	4.4	0.24	0.39	0.87	F	0	98	2	tax-free	Babson TF Short
89.9	75.2	11.44	10.46	0.63	0.00	6.0	0.19	0.20	0.97	B	0	98	2	fix-inc	Babson UMB Bond
25.2	28.0	9.49	9.20	0.18	0.17	1.9	0.51	0.63	1.50	B	81	1	18	agg gr	Babson UMB Heartland SC
113.6	120.9	16.24	15.01	0.40	1.26	2.4	0.72	0.84	1.83	B	76	3	21	growth	Babson UMB Stock
6.0	17.8	10.68	10.84	0.17	0.07	1.6	—	—	—	—	—	—	—	global	Babson UMB Worldwide
45.7	122.0	25.22	24.78	0.47	0.60	1.9	0.86	0.70	2.40	A	95	1	4	growth	Babson Value
64.0	87.1	21.11	22.01	0.00	0.66	0.0	0.97	0.52	3.16	A	93	4	3	agg gr	Baron Asset SC
—	—	—	—	—	—	—	—	—	—	—	—	—	—	gr-inc	Baron Growth & Inc
100.5	93.2	15.28	14.10	0.24	1.03	1.6	0.81	0.71	2.22	B	88	8	4	gr-inc	Bartlett Basic Value
123.1	90.7	10.29	9.48	0.52	0.00	5.5	0.19	0.21	0.94	C	0	99	1	fix-inc	Bartlett Fix Inc
—	17.0	—	9.55	—	—	—	—	—	—	—	0	98	2	fix-inc	Bartlett ST Bond
45.4	56.4	12.33	11.60	0.08	0.62	0.7	0.85	0.31	3.58	C	90	3	7	int'l	Bartlett Value Int'l
13.8	9.9	22.37	20.16	0.98	1.47	4.5	0.59	0.70	1.63	D	26	28	46	income	Bascom Hill Blncd
9.9	9.8	16.73	15.84	0.70	0.84	4.2	0.80	0.63	2.36	C	40	0	60	gr-inc	Bascom Hill Invest
50.5	42.0	13.18	11.64	0.31	0.00	2.7	0.63	0.56	1.94	D	50	36	14	global	BBK Diversa
220.0	148.8	6.52	5.70	0.00	0.00	0.0	0.71	0.20	3.70	F	89	2	9	int'l	BBK Int'l Equity
172.9	104.4	10.45	7.81	0.65	0.00	8.3	0.27	0.08	2.23	F	0	93	7	fix-inc	BBK Int'l Fix Inc
5.0	4.0	31.50	29.80	0.00	1.65	0.0	0.74	0.51	2.44	F	91	0	9	growth	Beacon Hill Mutual
1,050.4	447.0	9.84	9.26	0.48	0.00	5.2	0.04	0.06	0.39	C	0	90	10	fix-inc	Benham Adj Rate Gov
—	15.2	—	9.84	—	—	—	—	—	—	—	0	97	3	tax-free	Benham AZ Inter
123.8	96.2	9.60	8.54	0.56	0.00	6.6	0.40	0.34	1.58	A	0	100	0	tax-free	Benham CA Hi Yld
227.9	161.3	10.43	9.23	0.53	0.00	5.7	0.48	0.31	2.02	C	0	100	0	tax-free	Benham CA Insur
499.3	393.8	11.38	10.43	0.54	0.00	5.1	0.33	0.30	1.40	D	0	100	0	tax-free	Benham CA Inter
337.5	249.1	11.63	10.21	0.63	0.06	6.1	0.45	0.31	1.89	C	0	100	0	tax-free	Benham CA Long
131.0	106.3	10.35	9.90	0.39	0.00	3.9	—	—	—	—	0	100	0	tax-free	Benham CA Short
—	7.8	—	10.31	—	—	—	—	—	—	—	50	35	15	gr-inc	Benham Capital Mgr
96.5	97.6	12.12	11.53	0.30	0.26	2.5	0.92	0.87	2.30	D	99	0	1	growth	Benham Equity Growth
333.8	193.7	10.82	10.36	0.60	0.01	5.8	—	—	—	—	0	99	1	fix-inc	Benham Europ Gov
—	7.1	—	9.75	—	—	—	—	—	—	—	0	100	0	tax-free	Benham FL Inter
—	19.0	—	9.61	—	—	—	—	—	—	—	97	0	3	global	Benham Glob Nat Res
1,256.8	952.3	10.76	9.90	0.70	0.00	7.0	0.19	0.22	0.91	A	0	93	7	fix-inc	Benham GNMA Inc
618.9	570.6	13.67	11.33	0.02	0.03	0.2	0.38	0.01	8.43	D	100	0	0	prec met	Benham Gold Eqty
229.8	224.8	15.08	13.92	0.44	0.64	3.0	0.88	0.89	2.18	C	99	0	1	gr-inc	Benham Income & Gro
23.2	28.6	10.22	8.69	0.61	0.00	7.0	—	—	—	—	0	98	2	fix-inc	Benham LT Trsy/Agcy
82.0	62.1	11.11	10.19	0.51	0.04	5.0	0.32	0.28	1.40	D	0	100	0	tax-free	Benham Nat TF Inter
70.3	45.3	12.10	10.70	0.61	0.06	5.6	0.45	0.27	2.02	B	0	100	0	tax-free	Benham Nat TF Long
23.6	30.7	10.00	9.57	0.45	0.00	4.7	—	—	—	—	0	100	0	fix-inc	Benham ST Trsy/Agcy
80.1	80.5	94.57	95.29	0.00	0.00	6.5	0.08	0.04	0.90	B	0	99	1	fix-inc	Benham Target 1995
290.8	255.0	71.53	66.60	0.00	0.00	7.3	0.40	0.19	2.13	D	0	95	5	fix-inc	Benham Target 2000
127.7	101.6	50.57	46.07	0.00	0.00	7.4	0.60	0.22	2.96	D	0	100	0	fix-inc	Benham Target 2005

Stock and bond funds — comprehensive summary *continued*

Arranged in alphabetical order

No-Load Fund	1985	1986	1987	1988	1989	1990	1991	1992	1993	1994	Annualized 3 yrs.	Annualized 5 yrs.	Grew to after 3 yrs.	Grew to after 5 yrs.
Benham Target 2010	—	54.4[1]	-15.2[5]	15.7[1]	28.0[1]	0.3[4]	21.1[1]	9.8[1]	26.3[1]	-11.6[5]	7.0[1]	8.3[2]	12,260	14,883
Benham Target 2015	—	—	-19.3[5]	11.1[2]	33.5[1]	-3.4[5]	22.5[1]	7.8[3]	30.5[1]	-14.1[5]	6.5[2]	7.4[3]	12,085	14,300
Benham Target 2020	—	—	—	—	—	-4.5[5]	17.4[2]	8.3[2]	35.6[1]	-17.7[5]	6.6[2]	6.3[5]	12,097	13,558
Benham Trsy Note	17.6[1]	13.3[1]	-1.1[5]	5.2[5]	11.9[1]	9.2[2]	13.8[2]	6.5[2]	7.9[2]	-2.3[5]	3.9[3]	6.9[2]	11,229	13,948
Benham Util Inc	—	—	—	—	—	—	—	—	—	-10.0[5]	—	—	—	—
Berger 100	25.7[4]	20.1[1]	15.7[1]	1.7[5]	48.3[1]	-5.6[2]	88.8[1]	8.5[3]	21.2[2]	-6.7[4]	7.1[3]	17.0[1]	12,277	21,886
Berger 101	29.2[2]	15.1[4]	-2.9[5]	5.3[5]	20.3[3]	-8.0[4]	61.0[1]	5.0[4]	23.6[1]	-9.1[5]	5.7[4]	11.8[1]	11,800	17,478
Berger Sm Co Growth	—	—	—	—	—	—	—	—	—	13.7[1]	—	—	—	—
Bernstein CA Muni	—	—	—	—	—	—	9.5[5]	6.8[5]	8.3[5]	-3.2[2]	3.9[5]	—	11,202	—
Bernstein CA ST	—	—	—	—	—	—	—	—	—	—	—	—	—	—
Bernstein Dvsfd Muni ST	—	—	—	—	—	—	—	—	—	—	—	—	—	—
Bernstein Dvsfd Muni	—	—	—	—	—	6.8[3]	10.2[4]	6.5[5]	8.5[5]	-2.5[2]	4.1[5]	5.8[5]	11,267	13,258
Bernstein Gov Sht	—	—	—	—	—	9.0[3]	11.2[4]	5.4[4]	4.7[4]	0.4[2]	3.5[4]	6.1[4]	11,083	13,431
Bernstein Inter Dur	—	—	—	—	—	7.3[4]	17.1[1]	7.7[2]	10.4[3]	-3.2[3]	4.8[2]	7.7[2]	11,513	14,470
Bernstein Int'l Value	—	—	—	—	—	—	—	—	34.5[3]	3.8[2]	—	—	—	—
Bernstein NY Muni	—	—	—	—	—	6.7[3]	10.4[3]	6.9[5]	8.6[5]	-2.6[2]	4.2[4]	5.9[4]	11,315	13,323
Bernstein NY ST	—	—	—	—	—	—	—	—	—	—	—	—	—	—
Bernstein Short Dur	—	—	—	—	9.8[3]	8.3[4]	12.9[3]	6.4[2]	5.5[4]	0.5[2]	4.1[2]	6.6[3]	11,278	13,789
Berwyn Income	—	—	—	12.3[4]	10.9[5]	-0.1[2]	23.0[4]	21.8[1]	16.9[1]	-1.1[2]	12.1[1]	11.6[1]	14,072	17,296
Berwyn	23.6[4]	14.6[4]	2.9[2]	21.6[2]	16.6[4]	-23.8[5]	43.5[1]	20.6[1]	23.0[1]	4.2[1]	15.6[1]	11.1[1]	15,451	16,888
Blanchard Amer Eqty	—	—	—	—	—	—	—	—	-1.2[5]	-4.2[4]	—	—	—	—
Blanchard Cap Growth	—	—	—	—	—	—	—	—	—	—	—	—	—	—
Blanchard Emg Mkt	—	—	—	—	—	—	—	—	—	—	—	—	—	—
Blanchard Flex Inc	—	—	—	—	—	—	—	—	13.8[1]	-5.6[5]	—	—	—	—
Blanchard Flex TF	—	—	—	—	—	—	—	—	—	-5.6[2]	—	—	—	—
Blanchard Glob Growth	—	—	16.3[1]	7.4[4]	15.6[4]	-6.4[3]	10.6[4]	0.7[4]	24.5[3]	-7.5[4]	5.1[4]	3.7[5]	11,592	12,008
Blanchard Gro & Inc	—	—	—	—	—	—	—	—	—	—	—	—	—	—
Blanchard Prec Metals	—	—	—	—	8.1[5]	-22.9[4]	-2.3[2]	-18.5[4]	100.4[2]	-15.2[3]	11.5[2]	0.9[2]	13,857	10,442
Blanchard ST Bond	—	—	—	—	—	—	—	—	—	1.0[2]	—	—	—	—
Blanchard ST Global	—	—	—	—	—	—	—	3.6[5]	8.5[1]	-4.6[5]	2.4[5]	—	10,730	—
Bonnel Growth	—	—	—	—	—	—	—	—	—	—	—	—	—	—
Bramwell Growth	—	—	—	—	—	—	—	—	—	—	—	—	—	—
Brandywine Blue	—	—	—	—	—	—	40.1[2]	13.1[2]	27.2[1]	2.3[2]	13.8[1]	—	14,722	—
Brandywine	—	16.4[2]	2.6[2]	17.7[3]	33.1[2]	0.6[1]	49.2[3]	15.7[2]	22.6[1]	0.0[2]	12.3[1]	16.3[1]	14,179	21,279
Bridges Investment	28.6[2]	16.9[3]	1.7[3]	5.5[5]	22.3[3]	1.8[1]	20.8[4]	5.9[4]	3.5[5]	0.4[2]	3.2[4]	6.2[4]	11,004	13,537
Bridgeway Agg Gro	—	—	—	—	—	—	—	—	—	—	—	—	—	—
Bridgeway Soc Resp	—	—	—	—	—	—	—	—	—	—	—	—	—	—
Bridgeway Ult Sm Co SC	—	—	—	—	—	—	—	—	—	—	—	—	—	—
Brinson Glob Bd	—	—	—	—	—	—	—	—	—	-3.5[3]	—	—	—	—
Brinson Glob Eqty	—	—	—	—	—	—	—	—	—	—	—	—	—	—
Brinson Global	—	—	—	—	—	—	—	—	11.2[5]	-1.9[3]	—	—	—	—
Brinson Non US Bd	—	—	—	—	—	—	—	—	—	—	—	—	—	—
Brinson Non US Eqty	—	—	—	—	—	—	—	—	—	0.9[3]	—	—	—	—
Brinson US Blncd	—	—	—	—	—	—	—	—	—	—	—	—	—	—
Brinson US Bond	—	—	—	—	—	—	—	—	—	—	—	—	—	—
Brinson US Eqty	—	—	—	—	—	—	—	—	—	—	—	—	—	—
Brown Cap Blncd	—	—	—	—	—	—	—	—	8.1[4]	-1.2[4]	—	—	—	—
Brown Cap Equity	—	—	—	—	—	—	—	—	6.8[4]	-0.8[3]	—	—	—	—
Brown Cap Sm Co SC	—	—	—	—	—	—	—	—	5.9[5]	4.8[1]	—	—	—	—
Bruce	38.4[1]	29.6[1]	-18.0[5]	12.9[4]	15.5[4]	-1.1[2]	1.3[5]	10.6[2]	19.4[1]	-16.1[5]	3.5[4]	2.1[5]	11,082	11,098
BSR Gro & Inc	—	—	—	—	—	—	—	2.5[5]	10.2[3]	-0.5[3]	4.0[4]	—	11,232	—
BSR S-I Fix	—	—	—	—	—	—	—	6.5[2]	8.4[1]	-2.3[5]	4.1[2]	—	11,276	—
Bull & Bear Glob Inc	20.6[4]	6.0[5]	-6.4[5]	5.0[5]	-3.1[5]	-3.0[5]	18.0[2]	13.1[1]	24.9[1]	-13.4[5]	6.9[1]	6.9[3]	12,229	13,986
Bull & Bear Gold	2.6[2]	35.0[4]	30.4[4]	-13.5[1]	19.3[4]	-22.1[3]	-1.2[2]	-17.2[3]	87.6[3]	-13.8[3]	10.2[4]	0.6[3]	13,391	10,306
Bull & Bear Muni Inc	22.4[1]	19.2[2]	-0.9[2]	11.7[3]	8.9[4]	3.9[5]	13.4[1]	6.0[5]	10.6[5]	-9.8[5]	1.9[5]	4.5[5]	10,580	12,464
Bull & Bear Qual Gro	—	—	—	—	—	—	—	—	—	-8.0[5]	—	—	—	—
Bull & Bear Spec Eqty	—	—	-6.4[4]	22.7[2]	42.3[1]	-36.4[5]	40.5[3]	28.4[1]	16.4[3]	-16.5[5]	7.6[3]	2.2[5]	12,467	11,144
Bull & Bear US Gov	—	—	5.4[1]	4.5[5]	10.4[4]	7.8[2]	15.3[4]	5.2[5]	10.3[4]	-4.7[3]	3.4[5]	6.6[4]	11,059	13,742
Bull & Bear US & Overs	—	—	—	8.0[3]	10.8[5]	-8.6[4]	22.6[1]	-2.6[5]	26.7[3]	-13.1[5]	2.3[5]	3.8[4]	10,719	12,020
CA Inv Tr-CA Insur	—	—	—	—	—	—	—	—	12.0[4]	-5.0[1]	—	—	—	—

See Chapter 3 for explanation of symbols

Stock and bond funds — comprehensive summary *continued*

Arranged in alphabetical order

Total Net Assets $Million December 31 1993	1994	NAV per share December 31 1993	1994	1994 per share distributions Income	Capital gains	Yield % 12/31/94	beta	R²	Std. Dev.	Sharpe Ratio	% Distribution of Portfolio 12/31/94 Stocks	Bonds	Cash	Objective	No-Load Fund
62.8	55.6	37.29	32.98	0.00	0.00	7.5	0.73	0.24	3.53	D	0	99	1	fix-inc	Benham Target 2010
76.8	134.0	28.06	24.11	0.00	0.00	7.5	0.92	0.26	4.25	F	0	100	0	fix-inc	Benham Target 2015
52.5	125.5	19.76	16.27	0.00	0.00	7.5	1.11	0.28	4.95	F	0	100	0	fix-inc	Benham Target 2020
390.8	296.2	10.51	9.76	0.51	0.00	5.2	0.17	0.16	0.99	D	0	100	0	fix-inc	Benham Trsy Note
194.0	153.3	10.24	8.79	0.43	0.00	4.9	—	—	—	—	98	2	0	income	Benham Util Inc
1,648.7	2,113.0	16.81	15.69	0.00	0.00	0.0	1.39	0.56	4.37	C	89	0	11	agg gr	Berger 100
189.3	368.3	11.92	10.71	0.13	0.00	1.2	0.98	0.72	2.67	D	70	14	16	gr-inc	Berger 101
0.5	291.2	2.50	2.84	0.00	0.00	0.1	—	—	—	—	76	0	24	agg gr	Berger Sm Co Growth
162.8	160.8	13.78	12.73	0.62	0.00	4.9	0.27	0.33	1.10	D	0	93	7	tax-free	Bernstein CA Muni
—	42.0	—	12.42	—	—	—	—	—	—	—	0	94	6	tax-free	Bernstein CA ST
—	88.1	—	12.43	—	—	—	—	—	—	—	0	95	5	tax-free	Bernstein Dvsfd Muni ST
487.3	504.4	13.70	12.74	0.62	0.00	4.9	0.27	0.32	1.10	C	0	95	5	tax-free	Bernstein Dvsfd Muni
190.1	143.4	12.66	12.15	0.56	0.00	4.6	0.10	0.21	0.47	B	0	90	10	fix-inc	Bernstein Gov Sht
727.8	842.3	13.49	12.37	0.70	0.00	5.6	0.25	0.25	1.15	B	0	100	0	fix-inc	Bernstein Inter Dur
705.1	1429.1	15.59	15.43	0.11	0.63	0.7	—	—	—	—	—	—	—	int'l	Bernstein Int'l Value
364.8	376.6	13.71	12.72	0.64	0.00	5.1	0.27	0.31	1.13	B	0	93	7	tax-free	Bernstein NY Muni
—	49.8	—	12.39	—	—	—	—	—	—	—	0	96	4	tax-free	Bernstein NY ST
507.0	507.1	12.66	12.14	0.59	0.00	4.8	0.10	0.24	0.46	A	0	96	4	fix-inc	Bernstein Short Dur
30.4	55.8	11.63	10.74	0.73	0.03	6.8	0.41	0.30	1.75	A	16	80	4	income	Berwyn Income
47.3	63.5	17.67	17.55	0.07	0.78	0.4	1.03	0.48	3.45	A	98	1	1	gr-inc	Berwyn
19.9	10.5	9.87	9.23	0,20	0.03	2.2	—	—	—	—	98	0	2	growth	Blanchard Amer Eqty
—	0.8	—	6.81	—	—	—	—	—	—	—	97	3	0	growth	Blanchard Cap Growth
—	16.3	—	7.31	—	—	—	—	—	—	—	93	2	5	int'l	Blanchard Emg Mkt
690.5	272.1	5.15	4.55	0.32	0.00	7.0	—	—	—	—	0	98	2	fix-inc	Blanchard Flex Inc
24.6	18.0	5.18	4.65	0.24	0.00	5.2	—	—	—	—	0	98	2	tax-free	Blanchard Flex TF
95.6	93.8	10.48	9.47	0.19	0.03	2.0	0.70	0.52	2.23	F	62	9	29	global	Blanchard Glob Growth
—	1.4	—	6.80	—	—	—	—	—	—	—	89	11	0	gr-inc	Blanchard Gro & Inc
72.1	77.2	9.64	6.99	0.90	0.28	12.4	0.33	0.01	7.73	C	88	3	9	prec met	Blanchard Prec Metals
32.0	24.2	3.00	2.88	0.15	0.00	5.2	—	—	—	—	0	96	4	fix-inc	Blanchard ST Bond
631.8	305.7	1.87	1.68	0.11	0.00	6.3	0.08	0.06	0.77	F	0	62	38	fix-inc	Blanchard ST Global
—	2.6	—	10.06	—	—	—	—	—	—	—	25	0	75	growth	Bonnel Growth
—	13.4	—	10.25	—	—	—	—	—	—	—	94	0	6	growth	Bramwell Growth
8.3	32.0	16.77	17.05	0.00	0.11	0.0	1.14	0.51	3.75	B	87	0	13	growth	Brandywine Blue
1,527.5	2,299.3	24.97	23.50	0.00	1.45	0.0	1.30	0.59	3.97	B	87	0	13	agg gr	Brandywine
20.0	18.1	17.80	17.10	0.59	0.18	3.4	0.70	0.88	1.72	D	69	27	4	gr-inc	Bridges Investment
—	0.2	—	10.65	—	—	—	—	—	—	—	93	0	7	agg gr	Bridgeway Agg Gro
—	0.1	—	9.87	—	—	—	—	—	—	—	85	0	15	growth	Bridgeway Soc Resp
—	0.4	—	9.99	—	—	—	—	—	—	—	93	0	7	agg gr	Bridgeway Ult Sm Co SC
26.7	47.8	10.06	9.61	0.10	0.00	1.0	—	—	—	—	1	95	4	fix-inc	Brinson Glob Bd
—	20.0	—	9.43	—	—	—	—	—	—	—	96	1	3	global	Brinson Glob Eqty
252.3	317.3	10.79	10.31	0.18	0.09	1.7	—	—	—	—	38	57	5	global	Brinson Global
—	—	—	—	—	—	—	—	—	—	—	—	—	—	fix-inc	Brinson Non US Bd
53.6	113.8	9.64	9.68	0.05	0.00	0.5	—	—	—	—	66	30	4	int'l	Brinson Non US Eqty
—	—	—	—	—	—	—	—	—	—	—	—	—	—	income	Brinson US Blncd
—	—	—	—	—	—	—	—	—	—	—	—	—	—	fix-inc	Brinson US Bond
—	15.5	—	9.67	—	—	—	—	—	—	—	99	0	1	gr-inc	Brinson US Eqty
1.1	1.4	11.34	10.89	0.09	0.00	0.8	—	—	—	—	—	—	—	gr-inc	Brown Cap Blncd
0.6	0.9	11.67	11.45	0.00	0.00	0.0	—	—	—	—	—	—	—	growth	Brown Cap Equity
1.7	2.3	10.97	11.24	0.00	0.00	0.0	—	—	—	—	—	—	—	agg gr	Brown Cap Sm Co SC
2.5	2.0	112.02	90.56	3.47	0.00	3.8	0.95	0.33	3.87	F	15	75	10	gr-inc	Bruce
19.7	19.0	12.63	11.94	0.07	0.55	0.5	0.95	0.83	2.43	F	99	0	1	gr-inc	BSR Gro & Inc
43.9	33.5	10.76	9.92	0.60	0.00	6.0	0.14	0.14	0.90	D	0	98	2	fix-inc	BSR S-I Fix
57.6	40.9	9.94	7.97	0.66	0.00	8.3	0.10	—	—	—	1	92	7	fix-inc	Bull & Bear Glob Inc
56.9	38.5	18.52	14.50	0.00	1.45	0.0	0.43	0.02	7.56	D	79	9	12	prec met	Bull & Bear Gold
21.3	17.0	17.63	15.25	0.68	0.00	4.4	0.52	0.34	2.05	F	0	98	2	tax-free	Bull & Bear Muni Inc
1.1	4.2	14.47	13.32	0.00	0.00	0.0	—	—	—	—	99	0	1	gr-inc	Bull & Bear Qual Gro
73.9	45.5	23.13	19.11	0.00	0.19	0.0	1.54	0.43	5.55	D	119	0	-19	agg gr	Bull & Bear Spec Eqty
21.3	15.9	15.60	14.22	0.65	0.00	4.6	0.24	0.17	1.33	D	0	72	28	fix-inc	Bull & Bear US Gov
12.2	8.5	8.71	7.08	0.00	0.49	0.0	0.91	0.38	3.47	F	91	8	1	global	Bull & Bear US & Overs
17.6	20.0	10.71	9.75	0.43	0.00	4.4	—	—	—	—	0	99	1	tax-free	CA Inv Tr-CA Insur

35

Stock and bond funds — comprehensive summary *continued*

Arranged in alphabetical order

No-Load Fund	1985	1986	1987	1988	1989	1990	1991	1992	1993	1994	Annualized 3 yrs.	Annualized 5 yrs.	What $10,000 grew to after 3 yrs.	5 yrs.
CA Inv Tr-CA TF	—	22.7[1]	-1.3[2]	10.6[4]	9.9[2]	6.7[3]	12.1[3]	8.8[3]	14.7[1]	-8.6[5]	4.5[3]	6.4[3]	11,410	13,646
CA Inv Tr-S&P 500	—	—	—	—	—	—	—	—	9.8[4]	1.0[2]	—	—	—	—
CA Inv Tr-S&P MidCap	—	—	—	—	—	—	—	—	12.9[3]	-3.9[4]	—	—	—	—
CA Inv Tr-US Gov	—	11.9[4]	2.0[2]	6.4[5]	13.5[2]	8.5[2]	17.4[2]	8.4[2]	15.8[2]	-7.0[4]	5.3[2]	8.3[2]	11,676	14,877
Caldwell Fund	—	20.7[1]	-1.6[4]	11.2[5]	13.7[5]	-1.4[2]	22.6[4]	10.4[2]	10.9[3]	-1.1[3]	6.6[2]	7.9[3]	12,105	14,627
Caldwell Gov	—	—	—	—	—	—	—	—	5.9[5]	-0.3[1]	—	—	—	—
Caldwell Growth Stk	—	—	—	—	—	—	—	—	2.4[5]	-8.9[5]	—	—	—	—
Caldwell Tax-Free	—	—	—	—	—	—	—	—	4.2[5]	-1.8[1]	—	—	—	—
Camco Inter Term	—	—	—	—	—	—	—	—	5.8[5]	1.7[1]	—	—	—	—
Camco Short Term	—	—	—	—	—	—	—	—	4.0[5]	2.1[1]	—	—	—	—
Camco Total Ret	—	—	—	—	—	—	—	—	6.4[5]	1.3[1]	—	—	—	—
Capp-Rush Emg Gro SC	—	—	—	—	—	—	—	—	22.5[1]	-7.0[5]	—	—	—	—
Capp-Rush Gold	—	—	—	—	—	—	—	—	—	—	—	—	—	—
Capp-Rush Growth	—	—	—	—	—	—	—	—	14.4[2]	4.6[1]	—	—	—	—
Capp-Rush Util	—	—	—	—	—	—	—	—	6.1[5]	-13.3[5]	—	—	—	—
Capstone Gov Inc	20.5[4]	16.0[2]	3.7[1]	11.8[1]	7.3[4]	-1.1[5]	6.6[5]	3.6[5]	3.3[5]	1.2[1]	2.7[5]	2.7[5]	10,823	11,410
Century Shares	43.4[2]	9.6[4]	-8.0[4]	15.7[3]	41.6[2]	-7.8[3]	31.4[4]	27.0[1]	-0.4[5]	-3.9[3]	6.7[4]	8.1[4]	12,156	14,724
CGM American TF	—	—	—	—	—	—	—	—	—	-8.2[4]	—	—	—	—
CGM Capital Dev.‡	46.2[1]	28.4[1]	15.9[1]	-0.3[5]	17.9[4]	1.5[1]	99.1[1]	17.4[1]	28.7[1]	-22.9[5]	5.2[4]	18.7[1]	11,647	23,534
CGM Fixed Inc	—	—	—	—	—	—	—	—	18.9[1]	-8.0[5]	—	—	—	—
CGM Mutual	34.4[1]	25.0[1]	13.8[1]	3.2[5]	21.6[3]	1.1[1]	40.9[1]	6.0[4]	21.8[1]	-9.7[5]	5.3[4]	10.7[1]	11,661	16,618
CGM Realty	—	—	—	—	—	—	—	—	—	—	—	—	—	—
Charter Cap Blue Chip	13.5[5]	16.3[2]	-4.9[5]	1.8[5]	9.2[5]	-1.7[2]	45.8[1]	-5.7[5]	1.9[5]	-4.9[5]	-2.9[5]	5.6[5]	9,145	13,111
Clipper	26.5[3]	18.7[2]	2.9[2]	19.6[2]	22.0[3]	-7.6[4]	32.5[2]	15.9[1]	11.3[3]	-2.5[4]	7.9[2]	9.0[2]	12,570	15,389
Cohen & Steers Realty	—	—	—	—	—	—	—	19.9[2]	18.7[3]	8.3[1]	15.5[2]	—	15,422	—
Columbia Balanced	—	—	—	—	—	—	—	8.9[3]	13.6[3]	0.1[2]	7.4[2]	—	12,384	—
Columbia Common Stk	—	—	—	—	—	—	—	10.0[3]	16.4[2]	2.1[2]	9.3[2]	—	13,071	—
Columbia Fix Inc	20.2[2]	12.3[2]	0.9[4]	7.6[2]	14.4[1]	8.3[3]	16.8[2]	8.0[1]	10.5[3]	-3.5[4]	4.8[1]	7.8[1]	11,517	14,573
Columbia Growth	32.0[2]	6.9[4]	14.7[1]	10.8[4]	28.9[3]	-3.3[2]	34.2[4]	11.8[3]	13.0[4]	-0.6[3]	7.9[3]	10.3[3]	12,557	16,288
Columbia High Yld	—	—	—	—	—	—	—	—	—	-0.9[1]	—	—	—	—
Columbia Int'l Stk	—	—	—	—	—	—	—	—	33.4[3]	-2.5[3]	—	—	—	—
Columbia Muni Bd	19.8[3]	16.8[5]	1.4[1]	10.2[4]	9.0[4]	6.9[2]	11.7[3]	6.5[5]	10.7[5]	-4.7[1]	4.0[4]	6.1[4]	11,236	13,418
Columbia Real Est	—	—	—	—	—	—	—	—	—	—	—	—	—	—
Columbia Special	—	15.6[2]	3.0[2]	42.6[1]	31.8[2]	-12.4[4]	50.3[2]	13.7[2]	21.7[2]	2.3[2]	12.3[1]	13.3[2]	14,152	18,638
Columbia US Gov	—	—	4.1[3]	5.3[5]	9.6[4]	9.3[2]	12.7[3]	5.8[3]	5.9[3]	0.0[3]	3.9[3]	6.7[3]	11,201	13,799
Concorde Value	—	—	—	13.9[4]	4.6[5]	-16.7[5]	27.4[3]	14.6[1]	9.7[4]	-3.3[4]	6.7[2]	5.2[5]	12,155	12,901
Copley	24.9[4]	17.5[2]	-8.3[5]	19.9[2]	17.8[4]	-1.5[2]	17.1[5]	17.7[1]	10.2[3]	-7.7[5]	6.2[3]	6.7[4]	11,967	13,803
Cornerstone Growth	—	—	-23.0[5]	7.0[4]	8.2[5]	-16.2[4]	34.6[4]	-3.8[5]	5.1[5]	7.6[1]	2.9[4]	4.2[5]	10,883	12,282
Countdown Ret 2010	—	—	—	—	—	—	—	—	—	—	—	—	—	—
Countdown Ret 2020	—	—	—	—	—	—	—	—	—	—	—	—	—	—
Crabbe Hsn Asst All	—	—	—	—	—	—	21.2[4]	12.2[1]	18.2[1]	-0.9[2]	9.6[1]	—	13,151	—
Crabbe Hsn Eqty	—	—	—	—	—	—	35.0[2]	16.3[1]	26.0[1]	1.5[2]	14.1[1]	—	14,868	—
Crabbe Hsn Gov Bd	—	—	—	—	—	7.4[3]	13.2[5]	5.5[5]	5.9[5]	-2.1[1]	3.0[5]	5.9[5]	10,932	13,291
Crabbe Hsn Income	—	—	—	—	—	5.9[4]	16.2[3]	6.0[5]	6.3[5]	-3.6[3]	2.8[5]	6.0[5]	10,854	13,357
Crabbe Hsn OR Muni	—	—	—	—	—	—	9.8[4]	7.3[3]	8.9[5]	-2.7[2]	4.4[4]	—	11,376	—
Crabbe Hsn Real Est	—	—	—	—	—	—	—	—	—	—	—	—	—	—
Crabbe Hsn Spec SC	—	—	-17.4[5]	19.5[2]	17.3[4]	3.8[1]	17.1[5]	33.4[1]	34.5[1]	11.7[1]	26.1[1]	19.5[1]	20,052	24,364
Crescent Fund	—	—	—	—	—	—	—	—	—	4.3[1]	—	—	—	—
Crowley Growth	—	—	—	—	—	-0.8[2]	15.6[5]	3.6[5]	3.2[5]	3.9[1]	3.6[4]	5.0[5]	11,103	12,730
Crowley Income	—	—	—	—	—	9.0[2]	11.4[5]	7.2[3]	9.6[4]	-1.8[1]	4.9[3]	7.0[3]	11,538	14,016
CT&T Gro & Inc	—	—	—	—	—	—	—	—	—	0.5[2]	—	—	—	—
CT&T Inter Fix	—	—	—	—	—	—	—	—	—	-2.8[3]	—	—	—	—
CT&T Inter Muni	—	—	—	—	—	—	—	—	—	-2.2[1]	—	—	—	—
CT&T M&C Blncd	—	—	—	—	—	—	—	—	—	—	—	—	—	—
CT&T M&C Growth	—	—	—	—	—	—	—	—	—	—	—	—	—	—
CT&T Talon	—	—	—	—	—	—	—	—	—	—	—	—	—	—
C&O Agg Growth SC	—	—	—	—	—	—	—	15.1[2]	14.9[3]	-1.0[3]	9.4[2]	—	13,096	—
Delafield Fund	—	—	—	—	—	—	—	—	—	5.6[1]	—	—	—	—
DFA 1 Yr Fix Inc.‡	10.5[5]	8.9[5]	6.4[1]	7.4[1]	9.5[4]	9.1[3]	8.7[5]	5.2[4]	4.4[4]	2.5[1]	4.0[2]	5.9[4]	11,249	13,335
DFA 5 Yr Gov.‡	—	—	—	6.3[3]	9.5[4]	10.8[1]	14.5[1]	7.3[1]	8.3[1]	-3.2[5]	4.0[2]	7.4[1]	11,251	14,280

See Chapter 3 for explanation of symbols

Stock and bond funds — comprehensive summary *continued*

Arranged in alphabetical order

Total Net Assets $Million		NAV per share		1994 per share distributions		Yield %	Risk Analysis				% Distribution of Portfolio			Objective	No-Load Fund
December 31		December 31		Income	Capital gains	12/31/94	beta	R²	Std. Dev.	Sharpe Ratio	12/31/94				
1993	1994	1993	1994								Stocks	Bonds	Cash		
281.3	218.0	13.18	11.23	0.62	0.00	5.5	0.55	0.33	2.22	F	0	99	1	tax-free	CA Inv Tr-CA TF
13.0	14.7	11.15	10.90	0.32	0.00	2.9	—	—	—	—	99	0	1	gr-inc	CA Inv Tr-S&P 500
19.3	20.3	12.27	11.10	0.22	0.00	2.0	—	—	—	—	98	0	2	growth	CA Inv Tr-S&P MidCap
35.3	26.8	11.29	9.84	0.67	0.00	6.8	0.43	0.26	1.96	C	0	97	3	fix-inc	CA Inv Tr-US Gov
3.8	3.8	15.05	13.95	0.43	0.50	3.1	0.76	0.72	2.08	C	93	0	7	gr-inc	Caldwell Fund
6.0	6.0	9.93	9.44	0.46	0.00	4.9	—	—	—	—	0	95	5	fix-inc	Caldwell Gov
1.6	1.4	10.24	9.34	0.01	0.00	0.1	—	—	—	—	—	—	—	growth	Caldwell Growth Stk
0.6	0.6	9.98	9.39	0.41	0.00	4.4	—	—	—	—	0	96	4	tax-free	Caldwell Tax-Free
0.1	0.1	10.01	9.84	0.34	0.00	3.5	—	—	—	—	0	100	0	fix-inc	Camco Inter Term
0.0	0.1	10.07	9.92	0.36	0.00	3.6	—	—	—	—	0	100	0	fix-inc	Camco Short Term
2.0	0.2	10.01	9.78	0.35	0.00	3.6	—	—	—	—	0	100	0	fix-inc	Camco Total Ret
12.4	19.9	12.52	11.65	0.00	0.00	0.0	—	—	—	—	94	0	6	agg gr	Capp-Rush Emg Gro SC
—	6.2	—	8.80	—	—	—	—	—	—	—	89	0	11	prec met	Capp-Rush Gold
4.7	15.8	11.49	12.00	0.01	0.00	0.1	—	—	—	—	97	0	3	growth	Capp-Rush Growth
11.4	19.6	10.47	8.62	0.45	0.00	5.2	—	—	—	—	87	0	13	income	Capp-Rush Util
33.8	8.4	4.80	4.73	0.12	0.00	2.6	0.03	0.05	0.35	B	0	95	5	fix-inc	Capstone Gov Inc
233.8	206.1	24.04	21.77	0.45	0.88	2.0	0.74	0.34	3.00	D	97	2	1	sector	Century Shares
4.8	10.1	10.25	8.83	0.58	0.00	6.6	—	—	—	—	0	100	0	tax-free	CGM American TF
523.8	401.7	27.71	20.58	0.07	0.71	0.3	1.75	0.64	5.15	D	99	0	1	agg gr	CGM Capital Dev
32.9	28.7	11.17	9.57	0.73	0.00	7.7	—	—	—	—	0	98	2	fix-inc	CGM Fixed Inc
947.1	1,063.4	28.88	25.05	1.04	0.00	4.2	0.92	0.63	2.69	D	63	36	1	gr-inc	CGM Mutual
—	34.3	—	9.71	—	—	—	—	—	—	—	99	0	1	sector	CGM Realty
9.5	6.1	13.10	12.31	0.16	0.00	1.3	0.92	0.59	2.79	F	71	2	27	growth	Charter Cap Blue Chip
239.8	247.1	50.05	46.09	0.71	2.00	1.5	1.18	0.75	3.18	C	92	6	2	gr-inc	Clipper.
155.8	458.5	31.92	32.90	1.66	0.00	5.0	0.45	0.08	3.71	B	91	0	9	sector	Cohen & Steers Realty
186.6	249.7	17.91	17.28	0.64	0.00	3.7	0.63	0.82	1.63	B	50	45	5	income	Columbia Balanced
100.7	124.3	15.29	15.16	0.25	0.19	1.6	0.96	0.90	2.35	B	92	1	7	growth	Columbia Common Stk
300.5	252.1	13.44	12.15	0.83	0.00	6.8	0.25	0.20	1.32	C	0	96	4	fix-inc	Columbia Fix Inc
605.4	591.7	26.38	24.84	0.26	1.11	1.0	1.22	0.85	3.09	C	93	2	5	agg gr	Columbia Growth
5.9	12.8	9.94	9.04	0.80	0.00	8.9	—	—	—	—	0	96	4	fix-inc	Columbia High Yld
72.4	118.5	12.96	12.43	0.00	0.21	0.0	—	—	—	—	90	4	6	int'l	Columbia Int'l Stk
428.9	339.8	12.71	11.48	0.64	0.00	5.6	0.35	0.34	1.38	C	0	97	3	tax-free	Columbia Muni Bd
—	17.4	—	11.72	—	—	—	—	—	—	—	94	0	6	sector	Columbia Real Est
772.7	889.5	19.51	18.69	0.07	1.19	0.4	1.12	0.58	3.45	A	88	2	10	agg gr	Columbia Special
35.9	33.5	8.36	7.99	0.37	0.00	4.6	0.08	0.07	0.70	C	0	98	2	fix-inc	Columbia US Gov
12.5	11.2	11.90	11.02	0.06	0.42	0.5	0.68	0.55	2.11	C	91	0	9	gr-inc	Concorde Value
80.7	73.5	21.35	19.71	0.00	0.00	0.0	0.49	0.17	2.81	D	72	3	25	gr-inc	Copley
3.9	5.8	7.77	8.39	0.02	0.00	0.2	0.67	0.43	2.41	D	100	0	0	agg gr	Cornerstone Growth
—	0.2	—	7.50	—	—	—	—	—	—	—	—	—	—	growth	Countdown Ret 2010
—	0.2	—	7.46	—	—	—	—	—	—	—	—	—	—	growth	Countdown Ret 2020
91.9	107.1	13.07	12.17	0.32	0.47	2.5	0.61	0.74	1.64	A	55	40	5	income	Crabbe Hsn Asst All
41.3	155.5	15.84	15.69	0.15	0.24	0.9	0.86	0.74	2.31	A	80	0	20	growth	Crabbe Hsn Eqty
10.8	9.1	10.86	10.15	0.48	0.00	4.7	0.14	0.13	0.87	C	0	85	15	fix-inc	Crabbe Hsn Gov Bd
6.7	6.0	10.44	9.52	0.55	0.00	5.8	0.20	0.19	1.07	F	0	88	12	fix-inc	Crabbe Hsn Income
30.1	26.5	12.82	11.87	0.54	0.07	4.5	0.30	0.33	1.22	B	0	97	3	tax-free	Crabbe Hsn OR Muni
—	17.2	—	9.64	—	—	—	—	—	—	—	100	0	0	sector	Crabbe Hsn Real Est
29.0	377.5	12.40	13.34	0.04	0.45	0.3	1.34	0.38	5.15	A	69	1	30	growth	Crabbe Hsn Spec SC
9.7	14.0	10.70	10.55	0.17	0.00	1.6	—	—	—	—	—	—	—	gr-inc	Crescent Fund
4.7	5.5	10.20	10.08	0.12	0.40	1.1	—	—	—	—	34	54	12	growth	Crowley Growth
5.5	6.6	10.92	10.09	0.63	0.00	6.2	—	—	—	—	0	94	6	fix-inc	Crowley Income
10.2	12.5	10.14	10.11	0.08	0.00	0.8	—	—	—	—	88	0	12	gr-inc	CT&T Gro & Inc
10.0	12.9	10.00	9.13	0.59	0.00	6.4	—	—	—	—	0	93	7	fix-inc	CT&T Inter Fix
9.0	10.4	10.00	9.47	0.31	0.00	3.3	—	—	—	—	1	97	2	tax-free	CT&T Inter Muni
—	6.8	—	9.84	—	—	—	—	—	—	—	61	38	1	income	CT&T M&C Blncd
—	11.2	—	9.77	—	—	—	—	—	—	—	101	0	-1	growth	CT&T M&C Growth
—	5.1	—	10.13	—	—	—	—	—	—	—	72	0	28	growth	CT&T Talon
18.9	36.0	12.31	11.71	0.26	0.22	2.2	0.79	0.33	3.22	B	35	5	60	agg gr	C&O Agg Growth SC
2.2	10.1	10.17	10.47	0.11	0.16	1.0	—	—	—	—	86	2	12	gr-inc	Delafield Fund
599.0	573.0	101.95	99.78	4.57	0.07	4.6	0.04	0.12	0.24	A	0	0	100	fix-inc	DFA 1 Yr Fix Inc
185.0	222.0	105.35	97.09	4.95	0.00	5.1	0.19	0.14	1.13	D	0	98	2	fix-inc	DFA 5 Yr Gov

No-Load Fund	1985	1986	1987	1988	1989	1990	1991	1992	1993	1994	Annualized 3 yrs.	Annualized 5 yrs.	What $10,000 grew to after 3 yrs.	5 yrs.
DFA Cont Sm Co.‡	—	—	—	—	44.6[1]	-4.0[1]	-4.2[5]	-19.8[5]	25.3[5]	11.0[1]	3.7[5]	0.5[5]	11,159	10,257
DFA Emg Mkts‡	—	—	—	—	—	—	—	—	—	—	—	—	—	—
DFA Glob Fix Inc.‡	—	—	—	—	—	—	12.7[5]	6.5[4]	12.3[3]	-4.3[3]	4.6[3]	—	11,435	—
DFA Inter Gov.‡	—	—	—	—	—	—	16.8[2]	7.6[2]	12.3[1]	-4.8[5]	4.8[2]	—	11,502	—
DFA Int'l High BTM.‡	—	—	—	—	—	—	—	—	—	8.8[1]	—	—	—	—
DFA Int'l Sm Cap Val.‡	—	—	—	—	—	—	—	—	—	—	—	—	—	—
DFA Int'l Value‡	—	—	—	—	—	—	—	—	—	—	—	—	—	—
DFA Japan Sm Co.‡	—	—	87.6[1]	32.4[1]	38.5[1]	-33.4[5]	7.1[4]	-26.1[5]	14.2[5]	29.5[1]	3.0[5]	-4.9[5]	10,924	7,799
DFA Lrg Cap Int'l.‡	—	—	—	—	—	—	—	-13.1[4]	25.9[5]	5.3[1]	4.8[4]	—	11,518	—
DFA Pac Rim Sm Co‡	—	—	—	—	—	—	—	—	—	-12.1[5]	—	—	—	—
DFA Real Estate‡	—	—	—	—	—	—	—	—	—	-8.4[4]	—	—	—	—
DFA UK Small Co.‡	—	—	51.3[1]	6.7[5]	-6.3[5]	-6.6[2]	14.7[2]	-14.1[5]	30.6[4]	4.6[2]	5.5[4]	4.7[3]	11,742	12,577
DFA US 6-10 Sm Co SC‡	—	—	—	—	—	—	—	—	13.7[4]	-1.4[3]	—	—	—	—
DFA US 9-10 Sm Co SC‡	24.6[4]	6.8[4]	-9.3[5]	22.8[2]	10.2[5]	-21.6[5]	44.5[3]	23.3[1]	21.0[2]	3.1[1]	15.4[1]	11.8[2]	15,381	17,435
DFA US Lrg Cap Val‡	—	—	—	—	—	—	—	—	—	-4.6[5]	—	—	—	—
DFA US Lrg Co.‡	—	—	—	—	—	—	30.0[2]	7.3[3]	9.8[4]	1.3[2]	6.1[3]	—	11,932	—
DFA US Sm Cap Val SC‡	—	—	—	—	—	—	—	—	—	1.2[2]	—	—	—	—
Dodge & Cox Blncd	32.5[1]	19.2[2]	7.4[1]	11.6[4]	23.0[2]	1.0[2]	20.6[5]	10.6[2]	15.9[2]	2.1[1]	9.4[1]	9.8[2]	13,090	15,946
Dodge & Cox Income	—	—	—	—	—	7.4[4]	17.9[1]	7.8[2]	11.3[2]	-2.9[3]	5.2[1]	8.1[1]	11,655	14,751
Dodge & Cox Stock	37.8[1]	18.9[2]	12.3[1]	13.8[4]	26.9[2]	-5.1[3]	21.4[4]	10.8[2]	18.3[1]	5.2[1]	11.3[1]	9.7[1]	13,799	15,907
Domini Social Eqty	—	—	—	—	—	—	7.8[5]	12.4[2]	6.5[5]	-0.4[3]	6.1[3]	—	11,927	—
Dreman Contrarian	—	—	—	—	18.3[4]	-6.1[4]	26.7[4]	11.3[2]	9.1[4]	0.0[3]	6.7[3]	7.6[4]	12,138	14,444
Dreman Fixed Inc	—	—	—	—	9.1[4]	9.8[1]	11.9[4]	5.2[4]	6.1[3]	-1.2[4]	3.3[4]	6.3[4]	11,026	13,543
Dreman High Return	—	—	—	—	18.5[4]	-8.6[4]	47.5[1]	19.8[1]	9.2[4]	-1.0[3]	9.0[2]	11.8[1]	12,954	17,465
Dreman Small Cap SC	—	—	—	—	—	—	—	—	2.5[5]	0.2[2]	—	—	—	—
Dreyfus 100% US Inter	—	—	—	5.8[5]	12.9[3]	8.6[3]	15.2[3]	7.2[2]	10.4[3]	-4.0[4]	4.4[3]	7.3[2]	11,364	14,217
Dreyfus 100% US Long	—	—	—	8.2[3]	16.2[1]	7.0[3]	18.3[2]	7.6[3]	16.6[2]	-9.2[5]	4.4[3]	7.6[3]	11,388	14,415
Dreyfus 100% US Short	—	—	—	—	—	—	—	7.1[1]	7.0[2]	-0.3[3]	4.5[1]	—	11,419	—
Dreyfus A Bonds Plus	23.1[2]	14.0[4]	-1.1[4]	9.0[2]	14.1[2]	4.8[4]	18.7[2]	8.2[2]	14.9[2]	-6.1[4]	5.3[2]	7.7[2]	11,661	14,496
Dreyfus Apprec	35.6[2]	15.0[2]	4.4[2]	16.6[3]	27.0[3]	-1.9[2]	38.3[4]	4.6[4]	0.7[5]	3.6[1]	3.0[4]	8.2[4]	10,912	14,811
Dreyfus Asst:Gro	—	—	—	—	—	—	—	—	—	—	—	—	—	—
Dreyfus Asst:Inc	—	—	—	—	—	—	—	—	—	—	—	—	—	—
Dreyfus Asst:Tot Ret	—	—	—	—	—	—	—	—	—	1.7[1]	—	—	—	—
Dreyfus Balanced	—	—	—	—	—	—	—	—	10.8[4]	4.0[1]	—	—	—	—
Dreyfus Bond Mkt Idx	—	—	—	—	—	—	—	—	—	-3.4[4]	—	—	—	—
Dreyfus CA Inter	—	—	—	—	—	—	—	—	14.4[1]	-5.5[5]	—	—	—	—
Dreyfus CA TE	18.0[4]	17.7[3]	-1.7[3]	9.7[4]	8.6[4]	6.8[3]	10.4[5]	6.7[5]	11.9[4]	-7.1[4]	3.5[5]	5.5[5]	11,085	13,059
Dreyfus Core Value	35.0[1]	22.5[1]	0.5[3]	19.6[2]	24.9[2]	-13.7[5]	22.9[5]	4.0[5]	16.5[2]	0.4[3]	6.8[3]	5.2[5]	12,165	12,906
Dreyfus CT Inter	—	—	—	—	—	—	—	—	12.8[1]	-4.7[4]	—	—	—	—
Dreyfus Discpl MidCap	—	—	—	—	—	—	—	—	—	-6.7[5]	—	—	—	—
Dreyfus Discpl Stk	—	—	—	10.7[5]	32.4[1]	0.2[2]	33.6[1]	7.1[3]	11.8[3]	-1.2[4]	5.8[4]	9.6[1]	11,835	15,844
Dreyfus Edison Elec	—	—	—	—	—	—	—	7.3[4]	10.5[4]	-12.9[5]	1.1[5]	—	10,328	—
Dreyfus Equity Inc	—	—	—	—	—	—	—	—	—	—	—	—	—	—
Dreyfus European	—	—	—	0.2[5]	19.2[3]	2.2[1]	12.6[2]	-3.7[3]	18.8[5]	-3.1[4]	3.5[5]	5.0[3]	11,088	12,760
Dreyfus FL Inter	—	—	—	—	—	—	—	—	12.8[1]	-4.9[4]	—	—	—	—
Dreyfus Fund	25.2[4]	16.2[3]	8.2[1]	8.8[5]	23.5[3]	-3.3[3]	27.9[3]	5.5[4]	6.3[5]	-4.3[5]	2.4[5]	5.9[4]	10,745	13,296
Dreyfus Global Bd	—	—	—	—	—	—	—	—	—	—	—	—	—	—
Dreyfus Global Growth.†	—	—	—	15.5[2]	21.0[3]	5.8[1]	17.6[2]	-2.8[5]	22.0[4]	-7.5[4]	3.1[5]	6.4[3]	10,967	13,644
Dreyfus GNMA	—	9.6[5]	1.8[3]	6.4[4]	11.5[4]	9.7[2]	14.4[4]	6.3[4]	7.1[4]	-2.8[3]	3.5[5]	6.8[4]	11,072	13,892
Dreyfus Gro & Inc	—	—	—	—	—	—	—	20.1[1]	18.5[1]	-5.2[5]	10.5[1]	—	13,497	—
Dreyfus Growth Oppty	30.7[2]	15.3[2]	6.8[2]	17.9[3]	14.7[5]	-6.6[4]	51.4[1]	-4.2[5]	2.0[5]	-6.4[5]	-2.9[5]	5.3[5]	9,152	12,947
Dreyfus Insur Muni	—	17.0[4]	-1.9[3]	10.2[4]	8.8[4]	7.1[2]	11.2[4]	7.7[5]	12.6[4]	-8.6[5]	3.5[5]	5.7[5]	11,080	13,189
Dreyfus Inter Muni	16.1[3]	15.4[2]	1.1[3]	8.0[2]	8.7[2]	6.8[3]	11.1[2]	8.7[1]	11.6[2]	-4.6[4]	5.0[2]	6.5[2]	11,572	13,720
Dreyfus Intl Eqty Allc	—	—	—	—	—	—	—	—	—	—	—	—	—	—
Dreyfus Int'l Eqty	—	—	—	—	—	—	—	—	—	-5.4[4]	—	—	—	—
Dreyfus Invst GNMA	—	—	—	—	—	—	—	7.0[2]	8.8[3]	-1.1[1]	4.8[2]	—	11,515	—
Dreyfus MA Inter	—	—	—	—	—	—	—	—	12.6[1]	-6.4[5]	—	—	—	—
Dreyfus MA TE	—	17.9[3]	-3.4[4]	10.5[4]	7.7[5]	6.1[4]	12.7[1]	7.5[5]	12.4[4]	-6.0[3]	4.3[4]	6.3[3]	11,357	13,575
Dreyfus Muni Bond	19.4[3]	17.3[3]	-1.7[3]	11.5[3]	9.4[3]	6.4[3]	12.0[3]	8.4[3]	12.7[3]	-7.0[3]	4.4[4]	6.3[3]	11,362	13,539
Dreyfus New Ldrs SC	—	12.3[3]	-5.0[4]	23.3[2]	31.3[2]	-11.9[4]	45.4[3]	9.4[3]	17.0[3]	-0.2[2]	8.5[3]	10.4[3]	12,784	16,382

See Chapter 3 for explanation of symbols

Total Net Assets $Million		NAV per share		1994 per share distributions		Yield % 12/31/94	Risk Analysis				% Distribution of Portfolio 12/31/94			Objective	No-Load Fund
December 31 1993	1994	December 31 1993	1994	Income	Capital gains		beta	R²	Std. Dev.	Sharpe Ratio	Stocks	Bonds	Cash		
283.0	345.0	13.40	14.67	0.18	0.03	1.2	0.27	0.03	3.80	F	99	0	1	int'l	DFA Cont Sm Co
—	15.0	—	10.48	—	—	—	—	—	—	—	96	0	4	int'l	DFA Emg Mkts
101.0	141.0	105.68	97.40	3.70	0.00	3.8	0.20	0.15	1.17	C	0	99	1	fix-inc	DFA Glob Fix Inc
54.0	61.0	114.12	101.89	6.83	0.03	6.7	0.27	0.19	1.44	D	0	98	2	fix-inc	DFA Inter Gov
73.0	114.0	10.70	11.50	0.14	0.00	1.2	—	—	—	—	97	0	3	int'l	DFA Int'l High BTM
—	—	—	—	—	—	—	—	—	—	—	—	—	—	int'l	DFA Int'l Sm Cap Val
73.0	235.0	10.70	10.11	—	—	0.0	—	—	—	F	98	0	2	int'l	DFA Int'l Value
220.0	342.0	20.15	25.25	0.03	0.80	0.1	0.43	0.01	9.01	F	98	0	2	int'l	DFA Japan Sm Co
89.0	58.0	11.95	11.79	0.08	0.23	0.7	0.69	0.14	4.29	D	97	0	3	int'l	DFA Lrg Cap Int'l
189.0	214.0	19.04	15.47	0.22	0.19	1.4	—	—	—	—	99	0	1	int'l	DFA Pac Rim Sm Co
24.0	33.0	11.31	9.92	0.41	0.00	4.2	—	—	—	—	96	0	4	sector	DFA Real Estate
193.0	215.0	22.40	22.96	0.47	0.02	2.0	0.87	0.13	5.85	F	99	0	1	int'l	DFA UK Small Co
141.0	115.0	11.67	10.25	0.26	0.94	2.3	—	—	—	—	98	0	2	agg gr	DFA US 6-10 Sm Co SC
643.0	663.0	8.25	8.49	0.02	0.00	0.2	1.03	0.45	3.61	A	99	0	1	agg gr	DFA US 9-10 Sm Co SC
97.0	207.0	10.81	10.00	0.32	0.00	3.2	—	—	—	—	97	0	3	growth	DFA US Lrg Cap Val
40.0	52.0	13.94	13.75	0.36	0.00	2.6	0.96	0.92	2.34	C	99	0	1	gr-inc	DFA US Lrg Co
101.0	357.0	11.23	11.23	0.13	0.00	1.2	—	—	—	—	99	0	1	agg gr	DFA US Sm Cap Val SC
486.9	725.2	46.40	45.21	1.79	0.36	3.9	0.70	0.77	1.84	A	57	38	5	income	Dodge & Cox Blncd
180.0	195.4	11.89	10.74	0.76	0.05	7.1	0.27	0.20	1.39	B	0	97	3	fix-inc	Dodge & Cox Income
435.9	543.5	53.23	53.94	1.15	0.89	2.1	0.99	0.81	2.56	A	96	0	4	gr-inc	Dodge & Cox Stock
27.0	33.7	12.43	12.10	0.20	0.08	1.6	0.98	—	—	C	97	1	2	gr-inc	Domini Social Eqty
17.2	13.0	13.62	12.18	0.28	1.16	2.1	1.19	0.86	3.00	D	100	0	0	growth	Dreman Contrarian
5.2	4.5	10.09	9.44	0.53	0.00	5.6	0.11	0.11	0.73	D	0	66	34	fix-inc	Dreman Fixed Inc
28.4	35.0	15.50	15.11	0.24	0.00	1.6	1.12	0.74	3.04	C	98	0	2	growth	Dreman High Return
4.9	6.9	11.23	10.85	0.00	0.40	0.0	—	—	—	—	98	0	2	agg gr	Dreman Small Cap SC
253.4	185.3	13.60	12.16	0.91	0.00	7.5	0.22	0.15	1.33	C	0	98	2	fix-inc	Dreyfus 100% US Inter
215.0	123.4	15.68	13.26	1.01	0.00	7.6	0.43	0.24	2.04	D	0	98	2	fix-inc	Dreyfus 100% US Long
187.4	172.5	15.75	14.55	1.15	0.00	7.9	0.08	0.07	0.75	B	0	100	0	fix-inc	Dreyfus 100% US Short
633.6	484.3	15.18	13.24	0.94	0.07	7.1	0.35	0.24	1.69	C	0	96	4	fix-inc	Dreyfus A Bonds Plus
237.4	233.5	14.92	15.17	0.28	0.01	1.8	0.97	0.75	2.64	D	93	4	3	agg gr	Dreyfus Apprec
—	1.1	—	12.26	—	—	—	—	—	—	—	—	—	—	growth	Dreyfus Asst:Gro
—	1.1	—	12.57	—	—	—	—	—	—	—	—	—	—	income	Dreyfus Asst:Inc
47.8	50.0	12.68	12.48	0.37	0.05	2.9	—	—	—	—	—	—	—	income	Dreyfus Asst:Tot Ret
62.1	91.3	13.46	13.39	0.46	0.13	3.4	—	—	—	—	—	—	—	income	Dreyfus Balanced
11.0	5.9	9.98	9.10	0.54	0.00	5.9	—	—	—	—	0	100	0	fix-inc	Dreyfus Bond Mkt Idx
306.5	237.8	13.97	12.54	0.67	0.00	5.4	—	—	—	—	0	98	2	tax-free	Dreyfus CA Inter
1,840.1	1,433.4	15.56	13.61	0.82	0.05	6.0	0.41	0.31	1.73	F	0	99	1	tax-free	Dreyfus CA TE
349.6	318.1	27.80	24.55	0.40	2.97	1.5	1.02	0.84	2.58	C	95	2	3	growth	Dreyfus Core Value
138.3	124.3	13.77	12.47	0.66	0.00	5.3	—	—	—	—	0	98	2	tax-free	Dreyfus CT Inter
16.2	16.2	10.10	9.32	0.11	0.00	1.1	—	—	—	—	—	—	—	growth	Dreyfus Discpl MidCap
201.9	243.6	18.26	17.31	0.27	0.47	1.5	0.96	0.94	2.31	C	98	0	2	gr-inc	Dreyfus Discpl Stk
103.4	71.1	13.78	11.28	0.73	0.00	6.4	0.58	0.20	3.08	F	100	0	0	sector	Dreyfus Edison Elec
—	4.9	—	9.58	—	—	—	—	—	—	—	—	—	—	gr-inc	Dreyfus Equity Inc
10.6	10.1	12.37	10.27	0.10	1.51	0.9	0.80	0.26	3.71	F	99	0	1	int'l	Dreyfus European
535.5	409.4	13.85	12.52	0.65	0.01	5.2	—	—	—	—	0	96	4	tax-free	Dreyfus FL Inter
2,870.9	2,445.2	13.10	11.93	0.22	0.40	1.8	0.96	0.90	2.35	F	83	1	16	gr-inc	Dreyfus Fund
—	14.9	—	11.85	—	—	—	—	—	—	—	0	92	8	fix-inc	Dreyfus Global Bd
159.5	134.1	35.66	32.99	0.00	0.00	0.0	0.56	0.21	2.84	F	60	3	37	global	Dreyfus Global Growth
1,792.8	1,426.4	15.15	13.79	0.94	0.00	6.8	0.20	0.23	0.95	D	0	94	6	fix-inc	Dreyfus GNMA.
1,276.7	1,617.5	17.04	15.63	0.36	0.17	2.3	0.77	0.69	2.14	A	49	23	28	gr-inc	Dreyfus Gro & Inc
495.1	361.1	10.74	8.18	0.09	1.85	0.9	1.24	0.63	3.67	F	92	0	8	growth	Dreyfus Growth Oppty
287.6	215.7	19.08	16.51	0.95	0.00	5.8	0.49	0.30	2.10	F	0	99	1	tax-free	Dreyfus Insur Muni
1,824.2	1,449.2	14.61	13.14	0.75	0.06	5.7	0.36	0.32	1.46	C	0	100	0	tax-free	Dreyfus Inter Muni
—	12.8	—	9.75	—	—	—	—	—	—	—	—	—	—	int'l	Dreyfus Intl Eqty Allc
127.8	158.9	15.40	14.28	0.03	0.25	0.2	—	—	—	—	—	—	—	int'l	Dreyfus Int'l Eqty
54.1	44.9	15.39	14.15	1.08	0.00	7.6	0.19	0.18	1.06	A	0	93	7	fix-inc	Dreyfus Invst GNMA
90.6	67.0	13.72	12.22	0.62	0.02	5.1	—	—	—	—	0	96	4	tax-free	Dreyfus MA Inter
192.2	147.3	17.13	15.21	0.90	0.00	5.9	0.40	0.32	1.65	C	0	98	2	tax-free	Dreyfus MA TE
4,559.9	3,630.6	13.36	11.63	0.74	0.07	6.3	0.45	0.33	1.80	D	0	100	0	tax-free	Dreyfus Muni Bond
338.9	391.6	34.13	31.33	0.08	2.61	0.2	0.94	0.59	2.86	B	86	0	14	agg gr	Dreyfus New Ldrs SC

No-Load Fund	Total return percent with quintile ranks by objective										Annualized		What $10,000 grew to after	
	1985	1986	1987	1988	1989	1990	1991	1992	1993	1994	3 yrs.	5 yrs.	3 yrs.	5 yrs.
Dreyfus NJ Inter	—	—	—	—	—	—	—	—	12.5²	-5.2⁵	—	—	—	—
Dreyfus NJ Muni	—	—	—	12.6²	9.1⁴	7.9¹	12.1³	8.8³	13.0²	-6.0³	4.9²	6.9¹	11,548	13,975
Dreyfus NY Insur	—	—	—	11.3³	8.8⁴	5.9⁴	13.1¹	8.6³	11.1⁵	-6.6³	4.0⁴	6.2⁴	11,259	13,482
Dreyfus NY Inter	—	—	—	9.6¹	9.3¹	6.1⁵	11.1²	9.4¹	11.5³	-5.1⁵	5.0²	6.4³	11,575	13,644
Dreyfus NY TE	20.6²	17.1⁴	-2.7⁴	10.1⁴	8.9⁴	5.5⁵	12.4²	8.9³	12.6³	-7.0³	4.5³	6.2⁴	11,408	13,530
Dreyfus Special Gro	34.7²	7.6⁴	-3.5⁴	21.1²	19.2⁴	-4.9²	29.2⁵	26.1¹	20.2²	-18.3⁵	7.4³	8.8⁴	12,380	15,221
Dreyfus ST Income	—	—	—	—	—	—	—	—	9.2¹	0.1²	—	—	—	—
Dreyfus Strat Growth.†	—	—	—	5.1⁵	14.2⁵	-7.2³	32.7⁴	-15.4⁵	24.7¹	3.1¹	2.9⁵	6.0⁵	10,879	13,405
Dreyfus S&P 500 Idx	—	—	—	—	—	—	—	—	—	0.8²	—	—	—	—
Dreyfus S-I Gov	—	—	—	5.6⁵	11.3²	10.0¹	13.5²	7.0¹	7.3²	-0.8⁴	4.5¹	7.3¹	11,400	14,235
Dreyfus S-I Muni	—	—	—	5.8²	6.5⁴	6.7²	8.3²	6.7²	6.7²	-0.3⁴	4.3²	5.6²	11,346	13,101
Dreyfus Third Cent	29.7³	4.6⁵	2.5³	23.2¹	17.3⁴	3.5¹	38.0²	1.9⁵	5.3⁴	-7.5⁵	-0.3⁵	7.2⁴	9,923	14,170
Drey-Focus Lg Gro	—	—	—	—	—	—	—	—	—	-0.7³	—	—	—	—
Drey-Focus Lg Val	—	—	—	—	—	—	—	—	—	-1.0³	—	—	—	—
Drey-Focus Sm Gro SC	—	—	—	—	—	—	—	—	—	-6.6⁴	—	—	—	—
Drey-Focus Sm Val SC	—	—	—	—	—	—	—	—	—	-1.5⁴	—	—	—	—
Drey-General CA	—	—	—	—	—	7.7¹	10.9⁴	8.6³	13.7¹	-7.0³	4.7³	6.5³	11,483	13,724
Drey-General Muni	21.1²	17.1⁴	-7.1⁵	12.6²	11.5¹	7.6¹	15.0¹	9.8¹	13.3²	-7.3⁴	4.9³	7.4¹	11,535	14,275
Drey-General NY	—	—	—	6.0⁵	6.6⁵	6.6³	13.8¹	10.1¹	14.2¹	-7.2⁴	5.3²	7.2¹	11,665	14,147
Drey-Peoples Idx	—	—	—	—	—	-5.1³	29.8²	7.7³	9.5⁴	0.7²	5.9³	7.9³	11,874	14,625
Drey-Peoples MidCap	—	—	—	—	—	—	—	12.0²	13.5³	-4.0⁴	6.9³	—	12,206	—
Drey-Wilsh Lg Gro	—	—	—	—	—	—	—	—	-0.7⁵	2.3²	—	—	—	—
Drey-Wilsh Lg Val	—	—	—	—	—	—	—	—	13.3²	-5.2⁵	—	—	—	—
Drey-Wilsh Sm Gro	—	—	—	—	—	—	—	—	15.7³	-1.4³	—	—	—	—
Drey-Wilsh Sm Val	—	—	—	—	—	—	—	—	11.2³	-4.5⁴	—	—	—	—
Drey/Laurel Contrn	—	—	—	—	17.3⁴	-8.5⁴	41.6²	10.6²	21.2¹	-11.1⁵	6.0³	9.1³	11,913	15,427
Drey/Laurel Int'l	—	—	—	—	15.4⁴	-18.5⁵	6.6⁵	-10.4⁴	24.6⁵	3.5²	4.9⁴	0.1⁵	11,556	10,041
Drey/Laurel ST Bd	—	—	—	—	7.7⁵	8.4⁴	13.4³	4.9⁴	4.1⁵	0.2²	3.0⁵	6.1⁴	10,938	13,451
Drey/Laurel ST Gov	—	—	—	—	—	—	—	—	—	2.9¹	—	—	—	—
Dupree Inter Gov	—	—	—	—	—	—	—	—	11.9²	-5.9⁵	—	—	—	—
Dupree KY Sht-Med	—	—	—	5.1³	7.4²	6.8¹	7.5⁴	6.9¹	5.6⁴	1.0²	4.5¹	5.5²	11,403	13,095
Dupree KY TF Inc	15.9⁵	17.6³	-0.9²	10.4⁴	10.8¹	7.5¹	10.7⁴	9.1²	12.8³	-2.9¹	6.1¹	7.3¹	11,939	14,211
Dupree Tenn Sht-Med	—	—	—	—	—	—	—	—	—	—	—	—	—	—
Dupree Tenn TF Inc	—	—	—	—	—	—	—	—	—	-1.2¹	—	—	—	—
Eaton Vance ST Trsy	—	—	—	—	—	—	—	3.2⁵	2.4⁵	3.5¹	3.0⁵	—	10,927	—
Eclipse Balanced	—	—	—	—	—	1.4²	20.9⁵	12.0²	17.1¹	-0.1²	9.4¹	10.0¹	13,104	16,072
Eclipse Equity SC	—	—	—	12.7⁴	16.4⁵	-13.6⁴	31.2⁵	19.4¹	17.1³	-4.7⁴	10.0²	8.6⁴	13,320	15,089
Eclipse Gro & Inc	—	—	—	—	—	—	—	—	—	—	—	—	—	—
Eclipse Ultra Short	—	—	—	—	—	—	—	—	—	—	—	—	—	—
Evergreen Amer Ret	—	—	—	—	13.3⁵	-0.4²	18.7⁵	11.7²	14.1²	-2.9⁴	7.4²	7.9³	12,375	14,631
Evergreen Foundation	—	—	—	—	—	6.6¹	36.3¹	19.9¹	15.7²	-1.1²	11.1¹	14.8¹	13,722	19,930
Evergreen Fund	35.2¹	13.0³	-3.1⁴	22.9²	14.9⁵	-11.7⁵	39.9²	8.6³	6.3⁴	0.7²	5.1⁴	7.5⁴	11,618	14,349
Evergreen Glob RE	—	—	—	—	—	-19.5⁵	13.1⁵	9.7³	52.0¹	-14.1⁵	12.8³	5.5⁵	14,337	13,045
Evergreen Gro & Inc	—	-0.5⁵	-4.3⁵	24.5¹	25.4²	-4.5³	25.8⁴	13.8²	14.4²	1.7²	9.8²	9.8²	13,249	15,924
Evergreen Ltd Mkt SC	54.4¹	9.0⁴	-0.8³	26.1¹	20.9⁴	-10.4³	51.0²	10.1³	9.6⁴	-10.6⁵	2.6⁵	7.9⁴	10,796	14,604
Evergreen Nat TF	—	—	—	—	—	—	—	—	16.0¹	-7.9⁴	—	—	—	—
Evergreen Sm Cap SC	—	—	—	—	—	—	—	—	—	-0.8³	—	—	—	—
Evergreen S-I CA	—	—	—	—	—	—	—	—	8.5⁵	-1.8¹	—	—	—	—
Evergreen S-I Muni	—	—	—	—	—	—	—	7.4¹	7.2¹	-1.4⁵	4.3²	—	11,356	—
Evergreen Tax Found	—	—	—	—	—	—	—	—	—	3.4¹	—	—	—	—
Evergreen Tot Ret	31.5²	20.3¹	-9.1⁵	15.8³	16.8⁴	-6.2⁴	22.8⁴	9.9²	12.9³	-6.5⁵	5.1⁴	6.0⁴	11,605	13,368
Evergreen US Gov	—	—	—	—	—	—	—	—	—	-7.4⁴	—	—	—	—
Evergreen US RE	—	—	—	—	—	—	—	—	—	-10.9⁵	—	—	—	—
44 Wall St Eqty	22.4⁵	16.9¹	-41.9⁵	32.3¹	23.5³	-8.6³	25.7⁵	18.2¹	26.4¹	-11.7⁵	9.7²	8.7⁴	13,187	15,143
59 Wall Europe Eqty	—	—	—	—	—	—	8.3⁴	7.5¹	27.1¹	-3.9⁴	9.5²	—	13,124	—
59 Wall Pac Basin	—	—	—	—	—	—	11.2³	6.1¹	74.9¹	-21.5⁵	13.4¹	—	14,568	—
59 Wall Sm Co SC	—	—	—	—	—	—	—	10.6³	12.2⁴	-10.5⁵	3.6⁴	—	11,107	—
59 Wall S-I TF	—	—	—	—	—	—	—	—	6.1³	0.3⁵	—	—	—	—
Fairmont	32.1²	14.0³	-7.8⁴	3.1⁵	6.9⁵	-22.1⁵	40.6³	14.0²	15.6³	7.3¹	12.2¹	9.1³	14,136	15,470
FAM Value SC	—	—	-19.5⁵	35.5¹	20.2⁴	-5.4³	47.4¹	25.0¹	0.2⁵	6.8¹	10.2²	13.3¹	13,382	18,659

See Chapter 3 for explanation of symbols

Stock and bond funds — comprehensive summary *continued*
Arranged in alphabetical order

Total Net Assets $Million December 31 1993	1994	NAV per share December 31 1993	1994	1994 per share distributions Income	Capital gains	Yield % 12/31/94	beta	R^2	Std. Dev.	Sharpe Ratio	Stocks	Bonds	Cash	Objective	No-Load Fund
241.3	212.8	13.93	12.56	0.66	0.00	5.2	—	—	—	—	0	95	5	tax-free	Dreyfus NJ Inter
723.1	577.5	14.03	12.41	0.77	0.02	6.2	0.43	0.32	1.76	B	0	97	3	tax-free	Dreyfus NJ Muni
197.5	151.7	12.04	10.66	0.59	0.00	5.6	0.43	0.33	1.76	D	0	98	2	tax-free	Dreyfus NY Insur
419.0	338.1	18.69	16.89	0.86	0.00	5.1	0.36	0.31	1.49	C	0	99	1	tax-free	Dreyfus NY Inter
2,129.2	1,702.6	16.15	14.09	0.85	0.10	6.0	0.43	0.33	1.75	C	0	98	2	tax-free	Dreyfus NY TE
83.8	64.9	17.97	14.64	0.00	0.05	0.0	1.40	0.53	4.54	C	95	0	5	agg gr	Dreyfus Special Gro
320.7	223.5	12.42	11.60	0.83	0.00	7.2	—	—	—	—	0	92	8	fix-inc	Dreyfus ST Income
45.3	98.9	38.19	39.37	0.00	0.00	0.0	0.00	0.00	2.63	D	22	0	78	agg gr	Dreyfus Strat Growth
118.6	122.8	10.24	10.03	0.25	0.04	2.5	—	—	—	—	99	0	1	gr-inc	Dreyfus S&P 500 Idx
545.4	473.4	11.37	10.53	0.76	0.00	7.2	0.10	0.08	0.82	C	0	100	0	fix-inc	Dreyfus S-I Gov
573.9	427.3	13.31	12.70	0.57	0.00	4.5	0.14	0.23	0.67	C	0	99	1	tax-free	Dreyfus S-I Muni
523.0	347.7	8.26	6.53	0.07	1.01	0.9	0.98	0.74	2.65	F	91	0	9	growth	Dreyfus Third Cent
5.0	5.0	12.43	12.13	0.21	0.00	1.7	—	—	—	—	99	0	1	growth	Drey-Focus Lg Gro
5.0	5.0	12.42	11.97	0.32	0.00	2.7	—	—	—	—	99	0	1	growth	Drey-Focus Lg Val
5.0	5.0	12.54	11.59	0.12	0.00	1.0	—	—	—	—	99	0	1	agg gr	Drey-Focus Sm Gro SC
5.0	5.1	12.41	11.35	0.32	0.00	2.8	—	—	—	—	99	0	1	growth	Drey-Focus Sm Val SC
431.5	296.7	14.19	12.36	0.77	0.08	6.2	0.45	0.31	1.89	C	0	98	2	tax-free	Drey-General CA
1,252.0	826.9	15.84	13.72	0.86	0.12	6.2	0.44	0.28	1.93	C	0	99	1	tax-free	Drey-General Muni
400.3	293.6	21.14	18.40	1.13	0.12	6.1	0.45	0.30	1.89	B	0	98	2	tax-free	Drey-General NY
276.2	209.3	15.93	14.29	0.42	1.33	2.7	0.96	0.94	2.31	D	100	0	0	gr-inc	Drey-Peoples Idx
71.6	79.1	17.19	15.48	0.28	0.75	1.7	1.14	0.86	2.87	C	90	0	10	growth	Drey-Peoples MidCap
8.2	12.5	12.96	13.16	0.10	0.00	0.7	—	—	—	—	99	0	1	growth	Drey-Wilsh Lg Gro
12.5	15.4	14.11	12.88	0.40	0.10	3.1	—	—	—	—	99	0	1	gr-inc	Drey-Wilsh Lg Val
7.4	13.4	15.64	15.11	0.00	0.31	0.0	—	—	—	—	99	0	1	agg gr	Drey-Wilsh Sm Gro
19.2	27.8	14.35	13.18	0.45	0.07	3.4	—	—	—	—	99	0	1	growth	Drey-Wilsh Sm Val
3.8	2.5	16.95	13.87	0.00	1.18	0.0	1.22	0.71	3.37	D	97	1	2	growth	Drey/Laurel Contrn
3.7	5.1	12.68	12.94	0.19	0.00	1.5	0.69	0.16	4.07	D	85	0	15	int'l	Drey/Laurel Int'l
2.5	4.2	12.34	11.73	—	—	—	0.09	0.14	0.53	C	0	88	12	fix-inc	Drey/Laurel ST Bd
0.5	0.8	9.98	9.85	—	—	—	—	—	—	—	0	94	6	fix-inc	Drey/Laurel ST Gov
8.4	7.2	10.72	9.45	0.64	0.00	6.8	—	—	—	—	0	95	5	fix-inc	Dupree Inter Gov
70.8	61.9	5.30	5.15	0.20	0.00	3.9	0.11	0.22	0.54	B	0	94	6	tax-free	Dupree KY Sht-Med
271.2	246.8	7.72	7.09	0.40	0.00	5.7	0.24	0.18	1.34	A	0	99	1	tax-free	Dupree KY TF Inc
—	0.2	—	10.07	—	—	—	—	—	—	—	0	95	5	tax-free	Dupree Tenn Sht-Med
—	6.0	—	9.38	—	—	—	—	—	—	—	0	95	5	tax-free	Dupree Tenn TF Inc
0.0	1.3	55.58	57.52	0.00	0.00	0.0	0.00	0.00	0.06	A	0	0	100	fix-inc	Eaton Vance ST Trsy
21.7	27.7	18.63	17.75	0.56	0.31	3.1	0.64	0.72	1.74	A	60	39	1	income	Eclipse Balanced
197.1	195.1	13.35	11.83	0.03	0.87	0.2	1.04	0.68	2.95	B	94	0	6	agg gr	Eclipse Equity SC
—	—	—	—	—	—	—	—	—	—	—	—	—	—	gr-inc	Eclipse Gro & Inc
—	—	—	—	—	—	—	—	—	—	—	—	—	—	fix-inc	Eclipse Ultra Short
37.3	37.2	11.60	10.67	0.60	0.00	5.6	0.65	0.78	1.70	A	53	46	1	gr-inc	Evergreen Amer
239.8	331.5	13.12	12.27	0.42	0.28	3.4	0.83	0.77	2.20	A	60	31	9	income	Evergreen Foundation
629.7	454.9	14.20	12.03	0.07	2.16	0.5	1.02	0.75	2.74	D	100	0	0	growth	Evergreen Fund
142.5	98.2	14.75	12.06	0.10	0.52	0.8	0.90	0.26	4.15	C	99	0	1	sector	Evergreen Glob RE
77.9	73.6	15.41	14.52	0.14	1.01	0.9	0.98	0.87	2.45	B	94	2	4	growth	Evergreen Gro & Inc
103.8	81.7	21.70	15.70	0.00	3.68	0.0	1.02	0.39	3.82	F	99	0	1	agg gr	Evergreen Ltd Mkt SC
38.8	21.9	10.82	9.46	0.51	0.00	5.3	—	—	—	—	0	92	8	tax-free	Evergreen Nat TF
2.2	3.6	10.15	9.69	0.33	0.05	3.4	—	—	—	—	94	0	6	growth	Evergreen Sm Cap SC
30.6	25.2	10.41	9.78	0.42	0.03	4.3	—	—	—	—	0	95	5	tax-free	Evergreen S-I CA
63.3	44.8	10.58	9.97	0.46	0.00	4.7	0.18	0.33	0.73	F	0	100	0	tax-free	Evergreen S-I Muni
5.2	10.6	10.31	10.27	0.27	0.12	2.6	—	—	—	—	—	—	—	income	Evergreen Tax Found
1,195.4	944.5	19.62	17.03	1.08	0.25	6.3	0.77	0.73	2.08	D	71	27	2	gr-inc	Evergreen Tot Ret
6.6	4.0	9.99	8.66	0.56	0.04	6.4	—	—	—	—	0	94	6	fix-inc	Evergreen US Gov
4.5	8.6	10.71	9.22	0.20	0.12	2.1	—	—	—	—	94	0	6	sector	Evergreen US RE
8.9	7.7	6.41	5.56	0.00	0.10	0.0	0.95	0.59	2.88	B	94	6	0	agg gr	44 Wall St Eqty
100.8	101.2	31.66	27.91	0.00	2.41	0.0	0.90	0.34	3.65	B	0	98	2	int'l	59 Wall Europe Eqty
119.3	101.6	46.10	30.36	0.00	5.58	0.0	0.88	0.13	5.71	B	86	0	14	int'l	59 Wall Pac Basin
43.2	33.6	12.50	11.12	0.07	0.00	0.6	1.21	0.59	3.68	D	95	0	5	agg gr	59 Wall Sm Co SC
52.0	53.2	10.34	10.02	0.35	0.00	3.5	—	—	—	—	0	92	8	tax-free	59 Wall S-I TF
18.9	22.2	22.43	24.06	0.00	0.00	0.0	1.24	0.45	4.34	B	96	0	4	agg gr	Fairmont
220.2	210.3	20.40	21.04	0.12	0.63	0.6	0.72	0.36	2.81	B	93	0	7	growth	FAM Value SC

No-Load Fund	Total return percent with quintile ranks by objective										Annualized		What $10,000 grew to after	
	1985	1986	1987	1988	1989	1990	1991	1992	1993	1994	3 yrs.	5 yrs.	3 yrs.	5 yrs.
Fasciano SC	—	—	—	20.2[2]	22.4[4]	-1.2[2]	35.1[4]	7.7[4]	8.1[5]	3.7[1]	6.5[3]	10.0[3]	12,065	16,104
FBP Contrn Blncd	—	—	—	—	—	-7.9[5]	27.3[2]	13.9[1]	9.3[4]	1.8[1]	8.2[2]	8.3[3]	12,677	14,865
FBP Contrn Eqty	—	—	—	—	—	—	—	—	—	4.1[1]	—	—	—	—
Federated ARMS	—	8.8[5]	-1.8[4]	7.3[4]	15.9[1]	6.6[3]	15.7[3]	3.8[5]	4.4[5]	0.3[1]	2.8[5]	6.0[5]	10,865	13,406
Federated GNMA	19.5[3]	10.9[4]	3.5[1]	8.2[2]	15.1[1]	10.4[1]	15.3[3]	6.5[4]	6.3[5]	-2.5[2]	3.3[5]	7.0[3]	11,032	14,043
Federated Growth	34.7[1]	24.0[1]	-3.1[4]	28.8[1]	29.2[2]	-4.9[3]	35.0[2]	8.6[3]	6.6[4]	-11.9[5]	0.7[5]	5.6[5]	10,206	13,101
Federated Hi Yld	21.3[3]	15.9[3]	1.2[2]	16.2[1]	-1.2[5]	-12.9[5]	52.5[1]	15.0[1]	17.4[1]	-2.4[2]	9.6[1]	11.9[1]	13,176	17,514
Federated Income	16.9[5]	9.8[5]	4.6[1]	7.6[4]	12.5[3]	10.4[1]	13.9[4]	5.7[5]	5.6[5]	-1.6[1]	3.2[5]	6.7[4]	10,986	13,818
Federated Inter Gov	15.5[5]	12.0[3]	3.9[1]	5.3[5]	12.0[3]	9.4[2]	13.5[5]	6.7[3]	6.8[4]	-1.9[2]	3.8[3]	6.8[4]	11,183	13,880
Federated Inter Muni	—	10.4[5]	0.2[5]	5.1[5]	9.0[2]	6.5[4]	10.8[2]	7.2[4]	9.7[4]	-3.8[3]	4.2[4]	5.9[4]	11,311	13,344
Federated Max Cap	—	—	—	—	—	—	30.0[2]	7.2[3]	9.5[4]	1.2[2]	5.9[3]	—	11,888	—
Federated Mgd Agg Gro	—	—	—	—	—	—	—	—	—	—	—	—	—	—
Federated Mgd Gro & Inc	—	—	—	—	—	—	—	—	—	—	—	—	—	—
Federated Mgd Growth	—	—	—	—	—	—	—	—	—	—	—	—	—	—
Federated Mgd Income	—	—	—	—	—	—	—	—	—	—	—	—	—	—
Federated Mid Cap	—	—	—	—	—	—	—	—	11.2[3]	-4.3[4]	—	—	—	—
Federated Mini Cap SC	—	—	—	—	—	—	—	—	15.3[3]	-2.8[4]	—	—	—	—
Federated ST Income	—	—	4.8[2]	8.6[1]	9.4[4]	2.0[5]	13.9[2]	6.1[3]	5.5[4]	-0.5[3]	3.6[3]	5.3[5]	11,132	12,926
Federated ST Muni	12.1[1]	7.6[3]	2.3[4]	5.6[2]	6.4[4]	6.3[4]	7.3[4]	5.1[4]	4.1[5]	0.1[3]	3.1[5]	4.6[5]	10,950	12,489
Federated Stk & Bd	24.1[4]	13.8[4]	3.6[2]	9.3[5]	12.5[5]	0.2[2]	18.5[5]	7.3[3]	10.5[3]	-1.9[4]	5.2[4]	6.7[4]	11,632	13,811
Federated Stock	33.5[1]	17.4[2]	1.7[3]	12.7[4]	13.1[5]	-5.0[3]	29.0[2]	11.9[2]	12.5[3]	-0.5[3]	7.8[2]	9.0[2]	12,533	15,358
Federated S-I Gov	12.1[4]	9.4[4]	5.3[2]	5.7[4]	10.3[3]	9.3[2]	10.4[5]	5.2[4]	4.5[4]	0.7[2]	3.5[4]	6.0[4]	11,070	13,351
Federated US Gov	—	9.2[4]	-1.7[5]	6.0[3]	13.7[1]	8.8[3]	13.6[2]	8.2[1]	13.4[1]	-6.2[5]	4.8[1]	7.3[1]	11,502	14,211
FFB Lexcn Cap App	—	—	—	—	—	—	—	6.9[4]	7.2[4]	-4.5[4]	3.0[4]	—	10,941	—
FFB Lexcn Fix Inc	—	—	—	—	—	—	—	7.0[3]	11.4[3]	-3.0[2]	4.9[2]	—	11,554	—
FFB Lexcn Inter Gov	—	—	—	—	—	—	—	6.5[4]	7.4[4]	-1.9[2]	3.9[3]	—	11,220	—
FFB Lexcn Sel Value	—	—	—	—	—	—	—	—	13.5[2]	3.9[1]	—	—	—	—
FFB Lexcn Sm Co SC	—	—	—	—	—	—	—	—	8.8[4]	-7.9[5]	—	—	—	—
Fidelity Agg TF	—	17.4[3]	1.7[1]	13.4[1]	9.5[3]	7.5[1]	11.8[3]	9.2[2]	13.7[1]	-5.9[2]	5.3[1]	7.0[1]	11,681	14,033
Fidelity Asset Mgr	—	—	—	—	15.3[4]	5.3[1]	23.5[3]	13.3[1]	23.2[1]	-6.6[5]	9.3[1]	11.2[1]	13,043	16,963
Fidelity Asst Mgr Gro	—	—	—	—	—	—	—	19.1[1]	26.3[1]	-7.4[5]	11.7[1]	—	13,927	—
Fidelity Asst Mgr Inc	—	—	—	—	—	—	—	—	15.3[2]	-1.4[3]	—	—	—	—
Fidelity Balanced	—	—	1.9[2]	16.0[2]	19.5[3]	-0.4[3]	26.7[2]	7.9[3]	19.3[1]	-5.3[4]	6.8[3]	9.0[2]	12,192	15,381
Fidelity Blue Chip†	—	—	—	—	36.7[1]	3.5[1]	54.8[1]	6.2[4]	24.5[1]	9.9[1]	13.2[1]	18.4[1]	14,520	23,260
Fidelity CA Hi Yld	16.6[5]	17.5[3]	-3.7[4]	11.8[3]	9.6[3]	7.0[2]	10.2[5]	8.7[3]	13.1[2]	-8.9[5]	3.9[5]	5.7[5]	11,206	13,204
Fidelity CA Insur	—	—	-4.5[5]	11.6[3]	8.8[4]	7.0[2]	11.0[4]	9.2[2]	13.8[1]	-10.3[5]	3.7[5]	5.8[5]	11,152	13,242
Fidelity Canada	—	—	—	19.4[2]	27.0[2]	-5.5[1]	17.7[1]	-2.9[2]	25.5[5]	-12.0[5]	2.4[5]	3.6[4]	10,726	11,929
Fidelity Cap Apprect†	—	—	19.3[1]	37.6[1]	26.9[3]	-15.7[4]	9.8[5]	16.4[2]	33.4[1]	2.5[1]	16.7[1]	8.1[4]	15,911	14,725
Fidelity Cap & Inc	25.6[1]	18.0[2]	0.5[3]	12.6[1]	-3.2[5]	-3.9[5]	29.8[1]	28.1[1]	24.9[1]	-4.6[3]	15.1[1]	13.8[1]	15,257	19,044
Fidelity Contrafund†	27.0[3]	13.1[3]	-2.0[3]	21.0[2]	43.3[1]	3.9[1]	54.9[2]	15.9[2]	21.4[2]	-1.1[3]	11.6[1]	17.5[1]	13,912	22,392
Fidelity Convert	—	—	-5.0[4]	15.8[2]	26.2[1]	-2.9[3]	38.6[1]	22.0[1]	17.7[1]	-1.7[3]	12.2[1]	13.7[1]	14,113	18,999
Fidelity Curr: D-Mark†	—	—	—	—	—	21.4[1]	5.9[5]	1.2[5]	-1.3[5]	16.4[1]	5.1[2]	8.4[2]	11,623	14,941
Fidelity Curr: Sterling†	—	—	—	—	—	36.5[1]	6.3[5]	-12.1[5]	2.3[5]	9.9[1]	-0.4[5]	7.5[3]	9,880	14,331
Fidelity Curr: Yen.†	—	—	—	—	—	12.2[1]	15.0[4]	2.5[5]	13.1[2]	12.6[1]	9.3[1]	11.0[1]	13,053	16,846
Fidelity Discpl Eqty	—	—	—	—	35.8[1]	-0.8[2]	35.9[2]	13.2[2]	13.9[2]	3.0[2]	9.9[2]	12.3[1]	13,280	17,895
Fidelity Div Growth	—	—	—	—	—	—	—	—	—	4.3[1]	—	—	—	—
Fidelity Dvsfd Int'l	—	—	—	—	—	—	—	-13.8[5]	36.7[3]	1.1[2]	6.0[4]	—	11,906	—
Fidelity Emg Growth†	—	—	—	—	—	—	67.1[1]	8.4[3]	19.9[2]	-0.2[2]	9.0[2]	—	12,966	—
Fidelity Emg Mkts†	—	—	—	—	—	—	6.7[5]	5.8[1]	81.7[1]	-17.9[5]	16.4[1]	—	15,784	—
Fidelity Eqty Inc II	—	—	—	—	—	—	47.3[1]	19.0[1]	18.9[1]	3.2[1]	13.4[1]	—	14,600	—
Fidelity Eqty Inc	25.1[4]	16.9[3]	-1.6[4]	22.5[1]	18.7[4]	-14.0[5]	29.3[2]	14.7[1]	21.2[1]	0.3[2]	11.7[1]	9.2[2]	13,938	15,511
Fidelity Europe Cap App	—	—	—	—	—	—	—	—	—	6.9[1]	—	—	—	—
Fidelity Europe†	—	—	14.8[2]	5.8[5]	32.3[1]	-4.5[1]	4.0[5]	-2.5[2]	27.2[4]	6.2[1]	9.6[2]	5.5[2]	13,166	13,076
Fidelity Export	—	—	—	—	—	—	—	—	—	—	—	—	—	—
Fidelity Fifty	—	—	—	—	—	—	—	—	—	4.0[1]	—	—	—	—
Fidelity Fund	27.7[2]	15.6[3]	3.3[2]	17.9[3]	28.7[1]	-5.0[3]	24.1[4]	8.4[3]	18.3[1]	2.6[1]	9.6[1]	9.2[1]	13,164	15,518
Fidelity Glob Blncd	—	—	—	—	—	—	—	—	—	-11.4[5]	—	—	—	—
Fidelity Glob Bond	—	—	19.1[1]	3.7[5]	7.9[5]	12.2[1]	12.7[5]	4.4[5]	21.9[1]	-16.3[5]	2.1[5]	6.1[5]	10,649	13,464
Fidelity GNMA	—	12.7[2]	1.2[4]	7.2[3]	13.9[2]	10.5[1]	13.6[3]	6.7[3]	6.1[5]	-2.0[2]	3.5[4]	6.8[4]	11,093	13,921
Fidelity Gov Sec	17.6[5]	14.7[3]	1.1[2]	6.4[5]	12.6[3]	9.4[1]	16.0[3]	8.0[2]	12.3[3]	-5.2[3]	4.7[3]	7.8[2]	11,491	14,578

See Chapter 3 for explanation of symbols

Total Net Assets $Million		NAV per share		1994 per share distributions		Yield %	Risk Analysis				% Distribution of Portfolio 12/31/94			Objective	No-Load Fund
December 31 1993	1994	December 31 1993	1994	Income	Capital gains	12/31/94	beta	R^2	Std. Dev.	Sharpe Ratio	Stocks	Bonds	Cash		
17.4	17.7	17.68	17.18	0.00	1.14	0.0	0.66	0.45	2.28	C	83	0	17	agg gr	Fasciano SC
20.8	24.0	12.52	12.13	0.37	0.25	3.0	0.60	0.72	1.63	B	61	24	15	income	FBP Contrn Blncd
2.5	4.6	10.39	10.59	0.22	0.00	2.1	—	—	—		—	—	—	growth	FBP Contrn Eqty
2,322.2	1,009.0	9.91	9.46	0.48	0.00	5.1	0.06	0.12	0.36	B	0	98	2	fix-inc	Federated ARMS
1,936.7	1,437.7	11.58	10.48	0.81	0.00	7.7	0.21	0.24	0.99	D	0	99	1	fix-inc	Federated GNMA
461.3	280.9	24.07	19.96	0.27	0.68	1.3	0.96	0.63	2.82	F	74	11	15	growth	Federated Growth
455.8	349.5	9.42	8.35	0.85	0.00	10.2	0.23	0.12	1.56	A	0	94	6	fix-inc	Federated Hi Yld
1,725.6	1,142.2	10.47	9.60	0.70	0.00	7.3	0.15	0.15	0.85	C	0	95	5	fix-inc	Federated Income
938.2	732.2	10.73	10.01	0.52	0.00	5.2	0.13	0.13	0.86	B	0	98	2	fix-inc	Federated Inter Gov
327.6	270.1	11.02	10.08	0.53	0.00	5.3	0.31	0.30	1.33	F	0	98	2	tax-free	Federated Inter Muni
411.1	448.1	11.85	11.66	0.31	0.02	2.7	0.96	0.93	2.31	C	78	1	21	gr-inc	Federated Max Cap
—	—	—	—	—	—	—	—	—	—		—	—	—	agg gr	Federated Mgd Agg Gro
—	—	—	—	—	—	—	—	—	—		—	—	—	gr-inc	Federated Mgd Gro & Inc
—	—	—	—	—	—	—	—	—	—		—	—	—	growth	Federated Mgd Growth
—	—	—	—	—	—	—	—	—	—		—	—	—	income	Federated Mgd Income
20.4	43.6	11.23	10.38	0.18	0.19	1.7	—	—	—		95	0	5	growth	Federated Mid Cap
79.1	102.2	11.85	11.32	0.12	0.07	1.1	—	—	—		98	0	2	agg gr	Federated Mini Cap SC
358.0	237.3	9.06	8.50	0.51	0.00	6.0	0.07	0.11	0.48	B	0	97	3	fix-inc	Federated ST Income
344.5	290.2	10.35	9.96	0.40	0.00	4.0	0.10	0.26	0.44	D	0	97	3	tax-free	Federated ST Muni
127.7	122.0	16.69	15.74	0.00	0.00	0.0	0.55	0.78	1.44	B	42	55	3	gr-inc	Federated Stk & Bd
565.9	553.6	25.45	24.18	0.47	0.69	1.9	0.97	0.83	2.47	B	89	2	9	gr-inc	Federated Stock
875.0	685.9	10.52	10.11	0.48	0.00	4.7	0.07	0.13	0.42	B	0	98	2	fix-inc	Federated S-I Gov
104.0	143.1	10.56	9.35	0.56	0.00	6.0	0.38	0.25	1.73	F	0	100	0	fix-inc	Federated US Gov
151.7	128.2	11.54	10.66	0.17	0.00	1.6	1.07	0.86	2.68	F	92	0	8	growth	FFB Lexcn Cap App
94.3	86.8	10.58	9.67	0.54	0.00	5.6	0.23	0.16	1.37	B	0	61	39	fix-inc	FFB Lexcn Fix Inc
122.8	106.4	10.43	9.69	0.54	0.00	5.6	0.16	0.15	0.94	B	0	82	18	fix-inc	FFB Lexcn Inter Gov
31.9	59.5	11.50	11.04	0.25	0.00	2.2	—	—	—		—	—	—	gr-inc	FFB Lexcn Sel Value
23.5	21.5	11.88	10.87	0.08	0.00	0.7	—	—	—		—	—	—	agg gr	FFB Lexcn Sm Co SC
948.1	793.8	12.34	10.81	0.77	0.05	7.1	0.41	0.36	1.59	A	0	100	0	tax-free	Fidelity Agg TF
9,094.4	11,075.6	15.40	13.83	0.40	0.17	2.9	0.64	0.60	1.92	B	48	38	14	income	Fidelity Asset Mgr
1,795.0	2,852.9	14.25	12.84	0.19	0.17	1.5	0.89	0.68	2.49	A	70	30	0	gr-inc	Fidelity Asst Mgr Gro
292.4	476.2	11.06	10.42	0.49	0.00	4.7	—	—	—		18	66	16	income	Fidelity Asst Mgr Inc
4,684.5	4,999.1	13.39	12.29	0.40	0.00	3.3	0.39	0.25	1.77	B	19	80	1	income	Fidelity Balanced
1,094.7	3,287.0	24.17	25.95	0.00	0.58	0.0	1.06	0.73	2.89	A	90	1	9	growth	Fidelity Blue Chip
591.6	443.9	12.42	10.50	0.69	0.15	6.6	0.48	0.35	1.87	F	0	97	3	tax-free	Fidelity CA Hi Yld
311.1	197.3	11.07	9.23	0.56	0.17	6.1	0.54	0.34	2.15	F	0	97	3	tax-free	Fidelity CA Insur
109.0	332.9	18.19	16.00	0.01	0.00	0.1	0.86	0.33	3.51	F	95	1	4	int'l	Fidelity Canada
1,428.2	1,623.2	16.92	15.31	0.17	1.85	1.0	0.59	0.27	2.66	A	86	0	14	agg gr	Fidelity Cap Apprec
2,745.7	2,039.8	9.86	8.63	0.80	0.00	9.3	0.23	0.08	1.84	A	15	75	10	fix-inc	Fidelity Cap & Inc
6,193.3	8,682.4	30.84	30.28	0.00	0.22	0.0	1.00	0.78	2.64	A	84	1	15	agg gr	Fidelity Contrafund
1,063.9	891.3	16.45	15.36	0.80	0.00	5.2	0.72	0.56	2.24	A	24	72	4	income	Fidelity Convert
5.8	8.6	14.03	16.33	0.00	0.00	0.0	-0.15	0.01	3.21	F	0	0	100	fix-inc	Fidelity Curr: D-Mark
3.7	3.4	13.46	14.79	0.00	0.00	0.0	-0.11	0.00	3.77	F	0	0	100	fix-inc	Fidelity Curr: Sterling
2.3	3.5	15.03	16.93	0.00	0.00	0.0	-0.25	0.06	2.45	B	0	0	100	fix-inc	Fidelity Curr: Yen
795.8	1,160.1	18.18	17.94	0.25	0.52	1.4	1.04	0.84	2.64	B	90	0	10	growth	Fidelity Discpl Eqty
88.7	102.4	12.11	12.37	0.01	0.24	0.1	—	—	—		72	0	28	growth	Fidelity Div Growth
238.8	306.0	11.60	11.30	0.03	0.39	0.3	0.75	0.20	3.82	D	91	2	7	int'l	Fidelity Dvsfd Int'l
652.6	635.2	17.33	16.99	0.00	0.31	0.0	1.43	0.65	4.17	C	92	0	8	agg gr	Fidelity Emg Growth
1,908.8	1,508.3	19.70	16.13	0.04	0.00	0.2	1.06	0.20	5.69	A	105	4	-9	int'l	Fidelity Emg Mkts
5,021.9	7,697.5	18.41	17.72	0.39	0.88	2.1	0.84	0.78	2.20	A	79	7	14	gr-inc	Fidelity Eqty Inc II
6,641.9	7,412.8	33.84	30.70	0.98	2.22	3.1	0.87	0.82	2.24	A	80	18	2	gr-inc	Fidelity Eqty Inc
6.7	291.5	10.03	10.72	0.00	0.00	0.0	—	—	—		93	1	6	int'l	Fidelity Europe Cap App
494.9	478.9	19.12	20.00	0.20	0.11	1.0	0.72	0.21	3.68	B	89	3	8	int'l	Fidelity Europe
—	71.6	—	10.24	—	—	—	—	—	—		93	0	7	agg gr	Fidelity Export
51.3	60.6	10.58	10.88	0.02	0.10	0.2	—	—	—		76	0	24	agg gr	Fidelity Fifty
1,546.2	1,886.1	19.27	18.48	0.33	0.94	1.7	0.93	0.84	2.35	A	73	13	14	gr-inc	Fidelity Fund
331.3	236.5	13.16	11.56	0.10	0.00	0.9	—	—	—		41	57	2	global	Fidelity Glob Blncd
681.1	382.9	12.61	9.88	0.69	0.02	7.0	0.51	0.24	2.42	F	0	87	13	fix-inc	Fidelity Glob Bond
887.4	704.5	10.86	9.99	0.63	0.02	6.3	0.21	0.27	0.92	C	0	103	-3	fix-inc	Fidelity GNMA
753.4	611.2	10.34	9.17	0.62	0.02	6.7	0.31	0.23	1.52	C	0	99	1	fix-inc	Fidelity Gov Sec

No-Load Fund	1985	1986	1987	1988	1989	1990	1991	1992	1993	1994	Annualized 3 yrs.	Annualized 5 yrs.	What $10,000 grew to after 3 yrs.	What $10,000 grew to after 5 yrs.
Fidelity Gro & Inc†	—	35.2[1]	6.0[1]	23.0[1]	29.6[1]	-6.8[4]	41.8[1]	11.5[2]	19.5[1]	2.3[1]	10.9[1]	12.5[1]	13,631	18,028
Fidelity Growth Co	39.8[1]	13.0[3]	-1.7[3]	16.1[3]	41.6[1]	3.6[1]	48.3[3]	7.9[4]	16.2[3]	-2.2[3]	7.0[3]	13.5[1]	12,261	18,835
Fidelity Hi Yld TF	21.4[1]	18.9[2]	-3.7[4]	12.0[2]	11.4[1]	8.5[1]	10.2[5]	8.4[4]	10.6[5]	-7.5[4]	3.5[5]	5.8[4]	11,086	13,254
Fidelity Insur TF	—	18.3[3]	-2.2[4]	11.2[3]	9.5[3]	7.1[2]	11.6[4]	7.9[5]	13.8[1]	-7.7[4]	4.3[4]	6.3[3]	11,334	13,541
Fidelity Inter Bond	20.9[1]	13.2[1]	2.1[3]	7.1[4]	11.8[4]	7.5[4]	14.5[4]	6.1[4]	12.0[1]	-2.0[2]	5.2[1]	7.5[2]	11,637	14,329
Fidelity Int'l Gr & Inc	—	—	8.3[4]	11.5[4]	19.1[4]	-3.2[1]	8.0[4]	-3.3[2]	35.1[3]	-2.9[4]	8.3[3]	5.8[2]	12,684	13,255
Fidelity Int'l Value	—	—	—	—	—	—	—	—	—	—	—	—	—	—
Fidelity Inv Grd Bd	21.1[4]	13.6[4]	0.1[3]	7.9[3]	13.0[3]	6.1[4]	18.9[2]	8.3[2]	16.2[2]	-5.4[4]	6.0[2]	8.5[1]	11,914	15,022
Fidelity Japan	—	—	—	—	—	—	—	—	20.5[5]	16.5[1]	—	—	—	—
Fidelity Latin Amer†	—	—	—	—	—	—	—	—	—	-23.2[5]	—	—	—	—
Fidelity Low Pr Stk SC†	—	—	—	—	—	—	46.2[1]	29.0[1]	20.2[1]	4.8[1]	17.6[1]	—	16,243	—
Fidelity Ltd Muni	17.3[1]	15.2[2]	1.1[3]	8.2[2]	7.8[4]	7.0[2]	11.2[1]	8.2[2]	12.2[2]	-4.8[4]	5.0[2]	6.6[2]	11,561	13,748
Fidelity MA Hi Yld	19.6[3]	16.9[4]	-1.5[3]	10.7[4]	9.3[3]	7.4[1]	11.3[4]	9.3[2]	12.9[3]	-6.1[3]	5.0[2]	6.7[2]	11,589	13,850
Fidelity Magellan†	43.1[1]	23.7[1]	0.9[3]	22.7[2]	34.6[2]	-4.6[2]	40.9[3]	7.0[4]	24.6[1]	-1.8[3]	9.4[2]	12.0[2]	13,092	17,602
Fidelity Market Idx	—	—	—	—	—	—	30.3[2]	7.3[3]	9.6[4]	1.1[2]	5.9[3]	—	11,890	—
Fidelity MI Hi Yld	—	18.9[2]	-3.1[4]	13.0[1]	10.2[2]	5.2[5]	12.0[3]	9.5[1]	13.8[1]	-7.5[4]	4.9[3]	6.3[3]	11,531	13,584
Fidelity Mid-Cap Stk	—	—	—	—	—	—	—	—	—	—	—	—	—	—
Fidelity MN TF	—	17.0[4]	-4.1[5]	12.6[1]	9.5[3]	7.2[1]	8.5[5]	7.6[5]	12.4[4]	-5.9[3]	4.4[3]	5.8[4]	11,383	13,242
Fidelity Mrtg Sec	18.6[4]	10.9[4]	2.7[2]	6.7[4]	13.6[2]	10.4[1]	13.6[5]	5.5[5]	6.7[5]	1.9[1]	4.7[2]	7.5[2]	11,469	14,380
Fidelity Muni Bd	20.1[3]	19.5[1]	-1.6[3]	12.3[2]	9.6[3]	6.9[2]	11.9[3]	8.9[3]	13.2[2]	-8.6[5]	4.0[4]	6.1[4]	11,261	13,473
Fidelity New Millnm†	—	—	—	—	—	—	—	24.7[1]	0.8[2]	—	—	—	—	—
Fidelity New Mkts Inc	—	—	—	—	—	—	—	—	—	-16.2[5]	—	—	—	—
Fidelity NY Hi Yld	20.9[2]	16.8[4]	-2.4[4]	11.9[2]	9.2[4]	5.1[5]	13.3[1]	9.0[2]	12.9[3]	-8.0[4]	4.2[4]	6.1[4]	11,314	13,472
Fidelity NY Insured	—	17.3[3]	-3.2[4]	11.3[3]	9.2[4]	6.2[4]	12.5[2]	8.6[3]	12.8[3]	-8.0[4]	4.1[4]	6.1[4]	11,271	13,461
Fidelity OH TF	—	16.4[5]	-2.4[4]	13.0[1]	10.0[2]	7.5[1]	11.5[4]	8.7[3]	12.6[4]	-5.6[2]	4.9[2]	6.7[2]	11,551	13,837
Fidelity OTC SC†	69.0[1]	11.4[3]	1.6[2]	22.8[2]	30.4[2]	-4.7[2]	49.1[3]	14.9[2]	8.3[5]	-2.7[3]	6.6[3]	11.5[2]	12,107	17,200
Fidelity Overseas	78.7[1]	69.3[2]	18.4[2]	8.2[5]	16.9[4]	-6.6[2]	8.5[4]	-11.5[4]	40.0[3]	1.3[2]	7.9[3]	4.9[3]	12,554	12,725
Fidelity Pacific Basin	—	—	24.9[2]	10.4[4]	11.4[5]	-27.2[5]	12.5[2]	-7.6[4]	63.8[1]	-2.8[3]	13.7[1]	3.8[4]	14,702	12,053
Fidelity Puritan	28.5[2]	20.7[1]	-1.9[3]	18.8[1]	19.6[3]	-6.2[4]	24.4[3]	15.4[1]	21.4[1]	1.9[1]	12.6[1]	10.7[1]	14,275	16,650
Fidelity Real Estate	—	—	-7.7[3]	10.3[4]	13.8[4]	-8.6[3]	38.9[3]	19.4[2]	12.4[4]	1.9[2]	11.0[3]	11.7[3]	13,683	17,365
Fidelity Retrmnt Growth	28.7[3]	14.0[3]	9.3[1]	15.5[3]	30.3[2]	-10.2[3]	45.5[3]	10.6[3]	22.1[2]	0.1[2]	10.6[2]	12.0[2]	13,511	17,655
Fidelity SE Asia†	—	—	—	—	—	—	—	—	—	-21.8[5]	—	—	—	—
Fidelity Sel Air Trans†	—	12.8[3]	-20.1[5]	29.1[1]	26.3[3]	-18.2[5]	37.1[3]	6.6[4]	30.9[2]	-21.7[5]	3.0[5]	4.1[5]	10,914	12,239
Fidelity Sel Amer Gold†	—	18.1[5]	40.5[1]	-12.5[1]	22.0[3]	-17.2[1]	-6.1[3]	-3.1[1]	78.7[4]	-15.5[4]	13.6[2]	2.6[2]	14,640	11,377
Fidelity Sel Auto†	—	—	6.5[1]	20.1[2]	4.1[5]	-6.7[3]	37.3[3]	41.6[1]	35.4[1]	-12.8[5]	18.7[1]	16.4[2]	16,713	21,408
Fidelity Sel Biotech†	—	3.5[5]	-3.3[3]	4.1[5]	43.9[1]	44.4[1]	99.0[1]	-10.4[5]	0.7[5]	-18.2[5]	-9.6[5]	16.2[2]	7,385	21,209
Fidelity Sel Broker†	—	9.5[4]	-36.9[5]	18.6[2]	14.1[4]	-16.2[4]	82.3[1]	5.1[4]	49.3[1]	-17.3[5]	9.1[4]	14.7[2]	12,984	19,838
Fidelity Sel Chemicals†	—	26.9[1]	14.8[1]	21.0[2]	17.3[4]	-4.1[2]	38.7[3]	8.9[4]	12.7[4]	14.7[1]	12.1[3]	13.4[3]	14,079	18,714
Fidelity Sel Computer†	—	7.9[4]	-6.4[3]	-5.1[5]	6.8[5]	18.4[1]	31.0[4]	22.0[2]	28.9[2]	20.5[1]	23.7[1]	24.0[1]	18,930	29,364
Fidelity Sel Consmr Prod†	—	—	—	—	—	—	38.5[3]	8.6[4]	24.6[2]	-7.1[4]	7.9[4]	—	12,571	—
Fidelity Sel Const/Hous†	—	—	-12.4[5]	29.2[1]	16.6[4]	-9.6[3]	41.2[3]	18.7[2]	33.6[1]	-16.0[5]	10.1[3]	11.2[4]	13,331	17,018
Fidelity Sel Defense†	26.4[4]	5.0[5]	-23.2[5]	4.3[5]	8.8[5]	-4.6[3]	27.0[4]	0.0[5]	28.8[2]	1.8[3]	9.4[3]	9.7[4]	13,108	15,878
Fidelity Sel Devel Comm†	—	—	—	—	—	—	61.4[2]	17.2[3]	31.7[2]	15.1[1]	21.1[1]	—	17,778	—
Fidelity Sel Electronics†	—	-23.9[5]	-13.5[5]	-8.5[5]	15.7[4]	5.8[2]	35.3[3]	27.4[1]	32.2[1]	17.2[1]	25.4[1]	23.1[1]	19,734	28,248
Fidelity Sel Energy Serv†	—	-15.8[5]	-11.8[4]	-0.4[5]	59.4[1]	1.8[2]	-23.5[5]	3.4[4]	21.0[3]	0.6[3]	8.0[4]	-0.4[5]	12,580	9,795
Fidelity Sel Energy†	17.9[4]	5.5[4]	-1.8[2]	15.9[3]	42.8[1]	-4.5[2]	0.0[5]	-2.4[5]	19.1[3]	0.4[3]	5.3[4]	2.2[5]	11,670	11,145
Fidelity Sel Envir Serv†	—	—	—	—	—	-2.5[2]	7.7[5]	-1.4[5]	-0.6[5]	-9.6[4]	-3.9[5]	-1.4[5]	8,865	9,308
Fidelity Sel Financial†	41.7[2]	15.0[3]	-16.6[5]	12.1[4]	19.4[4]	-24.4[5]	61.5[2]	42.8[1]	17.6[3]	-3.7[3]	17.4[2]	14.6[3]	16,167	19,741
Fidelity Sel Food/Agr†	—	22.5[1]	7.5[1]	26.8[2]	38.9[2]	9.3[1]	34.1[4]	6.0[4]	8.8[5]	6.1[2]	7.0[4]	12.4[3]	12,238	17,935
Fidelity Sel Health†	59.4[1]	22.0[2]	-0.6[2]	8.8[4]	42.5[2]	24.3[1]	83.6[1]	-17.5[5]	2.4[5]	21.4[1]	0.9[5]	18.6[1]	10,264	23,419
Fidelity Sel Home Fincl†	—	27.5[1]	-7.9[4]	18.5[3]	9.3[5]	-15.1[4]	64.4[1]	57.8[1]	27.3[2]	2.7[2]	27.3[1]	23.5[1]	20,619	28,760
Fidelity Sel Indust Equip†	—	—	-9.3[4]	4.9[5]	18.0[4]	-15.5[4]	26.8[4]	11.3[3]	43.3[1]	3.1[2]	18.1[2]	12.0[3]	16,456	17,623
Fidelity Sel Indust Mat†	—	—	15.6[1]	10.8[4]	4.5[5]	-17.1[4]	35.8[3]	12.4[3]	21.4[3]	8.2[2]	13.8[2]	10.7[4]	14,751	16,607
Fidelity Sel Insurance†	—	7.7[4]	-12.2[5]	17.4[3]	37.9[2]	-9.8[3]	36.7[3]	22.5[2]	8.2[5]	-0.4[3]	9.7[3]	10.2[4]	13,205	16,280
Fidelity Sel Leisure†	56.5[1]	15.7[2]	5.7[2]	26.0[2]	31.2[3]	-22.3[5]	32.9[4]	16.2[3]	39.6[1]	-6.8[4]	14.8[2]	9.3[4]	15,112	15,611
Fidelity Sel Medical Del†	—	—	-12.2[4]	15.8[3]	58.0[1]	16.3[1]	77.7[1]	-13.2[5]	5.5[5]	19.8[1]	3.2[5]	17.8[2]	10,976	22,676
Fidelity Sel Multimedia†	—	—	19.9[1]	26.9[1]	32.6[3]	-26.2[5]	37.9[3]	21.5[2]	38.0[1]	4.0[2]	20.4[1]	12.1[3]	17,431	17,729
Fidelity Sel Nat Gas†	—	—	—	—	—	—	—	—	—	-6.8[4]	—	—	—	—
Fidelity Sel Pap/Forest†	—	—	3.9[2]	6.8[5]	4.0[5]	-15.2[4]	34.5[3]	12.1[3]	18.6[3]	14.1[1]	14.9[2]	11.6[3]	15,160	17,298
Fidelity Sel Prec Metals†	-10.5[4]	32.8[4]	37.5[2]	-23.9[5]	32.2[1]	-21.1[3]	1.5[1]	-21.9[5]	111.5[1]	-1.2[1]	17.8[1]	5.5[1]	16,328	13,074

See Chapter 3 for explanation of symbols

Total Net Assets $Million		NAV per share		1994 per share distributions		Yield % 12/31/94	Risk Analysis				% Distribution of Portfolio 12/31/94			Objective	No-Load Fund
December 31 1993	1994	December 31 1993	1994	Income	Capital gains		beta	R²	Std. Dev.	Sharpe Ratio	Stocks	Bonds	Cash		
7,684.0	9,344.9	22.22	21.09	0.40	1.24	1.8	0.85	0.84	2.15	A	81	20	-1	gr-inc	Fidelity Gro & Inc
2,542.7	2,993.4	29.06	27.26	0.22	0.92	0.8	1.19	0.76	3.20	C	93	1	6	agg gr	Fidelity Growth Co
2,108.6	1,671.3	12.95	11.25	0.76	0.00	6.7	0.45	0.36	1.75	D	0	98	2	tax-free	Fidelity Hi Yld TF
446.7	318.2	12.37	10.69	0.63	0.12	5.9	0.50	0.33	2.03	D	0	100	0	tax-free	Fidelity Insur TF
1,840.2	2,127.4	10.78	9.83	0.64	0.09	6.5	0.20	0.17	1.09	A	0	68	32	fix-inc	Fidelity Inter Bond
1,068.3	1,272.6	17.57	16.53	0.00	0.53	0.0	0.61	0.20	3.22	B	51	40	9	int'l	Fidelity Int'l Gr & Inc
—	32.7	—	9.79	—	—	—	—	—	—	—	62	2	36	int'l	Fidelity Int'l Value
1,042.4	995.1	7.89	6.85	0.50	0.12	7.4	0.31	0.25	1.44	B	0	78	22	fix-inc	Fidelity Inv Grd Bd
96.4	389.0	11.61	13.15	0.00	0.36	0.0	—	—	—	—	95	0	5	int'l	Fidelity Japan
798.9	616.1	16.10	12.37	0.00	0.00	0.0	—	—	—	—	85	4	11	int'l	Fidelity Latin Amer
2,060.1	2,354.5	17.30	16.00	0.09	2.05	0.5	0.89	0.55	2.82	A	73	1	26	growth	Fidelity Low Pr Stk SC
1,195.2	881.3	9.99	8.99	0.51	0.02	5.7	0.40	0.37	1.52	D	0	100	0	tax-free	Fidelity Ltd Muni
1375.4	993.8	12.13	10.48	0.70	0.23	6.6	0.43	0.35	1.68	A	0	98	2	tax-free	Fidelity MA Hi Yld
31,705.1	36,441.5	70.85	66.80	0.13	2.64	0.2	1.05	0.79	2.74	B	96	1	3	agg gr	Fidelity Magellan
299.9	306.7	34.60	34.15	0.80	0.00	2.3	1.00	1.00	2.29	C	96	0	4	gr-inc	Fidelity Market Idx
561.5	434.4	12.34	10.58	0.69	0.17	6.4	0.47	0.35	1.83	C	0	101	-1	tax-free	Fidelity MI Hi Yld
—	126.1	—	10.70	—	—	—	—	—	—	—	76	2	22	growth	Fidelity Mid-Cap Stk
341.2	277.4	11.52	10.14	0.63	0.08	6.2	0.41	0.33	1.63	C	0	98	2	tax-free	Fidelity MN TF
374.8	349.4	10.73	10.26	0.62	0.05	6.0	0.12	0.15	0.72	A	0	100	0	fix-inc	Fidelity Mrtg Sec
12,58.1	1,005.6	8.69	7.36	0.45	0.14	6.1	0.51	0.35	2.00	F	0	102	-2	tax-free	Fidelity Muni Bd
276.0	319.7	12.30	12.11	0.00	0.28	0.0	—	—	—	—	89	1	10	growth	Fidelity New Millnm
283.9	179.5	13.07	10.20	0.57	0.25	5.6	—	—	—	—	9	88	3	fix-inc	Fidelity New Mkts Inc
484.1	380.2	12.97	11.04	0.67	0.24	6.1	0.51	0.36	1.96	D	0	98	2	tax-free	Fidelity NY Hi Yld
409.7	300.8	12.24	10.50	0.63	0.15	5.9	0.49	0.34	1.95	F	0	99	1	tax-free	Fidelity NY Insured
456.5	349.5	12.02	10.52	0.66	0.19	6.2	0.41	0.33	1.68	B	0	99	1	tax-free	Fidelity OH TF
1,343.0	1,381.3	24.14	23.27	0.21	0.00	0.9	0.95	0.57	2.92	C	88	0	12	agg gr	Fidelity OTC SC
1,519.6	2,194.1	27.43	27.30	0.00	0.47	0.0	0.57	0.12	3.94	C	86	4	10	int'l	Fidelity Overseas
526.7	475.5	18.80	16.19	0.02	2.02	0.1	0.81	0.15	4.98	B	93	4	3	int'l	Fidelity Pacific Basin
8,988.2	11,769.4	15.75	14.81	0.54	0.71	3.5	0.69	0.68	1.95	A	63	32	5	income	Fidelity Puritan
424.4	555.7	13.57	13.20	0.63	0.00	4.8	0.58	0.16	3.44	C	89	2	9	sector	Fidelity Real Estate
2,848.2	3,184.9	18.14	16.24	0.22	1.68	1.2	1.05	0.81	2.71	A	64	7	29	agg gr	Fidelity Retrmnt Growth
1,186.4	660.9	16.41	12.84	0.00	0.00	0.0	—	—	—	—	94	1	5	int'l	Fidelity SE Asia
15.9	7.5	17.09	12.43	0.00	1.09	0.0	1.34	0.42	4.87	F	91	7	2	sector	Fidelity Sel Air Trans
365.3	314.2	23.55	19.91	0.00	0.00	0.0	0.34	0.01	7.10	A	88	3	9	prec met	Fidelity Sel Amer Gold
197.7	64.0	24.91	19.36	0.05	2.26	0.2	1.02	0.35	4.08	A	93	0	7	sector	Fidelity Sel Auto
557.2	396.1	28.61	23.41	0.00	0.00	0.0	1.33	0.28	5.97	F	77	0	23	sector	Fidelity Sel Biotech
94.4	21.9	18.30	15.14	0.00	0.00	0.0	1.31	0.39	4.94	D	80	2	18	sector	Fidelity Sel Broker
26.2	167.8	29.42	32.91	0.22	0.60	0.7	0.97	0.52	3.14	B	86	0	14	sector	Fidelity Sel Chemicals
61.5	175.4	24.35	29.33	0.00	0.00	0.0	1.40	0.36	5.51	A	93	4	3	sector	Fidelity Sel Computer
9.4	7.6	15.41	13.70	0.00	0.60	0.0	1.18	0.68	3.34	D	93	0	7	sector	Fidelity Sel Consmr Prod
64.9	17.5	19.59	15.95	0.00	0.52	0.0	1.09	0.46	3.77	C	83	0	17	sector	Fidelity Sel Const/Hous
2.7	3.7	18.27	18.32	0.00	0.27	0.0	0.97	0.52	3.15	C	78	1	21	sector	Fidelity Sel Defense
245.9	276.1	19.24	20.24	0.00	1.67	0.0	1.73	0.69	4.91	A	87	0	13	sector	Fidelity Sel Devel Comm
45.6	156.6	15.78	18.49	0.00	0.00	0.0	1.26	0.42	4.60	A	93	4	3	sector	Fidelity Sel Electronics
40.2	50.8	11.61	11.14	0.02	0.48	0.2	0.63	0.09	5.06	D	91	4	5	sector	Fidelity Sel Energy Serv
82.5	96.7	16.43	15.87	0.11	0.51	0.7	0.95	0.25	4.51	D	99	0	1	sector	Fidelity Sel Energy
50.7	32.1	11.20	10.13	0.00	0.00	0.0	1.34	0.52	4.39	F	94	0	6	sector	Fidelity Sel Envir Serv
126.1	94.2	49.79	43.12	0.59	4.13	1.3	1.30	0.54	4.17	B	80	0	20	sector	Fidelity Sel Financial
173.1	85.5	30.75	30.60	0.08	1.85	0.3	0.88	0.72	2.42	C	92	0	8	sector	Fidelity Sel Food/Agr
573.0	796.1	63.62	70.80	0.62	5.74	0.8	1.05	0.27	4.82	F	84	2	14	sector	Fidelity Sel Health
159.2	130.2	24.44	21.33	0.12	3.60	0.5	1.06	0.31	4.51	A	87	0	13	sector	Fidelity Sel Home Fincl
85.0	104.2	19.14	19.57	0.00	0.17	0.0	1.09	0.43	3.89	A	91	0	9	sector	Fidelity Sel Indust Equip
36.9	180.1	20.47	21.96	0.18	0.00	0.8	1.07	0.56	3.35	B	87	0	13	sector	Fidelity Sel Indust Mat
18.9	10.1	20.03	19.96	0.00	0.00	0.0	0.92	0.42	3.32	C	75	0	25	sector	Fidelity Sel Insurance
117.5	61.3	45.22	38.27	0.00	3.93	0.0	1.13	0.66	3.25	B	85	1	14	sector	Fidelity Sel Leisure
150.5	247.6	19.10	21.87	0.07	0.88	0.3	1.14	0.22	5.82	F	82	0	18	sector	Fidelity Sel Medical Del
65.1	26.6	23.84	21.23	0.00	3.21	0.0	1.19	0.63	3.52	A	91	1	8	sector	Fidelity Sel Multimedia
54.9	79.0	9.36	8.70	0.02	0.00	0.2	—	—	—	—	87	0	13	sector	Fidelity Sel Nat Gas
48.3	76.3	18.08	19.36	0.00	1.17	0.0	0.95	0.23	4.68	C	83	0	17	sector	Fidelity Sel Pap/Forest
500.7	453.3	18.13	17.68	0.23	0.00	1.3	0.31	0.01	7.44	A	91	0	9	prec met	Fidelity Sel Prec Metals

No-Load Fund	1985	1986	1987	1988	1989	1990	1991	1992	1993	1994	Annualized 3 yrs.	Annualized 5 yrs.	What $10,000 grew to after 3 yrs.	5 yrs.
Fidelity Sel Reg Banks†	—	—	-3.1^3	25.7^2	26.7^3	-20.7^5	65.6^1	48.5^1	11.0^4	0.2^3	18.2^1	16.8^2	16,528	21,708
Fidelity Sel Retail†	—	14.2^3	-7.4^3	38.7^1	29.6^3	-5.0^3	68.1^1	22.1^2	13.0^4	-5.0^4	9.4^3	15.9^2	13,105	20,920
Fidelity Sel Software†	—	13.9^3	9.4^1	9.1^4	12.1^5	0.9^2	45.8^2	35.5^1	32.5^1	0.4^3	21.7^1	21.5^1	18,027	26,510
Fidelity Sel Technology.†	7.5^5	-7.5^5	-11.8^4	-2.7^5	17.0^4	10.5^1	59.0^2	8.7^4	28.6^2	11.1^1	15.8^2	22.3^1	15,540	27,310
Fidelity Sel Telecomm†	—	19.8^2	15.2^1	27.7^1	50.9^1	-16.4^4	30.8^4	15.3^3	29.6^2	4.3^2	16.0^2	11.3^3	15,590	17,040
Fidelity Sel Transp.†	—	—	-17.5^5	38.5^1	28.5^3	-21.6^5	54.2^2	23.8^1	29.3^2	3.9^2	18.5^1	15.0^2	16,622	20,091
Fidelity Sel Util Gro.†	31.7^3	24.0^1	-9.3^4	16.5^3	39.0^2	0.5^2	20.9^5	10.5^3	12.5^4	-7.4^4	4.8^4	6.9^4	11,503	13,987
Fidelity Small Cap SC.†	—	—	—	—	—	—	—	—	—	-3.3^4	—	—	—	—
Fidelity Spart Agg Muni	—	—	—	—	—	—	—	—	—	-6.1^3	—	—	—	—
Fidelity Spart AZ Muni	—	—	—	—	—	—	—	—	—	—	—	—	—	—
Fidelity Spart Bond Strat	—	—	—	—	—	—	—	—	—	-7.7^5	—	—	—	—
Fidelity Spart CA Hi Yld	—	—	—	—	—	8.2^1	11.6^4	8.8^3	14.1^1	-9.0^5	4.2^4	6.4^3	11,297	13,630
Fidelity Spart CA Inter	—	—	—	—	—	—	—	—	—	-4.7^4	—	—	—	—
Fidelity Spart CT Hi Yld	—	—	—	10.1^4	10.4^1	6.6^3	10.6^5	8.2^4	12.9^3	-7.0^3	4.3^4	6.0^4	11,359	13,397
Fidelity Spart FL Muni	—	—	—	—	—	—	—	—	14.9^1	-6.7^3	—	—	—	—
Fidelity Spart GNMA	—	—	—	—	—	—	13.8^5	6.5^3	6.3^5	-1.5^1	3.7^4	—	11,151	—
Fidelity Spart Gov Inc	—	—	—	—	15.7^2	9.2^1	15.1^4	7.1^3	7.3^5	-3.6^3	3.5^4	6.8^4	11,081	13,924
Fidelity Spart Hi Inc	—	—	—	—	—	—	34.3^1	21.5^1	21.7^1	3.2^1	15.1^1	—	15,257	—
Fidelity Spart Inter Muni	—	—	—	—	—	—	—	—	—	-5.0^5	—	—	—	—
Fidelity Spart Inv Grd	—	—	—	—	—	—	—	—	15.8^2	-5.2^3	—	—	—	—
Fidelity Spart LT Gov	—	—	—	—	—	—	17.3^3	8.0^2	16.6^1	-12.2^5	3.4^4	—	11,062	—
Fidelity Spart Ltd Mat	—	—	—	10.4^3	9.1^2	—	11.9^4	5.8^3	6.4^3	-1.0^4	3.7^3	6.4^3	11,139	13,604
Fidelity Spart MD Muni	—	—	—	—	—	—	—	—	—	-7.5^4	—	—	—	—
Fidelity Spart Muni Inc	—	—	—	—	—	—	12.4^2	8.4^4	14.3^1	-8.9^5	4.1^4	—	11,290	—
Fidelity Spart NJ Hi Yld	—	—	—	6.4^5	10.4^2	7.1^1	12.3^3	8.8^3	13.1^2	-5.8^2	5.1^2	6.9^1	11,593	13,952
Fidelity Spart NY Hi Yld	—	—	—	—	—	—	13.7^1	9.5^1	13.4^2	-8.3^4	4.4^3	—	11,376	—
Fidelity Spart NY Inter	—	—	—	—	—	—	—	—	—	-4.3^3	—	—	—	—
Fidelity Spart PA Hi Yld	—	—	-5.8^5	14.3^1	9.8^3	7.2^1	12.5^2	9.1^2	13.2^2	-5.1^1	5.5^1	7.2^1	11,725	14,140
Fidelity Spart ST Inc	—	—	—	—	—	—	—	—	9.0^1	-4.6^5	—	—	—	—
Fidelity Spart S-I Gov	—	—	—	—	—	—	—	—	5.7^4	-0.5^3	—	—	—	—
Fidelity Spart S-I Muni	—	—	0.0^5	4.9^5	6.3^5	6.4^3	8.9^2	6.2^3	7.1^1	-0.1^4	4.4^1	5.7^1	11,365	13,165
Fidelity ST Bond	—	—	4.0^3	5.7^4	10.6^3	5.8^5	14.0^2	7.4^1	9.2^1	-4.1^5	4.0^2	6.3^4	11,251	13,571
Fidelity ST World Inc	—	—	—	—	—	—	—	5.0^4	12.5^1	-5.9^5	3.6^4	—	11,117	—
Fidelity Stk Selector	—	—	—	—	—	—	45.9^1	15.4^2	14.0^2	0.8^2	9.8^2	—	13,250	—
Fidelity S-I Gov	—	—	—	—	—	—	—	4.7^4	5.3^4	-1.4^4	2.8^5	—	10,870	—
Fidelity Trend	28.2^3	13.3^3	-4.2^4	24.3^2	31.6^2	-12.7^4	36.2^4	16.7^1	19.2^2	-6.7^4	9.1^2	9.1^3	12,978	15,432
Fidelity Utilities	—	—	—	14.8^3	25.8^1	1.9^2	21.1^5	10.9^2	15.5^2	-5.3^4	6.7^3	8.4^3	12,138	14,966
Fidelity Value	22.1^5	14.7^3	-8.6^5	29.0^1	23.0^3	-12.8^5	25.9^4	21.1^1	22.9^1	7.6^1	17.0^1	12.0^1	16,023	17,589
Fidelity Worldwide	—	—	—	—	—	—	7.8^5	6.2^1	36.5^1	3.0^1	14.3^1	—	14,922	—
Fiduciary Cap Gro SC	29.9^2	-0.1^5	-8.9^5	18.8^3	17.9^4	-11.7^3	36.3^4	14.4^2	14.7^3	0.4^2	9.6^2	9.7^3	13,175	15,859
Fiduciary Total Ret	—	—	12.3^1	20.8^2	13.2^5	-4.4^3	30.0^2	10.4^2	11.1^3	-2.0^4	6.3^3	8.4^2	12,010	14,934
First Eagle America	—	—	—	22.6^2	26.5^3	-17.6^5	20.9^5	24.3^1	23.9^1	-2.6^3	14.5^1	8.4^4	14,996	14,936
First Eagle Int'l	—	—	—	—	—	—	—	—	—	—	—	—	—	—
First Mutual	—	—	—	—	—	-4.5^2	26.2^5	2.2^5	15.2^3	-15.1^5	0.0^5	3.8^5	9,991	12,041
First Omaha Eqty	—	—	—	—	—	—	—	—	10.9^3	7.4^1	—	—	—	—
First Omaha Fix Inc	—	—	—	—	—	—	—	—	11.1^3	-4.8^3	—	—	—	—
First Omaha S-I Fix	—	—	—	—	—	—	—	—	6.4^3	-1.4^4	—	—	—	—
Flex-Fund Bond	—	12.6^1	-0.6^5	2.7^5	8.7^5	8.4^4	15.3^1	3.3^5	8.2^1	-1.0^4	3.4^4	6.7^3	11,063	13,821
Flex-Fund Growth	—	11.7^4	7.6^2	-5.7^5	10.2^5	4.3^1	21.4^5	6.4^4	7.2^4	-0.7^3	4.2^4	7.5^4	11,323	14,344
Flex-Fund Muirfield	—	—	—	—	14.0^5	2.4^1	29.6^3	6.7^4	8.2^4	2.7^2	5.9^3	9.5^2	11,862	15,737
Flex-Fund ST Glob	—	—	—	—	—	—	—	—	0.4^5	2.1^1	—	—	—	—
Fontaine Cap App	—	—	—	—	—	6.1^1	11.8^5	-4.0^5	14.1^3	2.3^2	3.9^4	5.9^5	11,215	13,302
Fontaine Glob Gro	—	—	—	—	—	—	—	—	13.4^5	-0.4^2	—	—	—	—
Fontaine Glob Inc	—	—	—	—	—	—	—	—	20.5^1	1.5^2	—	—	—	—
Founders Balanced	12.7^5	14.6^5	1.9^2	11.1^5	25.2^2	-5.0^4	22.8^4	6.0^4	21.8^1	-1.9^3	8.2^2	8.1^3	12,665	14,779
Founders Blue Chip	31.9^1	17.3^2	1.9^3	10.0^5	35.6^1	0.4^1	28.3^3	-0.3^5	14.5^1	0.5^2	4.7^4	8.2^3	11,479	14,793
Founders Discovery SC	—	—	—	—	—	13.1^1	62.5^2	15.2^2	10.8^4	-7.8^5	5.6^4	16.7^1	11,771	21,628
Founders Frontier SC	—	—	—	29.2^1	44.3^1	-7.5^3	49.3^2	8.9^3	16.5^3	-2.8^3	7.3^3	11.3^2	12,338	17,047
Founders Gov Sec	—	—	—	—	13.3^2	4.4^4	14.9^4	5.3^5	9.3^4	-7.5^5	2.1^5	5.0^5	10,648	12,772
Founders Growth	28.8^3	19.6^2	10.2^1	4.8^5	41.7^1	-10.6^5	47.4^1	4.3^5	25.5^1	-3.4^4	8.2^2	10.8^2	12,657	16,673

See Chapter 3 for explanation of symbols

Arranged in alphabetical order

Total Net Assets $Million		NAV per share		1994 per share distributions		Yield %	Risk Analysis				% Distribution of Portfolio			Objective	No-Load Fund
December 31		December 31							Std.	Sharpe	12/31/94				
1993	1994	1993	1994	Income	Capital gains	12/31/94	beta	R^2	Dev.	Ratio	Stocks	Bonds	Cash		
113.7	108.4	17.49	16.28	0.26	1.01	1.5	1.05	0.35	4.17	B	85	0	15	sector	Fidelity Sel Reg Banks
60.9	35.5	25.14	23.88	0.00	0.00	0.0	0.89	0.29	3.86	D	90	0	10	sector	Fidelity Sel Retail
164.8	211.5	27.55	27.29	0.00	0.33	0.0	1.70	0.43	6.15	B	87	2	11	sector	Fidelity Sel Software
229.8	227.4	38.73	41.36	0.00	1.50	0.0	1.44	0.55	4.59	B	95	5	0	sector	Fidelity Sel Technology
414.6	363.8	37.54	37.48	0.53	1.07	1.4	1.14	0.61	3.42	A	89	2	9	sector	Fidelity Sel Telecomm
10.3	11.1	20.76	19.29	0.00	2.19	0.0	1.02	0.62	3.03	A	92	0	8	sector	Fidelity Sel Transp
275.5	202.4	37.58	33.08	1.05	0.67	3.2	0.67	0.37	2.57	D	88	1	11	sector	Fidelity Sel Util Gro
666.3	664.8	10.82	10.45	0.01	0.00	0.1	—	—	—	—	91	0	9	agg gr	Fidelity Small Cap SC
37.2	57.4	10.46	9.23	0.60	0.00	6.5	—	—	—	—	0	101	-1	tax-free	Fidelity Spart Agg Muni
—	4.5	—	9.77	—	—	—	—	—	—	—	0	90	10	tax-free	Fidelity Spart AZ Muni
20.6	17.7	9.98	8.74	0.49	0.00	5.6	—	—	—	—	0	96	4	fix-inc	Fidelity Spart Bond Strat
596.8	371.9	11.23	9.46	0.61	0.18	6.4	0.47	0.33	1.89	D	0	98	2	tax-free	Fidelity Spart CA Hi Yld
1.0	38.0	10.00	9.07	0.47	0.00	5.2	—	—	—	—	0	96	4	tax-free	Fidelity Spart CA Inter
448.9	312.8	11.70	10.15	0.64	0.11	6.3	0.46	0.34	1.84	D	0	98	2	tax-free	Fidelity Spart CT Hi Yld
450.5	339.3	11.33	9.99	0.59	0.00	5.9	—	—	—	—	0	98	2	tax-free	Fidelity Spart FL Muni
579.4	347.8	10.10	9.32	0.62	0.00	6.7	0.19	0.23	0.91	C	0	105	-5	fix-inc	Fidelity Spart GNMA
376.0	231.9	10.68	9.59	0.71	0.00	7.4	0.27	0.31	1.11	D	0	98	2	fix-inc	Fidelity Spart Gov Inc
664.6	617.5	12.17	11.46	1.00	0.08	8.7	0.14	0.06	13.78	A	10	73	17	fix-inc	Fidelity Spart Hi Inc
278.2	205.9	10.44	9.41	0.51	0.00	5.4	—	—	—	—	0	103	-3	tax-free	Fidelity Spart Inter Muni
120.4	118.0	10.68	9.40	0.70	0.03	7.4	—	—	—	—	0	87	13	fix-inc	Fidelity Spart Inv Grd
69.7	71.7	12.40	10.27	0.52	0.11	5.1	0.55	0.28	2.42	F	0	97	3	fix-inc	Fidelity Spart LT Gov
1,356.6	830.6	10.00	9.35	0.55	0.00	5.9	0.12	0.21	0.61	B	0	100	0	fix-inc	Fidelity Spart Ltd Mat
39.4	35.5	10.39	9.07	0.55	0.00	6.1	—	—	—	—	0	94	6	tax-free	Fidelity Spart MD Muni
862.2	535.6	10.93	9.37	0.61	0.00	6.5	0.19	—	1.85	D	0	98	2	tax-free	Fidelity Spart Muni Inc
429.2	325.7	11.82	10.51	0.64	0.00	6.1	0.45	0.34	1.80	B	0	99	1	tax-free	Fidelity Spart NJ Hi Yld
443.8	284.8	11.31	9.50	0.61	0.28	6.3	0.52	0.36	2.03	D	0	98	2	tax-free	Fidelity Spart NY Hi Yld
1.0	31.8	10.01	9.12	0.47	0.00	5.1	—	—	—	—	0	95	5	tax-free	Fidelity Spart NY Inter
305.0	241.2	11.13	9.62	0.65	0.31	6.6	0.43	0.34	1.72	A	0	97	3	tax-free	Fidelity Spart PA Hi Yld
1,506.1	610.3	9.97	8.92	0.60	0.00	6.8	—	—	—	—	0	83	17	fix-inc	Fidelity Spart ST Inc
67.4	48.0	9.91	9.23	0.62	0.00	6.8	—	—	—	—	0	84	16	fix-inc	Fidelity Spart S-I Gov
1,188.2	913.1	10.11	9.66	0.44	0.00	4.5	0.08	—	—	B	0	101	-1	tax-free	Fidelity Spart S-I Muni
2,469.5	1,514.8	9.55	8.60	0.57	0.00	6.6	0.12	0.10	0.83	C	0	81	19	fix-inc	Fidelity ST Bond
418.1	265.8	10.19	8.90	0.71	0.00	7.9	0.20	0.13	1.24	F	0	54	46	fix-inc	Fidelity ST World Inc
624.7	786.7	18.75	17.91	0.15	0.81	0.8	0.97	0.61	2.86	B	93	0	7	growth	Fidelity Stk Selector
150.7	151.2	9.86	9.14	0.58	0.00	6.4	0.11	0.14	0.69	F	0	103	-3	fix-inc	Fidelity S-I Gov
1,393.2	1,193.8	59.08	50.99	0.16	3.89	0.3	1.36	0.90	3.35	B	93	2	5	agg gr	Fidelity Trend
1,456.0	1,079.6	15.18	13.06	0.54	0.80	4.0	0.73	0.43	2.61	D	74	9	17	income	Fidelity Utilities
1,716.1	3,720.4	40.23	40.81	0.17	2.28	0.4	0.88	0.73	2.39	A	92	3	5	growth	Fidelity Value
339.6	703.9	13.03	12.68	0.07	0.66	0.5	0.85	0.45	2.96	A	60	4	36	global	Fidelity Worldwide
48.7	39.3	19.63	17.76	0.04	1.88	0.2	0.80	0.61	2.40	A	85	5	10	agg gr	Fiduciary Cap Gro SC
2.8	0.8	12.08	11.03	0.14	0.67	1.2	0.63	—	—	—	0	59	41	gr-inc	Fiduciary Total Ret
108.3	105.1	15.04	12.70	0.00	2.00	0.0	1.28	0.72	3.54	A	98	2	0	agg gr	First Eagle America
—	20.2	—	12.37	—	—	—	—	—	—	—	76	6	18	int'l	First Eagle Int'l
25.1	18.4	10.03	8.32	0.00	0.00	0.0	—	—	—	—	—	—	—	agg gr	First Mutual
120.9	145.0	10.68	10.89	0.24	0.33	2.1	—	—	—	—	84	12	4	gr-inc	First Omaha Eqty
63.0	61.6	10.41	9.26	0.66	0.00	7.1	—	—	—	—	0	98	2	fix-inc	First Omaha Fix Inc
23.5	22.6	10.08	9.41	0.53	0.00	5.7	—	—	—	—	80	19	1	fix-inc	First Omaha S-I Fix
13.1	12.9	20.18	19.25	0.72	0.00	3.8	0.18	0.12	1.19	F	0	0	100	fix-inc	Flex-Fund Bond
26.1	22.0	13.45	13.08	0.27	0.00	2.1	0.50	0.37	1.93	D	0	0	100	growth	Flex-Fund Growth
64.8	81.8	5.36	5.34	0.14	0.02	2.6	0.48	0.48	1.59	B	0	0	100	growth	Flex-Fund Muirfield
14.7	3.9	9.41	9.32	0.29	0.00	3.1	—	—	—	—	0	88	12	fix-inc	Flex-Fund ST Glob
8.9	5.7	10.75	10.75	0.18	0.07	1.7	0.32	0.12	2.14	D	60	38	2	agg gr	Fontaine Cap App
0.3	0.3	10.34	9.61	0.16	0.53	1.6	—	—	—	—	39	44	17	global	Fontaine Glob Gro
0.7	0.7	10.78	10.16	0.39	0.39	3.7	—	—	—	—	29	56	15	fix-inc	Fontaine Glob Inc
72.6	96.0	8.93	8.56	0.20	0.00	2.3	0.66	0.65	1.90	B	58	29	13	income	Founders Balanced
307.4	312.2	6.49	6.16	0.06	0.31	0.9	0.95	0.78	2.50	D	73	5	22	gr-inc	Founders Blue Chip
226.1	187.5	21.55	19.88	0.00	0.00	0.0	1.15	0.42	4.16	D	71	0	29	agg gr	Founders Discovery SC
253.8	249.2	27.94	26.50	0.00	0.65	0.0	1.39	0.68	3.97	C	67	2	31	agg gr	Founders Frontier SC
28.7	21.5	10.02	8.78	0.50	0.00	5.7	0.29	0.20	1.48	F	0	83	17	fix-inc	Founders Gov Sec
343.0	310.1	12.38	11.63	0.00	0.34	0.0	1.48	0.72	4.11	D	83	2	15	growth	Founders Growth

No-Load Fund	Total return percent with quintile ranks by objective										Annualized		What $10,000 grew to after	
	1985	1986	1987	1988	1989	1990	1991	1992	1993	1994	3 yrs.	5 yrs.	3 yrs.	5 yrs.
Founders Oppty Bd	—	—	—	—	—	—	—	—	—	-10.0[5]	—	—	—	—
Founders Passport	—	—	—	—	—	—	—	—	—	-10.4[5]	—	—	—	—
Founders Special	15.2[5]	18.9[1]	5.2[2]	13.2[4]	39.1[1]	-10.4[3]	63.6[2]	8.3[3]	16.0[3]	-4.9[4]	6.1[3]	11.9[2]	11,949	17,511
Founders Worldwide Gro	—	—	—	—	—	6.7[1]	34.8[1]	1.5[4]	29.9[2]	-2.2[3]	8.9[3]	13.2[1]	12,900	18,547
Fremont Bond	—	—	—	—	—	—	—	—	—	-4.0[4]	—	—	—	—
Fremont CA Inter	—	—	—	—	—	—	10.1[4]	7.3[3]	9.3[4]	-4.9[4]	3.7[5]	—	11,150	—
Fremont Global	—	—	—	—	15.9[3]	-1.8[2]	18.6[2]	5.2[2]	19.6[4]	-4.2[3]	6.4[4]	7.0[2]	12,056	14,049
Fremont Growth	—	—	—	—	—	—	—	—	6.4[4]	0.4[3]	—	—	—	—
Fremont Int'l Gro	—	—	—	—	—	—	—	—	—	—	—	—	—	—
Fremont Int'l Sm Cap	—	—	—	—	—	—	—	—	—	—	—	—	—	—
Fremont US MicroCap SC	—	—	—	—	—	—	—	—	—	—	—	—	—	—
Fundamental CA Muni	17.2[4]	9.9[5]	1.5[1]	11.5[3]	5.5[5]	4.4[5]	8.8[5]	7.0[5]	15.8[1]	-19.9[5]	-0.3[5]	2.4[5]	9,926	11,269
Fundamental Hi Yld Muni	—	—	3.2[5]	5.9[5]	-5.8[5]	10.1[5]	6.3[5]	5.1[5]	-12.9[5]	-0.9[5]	0.2[5]	9,733	10,094	
Fundamental NY Muni	20.3[2]	17.0[4]	-7.4[5]	11.2[3]	9.6[3]	-1.0[5]	15.8[1]	11.8[1]	12.5[4]	-19.8[5]	0.3[5]	3.0[5]	10,097	11,572
Fundamental US Gov Strat	—	—	—	—	—	—	—	—	8.1[4]	-25.6[5]	—	—	—	—
FundTrust Agg Gro†	25.8[4]	14.9[2]	-1.0[3]	11.8[4]	21.9[4]	-7.5[3]	38.0[4]	5.5[4]	14.1[3]	-1.2[3]	5.9[4]	8.7[4]	11,892	15,190
FundTrust Gro & Inc†	23.7[4]	18.7[2]	-4.8[5]	19.2[2]	19.4[3]	-8.3[4]	23.3[4]	9.2[3]	12.7[3]	-0.2[3]	7.1[2]	6.8[4]	12,282	13,889
FundTrust Growth.†	25.0[4]	16.0[2]	-1.1[4]	14.4[4]	18.5[4]	-6.2[4]	28.8[4]	8.9[3]	12.5[3]	-0.5[3]	6.8[3]	8.0[3]	12,184	14,718
FundTrust Income.†	16.8[5]	8.2[5]	-0.2[5]	9.0[1]	7.8[5]	4.8[5]	14.2[4]	7.7[2]	10.5[2]	-3.9[4]	4.6[2]	6.5[4]	11,437	13,680
FundTrust Mgd Tot Ret.†	—	—	—	—	14.5[4]	0.3[1]	20.3[4]	6.3[4]	9.0[4]	-2.1[4]	4.3[4]	6.5[4]	11,347	13,689
Gabelli ABC	—	—	—	—	—	—	—	—	—	4.5[1]	—	—	—	—
Gabelli Asset	—	—	16.1[1]	31.1[1]	26.1[2]	-5.0[3]	18.1[5]	14.9[2]	21.8[1]	-0.2[3]	11.8[1]	9.4[2]	13,978	15,690
Gabelli Glob Convert	—	—	—	—	—	—	—	—	—	—	—	—	—	—
Gabelli Glob Couch Pot	—	—	—	—	—	—	—	—	—	—	—	—	—	—
Gabelli Glob Ent/Media	—	—	—	—	—	—	—	—	—	—	—	—	—	—
Gabelli Glob Growth	—	—	—	—	—	—	—	—	—	—	—	—	—	—
Gabelli Glob Telecomm	—	—	—	—	—	—	—	—	—	-3.7[3]	—	—	—	—
Gabelli Gold	—	—	—	—	—	—	—	—	—	—	—	—	—	—
Gabelli Growth	—	—	—	39.1[1]	40.1[1]	-2.0[2]	34.3[3]	4.5[4]	11.3[3]	-3.4[4]	4.0[4]	8.1[3]	11,235	14,790
Galaxy Asst Allc	—	—	—	—	—	—	—	6.6[4]	8.1[5]	-2.5[3]	4.0[5]	—	11,234	—
Galaxy Corp Bond	—	—	—	—	—	—	—	—	—	—	—	—	—	—
Galaxy CT Muni	—	—	—	—	—	—	—	—	—	-8.1[4]	—	—	—	—
Galaxy Eqty Growth	—	—	—	—	—	—	30.4[3]	6.1[4]	5.4[4]	0.6[2]	4.0[4]	—	11,251	—
Galaxy Eqty Income	—	—	—	—	—	—	22.3[4]	7.5[4]	8.1[5]	0.8[2]	5.4[4]	—	11,697	—
Galaxy Eqty Value	—	—	—	—	16.9[4]	-3.2[3]	23.3[4]	8.2[3]	14.8[2]	3.5[1]	8.7[2]	8.9[2]	12,854	15,345
Galaxy Hi Qual Bd	—	—	—	—	—	—	15.2[4]	6.8[4]	12.8[3]	-6.5[4]	4.1[4]	—	11,264	—
Galaxy Inter Bond	—	—	—	—	11.5[4]	5.9[5]	15.7[2]	7.2[2]	5.5[5]	-3.8[4]	2.9[5]	5.9[5]	10,883	13,333
Galaxy Int'l Eqty	—	—	—	—	—	—	—	-2.3[2]	31.7[4]	-2.5[3]	7.8[3]	—	12,535	—
Galaxy Lg Co Idx	—	—	—	—	—	—	29.1[2]	7.1[3]	9.6[4]	1.0[2]	5.8[3]	—	11,852	—
Galaxy MA Muni	—	—	—	—	—	—	—	—	—	-7.7[4]	—	—	—	—
Galaxy Muni Bd	—	—	—	—	—	—	—	—	—	-5.4[2]	—	—	—	—
Galaxy NY Muni	—	—	—	—	—	—	—	8.3[4]	12.3[4]	-7.2[4]	4.1[4]	—	11,279	—
Galaxy Sm Co Eqty SC	—	—	—	—	—	—	—	1.2[5]	22.8[1]	-0.1[2]	7.5[3]	—	12,415	—
Galaxy Sm Co Idx SC	—	—	—	—	—	—	44.6[3]	12.2[3]	11.3[4]	-3.7[4]	6.4[3]	—	12,029	—
Galaxy ST Bond	—	—	—	—	—	—	—	5.9[3]	6.4[3]	-0.4[3]	4.0[3]	—	11,233	—
Galaxy TE Bond	—	—	—	—	—	—	—	9.2[2]	11.9[4]	-5.4[2]	5.0[2]	—	11,569	—
Galaxy Trsy Idx	—	—	—	—	—	—	—	6.8[4]	10.2[4]	-3.7[3]	4.3[3]	—	11,333	—
Galaxy Util Idx	—	—	—	—	—	—	—	—	13.3[3]	-8.6[5]	—	—	—	—
Gateway Cincinnati	—	—	—	—	—	—	—	—	—	—	—	—	—	—
Gateway Idx Plus	16.0[5]	12.7[5]	-5.7[5]	19.8[2]	19.4[3]	10.3[1]	17.8[5]	5.2[4]	7.4[4]	5.6[1]	6.0[3]	9.2[2]	11,922	15,490
Gateway MidCap Idx	—	—	—	—	—	—	—	—	5.2[5]	-5.1[5]	—	—	—	—
Gateway Sm Cap Idx SC	—	—	—	—	—	—	—	—	—	-6.0[4]	—	—	—	—
GE Elfun Div Inc	—	—	—	—	21.5[3]	4.1[1]	18.0[5]	9.6[2]	8.9[4]	-0.3[3]	6.0[3]	7.9[3]	11,901	14,617
GE Elfun Glob Inc	—	—	—	—	24.7[2]	-8.5[3]	14.8[4]	5.9[2]	31.9[2]	-0.6[2]	11.6[1]	7.8[1]	13,883	14,581
GE Elfun Income	21.6[3]	16.3[2]	0.8[3]	7.5[4]	14.3[2]	8.6[2]	16.1[3]	6.6[4]	9.7[4]	-2.3[2]	4.6[3]	7.6[3]	11,427	14,416
GE Elfun TE Inc	21.4[1]	11.4[5]	0.3[1]	13.2[1]	9.2[4]	5.5[5]	12.1[3]	8.5[4]	12.1[4]	-5.8[2]	4.7[3]	6.3[3]	11,459	13,554
GE Elfun Trusts	36.1[1]	14.2[3]	3.2[3]	18.6[3]	35.9[1]	-3.8[3]	28.4[4]	9.3[3]	9.0[4]	0.2[3]	6.1[3]	8.1[3]	11,938	14,752
GE Fixed Income	—	—	—	—	—	—	—	—	—	-2.5[2]	—	—	—	—
GE Global Eqty	—	—	—	—	—	—	—	—	—	-1.9[2]	—	—	—	—
GE Int'l Eqty	—	—	—	—	—	—	—	—	—	—	—	—	—	—

See Chapter 3 for explanation of symbols

Total Net Assets $Million		NAV per share		1994 per share distributions		Yield %	Risk Analysis				% Distribution of Portfolio				
December 31 1993	1994	December 31 1993	1994	Income	Capital gains	12/31/94	beta	R^2	Std. Dev.	Sharpe Ratio	12/31/94 Stocks	Bonds	Cash	Objective	No-Load Fund
4.7	3.8	10.03	8.49	0.55	0.00	6.5	—	—	—	—	0	91	9	fix-inc	Founders Oppty Bd
18.4	16.5	10.53	9.42	0.02	0.00	0.2	—	—	—	—	—	—	—	global	Founders Passport
432.9	300.9	7.67	7.01	0.00	0.28	0.0	1.47	0.73	4.05	D	94	0	6	agg gr	Founders Special
84.6	104.9	17.94	17.09	0.00	0.46	0.0	1.04	0.50	3.47	D	70	4	26	global	Founders Worldwide Gro
12.0	59.8	10.10	9.15	0.55	0.00	6.0	—	—	—	—	0	100	0	fix-inc	Fremont Bond
62.8	54.9	11.09	10.03	0.52	0.00	5.2	0.34	0.31	1.38	F	0	98	2	tax-free	Fremont CA Inter
214.6	436.8	13.62	12.79	0.13	0.13	1.0	0.60	0.60	1.79	B	45	27	28	global	Fremont Global
42.6	23.4	11.18	10.11	0.22	0.90	2.0	—	—	—	—	100	0	0	growth	Fremont Growth
—	28.2	—	9.27	—	—	—	—	—	—	—	88	2	10	int'l	Fremont Int'l Gro
—	1.9	—	9.02	—	—	—	—	—	—	—	93	0	7	int'l	Fremont Int'l Sm Cap
—	2.1	—	10.13	—	—	—	—	—	—	—	66	0	34	agg gr	Fremont US MicroCap SC
16.3	10.6	9.49	7.10	0.55	0.00	7.8	0.21	—	—	—	0	100	0	tax-free	Fundamental CA Muni
1.1	1.0	7.27	5.92	0.43	0.00	7.3	0.41	0.42	1.48	F	0	100	0	tax-free	Fundamental Hi Yld Muni
274.3	213.2	1.18	0.88	0.07	0.01	7.3	0.60	0.29	2.59	F	0	100	0	tax-free	Fundamental NY Muni
62.7	19.1	2.01	1.37	0.14	0.00	10.3	—	—	—	—	0	100	0	fix-inc	Fundamental US Gov Strat
38.0	38.0	17.21	14.53	0.23	2.26	1.5	0.99	0.76	2.64	B	—	—	—	agg gr	FundTrust Agg Gro.
50.7	50.2	16.75	14.80	0.49	1.44	3.1	0.79	0.90	1.92	B	—	—	—	gr-inc	FundTrust Gro & Inc
26.4	33.8	15.12	13.06	0.15	1.83	1.1	0.88	0.86	2.21	B	—	—	—	growth	FundTrust Growth
72.1	74.0	10.56	9.49	0.67	0.00	7.1	0.24	0.23	1.14	C	—	—	—	fix-inc	FundTrust Income
25.4	16.2	12.10	10.21	0.49	1.17	4.4	0.50	0.41	1.81	A	—	—	—	gr-inc	FundTrust Mgd Tot Ret
8.9	26.1	10.03	9.57	0.33	0.58	3.3	—	—	—	—	—	—	—	growth	Gabelli ABC
948.0	940.2	23.30	22.21	0.26	0.79	1.1	0.83	0.76	2.22	A	88	5	7	growth	Gabelli Asset
—	15.3	—	9.93	—	—	—	—	—	—	—	—	—	—	income	Gabelli Glob Convert
—	24.8	—	10.25	—	—	—	—	—	—	—	—	—	—	global	Gabelli Glob Couch Pot
—	—	—	—	—	—	—	—	—	—	—	—	—	—	global	Gabelli Glob Ent/Media
—	—	—	—	—	—	—	—	—	—	—	—	—	—	global	Gabelli Glob Growth
—	137.8	10.20	9.73	—	—	—	—	—	—	—	—	—	—	global	Gabelli Glob Telecomm
—	17.5	—	11.07	—	—	—	—	—	—	—	—	—	—	prec met	Gabelli Gold
695.9	426.7	23.26	19.69	0.09	2.70	0.4	1.05	0.82	2.70	D	0	2	98	growth	Gabelli Growth
110.3	67.7	11.04	10.48	0.29	0.00	2.8	—	—	—	—	—	—	—	income	Galaxy Asst Allc
—	—	—	—	—	—	—	—	—	—	—	—	—	—	fix-inc	Galaxy Corp Bond
22.1	16.5	10.39	9.11	0.46	0.00	5.0	—	—	—	—	0	98	2	tax-free	Galaxy CT Muni
432.9	68.1	13.87	13.62	0.17	0.00	1.2	0.88	0.86	2.20	D	89	0	11	growth	Galaxy Eqty Growth.
126.9	61.0	12.58	12.17	0.29	0.00	2.4	0.68	0.83	1.75	D	94	0	6	income	Galaxy Eqty Income
181.9	73.6	12.84	11.88	0.17	0.00	1.5	0.89	0.85	2.23	B	94	0	6	gr-inc	Galaxy Eqty Value
161.9	25.1	10.89	9.55	0.65	0.00	6.8	0.32	0.20	1.65	D	0	100	0	fix-inc	Galaxy Hi Qual Bd
433.2	84.3	10.54	9.58	0.57	0.00	5.9	0.22	0.16	1.27	F	0	100	0	fix-inc	Galaxy Inter Bond
52.6	32.3	12.77	12.26	0.02	0.00	0.2	0.67	0.22	3.32	C	90	0	10	int'l	Galaxy Int'l Eqty
149.1	137.7	15.02	14.46	0.36	0.00	2.5	—	—	—	—	99	0	1	gr-inc	Galaxy Lg Co Idx
22.7	14.1	10.29	9.04	0.47	0.00	5.2	—	—	—	—	0	97	3	tax-free	Galaxy MA Muni
32.9	24.7	10.51	9.48	0.45	0.00	4.7	—	—	—	—	0	96	4	tax-free	Galaxy Muni Bd
71.8	39.2	11.10	9.81	0.50	0.00	5.1	0.48	0.33	1.92	F	0	99	1	tax-free	Galaxy NY Muni
61.9	27.1	12.37	12.16	0.00	0.00	0.0	1.44	0.57	4.50	C	100	0	0	agg gr	Galaxy Sm Co Eqty SC
263.6	230.6	18.16	16.38	0.26	0.00	1.6	—	—	—	—	99	0	1	agg gr	Galaxy Sm Co Idx SC
88.5	30.9	10.17	9.68	0.45	0.00	4.7	0.08	0.08	0.63	B	0	99	1	fix-inc	Galaxy ST Bond
144.3	31.3	11.07	9.95	0.53	0.00	5.3	—	—	—	—	0	95	5	tax-free	Galaxy TE Bond
152.8	104.8	10.83	9.63	0.61	0.00	6.4	—	—	—	—	0	99	1	fix-inc	Galaxy Trsy Idx
84.1	53.3	10.96	9.43	0.59	0.00	6.2	—	—	—	—	—	—	—	income	Galaxy Util Idx
—	3.2	—	9.91	—	—	—	—	—	—	—	—	—	—	growth	Gateway Cincinnati
199.5	164.7	15.85	15.48	0.27	0.97	1.6	0.37	0.55	1.18	A	98	0	2	gr-inc	Gateway Idx Plus
10.1	6.6	10.16	9.58	0.05	0.01	0.5	—	—	—	—	98	0	2	growth	Gateway MidCap Idx
12.6	9.7	10.35	9.63	0.00	0.10	0.0	—	—	—	—	100	0	0	agg gr	Gateway Sm Cap Idx SC
54.9	57.8	14.05	13.24	0.46	0.31	3.4	0.70	0.87	1.73	B	60	37	3	gr-inc	GE Elfun Div Inc
83.2	126.1	16.48	15.58	0.19	0.60	1.2	0.74	0.33	3.03	B	92	0	8	global	GE Elfun Glob Inc
198.7	184.8	11.68	10.55	0.70	0.16	6.5	0.21	0.17	1.19	C	0	96	4	fix-inc	GE Elfun Income
1,293.2	1,143.1	12.29	10.83	0.67	0.00	6.2	0.41	0.32	1.71	D	0	98	2	tax-free	GE Elfun TE Inc
937.6	900.6	33.76	30.91	0.77	2.17	2.3	0.98	0.91	2.40	C	98	0	2	growth	GE Elfun Trusts
7.4	15.0	12.09	11.11	0.68	0.00	6.1	—	—	—	—	0	97	3	fix-inc	GE Fixed Income
8.6	21.3	18.76	17.93	0.09	0.00	0.5	—	—	—	—	—	—	—	global	GE Global Eqty
—	0.7	—	14.37	—	—	—	—	—	—	—	—	—	—	int'l	GE Int'l Eqty

Arranged in alphabetical order

| No-Load Fund | Total return percent with quintile ranks by objective | | | | | | | | | | Annualized | | What $10,000 grew to after | |
	1985	1986	1987	1988	1989	1990	1991	1992	1993	1994	3 yrs.	5 yrs.	3 yrs.	5 yrs.
GE ST Gov	—	—	—	—	—	—	—	—	—	—	—	—	—	—
GE Strat Invest	—	—	—	—	—	—	—	—	—	-1.8[4]	—	—	—	—
GE S&S Prg: LT Inst	19.7[5]	17.9[2]	0.8[3]	7.4[4]	14.5[2]	9.4[1]	16.0[3]	6.9[3]	9.8[4]	-2.5[2]	4.6[3]	7.8[2]	11,446	14,524
GE S&S Prg: Mutual	26.8[3]	17.0[3]	-0.8[4]	14.9[4]	30.0[1]	-2.9[2]	29.2[2]	8.1[3]	11.5[3]	-1.8[4]	5.8[3]	8.3[2]	11,841	14,864
GE TE Bond	—	—	—	—	—	—	—	—	—	-7.4[4]	—	—	—	—
GE US Equity	—	—	—	—	—	—	—	—	—	-2.2[4]	—	—	—	—
General Securities	39.9[1]	9.1[4]	2.2[2]	14.0[3]	20.4[4]	-0.3[1]	35.8[4]	6.0[4]	6.2[5]	5.4[1]	5.9[4]	9.9[3]	11,863	16,061
Gibraltar Eqty Gro	27.6[3]	13.3[4]	-3.2[5]	11.3[4]	22.1[3]	-1.2[2]	28.9[2]	-2.4[5]	-3.3[5]	0.4[2]	-1.8[5]	3.8[5]	9,473	12,073
Gintel Erisa‡	24.1[4]	22.0[1]	-0.9[4]	22.0[2]	15.2[4]	-5.1[3]	13.5[5]	14.4[1]	5.3[5]	-21.3[5]	-1.8[5]	0.4[5]	9,481	10,209
Gintel	20.0[5]	20.8[1]	-14.3[5]	29.4[1]	23.4[3]	-6.7[4]	15.6[5]	24.7[1]	2.0[5]	-16.5[5]	2.0[5]	2.8[5]	10,618	11,451
GIT Equity Inc	25.7[3]	18.5[2]	-4.8[5]	13.2[4]	26.2[2]	0.6[1]	14.8[5]	3.2[5]	9.6[4]	-5.8[5]	2.1[5]	4.2[5]	10,653	12,301
GIT Gov Port	25.2[1]	13.0[2]	-1.1[5]	7.1[4]	11.1[4]	7.2[4]	13.4[5]	5.4[5]	9.6[3]	-3.6[4]	3.7[4]	6.3[5]	11,139	13,541
GIT Max Income	22.0[2]	9.1[5]	-2.8[4]	10.1[2]	2.9[5]	-7.6[5]	25.6[1]	12.0[1]	15.1[2]	-2.6[2]	7.9[1]	7.8[2]	12,554	14,580
GIT Select Gro	32.6[2]	21.2[1]	0.5[3]	15.7[3]	22.6[3]	-1.7[2]	22.9[4]	2.0[5]	4.8[5]	-5.2[5]	0.5[5]	4.1[5]	10,137	12,250
GIT Special Gro SC	47.2[1]	15.2[2]	-2.0[3]	24.7[1]	25.1[3]	-15.9[4]	25.7[5]	6.7[4]	14.9[3]	-4.0[4]	5.6[4]	4.5[5]	11,774	12,453
GIT TF AZ	—	—	—	—	—	6.7[3]	9.2[5]	8.5[4]	12.0[4]	-8.7[5]	3.5[5]	5.3[5]	11,088	12,922
GIT TF MD	—	—	—	—	—	—	—	—	—	-8.9[5]	—	—	—	—
GIT TF MO	—	—	—	—	—	5.9[4]	9.5[5]	8.0[4]	11.1[5]	-8.5[5]	3.2[5]	4.9[5]	10,981	12,728
GIT TF Nat	17.3[4]	19.4[2]	0.2[2]	8.6[5]	7.2[5]	5.5[5]	10.3[5]	8.2[4]	11.8[5]	-8.8[5]	3.3[5]	5.1[5]	11,024	12,832
GIT TF VA	—	—	—	6.9[5]	7.4[5]	5.9[4]	9.8[5]	7.5[5]	12.5[4]	-8.3[4]	3.5[5]	5.2[5]	11,090	12,896
GIT Wrldwd Growth	—	—	—	—	—	—	—	—	—	-24.1[5]	—	—	—	—
Golden Rainbow	—	—	—	—	—	—	—	9.9[2]	13.0[2]	-4.2[5]	6.0[3]	—	11,898	—
Gov St AL TF	—	—	—	—	—	—	—	—	—	-3.1[1]	—	—	—	—
Gov St Bond	—	—	—	—	—	—	—	6.6[3]	8.8[3]	-2.7[3]	4.1[3]	—	11,280	—
Gov St Equity	—	—	—	—	—	—	—	5.9[4]	2.5[5]	-2.2[4]	2.0[5]	—	10,623	—
Gradison Estab Value	28.8[3]	22.3[1]	12.4[1]	15.1[4]	16.0[5]	-8.1[4]	22.2[5]	10.2[2]	20.8[1]	0.3[3]	10.1[2]	8.4[3]	13,349	14,990
Gradison Oppty Value SC	28.1[3]	13.0[3]	-5.4[4]	23.6[2]	23.1[3]	-13.1[4]	35.9[4]	14.3[2]	11.1[4]	-2.2[3]	7.5[3]	8.0[4]	12,412	14,668
Grandich Contrarian	—	—	—	—	—	—	—	—	—	—	—	—	—	—
Green Cent Blncd	—	—	—	—	—	—	—	—	-0.5[5]	-4.3[5]	—	—	—	—
Greenspring	20.1[5]	16.0[2]	9.2[1]	15.9[3]	10.4[5]	-6.5[4]	19.2[5]	16.4[1]	14.6[2]	2.9[2]	11.1[1]	8.9[3]	13,727	15,309
GS ST Gov Agency	—	—	—	—	10.9[2]	9.0[3]	9.8[5]	6.1[3]	4.9[4]	0.4[2]	3.8[3]	6.0[4]	11,171	13,371
Guinness Flt China/HK	—	—	—	—	—	—	—	—	—	—	—	—	—	—
Guinness Flt Glob Gov	—	—	—	—	—	—	—	—	—	—	—	—	—	—
Harbor Bond	—	—	—	7.2[4]	13.7[2]	7.9[3]	19.6[1]	9.1[1]	12.4[1]	-3.7[4]	5.7[1]	8.8[1]	11,808	15,240
Harbor Cap App	—	—	—	15.3[4]	24.2[3]	-1.8[2]	54.8[1]	10.0[3]	12.1[3]	3.4[1]	8.4[2]	14.1[1]	12,746	19,368
Harbor Growth	—	—	2.9[3]	14.3[4]	23.0[3]	-6.7[4]	50.5[1]	-6.3[5]	18.4[2]	-11.4[5]	-0.6[5]	6.6[4]	9,822	13,794
Harbor Int'l Gro	—	—	—	—	—	—	—	—	—	-7.7[4]	—	—	—	—
Harbor Int'l‡	—	—	—	37.7[1]	36.8[1]	-9.8[3]	21.4[1]	-0.2[1]	45.4[2]	5.4[1]	15.2[1]	10.9[1]	15,301	16,764
Harbor Short Dur	—	—	—	—	—	—	—	4.7[5]	4.4[4]	2.7[1]	3.9[3]	—	11,229	—
Harbor Value	—	—	—	19.8[2]	29.8[1]	-5.6[3]	21.2[4]	7.5[3]	8.4[4]	0.7[2]	5.5[4]	6.1[4]	11,730	13,418
Haven Fund	—	—	—	—	—	—	—	—	—	—	—	—	—	—
Heartland Nebraska TF	—	—	—	—	—	—	—	—	—	-9.3[5]	—	—	—	—
Heartland US Gov	—	—	—	6.4[3]	11.3[2]	10.0[1]	17.0[1]	10.1[1]	17.8[1]	-9.6[5]	5.4[1]	8.6[1]	11,721	15,084
Heartland Val & Inc	—	—	—	—	—	—	—	—	—	-5.0[5]	—	—	—	—
Heartland Value SC	41.4[1]	11.0[4]	-8.4[4]	27.1[1]	6.6[5]	-17.1[5]	49.4[2]	42.5[1]	18.8[2]	1.7[2]	19.8[1]	16.3[1]	17,212	21,314
Heartland WI TF	—	—	—	—	—	—	—	—	10.8[5]	-6.6[3]	—	—	—	—
Henlopen Fund	—	—	—	—	—	—	—	—	29.9[1]	-2.7[4]	—	—	—	—
Hercules European	—	—	—	—	—	—	—	—	—	2.4[2]	—	—	—	—
Hercules Glob ST	—	—	—	—	—	—	—	—	—	-0.5[3]	—	—	—	—
Hercules Latin Amer	—	—	—	—	—	—	—	—	—	-18.1[5]	—	—	—	—
Hercules N Amer Gr&Inc	—	—	—	—	—	—	—	—	—	-13.0[5]	—	—	—	—
Hercules Pacific Bas	—	—	—	—	—	—	—	—	—	-1.8[3]	—	—	—	—
Hercules World Bond	—	—	—	—	—	—	—	—	—	-6.2[4]	—	—	—	—
Highmark Balncd	—	—	—	—	—	—	—	—	—	-1.2[2]	—	—	—	—
Highmark Bond	—	—	—	—	12.7[3]	8.2[2]	12.4[5]	8.2[2]	7.5[4]	-3.9[3]	3.8[4]	6.3[4]	11,177	13,587
Highmark Gov Bd	—	—	—	—	—	—	—	—	—	-1.9[1]	—	—	—	—
Highmark Growth	—	—	—	—	—	—	—	—	—	-4.9[5]	—	—	—	—
Highmark Inc Eqty	—	—	—	—	25.4[1]	-9.6[5]	30.5[1]	9.5[2]	12.8[4]	-0.6[2]	7.1[3]	7.7[3]	12,276	14,489
Highmark Inc & Gr	—	—	—	—	—	—	—	—	—	1.2[2]	—	—	—	—
Homestead ST Bond	—	—	—	—	—	—	—	6.3[2]	6.6[3]	0.1[3]	4.3[2]	—	11,340	—

See Chapter 3 for explanation of symbols

Arranged in alphabetical order

Total Net Assets $Million		NAV per share		1994 per share distributions		Yield %	Risk Analysis				% Distribution of Portfolio			Objective	No-Load Fund
December 31		December 31			Capital				Std.	Sharpe	12/31/94				
1993	1994	1993	1994	Income	gains	12/31/94	beta	R^2	Dev.	Ratio	Stocks	Bonds	Cash		
—	1.1	—	11.56	—	—	—	—	—	—	—	0	91	9	fix-inc	GE ST Gov
9.2	14.0	15.94	15.27	0.38	0.00	2.5	—	—	—	—	—	—	—	gr-inc	GE Strat Invest
3,170.3	2,741.4	11.64	10.52	0.73	0.00	7.0	0.22	0.21	1.11	B	0	96	4	fix-inc	GE S&S Prg: LT Inst
1,805.3	1,718.1	37.01	33.59	0.95	0.00	2.8	0.96	0.94	2.31	D	92	6	2	gr-inc	GE S&S Prg: Mutual
10.1	6.0	12.35	10.93	0.44	0.00	4.0	—	—	—	—	0	94	6	tax-free	GE TE Bond
9.9	16.7	16.26	15.53	0.28	0.00	1.8	—	—	—	—	98	0	2	gr-inc	GE US Equity
27.5	26.9	12.35	12.26	0.22	0.00	1.8	0.37	0.65	1.08	A	54	0	46	agg gr	General Securities
1.0	0.8	13.04	13.05	0.00	0.00	0.0	—	—	—	—	—	—	—	gr-inc	Gibraltar Eqty Gro
51.1	30.1	29.41	22.70	0.45	0.00	2.0	1.25	0.57	3.87	F	92	0	8	gr-inc	Gintel Erisa
136.1	88.3	15.11	12.46	0.04	0.12	0.3	1.17	0.46	4.08	F	87	0	13	growth	Gintel
3.9	3.2	16.57	14.45	0.39	0.23	2.7	0.48	—	—	—	—	—	—	gr-inc	GIT Equity Inc
9.4	7.5	10.01	9.30	0.35	0.00	3.8	0.28	0.23	1.37	F	0	80	20	fix-inc	GIT Gov Port
7.8	6.7	7.66	6.85	0.61	0.00	8.9	0.29	0.31	1.45	A	0	84	16	fix-inc	GIT Max Income
5.2	4.2	18.46	15.80	0.00	0.00	0.0	0.81	—	—	—	—	—	—	growth	GIT Select Gro
36.2	30.2	21.37	17.65	0.09	1.56	0.5	0.80	0.47	2.70	C	83	0	17	agg gr	GIT Special Gro SC
15.3	10.0	10.79	9.44	0.43	0.00	4.5	0.14	—	1.87	F	0	98	2	tax-free	GIT TF AZ
3.5	2.8	10.39	9.04	0.44	0.00	4.9	—	—	—	—	0	95	5	tax-free	GIT TF MD
13.9	10.5	10.75	9.41	0.43	0.00	4.6	0.14	—	1.78	F	0	96	4	tax-free	GIT TF MO
41.3	31.7	10.92	9.55	0.41	0.00	4.3	0.48	0.35	1.89	F	0	100	0	tax-free	GIT TF Nat
44.6	32.8	11.78	10.34	0.47	0.00	4.6	0.44	0.33	1.78	F	0	99	1	tax-free	GIT TF VA
4.0	3.9	14.88	9.89	0.05	1.43	0.5	—	—	—	—	—	—	—	global	GIT Wrldwd Growth
197.5	180.4	18.02	16.27	0.65	0.35	3.9	0.53	0.59	1.60	B	39	59	2	gr-inc	Golden Rainbow
8.3	12.9	10.40	9.62	0.46	0.00	4.8	—	—	—	—	0	97	3	tax-free	Gov St AL TF
21.9	26.0	21.70	19.83	1.29	0.00	6.5	0.19	0.17	1.05	C	0	97	3	fix-inc	Gov St Bond
26.7	29.3	23.46	22.45	0.35	0.00	1.6	0.85	0.81	2.19	F	97	0	3	growth	Gov St Equity
244.3	230.2	22.71	21.77	0.34	0.66	1.5	0.83	0.75	2.23	A	72	0	28	growth	Gradison Estab Value
83.9	82.9	18.38	17.43	0.11	0.44	0.6	0.80	0.53	2.55	B	72	0	28	agg gr	Gradison Oppty Value SC
—	2.0	—	9.84	—	—	—	—	—	—	—	65	0	35	agg gr	Grandich Contrarian
3.2	3.0	10.35	9.81	0.10	0.00	1.0	—	—	—	—	53	35	12	gr-inc	Green Cent Blncd
29.9	50.4	13.96	13.39	0.51	0.45	3.7	0.41	0.44	1.44	A	38	35	27	growth	Greenspring
340.3	160.0	10.05	9.49	0.59	0.00	6.3	0.09	0.12	0.58	B	0	82	18	fix-inc	GS ST Gov Agency
—	2.3	—	11.47	—	—	—	—	—	—	—	—	—	—	int'l	Guinness Flt China/HK
—	0.8	—	12.00	—	—	—	—	—	—	—	—	—	—	fix-inc	Guinness Flt Glob Gov
171.8	167.0	11.31	10.28	0.61	0.00	5.9	0.23	0.20	1.19	A	0	96	4	fix-inc	Harbor Bond
149.9	239.1	16.37	16.71	0.04	0.17	0.2	1.30	0.74	3.57	C	95	0	5	growth	Harbor Cap App
192.8	134.8	13.88	11.97	0.00	0.32	0.0	1.38	0.62	4.13	F	97	0	3	growth	Harbor Growth
20.6	69.0	11.20	10.27	0.06	0.00	0.6	—	—	—	—	98	0	2	int'l	Harbor Int'l Gro
2,537.9	2,953.1	24.32	24.45	0.25	0.94	1.0	1.05	0.38	4.04	A	96	0	4	int'l	Harbor Int'l
118.2	101.5	9.25	8.71	0.78	0.00	9.0	—	—	0.34	B	0	95	5	fix-inc	Harbor Short Dur
60.0	56.9	13.21	11.88	0.36	1.07	2.8	0.93	0.76	2.50	D	97	0	3	gr-inc	Harbor Value
—	44.1	—	9.93	—	—	—	—	—	—	—	91	3	6	growth	Haven Fund
9.0	12.5	9.56	8.23	0.45	0.00	5.5	—	—	—	—	0	98	2	tax-free	Heartland Nebraska TF
66.8	64.8	10.50	8.91	0.59	0.00	6.7	0.43	0.25	2.00	F	0	92	8	fix-inc	Heartland US Gov
5.8	9.9	10.45	9.53	0.41	0.00	4.3	—	—	—	—	76	22	2	gr-inc	Heartland Val & Inc
186.5	338.9	23.22	22.72	0.00	0.88	0.0	0.90	0.30	3.85	A	97	2	1	agg gr	Heartland Value SC
99.3	101.7	10.38	9.21	0.50	0.00	5.4	—	—	—	—	0	101	-1	tax-free	Heartland WI TF
5.2	9.0	12.51	11.98	0.00	0.19	0.0	—	—	—	—	97	1	2	growth	Henlopen Fund
5.2	18.4	10.03	10.18	0.02	0.00	0.2	—	—	—	—	—	—	—	int'l	Hercules European
0.7	1.1	9.99	9.81	0.14	0.00	1.4	—	—	—	—	0	90	10	fix-inc	Hercules Glob ST
8.8	28.3	11.05	9.05	0.00	0.00	0.0	—	—	—	—	—	—	—	int'l	Hercules Latin Amer
6.8	15.9	10.26	8.88	0.04	0.00	0.5	—	—	—	—	—	—	—	global	Hercules N Amer Gr&Inc
14.9	39.4	10.23	9.94	0.00	0.00	0.0	—	—	—	—	—	—	—	int'l	Hercules Pacific Bas
11.9	26.4	10.05	9.31	0.11	0.00	1.2	—	—	—	—	0	92	8	fix-inc	Hercules World Bond
15.2	23.8	10.04	9.54	0.38	0.00	3.9	—	—	—	—	—	—	—	income	Highmark Balncd
76.2	57.3	10.76	9.71	0.63	0.00	6.5	0.22	0.17	1.23	C	0	97	3	fix-inc	Highmark Bond
5.1	4.6	9.87	9.11	0.58	0.00	6.4	—	—	—	—	0	95	5	fix-inc	Highmark Gov Bd
2.1	16.8	10.45	9.68	0.11	0.00	1.2	—	—	—	—	—	—	—	growth	Highmark Growth
210.1	202.7	12.16	11.24	0.41	0.00	3.6	0.74	0.73	2.02	C	95	0	5	income	Highmark Inc Eqty
5.8	5.0	10.03	9.90	0.24	0.00	2.5	—	—	—	—	—	—	—	gr-inc	Highmark Inc & Gr
37.0	52.1	5.19	4.95	0.24	0.00	4.9	0.09	0.10	0.64	B	0	81	19	fix-inc	Homestead ST Bond

No-Load Fund	Total return percent with quintile ranks by objective										Annualized		What $10,000 grew to after	
	1985	1986	1987	1988	1989	1990	1991	1992	1993	1994	3 yrs.	5 yrs.	3 yrs.	5 yrs.
Homestead Value	—	—	—	—	—	—	17.2^5	11.7^2	18.8^1	2.5^1	10.8^1	—	13,602	—
Hough FL ST	—	—	—	—	—	—	—	—	—	1.2^1	—	—	—	—
Household Eqty Inc	—	—	—	—	—	—	—	—	—	-5.5^5	—	—	—	—
Household Fix Inc	—	—	—	—	—	—	—	—	—	-5.6^4	—	—	—	—
Household Gro Eqty	—	—	—	—	—	—	—	—	—	-4.5^4	—	—	—	—
Household ST Inc	—	—	—	—	—	—	—	—	—	-1.8^4	—	—	—	—
Household TE Inc	—	—	—	—	—	—	—	—	—	-3.1^1	—	—	—	—
Htchks & Wly Blncd	—	—	3.9^1	14.6^3	17.8^4	-0.5^3	20.5^5	9.4^3	12.5^4	0.8^2	7.5^2	8.3^3	12,411	14,885
Htchks & Wly Eq Inc	—	—	—	21.1^2	23.7^2	-18.1^5	34.6^1	14.0^1	15.8^2	-3.5^4	8.4^2	7.0^3	12,729	14,040
Htchks & Wly Int'l	—	—	—	—	—	—	20.3^1	-2.7^2	45.8^2	-3.0^4	11.2^2	—	13,764	—
Htchks & Wly Low Dur	—	—	—	—	—	—	—	—	—	5.1^1	—	—	—	—
Htchks & Wly Sm Cap SC	—	—	-1.7^3	8.9^4	20.5^4	-9.0^3	48.2^3	13.7^2	12.5^4	1.1^2	9.0^2	11.8^2	12,940	17,447
Htchks & Wly ST Invest	—	—	—	—	—	—	—	—	—	4.5^1	—	—	—	—
Htchks & Wly Tot Ret	—	—	—	—	—	—	—	—	—	—	—	—	—	—
IAI Balanced	—	—	—	—	—	—	—	—	5.0^5	-1.4^3	—	—	—	—
IAI Bond	20.1^4	12.1^4	2.1^2	6.4^5	15.9^1	7.0^3	17.3^3	6.8^3	12.3^3	-4.9^3	4.5^3	7.4^3	11,409	14,314
IAI Emg Growth SC	—	—	—	—	—	—	—	22.5^1	14.8^3	0.2^2	12.1^1	—	14,078	—
IAI Gov Bond	—	—	—	—	—	—	—	5.7^3	8.5^1	-2.3^4	3.9^3	—	11,209	—
IAI Gro & Inc	23.5^4	11.8^5	15.5^1	8.5^5	29.8^1	-6.7^4	26.6^3	4.0^5	10.0^3	-4.8^5	2.9^5	5.2^5	10,891	12,869
IAI Growth	—	—	—	—	—	—	—	—	—	0.7^2	—	—	—	—
IAI International	—	—	—	18.0^2	18.3^4	-13.1^4	16.6^2	-6.2^3	39.5^3	0.5^3	9.6^2	5.9^2	13,147	13,321
IAI MidCap	—	—	—	—	—	—	—	—	22.9^1	5.7^1	—	—	—	—
IAI MN TF	—	—	—	—	—	—	—	—	13.6^1	-8.4^4	—	—	—	—
IAI Regional	38.6^1	23.3^1	5.1^2	18.8^3	31.3^1	-0.3^2	35.3^2	3.5^5	9.0^4	0.7^2	4.3^4	8.9^3	11,357	15,319
IAI Reserve	—	5.9^1	6.8^2	8.8^5	8.4^4	8.0^5	3.3^5	3.3^5	2.8^1	—	3.1^4	5.1^5	10,962	12,823
IAI Value	12.8^5	1.4^5	14.1^1	24.3^1	22.6^3	-11.5^5	19.7^5	11.9^2	22.1^1	-9.1^5	7.5^3	5.7^5	12,419	13,162
Invesco Balanced	—	—	—	—	—	—	—	—	—	9.5^1	—	—	—	—
Invesco Dynamics	29.2^3	6.2^5	3.9^2	9.1^4	22.7^3	-6.4^3	66.9^1	13.2^2	19.1^2	-2.0^3	9.8^2	15.6^1	13,219	20,657
Invesco Emg Gro SC	—	—	—	—	—	—	—	25.7^1	23.4^1	-3.7^4	14.3^1	—	14,935	—
Invesco Europe Sm Co	—	—	—	—	—	—	—	—	—	—	—	—	—	—
Invesco Europe	—	—	-4.5^5	10.6^4	24.2^2	0.7^1	7.9^4	-7.6^3	24.6^5	-3.1^4	3.7^5	3.9^3	11,158	12,128
Invesco Gov Sec	—	14.3^3	-5.1^5	6.3^5	12.4^3	7.3^3	15.5^3	5.8^5	10.2^4	-7.2^4	2.7^5	6.0^5	10,817	13,403
Invesco Growth	28.4^3	8.2^5	-0.1^4	6.0^5	31.2^1	-1.2^2	42.2^1	2.9^5	18.0^2	-8.8^5	3.5^4	9.2^3	11,071	15,543
Invesco High Yld	26.5^1	14.5^3	3.5^1	13.5^1	3.7^5	-4.6^5	23.5^1	14.6^1	15.8^2	-5.1^3	8.0^1	8.2^2	12,589	14,842
Invesco Indust Inc	30.8^2	14.4^4	4.9^1	15.3^3	31.9^1	0.9^1	46.3^1	0.9^5	16.7^2	-3.9^4	4.2^4	10.8^1	11,322	16,713
Invesco Inter Gov	—	—	0.0^5	6.0^3	10.2^3	9.3^2	14.2^2	6.0^3	8.8^1	-1.7^4	4.3^1	7.2^1	11,346	14,159
Invesco Int'l Gro	—	—	—	—	—	-14.8^4	7.2^4	-12.5^4	27.9^4	0.6^3	4.0^5	0.6^5	11,250	10,281
Invesco Multi-Asst	—	—	—	—	—	—	—	—	—	-2.0^3	—	—	—	—
Invesco Pacific Bas	27.3^5	71.9^1	9.8^3	23.2^1	20.2^3	-24.5^5	13.2^2	-13.6^5	42.6^2	4.7^2	8.9^2	2.0^4	12,904	11,036
Invesco Select Inc	22.7^2	18.7^2	-1.6^4	10.4^2	8.2^4	4.9^4	18.7^2	10.4^1	11.4^3	-1.2^1	6.7^1	8.6^1	12,148	15,120
Invesco Small Co SC	—	—	—	—	—	—	—	—	—	-1.0^3	—	—	—	—
Invesco ST Bond	—	—	—	—	—	—	—	—	—	-0.6^3	—	—	—	—
Invesco Strat Enrgy	13.6^5	7.2^4	5.0^2	14.9^3	43.5^1	-16.5^4	-3.5^5	-13.2^5	16.7^4	-7.3^4	-2.1^5	-5.4^5	9,393	7,569
Invesco Strat Envrn	—	—	—	—	—	—	16.8^5	-18.7^5	-4.7^5	-11.4^5	-11.8^5	—	6,866	—
Invesco Strat Fncl	—	—	-11.2^4	17.1^3	36.9^2	-7.2^3	74.0^1	26.8^1	18.5^3	-5.9^4	12.2^3	18.0^1	14,138	22,840
Invesco Strat Gold	-4.5^2	38.7^2	16.0^5	-20.1^4	21.3^3	-23.2^4	-7.0^4	-8.2^2	72.6^4	-27.9^5	4.6^5	-4.0^5	11,432	8,169
Invesco Strat Health	31.5^3	29.5^1	7.0^1	16.1^3	59.5^1	25.8^1	91.8^1	-13.7^5	-8.4^5	0.9^3	-7.3^5	14.0^3	7,975	19,237
Invesco Strat Leisure	32.2^2	18.8^2	0.7^2	28.6^1	38.3^2	-11.0^4	52.7^2	23.4^1	35.7^1	-5.0^3	16.8^2	16.7^2	15,915	21,632
Invesco Strat Tech	27.3^4	21.9^2	-5.3^3	14.2^4	21.4^3	8.6^1	76.9^1	18.8^2	15.0^4	5.3^2	12.9^3	22.6^1	14,386	27,637
Invesco Strat Util	—	—	-4.9^3	14.2^4	31.5^3	-10.0^3	28.0^4	10.8^3	21.2^3	-9.9^5	6.6^4	6.9^4	12,097	13,938
Invesco TF Inter	—	—	—	—	—	—	—	—	—	-4.4^4	—	—	—	—
Invesco TF Long	22.9^1	22.2^1	-4.0^5	15.1^1	11.7^1	7.1^2	12.5^2	8.8^3	12.1^4	-7.5^4	4.1^4	6.3^3	11,283	13,599
Invesco Total Ret	—	—	—	14.9^3	17.9^4	-0.4^3	24.9^3	9.9^2	12.4^4	2.5^1	8.2^2	9.5^2	12,654	15,754
Invesco Value Eqty	—	—	5.3^2	25.7^1	21.3^3	-5.8^3	35.9^2	5.0^4	10.4^3	4.0^1	6.4^3	9.1^3	12,060	15,434
Invesco Wrld Cap Gds	—	—	—	—	—	—	—	—	—	—	—	—	—	—
Invesco Wrld Comm	—	—	—	—	—	—	—	—	—	—	—	—	—	—
Janus Balanced	—	—	—	—	—	—	—	—	10.6^3	0.0^2	—	—	—	—
Janus Enterprise	—	—	—	—	—	—	—	—	15.7^2	8.9^1	—	—	—	—
Janus Federal TE	—	—	—	—	—	—	—	—	—	-7.8^4	—	—	—	—
Janus Flex Inc	—	—	—	10.8^1	4.1^5	-4.6^5	26.0^1	12.0^1	15.7^1	-2.9^3	7.9^1	8.6^1	12,575	15,115

See Chapter 3 for explanation of symbols

Arranged in alphabetical order

Total Net Assets $Million		NAV per share		1994 per share distributions		Yield %	Risk Analysis				% Distribution of Portfolio			Objective	No-Load Fund
December 31 1993	1994	December 31 1993	1994	Income	Capital gains	12/31/94	beta	R²	Std. Dev.	Sharpe Ratio	12/31/94 Stocks	Bonds	Cash		
52.8	90.1	14.54	14.50	0.29	0.11	2.0	0.81	0.74	2.19	A	85	0	15	gr-inc	Homestead Value
5.0	9.6	10.04	9.77	0.40	0.00	4.1	—	—	—	—	0	71	29	tax-free	Hough FL ST
5.4	0.2	10.55	9.75	0.23	0.00	2.3	—	—	—	—	—	—	—	gr-inc	Household Eqty Inc
5.2	0.1	9.99	8.95	0.48	0.00	5.4	—	—	—	—	0	96	4	fix-inc	Household Fix Inc
5.3	0.1	10.36	9.70	0.03	0.00	0.3	—	—	—	—	—	—	—	growth	Household Gro Eqty
5.2	0.1	9.98	9.43	0.37	0.00	4.0	—	—	—	—	0	90	10	fix-inc	Household ST Inc
10.4	5.3	10.20	9.57	0.32	0.00	3.3	—	—	—	—	0	92	8	tax-free	Household TE Inc
33.9	34.1	16.44	15.16	0.81	0.59	5.1	0.50	0.65	1.43	A	51	48	1	income	Htchks & Wly Blncd
82.9	106.7	15.97	14.61	0.44	0.36	2.9	0.87	0.65	2.53	B	95	0	5	gr-inc	Htchks & Wly Eq Inc
10.3	27.7	17.88	16.58	0.31	0.45	1.8	0.76	0.23	3.75	A	96	0	4	int'l	Htchks & Wly Int'l
11.0	70.8	10.04	9.84	0.70	0.00	7.1	—	—	—	—	0	80	20	fix-inc	Htchks & Wly Low Dur
11.6	14.8	20.02	19.44	0.00	0.78	0.0	0.93	0.56	2.92	B	100	0	0	agg gr	Htchks & Wly Sm Cap SC
10.8	13.6	10.25	10.06	0.64	0.00	6.3	—	—	—	—	0	55	45	fix-inc	Htchks & Wly ST Invest
—	2.8	—	12.00	—	—	—	—	—	—	—	0	99	1	fix-inc	Htchks & Wly Tot Ret
64.7	42.1	10.83	9.95	0.32	0.38	3.3	—	—	—	—	51	42	7	income	IAI Balanced
110.0	80.4	9.76	8.66	0.49	0.13	5.7	0.36	0.25	1.67	D	0	98	2	fix-inc	IAI Bond
227.3	317.2	15.74	14.90	0.00	0.72	0.0	1.43	0.42	5.22	C	86	3	11	agg gr	IAI Emg Growth SC
42.2	39.1	10.33	9.60	0.47	0.03	4.9	0.17	0.14	1.04	D	0	91	9	fix-inc	IAI Gov Bond
130.7	104.6	14.51	13.06	0.10	0.65	0.8	0.96	0.85	2.43	F	82	15	3	gr-inc	IAI Gro & Inc
11.0	23.2	10.09	10.13	0.03	0.00	0.3	—	—	—	—	93	2	5	growth	IAI Growth
121.8	149.1	13.61	12.79	0.00	0.88	0.0	0.76	0.23	3.70	B	93	3	4	int'l	IAI International
43.9	84.8	13.93	14.05	0.00	0.63	0.0	—	—	—	—	90	2	8	growth	IAI MidCap
8.7	7.0	11.17	9.64	0.57	0.05	5.8	—	—	—	—	0	90	10	tax-free	IAI MN TF
650.8	514.0	21.45	20.15	0.20	1.19	1.0	0.91	0.79	2.39	D	80	0	20	growth	IAI Regional
91.7	78.1	10.04	9.85	0.46	0.00	4.7	0.03	0.19	0.17	A	0	51	49	fix-inc	IAI Reserve
32.2	34.6	12.11	10.18	0.03	0.84	0.2	0.88	0.54	2.80	C	79	10	11	growth	IAI Value
0.6	12.5	10.06	10.54	0.22	0.25	2.0	—	—	—	—	53	37	10	income	Invesco Balanced
319.2	338.9	12.83	10.24	0.00	2.30	0.0	1.38	0.63	4.09	C	81	2	17	agg gr	Invesco Dynamics
223.0	179.3	12.11	9.17	0.00	2.49	0.0	1.15	0.38	4.36	B	75	0	25	agg gr	Invesco Emg Gro SC
—	—	—	—	—	—	—	—	—	—	—	—	—	—	int'l	Invesco Europe Sm Co
307.2	245.6	12.83	12.29	0.16	0.00	1.3	0.88	0.28	3.92	F	94	3	3	int'l	Invesco Europe
34.5	31.4	7.79	6.81	0.43	0.00	6.3	0.36	0.25	1.68	F	0	96	4	fix-inc	Invesco Gov Sec
510.2	444.5	5.54	4.52	0.03	0.50	0.7	1.15	0.80	3.01	D	89	0	11	growth	Invesco Growth
306.1	210.8	7.43	6.38	0.65	0.03	10.1	0.28	0.22	1.39	A	0	90	10	fix-inc	Invesco High Yld
3,905.8	3,695.5	11.93	10.52	0.41	0.54	3.7	0.79	0.74	2.14	D	68	28	4	gr-inc	Invesco Indust Inc
40.8	31.5	12.72	11.81	0.70	0.00	5.9	0.08	0.03	1.12	F	0	97	3	fix-inc	Invesco Inter Gov
113.1	108.7	16.01	15.17	0.08	0.86	0.5	0.82	0.23	3.97	F	96	3	1	int'l	Invesco Int'l Gro
0.4	6.3	9.92	9.55	0.17	0.00	1.8	—	—	—	—	71	22	7	income	Invesco Multi-Asst
274.8	252.0	15.27	14.15	0.04	1.79	0.3	0.84	0.19	4.53	C	95	0	5	int'l	Invesco Pacific Bas
157.5	136.7	6.57	6.03	0.46	0.00	7.6	0.21	0.24	0.98	A	0	92	8	fix-inc	Invesco Select Inc
7.6	16.3	10.14	9.96	0.08	0.00	0.8	—	—	—	—	80	0	20	agg gr	Invesco Small Co SC
7.1	8.6	9.90	9.29	0.55	0.00	5.9	—	—	—	—	0	85	15	fix-inc	Invesco ST Bond
49.2	46.9	10.37	9.57	0.05	0.00	0.6	0.90	0.22	4.55	F	86	4	10	sector	Invesco Strat Enrgy
59.6	22.9	7.24	6.36	0.06	0.00	0.9	1.09	0.32	4.53	F	70	1	29	sector	Invesco Strat Envrn
339.2	236.4	15.91	14.64	0.35	0.00	2.4	1.08	0.53	3.47	B	68	0	32	sector	Invesco Strat Fncl
316.0	222.0	6.75	4.87	0.00	0.00	0.0	0.38	0.01	8.14	F	88	7	5	prec met	Invesco Strat Gold
566.2	488.5	35.14	35.47	0.00	0.00	0.0	1.14	0.25	5.34	F	89	5	6	sector	Invesco Strat Health
304.5	262.8	23.28	21.21	0.00	0.91	0.0	1.01	0.45	3.54	A	79	0	21	sector	Invesco Strat Leisure
251.6	310.1	23.59	24.04	0.00	0.79	0.0	1.53	0.51	5.09	C	91	3	6	sector	Invesco Strat Tech
174.5	122.5	10.68	9.32	0.32	0.00	3.4	0.78	0.56	2.41	C	74	20	6	sector	Invesco Strat Util
0.7	4.3	10.10	9.27	0.39	0.00	4.2	—	—	—	—	0	88	12	tax-free	Invesco TF Inter
337.4	254.1	16.54	14.52	0.81	0.00	5.6	0.44	0.33	1.77	B	0	82	18	tax-free	Invesco TF Long
240.6	293.7	18.26	18.10	0.57	0.05	3.1	0.69	0.84	1.75	B	55	45	0	income	Invesco Total Ret
108.8	108.1	17.41	16.63	0.31	1.17	1.7	0.92	0.84	2.33	C	92	0	8	growth	Invesco Value Eqty
—	3.5	—	9.06	—	—	—	—	—	—	—	97	2	1	sector	Invesco Wrld Cap Gds
—	15.8	—	10.40	—	—	—	—	—	—	—	43	0	57	global	Invesco Wrld Comm
77.4	93.4	12.19	11.63	0.56	0.00	4.8	—	—	—	—	28	23	49	gr-inc	Janus Balanced
258.6	354.1	21.92	22.98	0.52	0.38	2.2	—	—	—	—	71	0	29	growth	Janus Enterprise
29.2	24.2	7.31	6.39	0.36	0.00	5.6	—	—	—	—	0	93	7	tax-free	Janus Federal TE
469.6	353.9	9.74	8.75	0.72	0.00	8.2	0.25	0.23	1.17	A	0	80	20	fix-inc	Janus Flex Inc

Stock and bond funds — comprehensive summary *continued*

Arranged in alphabetical order

No-Load Fund	1985	1986	1987	1988	1989	1990	1991	1992	1993	1994	Annualized 3 yrs.	5 yrs.	What $10,000 grew to after 3 yrs.	5 yrs.
Janus Fund	24.6[4]	11.2[4]	3.9[3]	16.6[3]	46.3[1]	-0.7[2]	42.8[1]	6.9[4]	10.9[3]	-1.1[3]	5.4[4]	10.7[2]	11,722	16,615
Janus Growth & Inc	—	—	—	—	—	—	—	5.4[4]	6.7[4]	-4.9[5]	2.3[5]	—	10,695	—
Janus Inter Gov	—	—	—	—	—	—	—	4.9[4]	2.5[5]	-2.4[5]	1.6[5]	—	10,499	—
Janus Mercury	—	—	—	—	—	—	—	—	—	15.9[1]	—	—	—	—
Janus Overseas	—	—	—	—	—	—	—	—	—	—	—	—	—	—
Janus ST Bond	—	—	—	—	—	—	—	—	6.2[3]	0.4[2]	—	—	—	—
Janus Twenty.‡	23.4[4]	12.0[3]	-11.7[5]	19.1[3]	50.8[1]	0.6[1]	69.2[1]	2.0[5]	3.4[5]	-6.7[4]	-0.5[5]	10.9[2]	9,838	16,745
Janus Venture SC‡	31.5[2]	20.3[2]	5.2[2]	19.6[2]	38.7[1]	-0.4[2]	47.8[1]	7.4[3]	9.1[4]	5.5[1]	7.3[3]	12.7[1]	12,360	18,197
Janus Worldwide	—	—	—	—	—	—	—	9.0[1]	28.4[2]	3.6[1]	13.2[1]	—	14,503	—
Japan (Scudder)	38.9[4]	77.5[1]	32.9[1]	19.5[2]	11.4[5]	-16.3[5]	3.1[5]	-16.7[5]	23.6[5]	10.0[1]	4.2[5]	-0.5[5]	11,325	9,773
Jensen Portfolio	—	—	—	—	—	—	—	—	-7.3[5]	-1.8[4]	—	—	—	—
Jurika & Vyls Blncd	—	—	—	—	—	—	—	—	17.1[1]	-2.2[3]	—	—	—	—
Jurika & Vyls Mini Cap SC	—	—	—	—	—	—	—	—	—	—	—	—	—	—
Jurika & Vyls Val & Gro	—	—	—	—	—	—	—	—	—	—	—	—	—	—
Kaufmann SC	—	—	-37.2[5]	58.6[1]	46.9[1]	-6.1[2]	79.6[1]	11.3[3]	18.2[2]	9.0[1]	12.8[1]	19.3[1]	14,338	24,165
KPM Equity	—	—	—	—	—	—	—	—	—	—	—	—	—	—
KPM Fixed Inc	—	—	—	—	—	—	—	—	—	—	—	—	—	—
Leeb Prsnl Finance	—	—	—	—	—	—	—	6.2[4]	1.6[5]	-3.1[4]	1.5[5]	—	10,450	—
Legg Msn Amer Lead	—	—	—	—	—	—	—	—	—	-4.2[4]	—	—	—	—
Legg Msn Glob Gov	—	—	—	—	—	—	—	—	—	-1.6[1]	—	—	—	—
Legg Msn Gov Inter	—	—	—	6.3[5]	12.8[3]	9.1[2]	14.4[4]	6.2[4]	6.9[4]	-1.7[2]	3.7[4]	6.8[4]	11,155	13,912
Legg Msn High Yld	—	—	—	—	—	—	—	—	—	—	—	—	—	—
Legg Msn Invest Grd	—	—	—	7.4[3]	13.0[2]	5.8[5]	16.0[2]	6.8[3]	11.3[2]	-4.6[5]	4.3[3]	6.8[4]	11,342	13,920
Legg Msn Spec Invest SC	—	7.4[4]	-10.4[5]	19.7[3]	32.1[2]	0.5[1]	39.5[4]	15.3[2]	24.1[1]	-13.1[5]	7.6[3]	11.8[2]	12,444	17,452
Legg Msn Total Ret	—	1.4[5]	-7.8[5]	21.8[2]	16.3[5]	-16.8[5]	41.3[2]	14.3[2]	14.1[2]	-7.2[5]	6.6[3]	7.3[4]	12,103	14,226
Legg Msn Value	31.9[2]	9.4[5]	-7.3[5]	25.8[1]	20.2[4]	-16.9[5]	35.1[2]	11.4[2]	11.3[3]	1.3[2]	7.9[2]	7.1[4]	12,555	14,091
Lepercq-Istel	20.0[5]	8.1[5]	1.7[3]	7.1[5]	21.7[3]	-6.6[4]	17.2[5]	5.4[4]	13.5[2]	-5.0[5]	4.4[4]	4.5[5]	11,368	12,448
Lexington Convert.	—	—	—	—	7.2[5]	-3.4[3]	45.0[1]	11.2[2]	6.5[5]	1.3[1]	6.2[3]	10.9[1]	11,992	16,802
Lexington Corp Ldrs	35.8[1]	24.7[1]	1.9[3]	19.2[2]	30.3[1]	-4.2[3]	19.4[4]	9.6[2]	17.6[2]	-0.8[3]	8.6[2]	7.9[3]	12,791	14,628
Lexington Global	—	—	—	16.3[1]	25.1[1]	-16.8[5]	15.5[4]	-3.5[5]	31.9[1]	1.8[1]	9.0[2]	4.5[3]	12,955	12,460
Lexington GNMA	18.3[4]	11.9[3]	1.6[4]	6.8[4]	15.5[1]	9.2[2]	15.0[3]	5.2[5]	8.1[4]	-2.1[2]	3.6[4]	6.9[3]	11,131	13,975
Lexington Goldfund	13.0[1]	32.7[5]	46.3[1]	-15.0[2]	23.8[2]	-20.8[2]	-6.2[4]	-20.5[4]	87.0[3]	-7.3[2]	11.3[3]	0.5[4]	13,778	10,242
Lexington Gro & Inc	26.3[3]	20.2[1]	0.1[4]	9.4[5]	27.5[2]	-10.3[5]	24.8[3]	12.4[2]	13.2[2]	-3.1[4]	7.2[2]	6.7[4]	12,326	13,802
Lexington Int'l	—	—	—	—	—	—	—	—	—	5.9[1]	—	—	—	—
Lexington S-I Gov	—	—	—	—	—	—	—	—	—	-0.2[3]	—	—	—	—
Lexington TE Bond	—	—	0.2[2]	10.3[4]	7.4[5]	6.5[3]	9.4[5]	6.5[5]	10.9[5]	-6.5[3]	3.4[5]	5.2[5]	11,042	12,868
Lexington World Emg	26.7[5]	20.6[5]	-0.5[5]	10.5[4]	28.1[1]	-14.5[4]	24.2[1]	3.8[1]	63.4[1]	-13.8[5]	13.5[1]	9.2[1]	14,611	15,518
Lex-Ramrz Glob Inc	—	—	—	—	—	—	—	—	—	—	—	—	—	—
Lindner Bulwark	—	—	—	—	—	—	—	—	—	—	—	—	—	—
Lindner Dividend	17.0[5]	20.7[1]	-4.1[4]	24.1[1]	11.8[5]	-6.5[4]	27.3[2]	21.1[1]	14.9[2]	-3.3[4]	10.4[1]	9.9[1]	13,452	16,018
Lindner Fund	19.4[5]	14.0[3]	8.8[1]	20.4[2]	21.2[4]	-11.3[5]	23.4[4]	12.8[2]	19.8[2]	-0.7[3]	10.3[2]	8.0[4]	13,420	14,687
Lindner Int'l	—	—	—	—	—	—	—	—	—	—	—	—	—	—
Lindner Small Cap SC	—	—	—	—	—	—	—	—	—	—	—	—	—	—
Lindner Utility	—	—	—	—	—	—	—	—	—	-1.0[2]	—	—	—	—
LKCM Sm Cap SC	—	—	—	—	—	—	—	—	—	—	—	—	—	—
LMH Fund	22.7[5]	14.0[4]	-6.2[5]	18.0[3]	12.1[5]	-18.6[5]	18.4[5]	8.6[3]	7.2[4]	2.6[1]	6.1[3]	2.9[5]	11,938	11,511
Longleaf Partners	—	—	—	35.3[1]	23.3[3]	-16.4[5]	39.1[2]	20.5[1]	22.2[1]	9.0[1]	17.1[1]	13.3[1]	16,046	18,673
Longleaf Small Cap SC	—	—	—	—	32.9[2]	-30.1[5]	26.3[5]	6.8[4]	19.8[2]	3.7[1]	9.9[2]	3.2[5]	13,278	11,727
Loomis Syls Bond	—	—	—	—	—	—	—	14.3[1]	22.2[1]	-4.1[3]	10.2[1]	—	13,392	—
Loomis Syls Glob Bd	—	—	—	—	—	—	—	0.8[5]	14.6[2]	-8.7[5]	1.8[5]	—	10,546	—
Loomis Syls Gro & Inc	—	—	—	—	—	—	—	14.1[1]	11.9[3]	-0.9[3]	8.2[2]	—	12,653	—
Loomis Syls Growth	—	—	—	—	—	—	—	3.8[5]	9.2[4]	-3.7[4]	3.0[4]	—	10,926	—
Loomis Syls Int'l Eq	—	—	—	—	—	—	—	-5.1[3]	38.5[3]	-1.8[3]	8.9[2]	—	12,915	—
Loomis Syls Muni	—	—	—	—	—	—	—	9.4[1]	11.6[5]	-5.4[2]	4.9[2]	—	11,549	—
Loomis Syls Sm Cap SC	—	—	—	—	—	—	—	13.1[3]	24.7[1]	-8.3[5]	9.0[2]	—	12,932	—
Loomis Syls ST Bd	—	—	—	—	—	—	—	—	6.9[2]	1.8[1]	—	—	—	—
Loomis Syls US Gov	—	—	—	—	—	—	—	8.8[2]	15.8[2]	-6.3[4]	5.7[2]	—	11,797	—
Mairs & Power Gro	36.2[1]	5.4[5]	-2.6[4]	10.2[4]	28.1[2]	3.6[1]	42.0[1]	7.8[3]	12.8[3]	5.6[1]	8.7[2]	13.6[1]	12,848	18,905
Mairs & Power Inc	27.1[3]	15.3[4]	1.4[2]	13.9[3]	17.7[4]	1.4[2]	25.8[2]	5.9[4]	10.8[4]	-2.1[3]	4.8[4]	8.0[3]	11,494	14,662
Managers Balanced	—	—	—	18.4[2]	24.0[2]	-5.2[3]	29.6[2]	4.4[5]	6.6[5]	-3.1[4]	2.6[5]	5.8[5]	10,793	13,271

See Chapter 3 for explanation of symbols

Total Net Assets $Million December 31 1993	1994	NAV per share December 31 1993	1994	1994 per share distributions Income	Capital gains	Yield % 12/31/94	Risk Analysis beta	R²	Std. Dev.	Sharpe Ratio	% Distribution of Portfolio 12/31/94 Stocks	Bonds	Cash	Objective	No-Load Fund
9,199.6	9,400.6	19.39	18.78	0.01	0.39	0.0	0.87	0.85	2.18	C	58	2	40	growth	Janus Fund
513.8	456.5	14.69	13.88	0.09	0.00	0.7	1.07	0.75	2.89	F	62	19	19	gr-inc	Janus Growth & Inc
57.6	35.0	5.13	4.74	0.27	0.00	5.7	0.15	0.20	0.76	F	0	99	1	fix-inc	Janus Inter Gov
126.9	690.1	11.98	13.61	0.16	0.11	1.2	—	—	—	—	61	0	39	agg gr	Janus Mercury
—	65.4	—	10.05	—	—	—	—	—	—	—	53	0	47	int'l	Janus Overseas
53.5	45.5	3.00	2.83	0.18	0.00	6.4	—	—	—	—	0	94	6	fix-inc	Janus ST Bond
3,515.9	2,504.3	24.42	22.71	0.07	0.00	0.3	1.23	0.76	3.30	F	79	7	14	agg gr	Janus Twenty
1,778.7	1,496.1	48.88	48.68	0.03	2.84	0.1	0.93	0.70	2.59	C	69	4	27	growth	Janus Venture SC
935.2	1,542.6	25.03	24.39	0.54	1.01	2.1	0.96	0.56	3.00	A	55	3	42	global	Janus Worldwide
471.1	587.0	10.33	10.51	0.00	0.85	0.0	0.29	0.01	6.36	F	100	0	0	int'l	Japan (Scudder)
9.1	9.1	9.27	8.96	0.05	0.00	0.6	—	—	—	—	—	—	—	gr-inc	Jensen Portfolio
24.3	32.2	13.00	11.98	0.26	0.00	2.2	—	—	—	—	61	36	3	income	Jurika & Vyls Blncd
—	2.9	—	10.63	—	—	—	—	—	—	—	62	0	38	agg gr	Jurika & Vyls Mini Cap SC
—	1.6	—	10.54	—	—	—	—	—	—	—	65	0	35	gr-inc	Jurika & Vyls Val & Gro
965.4	1,590.6	3.45	3.76	0.00	0.00	0.0	1.37	0.52	4.49	B	94	3	3	agg gr	Kaufmann SC
—	8.9	—	10.11	—	—	—	—	—	—	—	—	—	—	growth	KPM Equity
—	2.4	—	9.70	—	—	—	—	—	—	—	0	93	7	fix-inc	KPM Fixed Inc
54.8	38.5	10.73	10.04	0.23	0.13	2.3	0.41	0.64	1.18	F	52	32	16	gr-inc	Leeb Prsnl Finance
51.9	56.1	10.06	9.53	0.11	0.00	1.2	—	—	—	—	88	0	12	growth	Legg Msn Amer Lead
161.1	145.1	10.27	9.52	0.59	0.00	6.2	—	—	—	—	0	88	12	fix-inc	Legg Msn Glob Gov
299.5	235.0	10.43	9.72	0.53	0.00	5.5	0.12	0.11	0.82	B	0	84	16	fix-inc	Legg Msn Gov Inter
—	53.4	—	13.56	—	—	—	—	—	—	—	0	8	92	fix-inc	Legg Msn High Yld
68.8	66.0	10.40	9.27	0.62	0.04	6.7	0.27	0.22	1.33	D	0	97	3	fix-inc	Legg Msn Invest Grd
510.0	605.7	22.14	19.03	0.00	0.23	0.0	1.34	0.62	3.99	C	90	2	8	agg gr	Legg Msn Spec Invest SC
175.1	193.3	14.00	12.15	0.29	0.60	2.4	0.94	0.71	2.59	C	80	12	8	growth	Legg Msn Total Ret
914.4	967.3	18.87	19.04	0.03	0.04	0.2	1.24	0.87	3.09	C	94	0	6	growth	Legg Msn Value
16.6	18.5	14.84	13.17	0.21	0.71	1.5	0.72	0.61	2.13	D	70	16	14	gr-inc	Lepercq-Istel
8.3	8.0	14.10	11.84	0.07	2.36	0.5	0.96	0.44	3.36	F	16	39	45	income	Lexington Convert
142.8	156.3	12.78	10.51	0.28	1.83	2.7	0.97	0.71	2.70	B	98	0	2	gr-inc	Lexington Corp Ldrs
87.0	67.4	13.51	11.17	0.00	2.59	0.0	0.82	0.36	3.19	C	90	0	10	global	Lexington Global
150.0	132.4	8.32	7.60	0.55	0.00	7.2	0.21	0.19	1.14	D	0	83	17	fix-inc	Lexington GNMA
159.5	158.8	6.90	6.37	0.03	0.00	0.4	0.37	0.01	7.71	C	92	5	3	prec met	Lexington Goldfund
134.5	124.3	16.16	14.36	0.16	1.13	1.1	0.97	0.80	2.51	C	91	0	9	gr-inc	Lexington Gro & Inc
0.1	17.8	10.00	10.37	0.00	0.22	0.0	—	—	—	—	88	0	12	int'l	Lexington Int'l
7.7	5.8	9.98	9.58	0.38	0.00	4.0	—	—	—	—	0	93	7	fix-inc	Lexington S-I Gov
14.6	10.6	10.95	9.80	0.45	0.00	4.5	—	—	—	—	—	—	—	tax-free	Lexington TE Bond
227.5	288.5	13.96	11.47	0.00	0.56	0.0	1.11	0.29	4.92	B	72	0	28	int'l	Lexington World Emg
—	—	—	—	—	—	—	—	—	—	—	—	—	—	fix-inc	Lex-Ramrz Glob Inc.
—	83.1	—	7.45	—	—	—	—	—	—	—	47	15	38	growth	Lindner Bulwark
1,374.5	1,605.2	27.32	23.97	1.90	0.57	7.9	0.41	0.45	1.41	A	23	72	5	income	Lindner Dividend
1,469.4	1,502.9	23.22	20.89	0.34	1.84	1.5	0.77	0.64	2.22	A	86	7	7	growth	Lindner Fund
—	—	—	—	—	—	—	—	—	—	—	—	—	—	int'l	Lindner Int'l
—	5.6	—	4.89	—	—	—	—	—	—	—	95	0	5	growth	Lindner Small Cap SC
6.6	43.4	10.61	10.27	0.15	0.09	1.4	—	—	—	—	78	15	7	income	Lindner Utility
—	22.1	—	10.50	—	—	—	—	—	—	—	90	0	10	agg gr	LKCM Sm Cap SC
6.5	5.8	18.56	18.65	0.39	0.00	2.1	0.80	0.69	2.24	C	99	0	1	gr-inc	LMH Fund
397.3	753.5	16.92	17.13	0.16	1.14	0.9	0.72	0.55	2.27	A	98	0	2	growth	Longleaf Partners
85.1	99.6	13.49	13.28	0.00	0.70	0.0	0.78	0.43	2.75	A	97	0	3	agg gr	Longleaf Small Cap SC
64.2	82.5	11.37	10.05	0.86	0.00	8.6	0.42	0.35	1.65	A	0	100	0	fix-inc	Loomis Syls Bond
21.4	25.7	11.06	9.82	0.28	0.00	2.9	0.28	0.09	2.22	F	0	95	5	fix-inc	Loomis Syls Glob Bd
20.8	25.7	12.49	11.80	0.15	0.43	1.2	0.97	0.80	2.51	B	97	0	3	gr-inc	Loomis Syls Gro & Inc
32.4	36.9	13.02	12.50	0.00	0.05	0.0	1.25	0.72	3.44	F	99	0	1	growth	Loomis Syls Growth
56.5	71.6	12.90	11.61	0.14	0.92	1.1	0.64	0.16	3.76	C	97	0	3	int'l	Loomis Syls Int'l Eq
5.1	7.3	11.54	10.41	0.52	0.00	5.0	0.45	0.33	1.84	C	0	91	9	tax-free	Loomis Syls Muni
67.8	74.1	14.13	12.85	0.00	0.11	0.0	1.23	0.47	4.21	C	92	0	8	agg gr	Loomis Syls Sm Cap SC
15.2	19.2	9.95	9.46	0.66	0.00	7.0	—	—	—	—	0	93	7	fix-inc	Loomis Syls ST Bd
18.6	17.3	10.53	9.22	0.65	0.00	7.0	0.45	0.23	2.15	C	0	100	0	fix-inc	Loomis Syls US Gov
39.1	41.9	38.84	39.37	0.65	0.98	1.6	0.94	0.70	2.63	B	98	0	2	growth	Mairs & Power Gro
13.4	13.0	56.38	52.42	2.06	0.74	3.9	0.58	0.74	1.56	D	60	36	4	income	Mairs & Power Inc
4.0	1.5	11.79	11.12	0.15	0.49	1.3	0.75	0.75	2.02	F	73	16	11	gr-inc	Managers Balanced

Arranged in alphabetical order

No-Load Fund	Total return percent with quintile ranks by objective										Annualized		What $10,000 grew to after	
	1985	1986	1987	1988	1989	1990	1991	1992	1993	1994	3 yrs.	5 yrs.	3 yrs.	5 yrs.
Managers Bond	19.1[5]	16.8[2]	1.9[2]	8.0[3]	13.1[3]	7.5[3]	19.0[2]	7.9[2]	11.6[3]	-7.2[4]	3.7[4]	7.4[3]	11,162	14,287
Managers Cap App	26.7[3]	11.1[3]	8.2[1]	19.2[3]	21.1[4]	-2.0[2]	32.0[5]	10.7[3]	12.5[4]	-1.5[3]	7.0[3]	9.7[3]	12,261	15,860
Managers Glob Bd	—	—	—	—	—	—	—	—	—	—	—	—	—	—
Managers Glob Oppty	—	—	—	—	—	—	—	—	—	—	—	—	—	—
Managers Inc Eqty	29.4[2]	21.9[1]	-5.2[4]	26.1[1]	22.2[2]	-13.0[5]	29.3[1]	10.0[2]	12.4[4]	1.0[1]	7.7[2]	7.0[4]	12,479	14,033
Managers Inter Mortg	—	—	3.3[2]	7.4[3]	14.7[1]	10.2[1]	18.2[1]	10.5[1]	11.4[2]	-25.0[5]	-2.6[5]	3.8[5]	9,236	12,028
Managers Int'l Eqty	—	58.5[3]	6.6[4]	8.9[5]	15.1[5]	-9.7[3]	18.2[1]	4.3[1]	38.2[3]	2.0[2]	13.7[1]	9.4[1]	14,700	15,691
Managers Muni Bd	18.5[4]	18.6[2]	0.3[1]	8.7[5]	9.3[4]	6.0[4]	10.7[5]	7.4[5]	10.8[5]	-5.6[2]	4.0[4]	5.7[5]	11,237	13,185
Managers Sht & Int	14.9[2]	11.4[2]	3.9[4]	5.8[4]	10.6[3]	7.2[5]	12.8[3]	11.6[1]	8.5[1]	-8.4[5]	3.5[4]	6.0[4]	11,086	13,406
Managers Spec Eqty SC	21.6[5]	6.7[4]	8.1[1]	25.3[1]	32.8[2]	-16.1[4]	49.3[3]	16.1[2]	17.4[3]	-2.0[3]	10.1[2]	10.9[2]	13,359	16,740
Managers ST Gov	—	—	—	5.9[4]	8.7[5]	7.1[5]	10.8[4]	3.9[5]	3.8[5]	-6.2[5]	0.4[5]	3.7[5]	10,119	12,007
Managers ST Muni	6.8[5]	7.3[5]	3.2[2]	4.7[5]	6.4[5]	5.5[5]	5.6[5]	4.2[5]	3.9[5]	0.4[2]	2.8[5]	3.9[5]	10,862	12,103
Marshall Balanced	—	—	—	—	—	—	—	—	—	-5.7[5]	—	—	—	—
Marshall Eqty Inc	—	—	—	—	—	—	—	—	—	-1.6[4]	—	—	—	—
Marshall Gov Inc	—	—	—	—	—	—	—	—	6.0[5]	-2.7[2]	—	—	—	—
Marshall Inter Bd	—	—	—	—	—	—	—	—	6.9[4]	-3.1[3]	—	—	—	—
Marshall Inter TF	—	—	—	—	—	—	—	—	—	—	—	—	—	—
Marshall Int'l Stk	—	—	—	—	—	—	—	—	—	—	—	—	—	—
Marshall MidCap Stk	—	—	—	—	—	—	—	—	—	-5.6[5]	—	—	—	—
Marshall ST Inc	—	—	—	—	—	—	—	—	3.7[5]	1.8[1]	—	—	—	—
Marshall ST TF	—	—	—	—	—	—	—	—	—	—	—	—	—	—
Marshall Stock	—	—	—	—	—	—	—	—	3.4[5]	-5.8[5]	—	—	—	—
Marshall Value Eqty	—	—	—	—	—	—	—	—	—	2.1[1]	—	—	—	—
Mathers	27.5[3]	13.8[3]	26.9[1]	13.7[4]	10.4[5]	10.4[1]	9.4[5]	3.1[5]	2.1[5]	-5.9[5]	-0.3[5]	3.7[5]	9,912	11,972
Matrix Emg Growth	—	—	—	—	—	—	—	—	—	—	—	—	—	—
Matrix Growth	—	—	0.3[4]	-2.0[5]	36.2[1]	-4.5[3]	34.2[3]	4.9[4]	9.3[4]	-4.8[5]	3.0[5]	7.0[4]	10,917	13,991
Matthews Asian Cnvrt	—	—	—	—	—	—	—	—	—	—	—	—	—	—
Matthews Pac Tiger	—	—	—	—	—	—	—	—	—	—	—	—	—	—
Maxus Equity	—	—	—	—	—	-10.8[5]	25.5[3]	18.2[1]	24.4[1]	1.1[2]	14.1[1]	10.7[1]	14,864	16,634
Maxus Income	—	6.6[5]	3.7[1]	7.7[4]	11.5[4]	1.6[4]	19.3[2]	10.1[1]	8.7[4]	-4.5[3]	4.6[3]	6.7[4]	11,434	13,854
Maxus Laureate	—	—	—	—	—	—	—	—	—	-3.2[4]	—	—	—	—
Merger	—	—	-10.7[5]	17.5[3]	9.6[5]	1.1[1]	16.9[5]	5.3[4]	17.7[2]	7.1[1]	9.9[2]	9.4[3]	13,282	15,690
Meridian Value	—	—	—	—	—	—	—	—	—	—	—	—	—	—
Meridian	27.0[4]	13.2[3]	-7.8[5]	18.1[3]	19.5[4]	4.6[1]	56.8[1]	15.5[2]	13.1[3]	0.5[2]	9.5[2]	16.6[1]	13,131	21,542
Merriman Asst All	—	—	—	—	—	1.0[2]	12.3[5]	2.8[5]	18.5[1]	-2.9[4]	5.8[3]	6.1[5]	11,829	13,417
Merriman Cap App	—	—	—	—	—	3.1[1]	21.9[5]	4.2[5]	3.6[5]	-0.6[3]	2.4[5]	6.2[5]	10,730	13,489
Merriman Flex Bd	—	—	—	—	8.4[5]	6.1[5]	13.3[5]	4.6[5]	14.5[1]	-1.7[2]	5.6[1]	7.2[2]	11,766	14,148
Merriman Gro & Inc	—	—	—	—	9.8[5]	3.8[1]	19.2[4]	-1.3[5]	2.8[5]	-0.2[3]	0.4[5]	4.6[5]	10,129	12,536
Merriman Levgd Gro	—	—	—	—	—	—	—	—	3.8[5]	-0.2[2]	—	—	—	—
MIM AFA Eqty Inc	—	—	—	—	—	—	—	11.2[2]	4.9[5]	-6.0[5]	3.1[5]	—	10,959	
MIM Bond Income	—	—	-1.1[4]	10.4[2]	3.0[5]	0.1[4]	15.6[3]	6.9[3]	3.0[5]	-3.6[3]	2.0[5]	4.2[5]	10,604	12,277
MIM Stock Apprec	—	—	—	-2.1[5]	16.3[5]	5.2[1]	77.0[1]	5.8[4]	10.4[4]	-10.4[5]	1.5[5]	14.3[1]	10,464	19,477
MIM Stock Growth	—	—	-10.9[5]	15.2[4]	8.4[5]	-5.9[4]	26.9[4]	-1.9[5]	2.2[5]	-11.7[5]	-4.0[5]	1.1[5]	8,847	10,567
MIM Stock Income	—	—	-2.0[4]	15.8[3]	7.9[5]	-3.3[3]	19.4[4]	4.9[5]	-0.7[5]	-1.8[4]	0.8[5]	3.4[5]	10,230	11,806
Monetta Fund.‡	—	—	1.5[3]	23.0[2]	15.2[5]	11.3[1]	55.9[1]	5.5[4]	0.5[5]	-6.2[5]	-0.2[5]	11.5[1]	9,942	17,254
Monetta Inter Bd	—	—	—	—	—	—	—	—	—	-1.0[1]	—	—	—	—
Monetta MidCap Eqty	—	—	—	—	—	—	—	—	—	2.2[2]	—	—	—	—
Montgmry Asst All	—	—	—	—	—	—	—	—	—	—	—	—	—	—
Montgmry CA TF S-I	—	—	—	—	—	—	—	—	—	0.0[3]	—	—	—	—
Montgmry Emg Mkts	—	—	—	—	—	—	—	—	58.6[1]	-7.7[4]	—	—	—	—
Montgmry Eqty Inc	—	—	—	—	—	—	—	—	—	—	—	—	—	—
Montgmry Glob Comm	—	—	—	—	—	—	—	—	—	-13.4[5]	—	—	—	—
Montgmry Glob Oppty	—	—	—	—	—	—	—	—	—	-8.5[4]	—	—	—	—
Montgmry Growth	—	—	—	—	—	—	—	—	—	20.9[1]	—	—	—	—
Montgmry Int'l Sm Cap	—	—	—	—	—	—	—	—	—	-13.3[5]	—	—	—	—
Montgmry Micro Cap SC	—	—	—	—	—	—	—	—	—	—	—	—	—	—
Montgmry Short Gov	—	—	—	—	—	—	—	—	8.1[1]	1.1[2]	—	—	—	—
Montgmry Sm Cap SC‡	—	—	—	—	—	—	98.7[1]	9.6[3]	24.3[1]	-9.9[5]	7.1[3]	—	12,271	—
MSB	27.7[2]	12.8[5]	4.8[2]	9.7[5]	26.9[2]	-7.5[4]	17.0[5]	10.7[2]	20.6[1]	-1.7[4]	9.5[1]	7.3[3]	13,124	14,209
Muhlenkamp	—	—	—	—	10.9[5]	-14.8[5]	45.3[1]	17.0[1]	18.6[1]	-7.3[5]	8.8[2]	9.8[1]	12,865	15,929

See Chapter 3 for explanation of symbols

Total Net Assets $Million		NAV per share		1994 per share distributions		Yield %	Risk Analysis				% Distribution of Portfolio 12/31/94			Objective	No-Load Fund
December 31 1993	1994	December 31 1993	1994	Income	Capital gains	12/31/94	beta	R²	Std. Dev.	Sharpe Ratio	Stocks	Bonds	Cash		
44.1	30.2	22.18	18.92	1.31	0.00	6.9	0.36	0.27	1.60	D	0	100	0	fix-inc	Managers Bond
69.1	84.2	25.17	23.25	0.05	0.00	0.2	1.11	0.82	2.87	B	81	0	19	agg gr	Managers Cap App
—	10.0	—	19.09	—	—	—	—	—	—	—	0	84	16	fix-inc	Managers Glob Bd
—	52.9	—	17.46	—	—	—	—	—	—	—	83	0	17	global	Managers Glob Oppty
40.9	47.6	27.89	24.90	0.63	1.20	2.4	0.88	0.83	2.24	C	91	1	8	income	Managers Inc Eqty
271.7	56.6	20.64	14.20	1.31	0.00	9.2	0.45	0.13	2.89	F	0	100	0	fix-inc	Managers Inter Mortg
62.1	86.5	35.92	36.35	0.03	0.00	0.1	0.65	0.27	2.90	A	82	8	10	int'l	Managers Int'l Eqty
17.7	20.0	24.32	21.63	1.12	0.12	5.1	0.40	0.33	1.60	D	0	100	0	tax-free	Managers Muni Bd
112.4	30.8	21.23	18.06	1.31	0.00	7.3	0.19	0.17	1.04	F	0	99	1	fix-inc	Managers Sht & Int
98.9	110.0	38.90	36.79	0.00	0.22	0.0	1.08	0.69	3.04	B	88	0	12	agg gr	Managers Spec Eqty SC
87.9	13.8	19.35	16.96	1.13	0.00	6.6	0.10	0.05	1.05	F	0	91	9	fix-inc	Managers ST Gov
4.3	10.0	20.00	19.41	0.60	0.00	3.1	0.06	0.23	0.26	A	0	100	0	tax-free	Managers ST Muni
25.5	2.5	10.03	9.02	0.45	0.00	5.0	—	—	—	—	—	—	—	income	Marshall Balanced
33.2	60.9	10.01	9.53	0.31	0.00	3.3	—	—	—	—	—	—	—	gr-inc	Marshall Eqty Inc
50.6	78.7	9.80	8.93	0.60	0.00	6.8	—	—	—	—	0	94	6	fix-inc	Marshall Gov Inc
312.4	326.1	9.93	9.04	0.59	0.00	6.5	—	—	—	—	0	91	9	fix-inc	Marshall Inter Bd
—	37.3	—	9.42	—	—	—	—	—	—	—	0	98	2	tax-free	Marshall Inter TF
—	74.8	—	9.33	—	—	—	—	—	—	—	—	—	—	int'l	Marshall Int'l Stk
15.9	69.3	10.13	9.55	0.01	0.00	0.1	—	—	—	—	—	—	—	growth	Marshall MidCap Stk
82.9	92.7	9.86	9.56	0.48	0.00	5.0	—	—	—	—	0	94	6	fix-inc	Marshall ST Inc
—	24.8	—	9.82	—	—	—	—	—	—	—	0	91	9	tax-free	Marshall ST TF
265.2	226.5	10.35	9.68	0.07	0.00	0.7	—	—	—	—	—	—	—	gr-inc	Marshall Stock
15.6	195.2	10.19	10.13	0.15	0.00	1.5	—	—	—	—	—	—	—	gr-inc	Marshall Value Eqty
435.9	293.3	15.11	13.55	0.68	0.00	5.0	0.17	0.09	1.28	F	24	72	4	growth	Mathers
—	—	—	—	—	—	—	—	—	—	—	—	—	—	agg gr	Matrix Emg Growth
19.2	17.2	14.51	13.45	0.05	0.31	0.4	0.97	0.80	2.52	F	96	0	4	growth	Matrix Growth
—	0.5	—	9.73	—	—	—	—	—	—	—	—	—	—	int'l	Matthews Asian Cnvrt
—	0.6	—	9.47	—	—	—	—	—	—	—	—	—	—	int'l	Matthews Pac Tiger
11.3	17.0	13.60	13.01	0.22	0.51	1.6	0.70	0.34	2.81	A	75	25	0	gr-inc	Maxus Equity
36.1	33.4	10.94	9.73	0.73	0.00	7.5	0.15	0.09	1.17	C	2	97	1	fix-inc	Maxus Income
2.1	2.0	9.96	9.64	0.00	0.00	0.0	—	—	—	—	—	—	—	agg gr	Maxus Laureate
27.2	171.2	12.96	13.17	0.00	0.71	0.0	0.07	0.02	1.18	A	80	0	20	agg gr	Merger
—	0.6	—	9.62	—	—	—	—	—	—	—	43	0	57	gr-inc	Meridian Value
160.3	256.5	25.87	25.12	0.17	0.70	0.7	1.11	0.57	3.42	C	71	0	29	growth	Meridian
28.7	25.8	11.71	10.23	0.18	0.96	1.6	0.39	0.37	1.46	C	23	0	77	income	Merriman Asst All
32.0	23.8	10.94	10.01	0.15	0.71	1.4	0.50	0.50	1.63	D	16	0	84	growth	Merriman Cap App
11.2	9.4	10.27	9.76	0.34	0.00	3.5	0.21	0.13	1.32	B	0	20	80	fix-inc	Merriman Flex Bd
14.5	9.9	11.05	9.97	0.20	0.86	1.9	0.31	0.45	1.05	F	25	0	75	gr-inc	Merriman Gro & Inc
5.8	5.8	10.63	10.15	0.12	0.34	1.2	—	—	—	—	—	—	—	agg gr	Merriman Levgd Gro
3.9	2.3	11.20	10.31	0.21	0.00	2.0	0.60	0.48	2.03	F	94	0	6	income	MIM AFA Eqty Inc
3.3	1.9	9.41	9.07	0.00	0.00	0.0	0.51	0.52	1.66	F	43	54	3	fix-inc	MIM Bond Income
58.4	41.0	15.43	13.82	0.00	0.00	0.0	1.11	0.39	4.21	F	98	0	2	agg gr	MIM Stock Apprec
9.3	6.6	11.40	9.97	0.00	0.10	0.0	1.00	0.72	2.74	F	100	0	0	growth	MIM Stock Growth
7.6	5.4	10.40	10.21	0.00	0.00	0.0	0.80	0.70	2.25	F	93	0	7	gr-inc	MIM Stock Income
524.3	364.9	15.54	14.52	0.00	0.06	0.0	1.01	0.56	3.15	F	81	0	19	growth	Monetta Fund
3.0	3.0	10.35	9.62	0.58	0.04	6.0	—	—	—	—	1	89	10	fix-inc	Monetta Inter Bd
9.8	11.7	12.54	12.20	0.00	0.60	0.0	—	—	—	—	90	0	10	growth	Monetta MidCap Eqty
—	9.5	—	14.10	—	—	—	—	—	—	—	40	50	10	income	Montgmry Asst All
11.3	8.3	12.07	11.64	0.43	0.00	3.7	—	—	—	—	0	100	0	tax-free	Montgmry CA TF S-I
610.2	878.0	15.58	13.65	0.00	0.79	0.0	—	—	—	—	86	0	14	int'l	Montgmry Emg Mkts
—	1.0	—	—	—	—	—	—	—	—	—	—	—	—	gr-inc	Montgmry Eqty Inc
220.9	216.4	16.18	13.98	0.00	0.03	0.0	—	—	—	—	96	0	4	global	Montgmry Glob Comm
10.1	13.2	14.22	12.53	0.00	0.50	0.0	—	—	—	—	91	0	9	global	Montgmry Glob Oppty
3.8	592.7	14.12	16.93	0.07	0.07	0.4	—	—	—	—	—	—	—	growth	Montgmry Growth
22.5	29.3	13.61	11.80	0.00	0.00	0.0	—	—	—	—	89	0	11	int'l	Montgmry Int'l Sm Cap
—	0.1	—	—	—	—	—	—	—	—	—	—	—	—	agg gr	Montgmry Micro Cap SC
24.0	19.0	10.10	9.63	0.58	0.00	6.0	—	—	—	—	0	100	0	fix-inc	Montgmry Short Gov
259.7	202.5	17.67	14.96	0.00	0.98	0.0	1.52	0.59	4.66	D	93	0	7	agg gr	Montgmry Sm Cap SC
45.2	35.9	16.79	13.39	0.37	0.00	2.8	0.88	0.64	2.56	B	95	0	5	gr-inc	MSB
12.1	16.6	17.86	16.21	0.07	0.28	0.4	1.04	0.67	2.95	C	81	6	13	gr-inc	Muhlenkamp

No-Load Fund	1985	1986	1987	1988	1989	1990	1991	1992	1993	1994	Annualized 3 yrs	Annualized 5 yrs	What $10,000 grew to after 3 yrs	What $10,000 grew to after 5 yrs
Mutual Beacon	23.3[5]	15.5[4]	12.7[1]	28.9[1]	17.4[4]	-8.2[4]	17.5[5]	22.9[1]	22.9[1]	5.6[1]	16.9[1]	11.5[1]	15,953	17,212
Mutual Discovery SC‡	—	—	—	—	—	—	—	—	35.8[1]	3.6[1]	—	—	—	—
Mutual Qualified	25.6[3]	16.9[3]	7.6[1]	30.3[1]	14.4[4]	-10.1[5]	21.0[4]	22.7[1]	22.7[1]	5.7[1]	16.7[1]	11.6[1]	15,911	17,307
Mutual Shares	26.6[3]	16.9[3]	6.2[1]	30.9[1]	14.9[4]	-9.8[5]	20.9[4]	21.3[1]	21.0[1]	4.5[1]	15.3[1]	10.8[1]	15,339	16,722
National Industries	10.7[5]	9.7[5]	2.6[2]	12.6[4]	24.5[2]	3.2[1]	32.0[2]	-0.6[5]	1.4[5]	-0.3[3]	0.2[5]	6.5[4]	10,054	13,695
Nbrgr-Ber Focus	22.5[4]	10.1[4]	0.6[3]	16.5[3]	29.8[2]	-5.9[4]	24.7[4]	21.1[1]	16.3[2]	0.9[2]	12.4[1]	10.8[2]	14,209	16,664
Nbrgr-Ber Genesis SC	—	—	—	—	17.3[4]	-16.2[4]	41.6[3]	15.6[2]	13.9[4]	-1.8[3]	8.9[3]	8.9[3]	12,929	15,328
Nbrgr-Ber Gov Inc	—	—	—	—	—	—	—	—	—	-3.3[3]	—	—	—	—
Nbrgr-Ber Guardian	25.3[4]	11.9[4]	-1.0[4]	28.0[1]	21.5[3]	-4.7[3]	34.3[2]	19.0[1]	14.5[2]	0.6[2]	11.1[1]	11.9[1]	13,703	17,539
Nbrgr-Ber Int'l Eqty	—	—	—	—	—	—	—	—	—	—	—	—	—	—
Nbrgr-Ber Ltd Mat	—	—	3.6[4]	6.7[3]	11.2[2]	8.7[3]	11.9[4]	5.2[4]	6.8[3]	-0.3[3]	3.9[3]	6.4[3]	11,199	13,611
Nbrgr-Ber Manhtn	37.1[1]	17.0[2]	0.4[4]	18.3[3]	29.1[2]	-8.1[4]	30.9[3]	17.8[1]	10.0[3]	-3.6[4]	7.7[3]	8.5[3]	12,489	15,032
Nbrgr-Ber Muni	—	—	6.8[3]	8.3[3]	6.9[2]	9.0[5]	6.9[5]	9.6[4]	—	-4.0[3]	4.0[5]	5.6[5]	11,249	13,108
Nbrgr-Ber NY Ins Inter	—	—	—	—	—	—	—	—	—	—	—	—	—	—
Nbrgr-Ber Partners	29.9[3]	17.3[2]	4.3[3]	15.4[3]	22.7[3]	-5.1[3]	22.4[5]	17.5[1]	16.5[2]	-1.9[4]	10.3[2]	9.3[2]	13,427	15,590
Nbrgr-Ber Social Resp	—	—	—	—	—	—	—	—	—	—	—	—	—	—
Nbrgr-Ber Ultra Sht	—	—	5.5[2]	6.9[2]	9.4[4]	8.4[4]	7.4[5]	3.6[5]	3.3[5]	2.2[1]	3.1[4]	5.0[5]	10,942	12,743
Nicholas Eqty Inc	—	—	—	—	—	—	—	—	—	4.1[1]	—	—	—	—
Nicholas Fund	29.7[3]	12.0[4]	-0.9[4]	18.0[3]	24.5[3]	-4.8[3]	41.9[1]	12.6[2]	5.9[4]	-2.9[4]	5.0[4]	9.4[2]	11,581	15,641
Nicholas II SC	33.8[2]	10.3[4]	7.7[2]	17.2[3]	17.7[4]	-6.2[4]	39.5[2]	9.4[3]	6.4[4]	1.0[2]	5.5[4]	9.0[3]	11,754	15,376
Nicholas Income	21.2[3]	11.4[4]	2.5[2]	11.5[2]	3.9[4]	-1.0[4]	23.0[1]	10.3[1]	13.0[2]	-0.2[1]	7.5[1]	8.7[1]	12,435	15,139
Nicholas Ltd Edit SC	—	—	—	27.3[1]	17.3[4]	-1.7[2]	43.2[1]	16.8[1]	9.0[4]	-3.1[4]	7.3[3]	11.7[1]	12,339	17,361
Nomura Pacific Bas	—	74.5[1]	32.6[1]	16.4[3]	22.7[3]	-15.2[4]	11.7[3]	-12.7[4]	40.4[2]	4.2[2]	8.5[3]	3.9[4]	12,779	12,102
North Carolina TF	—	—	—	—	—	—	—	—	—	-4.0[1]	—	—	—	—
Northeast Inv Gro	36.7[1]	24.4[1]	-3.4[4]	13.1[4]	32.9[1]	1.4[1]	36.8[2]	-0.8[5]	2.4[5]	0.0[3]	0.5[5]	7.1[4]	10,160	14,103
Northeast Inv Trust	25.6[1]	20.4[1]	0.1[3]	14.0[1]	0.0[5]	-9.2[5]	26.3[1]	17.4[1]	23.5[1]	2.2[1]	14.0[1]	11.2[1]	14,825	17,008
Northern Fix Inc	—	—	—	—	—	—	—	—	—	—	—	—	—	—
Northern Growth Eq	—	—	—	—	—	—	—	—	—	—	—	—	—	—
Northern Income Eq	—	—	—	—	—	—	—	—	—	—	—	—	—	—
Northern Inter TE	—	—	—	—	—	—	—	—	—	—	—	—	—	—
Northern Int'l Fixed	—	—	—	—	—	—	—	—	—	—	—	—	—	—
Northern Int'l Gro Eq	—	—	—	—	—	—	—	—	—	—	—	—	—	—
Northern Int'l Sel Eq	—	—	—	—	—	—	—	—	—	—	—	—	—	—
Northern Select Eq	—	—	—	—	—	—	—	—	—	—	—	—	—	—
Northern Sm Cap SC	—	—	—	—	—	—	—	—	—	—	—	—	—	—
Northern TE Bond	—	—	—	—	—	—	—	—	—	—	—	—	—	—
Northern US Gov	—	—	—	—	—	—	—	—	—	—	—	—	—	—
Northwest Growth	—	—	—	5.3[5]	5.6[5]	6.9[1]	23.6[4]	-1.3[5]	10.0[3]	-11.4[5]	-1.3[5]	4.9[5]	9,620	12,714
Northwest Idaho TE	—	—	—	7.8[5]	9.0[4]	5.8[4]	8.8[5]	6.8[5]	8.3[5]	-3.4[1]	3.8[5]	5.2[5]	11,173	12,866
Northwest WA TE	—	—	—	—	—	—	—	—	—	-6.3[3]	—	—	—	—
Ntnghm II-Invstk Fix	—	—	—	—	—	—	—	7.9[1]	10.8[2]	-4.0[4]	4.7[2]	—	11,476	—
Oak Hall Equity	—	—	—	—	—	—	—	—	42.3[1]	-11.6[5]	—	—	—	—
Oak Value	—	—	—	—	—	—	—	—	—	-1.6[4]	—	—	—	—
Oakmark Int'l	—	—	—	—	—	—	—	—	53.5[1]	-9.1[5]	—	—	—	—
Oakmark	—	—	—	—	—	—	—	48.9[1]	30.5[1]	3.3[1]	26.1[1]	—	20,062	—
Oberweis Emg Growth SC	—	—	—	6.0[5]	25.0[3]	0.4[1]	87.1[1]	13.7[2]	9.7[4]	-3.5[4]	6.4[3]	17.7[1]	12,037	22,610
Omni Investment	—	17.7[1]	8.5[1]	20.0[2]	26.4[3]	-22.0[5]	25.0[5]	19.7[1]	16.3[3]	6.7[1]	14.1[1]	7.7[4]	14,851	14,484
ORI Growth	—	—	—	—	—	—	—	—	—	3.2[2]	—	—	—	—
Pacifica Asset Pres	—	—	—	—	—	—	9.1[5]	4.7[5]	4.5[5]	2.4[1]	3.9[4]	—	11,201	—
Pacifica ST CA TF	—	—	—	—	—	—	—	—	—	1.1[1]	—	—	—	—
Papp L Roy Amer Abrd	—	—	—	—	—	—	—	7.4[1]	-0.7[5]	7.8[1]	4.8[5]	—	11,498	—
Papp L Roy Stock	—	—	—	—	—	1.5[1]	33.0[3]	13.5[2]	1.7[5]	-1.5[4]	4.4[4]	9.0[3]	11,371	15,349
Parnassus Balanced	—	—	—	—	—	—	—	—	15.9[2]	-5.3[4]	—	—	—	—
Parnassus CA TF	—	—	—	—	—	—	—	—	13.1[2]	-6.4[3]	—	—	—	—
Parnassus Fix Inc	—	—	—	—	—	—	—	—	10.6[3]	-6.8[4]	—	—	—	—
Pauze/Swanson Gov Tot	—	—	—	—	—	—	—	—	—	—	—	—	—	—
Pax World	25.8[3]	8.4[5]	2.4[2]	11.7[4]	24.7[2]	10.5[1]	20.7[5]	0.6[5]	-1.0[5]	2.6[1]	0.7[5]	6.4[4]	10,213	13,619
Payson Balanced	—	—	—	—	—	—	—	7.3[4]	15.3[2]	-4.2[4]	5.8[3]	—	11,847	—
Payson Value	—	—	—	—	—	—	—	—	19.2[1]	-3.7[4]	—	—	—	—
PBHG Emg Growth SC‡	—	—	—	—	—	—	—	—	—	23.8[1]	—	—	—	—

See Chapter 3 for explanation of symbols

Arranged in alphabetical order

Total Net Assets $Million		NAV per share		1994 per share distributions		Yield %	Risk Analysis				% Distribution of Portfolio			Objective	No-Load Fund
December 31		December 31			Capital				Std.	Sharpe	12/31/94				
1993	1994	1993	1994	Income	gains	12/31/94	beta	R^2	Dev.	Ratio	Stocks	Bonds	Cash		
1,060.8	2,056.4	31.09	31.03	0.59	1.21	1.8	0.67	0.68	1.89	A	69	11	20	gr-inc	Mutual Beacon
546.8	725.8	13.05	12.55	0.32	0.65	2.4	—	—	—	—	88	9	3	growth	Mutual Discovery SC
1,539.8	1,788.8	27.00	26.67	0.48	1.38	1.7	0.73	0.71	2.01	A	72	9	19	gr-inc	Mutual Qualified
3,527.1	3,745.3	80.96	78.69	1.50	4.40	1.8	0.75	0.72	2.06	A	76	7	17	gr-inc	Mutual Shares
33.4	31.0	12.71	11.92	0.07	0.69	0.6	0.86	0.70	2.41	F	79	0	21	gr-inc	National Industries
591.2	603.1	23.06	21.58	0.20	1.48	0.9	1.14	0.88	2.83	B	99	0	1	growth	Nbrgr-Ber Focus
124.9	108.0	8.26	7.80	0.00	0.31	0.0	0.88	0.53	2.83	B	98	0	2	agg gr	Nbrgr-Ber Genesis SC
11.8	10.1	10.01	9.04	0.61	0.00	6.8	—	—	—	—	0	91	9	fix-inc	Nbrgr-Ber Gov Inc
2,000.9	2,423.8	18.60	18.23	0.25	0.23	1.4	1.00	0.89	2.48	B	96	2	2	growth	Nbrgr-Ber Guardian
—	18.0	—	9.90	—	—	—	—	—	—	—	—	—	—	int'l	Nbrgr-Ber Int'l Eqty
347.6	293.0	10.36	9.76	0.56	0.00	5.8	0.10	0.12	0.65	C	0	72	28	fix-inc	Nbrgr-Ber Ltd Mat
522.9	462.2	11.11	10.00	0.01	0.70	0.1	1.33	0.76	3.58	D	99	0	1	growth	Nbrgr-Ber Manhtn
105.9	40.6	11.01	10.12	0.46	0.00	4.5	0.32	0.32	1.28	F	0	99	1	tax-free	Nbrgr-Ber Muni
—	10.0	—	9.20	—	—	—	—	—	—	—	0	92	8	tax-free	Nbrgr-Ber NY Ins Inter
1,127.7	1,245.2	20.62	18.52	0.11	1.60	0.5	1.16	0.89	2.86	B	94	2	4	growth	Nbrgr-Ber Partners
—	4.0	—	9.63	—	—	—	—	—	—	—	96	0	4	growth	Nbrgr-Ber Social Resp
105.9	90.5	9.61	9.45	0.37	0.00	3.9	0.03	0.12	0.20	A	0	42	58	fix-inc	Nbrgr-Ber Ultra Sht
2.1	10.9	9.98	10.11	0.28	0.00	2.8	—	—	—	—	57	32	11	gr-inc	Nicholas Eqty Inc
3,179.1	2,820.2	53.64	48.03	0.71	3.32	1.4	0.90	0.83	2.31	D	93	0	7	growth	Nicholas Fund
703.7	603.9	26.32	24.46	0.21	1.89	0.8	0.79	0.57	2.45	D	95	0	5	growth	Nicholas II SC
158.3	140.9	3.52	3.21	0.30	0.00	9.4	0.24	0.34	0.93	A	10	85	5	fix-inc	Nicholas Income
180.8	142.6	18.68	17.09	0.10	0.91	0.6	0.78	0.49	2.60	C	93	0	7	growth	Nicholas Ltd Edit SC
56.9	55.6	17.47	15.97	0.00	2.25	0.0	0.56	0.07	4.89	D	92	0	8	int'l	Nomura Pacific Bas.
6.5	2.5	10.46	9.63	0.42	0.00	4.3	—	—	—	—	0	95	5	tax-free	North Carolina TF
38.0	35.2	25.11	24.40	0.19	0.50	0.8	1.01	0.69	2.84	F	98	0	2	growth	Northeast Inv Gro
548.0	554.5	10.29	9.55	0.98	0.00	10.3	0.26	0.14	1.62	A	22	88	-10	fix-inc	Northeast Inv Trust
—	62.0	—	9.58	—	—	—	—	—	—	—	0	93	7	fix-inc	Northern Fix Inc
—	95.5	—	10.12	—	—	—	—	—	—	—	—	—	—	growth	Northern Growth Eq
—	35.6	—	9.53	—	—	—	—	—	—	—	—	—	—	gr-inc	Northern Income Eq
—	217.0	—	9.69	—	—	—	—	—	—	—	0	94	6	tax-free	Northern Inter TE
—	11.4	—	9.73	—	—	—	—	—	—	—	0	90	10	fix-inc	Northern Int'l Fixed
—	101.9	—	10.02	—	—	—	—	—	—	—	—	—	—	int'l	Northern Int'l Gro Eq
—	77.6	—	10.21	—	—	—	—	—	—	—	—	—	—	int'l	Northern Int'l Sel Eq
—	10.5	—	10.06	—	—	—	—	—	—	—	—	—	—	growth	Northern Select Eq
—	64.8	—	9.57	—	—	—	—	—	—	—	—	—	—	agg gr	Northern Sm Cap SC
—	119.7	—	9.57	—	—	—	—	—	—	—	0	91	9	tax-free	Northern TE Bond
—	110.2	—	9.64	—	—	—	—	—	—	—	0	94	6	fix-inc	Northern US Gov
1.4	1.0	6.60	5.85	0.00	0.00	0.0	0.86	0.54	2.72	F	97	0	3	growth	Northwest Growth
7.3	6.9	5.29	4.84	0.26	0.02	5.3	0.26	0.40	0.94	A	0	97	3	tax-free	Northwest Idaho TE
1.0	1.5	5.05	4.49	0.25	0.00	5.5	—	—	—	—	0	94	6	tax-free	Northwest WA TE
17.5	15.2	10.48	9.46	0.61	0.00	6.4	—	—	—	—	0	95	5	fix-inc	Ntnghm II-Invstk Fix
36.5	20.3	14.11	11.38	0.00	1.09	0.0	—	—	—	—	82	4	14	growth	Oak Hall Equity
4.0	7.8	11.99	10.98	0.00	0.00	0.0	—	—	—	—	—	—	—	growth	Oak Value
1,108.4	1,079.7	14.79	12.41	0.00	1.06	0.0	—	—	—	—	94	0	6	int'l	Oakmark Int'l
1,214.1	1,626.9	23.93	22.97	0.23	1.47	0.9	0.93	0.54	2.94	A	94	0	6	growth	Oakmark
101.2	90.1	22.19	21.41	0.00	0.00	0.0	1.62	0.37	6.32	D	94	6	0	agg gr	Oberweis Emg Growth SC
16.3	18.2	139.88	12.75	0.95	0.00	7.4	0.95	0.42	3.41	A	100	0	0	agg gr	Omni Investment
0.1	2.7	10.00	10.29	0.00	0.03	0.0	—	—	—	—	93	0	7	growth	ORI Growth
146.9	78.9	10.19	9.96	0.47	0.00	4.7	0.04	0.08	0.29	A	0	99	1	fix-inc	Pacifica Asset Pres
36.7	35.0	10.18	9.89	0.40	0.00	4.1	—	—	—	—	0	90	10	tax-free	Pacifica ST CA TF
10.9	11.6	11.45	12.24	0.09	0.00	0.8	0.92	0.52	2.98	D	98	0	2	int'l	Papp L Roy Amer Abrd
39.5	36.6	14.98	14.63	0.13	0.00	0.9	0.88	0.71	2.43	D	99	0	1	growth	Papp L Roy Stock
11.5	17.1	17.46	15.70	0.82	0.00	5.2	—	—	—	—	72	26	2	income	Parnassus Balanced
2.9	3.9	16.11	14.28	0.81	0.00	5.7	—	—	—	—	0	93	7	tax-free	Parnassus CA TF
4.2	4.5	15.89	13.79	1.04	0.00	7.5	—	—	—	—	0	98	2	fix-inc	Parnassus Fix Inc
—	18.2	—	9.09	—	—	—	—	—	—	—	0	89	11	fix-inc	Pauze/Swanson Gov Tot
464.4	388.3	13.55	13.39	0.50	0.00	3.7	0.52	0.55	1.63	F	63	27	10	income	Pax World
10.3	12.5	12.22	11.25	0.41	0.05	3.6	0.82	0.81	2.11	D	64	35	1	income	Payson Balanced
4.5	7.0	12.54	11.91	0.17	0.00	1.4	—	—	—	—	84	7	9	gr-inc	Payson Value
36.3	177.7	12.23	15.10	0.00	0.04	0.0	—	—	—	—	85	0	15	agg gr	PBHG Emg Growth SC

| No-Load Fund | Total return percent with quintile ranks by objective | | | | | | | | | | Annualized | | What $10,000 grew to after | |
	1985	1986	1987	1988	1989	1990	1991	1992	1993	1994	3 yrs.	5 yrs.	3 yrs.	5 yrs.
PBHG Growth.‡	—	23.0[1]	12.0[1]	6.9[4]	29.4[2]	-9.7[3]	51.6[2]	28.5[1]	46.5[1]	4.8[1]	25.4[1]	22.0[1]	19,721	26,993
PBHG Int'l	—	—	—	—	—	—	—	—	—	—	—	—	—	—
PDC&J Performance	20.6[5]	18.3[1]	-9.9[5]	12.6[4]	33.3[2]	-5.9[2]	30.5[5]	8.1[4]	14.3[3]	1.1[2]	7.7[3]	8.9[3]	12,484	15,335
PDC&J Preservation	—	9.9[5]	3.9[1]	5.1[5]	11.3[4]	9.3[1]	12.4[5]	6.3[4]	8.5[4]	-2.4[2]	4.0[4]	6.7[4]	11,247	13,822
Permanent Agg Growth.†	—	—	—	—	—	—	30.5[5]	19.9[1]	21.9[2]	1.0[2]	13.9[1]	—	14,765	—
Permanent Portfolio†	12.2[2]	13.6[2]	13.2[2]	1.3[5]	6.4[5]	-3.9[2]	7.9[5]	2.5[3]	15.5[5]	-2.9[3]	4.8[5]	3.6[5]	11,499	11,923
Permanent Treasy.†	—	—	—	6.4[3]	8.1[5]	7.3[5]	5.3[5]	2.9[5]	2.3[5]	3.3[1]	2.8[5]	4.2[5]	10,868	12,279
Permanent Vers Bd†	—	—	—	—	—	—	—	5.7[3]	3.8[5]	2.6[1]	4.0[2]	—	11,248	—
Perritt Capital Gro SC	—	—	—	—	2.0[5]	-16.8[5]	38.8[4]	6.5[4]	5.3[5]	-5.1[4]	2.1[5]	4.2[5]	10,642	12,293
Philadelphia	22.1[5]	7.6[5]	3.8[2]	15.2[4]	32.6[1]	-11.4[5]	5.7[5]	19.7[1]	17.6[2]	-8.6[5]	8.8[2]	3.8[5]	12,867	12,051
Pierpont Bond	—	—	—	—	10.4[4]	10.1[1]	13.4[5]	6.5[4]	8.3[4]	-3.0[2]	3.8[4]	6.9[4]	11,186	13,966
Pierpont Cap App SC	—	15.0[2]	-3.4[3]	13.7[4]	29.4[2]	-24.3[5]	59.6[2]	19.0[1]	8.6[4]	-5.9[4]	6.7[3]	8.0[4]	12,158	14,680
Pierpont Divsfd	—	—	—	—	—	—	—	—	—	-0.6[3]	—	—	—	—
Pierpont Emg Mkts	—	—	—	—	—	—	—	—	—	-7.0[4]	—	—	—	—
Pierpont Equity	—	18.5[2]	0.9[3]	13.0[4]	25.7[2]	1.4[1]	34.1[1]	8.7[3]	11.0[3]	-0.6[3]	6.3[3]	10.3[1]	11,997	16,316
Pierpont Int'l Eqty	—	—	—	—	—	—	10.6[3]	-10.8[4]	26.2[4]	5.7[1]	6.0[4]	—	11,893	—
Pierpont ST Bond	—	—	—	—	—	—	—	—	—	0.1[2]	—	—	—	—
Pierpont TE Bond	13.0[5]	13.4[5]	2.0[1]	7.3[5]	8.3[5]	6.9[2]	10.9[4]	7.5[5]	10.7[5]	-2.8[1]	5.0[2]	6.5[3]	11,568	13,714
Pierpont US Stock	—	—	—	—	—	—	—	—	—	—	—	—	—	—
PIMCO Low Dur‡	—	—	—	8.2[1]	11.5[2]	9.1[2]	13.5[2]	7.7[1]	7.8[2]	0.6[2]	5.3[1]	7.6[1]	11,676	14,451
PIMCO Short-Term‡	—	—	—	6.9[2]	9.4[4]	8.5[4]	6.7[5]	3.6[5]	4.6[4]	2.9[1]	3.7[3]	5.2[5]	11,156	12,906
PIMCO Tot Return‡	—	—	—	9.5[2]	14.2[2]	8.1[2]	19.5[2]	9.7[2]	12.5[3]	-3.6[3]	6.0[2]	9.0[1]	11,903	15,372
Pinnacle Fund	—	17.4[2]	15.2[1]	6.7[5]	31.0[1]	-3.2[3]	39.9[2]	-0.7[5]	3.3[5]	-1.1[4]	0.5[5]	6.6[4]	10,141	13,736
Portico Balanced	—	—	—	—	—	—	—	—	8.2[5]	-4.3[4]	—	—	—	—
Portico Bond Immdex	—	—	—	—	—	8.2[2]	16.6[3]	7.6[3]	11.0[3]	-3.1[2]	5.0[2]	7.9[2]	11,570	14,596
Portico Eqty Idx	—	—	—	—	—	-3.3[3]	30.0[3]	7.0[4]	9.1[4]	1.0[2]	5.7[3]	8.2[3]	11,792	14,822
Portico Gro & Inc	—	—	—	—	—	-0.3[2]	22.2[4]	5.5[4]	6.7[4]	0.1[2]	4.1[4]	6.5[4]	11,265	13,728
Portico Inter Bd Mkt	—	—	—	—	—	—	—	—	8.7[4]	-2.1[2]	—	—	—	—
Portico Int'l Eqty	—	—	—	—	—	—	—	—	—	—	—	—	—	—
Portico MidCore Gr	—	—	—	—	—	—	—	—	10.0[4]	-5.3[5]	—	—	—	—
Portico Spec Gro SC	—	—	—	—	—	1.0[1]	58.0[2]	7.2[4]	8.0[5]	-2.0[3]	4.3[4]	12.6[2]	11,348	18,103
Portico ST Bond	—	—	—	—	—	7.6[5]	14.2[2]	6.9[1]	6.5[3]	1.0[2]	4.7[1]	7.2[2]	11,491	14,123
Portico TE Inter	—	—	—	—	—	—	—	—	—	-1.7[1]	—	—	—	—
PRA Real Estate	—	—	—	—	—	-22.2[5]	23.5[5]	17.9[2]	19.7[3]	3.0[2]	13.3[2]	6.9[4]	14,534	13,969
Preferred Asst Allc	—	—	—	—	—	—	—	—	10.6[3]	-2.6[4]	—	—	—	—
Preferred Fix Inc	—	—	—	—	—	—	—	—	10.3[4]	-2.4[2]	—	—	—	—
Preferred Growth	—	—	—	—	—	—	—	—	16.1[2]	-1.1[3]	—	—	—	—
Preferred Int'l	—	—	—	—	—	—	—	—	41.5[2]	3.3[2]	—	—	—	—
Preferred ST Gov	—	—	—	—	—	—	—	—	5.6[4]	-0.7[3]	—	—	—	—
Preferred Value	—	—	—	—	—	—	—	—	8.8[4]	0.5[2]	—	—	—	—
Price, Rowe Adj Rate	—	—	—	—	—	—	—	4.0[5]	2.8[5]	-0.6[3]	2.0[5]	—	10,616	—
Price, Rowe Balanced	—	—	—	—	—	—	—	6.3[4]	13.4[3]	-2.0[3]	5.7[4]	—	11,797	—
Price, Rowe Blue Chip	—	—	—	—	—	—	—	—	—	0.8[2]	—	—	—	—
Price, Rowe CA TF	—	—	-6.7[5]	9.5[5]	8.5[4]	5.8[4]	12.1[3]	8.9[3]	12.5[4]	-5.7[2]	4.9[2]	6.5[3]	11,553	13,709
Price, Rowe Cap App	—	—	5.6[2]	21.2[2]	21.4[3]	-1.3[2]	21.4[5]	9.4[3]	15.7[2]	3.8[1]	9.5[2]	9.5[2]	13,126	15,733
Price, Rowe Cap Oppty	—	—	—	—	—	—	—	—	—	—	—	—	—	—
Price, Rowe Div Gro	—	—	—	—	—	—	—	—	19.4[1]	2.2[1]	—	—	—	—
Price, Rowe Eqty Idx	—	—	—	—	—	—	29.4[2]	7.2[3]	9.4[4]	1.0[2]	5.8[3]	—	11,850	—
Price, Rowe Eqty Inc	—	26.7[1]	3.7[1]	27.7[1]	13.7[4]	-6.7[4]	25.2[3]	14.1[1]	14.8[2]	4.5[1]	11.1[1]	9.9[2]	13,701	15,998
Price, Rowe Europe	—	—	—	—	—	—	7.3[4]	-5.6[3]	27.2[4]	4.1[2]	7.7[4]	—	12,505	—
Price, Rowe FL Ins Inter	—	—	—	—	—	—	—	—	—	-2.7[2]	—	—	—	—
Price, Rowe GA TF	—	—	—	—	—	—	—	—	—	-5.9[3]	—	—	—	—
Price, Rowe Glob Gov	—	—	—	—	—	—	11.3[5]	3.7[5]	11.1[2]	-3.3[3]	3.7[4]	—	11,148	—
Price, Rowe GNMA	—	11.0[4]	0.9[5]	5.9[5]	14.1[2]	10.0[2]	15.0[3]	6.5[4]	6.2[5]	-1.5[1]	3.6[4]	7.1[3]	11,129	14,084
Price, Rowe Gro & Inc	19.7[5]	8.0[5]	-4.7[5]	25.1[1]	19.3[3]	-11.1[5]	31.4[2]	15.3[1]	13.0[2]	-0.1[3]	9.2[1]	8.7[2]	13,006	15,198
Price, Rowe Growth Stk	35.2[1]	21.8[1]	3.4[3]	6.1[5]	25.4[2]	-4.3[3]	33.7[3]	6.0[4]	15.6[2]	0.9[2]	7.3[3]	9.6[2]	12,355	15,806
Price, Rowe High Yld	—	14.2[3]	3.0[1]	17.9[1]	-1.5[5]	-11.0[5]	30.9[1]	14.7[1]	21.8[1]	-8.1[5]	8.7[1]	8.4[1]	12,843	14,967
Price, Rowe Int'l Bond	—	—	27.6[1]	-1.3[5]	-3.2[5]	16.0[1]	17.7[1]	2.9[5]	19.4[1]	-1.9[2]	6.4[1]	10.5[1]	12,060	16,475
Price, Rowe Int'l Disc	—	—	—	—	41.7[1]	-12.9[4]	11.7[3]	-9.1[4]	49.8[1]	-7.6[4]	8.0[3]	4.1[3]	12,583	12,245
Price, Rowe Int'l Stk	44.7[3]	61.8[3]	8.0[4]	17.9[3]	23.7[3]	-8.9[2]	15.8[2]	-3.5[2]	40.1[2]	-0.8[3]	10.3[2]	7.2[1]	13,420	14,158

See Chapter 3 for explanation of symbols

Total Net Assets $Million December 31 1993	1994	NAV per share December 31 1993	1994	1994 per share distributions Income	Capital gains	Yield % 12/31/94	beta	R²	Std. Dev.	Sharpe Ratio	Stocks	Bonds	Cash	Objective	No-Load Fund
121.1	745.8	15.20	15.91	0.00	0.01	0.0	1.72	0.43	6.25	A	85	0	15	agg gr	PBHG Growth
—	15.0	—	9.75	—	—	—	—	—	—	—	—	—	—	int'l	PBHG Int'l
19.7	19.8	18.13	17.68	0.59	0.06	3.3	0.99	—	—	—	82	0	18	agg gr	PDC&J Performance
16.2	14.3	11.31	10.34	0.70	0.00	6.7	0.12	—	—	—	0	96	4	fix-inc	PDC&J Preservation
6.2	6.3	30.94	31.21	0.03	0.02	0.1	1.42	0.77	3.79	A	98	0	2	agg gr	Permanent Agg Growth
83.4	72.2	17.27	16.55	0.22	0.00	1.3	0.41	0.42	1.47	C	59	34	7	global	Permanent Portfolio
134.5	122.1	64.67	66.16	0.67	0.00	1.0	0.00	0.04	0.07	A	0	0	100	fix-inc	Permanent Treasy
36.3	23.9	54.37	54.42	1.33	0.02	2.4	0.03	0.02	0.46	A	0	99	1	fix-inc	Permanent Vers Bd
7.4	6.1	12.48	11.24	0.00	0.60	0.0	0.82	0.37	3.16	F	99	0	1	agg gr	Perritt Capital Gro SC
94.7	80.5	7.01	6.29	0.09	0.03	1.5	0.65	0.42	2.36	B	57	37	6	gr-inc	Philadelphia
105.7	110.5	10.42	9.55	0.56	0.00	5.9	0.22	0.17	1.22	C	0	94	6	fix-inc	Pierpont Bond
232.9	171.1	22.82	19.68	0.20	0.00	1.0	1.30	0.55	4.11	D	99	1	0	agg gr	Pierpont Cap App SC
0.1	15.9	10.10	9.82	0.08	0.00	0.8	—	—	—	—	—	—	—	gr-inc	Pierpont Divsfd
17.6	46.6	11.10	10.72	0.03	0.00	0.3	—	—	—	—	—	—	—	int'l	Pierpont Emg Mkts
244.3	229.1	19.22	16.61	0.28	0.00	1.7	0.99	0.91	2.42	C	94	5	1	gr-inc	Pierpont Equity
157.9	197.9	10.51	10.60	0.00	0.00	0.0	0.66	0.13	4.37	D	87	5	8	int'l	Pierpont Int'l Eqty
7.7	7.3	10.05	9.49	0.48	0.00	5.0	—	—	—	—	0	90	10	fix-inc	Pierpont ST Bond
493.0	330.6	11.60	11.04	0.52	0.00	4.7	0.30	0.30	1.25	A	0	98	2	tax-free	Pierpont TE Bond
—	—	—	—	—	—	—	—	—	—	—	—	—	—	growth	Pierpont US Stock
2,127.0	2,215.6	10.22	9.67	0.61	0.00	6.3	0.09	0.17	0.49	A	0	68	32	fix-inc	PIMCO Low Dur
60.3	97.8	10.00	9.79	0.49	0.00	5.0	0.03	0.18	0.14	A	0	49	51	fix-inc	PIMCO Short-Term
4,575.9	6,554.8	10.64	9.69	0.57	0.00	5.9	0.25	0.23	1.19	B	0	99	1	fix-inc	PIMCO Tot Return
15.1	13.0	21.15	18.83	0.09	0.00	0.5	0.95	—	—	—	—	—	—	growth	Pinnacle Fund
87.0	103.4	23.01	21.58	0.44	0.00	2.1	—	—	—	—	—	—	—	income	Portico Balanced
255.0	249.5	27.82	25.29	1.63	0.00	6.5	0.27	0.25	1.26	B	0	93	7	fix-inc	Portico Bond Immdex
76.5	106.5	32.91	32.38	0.78	0.00	2.4	0.96	—	—	—	99	0	1	growth	Portico Eqty Idx
165.3	162.3	23.18	22.17	0.43	0.00	1.9	0.73	—	—	—	—	—	—	gr-inc	Portico Gro & Inc
65.0	89.6	10.29	9.54	0.54	0.00	5.7	—	—	—	—	0	98	2	fix-inc	Portico Inter Bd Mkt
—	24.3	—	19.10	—	—	—	—	—	—	—	—	—	—	int'l	Portico Int'l Eqty
96.1	112.6	21.97	20.74	0.06	0.00	0.3	—	—	—	—	—	—	—	growth	Portico MidCore Gr
356.2	388.5	33.37	32.46	0.03	0.00	0.1	1.20	—	—	—	—	—	—	agg gr	Portico Spec Gro SC
137.3	116.3	10.40	9.92	0.58	0.00	5.8	0.09	0.11	0.62	B	0	99	1	fix-inc	Portico ST Bond
26.9	29.0	10.31	9.72	0.41	0.00	4.3	—	—	—	—	0	92	8	tax-free	Portico TE Inter
110.0	105.6	9.36	8.30	0.51	0.82	5.6	0.61	0.11	4.28	C	94	4	2	sector	PRA Real Estate
53.7	61.0	11.02	10.32	0.33	0.00	3.2	—	—	—	—	—	—	—	gr-inc	Preferred Asst Allc
40.6	46.7	10.34	9.58	0.52	0.00	5.4	—	—	—	—	0	90	10	fix-inc	Preferred Fix Inc
143.5	241.1	13.82	13.59	0.02	0.00	0.2	—	—	—	—	—	—	—	growth	Preferred Growth
65.8	107.6	11.75	11.58	0.12	0.00	1.1	—	—	—	—	—	—	—	int'l	Preferred Int'l
30.0	29.4	10.06	9.57	0.42	0.00	4.4	—	—	—	—	0	96	4	fix-inc	Preferred ST Gov
123.4	148.6	11.56	11.27	0.20	0.00	1.8	—	—	—	—	—	—	—	gr-inc	Preferred Value
250.2	120.9	4.77	4.51	0.23	0.00	5.1	0.02	0.02	0.37	F	0	11	89	fix-inc	Price, Rowe Adj Rate
340.4	392.0	12.02	11.14	0.43	0.20	3.8	0.69	0.81	1.79	C	54	37	9	income	Price, Rowe Balanced
24.5	39.0	11.24	11.11	0.11	0.11	1.0	—	—	—	—	87	0	13	growth	Price, Rowe Blue Chip
154.9	122.2	10.68	9.51	0.55	0.02	5.7	0.42	0.32	1.72	B	0	95	5	tax-free	Price, Rowe CA TF
535.7	655.0	12.66	12.10	0.35	0.69	2.7	0.53	0.72	1.45	A	51	30	19	growth	Price, Rowe Cap App
—	2.4	—	10.43	—	—	—	—	—	—	—	82	5	13	agg gr	Price, Rowe Cap Oppty
40.7	53.6	11.48	11.04	0.34	0.34	3.0	—	—	—	—	78	7	15	gr-inc	Price, Rowe Div Gro
167.0	270.2	13.48	13.09	0.36	0.16	2.7	0.95	0.93	2.30	D	87	0	13	gr-inc	Price, Rowe Eqty Idx
2,848.5	3,203.9	16.65	15.98	0.59	0.81	3.5	0.74	0.78	1.96	A	79	12	9	income	Price, Rowe Eqty Inc
289.5	366.5	11.86	12.17	0.12	0.05	1.0	0.78	0.26	3.61	C	94	2	4	int'l	Price, Rowe Europe
38.1	51.7	10.53	9.81	0.42	0.02	4.3	—	—	—	—	0	84	16	tax-free	Price, Rowe FL Ins Inter
20.2	20.9	10.60	9.43	0.50	0.05	5.3	—	—	—	—	0	96	4	tax-free	Price, Rowe GA TF
48.8	36.5	10.08	9.22	0.54	0.00	5.8	0.13	0.08	1.09	D	0	83	17	fix-inc	Price, Rowe Glob Gov
916.6	752.2	9.72	8.88	0.69	0.00	7.8	0.21	0.27	0.93	C	0	109	-9	fix-inc	Price, Rowe GNMA
1,170.5	1,228.9	16.57	15.63	0.49	0.42	3.1	0.87	0.80	2.28	B	79	13	8	gr-inc	Price, Rowe Gro & Inc
1,980.7	2,067.5	20.42	18.75	0.18	1.66	0.9	1.07	0.89	2.65	C	91	1	8	growth	Price, Rowe Growth Stk
1,622.2	1,040.4	9.22	7.75	0.74	0.00	9.6	0.37	0.26	1.68	A	7	84	9	fix-inc	Price, Rowe High Yld
741.6	738.1	10.34	9.34	0.60	0.21	6.3	0.09	0.01	2.05	C	0	79	21	fix-inc	Price, Rowe Int'l Bond
391.9	437.4	17.41	15.14	0.06	0.87	0.4	0.71	0.19	3.81	C	90	8	2	int'l	Price, Rowe Int'l Disc
4,296.1	5,786.9	12.16	11.32	0.12	0.62	1.0	0.81	0.27	3.70	B	91	2	7	int'l	Price, Rowe Int'l Stk

Stock and bond funds — comprehensive summary *continued*

Arranged in alphabetical order

No-Load Fund	1985	1986	1987	1988	1989	1990	1991	1992	1993	1994	Annualized 3 yrs.	Annualized 5 yrs.	What $10,000 grew to after 3 yrs.	What $10,000 grew to after 5 yrs.
Price, Rowe Japan	—	—	—	—	—	—	—	-13.4[5]	20.6[5]	15.1[1]	6.3[4]	—	12,022	—
Price, Rowe Latin Amer	—	—	—	—	—	—	—	—	—	-15.9[5]	—	—	—	—
Price, Rowe MD ST TF	—	—	—	—	—	—	—	—	—	0.7[2]	—	—	—	—
Price, Rowe MD TF	—	—	—	8.9[5]	9.6[3]	6.2[4]	11.2[4]	8.6[4]	12.7[3]	-5.0[1]	5.1[2]	6.5[2]	11,619	13,727
Price, Rowe Mid Cap	—	—	—	—	—	—	—	—	26.2[1]	0.3[3]	—	—	—	—
Price, Rowe New Amer	—	14.3[2]	-9.4[5]	18.5[3]	38.4[1]	-12.3[4]	62.0[2]	9.9[3]	17.4[2]	-7.4[5]	6.1[3]	11.2[2]	11,947	16,978
Price, Rowe New Asia	—	—	—	—	—	—	19.3[1]	11.2[1]	78.7[1]	-19.2[5]	17.1[1]	—	16,069	—
Price, Rowe New Era	23.3[4]	16.0[2]	17.7[1]	10.3[4]	24.3[3]	-8.8[4]	14.6[5]	2.1[5]	15.3[2]	5.2[1]	7.4[3]	5.3[5]	12,378	12,937
Price, Rowe New Horiz SC	24.2[4]	-0.1[5]	-7.4[4]	14.0[3]	26.2[3]	-9.6[3]	52.3[2]	10.6[3]	22.0[2]	0.3[2]	10.6[2]	13.2[2]	13,532	18,620
Price, Rowe New Inc	17.6[5]	13.9[1]	2.1[3]	7.6[3]	12.2[3]	8.8[3]	15.3[3]	5.0[5]	9.6[3]	-2.2[2]	4.0[3]	7.1[3]	11,245	14,100
Price, Rowe NJ TF	—	—	—	—	—	—	—	9.6[1]	14.0[1]	-6.1[3]	5.5[1]	—	11,733	—
Price, Rowe NY TF	—	—	-2.9[4]	10.5[4]	8.0[5]	5.3[5]	12.4[2]	10.4[1]	13.3[2]	-5.9[2]	5.6[1]	6.9[2]	11,772	13,931
Price, Rowe OTC SC	—	—	-12.5[5]	27.1[1]	19.1[4]	-20.5[5]	38.8[4]	13.9[2]	18.4[2]	0.1[2]	10.5[2]	8.3[4]	13,496	14,898
Price, Rowe Sci/Tech	—	—	—	13.3[4]	40.5[2]	-1.3[2]	60.2[2]	18.8[2]	24.3[3]	15.8[1]	19.6[1]	22.0[1]	17,085	27,022
Price, Rowe Sm Cap Val SC	—	—	—	—	18.0[4]	-11.3[5]	34.1[3]	20.9[1]	23.3[1]	-1.4[3]	13.7[1]	11.8[1]	14,691	17,471
Price, Rowe Spect-Gro	—	—	—	—	—	—	29.8[3]	7.2[4]	21.0[1]	1.4[2]	9.6[2]	—	13,153	—
Price, Rowe Spect-Inc	—	—	—	—	—	—	20.1[1]	7.8[1]	12.4[1]	-1.9[2]	5.9[1]	—	11,882	—
Price, Rowe ST Bond	12.5[4]	9.0[5]	5.2[2]	5.5[5]	9.9[3]	9.0[3]	11.2[4]	5.0[4]	6.6[3]	-2.9[5]	2.8[5]	5.7[5]	10,869	13,177
Price, Rowe ST Glob	—	—	—	—	—	—	—	—	7.9[2]	-2.9[5]	—	—	—	—
Price, Rowe TF Hi Yld	—	20.4[1]	0.2[2]	11.2[3]	10.3[2]	7.1[2]	11.7[3]	9.6[1]	13.0[2]	-4.4[1]	5.8[1]	7.2[1]	11,834	14,162
Price, Rowe TF Inc	16.9[5]	19.8[1]	-4.3[5]	7.9[5]	9.4[3]	5.9[4]	12.2[3]	9.4[2]	12.8[3]	-5.5[2]	5.3[2]	6.7[2]	11,660	13,846
Price, Rowe TF Ins Inter	—	—	—	—	—	—	—	—	12.7[1]	-2.6[2]	—	—	—	—
Price, Rowe TF S-I	11.8[2]	9.7[2]	2.2[4]	5.0[4]	6.9[3]	6.0[4]	7.9[3]	6.0[3]	6.3[2]	0.3[3]	4.2[3]	5.3[3]	11,309	12,937
Price, Rowe Trsy Inter	—	—	—	—	—	9.0[3]	14.8[1]	6.3[3]	8.0[2]	-2.3[4]	3.9[3]	7.0[2]	11,216	14,029
Price, Rowe Trsy Lng	—	—	—	—	—	6.7[3]	16.3[3]	5.8[5]	12.9[2]	-5.8[4]	4.0[4]	6.9[4]	11,260	13,966
Price, Rowe VA TF	—	—	—	—	—	—	—	9.2[2]	12.5[4]	-5.1[2]	5.3[1]	—	11,667	—
Price, Rowe Value	—	—	—	—	—	—	—	—	—	—	—	—	—	—
Price Pers Str-Blncd	—	—	—	—	—	—	—	—	—	—	—	—	—	—
Price Pers Str-Gro	—	—	—	—	—	—	—	—	—	—	—	—	—	—
Price Pers Str-Inc	—	—	—	—	—	—	—	—	—	—	—	—	—	—
Price Summit GNMA	—	—	—	—	—	—	—	—	—	-2.3[2]	—	—	—	—
Price Summit Ltd Trm	—	—	—	—	—	—	—	—	—	-3.2[5]	—	—	—	—
Price Summit Muni Inc	—	—	—	—	—	—	—	—	—	-4.7[1]	—	—	—	—
Price Summit Muni Inter	—	—	—	—	—	—	—	—	—	-1.7[1]	—	—	—	—
Primary Income	—	—	—	—	—	3.8[1]	21.5[4]	2.3[5]	15.4[2]	-2.6[3]	4.8[4]	7.7[3]	11,499	14,497
Primary Trend	—	—	3.7[2]	18.6[2]	8.9[5]	-1.7[2]	19.4[4]	0.3[5]	11.4[3]	-0.2[2]	3.7[4]	5.5[5]	11,150	13,087
Primary US Gov	—	—	—	—	—	8.3[3]	14.7[4]	3.6[5]	8.5[4]	-3.1[3]	2.9[5]	6.2[5]	10,878	13,509
Prudent Speculator SC	—	—	—	12.7[4]	-2.6[5]	-37.6[5]	63.8[1]	1.0[5]	3.1[5]	-9.0[5]	-1.8[5]	-0.6[5]	9,477	9,688
Quant Discp Gro	—	—	—	—	—	—	—	—	—	—	—	—	—	—
Quant Frgn Frntr	—	—	—	—	—	—	—	—	—	—	—	—	—	—
Quant Gro & Inc	—	20.0[2]	3.6[2]	17.0[3]	37.2[1]	-1.1[2]	27.8[3]	6.3[4]	11.9[3]	-0.7[3]	5.7[4]	8.3[2]	11,814	14,929
Quant Int'l Eqty	—	—	—	29.0[1]	17.2[4]	-28.2[5]	10.1[3]	-13.7[5]	32.2[4]	9.1[1]	7.6[4]	-0.3[5]	12,443	9,832
Quant Numeric II	—	—	—	—	—	—	—	—	—	—	—	—	—	—
Quant Numeric SC	—	—	—	—	—	—	—	—	28.9[1]	4.3[1]	—	—	—	—
Rainbow Fund	20.7[5]	15.9[2]	-3.8[4]	18.1[3]	9.7[5]	-9.7[3]	37.9[4]	-2.7[5]	-4.7[5]	-4.7[4]	-4.0[5]	2.0[5]	8,842	11,014
Reich & Tang Eqty	—	14.7[3]	5.1[2]	22.7[2]	17.8[4]	-5.8[3]	22.9[4]	16.4[1]	13.8[2]	1.7[2]	10.4[1]	9.3[2]	13,470	15,595
Reich & Tang Gov	—	—	0.2[3]	7.5[4]	13.5[2]	9.0[2]	13.7[5]	7.8[2]	10.2[4]	-6.2[4]	3.7[4]	6.7[4]	11,139	13,805
Retrmt Sys: Core Eq	—	—	—	—	—	—	—	5.1[4]	16.0[2]	5.8[1]	8.8[1]	—	12,892	—
Retrmt Sys: Emg Gr SC	—	—	—	—	—	—	—	16.7[2]	25.8[1]	10.4[1]	17.4[1]	—	16,196	—
Retrmt Sys: Inter Fix	—	—	—	—	—	—	—	6.7[3]	9.7[3]	-3.3[3]	4.2[3]	—	11,320	—
Reynolds Blue Chip	—	—	—	—	20.7[3]	0.1[2]	35.9[1]	0.1[5]	-5.2[5]	-0.6[3]	-1.9[5]	5.1[5]	9,431	12,825
Reynolds Opportunity	—	—	—	—	—	—	—	—	0.1[5]	1.7[2]	—	—	—	—
Reynolds US Gov	—	—	—	—	—	—	—	—	9.8[3]	-5.5[5]	—	—	—	—
Rightime	—	11.0[4]	19.2[1]	-1.3[5]	11.8[5]	1.2[1]	30.6[3]	5.0[4]	7.9[4]	0.7[2]	4.5[4]	8.6[3]	11,416	15,081
Robrtsn Stph Contrn	—	—	—	—	—	—	—	—	—	-5.5[4]	—	—	—	—
Robrtsn Stph Emg Gro SC	—	—	—	14.2[3]	44.4[1]	9.3[1]	58.7[2]	-2.4[5]	7.2[5]	8.0[1]	4.1[1]	14.4[1]	11,293	19,573
Robrtsn Stph Emg Mkts	—	—	—	—	—	—	—	—	—	—	—	—	—	—
Robrtsn Stph Val Gro	—	—	—	—	—	—	—	—	21.6[2]	23.1[1]	—	—	—	—
Royce Equity Inc	—	—	—	—	—	-15.4[5]	39.3[1]	19.4[1]	13.1[4]	-3.2[4]	9.3[1]	9.0[2]	13,058	15,403
Royce Low Price Stk SC	—	—	—	—	—	—	—	—	—	3.0[2]	—	—	—	—

See Chapter 3 for explanation of symbols

Total Net Assets $Million		NAV per share		1994 per share distributions		Yield %	Risk Analysis				% Distribution of Portfolio 12/31/94				
December 31 1993	1994	December 31 1993	1994	Income	Capital gains	12/31/94	beta	R²	Std. Dev.	Sharpe Ratio	Stocks	Bonds	Cash	Objective	No-Load Fund
71.1	169.3	9.61	10.24	0.00	0.81	0.0	0.08	0.00	6.00	D	97	0	3	int'l	Price, Rowe Japan
4.3	163.8	10.05	8.45	0.00	0.00	0.0	—	—	—	—	72	19	9	int'l	Price, Rowe Latin Amer
68.4	76.3	5.12	4.98	0.17	0.00	3.5	—	—	—	—	0	87	13	tax-free	Price, Rowe MD ST TF
826.3	675.2	10.67	9.56	0.56	0.02	5.9	0.41	0.33	1.66	A	0	97	3	tax-free	Price, Rowe MD TF
64.5	100.5	15.18	14.85	0.00	0.37	0.0	—	—	—	—	91	0	9	growth	Price, Rowe Mid Cap
618.6	646.1	28.04	25.42	0.00	0.53	0.0	1.40	0.64	4.11	D	96	0	4	agg gr	Price, Rowe New Amer
2,247.2	1,987.6	11.10	8.01	0.07	0.89	0.8	1.19	0.22	6.01	A	94	1	5	int'l	Price, Rowe New Asia
752.6	979.5	20.35	20.15	0.38	0.87	1.8	0.70	0.52	2.27	C	87	1	12	growth	Price, Rowe New Era
1,640.4	1,648.4	16.16	14.76	0.00	1.43	0.0	1.45	0.61	4.39	C	96	2	2	agg gr	Price, Rowe New Horiz SC
1,558.1	1,367.8	9.24	8.39	0.58	0.07	6.9	0.21	0.20	1.07	C	0	93	7	fix-inc	Price, Rowe New Inc
60.6	53.3	11.45	10.19	0.56	0.01	5.5	0.45	0.30	1.91	A	0	97	3	tax-free	Price, Rowe NJ TF
135.0	110.8	11.21	9.90	0.58	0.08	5.9	0.43	0.34	1.71	A	0	96	4	tax-free	Price, Rowe NY TF
204.6	196.7	15.39	13.80	0.03	1.56	0.2	0.86	0.47	2.93	B	88	2	10	agg gr	Price, Rowe OTC SC
500.3	915.1	18.95	21.64	0.00	0.30	0.0	1.59	0.53	5.13	B	87	1	12	sector	Price, Rowe Sci/Tech
453.8	408.4	14.68	14.92	0.14	0.92	1.0	0.69	0.44	2.42	A	94	4	2	growth	Price, Rowe Sm Cap Val SC
582.0	879.4	11.87	11.13	0.17	0.73	1.4	0.98	0.86	2.47	B	—	—	—	growth	Price, Rowe Spect-Gro
583.8	624.9	11.11	10.11	0.69	0.10	6.7	0.29	0.43	1.02	A	14	74	12	fix-inc	Price, Rowe Spect-Inc
677.8	474.9	5.05	4.63	0.28	0.00	6.0	0.09	0.11	0.65	D	0	89	11	fix-inc	Price, Rowe ST Bond
96.2	56.4	4.82	4.38	0.30	0.00	6.9	—	—	—	—	0	53	47	fix-inc	Price, Rowe ST Glob
955.2	802.2	12.46	11.16	0.72	0.04	6.5	0.37	0.35	1.45	A	0	93	7	tax-free	Price, Rowe TF Hi Yld
1,503.0	1,253.9	9.90	8.80	0.53	0.04	6.0	0.45	0.34	1.81	B	0	92	8	tax-free	Price, Rowe TF Inc
96.7	79.8	10.80	10.03	0.46	0.03	4.6	—	—	—	—	0	96	4	tax-free	Price, Rowe TF Ins Inter
528.9	451.1	5.38	5.18	0.22	0.00	4.2	0.14	0.30	0.58	C	0	81	19	tax-free	Price, Rowe TF S-I
170.8	163.1	5.38	4.94	0.30	0.02	6.1	0.15	0.10	1.06	D	0	99	1	fix-inc	Price, Rowe Trsy Inter
57.1	58.3	10.71	9.41	0.68	0.01	7.2	0.36	0.23	1.75	D	0	89	11	fix-inc	Price, Rowe Trsy Lng
163.9	143.9	11.24	10.10	0.57	0.01	5.6	0.44	0.33	1.78	A	0	86	14	tax-free	Price, Rowe VA TF
—	8.6	—	10.24	—	—	—	—	—	—	—	77	14	9	gr-inc	Price, Rowe Value
—	8.3	—	9.97	—	—	—	—	—	—	—	56	36	8	gr-inc	Price Pers Str-Blncd
—	6.5	—	10.09	—	—	—	—	—	—	—	74	20	6	growth	Price Pers Str-Gro
—	6.0	—	9.88	—	—	—	—	—	—	—	38	47	15	income	Price Pers Str-Inc
10.8	16.3	10.02	9.10	0.70	0.00	7.7	—	—	—	—	0	121	-21	fix-inc	Price Summit GNMA
12.4	17.3	5.05	4.56	0.33	0.00	7.3	—	—	—	—	0	95	5	fix-inc	Price Summit Ltd Trm
2.8	7.3	10.02	9.06	0.50	0.00	5.5	—	—	—	—	0	95	5	tax-free	Price Summit Muni Inc
4.1	16.2	10.10	9.49	0.44	0.00	4.7	—	—	—	—	0	74	26	tax-free	Price Summit Muni Inter
3.3	3.8	11.83	10.96	0.50	0.07	4.5	0.68	0.55	2.14	D	87	12	1	income	Primary Income
24.1	20.1	11.25	10.58	0.26	0.40	2.4	0.73	0.66	2.08	D	86	11	3	gr-inc	Primary Trend
1.4	1.3	10.40	9.52	0.52	0.04	5.4	0.18	0.14	1.06	F	0	98	2	fix-inc	Primary US Gov
3.6	2.5	6.94	6.32	0.00	0.00	0.0	1.06	0.20	5.61	F	96	0	4	agg gr	Prudent Speculator SC
—	—	—	—	—	—	—	—	—	—	—	—	—	—	growth	Quant Discp Gro
—	5.0	—	7.95	—	—	—	—	—	—	—	85	0	15	int'l	Quant Frgn Frntr
39.3	34.5	14.47	12.62	0.16	1.56	1.2	0.96	0.90	2.36	D	99	0	1	gr-inc	Quant Gro & Inc
23.6	29.0	9.49	10.22	0.00	0.13	0.0	0.67	0.17	3.81	C	96	0	4	int'l	Quant Int'l Eqty
—	—	—	—	—	—	—	—	—	—	—	—	—	—	agg gr	Quant Numeric II
34.3	47.8	15.29	14.92	0.00	0.99	0.0	—	—	—	—	92	0	8	agg gr	Quant Numeric SC
1.8	1.6	5.21	4.64	0.00	0.00	0.0	1.02	0.60	3.08	F	75	0	25	agg gr	Rainbow Fund
105.2	91.6	17.61	15.39	0.18	2.34	1.0	0.83	0.75	2.23	A	93	0	7	growth	Reich & Tang Eqty
20.0	18.6	10.50	9.57	0.00	0.28	0.0	0.20	0.16	1.17	B	0	99	1	fix-inc	Reich & Tang Gov
3.2	3.9	12.31	12.63	0.16	0.22	1.2	—	—	—	—	93	0	7	gr-inc	Retrmt Sys: Core Eq
1.3	2.0	13.41	14.46	0.00	0.33	0.0	—	—	—	—	99	0	1	agg gr	Retrmt Sys: Emg Gr SC
2.5	4.3	11.07	10.25	0.41	0.05	3.9	—	—	—	—	0	59	41	fix-inc	Retrmt Sys: Inter Fix
37.8	23.7	14.82	14.50	0.06	0.17	0.4	1.04	0.67	2.99	F	100	0	0	gr-inc	Reynolds Blue Chip
4.2	6.9	10.06	10.23	0.00	0.00	0.0	—	—	—	—	99	0	1	growth	Reynolds Opportunity
6.2	3.0	10.52	9.39	0.56	0.00	5.9	—	—	—	—	0	96	4	fix-inc	Reynolds US Gov
166.3	143.0	35.32	30.49	0.44	4.63	1.2	0.51	0.38	1.90	D	0	0	100	growth	Rightime
161.4	485.7	11.41	10.53	0.00	0.25	0.0	—	—	—	—	66	1	33	agg gr	Robrtsn Stph Contrn
169.7	176.1	17.98	17.32	0.00	2.10	0.0	1.48	0.36	5.83	F	87	0	13	agg gr	Robrtsn Stph Emg Gro SC
—	19.4	—	9.37	—	—	—	—	—	—	—	77	0	23	int'l	Robrtsn Stph Emg Mkts
23.1	132.5	13.06	15.88	0.00	0.20	0.0	—	—	—	—	98	0	2	agg gr	Robrtsn Stph Val Gro
84.7	77.1	5.58	5.12	0.18	0.10	3.5	0.50	0.47	1.68	A	74	23	3	income	Royce Equity Inc
0.1	1.9	5.00	5.07	0.09	0.00	1.8	—	—	—	—	—	—	—	growth	Royce Low Price Stk SC

Arranged in alphabetical order

No-Load Fund	Total return percent with quintile ranks by objective										Annualized		What $10,000 grew to after	
	1985	1986	1987	1988	1989	1990	1991	1992	1993	1994	3 yrs.	5 yrs.	3 yrs.	5 yrs.
Royce Micro-Cap SC	—	—	—	—	—	—	—	29.4[1]	23.7[1]	3.6[1]	18.3[1]	—	16,572	—
Royce Penn Mutual SC	26.5[4]	11.1[4]	1.4[3]	24.6[1]	16.7[5]	-11.5[5]	31.8[3]	16.2[1]	11.3[3]	-0.7[3]	8.7[2]	8.4[3]	12,832	14,966
Royce Premier SC	—	—	—	—	—	—	—	15.4[2]	19.0[2]	3.3[2]	12.4[1]	—	14,185	—
Royce Total Ret	—	—	—	—	—	—	—	—	—	5.1[1]	—	—	—	—
Royce Value	—	—	—	23.5[1]	13.4[5]	-13.6[5]	30.8[3]	16.0[2]	10.7[3]	-1.6[4]	8.1[2]	7.4[4]	12,630	14,273
RSI Tr-Act Mgd Bd	22.2[2]	15.8[3]	0.8[3]	6.5[4]	11.0[4]	7.7[3]	17.3[2]	6.7[4]	11.2[3]	-4.2[3]	4.4[3]	7.5[3]	11,364	14,348
RSI Tr-Core Eqty	31.9[1]	20.3[1]	1.2[3]	16.6[3]	33.5[1]	-3.2[2]	21.5[4]	6.3[4]	10.3[3]	1.3[2]	5.9[3]	6.9[4]	11,883	13,977
RSI Tr-Emg Gro SC	26.9[3]	16.1[2]	-9.5[5]	20.5[2]	12.6[5]	-10.5[3]	53.5[2]	15.8[2]	21.0[2]	3.5[1]	13.2[1]	14.8[1]	14,507	19,932
RSI Tr-Inter Bd	19.1[3]	13.7[1]	3.2[2]	7.2[3]	11.0[4]	9.5[2]	14.7[4]	6.0[4]	7.6[4]	-2.5[3]	3.6[4]	6.9[3]	11,116	13,958
RSI Tr-Int'l Eqty	44.8[3]	58.2[3]	10.5[3]	12.4[3]	13.6[5]	-12.5[3]	9.4[4]	-5.4[3]	30.4[4]	0.8[3]	7.5[4]	3.5[4]	12,427	11,889
RSI Tr-ST Invest	8.2[5]	6.6[5]	6.5[1]	7.1[1]	9.1[5]	8.2[4]	5.7[5]	3.1[5]	2.4[5]	3.4[1]	3.0[5]	4.5[5]	10,918	12,479
RSI Tr-Value Eqty	25.7[3]	12.1[5]	-0.2[4]	24.4[1]	14.4[5]	-9.2[4]	24.3[3]	8.4[3]	8.1[4]	-1.1[3]	5.0[4]	5.5[5]	11,587	13,072
Rushmore Amer Gas Idx	—	—	—	—	—	-10.5[4]	3.3[5]	11.3[3]	16.6[4]	-9.8[4]	5.4[4]	1.6[5]	11,707	10,822
Rushmore Gov Inter	—	10.5[5]	0.2[5]	6.8[4]	14.8[1]	6.5[4]	16.3[2]	7.0[2]	11.9[2]	-7.3[5]	3.5[4]	6.6[4]	11,097	13,747
Rushmore Gov Long	—	9.1[5]	-0.1[4]	7.9[3]	18.9[1]	4.5[4]	16.6[3]	6.1[4]	15.4[2]	-9.9[5]	3.3[5]	6.1[5]	11,026	13,427
Rushmore MD TF	16.2[5]	11.8[5]	1.1[1]	9.7[4]	6.7[5]	3.0[5]	10.2[5]	8.0[4]	11.9[4]	-5.2[2]	4.6[3]	5.4[5]	11,453	13,007
Rushmore VA TF	13.1[5]	12.1[5]	-1.1[2]	7.6[5]	8.0[5]	4.6[5]	10.8[4]	8.0[4]	11.8[4]	-5.0[1]	4.7[3]	5.9[4]	11,466	13,288
Rydex Gov Bd	—	—	—	—	—	—	—	—	—	—	—	—	—	—
Rydex Nova	—	—	—	—	—	—	—	—	—	-4.8[4]	—	—	—	—
Rydex OTC	—	—	—	—	—	—	—	—	—	—	—	—	—	—
Rydex Prec Met	—	—	—	—	—	—	—	—	—	-25.5[5]	—	—	—	—
Rydex Ursa	—	—	—	—	—	—	—	—	—	—	—	—	—	—
1784 Asset Alloc	—	—	—	—	—	—	—	—	—	-0.7[3]	—	—	—	—
1784 Gov Med	—	—	—	—	—	—	—	—	—	-3.7[4]	—	—	—	—
1784 Gro & Inc	—	—	—	—	—	—	—	—	—	-0.2[3]	—	—	—	—
1784 Income	—	—	—	—	—	—	—	—	—	—	—	—	—	—
1784 MA TE Inc	—	—	—	—	—	—	—	—	—	-5.5[2]	—	—	—	—
1784 ST Income	—	—	—	—	—	—	—	—	—	—	—	—	—	—
1784 TE Med Term	—	—	—	—	—	—	—	—	—	-3.0[2]	—	—	—	—
SAFECO CA TF	21.1[2]	19.8[1]	-2.1[3]	12.8[1]	9.9[2]	7.0[2]	12.6[2]	8.0[4]	13.2[2]	-9.2[5]	3.6[5]	6.0[4]	11,104	13,369
SAFECO Equity	31.9[2]	13.3[3]	-4.8[5]	25.3[1]	35.8[1]	-8.6[4]	27.9[4]	9.3[3]	30.9[1]	9.9[1]	16.3[1]	13.0[1]	15,724	18,390
SAFECO GNMA	—	—	0.9[5]	7.8[2]	12.9[2]	8.7[3]	14.8[3]	6.7[3]	7.1[4]	-4.3[4]	3.0[5]	6.4[5]	10,937	13,650
SAFECO Growth	20.5[5]	1.8[5]	7.0[1]	22.1[2]	19.2[4]	-15.0[4]	62.7[2]	-3.1[5]	22.2[1]	-1.6[3]	5.2[4]	10.0[3]	11,652	16,115
SAFECO Hi Yld Bd	—	—	—	—	2.0[5]	-3.6[5]	24.3[1]	13.9[1]	16.9[1]	-2.0[1]	9.3[1]	9.3[1]	13,042	15,628
SAFECO Income	31.6[1]	20.6[2]	-6.0[4]	19.0[1]	19.2[3]	-10.8[5]	23.3[4]	11.5[2]	12.6[4]	-1.1[2]	7.5[2]	6.4[4]	12,409	13,650
SAFECO Insur Muni	—	—	—	—	—	—	—	—	—	-10.4[5]	—	—	—	—
SAFECO Inter Muni	—	—	—	—	—	—	—	—	—	-5.6[5]	—	—	—	—
SAFECO Inter Trsy	—	—	—	—	10.3[4]	7.2[4]	13.5[5]	6.6[3]	10.8[2]	-3.6[4]	4.4[2]	6.7[4]	11,385	13,850
SAFECO Muni Bd	21.6[1]	19.8[1]	0.2[2]	13.9[1]	10.1[2]	6.7[3]	13.8[1]	8.8[3]	12.7[3]	-8.3[4]	4.0[4]	6.4[3]	11,241	13,641
SAFECO Northwest Gro	—	—	—	—	—	—	—	14.1[2]	1.0[5]	-1.6[4]	4.3[4]	—	11,346	—
SAFECO WA Muni	—	—	—	—	—	—	—	—	—	-8.7[5]	—	—	—	—
Salomon Capital	23.6[4]	13.7[3]	1.3[2]	-4.6[5]	39.7[1]	-9.1[3]	33.4[4]	4.9[4]	17.2[3]	-14.2[5]	1.8[5]	5.1[5]	10,551	12,804
Salomon Investors	26.9[3]	14.4[4]	0.7[4]	16.9[3]	21.8[3]	-6.5[4]	29.3[2]	7.4[3]	15.2[2]	-1.3[4]	6.9[2]	8.1[3]	12,215	14,771
Salomon NY Muni	—	—	—	—	—	—	—	—	—	-8.8[5]	—	—	—	—
Salomon Opportunity	32.9[2]	6.5[5]	4.4[2]	23.3[2]	20.9[4]	-16.0[4]	30.4[5]	13.8[2]	12.8[4]	0.8[2]	9.0[2]	7.2[5]	12,943	14,176
SBSF Capital Gro	—	—	—	—	—	—	—	—	—	-4.5[4]	—	—	—	—
SBSF Convert	—	—	—	—	18.9[3]	-5.0[4]	27.6[2]	11.3[2]	20.1[1]	-6.5[5]	7.7[2]	8.7[2]	12,498	15,149
SBSF Fund	28.3[3]	8.0[5]	-3.2[4]	17.2[3]	33.8[1]	-2.7[3]	19.0[5]	6.6[4]	20.4[1]	-5.6[5]	6.6[3]	7.0[4]	12,107	14,021
Schafer Value	—	10.1[5]	-0.4[4]	17.7[3]	35.7[1]	-10.8[5]	40.9[1]	18.7[1]	24.0[1]	-4.3[5]	12.1[1]	12.1[1]	14,081	17,702
Schooner Fund SC	—	—	—	—	—	—	—	—	—	-0.3[2]	—	—	—	—
Schroder Int'l Eqty	—	49.7[5]	3.7[4]	19.5[1]	22.1[3]	-11.4[3]	4.6[5]	-4.0[3]	45.7[2]	0.2[3]	11.9[2]	5.4[2]	14,019	12,989
Schroder Latin Amer	—	—	—	—	—	—	—	—	—	—	—	—	—	—
Schroder US Eqty	23.7[4]	11.9[3]	0.4[3]	12.2[4]	24.3[3]	-4.5[2]	38.2[4]	15.2[2]	12.5[4]	-5.2[4]	7.1[3]	10.2[3]	12,285	16,222
Schroder US Sm Co SC	—	—	—	—	—	—	—	—	—	4.5[1]	—	—	—	—
Schwab 1000	—	—	—	—	—	—	—	8.5[3]	9.6[4]	-0.1[3]	5.9[3]	—	11,884	—
Schwab CA Long	—	—	—	—	—	—	—	—	12.8[3]	-8.9[5]	—	—	—	—
Schwab CA S-I	—	—	—	—	—	—	—	—	—	-2.1[5]	—	—	—	—
Schwab Int'l Idx	—	—	—	—	—	—	—	—	—	3.8[2]	—	—	—	—
Schwab LT Gov	—	—	—	—	—	—	—	—	—	-5.7[4]	—	—	—	—
Schwab LT TF	—	—	—	—	—	—	—	—	13.5[1]	-7.0[4]	—	—	—	—

See Chapter 3 for explanation of symbols

Total Net Assets $Million		NAV per share		1994 per share distributions		Yield %	Risk Analysis				% Distribution of Portfolio				
December 31		December 31			Capital	12/31/94			Std.	Sharpe	12/31/94				
1993	1994	1993	1994	Income	gains		beta	R²	Dev.	Ratio	Stocks	Bonds	Cash	Objective	No-Load Fund
10.3	26.8	6.47	6.48	0.00	0.22	0.0	0.62	0.38	2.34	A	98	0	2	agg gr	Royce Micro-Cap SC
1,022.2	771.4	8.31	7.41	0.11	0.73	1.4	0.63	0.61	1.88	B	94	0	6	growth	Royce Penn Mutual SC
47.1	202.4	6.41	6.48	0.05	0.09	0.8	0.47	—	—	A	83	0	17	growth	Royce Premier SC
0.1	1.7	5.00	5.12	0.14	0.00	2.7	—	—	—	—	—	—	—	gr-inc	Royce Total Ret
185.8	166.9	9.73	9.11	0.05	0.41	0.5	0.65	0.60	1.96	B	90	0	10	growth	Royce Value
143.7	131.4	27.31	26.16	0.00	0.00	0.0	0.21	—	—	—	0	91	9	fix-inc	RSI Tr-Act Mgd Bd
147.2	144.3	34.99	35.45	0.00	0.00	0.0	0.91	—	—	—	—	—	—	gr-inc	RSI Tr-Core Eqty
57.1	51.6	35.97	37.24	0.00	0.00	0.0	1.48	—	—	—	—	—	—	agg gr	RSI Tr-Emg Gro SC
102.7	85.8	25.96	25.30	0.00	0.00	0.0	0.11	—	—	—	0	95	5	fix-inc	RSI Tr-Inter Bd
22.7	28.5	36.49	36.77	0.00	0.00	0.0	0.61	—	—	—	—	—	—	int'l	RSI Tr-Int'l Eqty
32.8	30.2	17.95	18.56	0.00	0.00	0.0	0.03	—	—	—	0	92	8	fix-inc	RSI Tr-ST Invest
37.6	35.1	26.30	26.00	0.00	0.00	0.0	0.94	—	—	—	—	—	—	gr-inc	RSI Tr-Value Eqty
230.3	176.2	11.96	10.36	0.44	0.00	4.2	0.83	0.36	3.26	D	99	0	1	sector	Rushmore Amer Gas Idx
20.8	9.2	9.84	8.57	0.56	0.00	6.5	0.37	0.22	1.85	F	0	100	0	fix-inc	Rushmore Gov Inter
17.2	33.1	10.31	8.69	0.61	0.00	7.0	0.52	0.25	2.40	F	0	100	0	fix-inc	Rushmore Gov Long
57.9	44.4	11.27	10.12	0.56	0.00	5.6	0.42	0.33	1.67	B	0	100	0	tax-free	Rushmore MD TF
34.2	27.9	11.51	10.36	0.58	0.00	5.6	0.41	0.32	1.68	B	0	100	0	tax-free	Rushmore VA TF
—	0.3	—	7.93	—	—	—	—	—	—	—	0	100	0	fix-inc	Rydex Gov Bd
3.2	58.4	10.71	9.99	0.09	0.12	0.9	—	—	—	—	100	0	0	agg gr	Rydex Nova
—	51.7	—	9.53	—	—	—	—	—	—	—	100	0	0	agg gr	Rydex OTC
2.4	28.4	10.67	7.90	0.05	0.00	0.6	—	—	—	—	100	0	0	prec met	Rydex Prec Met
—	142.2	—	10.30	—	—	—	—	—	—	—	100	0	0	agg gr	Rydex Ursa
5.0	7.1	10.09	9.76	0.25	0.00	2.6	—	—	—	—	—	—	—	gr-inc	1784 Asset Alloc
9.7	109.9	10.00	9.06	0.57	0.00	6.3	—	—	—	—	0	95	5	fix-inc	1784 Gov Med
99.1	193.1	10.69	10.47	0.11	0.00	1.1	—	—	—	—	0	95	5	gr-inc	1784 Gro & Inc
—	170.2	—	9.66	—	—	—	—	—	—	—	—	—	—	fix-inc	1784 Income
33.0	55.7	10.39	9.35	0.48	0.00	5.2	—	—	—	—	0	92	8	tax-free	1784 MA TE Inc
—	32.3	—	9.77	—	—	—	—	—	—	—	0	91	9	fix-inc	1784 ST Income
26.1	90.9	10.35	9.56	0.48	0.00	5.0	—	—	—	—	0	90	10	tax-free	1784 TE Med Term
84.2	58.1	12.43	10.58	0.64	0.10	6.0	0.49	0.31	2.04	F	0	97	3	tax-free	SAFECO CA TF
194.0	449.1	13.18	13.68	0.26	0.54	1.9	1.28	0.69	3.62	A	96	1	3	growth	SAFECO Equity
60.2	41.6	9.88	8.87	0.59	0.00	6.7	0.28	0.33	1.12	F	0	100	0	fix-inc	SAFECO GNMA
163.6	150.2	20.06	17.55	0.00	2.15	0.0	1.72	0.59	5.33	D	97	0	3	agg gr	SAFECO Growth
34.6	25.5	9.30	8.25	0.87	0.00	10.5	0.22	0.17	1.26	A	0	87	13	fix-inc	SAFECO Hi Yld Bd
201.0	180.7	17.77	16.54	0.81	0.24	4.8	0.72	0.76	1.93	B	58	40	2	income	SAFECO Income
4.0	7.3	10.82	9.24	0.46	0.00	5.0	—	—	—	—	0	96	4	tax-free	SAFECO Insur Muni
9.5	12.8	10.71	9.68	0.44	0.00	4.5	—	—	—	—	0	99	1	tax-free	SAFECO Inter Muni
14.9	12.6	10.52	9.64	0.50	0.00	5.2	0.25	0.18	1.32	D	0	97	3	fix-inc	SAFECO Inter Trsy
570.7	434.4	14.43	12.46	0.77	0.03	6.2	0.51	0.34	2.06	F	0	100	0	tax-free	SAFECO Muni Bd
39.2	34.2	12.45	12.12	0.04	0.10	0.3	0.80	0.46	2.74	D	99	0	1	growth	SAFECO Northwest Gro
3.3	5.9	10.82	9.42	0.47	0.00	5.0	—	—	—	—	0	98	2	tax-free	SAFECO WA Muni
113.8	87.5	20.84	15.62	0.03	0.00	0.2	1.50	0.82	3.88	F	93	4	3	agg gr	Salomon Capital
386.4	348.5	15.60	13.63	0.25	0.00	1.8	1.06	0.90	2.60	C	89	9	2	gr-inc	Salomon Investors
8.4	3.7	10.44	8.99	0.55	0.00	6.1	—	—	—	—	0	95	5	tax-free	Salomon NY Muni
116.4	108.8	30.01	28.39	0.37	1.48	1.2	0.90	0.77	2.38	A	87	2	11	agg gr	Salomon Opportunity
1.8	4.5	7.83	7.48	0.00	0.00	0.0	—	—	—	—	87	0	13	growth	SBSF Capital Gro
62.5	57.9	12.21	10.41	0.60	0.43	5.6	0.43	0.39	1.58	B	12	80	8	income	SBSF Convert
120.8	108.0	15.71	13.82	0.21	0.79	1.4	0.68	0.56	2.10	C	82	7	11	growth	SBSF Fund
25.2	72.5	36.78	33.23	0.33	1.64	0.9	1.01	0.75	2.70	A	100	0	0	gr-inc	Schafer Value
2.2	4.7	25.56	25.25	0.23	0.00	0.9	—	—	—	—	72	25	3	agg gr	Schooner Fund SC
358.1	174.6	21.94	19.44	0.00	2.54	0.0	0.71	0.20	3.66	A	96	2	2	int'l	Schroder Int'l Eqty
—	—	—	—	—	—	—	—	—	—	—	—	—	—	int'l	Schroder Latin Amer
20.7	17.7	8.76	7.79	0.05	0.46	0.6	1.16	0.76	3.11	C	93	0	7	agg gr	Schroder US Eqty
12.6	13.0	11.12	11.20	0.00	0.00	0.0	—	—	—	—	—	—	—	agg gr	Schroder US Sm Co SC
529.1	554.0	12.85	12.57	0.26	0.00	2.1	0.99	0.98	2.33	D	99	0	1	gr-inc	Schwab 1000
131.0	87.2	11.23	9.69	0.56	0.00	5.7	—	—	—	—	0	99	1	tax-free	Schwab CA Long
56.2	40.2	10.19	9.60	0.38	0.00	4.0	—	—	—	—	0	99	1	tax-free	Schwab CA S-I
112.8	138.1	10.04	10.31	0.12	0.00	1.1	—	—	—	—	99	0	1	int'l	Schwab Int'l Idx
4.4	8.0	10.22	9.00	0.64	0.00	7.1	—	—	—	—	0	98	2	fix-inc	Schwab LT Gov
49.0	36.8	10.62	9.37	0.51	0.00	5.5	—	—	—	—	0	99	1	tax-free	Schwab LT TF

Arranged in alphabetical order

No-Load Fund	Total return percent with quintile ranks by objective										Annualized		What $10,000 grew to after	
	1985	1986	1987	1988	1989	1990	1991	1992	1993	1994	3 yrs.	5 yrs.	3 yrs.	5 yrs.
Schwab Sm Cap Idx...	—	—	—	—	—	—	—	—	—	-3.1[4]	—	—	—	—
Schwab S-I Gov...	—	—	—	—	—	—	—	6.2[2]	7.9[2]	-2.9[5]	3.6[4]	—	11,126	—
Schwab S-I TF...	—	—	—	—	—	—	—	—	—	-1.1[4]	—	—	—	—
Schwartz Value SC...	—	—	—	—	—	—	—	—	—	-6.8[5]	—	—	—	—
SCM Portfolio...	—	—	—	—	6.9[5]	4.5[1]	9.8[5]	2.3[5]	6.6[5]	-0.9[3]	2.6[5]	4.4[5]	10,801	12,390
Scudder Balanced...	—	—	—	—	—	—	—	—	4.1[5]	-2.4[4]	—	—	—	—
Scudder CA TF...	18.3[4]	16.9[4]	-1.7[3]	11.9[2]	10.3[2]	6.4[3]	12.7[2]	9.4[2]	13.8[1]	-7.3[4]	4.9[3]	6.7[2]	11,544	13,835
Scudder Capital Gro...	36.6[2]	16.6[2]	-0.7[3]	29.7[1]	33.8[2]	-17.0[5]	42.8[3]	7.1[4]	20.1[2]	-9.9[5]	5.0[4]	6.6[5]	11,589	13,742
Scudder Development SC...	19.7[5]	7.8[4]	-1.4[3]	11.1[4]	23.2[3]	1.5[1]	71.9[1]	-2.0[5]	9.0[4]	-5.3[4]	0.4[5]	12.0[2]	10,110	17,637
Scudder Emg Mkts Inc...	—	—	—	—	—	—	—	—	—	-8.1[5]	—	—	—	—
Scudder Glob Sm Co...	—	—	—	—	—	—	—	-0.1[4]	38.2[1]	-7.7[4]	8.4[3]	—	12,746	—
Scudder Global...	—	—	3.0[5]	19.3[1]	37.4[1]	-6.4[3]	17.1[2]	4.5[2]	31.2[2]	-4.2[3]	9.5[2]	7.5[2]	13,131	14,385
Scudder GNMA...	—	11.2[4]	1.5[4]	6.8[4]	12.8[3]	10.1[2]	15.0[3]	7.0[3]	6.0[5]	-3.1[3]	3.2[5]	6.9[3]	10,994	13,927
Scudder Gold...	—	—	—	—	10.7[5]	-16.7[1]	-6.9[4]	-9.2[3]	59.5[5]	-7.4[2]	10.3[4]	0.8[3]	13,420	10,408
Scudder Gro & Inc...	34.5[1]	17.9[2]	3.5[2]	11.9[4]	26.4[2]	-2.3[2]	28.1[3]	9.5[2]	15.6[2]	2.6[1]	9.1[1]	10.2[1]	12,986	16,253
Scudder Grt Europe...	—	—	—	—	—	—	—	—	—	—	—	—	—	—
Scudder Hi Yld TF...	—	—	—	13.5[1]	10.3[2]	6.0[4]	13.5[1]	10.9[1]	13.9[1]	-8.4[5]	5.0[2]	6.8[2]	11,569	13,914
Scudder Income...	21.7[3]	14.6[3]	0.7[3]	8.9[2]	12.7[3]	8.3[2]	17.3[3]	6.7[4]	12.7[3]	-4.5[3]	4.7[3]	7.8[2]	11,482	14,581
Scudder Int'l Bond...	—	—	—	—	7.2[5]	21.1[1]	22.1[1]	7.7[2]	15.9[1]	-8.6[5]	4.5[2]	11.0[1]	11,398	16,851
Scudder Int'l Stk...	48.9[2]	50.8[4]	0.9[5]	18.8[2]	27.0[2]	-8.9[2]	11.8[3]	-2.4[2]	36.5[3]	-3.0[4]	8.9[2]	5.6[2]	12,926	13,158
Scudder Latin Amer...	—	—	—	—	—	—	—	—	74.3[1]	-9.4[5]	—	—	—	—
Scudder Ltd TF...	—	—	—	—	—	—	—	—	—	—	—	—	—	—
Scudder MA Ltd TF...	—	—	—	—	—	—	—	—	—	—	—	—	—	—
Scudder MA TF...	—	—	—	12.0[2]	9.8[2]	6.3[3]	12.2[2]	10.9[1]	14.3[1]	-6.2[3]	5.9[1]	7.3[1]	11,889	14,187
Scudder Medium TF...	11.0[5]	10.0[5]	3.2[1]	4.9[5]	6.0[5]	6.3[4]	12.1[1]	9.0[1]	11.0[3]	-3.5[3]	5.3[1]	6.8[1]	11,668	13,906
Scudder Mgd Muni...	17.4[4]	16.8[4]	0.3[1]	12.3[2]	11.1[1]	6.8[2]	12.2[2]	9.0[2]	13.3[2]	-6.0[3]	5.1[2]	6.8[2]	11,605	13,904
Scudder NY TF...	16.0[5]	14.2[5]	-0.6[2]	10.9[3]	10.1[2]	4.3[5]	14.4[1]	10.2[1]	12.9[3]	-7.2[4]	4.9[2]	6.6[2]	11,551	13,784
Scudder OH TF...	—	—	—	12.9[1]	9.5[3]	6.6[3]	11.8[3]	8.9[3]	12.3[4]	-5.5[2]	4.9[2]	6.6[2]	11,549	13,770
Scudder PA TF...	—	—	—	13.4[1]	10.2[2]	5.8[5]	12.4[2]	9.1[2]	13.2[2]	-5.9[2]	5.1[2]	6.7[2]	11,616	13,821
Scudder Pacific Opp...	—	—	—	—	—	—	—	—	60.1[1]	-17.1[5]	—	—	—	—
Scudder Qual Growth...	—	—	—	—	—	—	—	6.7[4]	0.0[5]	-1.3[4]	1.7[5]	—	10,523	—
Scudder ST Bond...	—	—	—	—	13.3[1]	9.9[1]	14.3[1]	5.6[3]	7.7[2]	-2.9[5]	3.4[4]	6.8[2]	11,043	13,868
Scudder ST Glob Inc...	—	—	—	—	—	—	—	5.5[3]	6.7[3]	-1.1[4]	3.7[3]	—	11,138	—
Scudder US Zero 2000...	—	—	-8.1[5]	11.7[1]	20.5[1]	4.6[4]	19.8[2]	8.1[2]	16.1[2]	-7.9[5]	4.9[2]	7.7[3]	11,554	14,480
Scudder Value...	—	—	—	—	—	—	—	—	11.6[3]	1.6[2]	—	—	—	—
Seafirst Asst Allc...	—	—	—	—	18.9[4]	4.2[1]	18.4[5]	5.5[4]	10.6[3]	-0.2[3]	5.2[4]	7.5[3]	11,640	14,360
Seafirst Blue Chip...	—	—	—	—	30.3[2]	-1.8[2]	22.5[5]	5.2[4]	13.4[3]	2.1[2]	6.8[3]	7.9[4]	12,175	14,654
Seafirst Bond...	—	—	—	—	12.2[3]	9.4[1]	13.3[5]	6.1[4]	7.2[5]	-2.3[2]	3.6[4]	6.6[4]	11,107	13,767
Selected Amer Sh...	33.3[1]	17.1[3]	0.2[4]	22.0[1]	20.0[3]	-3.9[3]	46.3[1]	5.8[4]	5.5[5]	-3.2[4]	2.6[5]	8.7[2]	10,800	15,177
Selected Spec Sh SC...	23.8[4]	7.3[5]	0.4[4]	19.6[2]	28.9[2]	-6.9[4]	25.1[4]	8.4[3]	10.8[3]	-2.5[4]	5.4[4]	6.4[5]	11,709	13,645
Selected US Gov...	—	—	—	2.9[5]	9.4[4]	8.4[2]	13.4[5]	5.4[5]	7.5[4]	-2.2[1]	3.5[4]	6.4[4]	11,073	13,620
Sentry...	32.8[2]	14.7[3]	-5.5[5]	16.9[3]	24.0[3]	5.2[1]	28.4[4]	7.5[3]	6.0[4]	-1.1[4]	4.0[4]	8.8[3]	11,257	15,246
Sequoia.‡...	27.9[3]	13.2[3]	6.7[2]	11.1[4]	27.8[2]	-3.9[3]	39.9[2]	9.4[3]	10.8[3]	3.4[1]	7.8[2]	11.0[2]	12,519	16,841
Seven Seas Emg Mkts...	—	—	—	—	—	—	—	—	—	—	—	—	—	—
Seven Seas Gro & Inc...	—	—	—	—	—	—	—	—	—	-0.3[3]	—	—	—	—
Seven Seas Inter Fix...	—	—	—	—	—	—	—	—	—	-4.4[5]	—	—	—	—
Seven Seas Matrix...	—	—	—	—	—	—	—	—	16.3[2]	-0.4[3]	—	—	—	—
Seven Seas Sm Cap SC...	—	—	—	—	—	—	—	—	13.0[4]	-1.0[3]	—	—	—	—
Seven Seas ST Gov...	—	—	—	—	—	—	—	—	4.8[4]	0.2[2]	—	—	—	—
Seven Seas S&P 500...	—	—	—	—	—	—	—	—	9.6[4]	1.3[2]	—	—	—	—
Seven Seas Yld Plus...	—	—	—	—	—	—	—	—	3.4[5]	4.1[1]	—	—	—	—
SIT Balanced...	—	—	—	—	—	—	—	—	—	-0.4[2]	—	—	—	—
SIT Bond...	—	—	—	—	—	—	—	—	—	-1.3[1]	—	—	—	—
SIT Develop Mkts...	—	—	—	—	—	—	—	—	—	—	—	—	—	—
SIT Gro & Inc...	23.3[5]	21.8[1]	5.4[1]	5.4[5]	31.3[1]	-1.8[2]	32.7[2]	4.9[5]	3.1[5]	2.8[1]	3.6[4]	7.7[3]	11,122	14,496
SIT Growth SC...	43.6[1]	10.3[4]	5.5[2]	9.8[4]	35.1[1]	-2.0[2]	65.5[1]	-2.1[5]	8.5[5]	-0.5[2]	1.9[5]	11.4[2]	10,573	17,142
SIT Int'l Growth...	—	—	—	—	—	—	—	2.7[1]	48.3[1]	-3.0[4]	13.9[1]	—	14,773	—
SIT MN TF Inc...	—	—	—	—	—	—	—	—	—	0.6[1]	—	—	—	—
SIT Sm Cap Gr SC...	—	—	—	—	—	—	—	—	—	—	—	—	—	—
SIT TF Income...	—	—	—	—	8.4[5]	7.3[1]	9.2[5]	7.7[5]	10.4[5]	-0.6[1]	5.7[1]	6.7[2]	11,816	13,843

See Chapter 3 for explanation of symbols

Stock and bond funds — comprehensive summary *continued*
Arranged in alphabetical order

Total Net Assets $Million		NAV per share		1994 per share distributions		Yield %	Risk Analysis				% Distribution of Portfolio			Objective	No-Load Fund
December 31		December 31			Capital				Std.	Sharpe	12/31/94				
1993	1994	1993	1994	Income	gains	12/31/94	beta	R²	Dev.	Ratio	Stocks	Bonds	Cash		
44.7	70.7	10.14	9.77	0.06	0.00	0.6	—	—	—	—	99	0	1	agg gr	Schwab Sm Cap Idx
271.7	160.0	10.38	9.55	0.54	0.00	5.6	0.14	0.12	0.94	D	0	97	3	fix-inc	Schwab S-I Gov
69.4	55.9	10.20	9.71	0.38	0.00	3.9	—	—	—	—	0	99	1	tax-free	Schwab S-I TF
40.7	45.1	19.44	18.12	0.00	0.00	0.0	—	—	—	—	—	—	—	growth	Schwartz Value SC
0.7	0.8	10.42	9.90	0.32	0.00	3.3	0.23	—	—	—	—	—	—	gr-inc	SCM Portfolio
64.1	66.1	12.23	11.63	0.31	0.00	2.6	—	—	—	—	—	—	—	gr-inc	Scudder Balanced
352.8	274.4	10.85	9.48	0.51	0.09	5.4	0.50	0.34	2.01	D	0	98	2	tax-free	Scudder CA TF
1,427.9	1,291.5	21.26	18.43	0.00	0.73	0.0	1.35	0.77	3.61	D	95	3	2	agg gr	Scudder Capital Gro
765.8	601.9	33.51	29.54	0.00	2.12	0.0	1.59	0.57	4.98	F	92	4	4	agg gr	Scudder Development SC
0.1	89.6	12.00	10.27	0.77	0.00	7.5	—	—	—	—	—	—	—	fix-inc	Scudder Emg Mkts Inc
219.8	235.3	16.53	15.18	0.00	0.08	0.0	0.73	0.31	3.06	D	84	8	8	global	Scudder Glob Sm Co
963.0	1,117.7	24.80	23.33	0.11	0.34	0.5	0.75	0.49	2.51	B	86	14	0	global	Scudder Global
610.3	417.0	15.06	13.66	0.94	0.00	6.8	0.26	0.29	1.13	D	0	88	12	fix-inc	Scudder GNMA
110.0	129.9	13.35	11.71	0.25	0.47	2.0	0.41	0.03	6.14	B	86	3	11	prec met	Scudder Gold
1,631.3	1,994.2	17.24	16.27	0.51	0.91	3.0	0.94	0.84	2.38	B	90	8	2	gr-inc	Scudder Gro & Inc
—	16.0	—	11.50	—	—	—	—	—	—	—	—	—	—	int'l	Scudder Grt Europe
315.9	259.8	12.55	10.86	0.66	0.00	6.1	0.49	0.33	2.00	C	0	96	4	tax-free	Scudder Hi Yld TF
508.9	464.1	13.72	12.32	0.76	0.02	6.2	0.33	0.27	1.46	C	0	90	10	fix-inc	Scudder Income
1,365.0	1,086.2	13.50	11.38	0.99	0.00	8.7	0.20	0.07	1.81	F	0	98	2	fix-inc	Scudder Int'l Bond
2,069.0	2,271.8	44.10	40.37	0.00	2.42	0.0	0.70	0.23	3.41	B	89	4	7	int'l	Scudder Int'l Stk
409.1	649.6	21.68	18.88	0.00	0.73	0.0	—	—	—	—	90	0	10	int'l	Scudder Latin Amer
—	96.1	—	11.57	—	—	—	—	—	—	—	0	93	7	tax-free	Scudder Ltd TF
—	49.2	—	11.58	—	—	—	—	—	—	—	0	92	8	tax-free	Scudder MA Ltd TF
375.6	277.5	14.21	12.57	0.76	0.01	6.0	0.49	0.34	1.94	A	0	92	8	tax-free	Scudder MA TF
1,012.0	703.1	11.36	10.39	0.55	0.03	5.3	0.34	0.33	1.36	A	0	98	2	tax-free	Scudder Medium TF
910.9	708.4	9.09	8.07	0.46	0.02	5.7	0.48	0.33	1.93	C	0	99	1	tax-free	Scudder Mgd Muni
229.0	182.1	11.17	9.81	0.52	0.05	5.3	0.50	0.32	2.06	D	0	99	1	tax-free	Scudder NY TF
85.0	72.9	13.59	12.11	0.70	0.04	5.8	0.45	0.32	1.82	B	0	93	7	tax-free	Scudder OH TF
76.5	67.8	13.99	12.41	0.74	0.03	6.0	0.44	0.33	1.75	B	0	99	1	tax-free	Scudder PA TF
453.7	422.3	19.07	15.71	0.10	0.00	0.6	—	—	—	—	89	0	11	int'l	Scudder Pacific Opp
123.9	112.4	15.92	14.47	0.15	1.09	1.0	1.21	0.81	3.14	F	96	0	4	growth	Scudder Qual Growth
3,196.7	2,138.8	12.01	10.92	0.76	0.00	6.9	0.12	0.13	0.73	C	0	93	7	fix-inc	Scudder ST Bond
940.0	496.9	11.53	10.54	0.86	0.00	8.2	0.07	0.06	0.71	C	0	92	8	fix-inc	Scudder ST Glob Inc
31.2	24.8	12.85	10.95	0.31	0.59	2.8	0.43	0.21	2.21	D	0	100	0	fix-inc	Scudder US Zero 2000
33.1	34.9	12.85	12.82	0.12	0.13	0.9	—	—	—	—	93	0	7	growth	Scudder Value
152.1	143.7	13.95	12.85	0.42	0.00	3.3	0.60	0.74	1.60	C	54	43	3	gr-inc	Seafirst Asst Allc
125.4	142.7	17.53	16.27	0.24	0.00	1.5	0.88	0.75	2.36	C	96	0	4	growth	Seafirst Blue Chip
82.0	56.6	11.14	10.24	0.58	0.00	5.6	0.17	0.14	1.02	C	0	94	6	fix-inc	Seafirst Bond
451.9	503.0	14.60	13.09	0.22	0.82	1.6	1.09	0.78	2.89	F	91	8	1	gr-inc	Selected Amer Sh
53.2	45.1	10.21	9.02	0.00	0.93	0.0	0.84	0.54	2.98	D	87	0	13	growth	Selected Spec Sh SC
10.3	10.2	9.20	8.49	0.51	0.00	6.0	0.20	0.18	1.08	C	0	98	2	fix-inc	Selected US Gov
76.6	75.7	14.85	13.75	0.17	0.76	1.2	0.76	0.69	2.13	D	97	0	3	growth	Sentry
1,512.1	1,548.3	54.84	55.59	0.42	0.66	0.7	0.83	0.56	2.59	C	90	0	10	growth	Sequoia
—	30.8	—	10.76	—	—	—	—	—	—	—	—	—	—	int'l	Seven Seas Emg Mkts
15.1	26.3	10.09	9.89	0.18	0.00	1.8	—	—	—	—	—	—	—	gr-inc	Seven Seas Gro & Inc
12.0	19.1	9.82	8.89	0.50	0.00	5.6	—	—	—	—	0	93	7	fix-inc	Seven Seas Inter Fix
89.3	138.3	11.93	11.56	0.26	0.00	2.3	—	—	—	—	—	—	—	growth	Seven Seas Matrix
37.5	4.0	11.92	10.94	0.22	0.00	2.0	—	—	—	—	90	0	10	agg gr	Seven Seas Sm Cap SC
22.7	9.1	9.90	9.46	0.46	0.00	4.8	—	—	—	—	0	92	8	fix-inc	Seven Seas ST Gov
309.9	302.3	10.63	10.44	0.30	0.00	2.9	—	—	—	—	98	0	2	gr-inc	Seven Seas S&P 500
1,234.7	1,209.9	10.00	9.96	0.43	0.00	4.4	—	—	—	—	0	95	5	fix-inc	Seven Seas Yld Plus
1.0	1.5	10.00	9.69	0.27	0.00	2.8	—	—	—	—	—	—	—	income	SIT Balanced
3.9	3.4	10.00	9.25	0.62	0.00	6.7	—	—	—	—	0	92	8	fix-inc	SIT Bond
—	3.8	—	9.75	—	—	—	—	—	—	—	—	—	—	int'l	SIT Develop Mkts
37.7	36.3	24.92	24.09	0.09	1.41	0.4	1.02	0.85	2.58	F	97	0	3	gr-inc	SIT Gro & Inc
332.3	303.1	12.66	11.51	0.00	1.04	0.0	1.37	0.69	3.90	F	92	0	8	agg gr	SIT Growth SC
64.9	65.3	15.66	14.88	0.04	0.27	0.3	0.87	0.30	3.69	A	92	1	7	int'l	SIT Int'l Growth
12.5	37.5	10.16	9.67	0.55	0.00	5.7	—	—	—	—	0	90	10	tax-free	SIT MN TF Inc
—	4.5	—	11.10	—	—	—	—	—	—	—	—	—	—	agg gr	SIT Sm Cap Gr SC
340.8	243.3	10.08	9.43	0.56	0.02	6.0	0.28	0.35	1.09	A	0	100	0	tax-free	SIT TF Income

No-Load Fund	Total return percent with quintile ranks by objective										Annualized		What $10,000 grew to after	
	1985	1986	1987	1988	1989	1990	1991	1992	1993	1994	3 yrs	5 yrs	3 yrs	5 yrs
SIT US Gov	—	—	—	7.9^3	11.0^4	10.9^1	12.8^5	5.5^5	7.3^5	1.8^1	4.8^3	7.6^3	11,518	14,406
Skyline Spcl Eqty II SC	—	—	—	—	—	—	—	—	—	-1.5^3	—	—	—	—
Skyline Special Eqty.‡	—	—	—	29.7^1	23.9^3	-9.3^3	46.5^3	42.4^1	22.8^1	-1.2^3	20.0^1	18.1^1	17,294	22,974
Smith Brdn Inter Gov	—	—	—	—	—	—	—	—	11.2^2	-1.7^2	—	—	—	—
Smith Brdn Mkt Track	—	—	—	—	—	—	—	—	13.2^2	1.8^2	—	—	—	—
Smith Brdn ST Gov	—	—	—	—	—	—	—	—	4.4	4.2^1	—	—	—	—
Smith Hayes Asst Allc	—	—	—	—	3.7^5	2.6^1	25.7^3	3.0^5	8.3^4	-4.2^5	2.3^5	6.6^4	10,691	13,793
Smith Hayes Blncd	—	—	—	—	13.7^4	3.9^1	13.6^5	2.1^5	13.2^3	-4.4^4	3.4^5	5.4^5	11,044	13,034
Smith Hayes Convert	—	—	—	—	12.0^5	-5.8^4	28.6^1	10.2^2	16.3^1	-8.0^5	5.7^4	7.4^4	11,802	14,300
Smith Hayes Gov Qual	—	—	—	—	12.4^3	6.8^3	14.2^4	6.6^4	5.3^5	-3.3^3	2.8^5	5.8^5	10,860	13,238
Smith Hayes Sm Cap SC	—	—	—	—	—	—	—	—	12.3^4	2.5^2	—	—	—	—
Smith Hayes Value	—	—	—	—	—	-13.0^5	21.1^5	9.8^3	12.1^3	-12.4^5	2.5^5	2.6^5	10,780	11,361
Sound Shore	—	20.6^1	-3.9^5	21.1^2	22.4^3	-10.6^5	32.2^3	21.2^1	12.0^3	0.3^3	10.8^1	10.0^2	13,607	16,080
Special Port Cash	—	—	—	—	—	8.5^3	8.1^5	5.7^4	4.8^5	2.7^1	4.4^2	5.9^5	11,370	13,330
Special Port Stk	39.3^1	20.4^1	-5.3^4	7.8^4	41.4^1	-4.2^2	67.7^1	1.9^5	10.2^4	-7.2^5	1.4^5	10.9^2	10,421	16,734
State Farm Blncd	36.1^1	14.9^4	7.8^1	11.4^4	25.7^1	10.0^1	39.2^1	5.4^4	3.3^5	5.0^1	4.6^4	11.9^1	11,431	17,504
State Farm Growth	33.8^2	12.9^3	8.8^1	11.7^4	31.9^1	4.4^1	41.9^2	2.1^5	0.6^5	6.0^1	2.9^5	10.0^2	10,887	16,125
State Farm Interim	15.5^2	11.1^2	4.7^3	5.9^4	12.0^1	9.4^1	12.3^3	6.3^2	6.8^3	-0.8^4	4.1^2	6.7^2	11,268	13,849
State Farm Muni Bd	23.0^1	18.8^2	3.7^1	9.5^5	10.3^2	7.2^1	11.1^4	7.8^5	9.8^5	-2.5^1	4.9^3	6.5^2	11,531	13,726
Steadman Amer Indust	7.8^5	-19.7^5	0.9^3	-11.1^5	5.8^5	-31.4^5	1.3^5	-6.5^5	9.1^4	-37.2^5	-13.8^5	-14.9^5	6,405	4,455
Steadman Associated	21.5^4	-2.7^5	-23.1^5	1.6^5	34.2^1	-25.0^5	24.6^3	5.6^4	10.7^4	-20.5^5	-2.4^5	-2.8^5	9,296	8,684
Steadman Investment	5.3^5	10.3^4	-17.5^5	-6.9^5	9.0^5	-15.8^5	33.9^3	-8.0^5	2.9^5	-33.8^5	-14.4^5	-6.7^5	6,267	7,068
Steadman Tech & Gro	-14.3^5	-11.3^5	-8.5^4	-25.9^5	29.9^2	-43.8^5	27.9^5	-5.3^5	-7.8^5	-37.1^5	-18.1^5	-17.0^5	5,493	3,949
SteinRoe Cap Oppty	24.9^4	16.7^2	8.7^1	-3.9^5	36.8^1	-29.1^5	62.7^2	2.4^4	27.5^1	0.0^2	9.3^2	8.6^4	13,059	15,070
SteinRoe Gov Inc	—	—	0.2^3	7.1^4	13.3^2	8.4^3	15.0^4	6.0^4	7.3^5	-3.3^3	3.2^5	6.5^4	10,996	13,709
SteinRoe Hi Yld Muni	21.0^2	18.9^2	-0.9^5	13.9^1	11.4^1	7.7^1	9.8^5	5.2^5	10.6^5	-4.2^1	3.7^5	5.7^5	11,148	13,182
SteinRoe Income	—	—	4.2^1	11.8^1	7.1^5	6.2^5	17.1^2	8.9^1	13.4^1	-4.1^4	5.8^1	8.0^1	11,834	14,709
SteinRoe Inter Bd	22.6^1	16.1^1	0.8^5	7.5^3	12.6^3	7.1^4	15.1^3	7.5^2	9.2^3	-2.8^3	4.5^2	7.1^3	11,411	14,068
SteinRoe Inter Muni	—	12.2^4	1.9^2	6.3^4	8.1^4	7.5^1	10.7^3	7.5^2	11.1^3	-3.5^3	4.9^2	6.5^2	11,527	13,716
SteinRoe Int'l	—	—	—	—	—	—	—	—	—	—	—	—	—	—
SteinRoe Ltd Mat Inc	—	—	—	—	—	—	—	—	—	0.0^3	—	—	—	—
SteinRoe Mgd Muni	22.7^1	21.8^1	0.5^1	10.9^3	10.6^1	7.0^2	11.9^3	8.1^4	11.3^3	-5.5^2	4.4^4	6.3^3	11,362	13,598
SteinRoe Prime Eqty	—	—	—	9.1^4	31.0^2	-1.8^2	32.3^3	10.0^3	12.9^3	-0.2^3	7.4^3	10.0^2	12,395	16,116
SteinRoe Spec Venture SC	—	—	—	—	—	—	—	—	—	—	—	—	—	—
SteinRoe Special	29.4^3	14.6^3	3.5^3	20.2^2	37.8^1	-5.8^4	33.9^3	14.0^2	20.4^1	-3.3^4	9.9^2	10.9^2	13,269	16,733
SteinRoe Stock	26.5^3	16.8^2	5.2^2	0.7^5	35.4^1	0.9^1	45.9^3	8.3^3	2.8^5	-3.8^4	2.3^5	9.6^3	10,716	15,780
SteinRoe Total Ret	25.6^4	17.0^3	0.3^3	7.9^5	20.2^2	-1.7^3	29.4^1	7.9^3	12.3^4	-4.1^4	5.1^4	8.1^3	11,618	14,776
SteinRoe Young Invest	—	—	—	—	—	—	—	—	—	—	—	—	—	—
Stratton Growth	27.4^3	10.7^5	-4.0^5	22.6^1	23.7^2	-6.7^4	22.0^4	6.7^4	6.4^5	7.1^1	6.7^2	6.7^4	12,160	13,834
Stratton Month Div Sh	29.7^2	20.3^2	-11.3^5	9.7^5	18.6^3	-3.8^4	34.9^1	10.3^2	6.6^5	-12.1^5	1.1^5	6.0^5	10,338	13,409
Stratton Sm Cap Yld SC	—	—	—	—	—	—	—	—	—	-2.7^4	—	—	—	—
Stratus Cap Apprec	—	—	—	—	—	—	—	—	—	-6.3^4	—	—	—	—
Stratus Eqty Inc	—	—	—	—	—	—	—	—	—	0.6^2	—	—	—	—
Stratus Gov Sec	—	—	—	—	—	—	—	—	—	-3.3^2	—	—	—	—
Stratus Inter Gov	—	—	—	—	—	—	—	6.0^4	7.0^4	-2.8^3	3.3^5	—	11,018	—
Stratus Variable Rate	—	—	—	—	—	—	—	—	—	—	—	—	—	—
Strong Advantage	—	—	—	—	9.4^4	6.6^5	10.6^4	8.4^1	7.9^2	3.6^1	6.6^1	7.4^1	12,115	14,289
Strong Amer Util	—	—	—	—	—	—	—	—	—	-2.6^3	—	—	—	—
Strong Asia Pacific	—	—	—	—	—	—	—	—	—	-5.3^4	—	—	—	—
Strong Asst Allc	19.4^4	17.6^3	-0.3^3	9.1^5	11.2^5	2.8^1	19.6^5	3.2^5	14.5^3	-1.5^3	5.2^4	7.4^4	11,640	14,311
Strong Common Stk SC‡	—	—	—	—	—	—	56.9^1	20.8^1	25.2^1	-0.5^3	14.6^1	—	15,046	—
Strong Discovery SC	—	—	—	24.4^2	23.9^3	-2.8^2	67.5^1	1.9^5	22.2^1	-5.7^4	5.5^4	13.8^1	11,733	19,115
Strong Gov Sec	—	—	3.4^1	10.5^1	9.4^4	8.1^3	16.7^2	9.2^1	12.7^1	-3.4^4	5.9^1	8.5^1	11,890	15,002
Strong Growth	—	—	—	—	—	—	—	—	—	17.3^1	—	—	—	—
Strong Hi Yld Muni	—	—	—	—	—	—	—	—	—	0.0^1	—	—	—	—
Strong Income	—	30.0^1	4.4^1	12.5^1	0.4^5	-6.2^5	14.8^4	9.4^2	16.8^1	-1.3^1	8.0^1	6.3^5	12,606	13,574
Strong Insur Muni	—	—	—	—	—	—	—	13.1^1	12.8^3	-6.5^3	6.1^1	—	11,932	—
Strong Int'l Bond	—	—	—	—	—	—	—	—	—	—	—	—	—	—
Strong Int'l Stk	—	—	—	—	—	—	—	—	47.8^2	-1.6^3	—	—	—	—
Strong Muni Bond	—	—	-1.7^3	7.6^5	7.1^5	4.8^5	13.4^1	12.2^1	11.8^5	-4.6^1	6.2^1	7.3^1	11,965	14,211

See Chapter 3 for explanation of symbols

Arranged in alphabetical order

Total Net Assets $Million December 31 1993	1994	NAV per share December 31 1993	1994	1994 per share distributions Income	Capital gains	Yield % 12/31/94	beta	R²	Std. Dev.	Sharpe Ratio	% Distribution of Portfolio 12/31/94 Stocks	Bonds	Cash	Objective	No-Load Fund
39.3	36.3	10.63	10.17	0.64	0.00	6.3	0.09	0.11	0.60	A	0	88	12	fix-inc	SIT US Gov
59.0	100.0	10.79	10.14	0.02	0.46	0.2	—	—	—	—	—	—	—	agg gr	Skyline Spcl Eqty II SC
228.0	203.0	17.83	15.64	0.00	1.93	0.0	0.97	0.46	3.36	A	97	0	3	agg gr	Skyline Special Eqty
4.9	33.3	10.36	9.47	0.58	0.13	6.1	—	—	—	—	0	111	-11	fix-inc	Smith Brdn Inter Gov
1.6	1.8	11.09	10.15	0.57	0.52	5.3	—	—	—	—	0	89	11	gr-inc	Smith Brdn Mkt Track
130.2	224.9	10.08	9.91	0.57	0.02	5.7	—	—	—	—	0	109	-9	fix-inc	Smith Brdn ST Gov
6.3	3.6	11.70	8.88	0.24	2.08	2.2	0.67	—	—	—	51	47	2	gr-inc	Smith Hayes Asst Allc
7.2	4.7	12.24	10.35	0.27	1.07	2.4	0.39	—	—	—	31	54	15	income	Smith Hayes Blncd
2.9	2.2	12.89	10.68	0.31	0.86	2.7	0.71	—	—	—	2	92	6	income	Smith Hayes Convert
9.4	7.2	10.92	9.95	0.61	0.00	6.1	0.15	—	—	—	0	98	2	fix-inc	Smith Hayes Gov Qual
4.9	8.6	12.25	12.14	0.00	0.40	0.0	—	—	—	—	97	0	3	agg gr	Smith Hayes Sm Cap SC
6.4	3.3	12.60	9.86	0.00	1.18	0.0	1.08	—	—	—	98	0	2	growth	Smith Hayes Value
58.2	56.7	16.50	15.46	0.22	0.87	1.3	0.85	0.75	2.29	A	85	0	15	growth	Sound Shore
25.6	27.2	9.67	9.37	0.55	0.00	5.9	0.23	—	—	—	0	90	10	fix-inc	Special Port Cash
76.7	75.8	36.15	33.36	0.00	0.19	0.0	1.18	—	—	—	82	0	18	agg gr	Special Port Stk
333.2	378.7	30.67	30.98	1.02	0.19	3.3	0.69	0.82	1.78	D	61	27	12	income	State Farm Blncd
736.0	796.1	22.21	22.90	0.45	0.18	2.0	0.89	0.74	2.41	F	94	0	6	growth	State Farm Growth
103.9	93.2	10.49	9.70	0.71	0.00	7.3	0.04	0.01	1.14	F	0	98	2	fix-inc	State Farm Interim
284.3	275.9	8.66	7.96	0.48	0.00	6.0	0.22	0.13	1.39	A	0	96	4	tax-free	State Farm Muni Bd
2.5	1.5	1.56	0.98	0.00	0.00	0.0	1.52	0.44	5.46	F	—	—	—	agg gr	Steadman Amer Indust
8.2	5.5	0.83	0.66	0.00	0.00	0.0	1.32	0.52	4.30	F	—	—	—	income	Steadman Associated
3.5	2.2	1.42	0.94	0.00	0.00	0.0	1.45	0.54	4.63	F	—	—	—	growth	Steadman Investment
1.5	0.9	2.48	1.56	0.00	0.00	0.0	1.52	0.32	6.35	F	—	—	—	agg gr	Steadman Tech & Gro
166.1	172.3	32.39	32.37	0.02	0.00	0.1	1.27	0.62	3.80	C	82	6	12	agg gr	SteinRoe Cap Oppty
56.4	44.4	10.16	9.26	0.57	0.00	6.2	0.26	0.23	1.23	D	0	88	12	fix-inc	SteinRoe Gov Inc
348.6	266.5	11.76	10.64	0.63	0.00	5.9	0.35	0.27	1.54	D	0	92	8	tax-free	SteinRoe Hi Yld Muni
161.8	152.9	10.14	9.06	0.67	0.00	7.4	0.30	0.26	1.34	A	0	94	6	fix-inc	SteinRoe Income
326.5	281.5	8.98	8.19	0.55	0.00	6.7	0.23	0.23	1.13	B	0	93	7	fix-inc	SteinRoe Inter Bd
258.5	215.5	11.62	10.70	0.52	0.00	4.8	0.34	0.31	1.40	B	0	92	8	tax-free	SteinRoe Inter Muni
—	74.0	—	9.88	—	—	—	—	—	—	—	94	3	3	int'l	SteinRoe Int'l
32.1	26.6	9.93	9.43	0.50	0.00	5.3	—	—	—	—	0	96	4	fix-inc	SteinRoe Ltd Mat Inc
781.4	604.6	9.36	8.36	0.49	0.00	5.8	0.39	0.30	1.66	C	0	96	4	tax-free	SteinRoe Mgd Muni
108.7	121.5	14.58	13.78	0.18	0.59	1.3	0.84	0.84	2.13	B	84	3	13	growth	SteinRoe Prime Eqty
—	18.3	—	10.41	—	—	—	—	—	—	—	88	0	12	agg gr	SteinRoe Spec Venture SC
1,167.2	1,167.7	24.00	21.72	0.15	1.31	0.7	1.02	0.80	2.67	B	92	3	5	growth	SteinRoe Special
369.1	302.6	24.39	20.29	0.15	3.02	0.6	1.08	0.77	2.89	F	95	1	4	agg gr	SteinRoe Stock
226.5	215.1	26.85	24.30	1.19	0.28	4.8	0.67	0.78	1.75	D	40	56	4	income	SteinRoe Total Ret
—	12.0	—	10.66	—	—	—	—	—	—	—	84	2	14	growth	SteinRoe Young Invest
24.6	26.6	20.05	19.61	0.54	1.28	2.6	0.77	0.73	2.10	C	87	2	11	gr-inc	Stratton Growth
176.4	121.9	29.17	23.78	1.92	0.00	8.1	0.53	0.24	2.52	F	85	9	6	income	Stratton Month Div Sh
7.8	13.7	26.62	25.38	0.53	0.00	2.1	—	—	—	—	86	0	14	growth	Stratton Sm Cap Yld SC
0.8	0.6	9.77	8.94	0.00	0.22	0.0	—	—	—	—	95	0	5	agg gr	Stratus Cap Apprec
12.3	11.2	10.25	9.97	0.23	0.11	2.3	—	—	—	—	99	0	1	gr-inc	Stratus Eqty Inc
12.6	12.7	9.86	9.18	0.36	0.00	3.9	—	—	—	—	0	96	4	fix-inc	Stratus Gov Sec
8.5	5.7	10.79	10.01	0.48	0.00	4.8	—	—	—	—	0	98	2	fix-inc	Stratus Inter Gov
—	—	—	—	—	—	—	—	—	—	—	—	—	—	fix-inc	Stratus Variable Rate
415.5	910.5	10.19	9.98	0.55	0.02	5.5	0.04	0.06	0.34	A	0	95	5	fix-inc	Strong Advantage
32.5	37.9	10.19	9.46	0.46	0.00	4.9	—	—	—	—	0	96	4	income	Strong Amer Util
0.1	57.7	10.00	9.35	0.01	0.12	0.1	—	—	—	—	89	1	10	int'l	Strong Asia Pacific
254.4	248.6	19.06	17.91	0.70	0.16	3.9	0.51	0.69	1.40	C	37	56	7	income	Strong Asst Allc
762.1	790.1	17.94	16.74	0.04	1.07	0.3	1.05	0.65	3.03	A	89	0	11	growth	Strong Common Stk SC
301.8	388.4	18.05	15.67	0.69	0.68	4.4	1.28	0.59	3.89	D	88	1	11	agg gr	Strong Discovery SC
222.0	276.8	10.61	9.63	0.62	0.00	6.5	0.26	0.23	1.28	A	0	104	-4	fix-inc	Strong Gov Sec
0.1	106.0	10.00	11.61	0.11	0.00	0.9	—	—	—	—	86	3	11	growth	Strong Growth
20.8	107.6	10.00	9.29	0.71	0.00	7.7	—	—	—	—	0	96	4	tax-free	Strong Hi Yld Muni
123.4	123.3	10.24	9.36	0.74	0.00	7.9	0.34	0.32	1.41	A	0	97	3	fix-inc	Strong Income
61.2	51.0	11.46	10.19	0.54	0.00	5.3	0.49	0.29	2.11	B	0	78	22	tax-free	Strong Insur Muni
—	10.0	—	10.36	—	—	—	—	—	—	—	0	91	9	fix-inc	Strong Int'l Bond
128.4	257.8	14.18	12.65	0.00	1.31	0.0	—	—	—	—	90	0	10	int'l	Strong Int'l Stk
398.9	279.8	10.25	9.23	0.56	0.00	6.0	0.42	0.32	1.75	A	0	82	18	tax-free	Strong Muni Bond

Stock and bond funds — comprehensive summary *continued*

Arranged in alphabetical order

No-Load Fund	1985	1986	1987	1988	1989	1990	1991	1992	1993	1994	Annualized 3 yrs.	5 yrs.	grew to after 3 yrs.	5 yrs.
Strong Opportunity	—	59.9[1]	11.8[1]	16.3[3]	18.5[4]	-11.3[5]	31.7[3]	17.4[1]	21.2[1]	3.2[2]	13.6[1]	11.4[1]	14,673	17,138
Strong ST Bond	—	—	—	10.1[1]	8.2[5]	5.1[5]	14.6[1]	6.7[2]	9.3[1]	-1.6[4]	4.7[1]	6.7[3]	11,474	13,816
Strong ST Global	—	—	—	—	—	—	—	—	—	—	—	—	—	—
Strong ST Muni	—	—	—	—	—	—	—	—	6.8[1]	-1.6[5]	—	—	—	—
Strong Total Return	25.4[4]	20.0[2]	6.0[1]	15.5[3]	2.6[5]	-7.1[4]	33.6[1]	0.5[5]	22.5[1]	-1.4[4]	6.7[2]	8.6[2]	12,149	15,075
TCW/DW Balanced	—	—	—	—	—	—	—	—	—	-9.7[5]	—	—	—	—
TCW/DW Inc & Gro	—	—	—	—	—	—	—	—	—	-3.3[4]	—	—	—	—
TCW/DW N Amer Gov	—	—	—	—	—	—	—	—	8.1[4]	-15.6[5]	—	—	—	—
TCW/DW N Amer Inter Inc	—	—	—	—	—	—	—	—	—	—	—	—	—	—
Tocqueville	—	—	—	20.4[2]	17.5[4]	1.4[1]	12.2[5]	17.0[1]	22.5[1]	-0.8[3]	12.5[1]	10.1[2]	14,218	16,173
Torchmark Gov Sec	—	—	—	—	—	—	—	—	—	-6.7[4]	—	—	—	—
Torchmark Insur TF	—	—	—	—	—	—	—	—	—	-8.7[5]	—	—	—	—
Torray	—	—	—	—	—	—	21.0[5]	21.0[1]	6.4[4]	2.4[2]	9.6[2]	—	13,181	—
Trent Equity	—	—	—	—	—	—	—	—	5.4[5]	-10.6[5]	—	—	—	—
TU&P Balanced	—	—	—	13.7[4]	19.9[3]	3.1[1]	27.0[3]	2.2[5]	4.5[5]	1.5[2]	2.7[5]	7.2[3]	10,834	14,180
TU&P Bond	—	—	—	—	—	—	—	—	8.3[4]	-2.7[2]	—	—	—	—
TU&P Growth	—	—	—	—	—	—	—	—	1.6[5]	0.4[3]	—	—	—	—
Tweedy Brwn Amer Value	—	—	—	—	—	—	—	—	—	-0.6[3]	—	—	—	—
Tweedy Brwn Glob Value	—	—	—	—	—	—	—	—	—	4.4[1]	—	—	—	—
Twentieth Cent Blncd	—	—	—	—	24.9[2]	1.8[1]	46.9[1]	-6.1[5]	7.2[4]	-0.1[2]	0.2[5]	8.5[2]	10,064	15,041
Twentieth Cent Eqty Inc	—	—	—	—	—	—	—	—	—	—	—	—	—	—
Twentieth Cent Giftrust	55.3[1]	28.0[1]	8.7[1]	11.1[4]	50.2[1]	-16.9[5]	84.9[1]	18.0[1]	31.4[1]	13.5[1]	20.7[1]	22.0[1]	17,598	27,042
Twentieth Cent Gov Inter	—	—	—	—	—	—	—	—	—	—	—	—	—	—
Twentieth Cent Gov ST	12.9[4]	9.1[4]	3.8[4]	5.6[5]	9.8[3]	7.5[5]	11.6[4]	4.4[5]	4.2[5]	-0.6[3]	2.6[5]	5.4[5]	10,812	12,979
Twentieth Cent Growth	33.9[2]	18.8[1]	13.0[1]	2.7[5]	43.1[1]	-3.9[2]	69.0[1]	-4.3[5]	3.8[5]	-1.5[3]	-0.7[5]	9.7[3]	9,782	15,895
Twentieth Cent Heritage	—	—	—	16.4[3]	35.1[1]	-9.2[4]	35.9[2]	10.1[3]	20.4[1]	-6.3[5]	7.5[3]	8.9[3]	12,418	15,326
Twentieth Cent Inter Bd	—	—	—	—	—	—	—	—	—	—	—	—	—	—
Twentieth Cent Int'l Emg	—	—	—	—	—	—	—	—	—	—	—	—	—	—
Twentieth Cent Int'l	—	—	—	—	—	—	—	4.8[1]	42.7[2]	-4.8[4]	12.5[1]	—	14,243	—
Twentieth Cent LT Bd	—	—	—	8.3[2]	13.7[2]	6.1[5]	17.3[1]	5.5[5]	10.1[3]	-4.6[5]	3.5[5]	6.6[4]	11,085	13,790
Twentieth Cent Ltd Trm	—	—	—	—	—	—	—	—	—	—	—	—	—	—
Twentieth Cent Select	33.8[2]	20.5[1]	5.6[2]	5.6[5]	39.5[1]	-0.4[2]	31.5[3]	-4.4[5]	14.7[2]	-8.0[5]	0.3[5]	5.7[5]	10,077	13,197
Twentieth Cent Strategic	—	—	—	—	—	—	—	—	—	—	—	—	—	—
Twentieth Cent TE Inter	—	—	—	6.0[4]	6.7[5]	6.3[4]	10.1[4]	7.2[4]	9.0[4]	-2.1[1]	4.6[3]	6.0[4]	11,436	13,375
Twentieth Cent TE Long	—	—	—	10.3[4]	9.8[3]	6.2[4]	12.2[2]	7.6[5]	12.1[4]	-5.6[2]	4.4[3]	6.3[3]	11,388	13,564
Twentieth Cent TE Short	—	—	—	—	—	—	—	—	—	2.4[1]	—	—	—	—
Twentieth Cent Ultra	26.2[3]	10.3[4]	6.7[1]	13.3[4]	37.0[1]	9.4[1]	86.5[1]	1.3[5]	21.8[2]	-3.6[4]	5.9[4]	19.4[1]	11,889	24,248
Twentieth Cent Value	—	—	—	—	—	—	—	—	—	4.0[1]	—	—	—	—
Twentieth Cent Vista	22.5[4]	26.3[1]	6.0[2]	2.4[5]	52.2[1]	-15.7[4]	73.7[1]	-2.1[5]	5.5[5]	4.7[1]	2.6[5]	9.6[3]	10,803	15,812
US All-Amer Eqty	—	—	—	—	—	—	26.7[3]	5.6[4]	10.0[3]	-5.3[5]	3.2[5]	—	11,002	—
US China Oppty	—	—	—	—	—	—	—	—	—	—	—	—	—	—
US Global Resrc	0.0[5]	30.9[1]	25.4[1]	-12.2[5]	22.1[3]	-16.0[5]	5.0[5]	-2.8[5]	20.5[1]	-9.7[5]	1.9[5]	-1.4[5]	10,580	9,340
US Gold Shares	-26.8[5]	37.5[3]	31.6[3]	-35.7[5]	64.7[1]	-34.2[5]	-15.7[5]	-50.8[5]	123.9[1]	-2.7[1]	2.3[5]	-9.9[5]	10,718	5,947
US Income	15.3[5]	5.6[5]	-4.3[4]	16.9[2]	37.9[1]	-8.7[5]	14.3[5]	8.1[3]	17.7[1]	-10.3[5]	4.5[5]	3.6[5]	11,417	11,919
US Inter Treas	—	—	—	—	—	—	—	—	13.2[1]	-4.9[5]	—	—	—	—
US Near Term TF	—	—	—	—	—	—	—	—	—	-0.1[1]	—	—	—	—
US Real Estate	—	—	—	20.8[2]	7.4[5]	-19.8[5]	55.4[2]	4.7[4]	0.9[5]	-11.6[5]	-2.3[5]	3.1[5]	9,337	11,631
US Spec Gov	—	—	—	—	—	—	—	—	—	-1.6[1]	—	—	—	—
US Tax Free	11.3[5]	16.9[1]	-0.2[5]	11.9[1]	8.2[3]	6.0[5]	9.5[5]	7.2[3]	11.8[2]	-5.2[5]	4.3[4]	5.7[5]	11,355	13,188
US World Gold	—	38.5[2]	31.1[4]	-18.8[4]	16.5[4]	-27.9[5]	-3.4[2]	-4.7[1]	89.8[2]	-16.9[5]	14.5[1]	0.9[2]	15,020	10,471
USAA Agg Growth SC	23.0[4]	5.6[5]	-0.8[3]	14.3[3]	16.6[4]	-12.0[4]	71.7[1]	-8.5[5]	8.1[5]	-0.8[3]	-0.6[5]	8.2[4]	9,813	14,833
USAA Balanced	—	—	—	—	—	1.4[2]	14.4[5]	5.1[4]	13.7[3]	-2.6[3]	5.2[4]	6.2[4]	11,635	13,493
USAA CA Bond	—	—	—	—	—	8.2[1]	10.9[4]	8.3[4]	12.7[3]	-9.3[5]	3.4[5]	5.8[4]	11,069	13,280
USAA Cornerstone	14.8[1]	40.8[1]	9.0[3]	8.4[3]	21.9[2]	-9.2[4]	16.3[3]	6.3[1]	23.8[4]	-1.1[2]	9.2[2]	6.6[3]	13,022	13,739
USAA Emg Mkts	—	—	—	—	—	—	—	—	—	—	—	—	—	—
USAA FL TF	—	—	—	—	—	—	—	—	—	-10.0[5]	—	—	—	—
USAA GNMA	—	—	—	—	—	—	—	6.1[4]	7.1[4]	0.0[1]	4.4[3]	—	11,362	—
USAA Gold	-20.7[4]	55.6[1]	15.7[5]	-17.1[3]	18.1[4]	-26.6[4]	-4.5[3]	-7.9[2]	58.3[5]	-9.4[3]	9.7[4]	-1.5[4]	13,214	9,266
USAA Growth & Inc	—	—	—	—	—	—	—	—	—	1.3[2]	—	—	—	—
USAA Growth	20.0[5]	10.0[4]	5.6[2]	6.6[5]	27.3[2]	-0.2[2]	27.8[4]	9.9[3]	7.5[4]	3.4[1]	6.9[3]	9.3[3]	12,203	15,574

See Chapter 3 for explanation of symbols

Total Net Assets $Million		NAV per share		1994 per share distributions		Yield % 12/31/94	Risk Analysis				% Distribution of Portfolio 12/31/94			Objective	No-Load Fund
December 31 1993	1994	December 31 1993	1994	Income	Capital gains		beta	R²	Std. Dev.	Sharpe Ratio	Stocks	Bonds	Cash		
443.5	805.7	28.23	27.71	0.13	1.28	0.5	1.07	0.81	2.77	A	87	4	9	growth	Strong Opportunity
1,531.6	1,041.1	10.23	9.42	0.65	0.00	6.9	0.12	0.14	0.70	B	0	96	4	fix-inc	Strong ST Bond
—	20.0	—	10.15	—	—	—	—	—	—	—	0	90	10	fix-inc	Strong ST Global
216.2	161.2	10.36	9.73	0.45	0.01	4.6	—	—	—	—	0	94	6	tax-free	Strong ST Muni
630.3	606.8	24.30	23.62	0.34	0.00	1.5	1.01	0.73	2.76	D	75	16	9	gr-inc	Strong Total Return
113.4	126.0	9.96	8.90	0.10	0.00	1.1	—	—	—	—	—	—	—	income	TCW/DW Balanced
58.2	56.1	10.65	9.71	0.55	0.00	5.7	—	—	—	—	—	—	—	gr-inc	TCW/DW Inc & Gro
2,853.4	880.9	10.03	7.87	0.67	0.00	8.5	—	—	—	—	0	93	7	fix-inc	TCW/DW N Amer Gov
—	4.6	—	9.12	—	—	—	—	—	—	—	0	92	8	fix-inc	TCW/DW N Amer Inter Inc
28.6	28.1	13.23	11.59	0.11	1.41	0.8	0.69	0.50	2.27	A	84	12	4	growth	Tocqueville
1.5	1.3	10.16	8.93	0.56	0.00	6.3	—	—	—	—	0	90	10	fix-inc	Torchmark Gov Sec
2.3	2.1	10.41	9.03	0.46	0.00	5.1	—	—	—	—	0	95	5	tax-free	Torchmark Insur TF
19.7	23.4	14.27	13.76	0.21	0.65	1.5	0.90	0.70	2.53	B	98	0	2	growth	Torray
5.3	3.7	11.60	8.45	0.00	1.92	0.0	—	—	—	—	100	0	0	agg gr	Trent Equity
22.4	17.6	13.65	12.02	0.28	1.54	2.1	0.71	0.73	1.93	F	67	32	1	gr-inc	TU&P Balanced
7.3	10.4	10.54	9.77	0.49	0.00	5.0	—	—	—	—	0	96	4	fix-inc	TU&P Bond
5.5	5.0	21.01	19.23	0.00	0.00	0.0	—	—	—	—	93	0	7	growth	TU&P Growth
3.1	35.7	9.94	9.82	0.06	0.00	0.6	—	—	—	—	78	0	22	gr-inc	Tweedy Brwn Amer Value
157.9	565.7	11.54	11.88	0.00	0.16	0.0	—	—	—	—	89	0	11	global	Tweedy Brwn Glob Value
683.8	689.3	16.00	15.27	0.44	0.27	2.8	0.83	0.73	2.26	F	55	35	10	gr-inc	Twentieth Cent Blncd
—	23.8	—	4.96	—	—	—	—	—	—	—	62	36	2	gr-inc	Twentieth Cent Eqty Inc
164.3	274.2	17.53	18.77	0.00	1.09	0.0	1.71	0.49	5.79	A	97	0	3	agg gr	Twentieth Cent Giftrust
—	7.7	—	9.45	—	—	—	—	—	—	—	0	96	4	fix-inc	Twentieth Cent Gov Inter
493.6	382.6	9.65	9.16	0.44	0.00	4.8	0.09	0.14	0.58	D	0	86	14	fix-inc	Twentieth Cent Gov ST
4,552.7	4,158.0	22.40	18.74	0.05	3.22	0.2	1.26	0.73	3.48	F	99	0	1	agg gr	Twentieth Cent Growth
724.0	851.6	10.61	9.35	0.03	0.54	0.3	1.28	0.74	3.48	C	92	5	3	growth	Twentieth Cent Heritage
—	5.0	—	9.44	—	—	—	—	—	—	—	0	92	8	fix-inc	Twentieth Cent Inter Bd
—	111.9	—	5.38	—	—	—	—	—	—	—	86	10	4	int'l	Twentieth Cent Int'l Emg
949.9	1,272.4	7.70	6.96	0.00	0.37	0.0	0.72	0.24	3.46	A	94	1	5	int'l	Twentieth Cent Int'l
158.3	118.9	9.88	8.85	0.59	0.00	6.6	0.25	0.21	1.29	F	0	91	9	fix-inc	Twentieth Cent LT Bd
—	4.6	—	9.58	—	—	—	—	—	—	—	0	95	5	fix-inc	Twentieth Cent Ltd Trm
4,938.0	3,995.2	39.46	33.10	0.28	2.87	0.8	1.13	0.82	2.93	F	96	0	4	growth	Twentieth Cent Select
														gr-inc	Twentieth Cent Strategic
97.4	77.0	10.66	9.88	0.47	0.08	4.7	0.28	0.34	1.11	A	0	95	5	tax-free	Twentieth Cent TE Inter
68.2	49.2	10.80	9.64	0.52	0.04	5.3	0.42	0.32	1.70	C	0	94	6	tax-free	Twentieth Cent TE Long
53.4	61.2	10.06	9.93	0.37	0.00	3.7	—	—	—	—	0	93	7	tax-free	Twentieth Cent TE Short
8,362.4	9,850.8	21.39	19.95	0.00	0.65	0.0	1.61	0.57	5.02	D	96	0	4	agg gr	Twentieth Cent Ultra
61.8	153.1	5.12	4.92	0.12	0.27	2.4	—	—	—	—	93	5	2	gr-inc	Twentieth Cent Value
796.6	820.2	10.27	10.72	0.00	0.03	0.0	1.59	0.58	4.92	F	94	0	6	agg gr	Twentieth Cent Vista
11.7	9.2	21.13	17.45	0.39	2.17	2.0	0.92	0.89	2.25	F	105	0	-5	gr-inc	US All-Amer Eqty
—	20.9	—	7.09	—	—	—	—	—	—	—	89	0	11	int'l	US China Oppty
23.9	20.4	6.50	5.56	0.28	0.03	5.0	0.88	0.46	3.05	F	96	0	4	growth	US Global Resrc
338.0	291.6	2.88	2.73	0.07	0.00	2.6	0.15	0.00	10.17	F	98	0	2	prec met	US Gold Shares
13.4	10.0	14.08	12.30	0.32	0.02	2.6	0.91	0.57	2.82	F	87	9	4	income	US Income
5.2	4.2	11.11	9.93	0.64	0.00	6.4	—	—	—	—	0	96	4	fix-inc	US Inter Treas
6.8	9.2	10.76	10.32	0.43	0.00	4.2	—	—	—	—	0	96	4	tax-free	US Near Term TF
18.0	11.0	10.69	9.27	0.18	0.00	1.9	1.10	0.37	4.27	F	99	0	1	sector	US Real Estate
24.7	7.4	10.02	9.42	0.45	0.00	4.7	—	—	—	—	0	98	2	fix-inc	US Spec Gov
21.2	16.1	12.24	10.89	0.72	0.00	6.6	0.40	0.31	1.69	F	0	98	2	tax-free	US Tax Free
168.6	182.5	17.65	14.63	0.03	0.00	0.2	0.60	0.03	8.34	B	97	0	3	prec met	US World Gold
288.5	283.8	20.22	18.46	0.00	1.55	0.0	1.46	0.55	4.63	F	95	0	5	agg gr	USAA Agg Growth SC
127.4	124.7	12.71	11.64	0.47	0.27	3.9	0.50	0.61	1.47	C	39	47	14	income	USAA Balanced
427.5	335.2	10.94	9.36	0.58	0.00	6.2	0.52	0.36	2.02	F	0	97	3	tax-free	USAA CA Bond
762.8	841.3	23.46	21.24	0.58	1.38	2.6	0.65	0.50	2.14	A	76	12	12	global	USAA Cornerstone
—	10.9	—	9.17	—	—	—	—	—	—	—	76	0	24	int'l	USAA Emg Mkts
21.6	37.4	9.98	8.51	0.48	0.00	5.7	—	—	—	—	0	86	14	tax-free	USAA FL TF
277.2	244.9	10.28	9.57	0.70	0.00	7.4	0.16	0.14	0.97	B	0	100	0	fix-inc	USAA GNMA
181.2	158.5	9.49	8.59	0.01	0.00	0.1	0.29	0.01	7.49	D	96	0	4	prec met	USAA Gold
95.1	150.5	10.38	10.18	0.22	0.11	2.1	—	—	—	—	93	1	6	gr-inc	USAA Growth & Inc
617.4	677.2	17.69	15.63	0.27	2.51	1.5	0.97	0.73	2.65	C	95	0	5	growth	USAA Growth

| No-Load Fund | Total return percent with quintile ranks by objective | | | | | | | | | | Annualized | | What $10,000 grew to after | |
	1985	1986	1987	1988	1989	1990	1991	1992	1993	1994	3 yrs.	5 yrs.	3 yrs.	5 yrs.
USAA Income Stk	—	—	—	19.4[1]	27.0[1]	-1.4[3]	27.2[2]	7.7[3]	11.6[4]	-0.7[2]	6.1[3]	8.4[3]	11,933	14,964
USAA Income	19.0[4]	12.6[2]	2.6[2]	9.9[1]	16.2[1]	7.7[4]	19.2[1]	8.3[1]	9.9[3]	-5.2[5]	4.1[3]	7.7[1]	11,285	14,484
USAA International	—	—	—	—	17.4[4]	-9.3[2]	13.4[2]	-0.3[2]	40.1[2]	2.7[2]	12.8[1]	8.1[1]	14,335	14,748
USAA NY Bond	—	—	—	—	—	—	13.8[1]	9.0[3]	13.5[2]	-9.0[5]	4.0[4]	—	11,244	
USAA ST Bond	—	—	—	—	—	—	—	—	—	0.0[3]	—	—		
USAA TE Inter	16.3[2]	13.6[3]	0.9[4]	8.7[2]	9.2[1]	6.7[3]	11.1[2]	8.5[2]	11.5[3]	-4.0[3]	5.1[1]	6.6[1]	11,606	13,765
USAA TE Long	19.8[3]	17.3[3]	-1.9[3]	12.5[2]	10.6[1]	6.6[3]	12.4[2]	8.6[3]	12.5[4]	-7.9[4]	4.0[4]	6.1[4]	11,250	13,472
USAA TE Short	9.5[3]	8.2[3]	2.5[3]	6.1[1]	7.4[1]	5.9[5]	7.7[3]	6.0[4]	5.5[4]	0.8[2]	4.1[3]	5.2[4]	11,273	12,855
USAA Texas TF	—	—	—	—	—	—	—	—	—	—	—	—		
USAA VA Bond	—	—	—	—	—	—	11.7[3]	8.5[4]	12.6[3]	-6.3[3]	4.6[3]	—	11,448	—
USAA World Growth	—	—	—	—	—	—	—	—	24.0[3]	0.6[2]	—	—	—	—
Valley Forge	10.5[5]	5.5[5]	4.7[2]	7.0[5]	13.0[5]	-5.4[3]	7.9[5]	9.3[3]	17.1[2]	5.9[1]	10.7[1]	6.7[4]	13,558	13,834
Value Line Adj Rate Gov	—	—	—	—	—	—	—	—	6.1[3]	-9.9[5]	—	—		
Value Line Agg Inc	—	—	-2.0[4]	6.3[5]	2.3[5]	-3.7[5]	26.6[1]	12.2[1]	19.0[1]	-4.1[3]	8.6[1]	9.3[1]	12,804	15,617
Value Line Asst All	—	—	—	—	—	—	—	—	—	3.4[1]	—	—		
Value Line Convert	—	16.7[4]	-6.1[5]	16.0[2]	10.7[5]	-3.9[4]	28.6[2]	13.8[1]	14.8[2]	-5.2[4]	7.4[2]	8.9[2]	12,384	15,311
Value Line Fund	35.6[1]	17.0[2]	5.0[2]	9.7[4]	31.4[1]	-0.8[2]	48.8[1]	4.7[4]	6.8[4]	-4.5[4]	2.2[5]	9.5[2]	10,682	15,774
Value Line Income	23.7[4]	16.6[4]	-2.3[3]	12.2[4]	22.5[2]	2.0[1]	28.4[2]	1.7[5]	8.2[5]	-4.3[4]	1.8[5]	6.7[4]	10,537	13,804
Value Line Lev Gro	27.1[3]	23.0[1]	2.8[2]	6.4[5]	32.3[2]	-1.7[2]	46.2[3]	-2.5[5]	16.2[3]	-3.7[4]	3.0[4]	9.4[3]	10,912	15,692
Value Line NY TE	—	—	—	10.8[3]	8.4[5]	4.5[5]	14.4[1]	9.5[1]	13.9[1]	-7.7[4]	4.8[3]	6.6[2]	11,508	13,754
Value Line Sm Cap	—	—	—	—	—	—	—	—	—	-0.6[3]	—	—		
Value Line Spec Sit	21.1[5]	5.1[5]	-9.3[5]	3.3[5]	21.7[4]	-4.5[2]	36.6[4]	-3.5[5]	13.0[4]	1.0[2]	3.3[4]	7.5[4]	11,021	14,382
Value Line TE Hi Yld	19.8[3]	13.7[5]	0.5[1]	11.0[3]	8.2[5]	6.2[4]	12.2[2]	7.9[5]	11.5[5]	-6.9[3]	3.8[5]	5.9[4]	11,193	13,339
Value Line US Gov	21.2[3]	10.7[5]	3.4[1]	7.9[3]	11.9[4]	10.3[1]	16.4[3]	6.3[4]	9.8[4]	-10.6[5]	1.4[5]	6.0[5]	10,432	13,386
Vangd Asset Alloc	—	—	—	—	23.7[2]	0.9[2]	25.4[2]	7.5[4]	13.5[3]	-2.3[3]	6.0[3]	8.6[2]	11,917	15,071
Vangd Bond Idx Inter	—	—	—	—	—	—	—	—	—	—	—	—	—	—
Vangd Bond Idx Long	—	—	—	—	—	—	—	—	—	—	—	—	—	—
Vangd Bond Idx Short	—	—	—	—	—	—	—	—	—	—	—	—	—	—
Vangd Bond Idx Total	—	—	1.5[4]	7.4[3]	13.6[2]	8.6[3]	15.2[3]	7.1[2]	9.7[3]	-2.7[3]	4.6[2]	7.5[2]	11,439	14,321
Vangd CA Insur Inter	—	—	—	—	—	—	—	—	—	—	—	—	—	—
Vangd CA Insur LT	—	—	-3.9[4]	12.1[2]	10.5[1]	7.0[2]	11.0[4]	9.4[2]	12.8[3]	-5.7[2]	5.2[2]	6.7[2]	11,640	13,826
Vangd Convert	—	—	-10.7[5]	15.7[3]	15.8[4]	-8.2[5]	34.2[1]	19.0[1]	13.5[3]	-5.7[5]	8.4[1]	9.4[2]	12,739	15,699
Vangd Equity Inc	—	—	—	—	26.5[1]	-11.9[5]	25.2[3]	9.2[3]	14.6[3]	-1.5[3]	7.2[3]	6.3[4]	12,317	13,579
Vangd Explorer SC	22.3[5]	-8.5[5]	-6.9[4]	25.8[1]	9.4[5]	-10.8[3]	55.9[2]	13.0[3]	15.4[3]	0.5[2]	9.4[2]	12.8[2]	13,108	18,228
Vangd FL Insur	—	—	—	—	—	—	—	—	13.4[2]	-4.7[1]	—	—		
Vangd GNMA	20.7[2]	11.7[3]	2.2[3]	8.8[1]	14.8[1]	10.3[1]	16.8[2]	6.9[3]	5.9[5]	-1.0[1]	3.9[3]	7.6[2]	11,208	14,438
Vangd Hi Yld Corp	22.0[2]	16.9[2]	2.6[2]	13.6[1]	1.9[5]	-6.0[5]	29.2[1]	14.2[1]	18.2[1]	-1.7[1]	9.9[1]	10.0[1]	13,276	16,127
Vangd Idx 500	31.2[2]	17.8[2]	4.7[2]	16.2[3]	31.4[1]	-3.4[3]	30.1[2]	7.5[3]	9.9[3]	1.2[2]	6.1[3]	8.5[2]	11,948	15,029
Vangd Idx Balanced	—	—	—	—	—	—	—	—	10.0[3]	-1.5[4]	—	—		
Vangd Idx Emg Mkt	—	—	—	—	—	—	—	—	—	—	—	—	—	—
Vangd Idx Europe	—	—	—	—	—	—	12.4[3]	-3.3[2]	29.2[4]	1.9[2]	8.4[3]	—	12,719	—
Vangd Idx Extend Mkt	—	—	—	19.7[2]	23.8[3]	-13.9[5]	41.8[2]	12.4[2]	14.5[2]	-1.8[4]	8.1[2]	9.1[3]	12,644	15,440
Vangd Idx Growth	—	—	—	—	—	—	—	—	1.5[5]	2.9[1]	—	—		
Vangd Idx Pacific	—	—	—	—	—	—	10.8[3]	-18.2[5]	35.5[3]	12.9[1]	7.8[3]	—	12,519	—
Vangd Idx Sm Cap SC	23.0[4]	0.2[5]	-7.0[4]	24.6[2]	10.5[5]	-18.1[5]	45.1[3]	18.2[1]	18.7[2]	-0.5[2]	11.7[1]	10.6[3]	13,947	16,566
Vangd Idx Total Mkt	—	—	—	—	—	—	—	—	10.6[3]	-0.1[3]	—	—		
Vangd Idx Value	—	—	—	—	—	—	—	—	18.2[1]	-0.6[3]	—	—		
Vangd Inter Corp	—	—	—	—	—	—	—	—	—	-4.2[4]	—	—		
Vangd Inter Trsy	—	—	—	—	—	—	—	7.8[1]	11.4[2]	-4.3[5]	4.7[2]	—	11,483	—
Vangd Int'l Growth	55.5[2]	56.7[4]	12.7[3]	11.6[4]	24.8[2]	-12.0[3]	4.7[5]	-5.8[3]	44.7[2]	0.7[3]	11.2[2]	4.8[3]	13,739	12,653
Vangd LT Corp	22.0[3]	14.3[3]	0.2[3]	9.7[2]	15.2[2]	6.2[3]	20.9[1]	9.8[1]	14.6[2]	-5.3[4]	6.0[2]	8.9[1]	11,914	15,298
Vangd LT Trsy	—	—	-2.9[4]	9.2[2]	17.9[1]	5.8[4]	17.4[2]	7.4[3]	16.8[1]	-7.0[4]	5.2[2]	7.7[2]	11,657	14,481
Vangd Morgan	30.1[2]	7.1[4]	5.0[2]	22.4[2]	22.6[4]	-1.5[2]	29.1[5]	9.5[3]	7.3[5]	-1.7[3]	4.9[4]	8.0[4]	11,556	14,691
Vangd Muni Hi Yld	21.7[1]	19.7[1]	-1.6[3]	13.8[1]	11.1[1]	5.9[4]	14.7[1]	9.9[1]	12.7[3]	-5.1[2]	5.5[1]	7.4[1]	11,751	14,280
Vangd Muni Insur LT	19.4[3]	18.6[2]	0.1[2]	12.8[1]	10.6[1]	7.0[2]	12.5[2]	9.2[2]	13.1[2]	-5.6[2]	5.2[2]	7.0[1]	11,656	14,033
Vangd Muni Inter	17.3[1]	15.8[1]	1.6[2]	10.0[1]	10.0[1]	7.2[1]	12.2[1]	8.9[1]	11.6[2]	-2.1[1]	5.9[1]	7.4[1]	11,885	14,289
Vangd Muni Long	20.8[2]	19.4[2]	-1.1[2]	12.2[1]	11.5[1]	6.8[2]	13.5[1]	9.3[1]	13.5[2]	-5.8[2]	5.3[1]	7.2[1]	11,687	14,165
Vangd Muni Ltd	—	—	—	6.4[1]	8.1[1]	7.0[1]	9.5[1]	6.6[2]	6.3[3]	0.1[3]	4.3[3]	5.8[1]	11,336	13,282
Vangd Muni Short	7.0[4]	7.4[4]	4.1[1]	5.6[3]	7.0[2]	6.6[3]	7.2[5]	4.7[5]	3.8[5]	1.6[1]	3.4[4]	4.8[4]	11,049	12,631
Vangd NJ Insur LT	—	—	—	—	10.4[1]	7.7[1]	11.2[4]	9.4[2]	13.4[2]	-5.2[2]	5.5[1]	7.1[1]	11,749	14,075

See Chapter 3 for explanation of symbols

Total Net Assets $Million		NAV per share		1994 per share distributions		Yield %	Risk Analysis				% Distribution of Portfolio 12/31/94			Objective	No-Load Fund
December 31 1993	1994	December 31 1993	1994	Income	Capital gains	12/31/94	beta	R^2	Std. Dev.	Sharpe Ratio	Stocks	Bonds	Cash		
1,129.9	1,171.7	14.13	13.06	0.75	0.22	5.6	0.85	0.77	2.24	D	75	22	3	income	USAA Income Stk
1,945.8	1,611.8	12.71	11.19	0.86	0.00	7.7	0.36	0.29	1.56	D	14	85	1	fix-inc	USAA Income
131.9	337.8	16.10	15.56	0.00	0.97	0.0	0.73	0.24	3.47	A	90	3	7	int'l	USAA International
61.3	45.8	11.83	10.17	0.61	0.00	6.0	0.51	0.35	2.00	F	0	102	-2	tax-free	USAA NY Bond
41.2	50.6	10.03	9.53	0.50	0.00	5.2	—	—	—	—	0	55	45	fix-inc	USAA ST Bond
1,660.9	1,416.1	13.26	12.02	0.69	0.03	5.7	0.35	0.32	1.42	B	0	99	1	tax-free	USAA TE Inter
2,014.0	1,661.2	14.18	12.22	0.78	0.09	6.3	0.44	0.33	1.77	D	0	98	2	tax-free	USAA TE Long
954.8	810.8	10.70	10.33	0.46	0.00	4.4	0.12	0.34	0.48	B	0	89	11	tax-free	USAA TE Short
—	4.7	—	9.48	—	—	—	—	—	—	—	0	101	-1	tax-free	USAA Texas TF
253.6	215.5	11.47	10.14	0.62	0.00	6.1	0.44	0.35	1.72	C	0	97	3	tax-free	USAA VA Bond
95.9	185.3	12.70	12.50	0.00	0.28	0.0	—	—	—	—	92	2	6	global	USAA World Growth
10.0	10.7	9.51	9.41	0.18	0.48	1.8	0.28	0.26	1.26	A	42	4	54	growth	Valley Forge
42.6	22.4	9.97	8.52	0.48	0.00	5.7	—	—	—	—	0	59	41	fix-inc	Value Line Adj Rate Gov
43.1	30.1	7.87	6.88	0.68	0.00	9.9	0.21	0.13	1.33	A	0	85	15	fix-inc	Value Line Agg Inc
13.2	22.4	10.55	10.74	0.06	0.11	0.6	—	—	—	—	53	10	37	income	Value Line Asst All
51.8	45.1	12.85	11.01	0.76	0.43	6.6	0.58	0.52	1.85	B	1	93	6	income	Value Line Convert
331.1	272.8	17.90	14.36	0.10	2.61	0.6	1.23	0.73	3.37	F	83	0	17	growth	Value Line Fund
162.3	131.6	6.77	6.21	0.21	0.05	3.4	0.70	0.72	1.90	F	57	31	12	income	Value Line Income
302.3	264.8	24.67	23.18	0.11	0.45	0.5	1.27	0.71	3.54	F	88	4	8	agg gr	Value Line Lev Gro
44.3	36.9	10.73	9.32	0.52	0.07	5.6	0.51	0.31	2.15	D	0	90	10	tax-free	Value Line NY TE
11.9	10.5	12.07	11.65	0.00	0.33	0.0	—	—	—	—	91	0	9	agg gr	Value Line Sm Cap
91.4	90.2	16.95	16.15	0.00	0.96	0.0	1.39	0.46	4.83	F	86	0	14	agg gr	Value Line Spec Sit
290.1	225.9	11.27	9.89	0.57	0.04	5.7	0.47	0.33	1.90	F	0	92	8	tax-free	Value Line TE Hi Yld
450.7	289.7	12.62	10.52	0.79	0.00	7.5	0.27	0.19	1.40	F	0	93	7	fix-inc	Value Line US Gov
1,125.8	1,125.6	14.45	13.54	0.57	0.00	4.2	0.75	0.74	2.03	D	50	48	2	income	Vangd Asset Alloc
—	71.4	—	9.18	—	—	—	—	—	—	—	0	97	3	fix-inc	Vangd Bond Idx Inter
—	8.6	—	8.96	—	—	—	—	—	—	—	0	96	4	fix-inc	Vangd Bond Idx Long
—	77.0	—	9.50	—	—	—	—	—	—	—	0	98	2	fix-inc	Vangd Bond Idx Short
1,540.2	1,730.7	10.06	9.17	0.62	0.00	6.8	0.24	0.23	1.13	B	0	98	2	fix-inc	Vangd Bond Idx Total
—	110.0	—	9.73	—	—	—	—	—	—	—	0	81	19	tax-free	Vangd CA Insur Inter
1,074.7	830.2	11.37	10.13	0.61	0.00	6.0	0.48	0.29	2.06	C	0	95	5	tax-free	Vangd CA Insur LT
204.4	170.7	11.91	10.55	0.51	0.18	4.8	0.79	0.61	2.34	C	4	91	5	income	Vangd Convert
1,067.9	859.0	13.66	12.77	0.58	0.09	4.5	0.81	0.69	2.28	C	86	0	14	income	Vangd Equity Inc
847.7	1,121.6	45.11	42.86	0.17	2.26	0.4	1.09	0.53	3.50	B	85	0	15	agg gr	Vangd Explorer SC
303.7	328.1	10.98	9.91	0.56	0.00	5.6	—	—	—	—	0	95	5	tax-free	Vangd FL Insur
7,073.2	5,777.8	10.37	9.58	0.68	0.01	7.1	0.18	0.20	0.96	B	0	98	2	fix-inc	Vangd GNMA
2,529.8	2,120.7	8.02	7.20	0.68	0.00	9.4	0.31	0.24	1.47	A	0	93	7	fix-inc	Vangd Hi Yld Corp
8,272.7	9,356.3	43.83	42.97	1.17	0.20	2.7	0.96	0.93	2.31	C	100	0	0	gr-inc	Vangd Idx 500
367.1	402.9	10.91	10.34	0.40	0.00	3.9	—	—	—	—	59	39	2	gr-inc	Vangd Idx Balanced
—	83.4	—	10.87	—	—	—	—	—	—	—	94	0	6	int'l	Vangd Idx Emg Mkt
600.8	715.0	11.88	11.76	0.28	0.06	2.4	0.79	0.25	3.73	C	98	0	2	int'l	Vangd Idx Europe
927.9	967.3	19.43	18.52	0.28	0.29	1.5	1.09	0.82	2.80	C	98	0	2	growth	Vangd Idx Extend Mkt
50.6	86.2	10.20	10.28	0.21	0.00	2.0	—	—	—	—	100	0	0	gr-inc	Vangd Idx Growth
493.6	697.1	10.13	11.30	0.08	0.06	0.7	0.65	0.06	6.57	D	99	0	1	int'l	Vangd Idx Pacific
488.9	605.4	15.67	14.99	0.22	0.37	1.4	1.12	0.63	3.32	A	98	0	2	agg gr	Vangd Idx Sm Cap SC
512.3	785.7	11.69	11.37	0.27	0.03	2.4	—	—	—	—	98	0	2	growth	Vangd Idx Total Mkt
190.1	296.9	11.73	11.12	0.38	0.16	3.4	—	—	—	—	100	0	0	gr-inc	Vangd Idx Value
64.8	151.5	9.94	8.95	0.58	0.00	6.4	—	—	—	—	0	98	2	fix-inc	Vangd Inter Corp
984.9	844.2	10.71	9.63	0.60	0.03	6.2	0.29	0.19	1.53	C	0	95	5	fix-inc	Vangd Inter Trsy
2,127.3	2,927.7	13.51	13.43	0.18	0.00	1.3	0.71	0.20	3.68	A	98	0	2	int'l	Vangd Int'l Growth
3,168.4	2,552.3	9.22	8.05	0.62	0.07	7.6	0.37	0.23	1.78	B	0	95	5	fix-inc	Vangd LT Corp
823.4	644.2	10.57	9.05	0.66	0.12	7.3	0.46	0.25	2.14	D	0	97	3	fix-inc	Vangd LT Trsy
1,135.2	1,074.8	12.01	11.36	0.14	0.31	1.2	1.12	0.92	2.73	C	93	0	7	agg gr	Vangd Morgan
1,857.5	1,572.6	11.01	9.66	0.63	0.17	6.4	0.46	0.30	1.96	B	0	92	8	tax-free	Vangd Muni Hi Yld
2,129.3	1,738.0	12.81	11.23	0.70	0.17	6.1	0.48	0.31	2.03	C	0	95	5	tax-free	Vangd Muni Insur LT
5,187.5	4,585.0	13.52	12.39	0.69	0.16	5.5	0.33	0.28	1.41	A	0	92	8	tax-free	Vangd Muni Inter
1,083.8	920.3	11.29	9.88	0.61	0.16	6.1	0.48	0.29	2.05	C	0	92	8	tax-free	Vangd Muni Long
1,808.5	1,629.5	10.82	10.37	0.46	0.00	4.4	0.13	0.26	0.60	D	0	79	21	tax-free	Vangd Muni Ltd
1,456.9	1,463.5	15.63	15.33	0.55	0.00	3.6	0.05	0.19	0.26	A	0	37	63	tax-free	Vangd Muni Short
758.8	653.9	11.91	10.67	0.62	0.00	5.8	0.47	0.32	1.93	B	0	93	7	tax-free	Vangd NJ Insur LT

No-Load Fund	1985	1986	1987	1988	1989	1990	1991	1992	1993	1994	Annualized 3 yrs.	5 yrs.	What $10,000 grew to after 3 yrs.	5 yrs.
Vangd NY Insur	—	—	-3.5[4]	12.0[2]	10.4[2]	6.3[3]	12.8[1]	9.7[1]	13.1[2]	-5.6[2]	5.4[1]	7.0[1]	11,711	14,039
Vangd OH Insur LT	—	—	—	—	—	—	12.0[3]	9.5[1]	12.9[3]	-5.1[2]	5.4[1]	—	11,723	—
Vangd PA Insur LT	—	—	-1.3[3]	12.3[2]	10.6[1]	6.9[2]	12.2[3]	10.2[1]	12.7[3]	-4.5[1]	5.8[1]	7.3[1]	11,856	14,226
Vangd Prefrd Stk	29.7[1]	24.7[1]	-7.7[5]	7.9[3]	18.7[1]	6.4[3]	20.9[1]	8.4[2]	13.0[2]	-7.9[5]	4.1[4]	7.7[2]	11,286	14,516
Vangd Primecap‡	35.8[1]	23.5[1]	-2.3[4]	14.7[4]	21.6[3]	-2.8[3]	33.0[3]	9.0[3]	18.0[2]	11.4[1]	12.7[1]	13.1[1]	14,328	18,534
Vangd Quantitative	—	—	4.0[2]	16.8[3]	31.9[1]	-2.5[2]	30.1[2]	7.0[4]	13.8[2]	-0.6[3]	6.6[3]	9.0[2]	12,104	15,355
Vangd Spec-Energy	14.4[5]	12.6[3]	6.1[2]	21.4[2]	43.4[1]	-1.4[2]	0.2[5]	6.2[4]	26.3[2]	-1.6[3]	9.7[3]	5.5[5]	13,194	13,036
Vangd Spec-Gold	-5.4[3]	49.7[1]	38.7[2]	-14.2[2]	30.4[2]	-20.0[2]	4.3[1]	-19.4[4]	93.2[2]	-5.4[1]	13.8[2]	4.2[1]	14,721	12,291
Vangd Spec-Health	45.6[1]	21.4[2]	-0.5[2]	28.4[1]	32.9[3]	16.8[1]	46.3[2]	-1.6[5]	11.8[4]	9.5[1]	6.4[4]	15.5[2]	12,047	20,577
Vangd Spec-Util	—	—	—	—	—	—	—	—	15.0[2]	-8.5[5]	—	—	—	—
Vangd ST Corp	14.9[3]	11.4[2]	4.5[3]	7.0[2]	11.5[2]	9.2[2]	13.1[3]	7.3[1]	7.0[2]	-0.1[3]	4.7[1]	7.2[1]	11,467	14,163
Vangd ST Federal	—	—	—	—	11.4[2]	9.3[1]	12.2[3]	6.2[3]	7.0[2]	-0.9[4]	4.0[2]	6.7[3]	11,255	13,804
Vangd ST Trsy	—	—	—	—	—	—	—	6.8[2]	6.3[3]	-0.5[3]	4.1[2]	—	11,293	—
Vangd Star:Cons Gro	—	—	—	—	—	—	—	—	—	—	—	—	—	—
Vangd Star:Growth	—	—	—	—	—	—	—	—	—	—	—	—	—	—
Vangd Star:Income	—	—	—	—	—	—	—	—	—	—	—	—	—	—
Vangd Star:Mod Gr	—	—	—	—	—	—	—	—	—	—	—	—	—	—
Vangd Star:Star	—	13.8[4]	1.6[3]	19.0[2]	18.6[4]	-3.6[3]	24.1[3]	10.5[2]	11.0[3]	-0.3[3]	6.9[2]	7.9[3]	12,227	14,623
Vangd Tax Mgd:Blncd	—	—	—	—	—	—	—	—	—	—	—	—	—	—
Vangd Tax Mgd:Cap App	—	—	—	—	—	—	—	—	—	—	—	—	—	—
Vangd Tax Mgd:Gro & Inc	—	—	—	—	—	—	—	—	—	—	—	—	—	—
Vangd Trust Int'l	40.4[4]	49.8[5]	24.0[2]	18.8[2]	25.9[2]	-12.2[3]	9.9[3]	-8.7[4]	30.5[4]	5.3[1]	7.8[3]	3.9[4]	12,533	12,094
Vangd Trust US	20.5[5]	13.5[4]	1.7[3]	24.6[1]	17.2[4]	-8.3[4]	26.5[3]	6.4[4]	17.2[2]	-3.9[5]	6.2[3]	6.8[4]	11,989	13,900
Vangd US Growth	36.6[1]	7.8[5]	-5.4[5]	8.8[4]	37.7[1]	4.6[1]	46.7[1]	2.8[5]	-1.4[5]	3.9[1]	1.7[5]	10.1[2]	10,522	16,148
Vangd Wellesley Inc	27.4[3]	18.2[3]	-1.9[3]	13.5[4]	20.8[2]	3.8[1]	21.4[4]	8.6[3]	14.6[3]	-4.4[4]	6.0[3]	8.4[3]	11,904	14,995
Vangd Wellington	28.4[2]	18.3[2]	2.3[3]	16.1[2]	21.5[2]	-2.8[3]	23.5[4]	7.9[3]	13.5[3]	-0.5[2]	6.8[3]	7.9[3]	12,187	14,617
Vangd Windsor II	—	21.5[1]	-2.1[5]	24.7[1]	27.7[2]	-10.0[5]	28.4[3]	11.9[2]	13.6[2]	-1.2[4]	7.9[2]	7.8[3]	12,564	14,522
Vangd Windsor‡	27.9[2]	20.3[1]	1.2[3]	28.7[1]	15.0[4]	-15.5[5]	28.4[3]	16.4[1]	19.3[1]	-0.1[3]	11.5[1]	8.5[2]	13,864	15,047
Vangd-Adml Inter	—	—	—	—	—	—	—	—	11.7[2]	-4.2[4]	—	—	—	—
Vangd-Adml Long	—	—	—	—	—	—	—	—	17.0[1]	-6.9[4]	—	—	—	—
Vangd-Adml Short	—	—	—	—	—	—	—	—	7.0[2]	-0.3[3]	—	—	—	—
Vista Bond	—	—	—	—	—	—	15.2[4]	7.1[3]	10.4[3]	-3.2[2]	4.6[3]	—	11,447	—
Vista Equity	—	—	—	—	—	—	31.3[3]	5.2[4]	8.6[4]	0.2[3]	4.6[4]	—	11,452	—
Vista ST Bond	—	—	—	—	—	—	9.1[5]	5.0[4]	4.5[4]	2.4[1]	4.0[2]	—	11,240	—
Volumetric	—	7.4[5]	-1.6[4]	20.0[2]	15.8[5]	-5.1[3]	34.8[2]	10.6[2]	2.1[5]	-2.1[4]	3.4[4]	7.2[4]	11,059	14,150
Vontobel EuroPac	—	—	—	—	—	—	18.7[1]	-3.5[2]	40.2[2]	-4.9[4]	8.8[3]	—	12,867	—
Vontobel Int'l Bd	—	—	—	—	—	—	—	—	—	—	—	—	—	—
Vontobel US Value	—	—	—	—	—	—	28.2[4]	5.6[4]	5.7[4]	0.3[3]	3.8[4]	—	11,197	—
Wade	19.0[5]	10.8[4]	10.3[1]	-10.2[5]	26.2[2]	-3.8[3]	15.6[5]	7.6[3]	9.3[4]	-1.3[4]	5.1[4]	5.2[5]	11,597	12,892
Warbg Pincus Balanced	—	—	—	—	—	3.1[1]	25.1[3]	7.5[4]	16.2[2]	1.3[1]	8.2[2]	10.3[1]	12,662	16,331
Warbg Pincus Cap App	—	—	—	21.4[2]	26.8[2]	-5.5[3]	26.3[4]	7.6[3]	15.7[2]	-2.9[4]	6.6[3]	7.6[4]	12,096	14,441
Warbg Pincus Emg Gro SC	—	—	—	—	21.8[4]	-9.9[3]	56.1[2]	12.1[3]	18.0[2]	-1.4[3]	9.3[2]	12.9[2]	13,047	18,349
Warbg Pincus Emg Mkts	—	—	—	—	—	—	—	—	—	—	—	—	—	—
Warbg Pincus Fix Inc	—	—	—	8.6[2]	9.3[5]	2.9[5]	16.9[2]	6.7[3]	11.2[2]	-0.8[1]	5.6[1]	7.2[2]	11,762	14,141
Warbg Pincus Glob Bd	—	—	—	—	—	—	14.7[4]	2.1[5]	19.5[1]	-5.5[5]	4.9[1]	—	11,537	—
Warbg Pincus Gro & Inc	—	—	—	—	20.7[3]	4.0[1]	13.1[5]	8.2[3]	37.0[1]	7.6[1]	16.8[1]	13.4[1]	15,945	18,753
Warbg Pincus Inter Gov	—	—	—	—	11.6[1]	8.9[3]	14.9[1]	6.7[2]	7.8[2]	-1.8[4]	4.1[2]	7.2[1]	11,290	14,130
Warbg Pincus Int'l	—	—	—	—	—	-4.6[1]	20.6[1]	-4.4[3]	51.3[1]	0.2[3]	13.2[1]	10.8[1]	14,491	16,678
Warbg Pincus Japan OTC	—	—	—	—	—	—	—	—	—	—	—	—	—	—
Warbg Pincus NY Muni	—	—	—	6.4[4]	6.9[5]	5.9[5]	9.5[5]	7.5[2]	9.9[4]	-0.6[1]	5.5[1]	6.4[3]	11,749	13,629
Warbg Pincus ST AfterTax	—	—	—	—	—	—	—	—	—	—	—	—	—	—
Wasatch Agg Eqty SC	—	—	-4.9[4]	-1.5[5]	32.0[2]	7.7[1]	50.7[2]	4.7[4]	22.4[1]	5.5[1]	10.6[2]	17.0[1]	13,529	21,960
Wasatch Growth	—	—	-4.2[5]	3.1[5]	25.0[2]	10.4[1]	40.8[2]	4.7[4]	11.1[3]	2.7[2]	6.1[3]	13.2[1]	11,948	18,565
Wasatch Income	—	—	6.1[1]	8.5[1]	14.7[1]	10.4[1]	13.6[2]	4.7[4]	4.0[5]	1.6[2]	3.4[4]	6.8[2]	11,063	13,880
Wasatch MidCap	—	—	—	—	—	—	—	—	-3.0[5]	8.1[1]	—	—	—	—
Wayne Hummer Growth	24.4[4]	13.8[3]	9.3[1]	7.0[5]	24.0[3]	5.0[1]	28.8[4]	10.4[2]	3.6[5]	-0.9[3]	4.2[4]	8.9[3]	11,324	15,324
Wayne Hummer Income	—	—	—	—	—	—	—	—	10.5[3]	-2.5[2]	—	—	—	—
Weitz Fix Inc	—	—	—	—	9.1[4]	9.0[2]	11.2[5]	5.5[5]	8.1[4]	-2.4[2]	3.7[4]	6.2[5]	11,135	13,496
Weitz Hickory	—	—	—	—	—	—	—	—	—	-17.2[5]	—	—	—	—
Weitz Prtnrs Value	—	—	—	—	—	—	—	—	—	-9.0[5]	—	—	—	—

See Chapter 3 for explanation of symbols

Stock and bond funds — comprehensive summary *continued*
Arranged in alphabetical order

Total Net Assets $Million		NAV per share		1994 per share distributions		Yield % 12/31/94	Risk Analysis				% Distribution of Portfolio 12/31/94			Objective	No-Load Fund
December 31 1993	1994	December 31 1993	1994	Income	Capital gains		beta	R^2	Std. Dev.	Sharpe Ratio	Stocks	Bonds	Cash		
822.9	699.0	11.15	9.94	0.59	0.00	5.9	0.45	0.30	1.92	B	0	96	4	tax-free	Vangd NY Insur
170.2	147.1	11.77	10.57	0.60	0.00	5.7	0.45	0.30	1.85	A	0	93	7	tax-free	Vangd OH Insur LT
1,510.4	1,299.3	11.44	10.30	0.63	0.00	6.1	0.43	0.31	1.79	A	0	94	6	tax-free	Vangd PA Insur LT
386.4	278.9	9.54	8.15	0.65	0.00	8.0	0.32	0.27	1.41	C	1	99	0	fix-inc	Vangd Prefrd Stk
790.9	1,553.7	18.42	19.98	0.12	0.41	0.6	1.21	0.75	3.25	B	86	0	14	growth	Vangd Primecap
530.7	596.0	16.45	15.56	0.39	0.40	2.5	1.00	0.94	2.40	C	96	0	4	gr-inc	Vangd Quantitative
269.6	445.5	15.06	14.29	0.24	0.29	1.7	1.00	0.28	4.50	D	97	0	3	sector	Vangd Spec-Energy
609.6	639.2	13.78	12.72	0.31	0.00	2.4	0.43	0.02	7.31	B	92	0	8	prec met	Vangd Spec-Gold
609.1	708.1	35.07	35.47	0.57	2.31	1.5	1.14	0.51	3.77	D	94	0	6	sector	Vangd Spec-Health
774.1	560.5	11.63	9.94	0.59	0.12	5.9	—	—	—	—	77	21	2	income	Vangd Spec-Util
3,482.9	2,905.8	10.90	10.30	0.59	0.00	5.7	0.10	0.10	0.71	B	0	97	3	fix-inc	Vangd ST Corp
1,921.8	1,504.8	10.34	9.69	0.54	0.01	5.6	0.10	0.11	0.73	C	0	97	3	fix-inc	Vangd ST Federal
705.5	704.0	10.38	9.79	0.52	0.02	5.3	0.10	0.11	0.70	B	0	96	4	fix-inc	Vangd ST Trsy
—	41.3	—	9.89	—	—	—					51	47	2	gr-inc	Vangd Star:Cons Gro
—	37.8	—	9.93	—	—	—					87	10	3	growth	Vangd Star:Growth
—	11.5	—	9.88	—	—	—					35	64	1	income	Vangd Star:Income
—	34.8	—	9.86	—	—	—					73	24	3	gr-inc	Vangd Star:Mod Gr
3,628.2	3,766.2	13.41	12.60	0.52	0.25	4.0	0.64	0.85	1.60	B	63	25	12	gr-inc	Vangd Star:Star
—	17.0	—	9.79	—	—	—					47	61	-8	income	Vangd Tax Mgd:Bl
—	69.0	—	9.95	—	—	—					100	0	0	growth	Vangd Tax Mgd:Cap
—	31.0	—	9.77	—	—	—					98	0	2	gr-inc	Vangd Tax Mgd:Gro &
982.3	1,053.2	31.04	31.48	0.56	0.63	1.7	0.57	0.15	3.47	C	98	0	2	int'l	Vangd Trust Int'l
118.7	112.8	30.65	29.09	0.34	0.03	1.2	1.09	0.80	2.84	D	97	0	3	gr-inc	Vangd Trust US
1,847.2	2,109.3	14.93	15.33	0.18	0.00	1.2	0.84	0.73	2.31	F	91	0	9	growth	Vangd US Growth
6,011.5	5,680.6	19.24	17.05	1.11	0.24	6.4	0.52	0.44	1.83	C	36	62	2	income	Vangd Wellesley Inc
8,075.8	8,809.4	20.40	19.39	0.88	0.03	4.5	0.70	0.73	1.91	C	64	35	1	income	Vangd Wellington
7,616.3	7,959.0	17.04	15.82	0.55	0.47	3.4	0.88	0.81	2.27	B	92	0	8	gr-inc	Vangd Windsor II
10,610.8	10,672.9	13.91	12.59	0.44	0.86	3.3	0.98	0.63	2.89	A	90	9	1	gr-inc	Vangd Windsor
319.8	319.9	10.48	9.45	0.59	0.01	6.2	—	—	—	—	0	95	5	fix-inc	Vangd-Adml Inter
92.1	118.1	10.71	9.22	0.67	0.10	7.3	—	—	—	—	0	96	4	fix-inc	Vangd-Adml Long
252.2	311.1	10.23	9.67	0.50	0.02	5.2	—	—	—	—	0	96	4	fix-inc	Vangd-Adml Short
55.9	50.9	11.03	9.99	0.67	0.00	6.7	0.25	0.22	1.22	B	0	99	1	fix-inc	Vista Bond
108.9	48.4	13.00	10.06	0.24	0.00	2.4	0.94	0.93	2.26	D	91	0	9	growth	Vista Equity
69.5	33.2	10.11	9.87	0.47	0.00	4.8	0.04	0.08	0.31	A	0	99	1	fix-inc	Vista ST Bond
11.8	11.2	16.09	14.35	0.03	1.40	0.2	0.99	0.73	2.71	D	86	0	14	growth	Volumetric
136.9	138.6	17.15	16.23	0.08	0.00	0.5	0.92	0.34	3.68	B	96	0	4	int'l	Vontobel EuroPac
—	10.2	—	9.48	—	—	—	—	—	—	—	0	91	9	fix-inc	Vontobel Int'l Bd
34.7	30.4	12.60	10.26	0.25	2.14	2.2	0.90	0.76	2.41	C	95	0	5	growth	Vontobel US Value
0.5	0.5	30.73	29.64	0.06	0.61	0.2	0.85	—	—	—	72	0	28	growth	Wade
0.7	0.8	10.73	9.00	0.36	1.51	3.4	0.61	—	—	B	36	72	-8	income	Warbg Pincus Balanced
158.9	145.3	14.06	12.66	0.00	0.98	0.0	1.14	0.87	2.86	C	79	0	21	growth	Warbg Pincus Cap App
183.1	222.8	22.31	21.99	0.00	0.00	0.0	1.16	0.47	3.98	C	95	0	5	agg gr	Warbg Pincus Emg Gro SC
—	—	—	—	—	—	—								int'l	Warbg Pincus Emg Mkts
84.0	105.2	10.24	9.49	0.66	0.00	7.0	0.19	0.19	1.01	A	0	99	1	fix-inc	Warbg Pincus Fix Inc
69.0	85.0	11.13	10.16	0.36	0.00	3.6	0.17	0.06	1.61	D	0	100	0	fix-inc	Warbg Pincus Glob Bd
34.5	628.0	12.95	13.64	0.11	0.18	0.8	0.61	0.21	3.15	A	62	0	38	gr-inc	Warbg Pincus Gro & Inc
64.4	44.1	10.29	9.55	0.56	0.00	5.9	0.15	0.10	1.07	D	0	99	1	fix-inc	Warbg Pincus Inter Gov
507.0	1,551.7	18.98	18.38	0.11	0.53	0.6	0.94	0.27	4.24	A	93	0	7	int'l	Warbg Pincus Int'l
—	22.3	—	9.63	—	—	—					86	0	14	int'l	Warbg Pincus Japan OTC
73.7	76.9	10.55	10.03	0.45	0.01	4.5	0.27	0.28	1.15	A	0	100	0	tax-free	Warbg Pincus NY Muni
—	1.0	—	9.94	—	—	—					0	83	17	fix-inc	Warbg Pincus ST AfterTax
29.0	55.5	19.50	19.06	0.00	1.51	0.0	1.17	0.52	3.82	C	93	0	7	agg gr	Wasatch Agg Eqty SC
16.2	8.5	15.14	11.61	0.00	3.94	0.0	1.07	0.48	3.62	D	89	0	11	growth	Wasatch Growth
3.7	3.0	10.00	9.57	0.59	0.00	6.1	0.10	0.09	0.76	C	0	95	5	fix-inc	Wasatch Income
1.6	1.2	10.79	11.64	0.00	0.03	0.0	—	—	—	—	—	—	—	growth	Wasatch MidCap
99.0	87.7	22.06	21.34	0.31	0.21	1.4	0.76	0.75	2.04	D	96	0	4	growth	Wayne Hummer Growth
36.5	25.3	15.62	14.27	0.97	0.00	6.8	—	—	—	—	0	93	7	fix-inc	Wayne Hummer Income
19.9	18.5	10.97	10.10	0.61	0.00	6.1	0.18	0.21	0.89	B	0	60	40	fix-inc	Weitz Fix Inc
2.5	3.2	13.36	10.61	0.28	0.00	2.6	—	—	—	—	—	—	—	growth	Weitz Hickory
—	51.3	10.00	8.28	0.00	0.82	—	—	—	—	—	87	7	6	growth	Weitz Prtnrs Value

No-Load Fund	1985	1986	1987	1988	1989	1990	1991	1992	1993	1994	Annualized 3 yrs.	Annualized 5 yrs.	What $10,000 grew to after 3 yrs.	What $10,000 grew to after 5 yrs.
Weitz Value	—	—	-0.6[4]	15.5[3]	22.1[3]	-5.2[3]	27.6[3]	13.6[1]	20.0[1]	-9.8[5]	7.1[2]	8.3[2]	12,296	14,867
Wertheim Eqty Value	—	—	—	—	—	—	—	—	—	—	—	—	—	—
Wertheim High Yld	—	—	—	—	—	—	—	—	—	—	—	—	—	—
Wertheim Invest Grd	—	—	—	—	—	—	—	—	—	—	—	—	—	—
Wertheim Small Cap SC	—	—	—	—	—	—	—	—	—	—	—	—	—	—
Wertheim ST Inv	—	—	—	—	—	—	—	—	—	—	—	—	—	—
Weston: New Cent Cap	—	—	—	—	—	-4.8[3]	36.5[1]	0.5[5]	13.8[2]	0.1[2]	4.6[4]	8.3[2]	11,450	14,879
Weston: New Cent Inc	—	—	—	—	—	-0.7[3]	22.9[4]	2.8[5]	15.5[2]	-2.4[3]	5.0[4]	7.2[4]	11,591	14,143
Westwood Balanced	—	—	—	—	—	—	—	5.9[4]	16.8[1]	0.1[2]	7.4[2]	—	12,375	—
Westwood Equity	—	—	—	12.7[4]	28.5[1]	-6.3[4]	21.2[4]	6.0[4]	17.2[2]	2.3[1]	8.3[2]	7.6[3]	12,706	14,430
Westwood Inter Bd	—	—	—	—	—	—	—	6.1[4]	10.5[2]	-5.6[5]	3.4[5]	—	11,068	—
Wm Blair Growth	23.8[4]	9.8[4]	8.0[1]	7.1[4]	30.4[2]	-2.0[2]	44.3[1]	7.6[3]	15.5[2]	6.5[1]	9.8[2]	13.4[1]	13,229	18,709
Wm Blair Income	—	—	—	—	—	—	15.1[1]	7.2[1]	7.8[2]	-0.7[4]	4.7[1]	—	11,466	—
Wm Blair Int'l Gro	—	—	—	—	—	—	—	—	33.5[3]	-0.1[3]	—	—	—	—
Wm Blair Ltd TF	—	—	—	—	—	—	—	—	—	—	—	—	—	—
Women's Equity	—	—	—	—	—	—	—	—	—	-0.1[3]	—	—	—	—
Wood Island Growth	33.2[2]	9.0[5]	3.2[3]	7.7[4]	26.3[2]	0.9[2]	25.0[4]	7.9[3]	11.3[3]	-6.4[5]	4.0[4]	7.2[4]	11,241	14,172
Woodward Eqty Idx	—	—	—	—	—	—	—	—	9.8[4]	1.0[2]	—	—	—	—
WPG Gov Sec	—	—	2.5[3]	7.9[2]	14.1[1]	8.9[2]	14.0[4]	7.9[1]	9.0[3]	-8.7[5]	2.4[5]	5.9[5]	10,737	13,325
WPG Growth SC	—	—	-3.2[3]	11.7[4]	25.0[3]	-12.8[4]	56.3[2]	6.3[4]	14.9[3]	-14.0[5]	1.6[5]	7.4[4]	10,494	14,312
WPG Growth & Inc	30.3[2]	11.4[5]	6.8[1]	9.5[5]	27.6[2]	-10.3[5]	40.7[1]	13.8[1]	9.5[4]	-5.5[5]	5.6[4]	8.3[3]	11,778	14,862
WPG Inter Muni	—	—	—	—	—	—	—	—	—	-2.3[1]	—	—	—	—
WPG International	—	—	—	—	—	-14.8[4]	0.3[5]	-5.5[3]	37.2[3]	-6.3[4]	6.7[4]	0.8[4]	12,146	10,388
WPG Quant Eqty	—	—	—	—	—	—	—	—	13.9[2]	0.3[3]	—	—	—	—
WPG Tudor	31.2[2]	12.4[3]	1.1[2]	15.2[3]	25.1[3]	-5.2[2]	45.8[3]	5.1[4]	13.4[4]	-9.8[5]	2.5[5]	8.3[4]	10,752	14,861
Wright Curr Inc	—	—	—	8.7[3]	14.2[2]	9.9[1]	15.3[4]	6.7[4]	6.6[5]	-3.3[2]	3.2[5]	6.9[4]	11,000	13,934
Wright Equi Belg\Lux	—	—	—	—	—	—	—	—	—	—	—	—	—	—
Wright Equi Dutch	—	—	—	—	—	—	10.0[3]	-8.2[4]	19.5[5]	11.7[1]	7.0[4]	—	12,253	—
Wright Equi Hong Kong	—	—	—	—	—	—	34.3[1]	16.2[1]	84.3[1]	-37.0[5]	10.5[2]	—	13,486	—
Wright Equi Italy	—	—	—	—	—	—	-8.5[5]	-33.6[5]	11.5[5]	5.0[2]	-8.1[5]	—	7,773	—
Wright Equi Japan	—	—	—	—	—	—	—	—	—	—	—	—	—	—
Wright Equi Mexico	—	—	—	—	—	—	—	—	—	—	—	—	—	—
Wright Equi Nordic	—	—	—	—	—	—	—	—	—	—	—	—	—	—
Wright Equi Spain	—	—	—	—	—	—	7.2[4]	-32.9[5]	21.6[5]	-9.5[5]	-9.6[5]	—	7,381	—
Wright Equi Swiss	—	—	—	—	—	—	—	—	—	—	—	—	—	—
Wright Gov Oblig	26.3[1]	19.9[2]	-3.0[4]	7.6[4]	16.3[1]	6.3[3]	17.6[2]	7.1[3]	15.9[2]	-8.7[5]	4.3[3]	7.2[3]	11,336	14,167
Wright Insur TF	—	14.7[5]	2.3[1]	6.4[5]	7.1[5]	5.9[4]	10.5[5]	7.9[4]	9.9[5]	-4.1[1]	4.4[3]	5.9[4]	11,376	13,316
Wright Int'l Blue Ch	—	—	—	—	—	-6.9[2]	17.2[2]	-3.9[3]	28.2[4]	-1.6[3]	6.6[4]	5.7[2]	12,115	13,216
Wright Jr Blue Ch SC	—	5.6[5]	-3.6[4]	15.2[3]	15.6[5]	-10.6[3]	37.0[4]	3.3[4]	7.9[5]	-2.8[3]	2.7[5]	5.8[5]	10,840	13,273
Wright Near Term	15.3[2]	13.1[1]	2.3[4]	5.8[4]	11.2[2]	8.2[4]	13.1[3]	6.3[2]	8.0[2]	-3.1[5]	3.6[4]	6.4[3]	11,115	13,603
Wright Qual Core Eqty	—	16.9[3]	1.0[3]	16.6[3]	23.0[3]	-2.9[2]	38.9[1]	8.0[3]	1.0[5]	-0.7[3]	2.7[5]	7.9[3]	10,830	14,604
Wright Sel Blue Ch	27.3[3]	14.2[4]	-1.7[4]	21.3[2]	24.6[2]	-3.3[3]	35.9[1]	4.7[5]	2.1[5]	-3.5[4]	1.0[5]	6.3[4]	10,310	13,552
Wright Total Ret	27.0[1]	20.5[1]	-3.1[5]	7.2[4]	13.6[2]	5.3[4]	15.4[4]	7.1[3]	11.0[3]	-6.6[4]	3.6[4]	6.2[5]	11,111	13,501
Yacktman	—	—	—	—	—	—	—	—	-6.6[5]	8.8[1]	—	—	—	—
ZSA Asset Alloc	—	—	—	—	—	—	—	—	16.7[2]	-12.8[5]	—	—	—	—
ZSA Equity	—	—	—	—	—	—	—	—	9.7[4]	-12.8[5]	—	—	—	—

See Chapter 3 for explanation of symbols

Total Net Assets $Million		NAV per share		1994 per share distributions		Yield %	Risk Analysis				% Distribution of Portfolio 12/31/94			Objective	No-Load Fund
December 31 1993	1994	December 31 1993	1994	Income	Capital gains	12/31/94	beta	R^2	Std. Dev.	Sharpe Ratio	Stocks	Bonds	Cash		
106.7	107.7	16.80	14.43	0.00	0.73	0.0	0.86	0.65	2.46	C	80	11	9	gr-inc	Weitz Value
—	26.8	—	9.14	—	—	—	—	—	—	—	92	0	8	gr-inc	Wertheim Eqty Value
—	17.7	—	8.48	—	—	—	—	—	—	—	1	91	8	fix-inc	Wertheim High Yld
—	19.3	—	9.09	—	—	—	—	—	—	—	0	98	2	fix-inc	Wertheim Invest Grd
—	24.8	—	9.49	—	—	—	—	—	—	—	90	0	10	agg gr	Wertheim Small Cap SC
—	32.2	—	9.86	—	—	—	—	—	—	—	0	53	47	fix-inc	Wertheim ST Inv
38.8	36.9	12.93	11.94	0.23	0.00	1.9	0.95	—	—	—	—	—	—	gr-inc	Weston: New Cent Cap
23.1	22.8	12.08	10.94	0.39	0.00	3.6	0.31	—	—	—	—	—	—	income	Weston: New Cent Inc
1.4	13.0	7.23	7.05	0.18	0.00	2.6	0.66	0.71	1.82	B	63	36	1	income	Westwood Balanced
4.9	10.1	5.35	5.21	0.06	0.20	1.1	0.94	0.72	2.58	B	91	9	0	gr-inc	Westwood Equity
8.3	4.6	10.40	9.32	0.50	0.00	5.4	0.26	0.23	1.24	F	0	94	6	fix-inc	Westwood Inter Bd
149.7	182.2	9.73	9.60	0.03	0.71	0.2	1.16	0.80	3.03	B	87	0	13	growth	Wm Blair Growth
203.5	149.5	10.58	9.85	0.65	0.00	6.6	0.13	0.10	0.95	C	0	89	11	fix-inc	Wm Blair Income
40.3	71.1	13.18	12.36	0.02	0.81	0.2	—	—	—	—	98	0	2	int'l	Wm Blair Int'l Gro
—	14.1	—	9.48	—	—	—	—	—	—	—	0	100	0	tax-free	Wm Blair Ltd TF
0.4	1.1	10.13	9.52	0.02	0.00	0.2	—	—	—	—	—	—	—	growth	Women's Equity
5.2	3.8	15.09	14.13	0.00	0.00	0.0	0.76	—	—	—	—	—	—	growth	Wood Island Growth
319.5	1.2	11.15	10.65	0.29	0.00	2.7	—	—	—	—	—	—	—	gr-inc	Woodward Eqty Idx
335.6	216.6	10.37	8.82	0.64	0.03	7.2	0.25	0.18	1.35	F	0	100	0	fix-inc	WPG Gov Sec
169.0	83.2	116.62	94.45	0.00	0.00	0.0	1.59	0.58	4.96	F	97	1	2	agg gr	WPG Growth SC
62.1	61.2	23.34	21.36	0.62	0.09	2.9	1.00	0.78	2.63	D	89	10	1	gr-inc	WPG Growth & Inc
12.3	14.1	10.15	9.51	0.41	0.00	4.3	—	—	—	—	0	92	8	tax-free	WPG Inter Muni
15.8	17.1	11.72	10.93	0.00	0.05	0.0	0.84	0.27	3.80	D	81	4	15	int'l	WPG International
46.4	73.5	5.58	5.44	0.11	0.05	1.9	—	—	—	—	—	—	—	growth	WPG Quant Eqty
237.5	143.8	23.40	19.34	0.00	1.79	0.0	1.53	0.59	4.68	F	98	2	0	agg gr	WPG Tudor
114.6	84.0	10.75	9.71	0.69	0.00	7.1	0.25	0.24	1.17	D	0	100	0	fix-inc	Wright Curr Inc
—	11.4	—	10.24	—	—	—	—	—	—	—	100	0	0	int'l	Wright Equi Belg\Lux
8.8	4.0	10.02	8.10	0.01	0.00	0.2	0.45	0.10	3.41	C	96	0	4	int'l	Wright Equi Dutch
15.7	19.8	20.99	13.02	0.20	0.00	1.5	1.17	0.14	7.54	D	97	0	3	int'l	Wright Equi Hong Kong
0.6	1.3	5.03	4.94	0.00	0.00	0.0	-0.31	0.01	8.00	F	100	0	0	int'l	Wright Equi Italy
—	8.6	—	9.66	—	—	—	—	—	—	—	100	0	0	int'l	Wright Equi Japan
—	13.1	—	6.48	—	—	—	—	—	—	—	100	0	0	int'l	Wright Equi Mexico
—	8.7	—	9.50	—	—	—	—	—	—	—	100	0	0	int'l	Wright Equi Nordic
0.8	6.4	6.53	5.89	0.02	0.00	0.3	1.01	0.15	6.22	F	98	0	2	int'l	Wright Equi Spain
—	3.8	—	9.43	—	—	—	—	—	—	—	100	0	0	int'l	Wright Equi Swiss
29.8	16.6	14.36	12.25	0.88	0.00	7.2	0.48	0.25	2.21	F	0	97	3	fix-inc	Wright Gov Oblig
17.8	15.0	12.17	11.02	0.55	0.00	5.0	0.35	0.38	1.30	B	0	98	2	tax-free	Wright Insur TF
100.5	201.1	13.41	13.09	0.10	0.00	0.8	0.66	0.22	3.34	D	100	0	0	int'l	Wright Int'l Blue Ch
68.2	37.4	11.95	11.00	0.10	0.00	0.9	0.94	0.64	2.75	D	96	0	4	agg gr	Wright Jr Blue Ch SC
379.7	213.3	10.84	9.92	0.59	0.00	5.9	0.18	0.18	1.00	D	0	99	1	fix-inc	Wright Near Term
88.4	51.1	12.71	11.39	0.15	0.00	1.3	0.83	0.75	2.25	F	100	0	0	gr-inc	Wright Qual Core Eqty
175.3	187.7	14.92	13.85	0.18	0.00	1.3	0.88	0.81	2.29	F	97	0	3	gr-inc	Wright Sel Blue Ch
255.4	143.8	13.01	11.43	0.73	0.00	6.4	0.31	0.22	1.54	D	0	99	1	fix-inc	Wright Total Ret
143.0	295.1	9.56	10.05	0.22	0.12	2.2	—	—	—	—	95	0	5	growth	Yacktman
9.4	10.7	11.84	10.24	0.08	0.00	0.8	—	—	—	—	—	—	—	gr-inc	ZSA Asset Alloc
2.4	8.6	11.46	9.99	0.00	0.00	0.0	—	—	—	—	—	—	—	agg gr	ZSA Equity

CHAPTER 5

Stock and bond funds – ranked within objective

By 1994 performance

AGGRESSIVE GROWTH FUNDS

No-Load Fund	1994	Annualized 3 years	5 years
PBHG Emg Growth SC	23.8[1]	—	—
Robrtsn Stph Val Gro	23.1[1]	—	—
Janus Mercury	15.9[1]	—	—
Berger Sm Co Growth	13.7[1]	—	—
Twentieth Cent Giftrust	13.5[1]	20.7[1]	22.0[1]
Retrmt Sys: Emg Gr SC	10.4[1]	17.4[1]	—
Kaufmann SC	9.0[1]	12.8[1]	19.3[1]
Robrtsn Stph Emg Gro SC	8.0[1]	4.1[4]	14.4[1]
Cornerstone Growth	7.6[1]	2.9[4]	4.2[5]
Baron Asset SC	7.4[1]	14.7[1]	10.5[3]
Fairmont	7.3[1]	12.2[1]	9.1[3]
Merger	7.1[1]	9.9[2]	9.4[3]
Omni Investment	6.7[1]	14.1[1]	7.7[4]
Wasatch Agg Eqty SC	5.5[1]	10.6[2]	17.0[1]
General Securities	5.4[1]	5.9[4]	9.9[3]
Brown Cap Sm Co SC	4.8[1]	—	—
PBHG Growth	4.7[1]	25.4[1]	22.0[1]
Twentieth Cent Vista	4.7[1]	2.6[5]	9.6[3]
Schroder US Sm Co SC	4.5[1]	—	—
Quant Numeric SC	4.3[1]	—	—
Fidelity Fifty	4.0[1]	—	—
Longleaf Small Cap SC	3.7[1]	9.9[2]	3.2[5]
Fasciano SC	3.7[1]	6.5[3]	10.0[3]
Dreyfus Apprec	3.6[1]	3.0[4]	8.2[4]
Royce Micro-Cap SC	3.6[1]	18.3[1]	—
RSI Tr-Emg Gro SC	3.5[1]	13.2[1]	14.8[1]
DFA US 9-10 Sm Co SC	3.1[1]	15.4[1]	11.8[2]
Dreyfus Strat Growth	3.1[1]	2.8[5]	6.0[5]
Fidelity Cap Apprec	2.5[1]	16.7[1]	8.0[4]
Smith Hayes Sm Cap SC	2.5[2]	—	—
Babson Enterprise SC	2.5[2]	14.1[1]	12.3[2]
Fontaine Cap App	2.3[2]	3.9[4]	5.9[5]
Columbia Special	2.3[2]	12.3[1]	13.3[2]
Heartland Value SC	1.7[2]	19.8[1]	16.3[1]
DFA US Sm Cap Val SC	1.2[2]	—	—
PDC&J Performance	1.1[2]	7.7[3]	8.9[3]
Htchks & Wly Sm Cap SC	1.1[2]	9.0[2]	11.8[2]
Permanent Agg Growth	1.0[2]	13.9[1]	—
Value Line Spec Sit	1.0[2]	3.3[4]	7.5[4]
Salomon Opportunity	0.8[2]	9.0[2]	7.2[5]
Babson UMB Heartland SC	0.7[2]	5.8[4]	5.0[5]
Vangd Explorer SC	0.5[2]	9.4[2]	12.8[2]
Fiduciary Cap Gro SC	0.4[2]	9.6[2]	9.7[3]
Price, Rowe New Horiz SC	0.3[2]	10.6[2]	13.2[2]
IAI Emg Growth SC	0.2[2]	12.1[1]	—
Dreman Small Cap SC	0.1[2]	—	—
Price, Rowe OTC SC	0.1[2]	10.5[2]	8.3[4]
Fidelity Retrmnt Growth	0.1[2]	10.6[2]	12.0[2]
Brandywine	0.0[2]	12.3[1]	16.3[1]
SteinRoe Cap Oppty	0.0[2]	9.3[2]	8.5[4]
AIC: Pin Oak SC	0.0[2]	—	—
Galaxy Sm Co Eqty SC	-0.1[2]	7.5[3]	—
Merriman Levgd Gro	-0.1[2]	—	—
Dreyfus New Ldrs SC	-0.2[2]	8.5[3]	10.4[3]
Fidelity Emg Growth	-0.2[2]	9.0[2]	—
Schooner Fund SC	-0.3[2]	—	—
SIT Growth SC	-0.5[2]	1.9[5]	11.4[2]
Vangd Idx Sm Cap SC	-0.5[2]	11.7[1]	10.6[3]
Columbia Growth	-0.6[3]	7.9[3]	10.2[3]
Value Line Sm Cap	-0.6[3]	—	—
USAA Agg Growth SC	-0.8[3]	-0.6[5]	8.2[4]
Seven Seas Sm Cap SC	-0.9[3]	—	—
C&O Agg Growth SC	-1.0[3]	9.4[2]	—
Invesco Small Co SC	-1.0[3]	—	—
Fidelity Contrafund	-1.1[3]	11.6[1]	17.5[1]
Skyline Special Eqty	-1.1[3]	20.0[1]	18.1[1]
FundTrust Agg Gro	-1.2[3]	5.9[4]	8.7[4]
DFA US 6-10 Sm Co SC	-1.3[3]	—	—
Drey-Wilsh Sm Gro	-1.4[3]	—	—
Warbg Pincus Emg Gro SC	-1.4[3]	9.3[2]	12.9[2]
Twentieth Cent Growth	-1.5[3]	-0.7[5]	9.7[3]
Managers Cap App	-1.5[3]	7.0[3]	9.7[3]
Skyline Spcl Eqty II SC	-1.5[3]	—	—
SAFECO Growth	-1.6[3]	5.2[4]	10.0[3]
Vangd Morgan	-1.7[3]	4.9[4]	8.0[4]
Fidelity Magellan	-1.8[3]	9.4[2]	12.0[2]
Nbrgr-Ber Genesis SC	-1.8[3]	8.9[3]	8.9[3]
Invesco Dynamics	-1.9[3]	9.7[2]	15.6[1]
Managers Spec Eqty SC	-2.0[3]	10.1[2]	10.9[2]
Portico Spec Gro SC	-2.0[3]	4.3[4]	12.6[2]
Fidelity Growth Co	-2.2[3]	7.0[3]	13.5[1]
Gradison Oppty Value SC	-2.2[3]	7.5[3]	8.0[4]
First Eagle America	-2.6[3]	14.5[1]	8.4[4]
Fidelity OTC SC	-2.7[3]	6.6[3]	11.5[2]
Wright Jr Blue Ch SC	-2.7[3]	2.7[5]	5.8[5]
Founders Frontier SC	-2.8[3]	7.3[3]	11.3[2]
Federated Mini Cap SC	-2.8[4]	—	—
Schwab Sm Cap Idx	-3.1[4]	—	—
Maxus Laureate	-3.2[4]	—	—
Fidelity Small Cap SC	-3.3[4]	—	—
API Growth	-3.4[4]	5.6[4]	8.4[4]
Oberweis Emg Growth SC	-3.5[4]	6.4[3]	17.7[1]
Twentieth Cent Ultra	-3.6[4]	5.9[4]	19.4[1]
Galaxy Sm Co Idx SC	-3.7[4]	6.4[3]	—
Value Line Lev Gro	-3.7[4]	3.0[4]	9.4[3]
Invesco Emg Gro SC	-3.7[4]	14.3[1]	—
SteinRoe Stock	-3.8[4]	2.3[5]	9.6[3]
GIT Special Gro SC	-3.9[4]	5.6[4]	4.5[5]
Ariel Growth SC	-4.2[4]	5.2[4]	5.5[5]
Eclipse Equity SC	-4.7[4]	10.0[2]	8.6[4]
Rainbow Fund	-4.7[4]	-4.0[5]	1.9[5]
Rydex Nova	-4.8[4]	—	—
Founders Special	-4.9[4]	6.1[3]	11.9[2]
Perritt Capital Gro SC	-5.1[4]	2.1[5]	4.2[5]
Schroder US Eqty	-5.2[4]	7.1[3]	10.2[3]
Scudder Development SC	-5.3[4]	0.4[5]	12.0[2]
Robrtsn Stph Contrn	-5.5[4]	—	—
Strong Discovery SC	-5.7[4]	5.5[4]	13.8[1]
Pierpont Cap App SC	-5.9[4]	6.7[3]	8.0[4]
Gateway Sm Cap Idx SC	-6.0[4]	—	—
Stratus Cap Apprec	-6.3[4]	—	—
Drey-Focus Sm Gro SC	-6.6[4]	—	—
Berger 100	-6.7[4]	7.1[3]	17.0[1]
Fidelity Trend	-6.7[4]	9.1[2]	9.1[3]
Janus Twenty	-6.7[4]	-0.5[5]	10.9[2]
Capp-Rush Emg Gro SC	-6.9[5]	—	—
Special Port Stk	-7.2[5]	1.4[5]	10.8[2]
Babson Enterprise II SC	-7.4[5]	9.1[2]	—
Price, Rowe New Amer	-7.4[5]	6.1[3]	11.2[2]

No-Load Fund	1994	Annualized 3 years	5 years
Founders Discovery SC	-7.7[5]	5.6[4]	16.7[1]
FFB Lexcn Sm Co SC	-7.9[5]	—	—
Loomis Syls Sm Cap SC	-8.3[5]	8.9[2]	—
Prudent Speculator SC	-8.9[5]	-1.8[5]	-0.6[5]
WPG Tudor	-9.8[5]	2.4[5]	8.2[4]
Scudder Capital Gro	-9.9[5]	5.0[4]	6.6[5]
Montgmry Sm Cap SC	-9.9[5]	7.1[3]	—
AARP Capital Growth	-10.0[5]	3.0[4]	5.3[5]
MIM Stock Apprec	-10.4[5]	1.5[5]	14.3[1]
59 Wall Sm Co SC	-10.5[5]	3.6[4]	—
Evergreen Ltd Mkt SC	-10.5[5]	2.6[5]	7.9[4]
Trent Equity	-10.6[5]	—	—
44 Wall St Eqty	-11.7[5]	9.7[2]	8.7[4]
ZSA Equity	-12.8[5]	—	—
Legg Msn Spec Invest SC	-13.1[5]	7.6[3]	11.8[2]
WPG Growth SC	-14.0[5]	1.6[5]	7.4[4]
Salomon Capital	-14.2[5]	1.8[5]	5.1[5]
First Mutual	-15.1[5]	0.0[5]	3.8[5]
Bull & Bear Spec Eqty	-16.5[5]	7.6[3]	2.2[5]
Dreyfus Special Gro	-18.3[5]	7.4[3]	8.8[4]
Arbor OVB Emg Gro	-18.4[5]	—	—
CGM Capital Dev	-22.9[5]	5.2[4]	18.7[1]
American Heritage	-35.4[5]	2.7[5]	8.1[4]
Steadman Tech & Gro	-37.1[5]	-18.1[5]	-17.0[5]
Steadman Amer Indust	-37.2[5]	-13.8[5]	-14.9[5]
GROWTH FUNDS			
Montgmry Growth	20.9[1]	—	—
Strong Growth	17.3[1]	—	—
AIC: Clvr Cap Eq	16.0[1]	11.9[1]	—
Crabbe Hsn Spec SC	11.7[1]	26.1[1]	19.5[1]
Vangd Primecap	11.4[1]	12.7[1]	13.1[1]
SAFECO Equity	9.9[1]	16.3[1]	13.0[1]
Fidelity Blue Chip	9.8[1]	13.2[1]	18.4[1]
Longleaf Partners	9.0[1]	17.1[1]	13.3[1]
Janus Enterprise	8.9[1]	—	—
Yacktman	8.8[1]	—	—
Wasatch MidCap	8.1[1]	—	—
Fidelity Value	7.6[1]	17.0[1]	12.0[1]
AIC: Rlstn Midwest Gr	7.2[1]	—	—
AIC: White Oak	7.2[1]	—	—
FAM Value SC	6.8[1]	10.2[2]	13.3[1]
Wm Blair Growth	6.5[1]	9.8[2]	13.3[1]
State Farm Growth	6.0[1]	2.9[5]	10.0[2]
Valley Forge	5.9[1]	10.7[1]	6.7[4]
IAI MidCap	5.7[1]	—	—
Mairs & Power Gro	5.6[1]	8.7[2]	13.6[1]
Janus Venture SC	5.5[1]	7.3[3]	12.7[1]
Armstrong Assoc	5.4[1]	9.0[2]	7.4[4]
Price, Rowe New Era	5.2[1]	7.4[3]	5.3[5]
Fidelity Low Pr Stk SC	4.8[1]	17.6[1]	—
Capp-Rush Growth	4.6[1]	—	—
Gabelli ABC	4.5[1]	—	—
Fidelity Div Growth	4.3[1]	—	—
FBP Contrn Eqty	4.0[1]	—	—
Invesco Value Eqty	4.0[1]	6.4[3]	9.1[3]
Crowley Growth	3.9[1]	3.6[4]	4.9[5]
Vangd US Growth	3.9[1]	1.7[5]	10.1[2]
Price, Rowe Cap App	3.8[1]	9.5[2]	9.5[2]
Mutual Discovery SC	3.6[1]	—	—
Harbor Cap App	3.4[1]	8.4[2]	14.1[1]

No-Load Fund	1994	Annualized 3 years	5 years
Sequoia	3.4[1]	7.8[2]	11.0[2]
USAA Growth	3.4[1]	6.9[3]	9.3[3]
Oakmark	3.3[1]	26.1[1]	—
Royce Premier SC	3.3[2]	12.4[1]	—
ORI Growth	3.2[2]	—	—
Strong Opportunity	3.2[2]	13.6[1]	11.4[1]
Royce Low Price Stk SC	3.0[2]	—	—
Fidelity Discpl Eqty	3.0[2]	9.9[2]	12.3[1]
Greenspring	2.9[2]	11.1[1]	8.9[3]
Babson UMB Stock	2.8[2]	6.8[3]	8.2[3]
Flex-Fund Muirfield	2.7[2]	5.9[3]	9.5[2]
Wasatch Growth	2.7[2]	6.1[3]	13.2[1]
Babson Value	2.5[2]	13.3[1]	10.6[2]
Torray	2.4[2]	9.6[2]	—
Brandywine Blue	2.3[2]	13.8[1]	—
Drey-Wilsh Lg Gro	2.3[2]	—	—
Monetta MidCap Eqty	2.2[2]	—	—
Columbia Common Stk	2.1[2]	9.3[2]	—
Seafirst Blue Chip	2.0[2]	6.8[3]	7.9[4]
Amcor Vntg Eqty	2.0[2]	—	—
Amtrust Value	1.8[2]	—	—
Evergreen Gro & Inc	1.7[2]	9.8[2]	9.8[2]
Reich & Tang Eqty	1.7[2]	10.4[1]	9.3[2]
Reynolds Opportunity	1.7[2]	—	—
Scudder Value	1.6[2]	—	—
Crabbe Hsn Eqty	1.5[2]	14.1[1]	—
Price, Rowe Spect-Gro	1.4[2]	9.6[2]	—
Legg Msn Value	1.3[2]	7.9[2]	7.1[4]
Portico Eqty Idx	1.0[2]	5.6[3]	8.2[3]
Nicholas II SC	1.0[2]	5.5[4]	9.0[3]
Price, Rowe Growth Stk	0.9[2]	7.3[3]	9.6[2]
Nbrgr-Ber Focus	0.9[2]	12.4[1]	10.8[2]
Price, Rowe Blue Chip	0.8[2]	—	—
Fidelity Stk Selector	0.8[2]	9.8[2]	—
Fidelity New Millnm	-0.8[2]	—	—
Evergreen Fund	0.7[2]	5.1[4]	7.5[4]
Rightime	0.7[2]	4.5[4]	8.6[3]
IAI Regional	0.7[2]	4.3[4]	8.9[3]
IAI Growth	0.7[2]	—	—
Nbrgr-Ber Guardian	0.6[2]	11.1[1]	11.9[1]
Galaxy Eqty Growth	0.6[2]	4.0[4]	—
Meridian	0.5[2]	9.5[2]	16.6[1]
TU&P Growth	0.4[3]	—	—
Fremont Growth	0.4[3]	—	—
Dreyfus Core Value	0.4[3]	6.8[3]	5.2[5]
WPG Quant Eqty	0.3[3]	—	—
Vontobel US Value	0.3[3]	3.8[4]	—
Gradison Estab Value	0.3[3]	10.1[2]	8.4[3]
Sound Shore	0.3[3]	10.8[1]	10.0[2]
Price, Rowe Mid Cap	0.3[3]	—	—
Beacon Hill Mutual	0.3[3]	-2.3[5]	4.6[5]
GE Elfun Trusts	0.2[3]	6.1[3]	8.1[3]
Vista Equity	0.2[3]	4.6[4]	—
Dreman Contrarian	0.0[3]	6.7[3]	7.6[4]
Northeast Inv Gro	0.0[3]	0.5[5]	7.1[4]
Women's Equity	0.0[3]	—	—
Vangd Idx Total Mkt	-0.1[3]	—	—
Gabelli Asset	-0.1[3]	11.8[1]	9.4[2]
SteinRoe Prime Eqty	-0.2[3]	7.4[3]	10.0[2]
Benham Equity Growth	-0.2[3]	5.0[4]	—

Stock and bond funds – ranked within objective continued

By 1994 performance

No-Load Fund	1994	Annualized 3 years	5 years	No-Load Fund	1994	Annualized 3 years	5 years
Analytic Enhncd Eqty...	-0.4[3]	—	—	GIT Select Gro...	-5.1[5]	0.5[5]	4.1[5]
Seven Seas Matrix...	-0.4[3]	—	—	Portico MidCore Gr...	-5.3[5]	—	—
Strong Common Stk SC...	-0.5[3]	14.6[1]	—	Arbor OVB Cap App...	-5.4[5]	—	—
FundTrust Growth...	-0.5[3]	6.8[3]	8.0[3]	Marshall MidCap Stk...	-5.6[5]	—	—
Babson Growth...	-0.6[3]	6.2[3]	6.4[5]	SBSF Fund...	-5.6[5]	6.6[3]	7.0[4]
Merriman Cap App...	-0.6[3]	2.4[5]	6.2[5]	Mathers...	-5.9[5]	-0.3[5]	3.7[5]
Lindner Fund...	-0.7[3]	10.3[2]	8.0[4]	Monetta Fund...	-6.2[5]	-0.2[5]	11.5[1]
Flex-Fund Growth...	-0.7[3]	4.2[4]	7.5[4]	Twentieth Cent Heritage...	-6.3[5]	7.5[3]	8.9[3]
Royce Penn Mutual SC...	-0.7[3]	8.7[2]	8.4[3]	Dreyfus Growth Oppty...	-6.4[5]	-2.9[5]	5.3[5]
Drey-Focus Lg Gro...	-0.7[3]	—	—	Wood Island Growth...	-6.4[5]	4.0[4]	7.2[4]
Evergreen Sm Cap SC...	-0.7[3]	—	—	Dreyfus Discpl MidCap...	-6.7[5]	—	—
Brown Cap Equity...	-0.8[3]	—	—	Schwartz Value SC...	-6.8[5]	—	—
Tocqueville...	-0.8[3]	12.4[1]	10.1[2]	Aquinas Eqty Gro...	-6.8[5]	—	—
Wayne Hummer Growth...	-0.9[3]	4.2[4]	8.9[3]	Legg Msn Total Ret...	-7.2[5]	6.6[3]	7.3[4]
Dreman High Return...	-1.0[3]	9.0[2]	11.8[1]	Acorn SC...	-7.5[5]	15.0[1]	13.1[1]
Drey-Focus Lg Val...	-1.0[3]	—	—	Dreyfus Third Cent...	-7.5[5]	-0.3[5]	7.2[4]
Janus Fund...	-1.1[3]	5.4[4]	10.7[2]	Twentieth Cent Select...	-8.0[5]	0.3[5]	5.7[5]
Preferred Growth...	-1.1[3]	—	—	Ariel Apprec...	-8.4[5]	3.8[4]	—
Pinnacle Fund...	-1.1[4]	0.5[5]	6.6[4]	Invesco Growth...	-8.8[5]	3.4[4]	9.2[3]
Sentry...	-1.1[4]	4.0[4]	8.8[3]	Caldwell Growth Stk...	-8.9[5]	—	—
Wade...	-1.3[4]	5.1[4]	5.2[5]	Weitz Prtnrs Value...	-9.0[5]	—	—
Scudder Qual Growth...	-1.3[4]	1.7[5]	—	IAI Value...	-9.1[5]	7.5[3]	5.6[5]
Price, Rowe Sm Cap Val SC...	-1.4[4]	13.7[1]	11.8[1]	US Global Resrc...	-9.7[5]	1.9[5]	-1.4[5]
Papp L Roy Stock...	-1.4[4]	4.4[4]	8.9[3]	Drey/Laurel Contrn...	-11.1[5]	6.0[3]	9.1[3]
Drey-Focus Sm Val SC...	-1.5[4]	—	—	Northwest Growth...	-11.4[5]	-1.3[5]	4.9[5]
SAFECO Northwest Gro...	-1.6[4]	4.3[4]	—	Harbor Growth...	-11.4[5]	-0.6[5]	6.6[4]
Oak Value...	-1.6[4]	—	—	Oak Hall Equity...	-11.6[5]	—	—
Royce Value...	-1.6[4]	8.1[2]	7.4[4]	MIM Stock Growth...	-11.7[5]	-4.0[5]	1.1[5]
Vangd Idx Extend Mkt...	-1.8[4]	8.1[2]	9.1[3]	Federated Growth...	-11.9[5]	0.7[5]	5.5[5]
Nbrgr-Ber Partners...	-1.9[4]	10.3[2]	9.3[2]	Smith Hayes Value...	-12.4[5]	2.5[5]	2.6[5]
Volumetric...	-2.1[4]	3.4[4]	7.2[4]	Gintel...	-16.5[5]	2.0[5]	2.7[5]
Gov St Equity...	-2.2[4]	2.0[5]	—	Weitz Hickory...	-17.2[5]	—	—
Selected Spec Sh SC...	-2.5[4]	5.4[4]	6.4[5]	Steadman Investment...	-33.8[5]	-14.4[5]	-6.7[5]
Stratton Sm Cap Yld SC...	-2.7[4]	—	—	**GROWTH-INCOME FUNDS**			
Analysts Inv Stk...	-2.7[4]	—	—	Warbg Pincus Gro & Inc...	7.6[1]	16.8[1]	13.4[1]
Henlopen Fund...	-2.7[4]	—	—	First Omaha Eqty...	7.4[1]	—	—
Warbg Pincus Cap App...	-2.9[4]	6.5[3]	7.6[4]	Stratton Growth...	7.1[1]	6.7[2]	6.7[4]
Nicholas Fund...	-2.9[4]	5.0[4]	9.4[2]	Retrmt Sys: Core Eq...	5.7[1]	8.8[1]	—
Nicholas Ltd Edit SC...	-3.0[4]	7.3[3]	11.7[1]	Mutual Qualified...	5.7[1]	16.7[1]	11.6[1]
SteinRoe Special...	-3.3[4]	9.9[2]	10.8[2]	Mutual Beacon...	5.6[1]	16.8[1]	11.5[1]
Founders Growth...	-3.3[4]	8.2[2]	10.8[2]	Delafield Fund...	5.6[1]	—	—
Gabelli Growth...	-3.4[4]	4.0[4]	8.1[3]	Gateway Idx Plus...	5.6[1]	6.0[3]	9.1[2]
Nbrgr-Ber Manhtn...	-3.6[4]	7.7[3]	8.5[3]	Dodge & Cox Stock...	5.2[1]	11.3[1]	9.7[1]
Loomis Syls Growth...	-3.6[4]	3.0[4]	—	Royce Total Ret...	5.1[1]	—	—
CA Inv Tr-S&P MidCap...	-3.9[4]	—	—	Mutual Shares...	4.5[1]	15.3[1]	10.8[1]
Drey-Peoples MidCap...	-4.0[4]	6.9[3]	—	Crescent Fund...	4.2[1]	—	—
Blanchard Amer Eqty...	-4.1[4]	—	—	Berwyn...	4.2[1]	15.6[1]	11.0[1]
Legg Msn Amer Lead...	-4.2[4]	—	—	Nicholas Eqty Inc...	4.1[1]	—	—
Federated Mid Cap...	-4.3[4]	—	—	Twentieth Cent Value...	4.0[1]	—	—
Babson Shadow Stk SC...	-4.3[4]	9.0[2]	7.9[4]	FFB Lexcn Sel Value...	3.9[1]	—	—
Household Gro Eqty...	-4.5[4]	—	—	Bascom Hill Invest...	3.9[1]	5.9[3]	6.1[4]
Value Line Fund...	-4.5[4]	2.2[5]	9.5[2]	Galaxy Eqty Value...	3.5[1]	8.7[2]	8.9[2]
SBSF Capital Gro...	-4.5[4]	—	—	Fidelity Eqty Inc II...	3.2[1]	13.4[1]	—
FFB Lexcn Cap App...	-4.5[4]	3.0[4]	—	AARP Growth & Inc...	3.1[1]	9.2[1]	10.0[1]
Drey-Wilsh Sm Val...	-4.5[4]	—	—	Vangd Idx Growth...	2.9[1]	—	—
DFA US Lrg Cap Val...	-4.5[5]	—	—	SIT Gro & Inc...	2.8[1]	3.6[4]	7.7[3]
Matrix Growth...	-4.8[5]	3.0[5]	6.9[4]	Fidelity Fund...	2.6[1]	9.6[1]	9.2[1]
Charter Cap Blue Chip...	-4.8[5]	-2.9[5]	5.6[5]	LMH Fund...	2.6[1]	6.1[3]	2.9[5]
Highmark Growth...	-4.9[5]	—	—	Scudder Gro & Inc...	2.6[1]	9.1[1]	10.2[1]
Gateway MidCap Idx...	-5.1[5]	—	—	Analytic Option Eqty...	2.5[1]	5.1[4]	5.9[4]

By 1994 performance

No-Load Fund	Total return percent with quintile ranks by objective			No-Load Fund	Total return percent with quintile ranks by objective		
	1994	Annualized 3 years	5 years		1994	Annualized 3 years	5 years
Homestead Value	2.5[1]	10.8[1]	—	Quant Gro & Inc	-0.7[3]	5.7[4]	8.3[2]
Fidelity Gro & Inc	2.3[1]	10.9[1]	12.5[1]	Wright Qual Core Eqty	-0.7[3]	2.7[5]	7.9[3]
Westwood Equity	2.3[1]	8.3[2]	7.6[3]	Lexington Corp Ldrs	-0.8[3]	8.6[2]	7.9[3]
Price, Rowe Div Gro	2.2[1]	—	—	Loomis Syls Gro & Inc	-0.9[3]	8.2[2]	—
Marshall Value Eqty	2.1[1]	—	—	SCM Portfolio	-0.9[3]	2.6[5]	4.4[5]
Smith Brdn Mkt Track	1.8[2]	—	—	Amer AAdv Gro & Inc	-1.0[3]	8.9[1]	9.0[2]
AIC: Rlstn Gr & Inc	1.7[2]	—	—	Caldwell Fund	-1.1[3]	6.6[2]	7.9[3]
TU&P Balanced	1.5[2]	2.7[5]	7.2[3]	RSI Tr-Value Eqty	-1.1[3]	5.0[4]	5.5[5]
RSI Tr-Core Eqty	1.3[2]	5.9[3]	6.9[4]	Vangd Windsor II	-1.2[4]	7.9[2]	7.7[3]
Seven Seas S&P 500	1.3[2]	—	—	Dreyfus Discpl Stk	-1.2[4]	5.8[4]	9.6[1]
USAA Growth & Inc	1.3[2]	—	—	Brown Cap Blncd	-1.2[4]	—	—
DFA US Lrg Co	1.3[2]	6.1[3]	—	Salomon Investors	-1.3[4]	6.9[2]	8.1[3]
Federated Max Cap	1.2[2]	5.9[3]	—	Strong Total Return	-1.4[4]	6.7[2]	8.6[2]
Vangd Idx 500	1.2[2]	6.1[3]	8.5[2]	Vangd Idx Balanced	-1.5[4]	—	—
Highmark Inc & Gr	1.2[2]	—	—	Marshall Eqty Inc	-1.6[4]	—	—
Maxus Equity	1.1[2]	14.1[1]	10.7[1]	MSB	-1.7[4]	9.5[1]	7.3[3]
ASM	1.1[2]	6.6[2]	—	GE S&S Prg: Mutual	-1.8[4]	5.8[3]	8.3[2]
Fidelity Market Idx	1.1[2]	5.9[3]	—	Jensen Portfolio	-1.8[4]	—	—
CA Inv Tr-S&P 500	1.0[2]	—	—	GE Strat Invest	-1.8[4]	—	—
Price, Rowe Eqty Idx	1.0[2]	5.8[3]	—	MIM Stock Income	-1.8[4]	0.8[5]	3.4[5]
Woodward Eqty Idx	1.0[2]	—	—	Federated Stk & Bd	-1.9[4]	5.2[4]	6.7[4]
Galaxy Lg Co Idx	1.0[2]	5.8[3]	—	Fiduciary Total Ret	-2.0[4]	6.3[3]	8.4[2]
Dreyfus S&P 500 Idx	0.8[2]	—	—	FundTrust Mgd Tot Ret	-2.1[4]	4.3[4]	6.5[4]
Harbor Value	0.7[2]	5.5[4]	6.1[4]	GE US Equity	-2.2[4]	—	—
Drey-Peoples Idx	0.7[2]	5.9[3]	7.9[3]	Scudder Balanced	-2.4[4]	—	—
Stratus Eqty Inc	0.6[2]	—	—	Clipper	-2.5[4]	7.9[2]	9.0[2]
Founders Blue Chip	0.5[2]	4.7[4]	8.1[3]	Preferred Asst Allc	-2.6[4]	—	—
CT&T Gro & Inc	0.5[2]	—	—	Anthem Gro & Inc	-2.7[4]	—	—
Preferred Value	0.5[2]	—	—	Evergreen Amer Ret	-2.9[4]	7.4[2]	7.9[3]
Bartlett Basic Value	0.4[2]	7.3[2]	7.1[3]	Aquinas Eqty Inc	-2.9[4]	—	—
Gibraltar Eqty Gro	0.4[2]	-1.8[5]	3.8[5]	Managers Balanced	-3.0[4]	2.6[5]	5.8[5]
Bridges Investment	0.4[2]	3.2[4]	6.2[4]	Lexington Gro & Inc	-3.1[4]	7.2[2]	6.7[4]
Fidelity Eqty Inc	0.3[2]	11.7[1]	9.2[2]	Leeb Prsnl Finance	-3.1[4]	1.5[5]	—
Portico Gro & Inc	0.1[2]	4.1[4]	6.5[4]	Selected Amer Sh	-3.2[4]	2.6[5]	8.7[2]
Weston: New Cent Cap	0.1[2]	4.6[4]	8.3[2]	TCW/DW Inc & Gro	-3.3[4]	—	—
Janus Balanced	0.0[2]	—	—	Concorde Value	-3.3[4]	6.7[2]	5.2[5]
Twentieth Cent Blncd	-0.1[2]	0.2[5]	8.5[2]	Htchks & Wly Eq Inc	-3.5[4]	8.4[2]	7.0[3]
Schwab 1000	-0.1[3]	5.9[3]	—	Wright Sel Blue Ch	-3.5[4]	1.0[5]	6.3[4]
Price, Rowe Gro & Inc	-0.1[3]	9.2[1]	8.7[2]	Payson Value	-3.7[4]	—	—
Vangd Windsor	-0.1[3]	11.5[1]	8.5[2]	Invesco Indust Inc	-3.9[4]	4.2[4]	10.8[1]
Merriman Gro & Inc	-0.2[3]	0.4[5]	4.6[5]	Vangd Trust US	-3.9[5]	6.2[3]	6.8[4]
FundTrust Gro & Inc	-0.2[3]	7.1[2]	6.8[4]	Advance Cap Eqty Univ	-4.0[5]	0.1[5]	2.3[5]
1784 Gro & Inc	-0.2[3]	—	—	Golden Rainbow	-4.2[5]	6.0[3]	—
Primary Trend	-0.2[3]	3.7[4]	5.5[5]	Smith Hayes Asst Allc	-4.2[5]	2.3[5]	6.6[4]
Seafirst Asst Allc	-0.2[3]	5.2[4]	7.5[3]	Dreyfus Fund	-4.2[5]	2.4[5]	5.9[4]
National Industries	-0.2[3]	0.2[5]	6.5[4]	Schafer Value	-4.3[5]	12.1[1]	12.1[1]
Seven Seas Gro & Inc	-0.3[3]	—	—	Green Cent Blncd	-4.3[5]	—	—
Vangd Star:Star	-0.3[3]	6.9[2]	7.9[3]	IAI Gro & Inc	-4.8[5]	2.9[5]	5.2[5]
GE Elfun Div Inc	-0.3[3]	6.0[3]	7.9[3]	Janus Growth & Inc	-4.9[5]	2.3[5]	—
Domini Social Eqty	-0.4[3]	6.1[3]	—	Heartland Val & Inc	-5.0[5]	—	—
Federated Stock	-0.4[3]	7.8[2]	9.0[2]	Lepercq-Istel	-5.0[5]	4.4[4]	4.5[5]
BSR Gro & Inc	-0.5[3]	3.9[4]	—	Drey-Wilsh Lg Val	-5.2[5]	—	—
Benham Income & Gro	-0.6[3]	6.1[3]	—	Dreyfus Gro & Inc	-5.2[5]	10.5[1]	—
Tweedy Brwn Amer Value	-0.6[3]	—	—	US All-Amer Eqty	-5.3[5]	3.2[5]	—
Reynolds Blue Chip	-0.6[3]	-1.9[5]	5.1[5]	Household Eqty Inc	-5.5[5]	—	—
Vangd Quantitative	-0.6[3]	6.6[3]	9.0[2]	WPG Growth & Inc	-5.5[5]	5.6[4]	8.2[3]
Vangd Idx Value	-0.6[3]	—	—	GIT Equity Inc	-5.8[5]	2.1[5]	4.2[5]
Pierpont Equity	-0.6[3]	6.3[3]	10.3[1]	Marshall Stock	-5.8[5]	—	—
Pierpont Divsfd	-0.6[3]	—	—	Evergreen Tot Ret	-6.5[5]	5.1[4]	6.0[4]
1784 Asset Alloc	-0.6[3]	—	—	Muhlenkamp	-7.3[5]	8.8[2]	9.8[1]

No-Load Fund	Total return percent with quintile ranks by objective		
	1994	Annualized 3 years	5 years
Fidelity Asst Mgr Gro...	-7.4[5]	11.7[1]	—
API Spec Mkts...	-7.4[5]	-1.0[5]	-2.2[5]
Copley...	-7.7[5]	6.2[3]	6.7[4]
Bull & Bear Qual Gro...	-7.9[5]	—	—
Philadelphia...	-8.6[5]	8.8[2]	3.8[5]
Berger 101...	-9.1[5]	5.7[4]	11.8[1]
CGM Mutual...	-9.7[5]	5.3[4]	10.7[1]
Weitz Value...	-9.8[5]	7.1[2]	8.3[2]
ZSA Asset Alloc...	-12.8[5]	—	—
Bruce...	-16.1[5]	3.5[4]	2.1[5]
Gintel Erisa...	-21.3[5]	-1.8[5]	0.4[5]
INCOME FUNDS			
Invesco Balanced...	9.5[1]	—	—
State Farm Blncd...	5.0[1]	4.6[4]	11.8[1]
Price, Rowe Eqty Inc...	4.5[1]	11.1[1]	9.9[2]
Dreyfus Balanced...	3.9[1]	—	—
Value Line Asst All...	3.4[1]	—	—
Evergreen Tax Found...	3.4[1]	—	—
Pax World...	2.6[1]	0.7[5]	6.4[4]
Invesco Total Ret...	2.5[1]	8.2[2]	9.5[2]
Avondale Total Ret...	2.3[1]	2.6[5]	6.5[4]
Dodge & Cox Blncd...	2.1[1]	9.4[1]	9.8[2]
Fidelity Puritan...	1.9[1]	12.6[1]	10.7[1]
FBP Contrn Blncd...	1.8[1]	8.2[2]	8.3[3]
Dreyfus Asst:Tot Ret...	1.7[1]	—	—
Warbg Pincus Balanced...	1.3[1]	8.2[2]	10.3[1]
Lexington Convert...	1.3[1]	6.2[3]	10.9[1]
Bascom Hill Blncd...	1.1[1]	4.6[4]	5.8[5]
Managers Inc Eqty...	1.0[1]	7.7[2]	7.0[4]
Htchks & Wly Blncd...	0.8[2]	7.5[2]	8.3[3]
Galaxy Eqty Income...	0.8[2]	5.4[4]	—
Columbia Balanced...	0.1[2]	7.4[2]	—
Westwood Balanced...	0.0[2]	7.4[2]	—
Eclipse Balanced...	0.0[2]	9.4[1]	10.0[1]
SIT Balanced...	-0.4[2]	—	—
API Cap Inc...	-0.4[2]	4.6[4]	6.2[5]
Vangd Wellington...	-0.4[2]	6.8[3]	7.9[3]
Highmark Inc Eqty...	-0.6[2]	7.1[3]	7.7[3]
USAA Income Stk...	-0.7[2]	6.1[3]	8.4[3]
Crabbe Hsn Asst All...	-0.9[2]	9.6[1]	—
Lindner Utility...	-1.0[2]	—	—
SAFECO Income...	-1.1[2]	7.5[2]	6.4[4]
Evergreen Foundation...	-1.1[2]	11.1[1]	14.8[1]
Berwyn Income...	-1.1[2]	12.1[1]	11.6[1]
Highmark Balncd...	-1.2[2]	—	—
Fidelity Asst Mgr Inc...	-1.4[3]	—	—
IAI Balanced...	-1.4[3]	—	—
Strong Asst Allc...	-1.5[3]	5.2[4]	7.4[4]
Vangd Equity Inc...	-1.5[3]	7.2[3]	6.3[4]
Amer AAdv Balncd...	-1.7[3]	7.2[3]	8.6[2]
Fidelity Convert...	-1.7[3]	12.1[1]	13.7[1]
Founders Balanced...	-1.9[3]	8.2[2]	8.1[3]
Invesco Multi-Asst...	-2.0[3]	—	—
Price, Rowe Balanced...	-2.0[3]	5.7[4]	—
Mairs & Power Inc...	-2.0[3]	4.8[4]	8.0[3]
Jurika & Vyls Blncd...	-2.2[3]	—	—
Vangd Asset Alloc...	-2.3[3]	6.0[3]	8.5[2]
Weston: New Cent Inc...	-2.4[3]	5.0[4]	7.2[4]
Galaxy Asst Allc...	-2.5[3]	4.0[5]	—
Strong Amer Util...	-2.6[3]	—	—

No-Load Fund	Total return percent with quintile ranks by objective		
	1994	Annualized 3 years	5 years
Primary Income...	-2.6[3]	4.8[4]	7.7[3]
USAA Balanced...	-2.6[3]	5.2[4]	6.2[4]
Advance Cap Blncd...	-2.7[4]	1.7[5]	4.2[5]
Merriman Asst All...	-2.9[4]	5.8[3]	6.1[5]
Anthem Balanced...	-3.0[4]	—	—
Aquinas Balanced...	-3.1[4]	—	—
Royce Equity Inc...	-3.2[4]	9.3[1]	9.0[2]
Lindner Dividend...	-3.3[4]	10.4[1]	9.9[1]
SteinRoe Total Ret...	-4.1[4]	5.1[4]	8.1[3]
Payson Balanced...	-4.2[4]	5.8[3]	—
Portico Balanced...	-4.3[4]	—	—
Value Line Income...	-4.3[4]	1.8[5]	6.7[4]
Smith Hayes Blncd...	-4.4[4]	3.4[5]	5.4[5]
Vangd Wellesley Inc...	-4.4[4]	6.0[3]	8.4[3]
Value Line Convert...	-5.2[4]	7.4[2]	8.9[2]
Fidelity Utilities...	-5.3[4]	6.7[3]	8.4[3]
Fidelity Balanced...	-5.3[4]	6.8[3]	9.0[2]
Parnassus Balanced...	-5.3[4]	—	—
Vangd Convert...	-5.6[5]	8.4[1]	9.4[2]
Marshall Balanced...	-5.6[5]	—	—
MIM AFA Eqty Inc...	-6.0[5]	3.1[5]	—
SBSF Convert...	-6.5[5]	7.7[2]	8.7[2]
Amana Income...	-6.5[5]	2.1[5]	4.9[5]
Fidelity Asset Mgr...	-6.5[5]	9.3[1]	11.1[1]
API Total Ret...	-6.8[5]	3.5[5]	3.0[5]
Smith Hayes Convert...	-8.0[5]	5.7[4]	7.4[4]
Vangd Spec-Util...	-8.5[5]	—	—
Galaxy Util Idx...	-8.6[5]	—	—
TCW/DW Balanced...	-9.7[5]	—	—
Benham Util Inc...	-10.0[5]	—	—
US Income...	-10.3[5]	4.5[5]	3.6[5]
Stratton Month Div Sh...	-12.1[5]	1.1[5]	6.0[5]
America's Utility...	-13.1[5]	—	—
Capp-Rush Util...	-13.3[5]	—	—
Steadman Associated...	-20.5[5]	-2.4[5]	-2.8[5]
SECTOR & INDUSTRY FUNDS			
Fidelity Sel Health...	21.4[1]	0.9[5]	18.6[1]
Fidelity Sel Computer...	20.5[1]	23.7[1]	24.0[1]
Fidelity Sel Medical Del...	19.8[1]	3.2[5]	17.8[2]
Fidelity Sel Electronics...	17.2[1]	25.4[1]	23.1[1]
Price, Rowe Sci/Tech...	15.8[1]	19.5[1]	22.0[1]
Fidelity Sel Devel Comm...	15.1[1]	21.1[1]	—
Fidelity Sel Chemicals...	14.7[1]	12.1[3]	13.4[3]
Fidelity Sel Pap/Forest...	14.1[1]	14.9[2]	11.6[3]
Fidelity Sel Technology...	11.1[1]	15.8[2]	22.3[1]
Vangd Spec-Health...	9.5[1]	6.4[4]	15.5[2]
Cohen & Steers Realty...	8.3[1]	15.5[2]	—
Fidelity Sel Indust Mat...	8.2[2]	13.8[2]	10.7[4]
Fidelity Sel Food/Agr...	6.1[2]	7.0[4]	12.4[3]
Invesco Strat Tech...	5.3[2]	12.9[3]	22.5[1]
Fidelity Sel Telecomm...	4.3[2]	16.0[2]	11.2[3]
Fidelity Sel Multimedia...	4.0[2]	20.3[1]	12.1[3]
Fidelity Sel Transp...	3.9[2]	18.5[1]	15.0[2]
Fidelity Sel Indust Equip...	3.1[2]	18.1[2]	12.0[3]
PRA Real Estate...	3.0[2]	13.3[2]	6.9[4]
Fidelity Sel Home Fincl...	2.7[2]	27.3[1]	23.5[1]
Fidelity Real Estate...	1.9[2]	11.0[3]	11.7[3]
Fidelity Sel Defense...	1.8[3]	9.4[3]	9.7[4]
Invesco Strat Health...	0.9[3]	-7.3[5]	14.0[3]
Fidelity Sel Energy Serv...	0.6[3]	8.0[4]	-0.4[5]

By 1994 performance

No-Load Fund	Total return percent with quintile ranks by objective 1994	Annualized 3 years	Annualized 5 years
Fidelity Sel Energy	0.4[3]	5.3[4]	2.2[5]
Fidelity Sel Software	0.4[3]	21.7[1]	21.5[1]
Fidelity Sel Reg Banks	0.2[3]	18.2[1]	16.8[2]
Fidelity Sel Insurance	-0.3[3]	9.7[3]	10.2[4]
Vangd Spec-Energy	-1.6[3]	9.7[3]	5.4[5]
Fidelity Sel Financial	-3.7[3]	17.4[2]	14.6[3]
Century Shares	-3.9[3]	6.7[4]	8.0[4]
Invesco Strat Leisure	-5.0[3]	16.8[2]	16.7[2]
Fidelity Sel Retail	-5.0[4]	9.4[3]	15.9[2]
Invesco Strat Fncl	-5.9[4]	12.2[3]	18.0[1]
Fidelity Sel Leisure	-6.8[4]	14.8[2]	9.3[4]
Fidelity Sel Nat Gas	-6.8[4]	—	—
Fidelity Sel Consmr Prod	-7.1[4]	7.9[4]	—
Invesco Strat Enrgy	-7.3[4]	-2.1[5]	-5.4[5]
Fidelity Sel Util Gro	-7.4[4]	4.8[4]	6.9[4]
DFA Real Estate	-8.4[4]	—	—
Fidelity Sel Envir Serv	-9.6[4]	-3.9[5]	-1.4[5]
Rushmore Amer Gas Idx	-9.8[4]	5.4[4]	1.6[5]
Invesco Strat Util	-9.9[5]	6.6[4]	6.9[4]
Evergreen US RE	-10.9[5]	—	—
Invesco Strat Envrn	-11.4[5]	-11.8[5]	—
US Real Estate	-11.6[5]	-2.3[5]	3.1[5]
Fidelity Sel Auto	-12.8[5]	18.7[1]	16.4[2]
Dreyfus Edison Elec	-12.9[5]	1.1[5]	—
Evergreen Glob RE	-14.1[5]	12.8[3]	5.5[5]
Fidelity Sel Const/Hous	-16.0[5]	10.1[3]	11.2[4]
Fidelity Sel Broker	-17.3[5]	9.1[4]	14.7[2]
Fidelity Sel Biotech	-18.2[5]	-9.6[5]	16.2[2]
Fidelity Sel Air Trans	-21.7[5]	3.0[5]	4.1[5]
PRECIOUS METALS FUNDS			
Fidelity Sel Prec Metals	-1.2[1]	17.8[1]	5.5[1]
US Gold Shares	-2.7[1]	2.3[5]	-9.9[5]
Vangd Spec-Gold	-5.4[1]	13.8[2]	4.2[1]
Lexington Goldfund	-7.3[2]	11.3[3]	0.5[4]
Scudder Gold	-7.4[2]	10.3[4]	0.8[3]
USAA Gold	-9.4[3]	9.7[4]	-1.5[4]
Bull & Bear Gold	-13.8[3]	10.2[4]	0.6[3]
Blanchard Prec Metals	-15.2[3]	11.5[2]	0.9[2]
Fidelity Sel Amer Gold	-15.4[4]	13.5[2]	2.6[2]
Benham Gold Eqty	-16.8[4]	11.3[3]	-0.3[4]
US World Gold	-16.9[5]	14.5[1]	0.9[2]
Rydex Prec Met	-25.5[5]	—	—
Invesco Strat Gold	-27.9[5]	4.6[5]	-4.0[5]
GLOBAL EQUITY FUNDS			
Tweedy Brwn Glob Value	4.4[1]	—	—
Babson UMB Worldwide	3.8[1]	—	—
Janus Worldwide	3.6[1]	13.2[1]	—
Fidelity Worldwide	3.0[1]	14.3[1]	—
Austin Global Eqty	2.1[1]	—	—
Lexington Global	1.8[1]	9.0[2]	4.5[3]
USAA World Growth	0.6[2]	—	—
Fontaine Glob Gro	-0.4[2]	—	—
GE Elfun Glob Inc	-0.6[2]	11.6[1]	7.8[1]
USAA Cornerstone	-1.1[2]	9.2[2]	6.6[3]
GE Global Eqty	-1.9[2]	—	—
Brinson Global	-1.9[3]	—	—
Founders Worldwide Gro	-2.2[3]	8.9[3]	13.1[1]
Permanent Portfolio	-2.9[3]	4.8[5]	3.6[5]
Gabelli Glob Telecomm	-3.7[3]	—	—
Fremont Global	-4.2[3]	6.4[4]	7.0[2]

No-Load Fund	Total return percent with quintile ranks by objective 1994	Annualized 3 years	Annualized 5 years
Scudder Global	-4.2[3]	9.5[2]	7.5[2]
Dreyfus Global Growth	-7.5[4]	3.1[5]	6.4[3]
Blanchard Glob Growth	-7.5[4]	5.0[4]	3.7[5]
Scudder Glob Sm Co	-7.7[4]	8.4[3]	—
Montgmry Glob Oppty	-8.5[4]	—	—
BBK Diversa	-9.4[4]	4.8[4]	3.8[4]
Founders Passport	-10.4[5]	—	—
Fidelity Glob Blncd	-11.4[5]	—	—
Hercules N Amer Gr&Inc	-13.0[5]	—	—
Bull & Bear US & Overs	-13.1[5]	2.3[5]	3.7[4]
Montgmry Glob Comm	-13.4[5]	—	—
GIT Wrldwd Growth	-24.1[5]	—	—
INTERNATIONAL FUNDS			
DFA Japan Sm Co	29.5[1]	3.0[5]	-4.9[5]
Fidelity Japan	16.5[1]	—	—
Price, Rowe Japan	15.1[1]	6.3[4]	—
Vangd Idx Pacific	12.9[1]	7.8[3]	—
Wright Equi Dutch	11.7[1]	7.0[4]	—
DFA Cont Sm Co	11.0[1]	3.7[5]	0.5[5]
Japan (Scudder)	10.0[1]	4.2[5]	-0.5[5]
Quant Int'l Eqty	9.1[1]	7.6[4]	-0.3[5]
DFA Int'l High BTM	8.8[1]	—	—
Papp L Roy Amer Abrd	7.8[1]	4.8[5]	—
Fidelity Europe Cap App	6.9[1]	—	—
Fidelity Europe	6.2[1]	9.6[2]	5.5[2]
Lexington Int'l	5.9[1]	—	—
Pierpont Int'l Eqty	5.6[1]	5.9[4]	—
Harbor Int'l	5.4[1]	15.2[1]	10.9[1]
DFA Lrg Cap Int'l	5.3[1]	4.8[4]	—
Vangd Trust Int'l	5.3[1]	7.8[3]	3.9[4]
Wright Equi Italy	5.0[2]	-8.1[5]	—
Invesco Pacific Bas	4.7[2]	8.9[2]	2.0[4]
DFA UK Small Co	4.6[2]	5.5[4]	4.7[3]
Nomura Pacific Bas	4.2[2]	8.5[3]	3.9[4]
Price, Rowe Europe	4.1[2]	7.7[4]	—
Schwab Int'l Idx	3.8[2]	—	—
Bernstein Int'l Value	3.8[2]	—	—
Drey/Laurel Int'l	3.5[2]	4.9[4]	0.1[5]
Preferred Int'l	3.3[2]	—	—
USAA International	2.7[2]	12.8[1]	8.1[1]
Hercules European	2.4[2]	—	—
Managers Int'l Eqty	2.0[2]	13.7[1]	9.4[1]
Vangd Idx Europe	1.9[2]	8.3[3]	—
Babson Stew Ivry Int'l	1.3[2]	10.0[2]	6.8[1]
Fidelity Overseas	1.3[2]	7.9[3]	4.9[3]
Amer AAdv Int'l	1.2[2]	8.8[3]	—
Fidelity Dvsfd Int'l	1.1[2]	6.0[4]	—
Brinson Non US Eqty	0.9[3]	—	—
RSI Tr-Int'l Eqty	0.8[3]	7.5[4]	3.5[4]
Vangd Int'l Growth	0.7[3]	11.2[2]	4.8[3]
Invesco Int'l Gro	0.6[3]	4.0[5]	0.6[5]
IAI International	0.5[3]	9.5[2]	5.9[2]
Schroder Int'l Eqty	0.2[3]	11.9[2]	5.4[2]
Warbg Pincus Int'l	0.2[3]	13.2[1]	10.8[1]
Wm Blair Int'l Gro	-0.1[3]	—	—
Bartlett Value Int'l	-0.5[3]	8.7[3]	5.9[2]
Price, Rowe Int'l Stk	-0.8[3]	10.3[2]	7.2[1]
Strong Int'l Stk	-1.6[3]	—	—
Wright Int'l Blue Ch	-1.6[3]	6.6[4]	5.7[2]
Loomis Syls Int'l Eq	-1.8[3]	8.9[2]	—

By 1994 performance

No-Load Fund	Total return percent with quintile ranks by objective	Annualized	
	1994	3 years	5 years
Hercules Pacific Bas...	-1.8[3]	—	—
Columbia Int'l Stk...	-2.5[3]	—	—
Galaxy Int'l Eqty...	-2.5[3]	7.8[3]	—
Fidelity Pacific Basin...	-2.8[3]	13.7[1]	3.8[4]
Fidelity Int'l Gr & Inc...	-2.9[4]	8.2[3]	5.8[2]
Htchks & Wly Int'l...	-3.0[4]	11.2[2]	—
Scudder Int'l Stk...	-3.0[4]	8.9[2]	5.6[2]
SIT Int'l Growth...	-3.0[4]	13.9[1]	—
Invesco Europe...	-3.0[4]	3.7[5]	3.9[3]
Dreyfus European...	-3.1[4]	3.5[5]	5.0[3]
Acorn Int'l...	-3.8[4]	—	—
59 Wall Europe Eqty...	-3.9[4]	9.5[2]	—
Twentieth Cent Int'l...	-4.8[4]	12.5[1]	—
Vontobel EuroPac...	-4.9[4]	8.8[3]	—
Strong Asia Pacific...	-5.3[4]	—	—
Dreyfus Int'l Eqty...	-5.4[4]	—	—
WPG International...	-6.3[4]	6.7[4]	0.8[4]
Pierpont Emg Mkts...	-7.0[4]	—	—
Price, Rowe Int'l Disc...	-7.6[4]	8.0[3]	4.1[3]
Montgmry Emg Mkts...	-7.7[4]	—	—
Harbor Int'l Gro...	-7.7[4]	—	—
Oakmark Int'l...	-9.1[5]	—	—
Scudder Latin Amer...	-9.4[5]	—	—
Wright Equi Spain...	-9.5[5]	-9.6[5]	—
Fidelity Canada...	-12.0[5]	2.4[5]	3.6[4]
DFA Pac Rim Sm Co...	-12.1[5]	—	—
BBK Int'l Equity...	-12.6[5]	2.2[5]	-2.6[5]
Montgmry Int'l Sm Cap...	-13.3[5]	—	—
Lexington World Emg...	-13.8[5]	13.5[1]	9.2[1]
Price, Rowe Latin Amer...	-15.9[5]	—	—
Scudder Pacific Opp...	-17.1[5]	—	—
Fidelity Emg Mkts...	-17.9[5]	16.4[1]	—
Hercules Latin Amer...	-18.1[5]	—	—
Price, Rowe New Asia...	-19.2[5]	17.1[1]	—
59 Wall Pac Basin...	-21.5[5]	13.4[1]	—
Fidelity SE Asia...	-21.8[5]	—	—
Fidelity Latin Amer...	-23.2[5]	—	—
Wright Equi Hong Kong...	-37.0[5]	10.5[2]	—
FIXED-INCOME FUNDS - LONG TERM			
Fidelity Curr: D-Mark...	16.4[1]	5.1[2]	8.4[2]
Fidelity Curr: Yen...	12.6[1]	9.3[1]	11.0[1]
Fidelity Curr: Sterling...	9.9[1]	-0.4[5]	7.5[3]
Fidelity Spart Hi Inc...	3.2[1]	15.1[1]	—
Pacifica Asset Pres...	2.4[1]	3.9[4]	—
Northeast Inv Trust...	2.2[1]	14.0[1]	11.2[1]
SIT US Gov...	1.8[1]	4.8[3]	7.6[3]
Camco Total Ret...	1.2[1]	—	—
Capstone Gov Inc...	1.2[1]	2.7[5]	2.7[5]
Benham Target 1995...	0.8[1]	5.0[2]	8.0[2]
Federated ARMS...	0.3[1]	2.8[5]	6.0[5]
Nicholas Income...	-0.2[1]	7.5[1]	8.6[1]
Caldwell Gov...	-0.3[1]	—	—
Columbia High Yld...	-0.9[1]	—	—
Analytic Master Fix...	-1.1[1]	—	—
Invesco Select Inc...	-1.2[1]	6.7[1]	8.6[1]
Strong Income...	-1.3[1]	8.0[1]	6.3[5]
SIT Bond...	-1.3[1]	—	—
Federated Income...	-1.6[1]	3.2[5]	6.7[4]
Vangd Hi Yld Corp...	-1.7[1]	9.9[1]	10.0[1]
Crowley Income...	-1.8[1]	4.9[3]	7.0[3]

No-Load Fund	Total return percent with quintile ranks by objective	Annualized	
	1994	3 years	5 years
Highmark Gov Bd...	-1.9[1]	—	—
SAFECO Hi Yld Bd...	-2.0[1]	9.3[1]	9.3[1]
Crabbe Hsn Gov Bd...	-2.1[1]	3.0[5]	5.9[5]
Selected US Gov...	-2.2[1]	3.5[4]	6.4[4]
Seafirst Bond...	-2.3[2]	3.6[4]	6.6[4]
GE Elfun Income...	-2.3[2]	4.5[3]	7.6[3]
Weitz Fix Inc...	-2.3[2]	3.6[4]	6.2[5]
Preferred Fix Inc...	-2.4[2]	—	—
Federated Hi Yld...	-2.4[2]	9.6[1]	11.9[1]
PDC&J Preservation...	-2.4[2]	4.0[4]	6.7[4]
Wayne Hummer Income...	-2.5[2]	—	—
GE S&S Prg: LT Inst...	-2.5[2]	4.6[3]	7.7[2]
GE Fixed Income...	-2.5[2]	—	—
GIT Max Income...	-2.6[2]	7.9[1]	7.8[2]
TU&P Bond...	-2.7[2]	—	—
Marshall Gov Inc...	-2.7[2]	—	—
AIC: Clvr Cap Fix...	-2.8[2]	4.8[3]	—
FFB Lexcn Fix Inc...	-3.0[2]	4.9[2]	—
Pierpont Bond...	-3.0[2]	3.8[4]	6.9[4]
Portico Bond Immdex...	-3.1[2]	5.0[2]	7.9[2]
Aquinas Fix Inc...	-3.1[2]	—	—
Babson UMB Bond...	-3.1[2]	3.8[4]	6.5[4]
Amcor Vntg Fix Inc...	-3.1[2]	—	—
Vista Bond...	-3.2[2]	4.6[3]	—
Babson Bond-Port L...	-3.3[2]	5.3[2]	7.7[3]
SteinRoe Gov Inc...	-3.3[2]	3.2[5]	6.5[4]
Stratus Gov Sec...	-3.3[2]	—	—
Wright Curr Inc...	-3.3[2]	3.2[5]	6.9[4]
Smith Hayes Gov Qual...	-3.3[3]	2.8[5]	5.8[5]
Brinson Glob Bd...	-3.5[3]	—	—
PIMCO Tot Return...	-3.6[3]	6.0[2]	9.0[1]
Crabbe Hsn Income...	-3.6[3]	2.8[5]	6.0[5]
Fidelity Spart Gov Inc...	-3.6[3]	3.5[4]	6.8[4]
MIM Bond Income...	-3.6[3]	2.0[5]	4.2[5]
Galaxy Trsy Idx...	-3.7[3]	4.3[3]	—
Highmark Bond...	-3.9[3]	3.8[4]	6.3[4]
Loomis Syls Bond...	-4.1[3]	10.2[1]	—
Value Line Agg Inc...	-4.1[3]	8.6[1]	9.3[1]
RSI Tr-Act Mgd Bd...	-4.2[3]	4.4[3]	7.5[3]
Alliance World Inc...	-4.2[3]	—	—
DFA Glob Fix Inc...	-4.3[3]	4.6[3]	—
AARP Hi Qual Bd...	-4.5[3]	4.0[4]	6.9[3]
Maxus Income...	-4.5[3]	4.6[3]	6.7[4]
Scudder Income...	-4.5[3]	4.7[3]	7.8[2]
Fidelity Cap & Inc...	-4.6[3]	15.1[1]	13.7[1]
Advance Cap Bond...	-4.6[3]	4.4[3]	7.1[3]
Bull & Bear US Gov...	-4.7[3]	3.4[5]	6.6[4]
First Omaha Fix Inc...	-4.8[3]	—	—
IAI Bond...	-4.9[3]	4.5[3]	7.4[3]
Arbor OVB Gov...	-5.1[3]	—	—
Invesco High Yld...	-5.1[3]	8.0[1]	8.2[2]
Fidelity Spart Inv Grd...	-5.2[3]	—	—
Fidelity Gov Sec...	-5.2[3]	4.7[3]	7.8[2]
Vangd LT Corp...	-5.3[4]	6.0[2]	8.9[1]
Advance Cap Ret Inc...	-5.3[4]	—	—
Fidelity Inv Grd Bd...	-5.4[4]	6.0[2]	8.5[1]
Household Fix Inc...	-5.6[4]	—	—
Schwab LT Gov...	-5.7[4]	—	—
Price, Rowe Trsy Lng...	-5.7[4]	4.0[4]	6.9[4]
Dreyfus A Bonds Plus...	-6.1[4]	5.3[2]	7.7[2]

No-Load Fund	Total return percent with quintile ranks by objective			No-Load Fund	Total return percent with quintile ranks by objective		
	1994	Annualized 3 years	5 years		1994	Annualized 3 years	5 years
Reich & Tang Gov....	**-6.2**[4]	3.7[4]	6.7[4]	Merriman Flex Bd....	**-1.7**[2]	5.6[1]	7.2[2]
Hercules World Bond...	**-6.2**[4]	—	—	Smith Brdn Inter Gov....	**-1.7**[2]	—	—
Loomis Syls US Gov....	**-6.3**[4]	5.7[2]	—	Legg Msn Gov Inter....	**-1.7**[2]	3.7[4]	6.8[4]
Analysts Inv Fix....	**-6.4**[4]	—	—	Price, Rowe Int'l Bond....	**-1.8**[2]	6.4[1]	10.5[1]
Galaxy Hi Qual Bd....	**-6.5**[4]	4.0[4]	—	FFB Lexcn Inter Gov....	**-1.9**[2]	3.9[3]	—
AIC: Rlstn Gov Sec....	**-6.5**[4]	—	—	Federated Inter Gov....	**-1.9**[2]	3.8[3]	6.8[4]
Advance Cap LT Inc....	**-6.5**[4]	—	—	Price, Rowe Spect-Inc....	**-1.9**[2]	5.9[1]	—
Wright Total Ret....	**-6.6**[4]	3.6[4]	6.2[5]	Fidelity Inter Bond....	**-2.0**[2]	5.2[1]	7.5[2]
Torchmark Gov Sec....	**-6.7**[4]	—	—	Fidelity GNMA....	**-2.0**[2]	3.5[4]	6.8[4]
Parnassus Fix Inc....	**-6.8**[4]	—	—	Portico Inter Bd Mkt....	**-2.1**[2]	—	—
Vangd-Adml Long....	**-6.8**[4]	—	—	Lexington GNMA....	**-2.1**[2]	3.6[4]	6.9[3]
Benham Target 2000....	**-6.9**[4]	5.3[2]	8.4[2]	Babson Bond-Port S....	**-2.1**[2]	4.3[3]	7.0[3]
CA Inv Tr-US Gov....	**-7.0**[4]	5.3[2]	8.3[2]	Price, Rowe New Inc....	**-2.2**[2]	4.0[3]	7.1[3]
Vangd LT Trsy....	**-7.0**[4]	5.2[2]	7.7[2]	Price Summit GNMA....	**-2.3**[2]	—	—
Invesco Gov Sec....	**-7.2**[4]	2.7[5]	6.0[5]	Asset Mgmt Mrtg Sec....	**-2.3**[2]	3.5[4]	6.9[3]
Managers Bond....	**-7.2**[4]	3.7[4]	7.4[3]	Federated GNMA....	**-2.5**[2]	3.3[5]	7.0[3]
Evergreen US Gov....	**-7.4**[4]	—	—	RSI Tr-Inter Bd....	**-2.5**[3]	3.6[4]	6.9[3]
Anthem Gov Sec....	**-7.5**[5]	—	—	Vangd Bond Idx Total....	**-2.7**[3]	4.6[2]	7.4[2]
Founders Gov Sec....	**-7.5**[5]	2.1[5]	5.0[5]	Gov St Bond....	**-2.7**[3]	4.1[3]	—
Fidelity Spart Bond Strat....	**-7.7**[5]	—	—	SteinRoe Inter Bd....	**-2.8**[3]	4.5[2]	7.1[3]
Vangd Prefrd Stk....	**-7.9**[5]	4.1[4]	7.7[2]	Dreyfus GNMA....	**-2.8**[3]	3.5[5]	6.8[4]
Scudder US Zero 2000....	**-7.9**[5]	4.9[2]	7.7[3]	CT&T Inter Fix....	**-2.8**[3]	—	—
CGM Fixed Inc....	**-8.0**[5]	—	—	Stratus Inter Gov....	**-2.8**[3]	3.3[5]	—
Scudder Emg Mkts Inc....	**-8.1**[5]	—	—	Dodge & Cox Income....	**-2.9**[3]	5.2[1]	8.1[1]
Price, Rowe High Yld....	**-8.1**[5]	8.7[1]	8.4[1]	Bartlett Fix Inc....	**-2.9**[3]	3.5[4]	6.1[5]
Wright Gov Oblig....	**-8.7**[5]	4.3[3]	7.2[3]	Janus Flex Inc....	**-2.9**[3]	7.9[1]	8.6[1]
Loomis Syls Glob Bd....	**-8.7**[5]	1.8[5]	—	Marshall Inter Bd....	**-3.1**[3]	—	—
Benham Target 2005....	**-8.9**[5]	6.7[2]	8.8[1]	Scudder GNMA....	**-3.1**[3]	3.2[5]	6.8[3]
Benham LT Trsy/Agcy....	**-9.1**[5]	—	—	Primary US Gov....	**-3.1**[3]	2.8[5]	6.2[5]
Dreyfus 100% US Long....	**-9.2**[5]	4.4[3]	7.6[3]	Bernstein Inter Dur....	**-3.2**[3]	4.8[2]	7.7[2]
Rushmore Gov Long....	**-9.9**[5]	3.3[5]	6.1[5]	Price, Rowe Glob Gov....	**-3.2**[3]	3.7[4]	—
Founders Oppty Bd....	**-10.0**[5]	—	—	Nbrgr-Ber Gov Inc....	**-3.3**[3]	—	—
Value Line US Gov....	**-10.6**[5]	1.4[5]	6.0[5]	Retrmt Sys: Inter Fix....	**-3.3**[3]	4.2[3]	—
Benham Target 2010....	**-11.6**[5]	7.0[1]	8.3[2]	Strong Gov Sec....	**-3.4**[3]	5.9[1]	8.5[1]
Fidelity Spart LT Gov....	**-12.2**[5]	3.4[4]	—	Dreyfus Bond Mkt Idx....	**-3.4**[4]	—	—
Bull & Bear Glob Inc....	**-13.4**[5]	6.9[1]	6.9[3]	Columbia Fix Inc....	**-3.5**[4]	4.8[1]	7.8[1]
Benham Target 2015....	**-14.1**[5]	6.5[2]	7.4[3]	GIT Gov Port....	**-3.6**[4]	3.7[4]	6.3[5]
TCW/DW N Amer Gov....	**-15.6**[5]	—	—	SAFECO Inter Trsy....	**-3.6**[4]	4.4[2]	6.7[4]
Fidelity New Mkts Inc....	**-16.1**[5]	—	—	Harbor Bond....	**-3.7**[4]	5.7[1]	8.8[1]
Benham Target 2020....	**-17.7**[5]	6.6[2]	6.3[5]	1784 Gov Med....	**-3.7**[4]	—	—
BBK Int'l Fix Inc....	**-19.2**[5]	-0.3[5]	—	Galaxy Inter Bond....	**-3.7**[4]	2.9[5]	5.9[5]
Fundamental US Gov Strat....	**-25.6**[5]	—	—	FundTrust Income....	**-3.9**[4]	4.6[2]	6.5[4]
FIXED-INCOME FUNDS - INTER TERM				Dreyfus 100% US Inter....	**-4.0**[4]	4.4[3]	7.3[2]
Seven Seas Yld Plus....	**4.1**[1]	—	—	Ntnghm II-Invstk Fix....	**-4.0**[4]	4.7[2]	—
Special Port Cash....	**2.7**[1]	4.4[2]	5.9[5]	Fremont Bond....	**-4.0**[4]	—	—
Asset Mgmt ARM....	**1.9**[1]	3.7[4]	—	SteinRoe Income....	**-4.1**[4]	5.8[1]	8.0[1]
Fidelity Mrtg Sec....	**1.9**[1]	4.7[2]	7.5[2]	Vangd Inter Corp....	**-4.2**[4]	—	—
Camco Inter Term....	**1.7**[1]	—	—	Vangd-Adml Inter....	**-4.2**[4]	—	—
Benham Europ Gov....	**1.5**[1]	—	—	SAFECO GNMA....	**-4.3**[4]	3.0[5]	6.4[5]
USAA GNMA....	**0.0**[1]	4.3[3]	—	Vangd Inter Trsy....	**-4.3**[5]	4.7[2]	—
Warbg Pincus Fix Inc....	**-0.8**[1]	5.6[1]	7.2[2]	Seven Seas Inter Fix....	**-4.4**[5]	—	—
Vangd GNMA....	**-1.0**[1]	3.9[3]	7.6[2]	Twentieth Cent LT Bd....	**-4.5**[5]	3.5[5]	6.6[4]
Monetta Inter Bd....	**-1.0**[1]	—	—	Legg Msn Invest Grd....	**-4.6**[5]	4.3[3]	6.8[4]
Dreyfus Invst GNMA....	**-1.1**[1]	4.8[2]	—	DFA Inter Gov....	**-4.7**[5]	4.8[2]	—
Benham GNMA Inc....	**-1.5**[1]	4.2[3]	7.6[2]	US Inter Treas....	**-4.9**[5]	—	—
Price, Rowe GNMA....	**-1.5**[1]	3.6[4]	7.1[3]	USAA Income....	**-5.2**[5]	4.1[3]	7.7[1]
Fidelity Spart GNMA....	**-1.5**[1]	3.7[4]	—	Warbg Pincus Glob Bd....	**-5.5**[5]	4.9[1]	—
Legg Msn Glob Gov....	**-1.6**[1]	—	—	Reynolds US Gov....	**-5.5**[5]	—	—
US Spec Gov....	**-1.6**[1]	—	—	Blanchard Flex Inc....	**-5.6**[5]	—	—
Asset Mgmt Inter Mrtg....	**-1.6**[1]	4.3[3]	6.9[3]	Westwood Inter Bd....	**-5.6**[5]	3.4[5]	—

No-Load Fund	Total return percent with quintile ranks by objective			No-Load Fund	Total return percent with quintile ranks by objective		
	1994	Annualized 3 years	5 years		1994	Annualized 3 years	5 years
Dupree Inter Gov.....................	-5.9[5]	—	—	Price, Rowe Adj Rate...................	-0.6[3]	2.0[5]	—
Rushmore Gov Inter..................	-7.3[5]	3.5[4]	6.6[4]	Invesco ST Bond........................	-0.6[3]	—	—
Scudder Int'l Bond...................	-8.6[5]	4.5[2]	11.0[1]	Preferred ST Gov.......................	-0.7[3]	—	—
WPG Gov Sec...........................	-8.7[5]	2.4[5]	5.9[5]	Wm Blair Income.......................	-0.7[4]	4.7[1]	—
Fidelity Glob Bond...................	-16.3[5]	2.1[5]	6.1[5]	Dreyfus S-I Gov.........................	-0.8[4]	4.5[1]	7.3[1]
Managers Inter Mortg..............	-25.0[5]	-2.6[5]	3.8[5]	State Farm Interim.....................	-0.8[4]	4.1[2]	6.7[2]
FIXED-INCOME FUNDS - SHORT TERM				Vangd ST Federal......................	-0.9[4]	4.0[2]	6.7[3]
Htchks & Wly Low Dur..............	5.1[1]	—	—	Flex-Fund Bond.........................	-1.0[4]	3.4[4]	6.7[3]
Htchks & Wly ST Invest............	4.5[1]	—	—	Fidelity Spart Ltd Mat................	-1.0[4]	3.7[3]	6.3[3]
Smith Brdn ST Gov..................	4.2[1]	—	—	Benham Adj Rate Gov................	-1.0[4]	2.6[5]	—
Strong Advantage....................	3.6[1]	6.6[1]	7.4[1]	Scudder ST Glob Inc..................	-1.1[4]	3.7[3]	—
Eaton Vance ST Trsy................	3.5[1]	3.0[5]	—	Dreman Fixed Inc......................	-1.2[4]	3.3[4]	6.3[4]
RSI Tr-ST Invest.......................	3.4[1]	3.0[5]	4.5[5]	First Omaha S-I Fix...................	-1.4[4]	—	—
Permanent Treasy....................	3.3[1]	2.8[5]	4.2[5]	Fidelity S-I Gov........................	-1.4[4]	2.8[5]	—
PIMCO Short-Term...................	2.9[1]	3.7[3]	5.2[5]	Strong ST Bond........................	-1.6[4]	4.7[1]	6.7[3]
Drey/Laurel ST Gov.................	2.8[1]	—	—	Invesco Inter Gov.....................	-1.7[4]	4.3[1]	7.2[1]
IAI Reserve.............................	2.7[1]	3.1[4]	5.1[5]	AARP GNMA & Trsy.................	-1.7[4]	3.5[4]	6.9[2]
Harbor Short Dur.....................	2.7[1]	3.9[3]	—	Warbg Pincus Inter Gov............	-1.8[4]	4.1[2]	7.2[1]
Permanent Vers Bd..................	2.6[1]	4.0[2]	—	Household ST Inc......................	-1.8[4]	—	—
DFA 1 Yr Fix Inc......................	2.5[1]	4.0[2]	5.9[4]	Price, Rowe Trsy Inter...............	-2.2[4]	3.9[3]	7.0[2]
Vista ST Bond.........................	2.4[1]	4.0[2]	—	IAI Gov Bond...........................	-2.3[4]	3.9[3]	—
Nbrgr-Ber Ultra Sht..................	2.2[1]	3.0[4]	5.0[5]	BSR S-I Fix..............................	-2.3[5]	4.1[2]	—
Flex-Fund ST Glob...................	2.1[1]	—	—	Benham Trsy Note.....................	-2.3[5]	3.9[3]	6.9[2]
Camco Short Term...................	2.1[1]	—	—	Janus Inter Gov........................	-2.4[5]	1.6[5]	—
Marshall ST Inc.......................	1.8[1]	—	—	Schwab S-I Gov.......................	-2.9[5]	3.6[4]	—
Loomis Syls ST Bd..................	1.8[1]	—	—	Scudder ST Bond......................	-2.9[5]	3.4[4]	6.8[2]
Wasatch Income......................	1.6[2]	3.4[4]	6.8[2]	Price, Rowe ST Glob.................	-2.9[5]	—	—
Fontaine Glob Inc....................	1.5[2]	—	—	Price, Rowe ST Bond.................	-2.9[5]	2.8[5]	5.7[5]
Amer AAdv Ltd Inc..................	1.3[2]	4.5[1]	7.1[2]	Wright Near Term......................	-3.1[5]	3.6[4]	6.3[3]
Montgmry Short Gov................	1.1[2]	—	—	Price Summit Ltd Trm................	-3.1[5]	—	—
Blanchard ST Bond..................	1.0[2]	—	—	DFA 5 Yr Gov...........................	-3.2[5]	4.0[2]	7.4[1]
Portico ST Bond......................	1.0[2]	4.7[1]	7.1[2]	Fidelity ST Bond.......................	-4.1[5]	4.0[2]	6.3[4]
Federated S-I Gov...................	0.7[2]	3.4[4]	5.9[4]	Blanchard ST Global.................	-4.6[5]	2.4[5]	—
PIMCO Low Dur......................	0.6[2]	5.3[1]	7.6[1]	Fidelity Spart ST Inc.................	-4.6[5]	—	—
Bernstein Short Dur.................	0.5[2]	4.1[2]	6.6[3]	Fidelity ST World Inc.................	-5.9[5]	3.6[4]	—
Bernstein Gov Sht....................	0.4[2]	3.5[4]	6.1[4]	Managers ST Gov.....................	-6.2[5]	0.4[5]	3.7[5]
Asset Mgmt ST Gov.................	0.4[2]	4.2[2]	6.7[3]	Federated US Gov.....................	-6.2[5]	4.8[1]	7.3[1]
GS ST Gov Agency..................	0.4[2]	3.8[3]	6.0[4]	Managers Sht & Int...................	-8.4[5]	3.5[4]	6.0[4]
Janus ST Bond........................	0.4[2]	—	—	Heartland US Gov.....................	-9.6[5]	5.4[1]	8.6[1]
Benham ST Trsy/Agcy..............	0.3[2]	—	—	Value Line Adj Rate Gov............	-9.9[5]	—	—
Drey/Laurel ST Bd...................	0.2[2]	3.0[5]	6.1[4]	**TAX-FREE FUNDS - LONG TERM**			
Seven Seas ST Gov..................	0.2[2]	—	—	SIT MN TF Inc..........................	0.6[1]	—	—
Dreyfus ST Income..................	0.1[2]	—	—	Strong Hi Yld Muni...................	0.0[1]	—	—
Pierpont ST Bond....................	0.1[2]	—	—	US Near Term TF.......................	-0.1[1]	—	—
Homestead ST Bond................	0.1[3]	4.3[2]	—	SIT TF Income..........................	-0.6[1]	5.7[1]	6.7[2]
Analytic ST Gov......................	0.0[3]	—	—	Dupree Tenn TF Inc...................	-1.2[1]	—	—
USAA ST Bond........................	0.0[3]	—	—	Caldwell Tax-Free.....................	-1.8[1]	—	—
SteinRoe Ltd Mat Inc...............	0.0[3]	—	—	State Farm Muni Bd..................	-2.5[1]	4.9[3]	6.5[2]
Columbia US Gov....................	0.0[3]	3.9[3]	6.7[3]	Pierpont TE Bond.....................	-2.8[1]	5.0[2]	6.5[3]
Vangd ST Corp........................	-0.1[3]	4.7[1]	7.2[1]	Dupree KY TF Inc......................	-2.9[1]	6.1[1]	7.3[1]
Lexington S-I Gov....................	-0.2[3]	—	—	Household TE Inc......................	-3.1[1]	—	—
Dreyfus 100% US Short............	-0.3[3]	4.5[1]	—	Gov St AL TF...........................	-3.1[1]	—	—
Vangd-Adml Short....................	-0.3[3]	—	—	Northwest Idaho TE...................	-3.4[1]	3.8[5]	5.2[5]
Nbrgr-Ber Ltd Mat....................	-0.3[3]	3.8[3]	6.4[3]	North Carolina TF.....................	-4.0[1]	—	—
Galaxy ST Bond......................	-0.3[3]	4.0[3]	—	Wright Insur TF........................	-4.1[1]	4.4[3]	5.9[4]
Hercules Glob ST.....................	-0.4[3]	—	—	SteinRoe Hi Yld Muni................	-4.2[1]	3.7[5]	5.7[5]
Vangd ST Trsy........................	-0.5[3]	4.1[2]	—	Price, Rowe TF Hi Yld...............	-4.4[1]	5.8[1]	7.2[1]
Fidelity Spart S-I Gov..............	-0.5[3]	—	—	Vangd PA Insur LT....................	-4.5[1]	5.8[1]	7.3[1]
Federated ST Income...............	-0.5[3]	3.6[3]	5.3[5]	Strong Muni Bond....................	-4.6[1]	6.2[1]	7.3[1]
Twentieth Cent Gov ST.............	-0.6[3]	2.6[5]	5.4[5]	Price Summit Muni Inc..............	-4.7[1]	—	—

By 1994 performance

No-Load Fund	1994	Annualized 3 years	Annualized 5 years
Columbia Muni Bd	-4.7[1]	4.0[4]	6.1[4]
Vangd FL Insur	-4.7[1]	—	—
CA Inv Tr-CA Insur	-5.0[1]	—	—
Arbor OVB WV TE	-5.0[1]	—	—
Price, Rowe MD TF	-5.0[1]	5.1[2]	6.5[2]
Rushmore VA TF	-5.0[1]	4.7[3]	5.9[4]
Fidelity Spart PA Hi Yld	-5.1[1]	5.4[1]	7.2[1]
Vangd Muni Hi Yld	-5.1[2]	5.5[1]	7.4[1]
Price, Rowe VA TF	-5.1[2]	5.3[1]	—
Vangd OH Insur LT	-5.1[2]	5.4[1]	—
Vangd NJ Insur LT	-5.2[2]	5.5[1]	7.1[1]
Rushmore MD TF	-5.2[2]	4.6[3]	5.4[5]
Benham CA Hi Yld	-5.3[2]	5.4[1]	6.5[3]
Galaxy Muni Bd	-5.4[2]	—	—
Galaxy TE Bond	-5.4[2]	5.0[2]	—
Loomis Syls Muni	-5.4[2]	4.9[2]	—
1784 MA TE Inc	-5.4[2]	—	—
Price, Rowe TF Inc	-5.5[2]	5.3[2]	6.7[2]
Scudder OH TF	-5.5[2]	4.9[2]	6.6[2]
SteinRoe Mgd Muni	-5.5[2]	4.3[4]	6.3[3]
Fidelity OH TF	-5.6[2]	4.9[2]	6.7[2]
Managers Muni Bd	-5.6[2]	4.0[4]	5.7[5]
Vangd Muni Insur LT	-5.6[2]	5.2[2]	7.0[1]
Blanchard Flex TF	-5.6[2]	—	—
Vangd NY Insur	-5.6[2]	5.4[1]	7.0[1]
Twentieth Cent TE Long	-5.6[2]	4.4[3]	6.3[3]
Vangd CA Insur LT	-5.7[2]	5.2[2]	6.7[2]
Price, Rowe CA TF	-5.7[2]	4.9[2]	6.5[3]
Fidelity Spart NJ Hi Yld	-5.7[2]	5.0[2]	6.9[1]
Vangd Muni Long	-5.8[2]	5.3[1]	7.2[1]
GE Elfun TE Inc	-5.8[2]	4.6[3]	6.3[3]
Price, Rowe NY TF	-5.9[2]	5.6[1]	6.9[2]
Scudder PA TF	-5.9[2]	5.1[2]	6.7[2]
Fidelity Agg TF	-5.9[2]	5.3[1]	7.0[1]
Price, Rowe GA TF	-5.9[3]	—	—
Fidelity MN TF	-5.9[3]	4.4[3]	5.8[4]
Dreyfus NJ Muni	-6.0[3]	4.9[2]	6.9[1]
Dreyfus MA TE	-6.0[3]	4.3[4]	6.3[3]
Scudder Mgd Muni	-6.0[3]	5.1[2]	6.8[2]
Price, Rowe NJ TF	-6.1[3]	5.5[1]	—
Fidelity MA Hi Yld	-6.1[3]	5.0[2]	6.7[2]
Fidelity Spart Agg Muni	-6.1[3]	—	—
Benham Nat TF Long	-6.2[3]	5.4[1]	7.1[1]
Scudder MA TF	-6.2[3]	5.9[1]	7.2[1]
AARP Insur TF Gen	-6.2[3]	4.7[3]	6.5[3]
USAA VA Bond	-6.3[3]	4.6[3]	—
Northwest WA TE	-6.3[3]	—	—
Parnassus CA TF	-6.4[3]	—	—
Benham CA Long	-6.4[3]	4.8[3]	6.5[3]
Strong Insur Muni	-6.5[3]	6.1[1]	—
Benham CA Insur	-6.5[3]	5.0[2]	6.6[2]
Lexington TE Bond	-6.5[3]	3.4[5]	5.2[5]
Heartland WI TF	-6.6[3]	—	—
Dreyfus NY Insur	-6.6[3]	4.0[4]	6.2[4]
Fidelity Spart FL Muni	-6.7[3]	—	—
Value Line TE Hi Yld	-6.9[3]	3.8[5]	5.9[4]
Dreyfus NY TE	-7.0[3]	4.5[3]	6.2[4]
Dreyfus Muni Bond	-7.0[3]	4.3[4]	6.2[3]
Drey-General CA	-7.0[3]	4.7[3]	6.5[3]
Fidelity Spart CT Hi Yld	-7.0[3]	4.3[4]	6.0[4]
Schwab LT TF	-7.0[4]	—	—
Dreyfus CA TE	-7.1[4]	3.5[5]	5.5[5]
Scudder NY TF	-7.2[4]	4.9[2]	6.6[2]
Drey-General NY	-7.2[4]	5.3[2]	7.2[1]
Galaxy NY Muni	-7.2[4]	4.1[4]	—
Scudder CA TF	-7.3[4]	4.9[3]	6.7[2]
Drey-General Muni	-7.3[4]	4.9[3]	7.4[1]
GE TE Bond	-7.4[4]	—	—
Babson TF Long	-7.4[4]	4.1[4]	6.0[4]
Fidelity Hi Yld TF	-7.4[4]	3.5[5]	5.8[4]
Invesco TF Long	-7.5[4]	4.1[4]	6.3[3]
Fidelity Spart MD Muni	-7.5[4]	—	—
Fidelity MI Hi Yld	-7.5[4]	4.9[3]	6.3[3]
Galaxy MA Muni	-7.7[4]	—	—
Fidelity Insur TF	-7.7[4]	4.3[4]	6.3[3]
Value Line NY TE	-7.7[4]	4.8[3]	6.6[2]
Janus Federal TE	-7.8[4]	—	—
USAA TE Long	-7.9[4]	4.0[4]	6.1[4]
Evergreen Nat TF	-7.9[4]	—	—
Fidelity NY Insured	-8.0[4]	4.1[4]	6.1[4]
Fidelity NY Hi Yld	-8.0[4]	4.2[4]	6.1[4]
Galaxy CT Muni	-8.1[4]	—	—
CGM American TF	-8.2[4]	—	—
SAFECO Muni Bd	-8.2[4]	4.0[4]	6.4[3]
GIT TF VA	-8.3[4]	3.5[5]	5.2[5]
Fidelity Spart NY Hi Yld	-8.3[4]	4.4[3]	—
IAI MN TF	-8.4[4]	—	—
Scudder Hi Yld TF	-8.4[5]	5.0[2]	6.8[2]
GIT TF MO	-8.5[5]	3.2[5]	4.9[5]
Dreyfus Insur Muni	-8.6[5]	3.5[5]	5.7[5]
CA Inv Tr-CA TF	-8.6[5]	4.5[3]	6.4[3]
Fidelity Muni Bd	-8.6[5]	4.0[4]	6.1[4]
Torchmark Insur TF	-8.7[5]	—	—
SAFECO WA Muni	-8.7[5]	—	—
GIT TF AZ	-8.7[5]	3.5[5]	5.3[5]
Salomon NY Muni	-8.8[5]	—	—
GIT TF Nat	-8.8[5]	3.3[5]	5.1[5]
GIT TF MD	-8.9[5]	—	—
Fidelity Spart Muni Inc	-8.9[5]	4.1[4]	—
Fidelity CA Hi Yld	-8.9[5]	3.9[5]	5.7[5]
Schwab CA Long	-8.9[5]	—	—
Fidelity Spart CA Hi Yld	-9.0[5]	4.1[4]	6.4[3]
USAA NY Bond	-9.0[5]	4.0[4]	—
SAFECO CA TF	-9.2[5]	3.6[5]	6.0[4]
USAA CA Bond	-9.3[5]	3.4[5]	5.8[4]
Heartland Nebraska TF	-9.3[5]	—	—
Bull & Bear Muni Inc	-9.8[5]	1.9[5]	4.5[5]
USAA FL TF	-10.0[5]	—	—
Fidelity CA Insur	-10.2[5]	3.7[5]	5.8[5]
SAFECO Insur Muni	-10.4[5]	—	—
Fundamental Hi Yld Muni	-12.9[5]	-0.9[5]	0.2[5]
Fundamental NY Muni	-19.8[5]	0.3[5]	3.0[5]
Fundamental CA Muni	-19.9[5]	-0.2[5]	2.4[5]
TAX-FREE FUNDS - INTER TERM			
Warbg Pincus NY Muni	-0.6[1]	5.5[1]	6.4[3]
Price Summit Muni Inter	-1.7[1]	—	—
Portico TE Inter	-1.7[1]	—	—
Evergreen S-I CA	-1.8[1]	—	—
Twentieth Cent TE Inter	-2.1[1]	4.6[3]	6.0[4]
Vangd Muni Inter	-2.1[1]	5.9[1]	7.4[1]

Stock and bond funds – ranked within objective *continued*

By 1994 performance

No-Load Fund	Total return percent with quintile ranks by objective			No-Load Fund	Total return percent with quintile ranks by objective		
	1994	Annualized 3 years	5 years		1994	Annualized 3 years	5 years
CT&T Inter Muni...	-2.2[1]	—	—	US Tax Free...	-5.2[5]	4.3[4]	5.7[5]
WPG Inter Muni...	-2.3[1]	—	—	Amcor Vntg Inter TF...	-5.4[5]	—	—
Bernstein Dvsfd Muni...	-2.5[2]	4.1[5]	5.8[5]	Dreyfus CA Inter...	-5.5[5]	—	—
Bernstein NY Muni...	-2.5[2]	4.2[4]	5.9[4]	SAFECO Inter Muni...	-5.6[5]	—	—
Price, Rowe TF Ins Inter...	-2.6[2]	—	—	Dreyfus MA Inter...	-6.4[5]	—	—
Price, Rowe FL Ins Inter...	-2.6[2]	—	—	**TAX-FREE FUNDS - SHORT TERM**			
Crabbe Hsn OR Muni...	-2.7[2]	4.4[4]	—	Twentieth Cent TE Short...	2.4[1]	—	—
1784 TE Med Term...	-3.0[2]	—	—	Vangd Muni Short...	1.6[1]	3.4[4]	4.8[4]
Bernstein CA Muni...	-3.2[2]	3.9[5]	—	Hough FL ST...	1.2[1]	—	—
Benham Nat TF Inter...	-3.4[3]	4.5[3]	6.4[3]	Pacifica ST CA TF...	1.1[1]	—	—
Scudder Medium TF...	-3.5[3]	5.3[1]	6.8[1]	Dupree KY Sht-Med...	1.0[2]	4.5[1]	5.5[2]
SteinRoe Inter Muni...	-3.5[3]	4.9[2]	6.5[2]	USAA TE Short...	0.8[2]	4.1[3]	5.2[4]
Benham CA Inter...	-3.7[3]	4.5[3]	6.2[3]	Price, Rowe MD ST TF...	0.6[2]	—	—
Federated Inter Muni...	-3.8[3]	4.2[4]	5.9[4]	Managers ST Muni...	0.3[2]	2.8[5]	3.9[5]
Nbrgr-Ber Muni...	-4.0[3]	4.0[5]	5.6[5]	59 Wall S-I TF...	0.3[3]	—	—
USAA TE Inter...	-4.0[3]	5.1[1]	6.6[1]	Price, Rowe TF S-I...	0.3[3]	4.2[3]	5.3[3]
Fidelity Spart NY Inter...	-4.3[3]	—	—	Federated ST Muni...	0.1[3]	3.1[5]	4.5[5]
Invesco TF Inter...	-4.4[4]	—	—	Vangd Muni Ltd...	0.1[3]	4.3[3]	5.8[1]
Dreyfus Inter Muni...	-4.6[4]	5.0[2]	6.5[2]	Montgmry CA TF S-I...	0.0[3]	—	—
Fidelity Spart CA Inter...	-4.7[4]	—	—	Fidelity Spart S-I Muni...	-0.1[4]	4.4[1]	5.7[1]
Dreyfus CT Inter...	-4.7[4]	—	—	Dreyfus S-I Muni...	-0.3[4]	4.3[2]	5.6[2]
Fidelity Ltd Muni...	-4.8[4]	5.0[2]	6.6[2]	Benham CA Short...	-0.6[4]	—	—
Fremont CA Inter...	-4.9[4]	3.7[5]	—	Schwab S-I TF...	-1.1[4]	—	—
Dreyfus FL Inter...	-4.9[4]	—	—	Evergreen S-I Muni...	-1.4[5]	4.3[2]	—
Fidelity Spart Inter Muni...	-5.0[5]	—	—	Strong ST Muni...	-1.6[5]	—	—
Dreyfus NY Inter...	-5.1[5]	5.0[2]	6.4[3]	Babson TF Short...	-1.7[5]	3.7[4]	5.4[3]
Dreyfus NJ Inter...	-5.2[5]	—	—	Schwab CA S-I...	-2.1[5]	—	—

Stock and bond funds – ranked within objective
By 1992 - 1994 performance

No-Load Fund	Total return percent with quintile ranks by objective		
	1994	Annualized 3 years	5 years
AGGRESSIVE GROWTH FUNDS			
PBHG Growth	4.7[1]	**25.4[1]**	22.0[1]
Twentieth Cent Giftrust	13.5[1]	**20.7[1]**	22.0[1]
Skyline Special Eqty	-1.1[3]	**20.0[1]**	18.1[1]
Heartland Value SC	1.7[2]	**19.8[1]**	16.3[1]
Royce Micro-Cap SC	3.6[1]	**18.3[1]**	—
Retrmt Sys: Emg Gr SC	10.4[1]	**17.4[1]**	—
Fidelity Cap Apprec	2.5[1]	**16.7[1]**	8.0[4]
DFA US 9-10 Sm Co SC	3.1[1]	**15.4[1]**	11.8[2]
Baron Asset SC	7.4[1]	**14.7[1]**	10.5[3]
First Eagle America	-2.6[3]	**14.5[1]**	8.4[4]
Invesco Emg Gro SC	-3.7[4]	**14.3[1]**	—
Omni Investment	6.7[1]	**14.1[1]**	7.7[4]
Babson Enterprise SC	2.5[2]	**14.1[1]**	12.3[2]
Permanent Agg Growth	1.0[2]	**13.9[1]**	—
RSI Tr-Emg Gro SC	3.5[1]	**13.2[1]**	14.8[1]
Kaufmann SC	9.0[1]	**12.8[1]**	19.3[1]
Brandywine	0.0[2]	**12.3[1]**	16.3[1]
Columbia Special	2.3[2]	**12.3[1]**	13.3[2]
Fairmont	7.3[1]	**12.2[1]**	9.1[3]
IAI Emg Growth SC	0.2[2]	**12.1[1]**	—
Vangd Idx Sm Cap SC	-0.5[2]	**11.7[1]**	10.6[3]
Fidelity Contrafund	-1.1[3]	**11.6[1]**	17.5[1]
Price, Rowe New Horiz SC	0.3[2]	**10.6[2]**	13.2[2]
Wasatch Agg Eqty SC	5.5[1]	**10.6[2]**	17.0[1]
Fidelity Retrmnt Growth	0.1[2]	**10.6[2]**	12.0[2]
Price, Rowe OTC SC	0.1[2]	**10.5[2]**	8.3[4]
Managers Spec Eqty SC	-2.0[3]	**10.1[2]**	10.9[2]
Eclipse Equity SC	-4.7[4]	**10.0[2]**	8.6[4]
Merger	7.1[1]	**9.9[2]**	9.4[3]
Longleaf Small Cap SC	3.7[1]	**9.9[2]**	3.2[5]
Invesco Dynamics	-1.9[3]	**9.7[2]**	15.6[1]
44 Wall St Eqty	-11.7[5]	**9.7[2]**	8.7[4]
Fiduciary Cap Gro SC	0.4[2]	**9.6[2]**	9.7[3]
Vangd Explorer SC	0.5[2]	**9.4[2]**	12.8[2]
C&O Agg Growth SC	-1.0[3]	**9.4[2]**	—
Fidelity Magellan	-1.8[3]	**9.4[2]**	12.0[2]
SteinRoe Cap Oppty	0.0[2]	**9.3[2]**	8.5[4]
Warbg Pincus Emg Gro SC	-1.4[3]	**9.3[2]**	12.9[2]
Babson Enterprise II SC	-7.4[5]	**9.1[2]**	—
Fidelity Trend	-6.7[4]	**9.1[2]**	9.1[3]
Fidelity Emg Growth	-0.2[2]	**9.0[2]**	—
Salomon Opportunity	0.8[2]	**9.0[2]**	7.2[5]
Htchks & Wly Sm Cap SC	1.1[2]	**9.0[2]**	11.8[2]
Loomis Syls Sm Cap SC	-8.3[5]	**8.9[2]**	—
Nbrgr-Ber Genesis SC	-1.8[3]	**8.9[3]**	8.9[3]
Dreyfus New Ldrs SC	-0.2[2]	**8.5[3]**	10.4[3]
Columbia Growth	-0.6[3]	**7.9[3]**	10.2[3]
PDC&J Performance	1.1[2]	**7.7[3]**	8.9[3]
Bull & Bear Spec Eqty	-16.5[5]	**7.6[3]**	2.2[5]
Legg Msn Spec Invest SC	-13.1[5]	**7.6[3]**	11.8[2]
Galaxy Sm Co Eqty SC	-0.1[2]	**7.5[3]**	—
Gradison Oppty Value SC	-2.2[3]	**7.5[3]**	8.0[4]
Dreyfus Special Gro	-18.3[5]	**7.4[3]**	8.8[4]
Founders Frontier SC	-2.8[3]	**7.3[3]**	11.3[2]
Schroder US Eqty	-5.2[4]	**7.1[3]**	10.2[3]
Berger 100	-6.7[4]	**7.1[3]**	17.0[1]
Montgmry Sm Cap SC	-9.9[5]	**7.1[3]**	—
Fidelity Growth Co	-2.2[3]	**7.0[3]**	13.5[1]
Managers Cap App	-1.5[3]	**7.0[3]**	9.7[3]

No-Load Fund	Total return percent with quintile ranks by objective		
	1994	Annualized 3 years	5 years
Pierpont Cap App SC	-5.9[4]	**6.7[3]**	8.0[4]
Fidelity OTC SC	-2.7[3]	**6.6[3]**	11.5[2]
Fasciano SC	3.7[1]	**6.5[3]**	10.0[3]
Oberweis Emg Growth SC	-3.5[4]	**6.4[3]**	17.7[1]
Galaxy Sm Co Idx SC	-3.7[4]	**6.4[3]**	—
Founders Special	-4.9[4]	**6.1[3]**	11.9[2]
Price, Rowe New Amer	-7.4[5]	**6.1[3]**	11.2[2]
FundTrust Agg Gro	-1.2[3]	**5.9[4]**	8.7[4]
Twentieth Cent Ultra	-3.6[4]	**5.9[4]**	19.4[1]
General Securities	5.4[1]	**5.9[4]**	9.9[3]
Babson UMB Heartland SC	0.7[2]	**5.8[4]**	5.0[5]
GIT Special Gro SC	-3.9[4]	**5.6[4]**	4.5[5]
Founders Discovery SC	-7.7[5]	**5.6[4]**	16.7[1]
API Growth	-3.4[4]	**5.6[4]**	8.4[4]
Strong Discovery SC	-5.7[4]	**5.5[4]**	13.8[1]
SAFECO Growth	-1.6[3]	**5.2[4]**	10.0[3]
CGM Capital Dev	-22.9[5]	**5.2[4]**	18.7[1]
Ariel Growth SC	-4.2[4]	**5.2[4]**	5.5[5]
Scudder Capital Gro	-9.9[5]	**5.0[4]**	6.6[5]
Vangd Morgan	-1.7[3]	**4.9[4]**	8.0[4]
Portico Spec Gro SC	-2.0[3]	**4.3[4]**	12.6[2]
Robrtsn Stph Emg Gro SC	8.0[1]	**4.1[4]**	14.4[1]
Fontaine Cap App	2.3[2]	**3.9[4]**	5.9[5]
59 Wall Sm Co SC	-10.5[5]	**3.6[4]**	—
Value Line Spec Sit	1.0[2]	**3.3[4]**	7.5[4]
AARP Capital Growth	-10.0[5]	**3.0[4]**	5.3[5]
Dreyfus Apprec	3.6[1]	**3.0[4]**	8.2[4]
Value Line Lev Gro	-3.7[4]	**3.0[4]**	9.4[3]
Cornerstone Growth	7.6[1]	**2.9[4]**	4.2[5]
Dreyfus Strat Growth	3.1[1]	**2.8[5]**	6.0[5]
Wright Jr Blue Ch SC	-2.7[3]	**2.7[5]**	5.8[5]
American Heritage	-35.4[5]	**2.7[5]**	8.1[4]
Twentieth Cent Vista	4.7[1]	**2.6[5]**	9.6[3]
Evergreen Ltd Mkt SC	-10.5[5]	**2.6[5]**	7.9[4]
WPG Tudor	-9.8[5]	**2.4[5]**	8.2[4]
SteinRoe Stock	-3.8[4]	**2.3[5]**	9.6[3]
Perritt Capital Gro SC	-5.1[4]	**2.1[5]**	4.2[5]
SIT Growth SC	-0.5[2]	**1.9[5]**	11.4[2]
Salomon Capital	-14.2[5]	**1.8[5]**	5.1[5]
WPG Growth SC	-14.0[5]	**1.6[5]**	7.4[4]
MIM Stock Apprec	-10.4[5]	**1.5[5]**	14.3[1]
Special Port Stk	-7.2[5]	**1.4[5]**	10.8[2]
Scudder Development SC	-5.3[4]	**0.4[5]**	12.0[2]
First Mutual	-15.1[5]	**0.0[5]**	3.8[5]
Janus Twenty	-6.7[4]	**-0.5[5]**	10.9[2]
USAA Agg Growth SC	-0.8[3]	**-0.6[5]**	8.2[4]
Twentieth Cent Growth	-1.5[3]	**-0.7[5]**	9.7[3]
Prudent Speculator SC	-8.9[5]	**-1.8[5]**	-0.6[5]
Rainbow Fund	-4.7[4]	**-4.0[5]**	1.9[5]
Steadman Amer Indust	-37.2[5]	**-13.8[5]**	-14.9[5]
Steadman Tech & Gro	-37.1[5]	**-18.1[5]**	-17.0[5]
GROWTH FUNDS			
Oakmark	3.3[1]	**26.1[1]**	—
Crabbe Hsn Spec SC	11.7[1]	**26.1[1]**	19.5[1]
Fidelity Low Pr Stk SC	4.8[1]	**17.6[1]**	—
Longleaf Partners	9.0[1]	**17.1[1]**	13.3[1]
Fidelity Value	7.6[1]	**17.0[1]**	12.0[1]
SAFECO Equity	9.9[1]	**16.3[1]**	13.0[1]
Acorn SC	-7.5[5]	**15.0[1]**	13.1[1]
Strong Common Stk SC	-0.5[3]	**14.6[1]**	—

No-Load Fund	Total return percent with quintile ranks by objective			No-Load Fund	Total return percent with quintile ranks by objective		
	1994	Annualized 3 years	5 years		1994	Annualized 3 years	5 years
Crabbe Hsn Eqty	1.5[2]	**14.1[1]**	—	Invesco Value Eqty	4.0[1]	**6.4[3]**	9.1[3]
Brandywine Blue	2.3[2]	**13.8[1]**	—	Babson Growth	-0.6[3]	**6.2[3]**	6.4[5]
Price, Rowe Sm Cap Val SC	-1.4[4]	**13.7[1]**	11.8[1]	Wasatch Growth	2.7[2]	**6.1[3]**	13.2[1]
Strong Opportunity	3.2[2]	**13.6[1]**	11.4[1]	GE Elfun Trusts	0.2[3]	**6.1[3]**	8.1[3]
Babson Value	2.5[2]	**13.3[1]**	10.6[2]	Drey/Laurel Contrn	-11.1[5]	**6.0[3]**	9.1[3]
Fidelity Blue Chip	9.8[1]	**13.2[1]**	18.4[1]	Flex-Fund Muirfield	2.7[2]	**5.9[3]**	9.5[2]
Vangd Primecap	11.4[1]	**12.7[1]**	13.1[1]	Portico Eqty Idx	1.0[2]	**5.6[3]**	8.2[3]
Tocqueville	-0.8[3]	**12.4[1]**	10.1[2]	Nicholas II SC	1.0[2]	**5.5[4]**	9.0[3]
Nbrgr-Ber Focus	0.9[2]	**12.4[1]**	10.8[2]	Janus Fund	-1.1[3]	**5.4[4]**	10.7[2]
Royce Premier SC	3.3[2]	**12.4[1]**	—	Selected Spec Sh SC	-2.5[4]	**5.4[4]**	6.4[5]
AIC: Clvr Cap Eq	16.0[1]	**11.9[1]**	—	Evergreen Fund	0.7[2]	**5.1[4]**	7.5[4]
Gabelli Asset	-0.1[3]	**11.8[1]**	9.4[2]	Wade	-1.3[4]	**5.1[4]**	5.2[5]
Greenspring	2.9[2]	**11.1[1]**	8.9[3]	Nicholas Fund	-2.9[4]	**5.0[4]**	9.4[2]
Nbrgr-Ber Guardian	0.6[2]	**11.1[1]**	11.9[1]	Benham Equity Growth	-0.2[3]	**5.0[4]**	—
Sound Shore	0.3[3]	**10.8[1]**	10.0[2]	Vista Equity	0.2[3]	**4.6[4]**	—
Valley Forge	5.9[1]	**10.7[1]**	6.7[4]	Rightime	0.7[2]	**4.5[4]**	8.6[3]
Reich & Tang Eqty	1.7[2]	**10.4[1]**	9.3[2]	Papp L Roy Stock	-1.4[4]	**4.4[4]**	8.9[3]
Nbrgr-Ber Partners	-1.9[4]	**10.3[2]**	9.3[2]	IAI Regional	0.7[2]	**4.3[4]**	8.9[3]
Lindner Fund	-0.7[3]	**10.3[2]**	8.0[4]	SAFECO Northwest Gro	-1.6[4]	**4.3[4]**	—
FAM Value SC	6.8[1]	**10.2[2]**	13.3[1]	Wayne Hummer Growth	-0.9[3]	**4.2[4]**	8.9[3]
Gradison Estab Value	0.3[3]	**10.1[2]**	8.4[3]	Flex-Fund Growth	-0.7[3]	**4.2[4]**	7.5[4]
Fidelity Discpl Eqty	3.0[2]	**9.9[2]**	12.3[1]	Sentry	-1.1[4]	**4.0[4]**	8.8[3]
SteinRoe Special	-3.3[4]	**9.9[2]**	10.8[2]	Galaxy Eqty Growth	0.6[2]	**4.0[4]**	—
Fidelity Stk Selector	0.8[2]	**9.8[2]**	—	Wood Island Growth	-6.4[5]	**4.0[4]**	7.2[4]
Evergreen Gro & Inc	1.7[2]	**9.8[2]**	9.8[2]	Gabelli Growth	-3.4[4]	**4.0[4]**	8.1[3]
Wm Blair Growth	6.5[1]	**9.8[2]**	13.3[1]	Vontobel US Value	0.3[3]	**3.8[4]**	—
Torray	2.4[2]	**9.6[2]**	—	Ariel Apprec	-8.4[5]	**3.8[4]**	—
Price, Rowe Spect-Gro	1.4[2]	**9.6[2]**	—	Crowley Growth	3.9[1]	**3.6[4]**	4.9[5]
Meridian	0.5[2]	**9.5[2]**	16.6[1]	Invesco Growth	-8.8[5]	**3.4[4]**	9.2[3]
Price, Rowe Cap App	3.8[1]	**9.5[2]**	9.5[2]	Volumetric	-2.1[4]	**3.4[4]**	7.2[4]
Columbia Common Stk	2.1[2]	**9.3[2]**	—	FFB Lexcn Cap App	-4.5[4]	**3.0[4]**	—
Dreman High Return	-1.0[3]	**9.0[2]**	11.8[1]	Loomis Syls Growth	-3.6[4]	**3.0[4]**	—
Babson Shadow Stk SC	-4.3[4]	**9.0[2]**	7.9[4]	Matrix Growth	-4.8[5]	**3.0[5]**	6.9[4]
Armstrong Assoc	5.4[1]	**9.0[2]**	7.4[4]	State Farm Growth	6.0[1]	**2.9[5]**	10.0[2]
Mairs & Power Gro	5.6[1]	**8.7[2]**	13.6[1]	Smith Hayes Value	-12.4[5]	**2.5[5]**	2.6[5]
Royce Penn Mutual SC	-0.7[3]	**8.7[2]**	8.4[3]	Merriman Cap App	-0.6[3]	**2.4[5]**	6.2[5]
Harbor Cap App	3.4[1]	**8.4[2]**	14.1[1]	Value Line Fund	-4.5[4]	**2.2[5]**	9.5[2]
Founders Growth	-3.3[4]	**8.2[2]**	10.8[2]	Gov St Equity	-2.2[4]	**2.0[5]**	—
Vangd Idx Extend Mkt	-1.8[4]	**8.1[2]**	9.1[3]	Gintel	-16.5[5]	**2.0[5]**	2.7[5]
Royce Value	-1.6[4]	**8.1[2]**	7.4[4]	US Global Resrc	-9.7[5]	**1.9[5]**	-1.4[5]
Legg Msn Value	1.3[2]	**7.9[2]**	7.1[4]	Scudder Qual Growth	-1.3[4]	**1.7[5]**	—
Sequoia	3.4[1]	**7.8[2]**	11.0[2]	Vangd US Growth	3.9[1]	**1.7[5]**	10.1[2]
Nbrgr-Ber Manhtn	-3.6[4]	**7.7[3]**	8.5[3]	Federated Growth	-11.9[5]	**0.7[5]**	5.5[5]
IAI Value	-9.1[5]	**7.5[3]**	5.6[5]	Northeast Inv Gro	0.0[3]	**0.5[5]**	7.1[4]
Twentieth Cent Heritage	-6.3[5]	**7.5[3]**	8.9[3]	Pinnacle Fund	-1.1[4]	**0.5[5]**	6.6[4]
SteinRoe Prime Eqty	-0.2[3]	**7.4[3]**	10.0[2]	GIT Select Gro	-5.2[5]	**0.5[5]**	4.1[5]
Price, Rowe New Era	5.2[1]	**7.4[3]**	5.3[3]	Twentieth Cent Select	-8.0[5]	**0.3[5]**	5.7[5]
Janus Venture SC	5.5[1]	**7.3[3]**	12.7[1]	Monetta Fund	-6.2[5]	**-0.2[5]**	11.5[1]
Price, Rowe Growth Stk	0.9[2]	**7.3[3]**	9.6[2]	Dreyfus Third Cent	-7.5[5]	**-0.3[5]**	7.2[4]
Nicholas Ltd Edit SC	-3.0[4]	**7.3[3]**	11.7[1]	Mathers	-5.9[5]	**-0.3[5]**	3.7[5]
Drey-Peoples MidCap	-4.0[4]	**6.9[3]**	—	Harbor Growth	-11.4[5]	**-0.6[5]**	6.6[4]
USAA Growth	3.4[1]	**6.9[3]**	9.3[3]	Northwest Growth	-11.4[5]	**-1.3[5]**	4.9[5]
FundTrust Growth	-0.5[3]	**6.8[3]**	8.0[3]	Beacon Hill Mutual	0.3[3]	**-2.3[5]**	4.6[5]
Babson UMB Stock	2.8[2]	**6.8[3]**	8.2[3]	Dreyfus Growth Oppty	-6.4[5]	**-2.9[5]**	5.3[5]
Seafirst Blue Chip	2.0[2]	**6.8[3]**	7.9[4]	Charter Cap Blue Chip	-4.8[5]	**-2.9[5]**	5.6[5]
Dreyfus Core Value	0.4[3]	**6.8[3]**	5.2[5]	MIM Stock Growth	-11.7[5]	**-4.0[5]**	1.1[5]
Dreman Contrarian	0.0[3]	**6.7[3]**	7.6[4]	Steadman Investment	-33.8[5]	**-14.4[5]**	-6.7[5]
SBSF Fund	-5.6[5]	**6.6[3]**	7.0[4]	**GROWTH-INCOME FUNDS**			
Legg Msn Total Ret	-7.2[5]	**6.6[3]**	7.3[4]	Mutual Beacon	5.6[1]	**16.8[1]**	11.5[1]
Warbg Pincus Cap App	-2.9[4]	**6.5[3]**	7.6[4]	Warbg Pincus Gro & Inc	7.6[1]	**16.8[1]**	13.4[1]

No-Load Fund	Total return percent with quintile ranks by objective		
	1994	Annualized 3 years	5 years
Mutual Qualified...	5.7[1]	**16.7[1]**	11.6[1]
Berwyn...	4.2[1]	**15.6[1]**	11.0[1]
Mutual Shares...	4.5[1]	**15.3[1]**	10.8[1]
Maxus Equity...	1.1[2]	**14.1[1]**	10.7[1]
Fidelity Eqty Inc II...	3.2[1]	**13.4[1]**	—
Schafer Value...	-4.3[5]	**12.1[1]**	12.1[1]
Fidelity Eqty Inc...	0.3[2]	**11.7[1]**	9.2[2]
Fidelity Asst Mgr Gro...	-7.4[5]	**11.7[1]**	—
Vangd Windsor...	-0.1[3]	**11.5[1]**	8.5[2]
Dodge & Cox Stock...	5.2[1]	**11.3[1]**	9.7[1]
Fidelity Gro & Inc...	2.3[1]	**10.9[1]**	12.5[1]
Homestead Value...	2.5[1]	**10.8[1]**	—
Dreyfus Gro & Inc...	-5.2[5]	**10.5[1]**	—
Fidelity Fund...	2.6[1]	**9.6[1]**	9.2[1]
MSB...	-1.7[4]	**9.5[1]**	7.3[3]
AARP Growth & Inc...	3.1[1]	**9.2[1]**	10.0[1]
Price, Rowe Gro & Inc...	-0.1[3]	**9.2[1]**	8.7[2]
Scudder Gro & Inc...	2.6[1]	**9.1[1]**	10.2[1]
Amer AAdv Gro & Inc...	-1.0[3]	**8.9[1]**	9.0[2]
Retrmt Sys: Core Eq...	5.7[1]	**8.8[1]**	—
Philadelphia...	-8.6[5]	**8.8[2]**	3.8[5]
Muhlenkamp...	-7.3[5]	**8.8[2]**	9.8[1]
Galaxy Eqty Value...	3.5[1]	**8.7[2]**	8.9[2]
Lexington Corp Ldrs...	-0.8[3]	**8.6[2]**	7.9[3]
Htchks & Wly Eq Inc...	-3.5[4]	**8.4[2]**	7.0[3]
Westwood Equity...	2.3[1]	**8.3[2]**	7.6[3]
Loomis Syls Gro & Inc...	-0.9[3]	**8.2[2]**	—
Clipper...	-2.5[4]	**7.9[2]**	9.0[2]
Vangd Windsor II...	-1.2[4]	**7.9[2]**	7.7[3]
Federated Stock...	-0.4[3]	**7.8[2]**	9.0[2]
Evergreen Amer Ret...	-2.9[4]	**7.4[2]**	7.9[3]
Bartlett Basic Value...	0.4[2]	**7.3[2]**	7.1[3]
Lexington Gro & Inc...	-3.1[4]	**7.2[2]**	6.7[4]
Weitz Value...	-9.8[5]	**7.1[2]**	8.3[2]
FundTrust Gro & Inc...	-0.2[3]	**7.1[2]**	6.8[4]
Vangd Star:Star...	-0.3[3]	**6.9[2]**	7.9[3]
Salomon Investors...	-1.3[4]	**6.9[2]**	8.1[3]
Stratton Growth...	7.1[1]	**6.7[2]**	6.7[4]
Concorde Value...	-3.3[4]	**6.7[2]**	5.2[5]
Strong Total Return...	-1.4[4]	**6.7[2]**	8.6[2]
ASM...	1.1[2]	**6.6[2]**	
Caldwell Fund...	-1.1[3]	**6.6[2]**	7.9[3]
Vangd Quantitative...	-0.6[3]	**6.6[2]**	9.0[2]
Fiduciary Total Ret...	-2.0[4]	**6.3[3]**	8.4[2]
Pierpont Equity...	-0.6[3]	**6.3[3]**	10.3[1]
Vangd Trust US...	-3.9[5]	**6.2[3]**	6.8[4]
Copley...	-7.7[5]	**6.2[3]**	6.7[4]
Vangd Idx 500...	1.2[2]	**6.1[3]**	8.5[2]
LMH Fund...	2.6[1]	**6.1[3]**	2.9[5]
Benham Income & Gro...	-0.6[3]	**6.1[3]**	—
DFA US Lrg Co...	1.3[2]	**6.1[3]**	—
Domini Social Eqty...	-0.4[3]	**6.1[3]**	—
Gateway Idx Plus...	5.6[1]	**6.0[3]**	9.1[2]
GE Elfun Div Inc...	-0.3[3]	**6.0[3]**	7.9[3]
Golden Rainbow...	-4.2[5]	**6.0[3]**	—
Fidelity Market Idx...	1.1[2]	**5.9[3]**	—
Federated Max Cap...	1.2[2]	**5.9[3]**	—
Bascom Hill Invest...	3.9[1]	**5.9[3]**	6.1[4]
Schwab 1000...	-0.1[3]	**5.9[3]**	—
RSI Tr-Core Eqty...	1.3[2]	**5.9[3]**	6.9[4]

No-Load Fund	Total return percent with quintile ranks by objective		
	1994	Annualized 3 years	5 years
Drey-Peoples Idx...	0.7[2]	**5.9[3]**	7.9[3]
Galaxy Lg Co Idx...	1.0[2]	**5.8[3]**	—
Price, Rowe Eqty Idx...	1.0[2]	**5.8[3]**	—
GE S&S Prg: Mutual...	-1.8[4]	**5.8[3]**	8.3[2]
Dreyfus Discpl Stk...	-1.2[4]	**5.8[4]**	9.6[1]
Quant Gro & Inc...	-0.7[3]	**5.7[4]**	8.3[2]
Berger 101...	-9.1[5]	**5.7[4]**	11.8[1]
WPG Growth & Inc...	-5.5[5]	**5.6[4]**	8.2[3]
Harbor Value...	0.7[2]	**5.5[4]**	6.1[4]
CGM Mutual...	-9.7[5]	**5.3[4]**	10.7[1]
Seafirst Asst Allc...	-0.2[3]	**5.2[4]**	7.5[3]
Federated Stk & Bd...	-1.9[4]	**5.2[4]**	6.7[4]
Analytic Option Eqty...	2.5[1]	**5.1[4]**	5.9[4]
Evergreen Tot Ret...	-6.5[5]	**5.1[4]**	6.0[4]
RSI Tr-Value Eqty...	-1.1[3]	**5.0[4]**	5.5[5]
Founders Blue Chip...	0.5[2]	**4.7[4]**	8.1[3]
Weston: New Cent Cap...	0.1[2]	**4.6[4]**	8.3[2]
Lepercq-Istel...	-5.0[5]	**4.4[4]**	4.5[5]
FundTrust Mgd Tot Ret...	-2.1[4]	**4.3[4]**	6.5[4]
Invesco Indust Inc...	-3.9[4]	**4.2[4]**	10.8[1]
Portico Gro & Inc...	0.1[2]	**4.1[4]**	6.5[4]
BSR Gro & Inc...	-0.5[3]	**3.9[4]**	—
Primary Trend...	-0.2[3]	**3.7[4]**	5.5[5]
SIT Gro & Inc...	2.8[1]	**3.6[4]**	7.7[3]
Bruce...	-16.1[5]	**3.5[4]**	2.1[5]
Bridges Investment...	0.4[2]	**3.2[5]**	6.2[4]
US All-Amer Eqty...	-5.3[5]	**3.2[5]**	—
IAI Gro & Inc...	-4.8[5]	**2.9[5]**	5.2[5]
TU&P Balanced...	1.5[2]	**2.7[5]**	7.2[3]
Wright Qual Core Eqty...	-0.7[3]	**2.7[5]**	7.9[3]
SCM Portfolio...	-0.9[3]	**2.6[5]**	4.4[5]
Selected Amer Sh...	-3.2[4]	**2.6[5]**	8.7[2]
Managers Balanced...	-3.0[4]	**2.6[5]**	5.8[5]
Dreyfus Fund...	-4.2[5]	**2.4[5]**	5.9[4]
Janus Growth & Inc...	-4.9[5]	**2.3[5]**	—
Smith Hayes Asst Allc...	-4.2[5]	**2.3[5]**	6.6[4]
GIT Equity Inc...	-5.8[5]	**2.1[5]**	4.2[5]
Leeb Prsnl Finance...	-3.1[4]	**1.5[5]**	
Wright Sel Blue Ch...	-3.5[4]	**1.0[5]**	6.3[4]
MIM Stock Income...	-1.8[4]	**0.8[5]**	3.4[5]
Merriman Gro & Inc...	-0.2[3]	**0.4[5]**	4.6[5]
Twentieth Cent Blncd...	-0.1[2]	**0.2[5]**	8.5[2]
National Industries...	-0.2[3]	**0.2[5]**	6.5[4]
Advance Cap Eqty Univ...	-4.0[5]	**0.1[5]**	2.3[5]
API Spec Mkts...	-7.4[5]	**-1.0[5]**	-2.2[5]
Gintel Erisa...	-21.3[5]	**-1.8[5]**	0.4[5]
Gibraltar Eqty Gro...	0.4[2]	**-1.8[5]**	3.8[5]
Reynolds Blue Chip...	-0.6[3]	**-1.9[5]**	5.1[5]
INCOME FUNDS			
Fidelity Puritan...	1.9[1]	**12.6[1]**	10.7[1]
Fidelity Convert...	-1.7[3]	**12.2[1]**	13.7[1]
Berwyn Income...	-1.1[2]	**12.1[1]**	11.6[1]
Evergreen Foundation...	-1.1[2]	**11.1[1]**	14.8[1]
Price, Rowe Eqty Inc...	4.5[1]	**11.1[1]**	9.9[2]
Lindner Dividend...	-3.3[4]	**10.4[1]**	9.9[1]
Crabbe Hsn Asst All...	-0.9[2]	**9.6[1]**	—
Eclipse Balanced...	0.0[2]	**9.4[1]**	10.0[1]
Dodge & Cox Blncd...	2.1[1]	**9.4[1]**	9.8[2]
Royce Equity Inc...	-3.2[4]	**9.3[1]**	9.0[2]
Fidelity Asset Mgr...	-6.5[5]	**9.3[1]**	11.1[1]

By 1992 - 1994 performance

No-Load Fund	Total return percent with quintile ranks by objective			No-Load Fund	Total return percent with quintile ranks by objective		
	1994	Annualized 3 years	5 years		1994	Annualized 3 years	5 years
Vangd Convert...	-5.6[5]	**8.4[1]**	9.4[2]	Fidelity Sel Financial...	-3.7[3]	**17.4[2]**	14.6[3]
FBP Contrn Blncd...	1.8[1]	**8.2[2]**	8.3[3]	Invesco Strat Leisure...	-5.0[3]	**16.8[2]**	16.7[2]
Founders Balanced...	-1.9[3]	**8.2[2]**	8.1[3]	Fidelity Sel Telecomm...	4.3[2]	**16.0[2]**	11.2[3]
Warbg Pincus Balanced...	1.3[1]	**8.2[2]**	10.3[1]	Fidelity Sel Technology...	11.1[1]	**15.8[2]**	22.3[1]
Invesco Total Ret...	2.5[1]	**8.2[2]**	9.5[2]	Cohen & Steers Realty...	8.3[1]	**15.5[2]**	—
SBSF Convert...	-6.5[5]	**7.7[2]**	8.7[2]	Fidelity Sel Pap/Forest...	14.1[1]	**14.9[2]**	11.6[3]
Managers Inc Eqty...	1.0[1]	**7.7[2]**	7.0[4]	Fidelity Sel Leisure...	-6.8[4]	**14.8[2]**	9.3[4]
Htchks & Wly Blncd...	0.8[2]	**7.5[2]**	8.3[3]	Fidelity Sel Indust Mat...	8.2[2]	**13.8[2]**	10.7[4]
SAFECO Income...	-1.1[2]	**7.5[2]**	6.4[4]	PRA Real Estate...	3.0[2]	**13.3[2]**	6.9[4]
Value Line Convert...	-5.2[4]	**7.4[2]**	8.9[2]	Invesco Strat Tech...	5.3[2]	**12.9[3]**	22.5[1]
Columbia Balanced...	0.1[2]	**7.4[2]**	—	Evergreen Glob RE...	-14.1[5]	**12.8[3]**	5.5[5]
Westwood Balanced...	0.0[2]	**7.4[2]**	—	Invesco Strat Fncl...	-5.9[4]	**12.2[3]**	18.0[1]
Amer AAdv Balncd...	-1.7[3]	**7.2[2]**	8.6[2]	Fidelity Sel Chemicals...	14.7[1]	**12.1[3]**	13.4[3]
Vangd Equity Inc...	-1.5[3]	**7.2[3]**	6.3[4]	Fidelity Real Estate...	1.9[2]	**11.0[3]**	11.7[3]
Highmark Inc Eqty...	-0.6[2]	**7.1[3]**	7.7[3]	Fidelity Sel Const/Hous...	-16.0[5]	**10.1[3]**	11.2[4]
Fidelity Balanced...	-5.3[4]	**6.8[3]**	9.0[2]	Fidelity Sel Insurance...	-0.3[3]	**9.7[3]**	10.2[4]
Vangd Wellington...	-0.4[2]	**6.8[3]**	7.9[3]	Vangd Spec-Energy...	-1.6[3]	**9.7[3]**	5.4[5]
Fidelity Utilities...	-5.3[4]	**6.7[3]**	8.4[3]	Fidelity Sel Defense...	1.8[3]	**9.4[3]**	9.7[4]
Lexington Convert...	1.3[1]	**6.2[3]**	10.9[1]	Fidelity Sel Retail...	-5.0[4]	**9.4[3]**	15.9[2]
USAA Income Stk...	-0.7[2]	**6.1[3]**	8.4[3]	Fidelity Sel Broker...	-17.3[5]	**9.1[4]**	14.7[2]
Vangd Asset Alloc...	-2.3[3]	**6.0[3]**	8.5[2]	Fidelity Sel Energy Serv...	0.6[3]	**8.0[4]**	-0.4[5]
Vangd Wellesley Inc...	-4.4[4]	**6.0[3]**	8.4[3]	Fidelity Sel Consmr Prod...	-7.1[4]	**7.9[4]**	—
Payson Balanced...	-4.2[4]	**5.8[3]**	—	Fidelity Sel Food/Agr...	6.1[2]	**7.0[4]**	12.4[3]
Merriman Asst All...	-2.9[4]	**5.8[3]**	6.1[5]	Century Shares...	-3.9[3]	**6.7[4]**	8.0[4]
Smith Hayes Convert...	-8.0[5]	**5.7[4]**	7.4[4]	Invesco Strat Util...	-9.9[5]	**6.6[4]**	6.9[4]
Price, Rowe Balanced...	-2.0[3]	**5.7[4]**	—	Vangd Spec-Health...	9.5[1]	**6.4[4]**	15.5[2]
Galaxy Eqty Income...	0.8[2]	**5.4[4]**	—	Rushmore Amer Gas Idx...	-9.8[4]	**5.4[4]**	1.6[5]
Strong Asst Allc...	-1.5[3]	**5.2[4]**	7.4[4]	Fidelity Sel Energy...	0.4[3]	**5.3[4]**	2.2[5]
USAA Balanced...	-2.6[3]	**5.2[4]**	6.2[4]	Fidelity Sel Util Gro...	-7.4[4]	**4.8[4]**	6.9[4]
SteinRoe Total Ret...	-4.1[4]	**5.1[4]**	8.1[3]	Fidelity Sel Medical Del...	19.8[1]	**3.2[5]**	17.8[2]
Weston: New Cent Inc...	-2.4[3]	**5.0[4]**	7.2[4]	Fidelity Sel Air Trans...	-21.7[5]	**3.0[5]**	4.1[5]
Primary Income...	-2.6[3]	**4.8[4]**	7.7[3]	Dreyfus Edison Elec...	-12.9[5]	**1.1[5]**	—
Mairs & Power Inc...	-2.0[3]	**4.8[4]**	8.0[3]	Fidelity Sel Health...	21.4[1]	**0.9[5]**	18.6[1]
API Cap Inc...	-0.4[2]	**4.6[4]**	6.2[5]	Invesco Strat Enrgy...	-7.3[4]	**-2.1[5]**	-5.4[5]
State Farm Blncd...	5.0[1]	**4.6[4]**	11.8[1]	US Real Estate...	-11.6[5]	**-2.3[5]**	3.1[5]
Bascom Hill Blncd...	1.1[1]	**4.6[4]**	5.8[5]	Fidelity Sel Envir Serv...	-9.6[4]	**-3.9[5]**	-1.4[5]
US Income...	-10.3[5]	**4.5[5]**	3.6[5]	Invesco Strat Health...	0.9[3]	**-7.3[5]**	14.0[3]
Galaxy Asst Allc...	-2.5[3]	**4.0[5]**	—	Fidelity Sel Biotech...	-18.2[5]	**-9.6[5]**	16.2[2]
API Total Ret...	-6.8[5]	**3.5[5]**	3.0[5]	Invesco Strat Envrn...	-11.4[5]	**-11.8[5]**	—
Smith Hayes Blncd...	-4.4[4]	**3.4[5]**	5.4[5]	**PRECIOUS METALS FUNDS**			
MIM AFA Eqty Inc...	-6.0[5]	**3.1[5]**	—	Fidelity Sel Prec Metals...	-1.2[1]	**17.8[1]**	5.5[1]
Avondale Total Ret...	2.3[1]	**2.6[5]**	6.5[4]	US World Gold...	-16.9[5]	**14.5[1]**	0.9[2]
Amana Income...	-6.5[5]	**2.1[5]**	4.9[5]	Vangd Spec-Gold...	-5.4[1]	**13.8[2]**	4.2[1]
Value Line Income...	-4.3[4]	**1.8[5]**	6.7[4]	Fidelity Sel Amer Gold...	-15.5[4]	**13.5[2]**	2.6[2]
Advance Cap Blncd...	-2.7[4]	**1.7[5]**	4.2[5]	Blanchard Prec Metals...	-15.2[3]	**11.5[2]**	0.9[2]
Stratton Month Div Sh...	-12.1[5]	**1.1[5]**	6.0[5]	Benham Gold Eqty...	-16.8[4]	**11.3[3]**	-0.3[4]
Pax World...	2.6[1]	**0.7[5]**	6.4[4]	Lexington Goldfund...	-7.3[2]	**11.3[3]**	0.5[4]
Steadman Associated...	-20.5[5]	**-2.4[5]**	-2.8[5]	Scudder Gold...	-7.4[2]	**10.3[4]**	0.8[3]
SECTOR & INDUSTRY FUNDS				Bull & Bear Gold...	-13.8[3]	**10.2[4]**	0.6[3]
Fidelity Sel Home Fincl...	2.7[2]	**27.3[1]**	23.5[1]	USAA Gold...	-9.4[3]	**9.7[4]**	-1.5[4]
Fidelity Sel Electronics...	17.2[1]	**25.4[1]**	23.1[1]	Invesco Strat Gold...	-27.9[5]	**4.6[5]**	-4.0[5]
Fidelity Sel Computer...	20.5[1]	**23.7[1]**	24.0[1]	US Gold Shares...	-2.7[1]	**2.3[5]**	-9.9[5]
Fidelity Sel Software...	0.4[3]	**21.7[1]**	21.5[1]	**GLOBAL EQUITY FUNDS**			
Fidelity Sel Devel Comm...	15.1[1]	**21.1[1]**	—	Fidelity Worldwide...	3.0[1]	**14.3[1]**	—
Fidelity Sel Multimedia...	4.0[2]	**20.3[1]**	12.1[3]	Janus Worldwide...	3.6[1]	**13.2[1]**	—
Price, Rowe Sci/Tech...	15.8[1]	**19.5[1]**	22.0[1]	GE Elfun Glob Inc...	-0.6[2]	**11.6[1]**	7.8[1]
Fidelity Sel Auto...	-12.8[5]	**18.7[1]**	16.4[2]	Scudder Global...	-4.2[3]	**9.5[2]**	7.5[2]
Fidelity Sel Transp...	3.9[2]	**18.5[1]**	15.0[2]	USAA Cornerstone...	-1.1[2]	**9.2[2]**	6.6[3]
Fidelity Sel Reg Banks...	0.2[3]	**18.2[1]**	16.8[2]	Lexington Global...	1.8[1]	**9.0[2]**	4.5[3]
Fidelity Sel Indust Equip...	3.1[2]	**18.1[2]**	12.0[3]	Founders Worldwide Gro...	-2.2[3]	**8.9[3]**	13.1[1]

Stock and bond funds – ranked within objective *continued*

By 1992 - 1994 performance

| No-Load Fund | Total return percent with quintile ranks by objective | | | No-Load Fund | Total return percent with quintile ranks by objective | | |
	1994	Annualized 3 years	5 years		1994	Annualized 3 years	5 years
Scudder Glob Sm Co	-7.7[4]	8.4[3]	—	DFA Japan Sm Co	29.5[1]	3.0[5]	-4.9[5]
Fremont Global	-4.2[3]	6.4[4]	7.0[2]	Fidelity Canada	-12.0[5]	2.4[5]	3.6[4]
Blanchard Glob Growth	-7.5[4]	5.0[4]	3.7[5]	BBK Int'l Equity	-12.6[5]	2.2[5]	-2.6[5]
BBK Diversa	-9.4[4]	4.8[4]	3.8[4]	Wright Equi Italy	5.0[2]	-8.1[5]	—
Permanent Portfolio	-2.9[3]	4.8[5]	3.6[5]	Wright Equi Spain	-9.5[5]	-9.6[5]	—
Dreyfus Global Growth	-7.5[4]	3.1[5]	6.4[3]	**FIXED-INCOME FUNDS - LONG TERM**			
Bull & Bear US & Overs	-13.1[5]	2.3[5]	3.7[4]	Fidelity Cap & Inc	-4.6[3]	15.1[1]	13.7[1]
INTERNATIONAL EQUITY FUNDS				Fidelity Spart Hi Inc	3.2[1]	15.1[1]	—
Price, Rowe New Asia	-19.2[5]	17.1[1]	—	Northeast Inv Trust	2.2[1]	14.0[1]	11.2[1]
Fidelity Emg Mkts	-17.9[5]	16.4[1]	—	Loomis Syls Bond	-4.1[3]	10.2[1]	—
Harbor Int'l	5.4[1]	15.2[1]	10.9[1]	Vangd Hi Yld Corp	-1.7[1]	9.9[1]	10.0[1]
SIT Int'l Growth	-3.0[4]	13.9[1]	—	Federated Hi Yld	-2.4[2]	9.6[1]	11.9[1]
Fidelity Pacific Basin	-2.8[3]	13.7[1]	3.8[4]	Fidelity Curr: Yen	12.6[1]	9.3[1]	11.0[1]
Managers Int'l Eqty	2.0[2]	13.7[1]	9.4[1]	SAFECO Hi Yld Bd	-2.0[1]	9.3[1]	9.3[1]
Lexington World Emg	-13.8[5]	13.5[1]	9.2[1]	Price, Rowe High Yld	-8.1[5]	8.7[1]	8.4[1]
59 Wall Pac Basin	-21.5[5]	13.4[1]		Value Line Agg Inc	-4.1[3]	8.6[1]	9.3[1]
Warbg Pincus Int'l	0.2[3]	13.2[1]	10.8[1]	Strong Income	-1.3[1]	8.0[1]	6.3[5]
USAA International	2.7[2]	12.8[1]	8.1[1]	Invesco High Yld	-5.1[3]	8.0[1]	8.2[2]
Twentieth Cent Int'l	-4.8[4]	12.5[1]	—	GIT Max Income	-2.6[2]	7.9[1]	7.8[2]
Schroder Int'l Eqty	0.2[3]	11.9[2]	5.4[2]	Nicholas Income	-0.2[1]	7.5[1]	8.6[1]
Htchks & Wly Int'l	-3.0[4]	11.2[2]	—	Benham Target 2010	-11.6[5]	7.0[1]	8.3[2]
Vangd Int'l Growth	0.7[3]	11.2[2]	4.8[3]	Bull & Bear Glob Inc	-13.4[5]	6.9[1]	6.9[3]
Wright Equi Hong Kong	-37.0[5]	10.5[2]	—	Invesco Select Inc	-1.2[1]	6.7[1]	8.6[1]
Price, Rowe Int'l Stk	-0.8[3]	10.3[2]	7.2[1]	Benham Target 2005	-8.9[5]	6.7[2]	8.8[1]
Babson Stew Ivry Int'l	1.3[2]	10.0[2]	6.8[1]	Benham Target 2020	-17.7[5]	6.6[2]	6.3[5]
Fidelity Europe	6.2[1]	9.6[2]	5.5[2]	Benham Target 2015	-14.1[5]	6.5[2]	7.4[3]
IAI International	0.5[3]	9.5[2]	5.9[2]	Fidelity Inv Grd Bd	-5.4[4]	6.0[2]	8.5[1]
59 Wall Europe Eqty	-3.9[4]	9.5[2]	—	Vangd LT Corp	-5.3[4]	6.0[2]	8.9[1]
Scudder Int'l Stk	-3.0[4]	8.9[2]	5.6[2]	PIMCO Tot Return	-3.6[3]	6.0[2]	9.0[1]
Loomis Syls Int'l Eq	-1.8[3]	8.9[2]	—	Loomis Syls US Gov	-6.3[4]	5.7[2]	—
Invesco Pacific Bas	4.7[2]	8.9[2]	2.0[4]	CA Inv Tr-US Gov	-7.0[4]	5.3[2]	8.3[2]
Amer AAdv Int'l	1.2[2]	8.8[3]	—	Babson Bond-Port L	-3.3[2]	5.3[2]	7.7[3]
Vontobel EuroPac	-4.9[4]	8.8[3]	—	Benham Target 2000	-6.9[4]	5.3[2]	8.4[2]
Bartlett Value Int'l	-0.5[3]	8.7[3]	5.9[2]	Dreyfus A Bonds Plus	-6.1[4]	5.3[2]	7.7[2]
Nomura Pacific Bas	4.2[2]	8.5[3]	3.9[4]	Vangd LT Trsy	-7.0[4]	5.2[2]	7.7[2]
Vangd Idx Europe	1.9[2]	8.3[3]	—	Fidelity Curr: D-Mark	16.4[1]	5.1[2]	8.4[2]
Fidelity Int'l Gr & Inc	-2.9[4]	8.2[3]	5.8[2]	Portico Bond Immdex	-3.1[2]	5.0[2]	7.9[2]
Price, Rowe Int'l Disc	-7.6[4]	8.0[3]	4.1[3]	Benham Target 1995	0.8[1]	5.0[2]	8.0[2]
Fidelity Overseas	1.3[2]	7.9[3]	4.9[3]	Scudder US Zero 2000	-7.9[5]	4.9[2]	7.7[3]
Galaxy Int'l Eqty	-2.5[3]	7.8[3]		FFB Lexcn Fix Inc	-3.0[2]	4.9[2]	—
Vangd Trust Int'l	5.3[1]	7.8[3]	3.9[4]	Crowley Income	-1.8[1]	4.9[3]	7.0[3]
Vangd Idx Pacific	12.9[1]	7.8[3]	—	SIT US Gov	1.8[1]	4.8[3]	7.6[3]
Price, Rowe Europe	4.1[2]	7.7[4]	—	AIC: Clvr Cap Fix	-2.8[2]	4.8[3]	—
Quant Int'l Eqty	9.1[1]	7.6[4]	-0.3[5]	Fidelity Gov Sec	-5.2[3]	4.7[3]	7.8[2]
RSI Tr-Int'l Eqty	0.8[3]	7.5[4]	3.5[4]	Scudder Income	-4.5[3]	4.7[3]	7.8[2]
Wright Equi Dutch	11.7[1]	7.0[4]	—	Vista Bond	-3.2[2]	4.6[3]	—
WPG International	-6.3[4]	6.7[4]	0.8[4]	GE S&S Prg: LT Inst	-2.5[2]	4.6[3]	7.7[2]
Wright Int'l Blue Ch	-1.6[3]	6.6[4]	5.7[2]	DFA Glob Fix Inc	-4.3[3]	4.6[3]	—
Price, Rowe Japan	15.1[1]	6.3[4]	—	Maxus Income	-4.5[3]	4.6[3]	6.7[4]
Fidelity Dvsfd Int'l	1.1[2]	6.0[4]	—	GE Elfun Income	-2.3[2]	4.5[3]	7.6[3]
Pierpont Int'l Eqty	5.7[1]	5.9[4]	—	IAI Bond	-4.9[3]	4.5[3]	7.4[3]
DFA UK Small Co	4.6[2]	5.5[4]	4.7[3]	Dreyfus 100% US Long	-9.2[5]	4.4[3]	7.6[3]
Drey/Laurel Int'l	3.5[2]	4.9[4]	0.1[5]	Advance Cap Bond	-4.6[3]	4.4[3]	7.1[3]
DFA Lrg Cap Int'l	5.3[1]	4.8[4]	—	RSI Tr-Act Mgd Bd	-4.2[3]	4.4[3]	7.5[3]
Papp L Roy Amer Abrd	7.8[1]	4.8[5]	—	Wright Gov Oblig	-8.7[5]	4.3[3]	7.2[3]
Japan (Scudder)	10.0[1]	4.2[5]	-0.5[5]	Galaxy Trsy Idx	-3.7[3]	4.3[3]	—
Invesco Int'l Gro	0.6[3]	4.0[5]	0.6[5]	Vangd Prefrd Stk	-7.9[5]	4.1[4]	7.7[2]
DFA Cont Sm Co	11.0[1]	3.7[5]	0.5[5]	Galaxy Hi Qual Bd	-6.5[4]	4.0[4]	—
Invesco Europe	-3.0[4]	3.7[5]	3.9[3]	Price, Rowe Trsy Lng	-5.7[4]	4.0[4]	6.9[4]
Dreyfus European	-3.1[4]	3.5[5]	5.0[3]	AARP Hi Qual Bd	-4.5[3]	4.0[4]	6.9[3]

No-Load Fund	Total return percent with quintile ranks by objective			No-Load Fund	Total return percent with quintile ranks by objective		
	1994	Annualized 3 years	5 years		1994	Annualized 3 years	5 years
PDC&J Preservation	-2.4[2]	4.0[4]	6.7[4]	Retrmt Sys: Inter Fix	-3.3[3]	4.2[2]	—
Pacifica Asset Pres	2.4[1]	3.9[4]	—	Benham GNMA Inc	-1.5[1]	4.2[2]	7.6[2]
Babson UMB Bond	-3.1[2]	3.8[4]	6.5[4]	USAA Income	-5.2[5]	4.1[3]	7.7[1]
Pierpont Bond	-3.0[2]	3.8[4]	6.9[4]	Gov St Bond	-2.7[3]	4.1[3]	—
Highmark Bond	-3.9[3]	3.8[4]	6.3[4]	Price, Rowe New Inc	-2.2[2]	4.0[3]	7.1[3]
Managers Bond	-7.2[4]	3.7[4]	7.4[3]	FFB Lexcn Inter Gov	-1.9[2]	3.9[3]	—
Reich & Tang Gov	-6.2[4]	3.7[4]	6.7[4]	Vangd GNMA	-1.0[1]	3.9[3]	7.6[2]
Weitz Fix Inc	-2.3[2]	3.6[4]	6.2[5]	Federated Inter Gov	-1.9[2]	3.8[3]	6.8[4]
Wright Total Ret	-6.6[4]	3.6[4]	6.2[5]	Legg Msn Gov Inter	-1.7[2]	3.7[4]	6.8[4]
Seafirst Bond	-2.3[2]	3.6[4]	6.6[4]	Fidelity Spart GNMA	-1.5[1]	3.7[4]	—
Fidelity Spart Gov Inc	-3.6[3]	3.5[4]	6.8[4]	Price, Rowe Glob Gov	-3.2[3]	3.7[4]	—
Selected US Gov	-2.2[1]	3.5[4]	6.4[4]	Asset Mgmt ARM	1.9[1]	3.7[4]	—
Fidelity Spart LT Gov	-12.2[5]	3.4[4]	—	GIT Gov Port	-3.6[4]	3.7[4]	6.3[5]
Bull & Bear US Gov	-4.7[3]	3.4[5]	6.6[4]	Lexington GNMA	-2.1[2]	3.6[4]	6.9[3]
Rushmore Gov Long	-9.9[5]	3.3[5]	6.1[5]	Price, Rowe GNMA	-1.5[1]	3.6[4]	7.1[3]
Wright Curr Inc	-3.3[2]	3.2[5]	6.9[4]	RSI Tr-Inter Bd	-2.5[3]	3.6[4]	6.9[3]
SteinRoe Gov Inc	-3.3[2]	3.2[5]	6.5[4]	Bartlett Fix Inc	-2.9[3]	3.5[4]	6.1[5]
Federated Income	-1.6[1]	3.2[5]	6.7[4]	Asset Mgmt Mrtg Sec	-2.3[2]	3.5[4]	6.9[3]
Crabbe Hsn Gov Bd	-2.1[1]	3.0[5]	5.9[5]	Rushmore Gov Inter	-7.3[5]	3.5[4]	6.6[4]
Federated ARMS	0.3[1]	2.8[5]	6.0[5]	Fidelity GNMA	-2.0[2]	3.5[4]	6.8[4]
Smith Hayes Gov Qual	-3.3[3]	2.8[5]	5.8[5]	Twentieth Cent LT Bd	-4.5[5]	3.5[5]	6.6[4]
Crabbe Hsn Income	-3.6[3]	2.8[5]	6.0[5]	Dreyfus GNMA	-2.8[3]	3.5[5]	6.8[4]
Capstone Gov Inc	1.2[1]	2.7[5]	2.7[5]	Westwood Inter Bd	-5.6[5]	3.4[5]	—
Invesco Gov Sec	-7.2[4]	2.7[5]	6.0[5]	Federated GNMA	-2.5[2]	3.3[5]	7.0[3]
Founders Gov Sec	-7.5[5]	2.1[5]	5.0[5]	Stratus Inter Gov	-2.8[3]	3.3[5]	—
MIM Bond Income	-3.6[3]	2.0[5]	4.2[5]	Scudder GNMA	-3.1[3]	3.2[5]	6.8[3]
Loomis Syls Glob Bd	-8.7[5]	1.8[5]	—	SAFECO GNMA	-4.3[4]	3.0[5]	6.4[5]
Value Line US Gov	-10.6[5]	1.4[5]	6.0[5]	Galaxy Inter Bond	-3.7[4]	2.9[5]	5.9[5]
BBK Int'l Fix Inc	-19.2[5]	-0.3[5]	—	Primary US Gov	-3.1[3]	2.8[5]	6.2[5]
Fidelity Curr: Sterling	9.9[1]	-0.4[5]	7.5[3]	WPG Gov Sec	-8.7[5]	2.4[5]	5.9[5]
FIXED-INCOME FUNDS - INTER TERM				Fidelity Glob Bond	-16.3[5]	2.1[5]	6.1[5]
Janus Flex Inc	-2.9[3]	7.9[1]	8.6[1]	Managers Inter Mortg	-25.0[5]	-2.6[5]	3.8[5]
Price, Rowe Int'l Bond	-1.8[2]	6.4[1]	10.5[1]	**FIXED-INCOME FUNDS - SHORT TERM**			
Strong Gov Sec	-3.4[4]	5.9[1]	8.5[1]	Strong Advantage	3.6[1]	6.6[1]	7.4[1]
Price, Rowe Spect-Inc	-1.9[2]	5.9[1]	—	Heartland US Gov	-9.6[5]	5.4[1]	8.6[1]
SteinRoe Income	-4.1[4]	5.8[1]	8.0[1]	PIMCO Low Dur	0.6[2]	5.3[1]	7.6[1]
Harbor Bond	-3.7[4]	5.7[1]	8.8[1]	Federated US Gov	-6.2[5]	4.8[1]	7.3[1]
Merriman Flex Bd	-1.7[2]	5.6[1]	7.2[2]	Portico ST Bond	1.0[2]	4.7[1]	7.1[2]
Warbg Pincus Fix Inc	-0.8[1]	5.6[1]	7.2[2]	Strong ST Bond	-1.6[4]	4.7[1]	6.7[3]
Dodge & Cox Income	-2.9[3]	5.2[1]	8.1[1]	Vangd ST Corp	-0.1[3]	4.7[1]	7.2[1]
Fidelity Inter Bond	-2.0[2]	5.2[1]	7.5[2]	Wm Blair Income	-0.7[4]	4.7[1]	—
Warbg Pincus Glob Bd	-5.5[5]	4.9[1]	—	Amer AAdv Ltd Inc	1.3[2]	4.5[1]	7.1[2]
Columbia Fix Inc	-3.5[4]	4.8[1]	7.8[1]	Dreyfus 100% US Short	-0.3[3]	4.5[1]	—
Dreyfus Invst GNMA	-1.1[1]	4.8[2]	—	Dreyfus S-I Gov	-0.8[4]	4.5[1]	7.3[1]
Bernstein Inter Dur	-3.2[3]	4.8[2]	7.7[2]	Invesco Inter Gov	-1.7[4]	4.3[1]	7.2[1]
DFA Inter Gov	-4.8[5]	4.8[2]	—	Homestead ST Bond	0.1[3]	4.3[2]	—
Vangd Inter Trsy	-4.3[5]	4.7[2]	—	Asset Mgmt ST Gov	0.4[2]	4.2[2]	6.7[3]
Ntnghm II-Invstk Fix	-4.0[4]	4.7[2]	—	Vangd ST Trsy	-0.5[3]	4.1[2]	—
Fidelity Mrtg Sec	1.9[1]	4.7[2]	7.5[2]	Warbg Pincus Inter Gov	-1.8[4]	4.1[2]	7.2[1]
Vangd Bond Idx Total	-2.7[3]	4.6[2]	7.4[2]	Bernstein Short Dur	0.5[2]	4.1[2]	6.6[3]
FundTrust Income	-3.9[4]	4.6[2]	6.5[4]	BSR S-I Fix	-2.3[5]	4.1[2]	—
SteinRoe Inter Bd	-2.8[3]	4.5[2]	7.1[3]	State Farm Interim	-0.8[4]	4.1[2]	6.7[2]
Scudder Int'l Bond	-8.6[5]	4.5[2]	11.0[1]	Vangd ST Federal	-0.9[4]	4.0[2]	6.7[3]
SAFECO Inter Trsy	-3.6[4]	4.4[2]	6.7[4]	DFA 5 Yr Gov	-3.2[5]	4.0[2]	7.4[1]
Special Port Cash	2.7[1]	4.4[2]	5.9[5]	Fidelity ST Bond	-4.1[5]	4.0[2]	6.3[4]
Dreyfus 100% US Inter	-4.0[4]	4.4[3]	7.3[2]	DFA 1 Yr Fix Inc	2.5[1]	4.0[2]	5.9[4]
USAA GNMA	0.0[1]	4.3[3]	—	Permanent Vers Bd	2.6[1]	4.0[2]	—
Babson Bond-Port S	-2.1[2]	4.3[3]	7.0[3]	Vista ST Bond	2.4[1]	4.0[2]	—
Legg Msn Invest Grd	-4.6[5]	4.3[3]	6.8[4]	Galaxy ST Bond	-0.3[3]	4.0[3]	—
Asset Mgmt Inter Mrtg	-1.6[1]	4.3[3]	6.9[3]	Harbor Short Dur	2.7[1]	3.9[3]	—

Stock and bond funds – ranked within objective continued
By 1992 - 1994 performance

No-Load Fund	Total return percent with quintile ranks by objective			No-Load Fund	Total return percent with quintile ranks by objective		
	1994	Annualized 3 years	5 years		1994	Annualized 3 years	5 years
Benham Trsy Note	-2.3[5]	3.9[3]	6.9[2]	Scudder PA TF	-5.9[2]	5.1[2]	6.7[2]
Price, Rowe Trsy Inter	-2.2[4]	3.9[3]	7.0[2]	Scudder Mgd Muni	-6.0[3]	5.1[2]	6.8[2]
IAI Gov Bond	-2.3[4]	3.9[3]	—	Fidelity Spart NJ Hi Yld	-5.7[2]	5.0[2]	6.9[1]
Columbia US Gov	0.0[3]	3.9[3]	6.7[3]	Fidelity MA Hi Yld	-6.1[3]	5.0[2]	6.7[2]
Nbrgr-Ber Ltd Mat	-0.3[3]	3.8[3]	6.4[3]	Benham CA Insur	-6.5[3]	5.0[2]	6.6[2]
GS ST Gov Agency	0.4[2]	3.8[3]	6.0[4]	Scudder Hi Yld TF	-8.4[5]	5.0[2]	6.8[2]
PIMCO Short-Term	2.9[1]	3.7[3]	5.2[5]	Galaxy TE Bond	-5.4[2]	5.0[2]	—
Fidelity Spart Ltd Mat	-1.0[4]	3.7[3]	6.3[3]	Pierpont TE Bond	-2.8[1]	5.0[2]	6.5[3]
Scudder ST Glob Inc	-1.1[4]	3.7[3]	—	Price, Rowe CA TF	-5.7[2]	4.9[2]	6.5[3]
Federated ST Income	-0.5[3]	3.6[3]	5.3[5]	Scudder NY TF	-7.2[4]	4.9[2]	6.6[2]
Schwab S-I Gov	-2.9[5]	3.6[4]	—	Fidelity OH TF	-5.6[2]	4.9[2]	6.7[2]
Fidelity ST World Inc	-5.9[5]	3.6[4]	—	Scudder OH TF	-5.5[2]	4.9[2]	6.6[2]
Wright Near Term	-3.1[5]	3.6[4]	6.3[3]	Loomis Syls Muni	-5.4[2]	4.9[2]	—
AARP GNMA & Trsy	-1.7[4]	3.5[4]	6.9[2]	Dreyfus NJ Muni	-6.0[3]	4.9[2]	6.9[1]
Managers Sht & Int	-8.4[5]	3.5[4]	6.0[4]	Scudder CA TF	-7.3[4]	4.9[3]	6.7[2]
Bernstein Gov Sht	0.4[2]	3.5[4]	6.1[4]	Drey-General Muni	-7.3[4]	4.9[3]	7.4[1]
Federated S-I Gov	0.7[2]	3.4[4]	5.9[4]	Fidelity MI Hi Yld	-7.5[4]	4.9[3]	6.3[3]
Flex-Fund Bond	-1.0[4]	3.4[4]	6.7[3]	State Farm Muni Bd	-2.5[1]	4.9[3]	6.5[2]
Wasatch Income	1.6[2]	3.4[4]	6.8[2]	Value Line NY TE	-7.7[4]	4.8[3]	6.6[2]
Scudder ST Bond	-2.9[5]	3.4[4]	6.8[2]	Benham CA Long	-6.4[3]	4.8[3]	6.5[3]
Dreman Fixed Inc	-1.2[4]	3.3[4]	6.3[4]	Drey-General CA	-7.0[3]	4.7[3]	6.5[3]
IAI Reserve	2.7[1]	3.1[4]	5.1[5]	AARP Insur TF Gen	-6.2[3]	4.7[3]	6.5[3]
Nbrgr-Ber Ultra Sht	2.2[1]	3.0[4]	5.0[5]	Rushmore VA TF	-5.0[1]	4.7[3]	5.9[4]
Drey/Laurel ST Bd	0.2[2]	3.0[5]	6.1[4]	GE Elfun TE Inc	-5.8[2]	4.6[3]	6.3[3]
Eaton Vance ST Trsy	3.5[1]	3.0[5]	—	Rushmore MD TF	-5.2[2]	4.6[3]	5.4[5]
RSI Tr-ST Invest	3.4[1]	3.0[5]	4.5[5]	USAA VA Bond	-6.3[3]	4.6[3]	—
Fidelity S-I Gov	-1.4[4]	2.8[5]	—	CA Inv Tr-CA TF	-8.6[5]	4.5[3]	6.4[3]
Price, Rowe ST Bond	-2.9[5]	2.8[5]	5.7[5]	Dreyfus NY TE	-7.0[3]	4.5[3]	6.2[4]
Permanent Treasy	3.3[1]	2.8[5]	4.2[5]	Twentieth Cent TE Long	-5.6[2]	4.4[3]	6.3[3]
Twentieth Cent Gov ST	-0.6[3]	2.6[5]	5.4[5]	Fidelity MN TF	-5.9[3]	4.4[3]	5.8[4]
Benham Adj Rate Gov	-1.0[4]	2.6[5]	—	Wright Insur TF	-4.1[1]	4.4[3]	5.9[4]
Blanchard ST Global	-4.6[5]	2.4[5]	—	Fidelity Spart NY Hi Yld	-8.3[4]	4.4[3]	—
Price, Rowe Adj Rate	-0.6[3]	2.0[5]	—	Dreyfus Muni Bond	-7.0[3]	4.3[4]	6.2[3]
Janus Inter Gov	-2.4[5]	1.6[5]	—	SteinRoe Mgd Muni	-5.5[2]	4.3[4]	6.3[3]
Managers ST Gov	-6.2[5]	0.4[5]	3.7[5]	Fidelity Spart CT Hi Yld	-7.0[3]	4.3[4]	6.0[4]
TAX-FREE FUNDS - LONG TERM				Dreyfus MA TE	-6.0[3]	4.3[4]	6.3[3]
Strong Muni Bond	-4.6[1]	6.2[1]	7.3[1]	Fidelity Insur TF	-7.7[4]	4.3[4]	6.3[3]
Dupree KY TF Inc	-2.9[1]	6.1[1]	7.3[1]	Fidelity NY Hi Yld	-8.0[4]	4.2[4]	6.1[4]
Strong Insur Muni	-6.5[3]	6.1[1]	—	Fidelity Spart CA Hi Yld	-9.0[5]	4.1[4]	6.4[3]
Scudder MA TF	-6.2[3]	5.9[1]	7.2[1]	Fidelity Spart Muni Inc	-8.9[5]	4.1[4]	—
Vangd PA Insur LT	-4.5[1]	5.8[1]	7.3[1]	Invesco TF Long	-7.5[4]	4.1[4]	6.3[3]
Price, Rowe TF Hi Yld	-4.4[1]	5.8[1]	7.2[1]	Galaxy NY Muni	-7.2[4]	4.1[4]	—
SIT TF Income	-0.6[1]	5.7[1]	6.7[2]	Fidelity NY Insured	-8.0[4]	4.1[4]	6.1[4]
Price, Rowe NY TF	-5.9[2]	5.6[1]	6.9[2]	Babson TF Long	-7.4[4]	4.1[4]	6.0[4]
Vangd Muni Hi Yld	-5.1[2]	5.5[1]	7.4[1]	Fidelity Muni Bd	-8.6[5]	4.0[4]	6.1[4]
Vangd NJ Insur LT	-5.2[2]	5.5[1]	7.1[1]	Dreyfus NY Insur	-6.6[3]	4.0[4]	6.2[4]
Price, Rowe NJ TF	-6.1[3]	5.5[1]	—	USAA TE Long	-7.9[4]	4.0[4]	6.1[4]
Fidelity Spart PA Hi Yld	-5.1[1]	5.4[1]	7.2[1]	USAA NY Bond	-9.0[5]	4.0[4]	—
Vangd OH Insur LT	-5.1[2]	5.4[1]	—	SAFECO Muni Bd	-8.2[4]	4.0[4]	6.4[3]
Vangd NY Insur	-5.6[2]	5.4[1]	7.0[1]	Managers Muni Bd	-5.6[2]	4.0[4]	5.7[5]
Benham Nat TF Long	-6.2[3]	5.4[1]	7.1[1]	Columbia Muni Bd	-4.7[1]	4.0[4]	6.1[4]
Benham CA Hi Yld	-5.3[2]	5.4[1]	6.5[3]	Fidelity CA Hi Yld	-8.9[5]	3.9[5]	5.7[5]
Vangd Muni Long	-5.8[2]	5.3[1]	7.2[1]	Value Line TE Hi Yld	-6.9[3]	3.8[5]	5.9[4]
Fidelity Agg TF	-5.9[2]	5.3[1]	7.0[1]	Northwest Idaho TE	-3.4[1]	3.8[5]	5.2[5]
Price, Rowe VA TF	-5.1[2]	5.3[1]	—	Fidelity CA Insur	-10.2[5]	3.7[5]	5.8[5]
Drey-General NY	-7.2[4]	5.3[2]	7.2[1]	SteinRoe Hi Yld Muni	-4.2[1]	3.7[5]	5.7[5]
Price, Rowe TF Inc	-5.5[2]	5.3[2]	6.7[2]	SAFECO CA TF	-9.2[5]	3.6[5]	6.0[4]
Vangd Muni Insur LT	-5.6[2]	5.2[2]	7.0[1]	GIT TF VA	-8.3[4]	3.5[5]	5.2[5]
Vangd CA Insur LT	-5.7[2]	5.2[2]	6.7[2]	GIT TF AZ	-8.7[5]	3.5[5]	5.3[5]
Price, Rowe MD TF	-5.0[1]	5.1[2]	6.5[2]	Fidelity Hi Yld TF	-7.4[4]	3.5[5]	5.8[4]

Stock and bond funds – ranked within objective continued

By 1992 - 1994 performance

No-Load Fund	Total return percent with quintile ranks by objective			No-Load Fund	Total return percent with quintile ranks by objective		
	1994	Annualized 3 years	5 years		1994	Annualized 3 years	5 years
Dreyfus CA TE	-7.1[4]	**3.5[5]**	5.5[5]	Benham Nat TF Inter	-3.4[3]	**4.5[3]**	6.4[3]
Dreyfus Insur Muni	-8.6[5]	**3.5[5]**	5.7[5]	Crabbe Hsn OR Muni	-2.7[2]	**4.4[4]**	—
USAA CA Bond	-9.3[5]	**3.4[5]**	5.8[4]	US Tax Free	-5.2[5]	**4.3[4]**	5.7[5]
Lexington TE Bond	-6.5[3]	**3.4[5]**	5.2[5]	Bernstein NY Muni	-2.5[2]	**4.2[4]**	5.9[4]
GIT TF Nat	-8.8[5]	**3.3[5]**	5.1[5]	Federated Inter Muni	-3.8[3]	**4.2[4]**	5.9[4]
GIT TF MO	-8.5[5]	**3.2[5]**	4.9[5]	Bernstein Dvsfd Muni	-2.5[2]	**4.1[5]**	5.8[5]
Bull & Bear Muni Inc	-9.8[5]	**1.9[5]**	4.5[5]	Nbrgr-Ber Muni	-4.0[3]	**4.0[5]**	5.6[5]
Fundamental NY Muni	-19.8[5]	**0.3[5]**	3.0[5]	Bernstein CA Muni	-3.2[2]	**3.9[5]**	—
Fundamental CA Muni	-19.9[5]	**-0.2[5]**	2.4[5]	Fremont CA Inter	-4.9[4]	**3.7[5]**	—
Fundamental Hi Yld Muni	-12.9[5]	**-0.9[5]**	0.2[5]	*TAX-FREE FUNDS - SHORT TERM*			
TAX-FREE FUNDS - INTER TERM				Dupree KY Sht-Med	1.0[2]	**4.5[1]**	5.5[2]
Vangd Muni Inter	-2.1[1]	**5.9[1]**	7.4[1]	Fidelity Spart S-I Muni	-0.1[4]	**4.4[1]**	5.7[1]
Warbg Pincus NY Muni	-0.6[1]	**5.5[1]**	6.4[3]	Evergreen S-I Muni	-1.4[5]	**4.3[2]**	—
Scudder Medium TF	-3.5[3]	**5.3[1]**	6.8[1]	Dreyfus S-I Muni	-0.3[4]	**4.3[2]**	5.6[2]
USAA TE Inter	-4.0[3]	**5.1[1]**	6.6[1]	Vangd Muni Ltd	0.1[3]	**4.3[3]**	5.8[1]
Dreyfus NY Inter	-5.1[5]	**5.0[2]**	6.4[3]	Price, Rowe TF S-I	0.3[3]	**4.2[3]**	5.3[3]
Dreyfus Inter Muni	-4.6[4]	**5.0[2]**	6.5[2]	USAA TE Short	0.8[2]	**4.1[3]**	5.2[4]
Fidelity Ltd Muni	-4.8[4]	**5.0[2]**	6.6[2]	Babson TF Short	-1.7[5]	**3.7[4]**	5.4[3]
SteinRoe Inter Muni	-3.5[3]	**4.9[2]**	6.5[2]	Vangd Muni Short	1.6[1]	**3.4[4]**	4.8[4]
Twentieth Cent TE Inter	-2.1[1]	**4.6[3]**	6.0[4]	Federated ST Muni	0.1[3]	**3.1[5]**	4.5[5]
Benham CA Inter	-3.7[3]	**4.5[3]**	6.2[3]	Managers ST Muni	0.3[2]	**2.8[5]**	3.9[5]

Stock and bond funds – ranked within objective

By 1990-1994 performance

No-Load Fund	Total return percent with quintile ranks by objective			No-Load Fund	Total return percent with quintile ranks by objective		
	1994	Annualized 3 years	5 years		1994	Annualized 3 years	5 years
AGGRESSIVE GROWTH FUNDS				FundTrust Agg Gro	-1.2[3]	5.9[4]	**8.7[4]**
Twentieth Cent Giftrust	13.5[1]	20.7[1]	**22.0[1]**	44 Wall St Eqty	-11.7[5]	9.7[2]	**8.7[4]**
PBHG Growth	4.7[1]	25.4[1]	**22.0[1]**	Eclipse Equity SC	-4.7[4]	10.0[2]	**8.6[4]**
Twentieth Cent Ultra	-3.6[4]	5.9[4]	**19.4[1]**	SteinRoe Cap Oppty	0.0[2]	9.3[2]	**8.5[4]**
Kaufmann SC	9.0[1]	12.8[1]	**19.3[1]**	API Growth	-3.4[4]	5.6[4]	**8.4[4]**
CGM Capital Dev	-22.9[5]	5.2[4]	**18.7[1]**	First Eagle America	-2.6[3]	14.5[1]	**8.4[4]**
Skyline Special Eqty	-1.1[3]	20.0[1]	**18.1[1]**	Price, Rowe OTC SC	0.1[2]	10.5[2]	**8.3[4]**
Oberweis Emg Growth SC	-3.5[4]	6.4[3]	**17.7[1]**	WPG Tudor	-9.8[5]	2.4[5]	**8.2[4]**
Fidelity Contrafund	-1.1[3]	11.6[1]	**17.5[1]**	USAA Agg Growth SC	-0.8[3]	-0.6[5]	**8.2[4]**
Wasatch Agg Eqty SC	5.5[1]	10.6[2]	**17.0[1]**	Dreyfus Apprec	3.6[1]	3.0[4]	**8.2[4]**
Berger 100	-6.7[4]	7.1[3]	**17.0[1]**	American Heritage	-35.4[5]	2.7[5]	**8.1[4]**
Founders Discovery SC	-7.7[5]	5.6[4]	**16.7[1]**	Fidelity Cap Apprec	2.5[1]	16.7[1]	**8.0[4]**
Heartland Value SC	1.7[2]	19.8[1]	**16.3[1]**	Vangd Morgan	-1.7[3]	4.9[4]	**8.0[4]**
Brandywine	0.0[2]	12.3[1]	**16.3[1]**	Pierpont Cap App SC	-5.9[4]	6.7[3]	**8.0[4]**
Invesco Dynamics	-1.9[3]	9.7[2]	**15.6[1]**	Gradison Oppty Value SC	-2.2[3]	7.5[3]	**8.0[4]**
RSI Tr-Emg Gro SC	3.5[1]	13.2[1]	**14.8[1]**	Evergreen Ltd Mkt SC	-10.5[5]	2.6[5]	**7.9[4]**
Robrtsn Stph Emg Gro SC	8.0[1]	4.1[4]	**14.4[1]**	Omni Investment	6.7[1]	14.1[1]	**7.7[4]**
MIM Stock Apprec	-10.4[5]	1.5[5]	**14.3[1]**	Value Line Spec Sit	1.0[2]	3.3[4]	**7.5[4]**
Strong Discovery SC	-5.7[4]	5.5[4]	**13.8[1]**	WPG Growth SC	-14.0[5]	1.6[5]	**7.4[4]**
Fidelity Growth Co	-2.2[3]	7.0[3]	**13.5[1]**	Salomon Opportunity	0.8[2]	9.0[2]	**7.2[5]**
Columbia Special	2.3[2]	12.3[1]	**13.3[2]**	Scudder Capital Gro	-9.9[5]	5.0[4]	**6.6[5]**
Price, Rowe New Horiz SC	0.3[2]	10.6[2]	**13.2[2]**	Dreyfus Strat Growth	3.1[1]	2.8[5]	**6.0[5]**
Warbg Pincus Emg Gro SC	-1.4[3]	9.3[2]	**12.9[2]**	Fontaine Cap App	2.3[2]	3.9[4]	**5.9[5]**
Vangd Explorer SC	0.5[2]	9.4[2]	**12.8[2]**	Wright Jr Blue Ch SC	-2.7[3]	2.7[5]	**5.8[5]**
Portico Spec Gro SC	-2.0[3]	4.3[4]	**12.6[2]**	Ariel Growth SC	-4.2[4]	5.2[4]	**5.5[5]**
Babson Enterprise SC	2.5[2]	14.1[1]	**12.3[2]**	AARP Capital Growth	-10.0[5]	3.0[4]	**5.3[5]**
Fidelity Retrmnt Growth	0.1[2]	10.6[2]	**12.0[2]**	Salomon Capital	-14.2[5]	1.8[5]	**5.1[5]**
Scudder Development SC	-5.3[4]	0.4[5]	**12.0[2]**	Babson UMB Heartland SC	0.7[2]	5.8[4]	**5.0[5]**
Fidelity Magellan	-1.8[3]	9.4[2]	**12.0[2]**	GIT Special Gro SC	-3.9[4]	5.6[4]	**4.5[5]**
Founders Special	-4.9[4]	6.1[3]	**11.9[2]**	Perritt Capital Gro SC	-5.1[4]	2.1[5]	**4.2[5]**
Legg Msn Spec Invest SC	-13.1[5]	7.6[3]	**11.8[2]**	Cornerstone Growth	7.6[1]	2.9[4]	**4.2[5]**
Htchks & Wly Sm Cap SC	1.1[2]	9.0[2]	**11.8[2]**	First Mutual	-15.1[5]	0.0[5]	**3.8[5]**
DFA US 9-10 Sm Co SC	3.1[1]	15.4[1]	**11.8[2]**	Longleaf Small Cap SC	3.7[1]	9.9[2]	**3.2[5]**
Fidelity OTC SC	-2.7[3]	6.6[3]	**11.5[2]**	Bull & Bear Spec Eqty	-16.5[5]	7.6[3]	**2.2[5]**
SIT Growth SC	-0.5[2]	1.9[5]	**11.4[2]**	Rainbow Fund	-4.7[4]	-4.0[5]	**1.9[5]**
Founders Frontier SC	-2.8[3]	7.3[3]	**11.3[2]**	Prudent Speculator SC	-8.9[5]	-1.8[5]	**-0.6[5]**
Price, Rowe New Amer	-7.4[5]	6.1[3]	**11.2[2]**	Steadman Amer Indust	-37.2[5]	-13.8[5]	**-14.9[5]**
Janus Twenty	-6.7[4]	-0.5[5]	**10.9[2]**	Steadman Tech & Gro	-37.1[5]	-18.1[5]	**-17.0[5]**
Managers Spec Eqty SC	-2.0[3]	10.1[2]	**10.9[2]**	**GROWTH FUNDS**			
Special Port Stk	-7.2[5]	1.4[5]	**10.8[2]**	Crabbe Hsn Spec SC	11.7[1]	26.1[1]	**19.5[1]**
Vangd Idx Sm Cap SC	-0.5[2]	11.7[1]	**10.6[3]**	Fidelity Blue Chip	9.8[1]	13.2[1]	**18.4[1]**
Baron Asset SC	7.4[1]	14.7[1]	**10.5[3]**	Meridian	0.5[2]	9.5[2]	**16.6[1]**
Dreyfus New Ldrs SC	-0.2[2]	8.5[3]	**10.4[3]**	Harbor Cap App	3.4[1]	8.4[2]	**14.1[1]**
Columbia Growth	-0.6[3]	7.9[3]	**10.2[3]**	Mairs & Power Gro	5.6[1]	8.7[2]	**13.6[1]**
Schroder US Eqty	-5.2[4]	7.1[3]	**10.2[3]**	Wm Blair Growth	6.5[1]	9.8[2]	**13.3[1]**
SAFECO Growth	-1.6[3]	5.2[4]	**10.0[3]**	Longleaf Partners	9.0[1]	17.1[1]	**13.3[1]**
Fasciano SC	3.7[1]	6.5[3]	**10.0[3]**	FAM Value SC	6.8[1]	10.2[2]	**13.3[1]**
General Securities	5.4[1]	5.9[4]	**9.9[3]**	Wasatch Growth	2.7[2]	6.1[3]	**13.2[1]**
Twentieth Cent Growth	-1.5[3]	-0.7[5]	**9.7[3]**	Vangd Primecap	11.4[1]	12.7[1]	**13.1[1]**
Managers Cap App	-1.5[3]	7.0[3]	**9.7[3]**	Acorn SC	-7.5[5]	15.0[1]	**13.1[1]**
Fiduciary Cap Gro SC	0.4[2]	9.6[2]	**9.7[3]**	SAFECO Equity	9.9[1]	16.3[1]	**13.0[1]**
Twentieth Cent Vista	4.7[1]	2.6[5]	**9.6[3]**	Janus Venture SC	5.5[1]	7.3[3]	**12.7[1]**
SteinRoe Stock	-3.8[4]	2.3[5]	**9.6[3]**	Fidelity Discpl Eqty	3.0[2]	9.9[2]	**12.3[1]**
Value Line Lev Gro	-3.7[4]	3.0[4]	**9.4[3]**	Fidelity Value	7.6[1]	17.0[1]	**12.0[1]**
Merger	7.1[1]	9.9[2]	**9.4[3]**	Nbrgr-Ber Guardian	0.6[2]	11.1[1]	**11.9[1]**
Fairmont	7.3[1]	12.2[1]	**9.1[3]**	Price, Rowe Sm Cap Val SC	-1.4[4]	13.7[1]	**11.8[1]**
Fidelity Trend	-6.7[4]	9.1[2]	**9.1[3]**	Dreman High Return	-1.0[3]	9.0[2]	**11.8[1]**
PDC&J Performance	1.1[2]	7.7[3]	**8.9[3]**	Nicholas Ltd Edit SC	-3.0[4]	7.3[3]	**11.7[1]**
Nbrgr-Ber Genesis SC	-1.8[3]	8.9[3]	**8.9[3]**	Monetta Fund	-6.2[5]	-0.2[5]	**11.5[1]**
Dreyfus Special Gro	-18.3[5]	7.4[3]	**8.8[4]**	Strong Opportunity	3.2[2]	13.6[1]	**11.4[1]**

No-Load Fund	Total return percent with quintile ranks by objective			No-Load Fund	Total return percent with quintile ranks by objective		
	1994	Annualized 3 years	5 years		1994	Annualized 3 years	5 years
Sequoia	3.4[1]	7.8[2]	**11.0[2]**	Pinnacle Fund	-1.1[4]	0.5[5]	**6.6[4]**
SteinRoe Special	-3.3[4]	9.9[2]	**10.8[2]**	Babson Growth	-0.6[3]	6.2[3]	**6.4[5]**
Founders Growth	-3.3[4]	8.2[2]	**10.8[2]**	Selected Spec Sh SC	-2.5[4]	5.4[4]	**6.4[5]**
Nbrgr-Ber Focus	0.9[2]	12.4[1]	**10.8[2]**	Merriman Cap App	-0.6[3]	2.4[5]	**6.2[5]**
Janus Fund	-1.1[3]	5.4[4]	**10.7[2]**	Twentieth Cent Select	-8.0[5]	0.3[5]	**5.7[5]**
Babson Value	2.5[2]	13.3[1]	**10.6[2]**	IAI Value	-9.1[5]	7.5[3]	**5.6[5]**
Tocqueville	-0.8[3]	12.4[1]	**10.1[2]**	Charter Cap Blue Chip	-4.8[5]	-2.9[5]	**5.6[5]**
Vangd US Growth	3.9[1]	1.7[5]	**10.1[2]**	Federated Growth	-11.9[5]	0.7[5]	**5.5[5]**
State Farm Growth	6.0[1]	2.9[5]	**10.0[2]**	Dreyfus Growth Oppty	-6.4[5]	-2.9[5]	**5.3[5]**
SteinRoe Prime Eqty	-0.2[3]	7.4[3]	**10.0[2]**	Price, Rowe New Era	5.2[1]	7.4[3]	**5.3[5]**
Sound Shore	0.3[3]	10.8[1]	**10.0[2]**	Dreyfus Core Value	0.4[3]	6.8[3]	**5.2[5]**
Evergreen Gro & Inc	1.7[2]	9.8[2]	**9.8[2]**	Wade	-1.3[4]	5.1[4]	**5.2[5]**
Price, Rowe Growth Stk	0.9[2]	7.3[3]	**9.6[2]**	Crowley Growth	3.9[1]	3.6[4]	**4.9[5]**
Value Line Fund	-4.5[4]	2.2[5]	**9.5[2]**	Northwest Growth	-11.4[5]	-1.3[5]	**4.9[5]**
Flex-Fund Muirfield	2.7[2]	5.9[3]	**9.5[2]**	Beacon Hill Mutual	0.3[3]	-2.3[5]	**4.6[5]**
Price, Rowe Cap App	3.8[1]	9.5[2]	**9.5[2]**	GIT Select Gro	-5.2[5]	0.5[5]	**4.1[5]**
Gabelli Asset	-0.1[3]	11.8[1]	**9.4[2]**	Mathers	-5.9[5]	-0.3[5]	**3.7[5]**
Nicholas Fund	-2.9[4]	5.0[4]	**9.4[2]**	Gintel	-16.5[5]	2.0[5]	**2.7[5]**
Reich & Tang Eqty	1.7[2]	10.4[1]	**9.3[2]**	Smith Hayes Value	-12.4[5]	2.5[5]	**2.6[5]**
Nbrgr-Ber Partners	-1.9[4]	10.3[2]	**9.3[2]**	MIM Stock Growth	-11.7[5]	-4.0[5]	**1.1[5]**
USAA Growth	3.4[1]	6.9[3]	**9.3[3]**	US Global Resrc	-9.7[5]	1.9[5]	**-1.4[5]**
Invesco Growth	-8.8[5]	3.4[4]	**9.2[3]**	Steadman Investment	-33.8[5]	-14.4[5]	**-6.7[5]**
Vangd Idx Extend Mkt	-1.8[4]	8.1[2]	**9.1[3]**	***GROWTH-INCOME FUNDS***			
Invesco Value Eqty	4.0[1]	6.4[3]	**9.1[3]**	Warbg Pincus Gro & Inc	7.6[1]	16.8[1]	**13.4[1]**
Drey/Laurel Contrn	-11.1[5]	6.0[3]	**9.1[3]**	Fidelity Gro & Inc	2.3[1]	10.9[1]	**12.5[1]**
Nicholas II SC	1.0[2]	5.5[4]	**9.0[3]**	Schafer Value	-4.3[5]	12.1[1]	**12.1[1]**
Papp L Roy Stock	-1.4[4]	4.4[4]	**8.9[3]**	Berger 101	-9.1[5]	5.7[4]	**11.8[1]**
Twentieth Cent Heritage	-6.3[5]	7.5[3]	**8.9[3]**	Mutual Qualified	5.7[1]	16.7[1]	**11.6[1]**
Wayne Hummer Growth	-0.9[3]	4.2[4]	**8.9[3]**	Mutual Beacon	5.6[1]	16.8[1]	**11.5[1]**
IAI Regional	0.7[2]	4.3[4]	**8.9[3]**	Berwyn	4.2[1]	15.6[1]	**11.0[1]**
Greenspring	2.9[2]	11.1[1]	**8.9[3]**	Mutual Shares	4.5[1]	15.3[1]	**10.8[1]**
Sentry	-1.1[4]	4.0[4]	**8.8[3]**	Invesco Indust Inc	-3.9[4]	4.2[4]	**10.8[1]**
Rightime	0.7[2]	4.5[4]	**8.6[3]**	Maxus Equity	1.1[2]	14.1[1]	**10.7[1]**
Nbrgr-Ber Manhtn	-3.6[4]	7.7[3]	**8.5[3]**	CGM Mutual	-9.7[5]	5.3[4]	**10.7[1]**
Gradison Estab Value	0.3[3]	10.1[2]	**8.4[3]**	Pierpont Equity	-0.6[3]	6.3[3]	**10.3[1]**
Royce Penn Mutual SC	-0.7[3]	8.7[2]	**8.4[3]**	Scudder Gro & Inc	2.6[1]	9.1[1]	**10.2[1]**
Portico Eqty Idx	1.0[2]	5.6[3]	**8.2[3]**	AARP Growth & Inc	3.1[1]	9.2[1]	**10.0[1]**
Babson UMB Stock	2.8[2]	6.8[3]	**8.2[3]**	Muhlenkamp	-7.3[5]	8.8[2]	**9.8[1]**
Gabelli Growth	-3.4[4]	4.0[4]	**8.1[3]**	Dodge & Cox Stock	5.2[1]	11.3[1]	**9.7[1]**
GE Elfun Trusts	0.2[3]	6.1[3]	**8.1[3]**	Dreyfus Discpl Stk	-1.2[4]	5.8[4]	**9.6[1]**
FundTrust Growth	-0.5[3]	6.8[3]	**8.0[3]**	Fidelity Fund	2.6[1]	9.6[1]	**9.2[1]**
Lindner Fund	-0.7[3]	10.3[2]	**8.0[4]**	Fidelity Eqty Inc	0.3[2]	11.7[1]	**9.2[2]**
Seafirst Blue Chip	2.0[2]	6.8[3]	**7.9[4]**	Gateway Idx Plus	5.6[1]	6.0[3]	**9.1[2]**
Babson Shadow Stk SC	-4.3[4]	9.0[2]	**7.9[4]**	Clipper	-2.5[4]	7.9[2]	**9.0[2]**
Dreman Contrarian	0.0[3]	6.7[3]	**7.6[4]**	Amer AAdv Gro & Inc	-1.0[3]	8.9[1]	**9.0[2]**
Warbg Pincus Cap App	-2.9[4]	6.5[3]	**7.6[4]**	Federated Stock	-0.4[3]	7.8[2]	**9.0[2]**
Evergreen Fund	0.7[2]	5.1[4]	**7.5[4]**	Vangd Quantitative	-0.6[3]	6.6[3]	**9.0[2]**
Flex-Fund Growth	-0.7[3]	4.2[4]	**7.5[4]**	Galaxy Eqty Value	3.5[1]	8.7[2]	**8.9[2]**
Armstrong Assoc	5.4[1]	9.0[2]	**7.4[4]**	Price, Rowe Gro & Inc	-0.1[3]	9.2[1]	**8.7[2]**
Royce Value	-1.6[4]	8.1[2]	**7.4[4]**	Selected Amer Sh	-3.2[4]	2.6[5]	**8.7[2]**
Legg Msn Total Ret	-7.2[5]	6.6[3]	**7.3[4]**	Strong Total Return	-1.4[4]	6.7[2]	**8.6[2]**
Wood Island Growth	-6.4[5]	4.0[4]	**7.2[4]**	Vangd Windsor	-0.1[3]	11.5[1]	**8.5[2]**
Dreyfus Third Cent	-7.5[5]	-0.3[5]	**7.2[4]**	Twentieth Cent Blncd	-0.1[2]	0.2[5]	**8.5[2]**
Volumetric	-2.1[4]	3.4[4]	**7.2[4]**	Vangd Idx 500	1.2[2]	6.1[3]	**8.5[2]**
Northeast Inv Gro	0.0[3]	0.5[5]	**7.1[4]**	Fiduciary Total Ret	-2.0[4]	6.3[3]	**8.4[2]**
Legg Msn Value	1.3[2]	7.9[2]	**7.1[4]**	Quant Gro & Inc	-0.7[3]	5.7[4]	**8.3[2]**
SBSF Fund	-5.6[5]	6.6[3]	**7.0[4]**	Weston: New Cent Cap	0.1[2]	4.6[4]	**8.3[2]**
Matrix Growth	-4.8[5]	3.0[5]	**6.9[4]**	Weitz Value	-9.8[5]	7.1[2]	**8.3[2]**
Valley Forge	5.9[1]	10.7[1]	**6.7[4]**	GE S&S Prg: Mutual	-1.8[4]	5.8[3]	**8.3[2]**
Harbor Growth	-11.4[5]	-0.6[5]	**6.6[4]**	WPG Growth & Inc	-5.5[5]	5.6[4]	**8.2[3]**

Stock and bond funds – ranked within objective continued

By 1990-1994 performance

No-Load Fund	Total return percent with quintile ranks by objective			No-Load Fund	Total return percent with quintile ranks by objective		
	1994	Annualized 3 years	5 years		1994	Annualized 3 years	5 years
Founders Blue Chip...	0.5[2]	4.7[4]	8.1[3]	Fidelity Puritan...	1.9[1]	12.6[1]	10.7[1]
Salomon Investors...	-1.3[4]	6.9[2]	8.1[3]	Warbg Pincus Balanced...	1.3[1]	8.2[2]	10.3[1]
Evergreen Amer Ret...	-2.9[4]	7.4[2]	7.9[3]	Eclipse Balanced...	0.0[2]	9.4[1]	10.0[1]
Lexington Corp Ldrs...	-0.8[3]	8.6[2]	7.9[3]	Lindner Dividend...	-3.3[4]	10.4[1]	9.9[1]
Caldwell Fund...	-1.1[3]	6.6[2]	7.9[3]	Price, Rowe Eqty Inc...	4.5[1]	11.1[1]	9.9[2]
Drey-Peoples Idx...	0.7[2]	5.9[3]	7.9[3]	Dodge & Cox Blncd...	2.1[1]	9.4[1]	9.8[2]
Vangd Star:Star...	-0.3[3]	6.9[2]	7.9[3]	Invesco Total Ret...	2.5[1]	8.2[2]	9.5[2]
GE Elfun Div Inc...	-0.3[3]	6.0[3]	7.9[3]	Vangd Convert...	-5.6[5]	8.4[1]	9.4[2]
Wright Qual Core Eqty...	-0.7[3]	2.7[5]	7.9[3]	Royce Equity Inc...	-3.2[4]	9.3[1]	9.0[2]
Vangd Windsor II...	-1.2[4]	7.9[2]	7.7[3]	Fidelity Balanced...	-5.3[4]	6.8[3]	9.0[2]
SIT Gro & Inc...	2.8[1]	3.6[4]	7.7[3]	Value Line Convert...	-5.2[4]	7.4[2]	8.9[2]
Westwood Equity...	2.3[1]	8.3[2]	7.6[3]	SBSF Convert...	-6.5[5]	7.7[2]	8.7[2]
Seafirst Asst Allc...	-0.2[3]	5.2[4]	7.5[3]	Amer AAdv Balncd...	-1.7[3]	7.2[2]	8.6[2]
MSB...	-1.7[4]	9.5[1]	7.3[3]	Vangd Asset Alloc...	-2.3[3]	6.0[3]	8.5[2]
TU&P Balanced...	1.5[2]	2.7[5]	7.2[3]	Vangd Wellesley Inc...	-4.4[4]	6.0[3]	8.4[3]
Bartlett Basic Value...	0.4[2]	7.3[2]	7.1[3]	Fidelity Utilities...	-5.3[4]	6.7[3]	8.4[3]
Htchks & Wly Eq Inc...	-3.5[4]	8.4[2]	7.0[3]	USAA Income Stk...	-0.7[2]	6.1[3]	8.4[3]
RSI Tr-Core Eqty...	1.3[2]	5.9[3]	6.9[4]	Htchks & Wly Blncd...	0.8[2]	7.5[2]	8.3[3]
Vangd Trust US...	-3.9[5]	6.2[3]	6.8[4]	FBP Contrn Blncd...	1.8[1]	8.2[2]	8.3[3]
FundTrust Gro & Inc...	-0.2[3]	7.1[2]	6.8[4]	Founders Balanced...	-1.9[3]	8.2[2]	8.1[3]
Stratton Growth...	7.1[1]	6.7[2]	6.7[4]	SteinRoe Total Ret...	-4.1[4]	5.1[4]	8.1[3]
Federated Stk & Bd...	-1.9[4]	5.2[4]	6.7[4]	Mairs & Power Inc...	-2.0[3]	4.8[4]	8.0[3]
Copley...	-7.7[5]	6.2[3]	6.7[4]	Vangd Wellington...	-0.4[2]	6.8[3]	7.9[3]
Lexington Gro & Inc...	-3.1[4]	7.2[2]	6.7[4]	Primary Income...	-2.6[3]	4.8[4]	7.7[3]
Smith Hayes Asst Allc...	-4.2[5]	2.3[5]	6.6[4]	Highmark Inc Eqty...	-0.6[2]	7.1[3]	7.7[3]
Portico Gro & Inc...	0.1[2]	4.1[4]	6.5[4]	Strong Asst Allc...	-1.5[3]	5.2[4]	7.4[4]
National Industries...	-0.2[3]	0.2[5]	6.5[4]	Smith Hayes Convert...	-8.0[5]	5.7[4]	7.4[4]
FundTrust Mgd Tot Ret...	-2.1[4]	4.3[4]	6.5[4]	Weston: New Cent Inc...	-2.4[3]	5.0[4]	7.2[4]
Wright Sel Blue Ch...	-3.5[4]	1.0[5]	6.3[4]	Managers Inc Eqty...	1.0[1]	7.7[2]	7.0[4]
Bridges Investment...	0.4[2]	3.2[4]	6.2[4]	Value Line Income...	-4.3[4]	1.8[5]	6.7[4]
Bascom Hill Invest...	3.9[1]	5.9[3]	6.1[4]	Avondale Total Ret...	2.3[1]	2.6[5]	6.5[4]
Harbor Value...	0.7[2]	5.5[4]	6.1[4]	SAFECO Income...	-1.1[2]	7.5[2]	6.4[4]
Evergreen Tot Ret...	-6.5[5]	5.1[4]	6.0[4]	Pax World...	2.6[1]	0.7[5]	6.4[4]
Analytic Option Eqty...	2.5[1]	5.1[4]	5.9[4]	Vangd Equity Inc...	-1.5[3]	7.2[3]	6.3[4]
Dreyfus Fund...	-4.2[5]	2.4[5]	5.9[4]	USAA Balanced...	-2.6[3]	5.2[4]	6.2[4]
Managers Balanced...	-3.0[4]	2.6[5]	5.8[5]	API Cap Inc...	-0.4[2]	4.6[4]	6.2[4]
Primary Trend...	-0.2[3]	3.7[4]	5.5[5]	Merriman Asst All...	-2.9[4]	5.8[3]	6.1[5]
RSI Tr-Value Eqty...	-1.1[3]	5.0[4]	5.5[5]	Stratton Month Div Sh...	-12.1[5]	1.1[5]	6.0[5]
Concorde Value...	-3.3[4]	6.7[2]	5.2[5]	Bascom Hill Blncd...	1.1[1]	4.6[4]	5.8[5]
IAI Gro & Inc...	-4.8[5]	2.9[5]	5.2[5]	Smith Hayes Blncd...	-4.4[4]	3.4[5]	5.4[5]
Reynolds Blue Chip...	-0.6[3]	-1.9[5]	5.1[5]	Amana Income...	-6.5[5]	2.1[5]	4.9[5]
Merriman Gro & Inc...	-0.2[3]	0.4[5]	4.6[5]	Advance Cap Blncd...	-2.7[4]	1.7[5]	4.2[5]
Lepercq-Istel...	-5.0[5]	4.4[5]	4.5[5]	US Income...	-10.3[5]	4.5[5]	3.6[5]
SCM Portfolio...	-0.9[3]	2.6[5]	4.4[5]	API Total Ret...	-6.8[5]	3.5[5]	3.0[5]
GIT Equity Inc...	-5.8[5]	2.1[5]	4.2[5]	Steadman Associated...	-20.5[5]	-2.4[5]	-2.8[5]
Gibraltar Eqty Gro...	0.4[2]	-1.8[5]	3.8[5]	**SECTOR & INDUSTRY FUNDS**			
Philadelphia...	-8.6[5]	8.8[2]	3.8[5]	Fidelity Sel Computer...	20.5[1]	23.7[1]	24.0[1]
MIM Stock Income...	-1.8[4]	0.8[5]	3.4[5]	Fidelity Sel Home Fincl...	2.7[2]	27.3[1]	23.5[1]
LMH Fund...	2.6[1]	6.1[3]	2.9[5]	Fidelity Sel Electronics...	17.2[1]	25.4[1]	23.1[1]
Advance Cap Eqty Univ...	-4.0[5]	0.1[5]	2.3[5]	Invesco Strat Tech...	5.3[2]	12.9[3]	22.5[1]
Bruce...	-16.1[5]	3.5[4]	2.1[5]	Fidelity Sel Technology...	11.1[1]	15.8[2]	22.3[1]
Gintel Erisa...	-21.3[5]	-1.8[5]	0.4[5]	Price, Rowe Sci/Tech...	15.8[1]	19.5[1]	22.0[1]
API Spec Mkts...	-7.4[5]	-1.0[5]	-2.2[5]	Fidelity Sel Software...	0.4[3]	21.7[1]	21.5[1]
INCOME FUNDS				Fidelity Sel Health...	21.4[1]	0.9[5]	18.6[1]
Evergreen Foundation...	-1.1[2]	11.1[1]	14.8[1]	Invesco Strat Fncl...	-5.9[4]	12.2[3]	18.0[1]
Fidelity Convert...	-1.7[3]	12.2[1]	13.7[1]	Fidelity Sel Medical Del...	19.8[1]	3.2[5]	17.8[2]
State Farm Blncd...	5.0[1]	4.6[4]	11.8[1]	Fidelity Sel Reg Banks...	0.2[3]	18.2[1]	16.8[2]
Berwyn Income...	-1.1[2]	12.1[1]	11.6[1]	Invesco Strat Leisure...	-5.0[3]	16.8[2]	16.7[2]
Fidelity Asset Mgr...	-6.5[5]	9.3[1]	11.1[1]	Fidelity Sel Auto...	-12.8[5]	18.7[1]	16.4[2]
Lexington Convert...	1.3[1]	6.2[3]	10.9[1]	Fidelity Sel Biotech...	-18.2[5]	-9.6[5]	16.2[2]

Stock and bond funds – ranked within objective continued
By 1990-1994 performance

No-Load Fund	Total return percent with quintile ranks by objective			No-Load Fund	Total return percent with quintile ranks by objective		
	1994	Annualized 3 years	5 years		1994	Annualized 3 years	5 years
Fidelity Sel Retail	-5.0[4]	9.4[3]	**15.9[2]**	Lexington World Emg	-13.8[5]	13.5[1]	**9.2[1]**
Vangd Spec-Health	9.5[1]	6.4[4]	**15.5[2]**	USAA International	2.7[2]	12.8[1]	**8.1[1]**
Fidelity Sel Transp	3.9[2]	18.5[1]	**15.0[2]**	Price, Rowe Int'l Stk	-0.8[3]	10.3[2]	**7.2[1]**
Fidelity Sel Broker	-17.3[5]	9.1[4]	**14.7[2]**	Babson Stew Ivry Int'l	1.3[2]	10.0[2]	**6.8[1]**
Fidelity Sel Financial	-3.7[3]	17.4[2]	**14.6[3]**	IAI International	0.5[3]	9.5[2]	**5.9[1]**
Invesco Strat Health	0.9[3]	-7.3[5]	**14.0[3]**	Bartlett Value Int'l	-0.5[3]	8.7[3]	**5.9[2]**
Fidelity Sel Chemicals	14.7[1]	12.1[3]	**13.4[3]**	Fidelity Int'l Gr & Inc	-2.9[4]	8.2[3]	**5.8[2]**
Fidelity Sel Food/Agr	6.1[2]	7.0[4]	**12.4[3]**	Wright Int'l Blue Ch	-1.6[3]	6.6[4]	**5.7[2]**
Fidelity Sel Multimedia	4.0[2]	20.3[1]	**12.1[3]**	Scudder Int'l Stk	-3.0[4]	8.9[2]	**5.6[2]**
Fidelity Sel Indust Equip	3.1[2]	18.1[2]	**12.0[3]**	Fidelity Europe	6.2[1]	9.6[2]	**5.5[2]**
Fidelity Real Estate	1.9[2]	11.0[3]	**11.7[3]**	Schroder Int'l Eqty	0.2[3]	11.9[2]	**5.4[2]**
Fidelity Sel Pap/Forest	14.1[1]	14.9[2]	**11.6[3]**	Dreyfus European	-3.1[4]	3.5[5]	**5.0[3]**
Fidelity Sel Telecomm	4.3[2]	16.0[2]	**11.2[3]**	Fidelity Overseas	1.3[2]	7.9[3]	**4.9[3]**
Fidelity Sel Const/Hous	-16.0[5]	10.1[3]	**11.2[3]**	Vangd Int'l Growth	0.7[3]	11.2[2]	**4.8[3]**
Fidelity Sel Indust Mat	8.2[2]	13.8[2]	**10.7[4]**	DFA UK Small Co	4.6[2]	5.5[4]	**4.7[3]**
Fidelity Sel Insurance	-0.3[3]	9.7[3]	**10.2[4]**	Price, Rowe Int'l Disc	-7.6[4]	8.0[3]	**4.1[3]**
Fidelity Sel Defense	1.8[3]	9.4[3]	**9.7[4]**	Invesco Europe	-3.0[4]	3.7[5]	**3.9[3]**
Fidelity Sel Leisure	-6.8[4]	14.8[2]	**9.3[4]**	Nomura Pacific Bas	4.2[2]	8.5[3]	**3.9[4]**
Century Shares	-3.9[3]	6.7[4]	**8.0[4]**	Vangd Trust Int'l	5.3[1]	7.8[3]	**3.9[4]**
Fidelity Sel Util Gro	-7.4[4]	4.8[4]	**6.9[4]**	Fidelity Pacific Basin	-2.8[3]	13.7[1]	**3.8[4]**
PRA Real Estate	3.0[2]	13.3[2]	**6.9[4]**	Fidelity Canada	-12.0[5]	2.4[5]	**3.6[4]**
Invesco Strat Util	-9.9[5]	6.6[4]	**6.9[4]**	RSI Tr-Int'l Eqty	0.8[3]	7.5[4]	**3.5[5]**
Evergreen Glob RE	-14.1[5]	12.8[3]	**5.5[5]**	Invesco Pacific Bas	4.7[2]	8.9[2]	**2.0[4]**
Vangd Spec-Energy	-1.6[3]	9.7[3]	**5.4[5]**	WPG International	-6.3[4]	6.7[4]	**0.8[4]**
Fidelity Sel Air Trans	-21.7[5]	3.0[5]	**4.1[5]**	Invesco Int'l Gro	0.6[3]	4.0[5]	**0.6[5]**
US Real Estate	-11.6[5]	-2.3[5]	**3.1[5]**	DFA Cont Sm Co	11.0[1]	3.7[5]	**0.5[5]**
Fidelity Sel Energy	0.4[3]	5.3[4]	**2.2[5]**	Drey/Laurel Int'l	3.5[2]	4.9[4]	**0.1[5]**
Rushmore Amer Gas Idx	-9.8[4]	5.4[4]	**1.6[5]**	Quant Int'l Eqty	9.1[1]	7.6[4]	**-0.3[5]**
Fidelity Sel Energy Serv	0.6[3]	8.0[4]	**-0.4[5]**	Japan (Scudder)	10.0[1]	4.2[5]	**-0.5[5]**
Fidelity Sel Envir Serv	-9.6[4]	-3.9[5]	**-1.4[5]**	BBK Int'l Equity	-12.6[5]	2.2[5]	**-2.6[5]**
Invesco Strat Enrgy	-7.3[4]	-2.1[5]	**-5.4[5]**	DFA Japan Sm Co	29.5[1]	3.0[5]	**-4.9[5]**
PRECIOUS METALS FUNDS				**FIXED-INCOME FUNDS - LONG TERM**			
Fidelity Sel Prec Metals	-1.2[1]	17.8[1]	**5.5[1]**	Fidelity Cap & Inc	-4.6[3]	15.1[1]	**13.7[1]**
Vangd Spec-Gold	-5.4[1]	13.8[2]	**4.2[1]**	Federated Hi Yld	-2.4[2]	9.6[1]	**11.9[1]**
Fidelity Sel Amer Gold	-15.5[4]	13.5[2]	**2.6[2]**	Northeast Inv Trust	2.2[1]	14.0[1]	**11.2[1]**
US World Gold	-16.9[5]	14.5[1]	**0.9[2]**	Fidelity Curr: Yen	12.6[1]	9.3[1]	**11.0[1]**
Blanchard Prec Metals	-15.2[3]	11.5[2]	**0.9[2]**	Vangd Hi Yld Corp	-1.7[1]	9.9[1]	**10.0[1]**
Scudder Gold	-7.4[2]	10.3[4]	**0.8[3]**	SAFECO Hi Yld Bd	-2.0[1]	9.3[1]	**9.3[1]**
Bull & Bear Gold	-13.8[3]	10.2[4]	**0.6[3]**	Value Line Agg Inc	-4.1[3]	8.6[1]	**9.3[1]**
Lexington Goldfund	-7.3[2]	11.3[3]	**0.5[4]**	PIMCO Tot Return	-3.6[3]	6.0[2]	**9.0[1]**
Benham Gold Eqty	-16.8[4]	11.3[3]	**-0.3[4]**	Vangd LT Corp	-5.3[4]	6.0[2]	**8.9[1]**
USAA Gold	-9.4[3]	9.7[4]	**-1.5[4]**	Benham Target 2005	-8.9[5]	6.7[2]	**8.8[1]**
Invesco Strat Gold	-27.9[5]	4.6[5]	**-4.0[5]**	Nicholas Income	-0.2[1]	7.5[1]	**8.6[1]**
US Gold Shares	-2.7[1]	2.3[5]	**-9.9[5]**	Invesco Select Inc	-1.2[1]	6.7[1]	**8.6[1]**
GLOBAL EQUITY FUNDS				Fidelity Inv Grd Bd	-5.4[4]	6.0[2]	**8.5[1]**
Founders Worldwide Gro	-2.2[3]	8.9[3]	**13.1[1]**	Price, Rowe High Yld	-8.1[5]	8.7[1]	**8.4[1]**
GE Elfun Glob Inc	-0.6[2]	11.6[1]	**7.8[1]**	Benham Target 2000	-6.9[4]	5.3[2]	**8.4[2]**
Scudder Global	-4.2[3]	9.5[2]	**7.5[2]**	Fidelity Curr: D-Mark	16.4[1]	5.1[2]	**8.4[2]**
Fremont Global	-4.2[3]	6.4[4]	**7.0[2]**	Benham Target 2010	-11.6[5]	7.0[1]	**8.3[2]**
USAA Cornerstone	-1.1[2]	9.2[2]	**6.6[3]**	CA Inv Tr-US Gov	-7.0[4]	5.3[2]	**8.3[2]**
Dreyfus Global Growth	-7.5[4]	3.1[5]	**6.4[3]**	Invesco High Yld	-5.1[3]	8.0[1]	**8.2[2]**
Lexington Global	1.8[1]	9.0[2]	**4.5[3]**	Benham Target 1995	0.8[1]	5.0[2]	**8.0[2]**
BBK Diversa	-9.4[4]	4.8[4]	**3.8[4]**	Portico Bond Immdex	-3.1[2]	5.0[2]	**7.9[2]**
Bull & Bear US & Overs	-13.1[5]	2.3[5]	**3.7[4]**	Scudder Income	-4.5[3]	4.7[3]	**7.8[2]**
Blanchard Glob Growth	-7.5[4]	5.0[4]	**3.7[5]**	GIT Max Income	-2.6[2]	7.9[1]	**7.8[2]**
Permanent Portfolio	-2.9[3]	4.8[5]	**3.6[5]**	Fidelity Gov Sec	-5.2[3]	4.7[3]	**7.8[2]**
INTERNATIONAL EQUITY FUNDS				GE S&S Prg: LT Inst	-2.5[2]	4.6[3]	**7.7[2]**
Harbor Int'l	5.4[1]	15.2[1]	**10.9[1]**	Vangd Prefrd Stk	-7.9[5]	4.1[4]	**7.7[2]**
Warbg Pincus Int'l	0.2[3]	13.2[1]	**10.8[1]**	Dreyfus A Bonds Plus	-6.1[4]	5.3[2]	**7.7[2]**
Managers Int'l Eqty	2.0[2]	13.7[1]	**9.4[1]**	Vangd LT Trsy	-7.0[4]	5.2[2]	**7.7[2]**

By 1990-1994 performance

No-Load Fund	1994	Annualized 3 years	Annualized 5 years
Scudder US Zero 2000...	-7.9[5]	4.9[2]	**7.7[3]**
Babson Bond-Port L...	-3.3[2]	5.3[2]	**7.7[3]**
GE Elfun Income...	-2.3[2]	4.5[3]	**7.6[3]**
Dreyfus 100% US Long...	-9.2[5]	4.4[3]	**7.6[3]**
SIT US Gov...	1.8[1]	4.8[3]	**7.6[3]**
RSI Tr-Act Mgd Bd...	-4.2[3]	4.4[3]	**7.5[3]**
Fidelity Curr: Sterling...	9.9[1]	-0.4[5]	**7.5[3]**
IAI Bond...	-4.9[3]	4.5[3]	**7.4[3]**
Benham Target 2015...	-14.1[5]	6.5[2]	**7.4[3]**
Managers Bond...	-7.2[4]	3.7[4]	**7.4[3]**
Wright Gov Oblig...	-8.7[5]	4.3[3]	**7.2[3]**
Advance Cap Bond...	-4.6[3]	4.4[3]	**7.1[3]**
Crowley Income...	-1.8[1]	4.9[3]	**7.0[3]**
AARP Hi Qual Bd...	-4.5[3]	4.0[4]	**6.9[3]**
Bull & Bear Glob Inc...	-13.4[5]	6.9[1]	**6.9[3]**
Price, Rowe Trsy Lng...	-5.7[4]	4.0[4]	**6.9[4]**
Pierpont Bond...	-3.0[2]	3.8[4]	**6.9[4]**
Wright Curr Inc...	-3.3[2]	3.2[5]	**6.9[4]**
Fidelity Spart Gov Inc...	-3.6[3]	3.5[4]	**6.8[4]**
Maxus Income...	-4.5[3]	4.6[3]	**6.7[4]**
PDC&J Preservation...	-2.4[2]	4.0[4]	**6.7[4]**
Federated Income...	-1.6[1]	3.2[5]	**6.7[4]**
Reich & Tang Gov...	-6.2[4]	3.7[4]	**6.7[4]**
Seafirst Bond...	-2.3[2]	3.6[4]	**6.6[4]**
Bull & Bear US Gov...	-4.7[3]	3.4[5]	**6.6[4]**
SteinRoe Gov Inc...	-3.3[2]	3.2[5]	**6.5[4]**
Babson UMB Bond...	-3.1[2]	3.8[4]	**6.5[4]**
Selected US Gov...	-2.2[1]	3.5[4]	**6.4[4]**
Highmark Bond...	-3.9[3]	3.8[4]	**6.3[4]**
Strong Income...	-1.3[1]	8.0[1]	**6.3[5]**
Benham Target 2020...	-17.7[5]	6.6[2]	**6.3[5]**
Wright Total Ret...	-6.6[4]	3.6[4]	**6.2[5]**
Weitz Fix Inc...	-2.3[2]	3.6[4]	**6.2[5]**
Rushmore Gov Long...	-9.9[5]	3.3[5]	**6.1[5]**
Federated ARMS...	0.3[1]	2.8[5]	**6.0[5]**
Invesco Gov Sec...	-7.2[4]	2.7[5]	**6.0[5]**
Value Line US Gov...	-10.6[5]	1.4[5]	**6.0[5]**
Crabbe Hsn Income...	-3.6[3]	2.8[5]	**6.0[5]**
Crabbe Hsn Gov Bd...	-2.1[1]	3.0[5]	**5.9[5]**
Smith Hayes Gov Qual...	-3.3[3]	2.8[5]	**5.8[5]**
Founders Gov Sec...	-7.5[5]	2.1[5]	**5.0[5]**
MIM Bond Income...	-3.6[3]	2.0[5]	**4.2[5]**
Capstone Gov Inc...	1.2[1]	2.7[5]	**2.7[5]**
FIXED-INCOME FUNDS - INTER TERM			
Scudder Int'l Bond...	-8.6[5]	4.5[2]	**11.0[1]**
Price, Rowe Int'l Bond...	-1.8[2]	6.4[1]	**10.5[1]**
Harbor Bond...	-3.7[4]	5.7[1]	**8.8[1]**
Janus Flex Inc...	-2.9[3]	7.9[1]	**8.6[1]**
Strong Gov Sec...	-3.4[4]	5.9[1]	**8.5[1]**
Dodge & Cox Income...	-2.9[3]	5.2[1]	**8.1[1]**
SteinRoe Income...	-4.1[4]	5.8[1]	**8.0[1]**
Columbia Fix Inc...	-3.5[4]	4.8[1]	**7.8[1]**
USAA Income...	-5.2[5]	4.1[3]	**7.7[1]**
Bernstein Inter Dur...	-3.2[3]	4.8[2]	**7.7[2]**
Vangd GNMA...	-1.0[1]	3.9[3]	**7.6[2]**
Benham GNMA Inc...	-1.5[1]	4.2[3]	**7.6[2]**
Fidelity Mrtg Sec...	1.9[1]	4.7[2]	**7.5[2]**
Fidelity Inter Bond...	-2.0[2]	5.2[1]	**7.5[2]**
Vangd Bond Idx Total...	-2.7[3]	4.6[2]	**7.4[2]**
Dreyfus 100% US Inter...	-4.0[4]	4.4[3]	**7.3[2]**

No-Load Fund	1994	Annualized 3 years	Annualized 5 years
Merriman Flex Bd...	-1.7[2]	5.6[1]	**7.2[2]**
Warbg Pincus Fix Inc...	-0.8[1]	5.6[1]	**7.2[2]**
Price, Rowe New Inc...	-2.2[2]	4.0[3]	**7.1[3]**
Price, Rowe GNMA...	-1.5[1]	3.6[4]	**7.1[3]**
SteinRoe Inter Bd...	-2.8[3]	4.5[2]	**7.1[3]**
Babson Bond-Port S...	-2.1[2]	4.3[3]	**7.0[3]**
Federated GNMA...	-2.5[2]	3.3[5]	**7.0[3]**
Asset Mgmt Inter Mrtg...	-1.6[1]	4.3[3]	**6.9[3]**
Lexington GNMA...	-2.1[2]	3.6[4]	**6.9[3]**
Asset Mgmt Mrtg Sec...	-2.3[2]	3.5[4]	**6.9[3]**
RSI Tr-Inter Bd...	-2.5[3]	3.6[4]	**6.9[3]**
Scudder GNMA...	-3.1[3]	3.2[5]	**6.8[3]**
Fidelity GNMA...	-2.0[2]	3.5[4]	**6.8[4]**
Legg Msn Invest Grd...	-4.6[5]	4.3[3]	**6.8[4]**
Legg Msn Gov Inter...	-1.7[2]	3.7[4]	**6.8[4]**
Dreyfus GNMA...	-2.8[3]	3.5[5]	**6.8[4]**
Federated Inter Gov...	-1.9[2]	3.8[3]	**6.8[4]**
SAFECO Inter Trsy...	-3.6[4]	4.4[2]	**6.7[4]**
Twentieth Cent LT Bd...	-4.5[5]	3.5[5]	**6.6[4]**
Rushmore Gov Inter...	-7.3[5]	3.5[4]	**6.6[4]**
FundTrust Income...	-3.9[4]	4.6[2]	**6.5[4]**
SAFECO GNMA...	-4.3[4]	3.0[5]	**6.4[5]**
GIT Gov Port...	-3.6[4]	3.7[4]	**6.3[5]**
Primary US Gov...	-3.1[3]	2.8[5]	**6.2[5]**
Fidelity Glob Bond...	-16.3[5]	2.1[5]	**6.1[5]**
Bartlett Fix Inc...	-2.9[3]	3.5[4]	**6.1[5]**
Galaxy Inter Bond...	-3.7[4]	2.9[5]	**5.9[5]**
Special Port Cash...	2.7[1]	4.4[2]	**5.9[5]**
WPG Gov Sec...	-8.7[5]	2.4[5]	**5.9[5]**
Managers Inter Mortg...	-25.0[5]	-2.6[5]	**3.8[5]**
FIXED-INCOME FUNDS - SHORT TERM			
Heartland US Gov...	-9.6[5]	5.4[1]	**8.6[1]**
PIMCO Low Dur...	0.6[2]	5.3[1]	**7.6[1]**
Strong Advantage...	3.6[1]	6.6[1]	**7.4[1]**
DFA 5 Yr Gov...	-3.2[5]	4.0[2]	**7.4[1]**
Dreyfus S-I Gov...	-0.8[4]	4.5[1]	**7.3[1]**
Federated US Gov...	-6.2[5]	4.8[1]	**7.3[1]**
Vangd ST Corp...	-0.1[3]	4.7[1]	**7.2[1]**
Invesco Inter Gov...	-1.7[4]	4.3[1]	**7.2[1]**
Warbg Pincus Inter Gov...	-1.8[4]	4.1[2]	**7.2[1]**
Portico ST Bond...	1.0[2]	4.7[1]	**7.1[2]**
Amer AAdv Ltd Inc...	1.3[2]	4.5[1]	**7.1[2]**
Price, Rowe Trsy Inter...	-2.2[4]	3.9[3]	**7.0[2]**
Benham Trsy Note...	-2.3[5]	3.9[3]	**6.9[2]**
AARP GNMA & Trsy...	-1.7[4]	3.5[4]	**6.9[2]**
Wasatch Income...	1.6[2]	3.4[4]	**6.8[2]**
Scudder ST Bond...	-2.9[5]	3.4[4]	**6.8[2]**
State Farm Interim...	-0.8[4]	4.1[2]	**6.7[2]**
Flex-Fund Bond...	-1.0[4]	3.4[4]	**6.7[3]**
Strong ST Bond...	-1.6[4]	4.7[1]	**6.7[3]**
Asset Mgmt ST Gov...	0.4[2]	4.2[2]	**6.7[3]**
Vangd ST Federal...	-0.9[4]	4.0[2]	**6.7[3]**
Columbia US Gov...	0.0[3]	3.9[3]	**6.7[3]**
Bernstein Short Dur...	0.5[2]	4.1[2]	**6.6[3]**
Nbrgr-Ber Ltd Mat...	-0.3[3]	3.8[3]	**6.4[3]**
Fidelity Spart Ltd Mat...	-1.0[4]	3.7[3]	**6.3[3]**
Wright Near Term...	-3.1[5]	3.6[4]	**6.3[3]**
Fidelity ST Bond...	-4.1[5]	4.0[2]	**6.3[4]**
Dreman Fixed Inc...	-1.2[4]	3.3[4]	**6.3[4]**
Drey/Laurel ST Bd...	0.2[2]	3.0[5]	**6.1[4]**

Stock and bond funds – ranked within objective continued

By 1990-1994 performance

No-Load Fund	Total return percent with quintile ranks by objective			No-Load Fund	Total return percent with quintile ranks by objective		
		Annualized				**Annualized**	
	1994	3 years	5 years		1994	3 years	5 years
Bernstein Gov Sht	0.4²	3.5⁴	**6.1⁴**	Dreyfus MA TE	-6.0³	4.3⁴	**6.3³**
Managers Sht & Int	-8.4⁵	3.5⁴	**6.0⁴**	Twentieth Cent TE Long	-5.6²	4.4³	**6.3³**
GS ST Gov Agency	0.4²	3.8³	**6.0⁴**	GE Elfun TE Inc	-5.8²	4.6³	**6.3³**
Federated S-I Gov	0.7²	3.4⁴	**5.9⁴**	Fidelity Insur TF	-7.7⁴	4.3⁴	**6.3³**
DFA 1 Yr Fix Inc	2.5¹	4.0²	**5.9⁴**	Dreyfus Muni Bond	-7.0³	4.3⁴	**6.2³**
Price, Rowe ST Bond	-2.9⁵	2.8⁵	**5.7⁵**	Dreyfus NY TE	-7.0³	4.5³	**6.2⁴**
Twentieth Cent Gov ST	-0.6³	2.6⁵	**5.4⁵**	Dreyfus NY Insur	-6.6³	4.0⁴	**6.2⁴**
Federated ST Income	-0.5³	3.6³	**5.3⁵**	Fidelity Muni Bd	-8.6⁵	4.0⁴	**6.1⁴**
PIMCO Short-Term	2.9¹	3.7³	**5.2⁵**	USAA TE Long	-7.9⁴	4.0⁴	**6.1⁴**
IAI Reserve	2.7¹	3.1⁴	**5.1⁵**	Fidelity NY Hi Yld	-8.0⁴	4.2⁴	**6.1⁴**
Nbrgr-Ber Ultra Sht	2.2¹	3.0⁴	**5.0⁵**	Fidelity NY Insured	-8.0⁴	4.1⁴	**6.1⁴**
RSI Tr-ST Invest	3.4¹	3.0⁵	**4.5⁵**	Columbia Muni Bd	-4.7¹	4.0⁴	**6.1⁴**
Permanent Treasy	3.3¹	2.8⁵	**4.2⁵**	Fidelity Spart CT Hi Yld	-7.0³	4.3⁴	**6.0⁴**
Managers ST Gov	-6.2⁵	0.4⁵	**3.7⁵**	Babson TF Long	-7.4⁴	4.1⁴	**6.0⁴**
TAX-FREE FUNDS - LONG TERM				SAFECO CA TF	-9.2⁵	3.6⁵	**6.0⁴**
Vangd Muni Hi Yld	-5.1²	5.5¹	**7.4¹**	Value Line TE Hi Yld	-6.9³	3.8⁵	**5.9⁴**
Drey-General Muni	-7.3⁴	4.9³	**7.4¹**	Wright Insur TF	-4.1¹	4.4³	**5.9⁴**
Vangd PA Insur LT	-4.5¹	5.8¹	**7.3¹**	Rushmore VA TF	-5.0¹	4.7³	**5.9⁴**
Dupree KY TF Inc	-2.9¹	6.1¹	**7.3¹**	USAA CA Bond	-9.3⁵	3.4⁵	**5.8⁴**
Strong Muni Bond	-4.6¹	6.2¹	**7.3¹**	Fidelity Hi Yld TF	-7.4⁴	3.5⁵	**5.8⁴**
Scudder MA TF	-6.2³	5.9¹	**7.2¹**	Fidelity MN TF	-5.9³	4.4³	**5.8⁴**
Vangd Muni Long	-5.8²	5.3¹	**7.2¹**	Fidelity CA Insur	-10.2⁵	3.7⁵	**5.8⁵**
Price, Rowe TF Hi Yld	-4.4¹	5.8¹	**7.2¹**	Fidelity CA Hi Yld	-8.9⁵	3.9⁵	**5.7⁵**
Drey-General NY	-7.2⁴	5.3²	**7.2¹**	Dreyfus Insur Muni	-8.6⁵	3.5⁵	**5.7⁵**
Fidelity Spart PA Hi Yld	-5.1¹	5.4¹	**7.2¹**	Managers Muni Bd	-5.6²	4.0⁴	**5.7⁵**
Benham Nat TF Long	-6.2³	5.4¹	**7.1¹**	SteinRoe Hi Yld Muni	-4.2¹	3.7⁵	**5.7⁵**
Vangd NJ Insur LT	-5.2²	5.5¹	**7.1¹**	Dreyfus CA TE	-7.1⁴	3.5⁵	**5.5⁵**
Vangd NY Insur	-5.6²	5.4¹	**7.0¹**	Rushmore MD TF	-5.2²	4.6³	**5.4⁵**
Vangd Muni Insur LT	-5.6²	5.2²	**7.0¹**	GIT TF AZ	-8.7⁵	3.5⁵	**5.3⁵**
Fidelity Agg TF	-5.9²	5.3¹	**7.0¹**	GIT TF VA	-8.3⁴	3.5⁵	**5.2⁵**
Dreyfus NJ Muni	-6.0³	4.9²	**6.9¹**	Lexington TE Bond	-6.5³	3.4⁵	**5.2⁵**
Fidelity Spart NJ Hi Yld	-5.7²	5.0²	**6.9¹**	Northwest Idaho TE	-3.4¹	3.8⁵	**5.2⁵**
Price, Rowe NY TF	-5.9²	5.6¹	**6.9²**	GIT TF Nat	-8.8⁵	3.3⁵	**5.1⁵**
Scudder Hi Yld TF	-8.4⁵	5.0²	**6.8²**	GIT TF MO	-8.5⁵	3.2⁵	**4.9⁵**
Scudder Mgd Muni	-6.0³	5.1²	**6.8²**	Bull & Bear Muni Inc	-9.8⁵	1.9⁵	**4.5⁵**
Fidelity MA Hi Yld	-6.1³	5.0²	**6.7²**	Fundamental NY Muni	-19.8⁵	0.3⁵	**3.0⁵**
Price, Rowe TF Inc	-5.5²	5.3²	**6.7²**	Fundamental CA Muni	-19.9⁵	-0.2⁵	**2.4⁵**
SIT TF Income	-0.6¹	5.7¹	**6.7²**	Fundamental Hi Yld Muni	-12.9⁵	-0.9⁵	**0.2⁵**
Fidelity OH TF	-5.6²	4.9²	**6.7²**	**TAX-FREE FUNDS - INTER TERM**			
Scudder CA TF	-7.3⁴	4.9³	**6.7²**	Vangd Muni Inter	-2.1¹	5.9¹	**7.4¹**
Vangd CA Insur LT	-5.7²	5.2²	**6.7²**	Scudder Medium TF	-3.5³	5.3¹	**6.8¹**
Scudder PA TF	-5.9²	5.1²	**6.7²**	USAA TE Inter	-4.0³	5.1¹	**6.6¹**
Scudder NY TF	-7.2⁴	4.9²	**6.6²**	Fidelity Ltd Muni	-4.8⁴	5.0²	**6.6²**
Scudder OH TF	-5.5²	4.9²	**6.6²**	Dreyfus Inter Muni	-4.6⁴	5.0²	**6.5²**
Benham CA Insur	-6.5³	5.0²	**6.6²**	SteinRoe Inter Muni	-3.5³	4.9²	**6.5²**
Value Line NY TE	-7.7⁴	4.8³	**6.6²**	Dreyfus NY Inter	-5.1⁵	5.0²	**6.4³**
Price, Rowe MD TF	-5.0¹	5.1²	**6.5²**	Warbg Pincus NY Muni	-0.6¹	5.5¹	**6.4³**
State Farm Muni Bd	-2.5¹	4.9³	**6.5²**	Benham Nat TF Inter	-3.4³	4.5³	**6.4³**
Drey-General CA	-7.0³	4.7³	**6.5³**	Benham CA Inter	-3.7³	4.5³	**6.2³**
Pierpont TE Bond	-2.8¹	5.0²	**6.5³**	Twentieth Cent TE Inter	-2.1¹	4.6³	**6.0⁴**
Benham CA Long	-6.4³	4.8³	**6.5³**	Federated Inter Muni	-3.8³	4.2⁴	**5.9⁴**
Price, Rowe CA TF	-5.7²	4.9³	**6.5³**	Bernstein NY Muni	-2.5²	4.2⁴	**5.9⁴**
AARP Insur TF Gen	-6.2³	4.7³	**6.5³**	Bernstein Dvsfd Muni	-2.5²	4.1⁵	**5.8⁵**
Benham CA Hi Yld	-5.3²	5.4¹	**6.5³**	US Tax Free	-5.2⁵	4.3⁴	**5.7⁵**
CA Inv Tr-CA TF	-8.6⁵	4.5³	**6.4³**	Nbrgr-Ber Muni	-4.0³	4.0⁵	**5.6⁵**
SAFECO Muni Bd	-8.2⁴	4.0⁴	**6.4³**	**TAX-FREE FUNDS - SHORT TERM**			
Fidelity Spart CA Hi Yld	-9.0⁵	4.1⁴	**6.4³**	Vangd Muni Ltd	0.1³	4.3³	**5.8¹**
Invesco TF Long	-7.5⁴	4.1⁴	**6.3³**	Fidelity Spart S-I Muni	-0.1⁴	4.4¹	**5.7¹**
SteinRoe Mgd Muni	-5.5²	4.3⁴	**6.3³**	Dreyfus S-I Muni	-0.3⁴	4.3²	**5.6²**
Fidelity MI Hi Yld	-7.5⁴	4.9³	**6.3³**	Dupree KY Sht-Med	1.0²	4.5¹	**5.5²**

102

Stock and bond funds – ranked within objective *continued*

By 1990-1994 performance

No-Load Fund	Total return percent with quintile ranks by objective			No-Load Fund	Total return percent with quintile ranks by objective		
	1994	Annualized 3 years	Annualized 5 years		1994	Annualized 3 years	Annualized 5 years
Babson TF Short...	-1.7[5]	3.7[4]	**5.4[3]**				
Price, Rowe TF S-I...	0.3[3]	4.2[3]	**5.3[3]**				
USAA TE Short...	0.8[2]	4.1[3]	**5.2[4]**				
Vangd Muni Short...	1.6[1]	3.4[4]	**4.8[4]**				
Federated ST Muni...	0.1[3]	3.1[5]	**4.5[5]**				
Managers ST Muni...	0.3[2]	2.8[5]	**3.9[5]**				

Stock and bond funds – ranked within objective *continued*

CHAPTER 6

Stock and bond funds — top 50

Ranked by 1994 performance   *Ranked by 1992-1994 performance*

No-Load Fund	Objective	Total return percent Annualized 1994	3 yrs.
1 DFA Japan Sm Co...	int'l	29.5	3.0
2 PBHG Emg Growth SC...	agg gr	23.8	—
3 Robrtsn Stph Val Gro...	agg gr	23.1	—
4 Fidelity Sel Health...	sector	21.4	0.9
5 Montgmry Growth...	growth	20.9	—
6 Fidelity Sel Computer...	sector	20.5	23.7
7 Fidelity Sel Medical Del...	sector	19.8	3.2
8 Strong Growth...	growth	17.3	—
9 Fidelity Sel Electronics...	sector	17.2	25.4
10 Fidelity Japan...	int'l	16.5	—
11 Fidelity Curr: D-Mark...	fix-inc	16.4	5.1
12 AIC: Clvr Cap Eq...	growth	16.0	11.9
13 Janus Mercury...	agg gr	15.9	—
14 Price, Rowe Sci/Tech...	sector	15.8	19.5
15 Fidelity Sel Devel Comm...	sector	15.1	21.1
16 Price, Rowe Japan...	int'l	15.1	6.3
17 Fidelity Sel Chemicals...	sector	14.7	12.1
18 Fidelity Sel Pap/Forest...	sector	14.1	14.9
19 Berger Sm Co Growth...	agg gr	13.7	—
20 Twentieth Cent Giftrust...	agg gr	13.5	20.7
21 Vangd Idx Pacific...	int'l	12.9	7.8
22 Fidelity Curr: Yen...	fix-inc	12.6	9.3
23 Crabbe Hsn Spec SC...	growth	11.7	26.1
24 Wright Equi Dutch...	int'l	11.7	7.0
25 Vangd Primecap...	growth	11.4	12.7
26 Fidelity Sel Technology...	sector	11.1	15.8
27 DFA Cont Sm Co...	int'l	11.0	3.7
28 Retrmt Sys: Emg Gr SC...	agg gr	10.4	17.4
29 Japan (Scudder)...	int'l	10.0	4.2
30 SAFECO Equity...	growth	9.9	16.3
31 Fidelity Curr: Sterling...	fix-inc	9.9	-0.4
32 Fidelity Blue Chip...	growth	9.8	13.2
33 Vangd Spec-Health...	sector	9.5	6.4
34 Invesco Balanced...	income	9.5	—
35 Quant Int'l Eqty...	int'l	9.1	7.6
36 Kaufmann SC...	agg gr	9.0	12.8
37 Longleaf Partners...	growth	9.0	17.1
38 Janus Enterprise...	growth	8.9	—
39 Yacktman...	growth	8.8	—
40 DFA Int'l High BTM...	int'l	8.8	—
41 Cohen & Steers Realty...	sector	8.3	15.5
42 Fidelity Sel Indust Mat...	sector	8.2	13.8
43 Wasatch MidCap...	growth	8.1	—
44 Robrtsn Stph Emg Gro SC...	agg gr	8.0	4.1
45 Papp L Roy Amer Abrd...	int'l	7.8	4.8
46 Fidelity Value...	growth	7.6	17.0
47 Warbg Pincus Gro & Inc...	gr-inc	7.6	16.8
48 Cornerstone Growth...	agg gr	7.6	2.9
49 First Omaha Eqty...	gr-inc	7.4	—
50 Baron Asset SC...	agg gr	7.4	14.7

No-Load Fund	Objective	Total return percent Annualized 1994	3 yrs.
1 Fidelity Sel Home Fincl...	sector	2.7	27.3
2 Oakmark...	growth	3.3	26.1
3 Crabbe Hsn Spec SC...	growth	11.7	26.1
4 Fidelity Sel Electronics...	sector	17.2	25.4
5 PBHG Growth...	agg gr	4.7	25.4
6 Fidelity Sel Computer...	sector	20.5	23.7
7 Fidelity Sel Software...	sector	0.4	21.7
8 Fidelity Sel Devel Comm...	sector	15.1	21.1
9 Twentieth Cent Giftrust...	agg gr	13.5	20.7
10 Fidelity Sel Multimedia...	sector	4.0	20.3
11 Skyline Special Eqty...	agg gr	-1.1	20.0
12 Heartland Value SC...	agg gr	1.7	19.8
13 Price, Rowe Sci/Tech...	sector	15.8	19.5
14 Fidelity Sel Auto...	sector	-12.8	18.7
15 Fidelity Sel Transp...	sector	3.9	18.5
16 Royce Micro-Cap SC...	agg gr	3.6	18.3
17 Fidelity Sel Reg Banks...	sector	0.2	18.2
18 Fidelity Sel Indust Equip...	sector	3.1	18.1
19 Fidelity Sel Prec Metals...	prec met	-1.2	17.8
20 Fidelity Low Pr Stk SC...	growth	4.8	17.6
21 Retrmt Sys: Emg Gr SC...	agg gr	10.4	17.4
22 Fidelity Sel Financial...	sector	-3.7	17.4
23 Price, Rowe New Asia...	int'l	-19.2	17.1
24 Longleaf Partners...	growth	9.0	17.1
25 Fidelity Value...	growth	7.6	17.0
26 Mutual Beacon...	gr-inc	5.6	16.8
27 Warbg Pincus Gro & Inc...	gr-inc	7.6	16.8
28 Invesco Strat Leisure...	sector	-5.0	16.8
29 Mutual Qualified...	gr-inc	5.7	16.7
30 Fidelity Cap Apprec...	agg gr	2.5	16.7
31 Fidelity Emg Mkts...	int'l	-17.9	16.4
32 SAFECO Equity...	growth	9.9	16.3
33 Fidelity Sel Telecomm...	sector	4.3	16.0
34 Fidelity Sel Technology...	sector	11.1	15.8
35 Berwyn...	gr-inc	4.2	15.6
36 Cohen & Steers Realty...	sector	8.3	15.5
37 DFA US 9-10 Sm Co SC...	agg gr	3.1	15.4
38 Mutual Shares...	gr-inc	4.5	15.3
39 Harbor Int'l...	int'l	5.4	15.2
40 Fidelity Cap & Inc...	fix-inc	-4.6	15.1
41 Fidelity Spart Hi Inc...	fix-inc	3.2	15.1
42 Acorn SC...	growth	-7.5	15.0
43 Fidelity Sel Pap/Forest...	sector	14.1	14.9
44 Fidelity Sel Leisure...	sector	-6.8	14.8
45 Baron Asset SC...	agg gr	7.4	14.7
46 Strong Common Stk SC...	growth	-0.5	14.6
47 US World Gold...	prec met	-16.9	14.5
48 First Eagle America...	agg gr	-2.6	14.5
49 Invesco Emg Gro SC...	agg gr	-3.7	14.3
50 Fidelity Worldwide...	global	3.0	14.3

Stock and bond funds – top 50 *continued*

Ranked by 1990-1994 performance

No-Load Fund	Objective	1994	Annualized 5 yrs.
1 Fidelity Sel Computer...	sector	20.5	**24.0**
2 Fidelity Sel Home Fincl...	sector	2.7	**23.5**
3 Fidelity Sel Electronics...	sector	17.2	**23.1**
4 Invesco Strat Tech...	sector	5.3	**22.6**
5 Fidelity Sel Technology...	sector	11.1	**22.3**
6 Twentieth Cent Giftrust...	agg gr	13.5	**22.0**
7 Price, Rowe Sci/Tech...	sector	15.8	**22.0**
8 PBHG Growth...	agg gr	4.8	**22.0**
9 Fidelity Sel Software...	sector	0.4	**21.5**
10 Crabbe Hsn Spec SC...	growth	11.7	**19.5**
11 Twentieth Cent Ultra...	agg gr	-3.6	**19.4**
12 Kaufmann SC...	agg gr	9.0	**19.3**
13 CGM Capital Dev...	agg gr	-22.9	**18.7**
14 Fidelity Sel Health...	sector	21.4	**18.6**
15 Fidelity Blue Chip...	growth	9.9	**18.4**
16 Skyline Special Eqty...	agg gr	-1.2	**18.1**
17 Invesco Strat Fncl...	sector	-5.9	**18.0**
18 Fidelity Sel Medical Del...	sector	19.8	**17.8**
19 Oberweis Emg Growth SC...	agg gr	-3.5	**17.7**
20 Fidelity Contrafund...	agg gr	-1.1	**17.5**
21 Wasatch Agg Eqty SC...	agg gr	5.5	**17.0**
22 Berger 100...	agg gr	-6.7	**17.0**
23 Fidelity Sel Reg Banks...	sector	0.2	**16.8**
24 Invesco Strat Leisure...	sector	-5.0	**16.7**
25 Founders Discovery SC...	agg gr	-7.8	**16.7**
26 Meridian...	growth	0.5	**16.6**
27 Fidelity Sel Auto...	sector	-12.8	**16.4**
28 Heartland Value SC...	agg gr	1.7	**16.3**
29 Brandywine...	agg gr	0.0	**16.3**
30 Fidelity Sel Biotech...	sector	-18.2	**16.2**
31 Fidelity Sel Retail...	sector	-5.0	**15.9**
32 Invesco Dynamics...	agg gr	-2.0	**15.6**
33 Vangd Spec-Health...	sector	9.5	**15.5**
34 Fidelity Sel Transp...	sector	3.9	**15.0**
35 RSI Tr-Emg Gro SC...	agg gr	3.5	**14.8**
36 Evergreen Foundation...	income	-1.1	**14.8**
37 Fidelity Sel Broker...	sector	-17.3	**14.7**
38 Fidelity Sel Financial...	sector	-3.7	**14.6**
39 Robrtsn Stph Emg Gro SC...	agg gr	8.0	**14.4**
40 MIM Stock Apprec...	agg gr	-10.4	**14.3**
41 Harbor Cap App...	growth	3.4	**14.1**
42 Invesco Strat Health...	sector	0.9	**14.0**
43 Strong Discovery SC...	agg gr	-5.7	**13.8**
44 Fidelity Cap & Inc...	fix-inc	-4.6	**13.8**
45 Fidelity Convert...	income	-1.7	**13.7**
46 Mairs & Power Gro...	growth	5.6	**13.6**
47 Fidelity Growth Co...	agg gr	-2.2	**13.5**
48 Warbg Pincus Gro & Inc...	gr-inc	7.6	**13.4**
49 Fidelity Sel Chemicals...	sector	14.7	**13.4**
50 Wm Blair Growth...	growth	6.5	**13.4**

Ranked by 1985-1994 performance

No-Load Fund	Objective	1994	Annualized 10 yrs.
1 Twentieth Cent Giftrust...	agg gr	13.5	**25.6**
2 Fidelity Sel Health...	sector	21.4	**21.5**
3 Invesco Strat Health...	sector	0.9	**20.6**
4 Vangd Spec-Health...	sector	9.5	**20.0**
5 Invesco Strat Leisure...	sector	-5.0	**19.8**
6 CGM Capital Dev...	agg gr	-22.9	**19.7**
7 Berger 100...	agg gr	-6.7	**19.2**
8 Fidelity Overseas...	int'l	1.3	**19.1**
9 Invesco Strat Tech...	sector	5.3	**18.9**
10 Twentieth Cent Ultra...	agg gr	-3.6	**18.8**
11 Fidelity Contrafund...	agg gr	-1.1	**18.5**
12 Fidelity OTC SC...	agg gr	-2.7	**18.1**
13 Price, Rowe Int'l Stk...	int'l	-0.8	**18.0**
14 Fidelity Magellan...	agg gr	-1.8	**17.9**
15 Janus Venture SC...	growth	5.5	**17.5**
16 Fidelity Sel Leisure...	sector	-6.8	**17.3**
17 Vangd Int'l Growth...	int'l	0.7	**17.1**
18 Fidelity Growth Co...	agg gr	-2.2	**17.0**
19 Vangd Trust Int'l...	int'l	5.3	**16.8**
20 Acorn SC...	growth	-7.5	**16.5**
21 Scudder Int'l Stk...	int'l	-3.0	**16.2**
22 SAFECO Equity...	growth	9.9	**16.1**
23 IAI Regional...	growth	0.7	**15.7**
24 Japan (Scudder)...	int'l	10.0	**15.6**
25 Fidelity Retrmnt Growth...	agg gr	0.1	**15.6**
26 SteinRoe Special...	growth	-3.3	**15.6**
27 SIT Growth SC...	agg gr	-0.5	**15.6**
28 Vangd Primecap...	growth	11.4	**15.5**
29 Dodge & Cox Stock...	gr-inc	5.2	**15.5**
30 Founders Growth...	growth	-3.4	**15.4**
31 Twentieth Cent Growth...	agg gr	-1.5	**15.4**
32 Mutual Beacon...	gr-inc	5.6	**15.4**
33 Heartland Value SC...	agg gr	1.7	**15.3**
34 State Farm Blncd...	income	5.0	**15.2**
35 Janus Fund...	growth	-1.1	**15.1**
36 Mutual Qualified...	gr-inc	5.7	**15.1**
37 Special Port Stk...	agg gr	-7.2	**15.0**
38 Twentieth Cent Vista...	agg gr	4.7	**15.0**
39 Meridian...	growth	0.5	**14.9**
40 Invesco Indust Inc...	gr-inc	-3.9	**14.8**
41 CGM Mutual...	gr-inc	-9.7	**14.8**
42 Founders Special...	agg gr	-4.9	**14.8**
43 Babson Enterprise SC...	agg gr	2.5	**14.8**
44 Mutual Shares...	gr-inc	4.5	**14.7**
45 Invesco Dynamics...	agg gr	-2.0	**14.7**
46 Invesco Pacific Bas...	int'l	4.7	**14.6**
47 Lexington Corp Ldrs...	gr-inc	-0.8	**14.6**
48 State Farm Growth...	growth	6.0	**14.6**
49 Managers Spec Eqty SC...	agg gr	-2.0	**14.6**
50 RSI Tr-Int'l Eqty...	int'l	0.8	**14.4**

CHAPTER 7

No-load fund groups

Families with 3 or more funds including one stock or bond fund
Arranged in alphabetical order by group and risk within group

Fund group/fund	Objective	Total Net Assets $ Millions 12/31/94	1994	3 years 1992-1994	5 years 1990-1994	1994	3 years ending 1994	5 years ending 1994
			Annualized Total Return % with quintile ranks by obj			Post quintile ranks for your funds here		
American Assoc of Retired Persons (Scudder)....								
AARP Capital Growth...	agg gr	631.6	-10.0[5]	3.0[4]	5.3[5]	___	___	___
AARP Growth & Inc...	gr-inc	2,298.7	3.1[1]	9.2[1]	10.0[1]	___	___	___
AARP Blncd Stk & Bd...	income	177.9	—	—	—	___	___	___
AARP GNMA & Trsy...	fix-inc	5,248.9	-1.7[4]	3.5[4]	6.9[2]	___	___	___
AARP Hi Qual Bd...	fix-inc	529.1	-4.5[3]	4.0[4]	6.9[3]	___	___	___
AARP Insur TF Gen...	tax-free	1,748.6	-6.2[3]	4.7[3]	6.5[3]	___	___	___
AARP Hi Qual MM...	money mkt	375.2	3.5[5]	2.8[5]	4.3[5]	___	___	___
AARP Hi Qual TF MM...	money mkt TF	131.4	2.0[5]	1.9[5]	—	___	___	___
Your average...		11,141.4				___	___	___
Advance Capital Funds...								
Advance Cap Eqty Univ...	gr-inc	12.6	-4.0[5]	0.1[5]	2.3[5]	___	___	___
Advance Cap Blncd...	income	44.2	-2.7[4]	1.7[5]	4.2[5]	___	___	___
Advance Cap Bond...	fix-inc	4.0	-4.6[3]	4.4[3]	7.1[3]	___	___	___
Advance Cap LT Inc...	fix-inc	1.2	-6.5[4]	—	—	___	___	___
Advance Cap Ret Inc...	fix-inc	84.2	-5.3[4]	—	—	___	___	___
Your average...		146.2				___	___	___
Advisors Inner Circle Funds								
AIC: Pin Oak SC...	agg gr	10.2	0.0[2]	—	—	___	___	___
AIC: Clvr Cap Eq...	growth	27.6	16.0[1]	11.9[1]	—	___	___	___
AIC: Rlstn Midwest Gr...	growth	31.4	7.2[1]	—	—	___	___	___
AIC: White Oak...	growth	5.8	7.2[1]	—	—	___	___	___
AIC: Rlstn Gr & Inc...	gr-inc	17.4	1.7[2]	—	—	___	___	___
AIC: Clvr Cap Fix...	fix-inc	9.8	-2.8[2]	4.8[3]	—	___	___	___
AIC: Rlstn Gov Sec...	fix-inc	7.4	-6.5[4]	—	—	___	___	___
Your average...		109.6				___	___	___
Alliance Capital...								
Alliance World Inc...	fix-inc	84.1	-4.2[3]	—	—	___	___	___
Alliance Money Res...	money mkt	1,808.5	3.3[5]	3.0[4]	4.5[4]	___	___	___
Alliance Cap Res...	money mkt	2,319.7	3.4[5]	3.0[4]	4.5[4]	___	___	___
Alliance Muni MM...	money mkt TF	1,061.2	2.2[5]	2.2[4]	3.2[4]	___	___	___
Alliance Gov Res...	money mkt gov	2,068.1	3.3[5]	2.9[5]	4.3[5]	___	___	___
Your average...		7,341.6				___	___	___
Amcore Vintage Funds								
Amcor Vntg Eqty...	growth	131.1	2.0[2]	—	—	___	___	___
Amcor Vntg Fix Inc...	fix-inc	79.5	-3.1[2]	—	—	___	___	___
Amcor Vntg Inter TF...	tax-free	28.9	-5.4[5]	—	—	___	___	___
Amcor Vntg Gov Obl MM...	money mkt	117.6	3.7[4]	—	—	___	___	___
Your average...		357.1				___	___	___
American AAdvantage Funds								
Amer AAdv Int'l...	int'l	21.6	1.2[2]	8.8[3]	—	___	___	___
Amer AAdv Gro & Inc...	gr-inc	21.3	-1.0[3]	8.9[1]	9.0[2]	___	___	___

See Chapter 3 for explanation of symbols

Families with 3 or more funds including one stock or bond fund
Arranged in alphabetical order by group and risk within group

Fund group/fund	Objective	Total Net Assets $ Millions 12/31/94	1994	3 years 1992-1994	5 years 1990-1994	1994	3 years ending 1994	5 years ending 1994
				Annualized Total Return % with quintile ranks by obj			Post quintile ranks for your funds here	
Amer AAdv Balncd	income	212.5	-1.7[3]	7.2[2]	8.6[2]	___	___	___
Amer AAdv Ltd Inc	fix-inc	73.6	1.3[2]	4.5[1]	7.1[2]	___	___	___
Amer AAdv Mileage MM	money mkt	64.7	3.9[2]	3.6[1]	—	___	___	___
Amer AAdv Muni Miles	money mkt TF	10.9	2.4[3]	—	—	___	___	___
Amer AAdv Trsy MM	money mkt gov	9.3	3.8[2]	—	—	___	___	___
Your average		413.9				___	___	___
Analytic Investment Management								
Analytic Enhncd Eqty	growth	1.5	-0.4[3]	—	—	___	___	___
Analytic Option Eqty	gr-inc	48.2	2.5[1]	5.1[4]	5.9[4]	___	___	___
Analytic Master Fix	fix-inc	6.2	-1.1[1]	—	—	___	___	___
Analytic ST Gov	fix-inc	24.5	0.0[3]	—	—	___	___	___
Your average		80.4				___	___	___
Anthem Funds								
Anthem Agg Gro	agg gr	5.6	—	—	—	___	___	___
Anthem Value	growth	5.8	—	—	—	___	___	___
Anthem Gro & Inc	gr-inc	10.0	-2.7[4]	—	—	___	___	___
Anthem Eqty Inc	gr-inc	5.6	—	—	—	___	___	___
Anthem Balanced	income	8.0	-3.0[4]	—	—	___	___	___
Anthem Income	fix-inc	5.0	—	—	—	___	___	___
Anthem Gov Sec	fix-inc	2.9	-7.5[5]	—	—	___	___	___
Anthem Muni	tax-free	4.8	—	—	—	___	___	___
Anthem Inter Gov	fix-inc	5.4	—	—	—	___	___	___
Your average		53.1				___	___	___
American Pension Investors								
API Growth	agg gr	50.4	-3.4[4]	5.6[4]	8.4[4]	___	___	___
API Spec Mkts	gr-inc	2.0	-7.4[5]	-1.0[5]	-2.2[5]	___	___	___
API Cap Inc	income	3.0	-0.4[2]	4.6[4]	6.2[5]	___	___	___
API Total Ret	income	4.5	-6.8[5]	3.5[5]	3.0[5]	___	___	___
API Money Mkt	money mkt	—	—	—	—	___	___	___
Your average		59.9				___	___	___
Aquinas Funds								
Aquinas Eqty Gro	growth	10.1	-6.8[5]	—	—	___	___	___
Aquinas Eqty Inc	gr-inc	32.2	-2.9[4]	—	—	___	___	___
Aquinas Balanced	income	30.1	-3.1[4]	—	—	___	___	___
Aquinas Fix Inc	fix-inc	28.2	-3.1[2]	—	—	___	___	___
Your average		100.6				___	___	___
Arbor One Valley Bank								
Arbor OVB Emg Gro	agg gr	36.4	-18.4[5]	—	—	___	___	___
Arbor OVB Cap App	growth	71.4	-5.5[5]	—	—	___	___	___
Arbor OVB Gov	fix-inc	51.2	-5.1[3]	—	—	___	___	___
Arbor OVB WV TE	tax-free	2.0	-5.0[1]	—	—	___	___	___
Arbor OVB Prime Obl	money mkt	0.7	—	—	—	___	___	___
Your average		161.7				___	___	___

No-load fund groups *continued*

Families with 3 or more funds including one stock or bond fund
Arranged in alphabetical order by group and risk within group

Fund group/fund	Objective	Total Net Assets $ Millions 12/31/94	Annualized Total Return % with quintile ranks by obj 1994	3 years 1992-1994	5 years 1990-1994	Post quintile ranks for your funds here 1994	3 years ending 1994	5 years ending 1994
Asset Management Financial								
Asset Mgmt ARM...	fix-inc	863.0	1.9[1]	3.7[4]	—			
Asset Mgmt Inter Mrtg...	fix-inc	211.0	-1.6[1]	4.3[3]	6.9[3]			
Asset Mgmt Mrtg Sec...	fix-inc	59.0	-2.3[2]	3.5[4]	6.9[3]			
Asset Mgmt ST Gov...	fix-inc	165.0	0.4[2]	4.2[2]	6.7[3]			
Asset Mgmt Money Mkt...	money mkt	35.1	3.9[2]	3.3[2]	—			
Your average...		1,333.1						
Jones & Babson								
Babson Enterprise SC‡...	agg gr	190.5	2.5[2]	14.1[1]	12.3[2]			
Babson Enterprise II SC...	agg gr	36.8	-7.4[5]	9.1[2]	—			
Babson Shadow Stk SC...	growth	33.5	-4.3[4]	9.0[2]	7.9[4]			
Babson Stew Ivry Int'l...	int'l	55.2	1.3[2]	10.0[2]	6.8[1]			
Babson Growth...	growth	226.5	-0.6[3]	6.2[3]	6.4[5]			
Babson Value...	growth	122.0	2.5[2]	13.3[1]	10.6[2]			
Babson Buffalo Blncd...	income	32.9	—	—	—			
Babson Bond-Port L...	fix-inc	137.0	-3.3[2]	5.3[3]	7.7[3]			
Babson TF Long...	tax-free	26.6	-7.4[4]	4.1[4]	6.0[4]			
Babson Bond-Port S...	fix-inc	29.0	-2.1[2]	4.3[3]	7.0[3]			
Babson TF Short...	tax-free	28.4	-1.7[5]	3.7[4]	5.4[3]			
Babson Prime MM...	money mkt	42.8	3.4[5]	3.0[5]	4.4[5]			
Babson TF MM...	money mkt TF	10.5	2.4[3]	2.3[2]	3.3[2]			
Babson Fed MM...	money mkt gov	9.1	3.3[5]	2.9[5]	4.3[5]			
Your average...		980.8						
Bartlett & Company								
Bartlett Value Int'l...	int'l	56.4	-0.5[3]	8.7[3]	5.9[2]			
Bartlett Basic Value...	gr-inc	93.2	0.4[2]	7.3[2]	7.1[3]			
Bartlett Fix Inc...	fix-inc	90.7	-2.9[3]	3.5[4]	6.1[5]			
Bartlett ST Bond...	fix-inc	17.0	—	—	—			
Bartlett Cash Res...	money mkt	76.8	3.6[4]	3.3[3]	4.6[3]			
Your average...		334.1						
Bailard, Biehl, & Kaiser								
BBK Int'l Equity...	int'l	148.8	-12.6[5]	2.2[5]	-2.6[5]			
BBK Diversa...	global	42.0	-9.4[4]	4.8[4]	3.8[4]			
BBK Int'l Fix Inc...	fix-inc	104.4	-19.2[5]	-0.3[5]	—			
Your average...		295.2						
Benham Management								
Benham Gold Eqty...	prec met	570.6	-16.8[4]	11.3[3]	-0.3[4]			
Benham Glob Nat Res...	global	19.0	—	—	—			
Benham Equity Growth...	growth	97.6	-0.2[3]	5.0[4]	—			
Benham Capital Mgr...	gr-inc	7.8	—	—	—			
Benham Income & Gro...	gr-inc	224.8	-0.6[3]	6.1[3]	—			
Benham Util Inc...	income	153.3	-10.0[5]	—	—			
Benham Target 2020...	fix-inc	125.5	-17.7[5]	6.6[2]	6.3[5]			

No-load fund groups *continued*

Families with 3 or more funds including one stock or bond fund
Arranged in alphabetical order by group and risk within group

Fund group/fund	Objective	Total Net Assets $ Millions 12/31/94	1994	Annualized Total Return % with quintile ranks by obj 3 years 1992-1994	5 years 1990-1994	Post quintile ranks for your funds here 1994	3 years ending 1994	5 years ending 1994
Benham Target 2015	fix-inc	134.0	-14.1[5]	6.5[2]	7.4[3]	____	____	____
Benham Target 2010	fix-inc	55.6	-11.6[5]	7.0[1]	8.3[2]	____	____	____
Benham Target 2005	fix-inc	101.6	-8.9[5]	6.7[2]	8.8[1]	____	____	____
Benham Target 2000	fix-inc	255.0	-6.9[4]	5.3[2]	8.4[2]	____	____	____
Benham Target 1995	fix-inc	80.5	0.8[1]	5.0[2]	8.0[2]	____	____	____
Benham Europ Gov	fix-inc	193.7	1.5[1]	—	—	____	____	____
Benham LT TrsyAgcy	fix-inc	28.6	-9.1[5]	—	—	____	____	____
Benham CA Hi Yld	tax-free	96.2	-5.3[2]	5.4[1]	6.5[3]	____	____	____
Benham CA Long	tax-free	249.1	-6.4[3]	4.8[3]	6.5[3]	____	____	____
Benham CA Insur	tax-free	161.3	-6.5[3]	5.0[2]	6.6[2]	____	____	____
Benham Nat TF Long	tax-free	45.3	-6.2[3]	5.4[1]	7.1[1]	____	____	____
Benham GNMA Inc	fix-inc	952.3	-1.5[1]	4.2[3]	7.6[2]	____	____	____
Benham CA Inter	tax-free	393.8	-3.7[3]	4.5[3]	6.2[3]	____	____	____
Benham AZ Inter	tax-free	15.2	—	—	—	____	____	____
Benham FL Inter	tax-free	7.1	—	—	—	____	____	____
Benham Nat TF Inter	tax-free	62.1	-3.4[3]	4.5[3]	6.4[3]	____	____	____
Benham Adj Rate Gov	fix-inc	447.0	-1.0[4]	2.6[5]	—	____	____	____
Benham CA Short	tax-free	106.3	-0.6[4]	—	—	____	____	____
Benham ST TrsyAgcy	fix-inc	30.7	0.3[2]	—	—	____	____	____
Benham Trsy Note	fix-inc	296.2	-2.3[5]	3.9[3]	6.9[2]	____	____	____
Benham Prime MM	money mkt	1.5	4.5[1]	—	—	____	____	____
Benham Nat TF MM	money mkt TF	94.2	2.3[3]	2.2[4]	3.3[3]	____	____	____
Benham FL TF MM	money mkt TF	47.6	—	—	—	____	____	____
Benham CA TF MM	money mkt TF	376.9	2.4[3]	2.3[3]	3.2[4]	____	____	____
Benham CA Muni MM	money mkt TF	211.4	2.5[2]	2.5[2]	—	____	____	____
Benham Gov Agcy MM	money mkt gov	486.8	3.8[2]	3.3[2]	4.8[1]	____	____	____
Benham Cap Presv	money mkt gov	2,832.0	3.6[3]	3.2[2]	4.6[2]	____	____	____
Benham Cap Presv II	money mkt gov	261.0	3.5[4]	2.9[5]	4.3[5]	____	____	____
Your average		9,221.5				____	____	____
Berger Associates								
Berger Sm Co Growth	agg gr	291.2	13.7[1]	—	—	____	____	____
Berger 100	agg gr	2,113.0	-6.7[4]	7.1[3]	17.0[1]	____	____	____
Berger 101	gr-inc	368.3	-9.1[5]	5.7[4]	11.8[1]	____	____	____
Cash Acct Tr-MM*	money mkt	375.9	3.5[4]	3.0[5]	—	____	____	____
Cash Acct Tr-TF MM*	money mkt TF	68.2	2.3[4]	2.2[4]	—	____	____	____
Cash Acct Tr-Gov MM*	money mkt gov	117.6	3.5[4]	3.0[5]	—	____	____	____
Your average		2,772.5				____	____	____
Sanford Bernstein & Co								
Bernstein Int'l Value	int'l	1,429.1	3.8[2]	—	—	____	____	____
Bernstein NY Muni	tax-free	376.6	-2.5[2]	4.2[4]	5.9[4]	____	____	____
Bernstein CA Muni	tax-free	160.8	-3.2[2]	3.9[5]	—	____	____	____
Bernstein Dvsfd Muni	tax-free	504.4	-2.5[2]	4.1[5]	5.8[5]	____	____	____
Bernstein Inter Dur	fix-inc	842.3	-3.2[3]	4.8[2]	7.7[2]	____	____	____
Bernstein Short Dur	fix-inc	507.1	0.5[2]	4.1[2]	6.6[3]	____	____	____
Bernstein Gov Sht	fix-inc	143.4	0.4[2]	3.5[4]	6.1[4]	____	____	____

No-load fund groups *continued*

Families with 3 or more funds including one stock or bond fund
Arranged in alphabetical order by group and risk within group

Fund group/fund	Objective	Total Net Assets $ Millions 12/31/94	Annualized Total Return % with quintile ranks by obj 1994	3 years 1992-1994	5 years 1990-1994	Post quintile ranks for your funds here 1994	3 years ending 1994	5 years ending 1994
Bernstein CA ST...	tax-free	42.0	—	—	—			
Bernstein Dvsfd Muni ST...	tax-free	88.1	—	—	—			
Bernstein NY ST...	tax-free	49.8	—	—	—			
Your average...		4,143.6						
Blanchard Funds								
Blanchard Prec Metals...	prec met	77.2	-15.2[3]	11.5[2]	0.9[2]			
Blanchard Emg Mkt...	int'l	16.3	—	—	—			
Blanchard Cap Growth...	growth	0.8	—	—	—			
Blanchard Amer Eqty...	growth	10.5	-4.1[4]	—	—			
Blanchard Glob Growth...	global	93.8	-7.5[4]	5.0[4]	3.7[5]			
Blanchard Gro & Inc...	gr-inc	1.4	—	—	—			
Blanchard ST Global...	fix-inc	305.7	-4.6[5]	2.4[5]	—			
Blanchard Flex Inc...	fix-inc	272.1	-5.6[5]	—	—			
Blanchard Flex TF...	tax-free	18.0	-5.6[2]	—	—			
Blanchard ST Bond...	fix-inc	24.2	1.0[2]	—	—			
Blanchard Trsy MM...	money mkt gov	184.2	3.3[5]	3.4[1]	4.4[4]			
Your average...		1,004.2						
Bridgeway Funds								
Bridgeway Ult Sm Co SC...	agg gr	0.4	—	—	—			
Bridgeway Agg Gro...	agg gr	0.2	—	—	—			
Bridgeway Soc Resp...	growth	0.1	—	—	—			
Your average...		0.7						
Brinson Funds								
Brinson Non US Eqty...	int'l	113.8	0.9[3]	—	—			
Brinson Glob Eqty...	global	20.0	—	—	—			
Brinson Global...	global	317.3	-1.9[3]	—	—			
Brinson US Eqty...	gr-inc	15.5	—	—	—			
Brinson US Blncd...	income	—	—	—	—			
Brinson Non US Bd...	fix-inc	—	—	—	—			
Brinson Glob Bd...	fix-inc	47.8	-3.5[3]	—	—			
Brinson US Bond...	fix-inc	—	—	—	—			
Your average...		514.4						
Brown Capital								
Brown Cap Sm Co SC...	agg gr	2.3	4.8[1]	—	—			
Brown Cap Equity...	growth	0.9	-0.8[3]	—	—			
Brown Cap Blncd...	gr-inc	1.4	-1.2[4]	—	—			
Your average...		4.6						
Bull & Bear Advisors								
Bull & Bear Gold...	prec met	38.5	-13.8[3]	10.2[4]	0.6[3]			
Bull & Bear Spec Eqty...	agg gr	45.5	-16.5[5]	7.6[3]	2.2[5]			
Bull & Bear US & Overs...	global	8.5	-13.1[5]	2.3[5]	3.7[4]			
Bull & Bear Qual Gro...	gr-inc	4.2	-7.9[5]	—	—			

Families with 3 or more funds including one stock or bond fund
Arranged in alphabetical order by group and risk within group

Fund group/fund	Objective	Total Net Assets $ Millions 12/31/94	1994	3 years 1992-1994	5 years 1990-1994	1994	3 years ending 1994	5 years ending 1994
						Post quintile ranks for your funds here		
Bull & Bear Glob Inc...............	fix-inc	40.9	-13.4[5]	6.9[1]	6.9[3]	_____	_____	_____
Bull & Bear Muni Inc...............	tax-free	17.0	-9.8[5]	1.9[5]	4.5[5]	_____	_____	_____
Bull & Bear US Gov...	fix-inc	15.9	-4.7[3]	3.4[5]	6.6[4]	_____	_____	_____
Bull & Bear Dollar...............	money mkt	67.7	3.4[5]	3.0[5]	4.3[5]	_____	_____	_____
Your average...............		238.2				_____	_____	_____
California Investment Trust...............								
CA Inv Tr-S&P MidCap	growth	20.3	-3.9[4]	—	—	_____	_____	_____
CA Inv Tr-S&P 500...	gr-inc	14.7	1.0[2]	—	—	_____	_____	_____
CA Inv Tr-CA TF...	tax-free	218.0	-8.6[5]	4.5[3]	6.4[3]	_____	_____	_____
CA Inv Tr-CA Insur...	tax-free	20.0	-5.0[1]	—	—	_____	_____	_____
CA Inv Tr-US Gov...	fix-inc	26.8	-7.0[4]	5.3[2]	8.3[2]	_____	_____	_____
CA Inv Tr-CA MM...	money mkt TF	90.0	2.5[2]	2.4[2]	3.4[2]	_____	_____	_____
CA Inv Tr-Trsy MM...	money mkt gov	65.0	3.5[4]	3.1[3]	4.5[3]	_____	_____	_____
Your average...............		454.8				_____	_____	_____
Caldwell Funds...............								
Caldwell Growth Stk...	growth	1.4	-8.9[5]	—	—	_____	_____	_____
Caldwell Fund...	gr-inc	3.8	-1.1[3]	6.6[2]	7.9[3]	_____	_____	_____
Caldwell Gov...	fix-inc	6.0	-0.3[1]	—	—	_____	_____	_____
Caldwell Tax-Free...	tax-free	0.6	-1.8[1]	—	—	_____	_____	_____
Your average...............		11.8				_____	_____	_____
Consistent Asset Management...............								
Camco Total Ret...	fix-inc	0.2	1.2[1]	—	—	_____	_____	_____
Camco Inter Term...	fix-inc	0.1	1.7[1]	—	—	_____	_____	_____
Camco Short Term...	fix-inc	0.1	2.1[1]	—	—	_____	_____	_____
Your average...............		0.4				_____	_____	_____
Capital Growth Management...............								
CGM Capital Dev‡...	agg gr	401.7	-22.9[5]	5.2[4]	18.7[1]	_____	_____	_____
CGM Realty...	sector	34.3	—	—	—	_____	_____	_____
CGM Mutual...	gr-inc	1,063.4	-9.7[5]	5.3[4]	10.7[1]	_____	_____	_____
CGM American TF...	tax-free	10.1	-8.2[4]	—	—	_____	_____	_____
CGM Fixed Inc...	fix-inc	28.7	-8.0[5]	—	—	_____	_____	_____
Your average...............		1,538.2				_____	_____	_____
Columbia Funds...............								
Columbia Special...	agg gr	889.5	2.3[2]	12.3[1]	13.3[2]	_____	_____	_____
Columbia Growth...	agg gr	591.7	-0.6[3]	7.9[3]	10.2[3]	_____	_____	_____
Columbia Int'l Stk...	int'l	118.5	-2.5[3]	—	—	_____	_____	_____
Columbia Common Stk...	growth	124.3	2.1[2]	9.3[2]	—	_____	_____	_____
Columbia Real Est...	sector	17.4	—	—	—	_____	_____	_____
Columbia Balanced...	income	249.7	0.1[2]	7.4[2]	—	_____	_____	_____
Columbia High Yld...	fix-inc	12.8	-0.9[1]	—	—	_____	_____	_____
Columbia Fix Inc...	fix-inc	252.1	-3.5[4]	4.8[1]	7.8[1]	_____	_____	_____

No-load fund groups *continued*

Families with 3 or more funds including one stock or bond fund
Arranged in alphabetical order by group and risk within group

| Fund group/fund | Objective | Total Net Assets $ Millions 12/31/94 | Annualized Total Return % with quintile ranks by obj | | | Post quintile ranks for your funds here | | |
			1994	3 years 1992-1994	5 years 1990-1994	1994	3 years ending 1994	5 years ending 1994
Columbia Muni Bd	tax-free	339.8	-4.7[1]	4.0[4]	6.1[4]	___	___	___
Columbia US Gov	fix-inc	33.5	0.0[3]	3.9[3]	6.7[3]	___	___	___
Columbia Daily Inc	money mkt	730.1	3.7[4]	3.1[4]	4.6[4]	___	___	___
Your average		3,359.4				___	___	___
Crabbe Huson Funds								
Crabbe Hsn Spec SC	growth	377.5	11.7[1]	26.1[1]	19.5[1]	___	___	___
Crabbe Hsn Eqty	growth	155.5	1.5[2]	14.1[1]	—	___	___	___
Crabbe Hsn Real Est	sector	17.2	—	—	—	___	___	___
Crabbe Hsn Asst All	income	107.1	-0.9[2]	9.6[1]	—	___	___	___
Crabbe Hsn Income	fix-inc	6.0	-3.6[3]	2.8[5]	6.0[5]	___	___	___
Crabbe Hsn OR Muni	tax-free	26.5	-2.7[2]	4.4[4]	—	___	___	___
Crabbe Hsn Gov Bd	fix-inc	9.1	-2.1[1]	3.0[5]	5.9[5]	___	___	___
Crabbe Hsn Gov MM	money mkt gov	43.3	3.6[3]	3.1[4]	4.4[4]	___	___	___
Your average		742.2				___	___	___
Chicago Title & Trust								
CT&T Talon	growth	5.1	—	—	—	___	___	___
CT&T M&C Growth	growth	11.2	—	—	—	___	___	___
CT&T Gro & Inc	gr-inc	12.5	0.5[2]	—	—	___	___	___
CT&T M&C Blncd	income	6.8	—	—	—	___	___	___
CT&T Inter Fix	fix-inc	12.9	-2.8[3]	—	—	___	___	___
CT&T Inter Muni	tax-free	10.4	-2.2[1]	—	—	___	___	___
CT&T Money Mkt	money mkt	97.1	3.9[2]	—	—	___	___	___
Your average		156.0				___	___	___
Dimensional Fund Advisors								
DFA US 6-10 Sm Co SC‡	agg gr	115.0	-1.3[3]	—	—	___	___	___
DFA US 9-10 Sm Co SC‡	agg gr	663.0	3.1[1]	15.4[1]	11.8[2]	___	___	___
DFA US Sm Cap Val SC‡	agg gr	357.0	1.2[2]	—	—	___	___	___
DFA Emg Mkts‡	int'l	15.0	—	—	—	___	___	___
DFA Pac Rim Sm Co‡	int'l	214.0	-12.1[5]	—	—	___	___	___
DFA Japan Sm Co‡	int'l	342.0	29.5[1]	3.0[5]	-4.9[5]	___	___	___
DFA UK Small Co‡	int'l	215.0	4.6[2]	5.5[4]	4.7[3]	___	___	___
DFA Cont Sm Co.‡	int'l	345.0	11.0[1]	3.7[5]	0.5[5]	___	___	___
DFA Int'l Sm Cap Val‡	int'l	—	—	—	—	___	___	___
DFA Lrg Cap Int'l‡	int'l	58.0	5.3[1]	4.8[4]	—	___	___	___
DFA Int'l Value‡	int'l	235.0	—	—	—	___	___	___
DFA Int'l High BTM‡	int'l	114.0	8.8[1]	—	—	___	___	___
DFA US Lrg Co‡	gr-inc	52.0	1.3[2]	6.1[3]	—	___	___	___
DFA US Lrg Cap Val‡	growth	207.0	-4.5[5]	—	—	___	___	___
DFA Real Estate‡	sector	33.0	-8.4[4]	—	—	___	___	___
DFA Glob Fix Inc‡	fix-inc	141.0	-4.3[3]	4.6[3]	—	___	___	___
DFA Inter Gov‡	fix-inc	61.0	-4.8[5]	4.8[2]	—	___	___	___
DFA 5 Yr Gov‡	fix-inc	222.0	-3.2[5]	4.0[2]	7.4[1]	___	___	___
DFA 1 Yr Fix Inc‡	fix-inc	573.0	2.5[1]	4.0[2]	5.9[4]	___	___	___
Your average		3,962.0				___	___	___

Families with 3 or more funds including one stock or bond fund
Arranged in alphabetical order by group and risk within group

| Fund group/fund | Objective | Total Net Assets $ Millions 12/31/94 | Annualized Total Return % with quintile ranks by obj | | | Post quintile ranks for your funds here | | |
			1994	3 years 1992-1994	5 years 1990-1994	1994	3 years ending 1994	5 years ending 1994
Dodge & Cox...............								
Dodge & Cox Stock...	gr-inc	543.5	5.2[1]	11.3[1]	9.7[1]	____	____	____
Dodge & Cox Blncd...............................	income	725.2	2.1[1]	9.4[1]	9.8[2]	____	____	____
Dodge & Cox Income..........................	fix-inc	195.4	-2.9[3]	5.2[1]	8.1[1]	____	____	____
Your average.................		1,464.1				____	____	____
Dreman Asset Management								
Dreman Small Cap SC..	agg gr	6.9	0.1[2]	—	—	____	____	____
Dreman High Return..........................	growth	35.0	-1.0[3]	9.0[2]	11.8[1]	____	____	____
Dreman Contrarian..	growth	13.0	0.0[3]	6.7[3]	7.6[4]	____	____	____
Dreman Fixed Inc	fix-inc	4.5	-1.2[4]	3.3[4]	6.3[4]	____	____	____
Your average.................		59.4				____	____	____
Dreyfus Corporation								
Dreyfus Strat Growth†	agg gr	98.9	3.1[1]	2.8[5]	6.0[5]	____	____	____
Dreyfus Global Growth†	global	134.1	-7.5[4]	3.1[5]	6.4[3]	____	____	____
Dreyfus New Ldrs SC........................	agg gr	391.6	-0.2[2]	8.5[3]	10.4[3]	____	____	____
Dreyfus Apprec........................	agg gr	233.5	3.6[1]	3.0[4]	8.2[4]	____	____	____
Dreyfus Special Gro........................	agg gr	64.9	-18.3[5]	7.4[3]	8.8[4]	____	____	____
Drey-Focus Sm Gro SC........................	agg gr	5.0	-6.6[4]	—	—	____	____	____
Drey-Wilsh Sm Gro........................	agg gr	13.4	-1.4[3]	—	—	____	____	____
DreyLaurel Int'l...	int'l	5.1	3.5[2]	4.9[4]	0.1[5]	____	____	____
Dreyfus Intl Eqty Allc........................	int'l	12.8	—	—	—	____	____	____
Dreyfus European...	int'l	10.1	-3.1[4]	3.5[5]	5.0[3]	____	____	____
Dreyfus Int'l Eqty........................	int'l	158.9	-5.4[4]	—	—	____	____	____
Dreyfus Discpl MidCap........................	growth	16.2	-6.7[5]	—	—	____	____	____
Drey-Focus Lg Val........................	growth	5.0	-1.0[3]	—	—	____	____	____
DreyLaurel Contrn........................	growth	2.5	-11.1[5]	6.0[3]	9.1[3]	____	____	____
Drey-Focus Sm Val SC........................	growth	5.1	-1.5[4]	—	—	____	____	____
Dreyfus Asst:Gro...	growth	1.1	—	—	—	____	____	____
Drey-Focus Lg Gro........................	growth	5.0	-0.7[3]	—	—	____	____	____
Drey-Wilsh Sm Val........................	growth	27.8	-4.5[4]	—	—	____	____	____
Drey-Wilsh Lg Gro........................	growth	12.5	2.3[2]	—	—	____	____	____
Drey-Peoples MidCap........................	growth	79.1	-4.0[4]	6.9[3]	—	____	____	____
Dreyfus Third Cent........................	growth	347.7	-7.5[5]	-0.3[5]	7.2[4]	____	____	____
Dreyfus Growth Oppty........................	growth	361.1	-6.4[5]	-2.9[5]	5.3[5]	____	____	____
Dreyfus Core Value........................	growth	318.1	0.4[3]	6.8[3]	5.2[5]	____	____	____
Drey-Peoples Idx........................	gr-inc	209.3	0.7[2]	5.9[3]	7.9[3]	____	____	____
Dreyfus S&P 500 Idx........................	gr-inc	122.8	0.8[2]	—	—	____	____	____
Dreyfus Equity Inc........................	gr-inc	4.9	—	—	—	____	____	____
Drey-Wilsh Lg Val........................	gr-inc	15.4	-5.2[5]	—	—	____	____	____
Dreyfus Discpl Stk........................	gr-inc	243.6	-1.2[4]	5.8[4]	9.6[1]	____	____	____
Dreyfus Fund........................	gr-inc	2,445.2	-4.2[5]	2.4[5]	5.9[4]	____	____	____
Dreyfus Gro & Inc........................	gr-inc	1,617.5	-5.2[5]	10.5[1]	—	____	____	____
Dreyfus Asst:Inc........................	income	1.1	—	—	—	____	____	____
Dreyfus Asst:Tot Ret........................	income	50.0	1.7[1]	—	—	____	____	____
Dreyfus Balanced........................	income	91.3	3.9[1]	—	—	____	____	____

No-load fund groups *continued*

Families with 3 or more funds including one stock or bond fund
Arranged in alphabetical order by group and risk within group

Fund group/fund	Objective	Total Net Assets $ Millions 12/31/94	Annualized Total Return % with quintile ranks by obj			Post quintile ranks for your funds here		
			1994	3 years 1992-1994	5 years 1990-1994	1994	3 years ending 1994	5 years ending 1994
Dreyfus Edison Elec	sector	71.1	-12.9[5]	1.1[5]	—	_____	_____	_____
Dreyfus CA TE	tax-free	1,433.4	-7.1[4]	3.5[5]	5.5[5]	_____	_____	_____
Dreyfus NY TE	tax-free	1,702.6	-7.0[3]	4.5[3]	6.2[4]	_____	_____	_____
Dreyfus NJ Muni	tax-free	577.5	-6.0[3]	4.9[2]	6.9[1]	_____	_____	_____
Drey-General NY	tax-free	293.6	-7.2[4]	5.3[2]	7.2[1]	_____	_____	_____
Dreyfus NY Insur	tax-free	151.7	-6.6[3]	4.0[4]	6.2[4]	_____	_____	_____
Dreyfus Insur Muni	tax-free	215.7	-8.6[5]	3.5[5]	5.7[5]	_____	_____	_____
Dreyfus Muni Bond	tax-free	3,630.6	-7.0[3]	4.3[4]	6.2[3]	_____	_____	_____
Dreyfus MA TE	tax-free	147.3	-6.0[3]	4.3[4]	6.3[3]	_____	_____	_____
Drey-General CA	tax-free	296.7	-7.0[3]	4.7[3]	6.5[3]	_____	_____	_____
Drey-General Muni	tax-free	826.9	-7.3[4]	4.9[3]	7.4[1]	_____	_____	_____
Dreyfus 100% US Long	fix-inc	123.4	-9.2[5]	4.4[3]	7.6[3]	_____	_____	_____
Dreyfus A Bonds Plus	fix-inc	484.3	-6.1[4]	5.3[2]	7.7[2]	_____	_____	_____
Dreyfus Global Bd	fix-inc	14.9	—	—	—	_____	_____	_____
Dreyfus Invst GNMA	fix-inc	44.9	-1.1[1]	4.8[2]	—	_____	_____	_____
Dreyfus Bond Mkt Idx	fix-inc	5.9	-3.4[4]	—	—	_____	_____	_____
Dreyfus 100% US Inter	fix-inc	185.3	-4.0[4]	4.4[3]	7.3[2]	_____	_____	_____
Dreyfus GNMA	fix-inc	1,426.4	-2.8[3]	3.5[5]	6.8[4]	_____	_____	_____
Dreyfus NY Inter	tax-free	338.1	-5.1[5]	5.0[2]	6.4[3]	_____	_____	_____
Dreyfus CT Inter	tax-free	124.3	-4.7[4]	—	—	_____	_____	_____
Dreyfus FL Inter	tax-free	409.4	-4.9[4]	—	—	_____	_____	_____
Dreyfus MA Inter	tax-free	67.0	-6.4[5]	—	—	_____	_____	_____
Dreyfus Inter Muni	tax-free	1,449.2	-4.6[4]	5.0[2]	6.5[2]	_____	_____	_____
Dreyfus CA Inter	tax-free	237.8	-5.5[5]	—	—	_____	_____	_____
Dreyfus NJ Inter	tax-free	212.8	-5.2[5]	—	—	_____	_____	_____
Dreyfus S-I Muni	tax-free	427.3	-0.3[4]	4.3[2]	5.6[2]	_____	_____	_____
Dreyfus ST Income	fix-inc	223.5	0.1[2]	—	—	_____	_____	_____
DreyLaurel ST Bd	fix-inc	4.2	0.2[2]	3.0[5]	6.1[4]	_____	_____	_____
Dreyfus S-I Gov	fix-inc	473.4	-0.8[4]	4.5[1]	7.3[1]	_____	_____	_____
Dreyfus 100% US Short	fix-inc	172.5	-0.3[3]	4.5[1]	—	_____	_____	_____
DreyLaurel ST Gov	fix-inc	0.8	2.8[1]	—	—	_____	_____	_____
Drey-General MM	money mkt	575.6	3.5[5]	3.2[4]	4.6[3]	_____	_____	_____
Dreyfus BASIC MM	money mkt	1,719.2	4.3[1]	—	—	_____	_____	_____
DreyLaurel Cash Mgmt	money mkt	—	—	—	—	_____	_____	_____
Dreyfus MM Instr MM Ser	money mkt	170.4	3.4[5]	3.2[3]	—	_____	_____	_____
Dreyfus Liq Asst	money mkt	4,863.4	3.5[4]	3.2[3]	4.7[3]	_____	_____	_____
Dreyfus Wrld Dollar	money mkt	2,316.4	3.5[5]	3.3[2]	5.0[1]	_____	_____	_____
DreyLaurel Prime MM	money mkt	129.5	3.9[2]	3.4[1]	—	_____	_____	_____
Dreyfus BASIC Muni MM	money mkt TF	1,045.0	2.9[1]	—	—	_____	_____	_____
Drey-General NY MM	money mkt TF	680.7	2.5[2]	2.4[2]	3.4[2]	_____	_____	_____
DreyLaurel CA MM	money mkt TF	13.0	2.5[2]	2.6[1]	3.6[1]	_____	_____	_____
Dreyfus CT TF MM	money mkt TF	262.0	2.6[2]	2.6[1]	—	_____	_____	_____
DreyLaurel MA MM	money mkt TF	103.0	2.3[4]	2.2[5]	3.3[3]	_____	_____	_____
Dreyfus MI MM	money mkt TF	60.7	2.5[2]	2.4[2]	—	_____	_____	_____
DreyLaurel NY MM	money mkt TF	6.3	2.2[5]	2.4[2]	3.4[2]	_____	_____	_____
Dreyfus NJ MM	money mkt TF	763.5	2.5[2]	2.4[2]	3.5[1]	_____	_____	_____
DreyLaurel TxEx MM	money mkt TF	197.0	2.5[2]	2.4[2]	—	_____	_____	_____

Families with 3 or more funds including one stock or bond fund
Arranged in alphabetical order by group and risk within group

| Fund group/fund | Objective | Total Net Assets $ Millions 12/31/94 | Annualized Total Return % with quintile ranks by obj | | | Post quintile ranks for your funds here | | |
			1994	3 years 1992-1994	5 years 1990-1994	1994	3 years ending 1994	5 years ending 1994
Dreyfus OH MM..............................	money mkt TF	58.7	2.8[1]	2.8[1]	—	___	___	___
DreyLaurel TxFr MM......................	money mkt TF	—	2.5[2]	2.3[3]	3.3[3]	___	___	___
Drey-General CA MM.....................	money mkt TF	523.0	2.6[2]	2.6[1]	3.7[1]	___	___	___
Dreyfus NY MM.............................	money mkt TF	323.7	2.1[5]	2.0[5]	3.0[5]	___	___	___
Dreyfus PA MM..............................	money mkt TF	159.9	2.8[1]	2.7[1]	—	___	___	___
Dreyfus MA MM.............................	money mkt TF	141.2	2.6[1]	2.5[1]	—	___	___	___
Dreyfus CA TF MM.........................	money mkt TF	298.6	2.3[4]	2.3[3]	3.2[4]	___	___	___
Dreyfus Muni MM...........................	money mkt TF	1,002.5	2.4[3]	2.3[3]	3.3[3]	___	___	___
Drey-General Muni MM...................	money mkt TF	283.3	2.4[3]	2.4[2]	3.3[2]	___	___	___
Dreyfus 100% US MM.....................	money mkt gov	1,450.6	3.4[5]	3.2[2]	4.7[1]	___	___	___
Drey-General Gov MM.....................	money mkt gov	490.0	3.7[2]	3.3[2]	4.6[2]	___	___	___
Dreyfus MM Instr Gov....................	money mkt gov	465.9	3.3[5]	3.1[4]	4.5[3]	___	___	___
Dreyfus BASIC Gov MM..................	money mkt gov	658.1	4.2[1]	—	—	___	___	___
DreyLaurel Gov MM.......................	money mkt gov	25.0	3.6[3]	3.2[3]	4.4[4]	___	___	___
DreyLaurel Trsy MM......................	money mkt gov	240.9	3.7[2]	3.3[2]	—	___	___	___
Your average..............................		41,910.2				___	___	___
Dupree & Company.....................								
Dupree KY TF Inc..........................	tax-free	246.8	-2.9[1]	6.1[1]	7.3[1]	___	___	___
Dupree Tenn TF Inc.......................	tax-free	6.0	-1.2[1]	—	—	___	___	___
Dupree Inter Gov...........................	fix-inc	7.2	-5.9[5]	—	—	___	___	___
Dupree KY Sht-Med.......................	tax-free	61.9	1.0[2]	4.5[1]	5.5[2]	___	___	___
Dupree Tenn Sht-Med....................	tax-free	0.2	—	—	—	___	___	___
Your average..............................		322.1				___	___	___
Eclipse Funds.............................								
Eclipse Equity SC.........................	agg gr	195.1	-4.7[4]	10.0[2]	8.6[4]	___	___	___
Eclipse Gro & Inc..........................	gr-inc	—	—	—	—	___	___	___
Eclipse Balanced..........................	income	27.7	0.0[2]	9.4[1]	10.0[1]	___	___	___
Eclipse Ultra Short........................	fix-inc	—	—	—	—	___	___	___
Your average..............................		222.8				___	___	___
Fifty-Nine Wall Street..................								
59 Wall Sm Co SC........................	agg gr	33.6	-10.5[5]	3.6[4]	—	___	___	___
59 Wall Pac Basin.........................	int'l	101.6	-21.5[5]	13.4[1]	—	___	___	___
59 Wall Europe Eqty......................	int'l	101.2	-3.9[4]	9.5[2]	—	___	___	___
59 Wall S-I TF...............................	tax-free	53.2	0.3[3]	—	—	___	___	___
59 Wall St MM...............................	money mkt	—	—	—	—	___	___	___
59 Wall St Trsy MM.......................	money mkt gov	5.0	3.5[4]	—	—	___	___	___
Your average..............................		294.6				___	___	___
Federated Research.....................								
Federated Mini Cap SC..................	agg gr	102.2	-2.8[4]	—	—	___	___	___
Federated Mgd Agg Gro.................	agg gr	—	—	—	—	___	___	___
Federated Mid Cap........................	growth	43.6	-4.3[4]	—	—	___	___	___
Federated Growth..........................	growth	280.9	-11.9[5]	0.7[5]	5.5[5]	___	___	___
Federated Mgd Growth...................	growth	—	—	—	—	___	___	___

No-load fund groups *continued*

Families with 3 or more funds including one stock or bond fund
Arranged in alphabetical order by group and risk within group

Fund group/fund	Objective	Total Net Assets $ Millions 12/31/94	1994	3 years 1992-1994	5 years 1990-1994	1994	3 years ending 1994	5 years ending 1994
				Annualized Total Return % with quintile ranks by obj			Post quintile ranks for your funds here	
Federated Max Cap...	gr-inc	448.1	1.2[2]	5.9[3]	—	___	___	___
Federated Stock...	gr-inc	553.6	-0.4[3]	7.8[2]	9.0[2]	___	___	___
Federated Mgd Gro & Inc...	gr-inc	—	—	—	—	___	___	___
Federated Stk & Bd...	gr-inc	122.0	-1.9[4]	5.2[4]	6.7[4]	___	___	___
Federated Mgd Income...	income	—	—	—	—	___	___	___
Federated Hi Yld...	fix-inc	349.5	-2.4[2]	9.6[1]	11.9[1]	___	___	___
Federated Income...	fix-inc	1,142.2	-1.6[1]	3.2[5]	6.7[4]	___	___	___
Federated GNMA...	fix-inc	1,437.7	-2.5[2]	3.3[5]	7.0[3]	___	___	___
Federated ARMS...	fix-inc	1,009.0	0.3[1]	2.8[5]	6.0[5]	___	___	___
Federated Inter Muni...	tax-free	270.1	-3.8[3]	4.2[4]	5.9[4]	___	___	___
Federated Inter Gov...	fix-inc	732.2	-1.9[2]	3.8[3]	6.8[4]	___	___	___
Federated ST Muni...	tax-free	290.2	0.1[3]	3.1[5]	4.5[5]	___	___	___
Federated US Gov...	fix-inc	143.1	-6.2[5]	4.8[1]	7.3[1]	___	___	___
Federated S-I Gov...	fix-inc	685.9	0.7[2]	3.4[4]	5.9[4]	___	___	___
Federated ST Income...	fix-inc	237.3	-0.5[3]	3.6[3]	5.3[5]	___	___	___
Federated Prime MM...	money mkt	38.4	3.8[3]	3.1[4]	4.5[5]	___	___	___
Federated Muni Cash...	money mkt TF	490.2	2.2[5]	2.2[4]	3.3[3]	___	___	___
Federated OH Cash...	money mkt TF	144.6	2.3[4]	2.3[3]	—	___	___	___
Federated Gov Cash...	money mkt gov	415.5	3.4[5]	2.9[5]	—	___	___	___
Federated Trsy MM...	money mkt gov	428.1	3.9[1]	3.2[2]	—	___	___	___
Your average...		9,364.4				___	___	___
FFB Lexicon Funds ...						___	___	___
FFB Lexcn Sm Co SC...	agg gr	21.5	-7.9[5]	—	—	___	___	___
FFB Lexcn Cap App...	growth	128.2	-4.5[4]	3.0[4]	—	___	___	___
FFB Lexcn Sel Value...	gr-inc	59.5	3.9[1]	—	—	___	___	___
FFB Lexcn Fix Inc...	fix-inc	86.8	-3.0[2]	4.9[2]	—	___	___	___
FFB Lexcn Inter Gov...	fix-inc	106.4	-1.9[2]	3.9[3]	—	___	___	___
FFB Lexcn Cash Mgt...	money mkt	402.2	3.7[3]	3.3[2]	—	___	___	___
Your average...		804.6				___	___	___
Fidelity Research & Management ...								
Fidelity Sel Biotech† ...	sector	396.1	-18.2[5]	-9.6[5]	16.2[2]	___	___	___
Fidelity Sel Medical Del† ...	sector	247.6	19.8[1]	3.2[5]	17.8[2]	___	___	___
Fidelity Sel Health† ...	sector	796.1	21.4[1]	0.9[5]	18.6[1]	___	___	___
Fidelity Sel Devel Comm† ...	sector	276.1	15.1[1]	21.1[1]	—	___	___	___
Fidelity Sel Technology† ...	sector	227.4	11.1[1]	15.8[2]	22.3[1]	___	___	___
Fidelity Sel Software† ...	sector	211.5	0.4[3]	21.7[1]	21.5[1]	___	___	___
Fidelity Sel Electronics† ...	sector	156.6	17.2[1]	25.4[1]	23.1[1]	___	___	___
Fidelity Sel Computer† ...	sector	175.4	20.5[1]	23.7[1]	24.0[1]	___	___	___
Fidelity Sel Telecomm† ...	sector	363.8	4.3[2]	16.0[2]	11.2[3]	___	___	___
Fidelity Sel Defense† ...	sector	3.7	1.8[3]	9.4[3]	9.7[4]	___	___	___
Fidelity Sel Indust Equip† ...	sector	104.2	3.1[2]	18.1[2]	12.0[3]	___	___	___
Fidelity Sel Consmr Prod† ...	sector	7.6	-7.1[4]	7.9[4]	—	___	___	___
Fidelity Sel Energy Serv† ...	sector	50.8	0.6[3]	8.0[4]	-0.4[5]	___	___	___
Fidelity Sel Energy† ...	sector	96.7	0.4[3]	5.3[4]	2.2[5]	___	___	___
Fidelity Sel Nat Gas† ...	sector	79.0	-6.8[4]	—	—	___	___	___

Families with 3 or more funds including one stock or bond fund
Arranged in alphabetical order by group and risk within group

| Fund group/fund | Objective | Total Net Assets $ Millions 12/31/94 | Annualized Total Return % with quintile ranks by obj | | | Post quintile ranks for your funds here | | |
			1994	3 years 1992-1994	5 years 1990-1994	1994	3 years ending 1994	5 years ending 1994
Fidelity Sel Chemicals†...................	sector	167.8	14.7[1]	12.1[3]	13.4[3]	_____	_____	_____
Fidelity Sel PapForest†...................	sector	76.3	14.1[1]	14.9[2]	11.6[3]	_____	_____	_____
Fidelity Sel Envir Serv†..................	sector	32.1	-9.6[4]	-3.9[5]	-1.4[5]	_____	_____	_____
Fidelity Sel Indust Mat†..................	sector	180.1	8.2[2]	13.8[2]	10.7[4]	_____	_____	_____
Fidelity Sel Prec Metals†................	prec met	453.3	-1.2[1]	17.8[1]	5.5[1]	_____	_____	_____
Fidelity Sel Amer Gold†..................	prec met	314.2	-15.5[4]	13.5[2]	2.6[2]	_____	_____	_____
Fidelity Sel Air Trans†...................	sector	7.5	-21.7[5]	3.0[5]	4.1[5]	_____	_____	_____
Fidelity Sel Transp†.....................	sector	11.1	3.9[2]	18.5[1]	15.0[2]	_____	_____	_____
Fidelity Sel Auto†.......................	sector	64.0	-12.8[5]	18.7[1]	16.4[2]	_____	_____	_____
Fidelity Sel ConstHous†.................	sector	17.5	-16.0[5]	10.1[3]	11.2[4]	_____	_____	_____
Fidelity Sel FoodAgr†...................	sector	85.5	6.1[2]	7.0[4]	12.4[3]	_____	_____	_____
Fidelity Sel Multimedia†.................	sector	26.6	4.0[2]	20.3[1]	12.1[3]	_____	_____	_____
Fidelity Sel Leisure†....................	sector	61.3	-6.8[4]	14.8[2]	9.3[4]	_____	_____	_____
Fidelity Sel Retail†.....................	sector	35.5	-5.0[4]	9.4[3]	15.9[2]	_____	_____	_____
Fidelity Sel Home Fincl†................	sector	130.2	2.7[2]	27.3[1]	23.5[1]	_____	_____	_____
Fidelity Sel Broker†....................	sector	21.9	-17.3[5]	9.1[4]	14.7[2]	_____	_____	_____
Fidelity Sel Reg Banks†.................	sector	108.4	0.2[3]	18.2[1]	16.8[2]	_____	_____	_____
Fidelity Sel Financial†..................	sector	94.2	-3.7[3]	17.4[2]	14.6[3]	_____	_____	_____
Fidelity Sel Insurance†.................	sector	10.1	-0.3[3]	9.7[3]	10.2[4]	_____	_____	_____
Fidelity SE Asia†......................	int'l	660.9	-21.8[5]	—	—	_____	_____	_____
Fidelity Latin Amer†...................	int'l	616.1	-23.2[5]	—	—	_____	_____	_____
Fidelity Emg Mkts†....................	int'l	1,508.3	-17.9[5]	16.4[1]	—	_____	_____	_____
Fidelity Japan........................	int'l	389.0	16.5[1]	—	—	_____	_____	_____
Fidelity Pacific Basin..................	int'l	475.5	-2.8[3]	13.7[1]	3.8[4]	_____	_____	_____
Fidelity Europe Cap App...............	int'l	291.5	6.9[1]	—	—	_____	_____	_____
Fidelity Europe†......................	int'l	478.9	6.2[1]	9.6[2]	5.5[2]	_____	_____	_____
Fidelity Overseas.....................	int'l	2,194.1	1.3[2]	7.9[3]	4.9[3]	_____	_____	_____
Fidelity Dvsfd Int'l....................	int'l	306.0	1.1[2]	6.0[4]	—	_____	_____	_____
Fidelity Canada.......................	int'l	332.9	-12.0[5]	2.4[5]	3.6[4]	_____	_____	_____
Fidelity Emg Growth†..................	agg gr	635.2	-0.2[2]	9.0[2]	—	_____	_____	_____
Fidelity Small Cap SC†.................	agg gr	664.8	-3.3[4]	—	—	_____	_____	_____
Fidelity Fifty.........................	agg gr	60.6	4.0[1]	—	—	_____	_____	_____
Fidelity OTC SC†......................	agg gr	1,381.3	-2.7[3]	6.6[3]	11.5[2]	_____	_____	_____
Fidelity Export.......................	agg gr	71.6	—	—	—	_____	_____	_____
Fidelity Growth Co....................	agg gr	2,993.4	-2.2[3]	7.0[3]	13.5[1]	_____	_____	_____
Fidelity Low Pr Stk SC†................	growth	2,354.5	4.8[1]	17.6[1]	—	_____	_____	_____
Fidelity Retrmnt Growth...............	agg gr	3,184.9	0.1[2]	10.6[2]	12.0[2]	_____	_____	_____
Fidelity Trend.......................	agg gr	1,193.8	-6.7[4]	9.1[2]	9.1[3]	_____	_____	_____
Fidelity Magellan†....................	agg gr	36,441.5	-1.8[3]	9.4[2]	12.0[2]	_____	_____	_____
Fidelity Contrafund†..................	agg gr	8,682.4	-1.1[3]	11.6[1]	17.5[1]	_____	_____	_____
Fidelity Cap Apprec†..................	agg gr	1,623.2	2.5[1]	16.7[1]	8.0[4]	_____	_____	_____
Fidelity Worldwide....................	global	703.9	3.0[1]	14.3[1]	—	_____	_____	_____
Fidelity Mid-Cap Stk..................	growth	126.1	—	—	—	_____	_____	_____
Fidelity Blue Chip†...................	growth	3,287.0	9.8[1]	13.2[1]	18.4[1]	_____	_____	_____
Fidelity Stk Selector..................	growth	786.7	0.8[2]	9.8[2]	—	_____	_____	_____
Fidelity Discpl Eqty...................	growth	1,160.1	3.0[2]	9.9[2]	12.3[1]	_____	_____	_____
Fidelity Value.......................	growth	3,720.4	7.6[1]	17.0[1]	12.0[1]	_____	_____	_____

No-load fund groups   *continued*

Families with 3 or more funds including one stock or bond fund
Arranged in alphabetical order by group and risk within group

Fund group/fund	Objective	Total Net Assets $ Millions 12/31/94	1994	3 years 1992-1994	5 years 1990-1994	1994	3 years ending 1994	5 years ending 1994
Fidelity Div Growth...	growth	102.4	4.3[1]	—	—			
Fidelity New Millnm† ...	growth	319.7	0.8[2]	—	—			
Fidelity Int'l Value...	int'l	32.7	—	—	—			
Fidelity Int'l Gr & Inc...	int'l	1,272.6	-2.9[4]	8.2[3]	5.8[2]			
Fidelity Glob Blncd...	global	236.5	-11.4[5]	—	—			
Fidelity Market Idx...	gr-inc	306.7	1.1[2]	5.9[3]	—			
Fidelity Fund...	gr-inc	1,886.1	2.6[1]	9.6[1]	9.2[1]			
Fidelity Gro & Inc† ...	gr-inc	9,344.9	2.3[1]	10.9[1]	12.5[1]			
Fidelity Asst Mgr Gro...	gr-inc	2,852.9	-7.4[5]	11.7[1]	—			
Fidelity Eqty Inc II...	gr-inc	7,697.5	3.2[1]	13.4[1]	—			
Fidelity Eqty Inc...	gr-inc	7,412.8	0.3[2]	11.7[1]	9.2[2]			
Fidelity Real Estate...	sector	555.7	1.9[2]	11.0[3]	11.7[3]			
Fidelity Sel Util Gro† ...	sector	202.4	-7.4[4]	4.8[4]	6.9[4]			
Fidelity Utilities...	income	1,079.6	-5.3[4]	6.7[3]	8.4[3]			
Fidelity Asset Mgr...	income	11,075.6	-6.5[5]	9.3[1]	11.1[1]			
Fidelity Asst Mgr Inc...	income	476.2	-1.4[3]	—	—			
Fidelity Balanced...	income	4,999.1	-5.3[4]	6.8[3]	9.0[2]			
Fidelity Puritan...	income	11,769.4	1.9[1]	12.6[1]	10.7[1]			
Fidelity Convert...	income	891.3	-1.7[3]	12.2[1]	13.7[1]			
Fidelity Curr: Yen† ...	fix-inc	3.5	12.6[1]	9.3[1]	11.0[1]			
Fidelity Curr: Sterling† ...	fix-inc	3.4	9.9[1]	-0.4[5]	7.5[3]			
Fidelity Curr: D-Mark.† ...	fix-inc	8.6	16.4[1]	5.1[2]	8.4[2]			
Fidelity Cap & Inc...	fix-inc	2,039.8	-4.6[3]	15.1[1]	13.7[1]			
Fidelity Spart Hi Inc...	fix-inc	617.5	3.2[1]	15.1[1]	—			
Fidelity New Mkts Inc...	fix-inc	179.5	-16.1[5]	—	—			
Fidelity Agg TF...	tax-free	793.8	-5.9[2]	5.3[1]	7.0[1]			
Fidelity Spart Agg Muni...	tax-free	57.4	-6.1[3]	—	—			
Fidelity Spart NY Hi Yld...	tax-free	284.8	-8.3[4]	4.4[3]	—			
Fidelity NY Hi Yld...	tax-free	380.2	-8.0[4]	4.2[4]	6.1[4]			
Fidelity MA Hi Yld...	tax-free	993.8	-6.1[3]	5.0[2]	6.7[2]			
Fidelity Spart CA Hi Yld...	tax-free	371.9	-9.0[5]	4.1[4]	6.4[3]			
Fidelity CA Hi Yld...	tax-free	443.9	-8.9[5]	3.9[5]	5.7[5]			
Fidelity Spart PA Hi Yld...	tax-free	241.2	-5.1[1]	5.4[1]	7.2[1]			
Fidelity Spart NJ Hi Yld...	tax-free	325.7	-5.7[2]	5.0[2]	6.9[1]			
Fidelity Hi Yld TF...	tax-free	1,671.3	-7.4[4]	3.5[5]	5.8[4]			
Fidelity MN TF...	tax-free	277.4	-5.9[3]	4.4[3]	5.8[4]			
Fidelity MI Hi Yld...	tax-free	434.4	-7.5[4]	4.9[3]	6.3[3]			
Fidelity Spart CT Hi Yld...	tax-free	312.8	-7.0[3]	4.3[4]	6.0[4]			
Fidelity OH TF...	tax-free	349.5	-5.6[2]	4.9[2]	6.7[2]			
Fidelity Spart MD Muni...	tax-free	35.5	-7.5[4]	—	—			
Fidelity Spart AZ Muni...	tax-free	4.5	—	—	—			
Fidelity Glob Bond...	fix-inc	382.9	-16.3[5]	2.1[5]	6.1[5]			
Fidelity Spart FL Muni...	tax-free	339.3	-6.7[3]	—	—			
Fidelity Inv Grd Bd... †	fix-inc	995.1	-5.4[4]	6.0[2]	8.5[1]			
Fidelity NY Insured...	tax-free	300.8	-8.0[4]	4.1[4]	6.1[4]			
Fidelity Spart Inv Grd...	fix-inc	118.0	-5.2[3]	—	—			
Fidelity CA Insur...	tax-free	197.3	-10.2[5]	3.7[5]	5.8[5]			

Families with 3 or more funds including one stock or bond fund
Arranged in alphabetical order by group and risk within group

| Fund group/fund | Objective | Total Net Assets $ Millions 12/31/94 | Annualized Total Return % with quintile ranks by obj | | | Post quintile ranks for your funds here | | |
			1994	3 years 1992-1994	5 years 1990-1994	1994	3 years ending 1994	5 years ending 1994
Fidelity Insur TF...	tax-free	318.2	-7.7[4]	4.3[4]	6.3[3]	_____	_____	_____
Fidelity Spart Muni Inc...	tax-free	535.6	-8.9[5]	4.1[4]	—	_____	_____	_____
Fidelity Muni Bd...	tax-free	1,005.6	-8.6[5]	4.0[4]	6.1[4]	_____	_____	_____
Fidelity Spart LT Gov...	fix-inc	71.7	-12.2[5]	3.4[4]	—	_____	_____	_____
Fidelity Spart Bond Strat...	fix-inc	17.7	-7.7[5]	—	—	_____	_____	_____
Fidelity Mrtg Sec...	fix-inc	349.4	1.9[1]	4.7[2]	7.5[2]	_____	_____	_____
Fidelity GNMA...	fix-inc	704.5	-2.0[2]	3.5[4]	6.8[4]	_____	_____	_____
Fidelity Spart GNMA...	fix-inc	347.8	-1.5[1]	3.7[4]	—	_____	_____	_____
Fidelity Spart Gov Inc...	fix-inc	231.9	-3.6[3]	3.5[4]	6.8[4]	_____	_____	_____
Fidelity Spart NY Inter...	tax-free	31.8	-4.3[3]	—	—	_____	_____	_____
Fidelity Spart CA Inter...	tax-free	38.0	-4.7[4]	—	—	_____	_____	_____
Fidelity Spart Inter Muni...	tax-free	205.9	-5.0[5]	—	—	_____	_____	_____
Fidelity ST World Inc...	fix-inc	265.8	-5.9[5]	3.6[4]	—	_____	_____	_____
Fidelity Inter Bond...	fix-inc	2,127.4	-2.0[2]	5.2[1]	7.5[2]	_____	_____	_____
Fidelity Ltd Muni...	tax-free	881.3	-4.8[4]	5.0[2]	6.6[2]	_____	_____	_____
Fidelity Spart S-I Muni...	tax-free	913.1	-0.1[4]	4.4[1]	5.7[1]	_____	_____	_____
Fidelity Gov Sec...	fix-inc	611.2	-5.2[3]	4.7[3]	7.8[2]	_____	_____	_____
Fidelity ST Bond...	fix-inc	1,514.8	-4.1[5]	4.0[2]	6.3[4]	_____	_____	_____
Fidelity Spart Ltd Mat...	fix-inc	830.6	-1.0[4]	3.7[3]	6.3[3]	_____	_____	_____
Fidelity S-I Gov...	fix-inc	151.2	-1.4[4]	2.8[5]	—	_____	_____	_____
Fidelity Spart S-I Gov...	fix-inc	48.0	-0.5[3]	—	—	_____	_____	_____
Fidelity Spart ST Inc...	fix-inc	610.3	-4.6[5]	—	—	_____	_____	_____
Fidelity Cash MM...	money mkt	15,215.8	4.0[2]	3.5[1]	4.9[1]	_____	_____	_____
Fidelity Daily MM...	money mkt	2,226.8	3.9[2]	3.4[1]	4.8[2]	_____	_____	_____
Fidelity Select MM...	money mkt	669.0	3.7[3]	3.3[2]	4.7[2]	_____	_____	_____
Fidelity Spart MM...	money mkt	7,531.9	4.1[1]	3.7[1]	5.2[1]	_____	_____	_____
Fidelity CA TF MM...	money mkt TF	687.0	2.4[3]	2.3[3]	3.2[3]	_____	_____	_____
Fidelity CT TF MM...	money mkt TF	312.8	2.3[4]	2.2[3]	3.4[2]	_____	_____	_____
Fidelity MA TF MM...	money mkt TF	729.1	2.2[5]	2.0[5]	3.1[5]	_____	_____	_____
Fidelity MI Muni MM...	money mkt TF	220.2	2.4[3]	2.4[2]	—	_____	_____	_____
Fidelity NJ TF MM...	money mkt TF	413.3	2.3[3]	2.3[3]	3.3[2]	_____	_____	_____
Fidelity NY TF MM...	money mkt TF	715.4	2.3[3]	2.2[4]	3.1[5]	_____	_____	_____
Fidelity OH Muni MM...	money mkt TF	298.2	2.5[2]	2.5[2]	3.6[1]	_____	_____	_____
Fidelity Spart AZ MM...	money mkt TF	—	—	—	—	_____	_____	_____
Fidelity Spart CA MM...	money mkt TF	1,163.7	2.8[1]	2.7[1]	3.7[1]	_____	_____	_____
Fidelity Spart CT MM...	money mkt TF	162.5	2.4[3]	2.5[2]	—	_____	_____	_____
Fidelity Spart FL MM...	money mkt TF	627.4	2.6[1]	—	—	_____	_____	_____
Fidelity Spart MA MM...	money mkt TF	390.2	2.3[3]	2.3[2]	—	_____	_____	_____
Fidelity Spart Muni MM...	money mkt TF	2,133.7	2.8[1]	2.9[1]	—	_____	_____	_____
Fidelity Spart NJ MM...	money mkt TF	407.5	2.7[1]	2.5[2]	—	_____	_____	_____
Fidelity Spart NY MM...	money mkt TF	545.6	2.5[2]	2.4[2]	—	_____	_____	_____
Fidelity Spart PA MM...	money mkt TF	254.9	2.6[1]	2.6[1]	3.7[1]	_____	_____	_____
Fidelity TE MM...	money mkt TF	3,584.4	2.5[2]	2.5[2]	3.5[1]	_____	_____	_____
Fidelity Gov MM...	money mkt gov	1,148.6	3.9[1]	3.3[2]	4.6[2]	_____	_____	_____
Fidelity Spart Gov MM...	money mkt gov	737.8	3.9[1]	3.5[1]	—	_____	_____	_____
Fidelity Spart Trsy MM...	money mkt gov	1,771.2	3.7[2]	3.4[1]	4.8[1]	_____	_____	_____
Your average...		209,851.5				_____	_____	_____

No-load fund groups *continued*

Families with 3 or more funds including one stock or bond fund
Arranged in alphabetical order by group and risk within group

Fund group/fund	Objective	Total Net Assets $ Millions 12/31/94	1994	3 years 1992-1994	5 years 1990-1994	Post quintile ranks for your funds here 1994	3 years ending 1994	5 years ending 1994
First Omaha Funds....................................								
First Omaha Eqty..	gr-inc	145.0	7.4[1]	—	—			
First Omaha Fix Inc...	fix-inc	61.6	-4.8[3]	—	—			
First Omaha S-I Fix...	fix-inc	22.6	-1.4[4]	—	—			
First Omaha Gov MM...	money mkt gov	77.6	3.6[3]	—	—			
Your average..		306.8						
Flex-Funds (Meeder & Assoc)..................								
Flex-Fund Growth.......................................	growth	22.0	-0.7[3]	4.2[4]	7.5[4]			
Flex-Fund Muirfield.....................................	growth	81.8	2.7[2]	5.9[3]	9.5[2]			
Flex-Fund Bond..	fix-inc	12.9	-1.0[4]	3.4[4]	6.7[3]			
Flex-Fund ST Glob...	fix-inc	3.9	2.1[1]	—	—			
Flex-Fund MM...	money mkt	164.1	4.1[1]	3.6[1]	5.0[1]			
Your average..		284.7						
Fontaine Associates.................................								
Fontaine Cap App......................................	agg gr	5.7	2.3[2]	3.9[4]	5.9[5]			
Fontaine Glob Gro......................................	global	0.3	-0.4[2]	—	—			
Fontaine Glob Inc.......................................	fix-inc	0.7	1.5[2]	—	—			
Your average..		6.7						
Founders Asset Management....................								
Founders Discovery SC...	agg gr	187.5	-7.7[5]	5.6[4]	16.7[1]			
Founders Frontier SC...	agg gr	249.2	-2.8[3]	7.3[3]	11.3[2]			
Founders Special..	agg gr	300.9	-4.9[4]	6.1[3]	11.9[2]			
Founders Worldwide Gro...	global	104.9	-2.2[3]	8.9[3]	13.1[1]			
Founders Passport......................................	global	16.5	-10.4[5]	—	—			
Founders Growth..	growth	310.1	-3.3[4]	8.2[2]	10.8[2]			
Founders Blue Chip...	gr-inc	312.2	0.5[2]	4.7[4]	8.1[3]			
Founders Balanced.....................................	income	96.0	-1.9[3]	8.2[2]	8.1[3]			
Founders Oppty Bd.....................................	fix-inc	3.8	-10.0[5]	—	—			
Founders Gov Sec...	fix-inc	21.5	-7.5[5]	2.1[5]	5.0[5]			
Founders Money Mkt..................................	money mkt	203.5	3.5[5]	2.9[5]	4.3[5]			
Your average..		1,806.1						
Fremont Investment Advisors....................								
Fremont US MicroCap SC............................	agg gr	2.1	—	—	—			
Fremont Int'l Sm Cap..................................	int'l	1.9	—	—	—			
Fremont Int'l Gro..	int'l	28.2	—	—	—			
Fremont Growth..	growth	23.4	0.4[3]	—	—			
Fremont Global...	global	436.8	-4.2[3]	6.4[4]	7.0[2]			
Fremont Bond...	fix-inc	59.8	-4.0[4]	—	—			
Fremont CA Inter..	tax-free	54.9	-4.9[4]	3.7[5]	—			
Fremont Money Mkt.....................................	money mkt	241.4	4.0[2]	3.3[2]	4.8[2]			
Your average..		848.5						

120

No-load fund groups *continued*

Families with 3 or more funds including one stock or bond fund
Arranged in alphabetical order by group and risk within group

Fund group/fund	Objective	Total Net Assets $ Millions 12/31/94	Annualized Total Return % with quintile ranks by obj 1994	3 years 1992-1994	5 years 1990-1994	Post quintile ranks for your funds here 1994	3 years ending 1994	5 years ending 1994
Fundamental Portfolio Advisors								
Fundamental Hi Yld Muni..............................	tax-free	1.0	-12.9[5]	-0.9[5]	0.2[5]	_____	_____	_____
Fundamental NY Muni................................	tax-free	213.2	-19.8[5]	0.3[5]	3.0[5]	_____	_____	_____
Fundamental CA Muni................................	tax-free	10.6	-19.9[5]	-0.2[5]	2.4[5]	_____	_____	_____
Fundamental US Gov Strat...........................	fix-inc	19.1	-25.6[5]	—	—	_____	_____	_____
Fundamental TF MM...................................	money mkt TF	9.5	1.7[5]	2.0[5]	3.2[4]	_____	_____	_____
Your average..		253.4				_____	_____	_____
FundTrust								
FundTrust Agg Gro†.................................	agg gr	38.0	-1.2[3]	5.9[4]	8.7[4]	_____	_____	_____
FundTrust Growth.†................................	growth	33.8	-0.5[3]	6.8[3]	8.0[3]	_____	_____	_____
FundTrust Gro & Inc†..............................	gr-inc	50.2	-0.2[3]	7.1[2]	6.8[4]	_____	_____	_____
FundTrust Mgd Tot Ret†...........................	gr-inc	16.2	-2.1[4]	4.3[4]	6.5[4]	_____	_____	_____
FundTrust Income†................................	fix-inc	74.0	-3.9[4]	4.6[2]	6.5[4]	_____	_____	_____
FundTrust Money Mkt..............................	money mkt	115.2	4.0[1]	3.3[2]	—	_____	_____	_____
Your average..		327.4				_____	_____	_____
Gabelli Funds..								
Gabelli Gold...	prec met	17.5	—	—	—	_____	_____	_____
Gabelli Glob Telecomm............................	global	137.8	-3.7[3]	—	—	_____	_____	_____
Gabelli Glob Couch Pot............................	global	24.8	—	—	—	_____	_____	_____
Gabelli Glob EntMedia............................	global	—	—	—	—	_____	_____	_____
Gabelli Glob Growth................................	global	—	—	—	—	_____	_____	_____
Gabelli Growth.......................................	growth	426.7	-3.4[4]	4.0[4]	8.1[3]	_____	_____	_____
Gabelli Asset...	growth	940.2	-0.1[3]	11.8[1]	9.4[2]	_____	_____	_____
Gabelli ABC...	growth	26.1	4.5[1]	—	—	_____	_____	_____
Gabelli Glob Convert...............................	income	15.3	—	—	—	_____	_____	_____
Gabelli Treas MM....................................	money mkt gov	204.9	3.8[1]	—	—	_____	_____	_____
Your average..		1,793.3				_____	_____	_____
Galaxy Funds..								
Galaxy Sm Co Idx SC................................	agg gr	230.6	-3.7[4]	6.4[3]	—	_____	_____	_____
Galaxy Sm Co Eqty SC..............................	agg gr	27.1	-0.1[2]	7.5[3]	—	_____	_____	_____
Galaxy Int'l Eqty.....................................	int'l	32.3	-2.5[3]	7.8[3]	—	_____	_____	_____
Galaxy Eqty Growth.................................	growth	68.1	0.6[2]	4.0[4]	—	_____	_____	_____
Galaxy Lg Co Idx....................................	gr-inc	137.7	1.0[2]	5.8[3]	—	_____	_____	_____
Galaxy Eqty Value..................................	gr-inc	73.6	3.5[1]	8.7[2]	8.9[2]	_____	_____	_____
Galaxy Eqty Income................................	income	61.0	0.8[2]	5.4[4]	—	_____	_____	_____
Galaxy Asst Allc.....................................	income	67.7	-2.5[3]	4.0[5]	—	_____	_____	_____
Galaxy Util Idx.......................................	income	53.3	-8.6[5]	—	—	_____	_____	_____
Galaxy Corp Bond...................................	fix-inc	—	—	—	—	_____	_____	_____
Galaxy Hi Qual Bd...................................	fix-inc	25.1	-6.5[4]	4.0[4]	—	_____	_____	_____
Galaxy Trsy Idx......................................	fix-inc	104.8	-3.7[3]	4.3[3]	—	_____	_____	_____
Galaxy Inter Bond...................................	fix-inc	84.3	-3.7[4]	2.9[5]	5.9[5]	_____	_____	_____
Galaxy ST Bond......................................	fix-inc	30.9	-0.3[3]	4.0[3]	—	_____	_____	_____
Galaxy CT Muni......................................	tax-free	16.5	-8.1[4]	—	—	_____	_____	_____
Galaxy Muni Bd......................................	tax-free	24.7	-5.4[2]	—	—	_____	_____	_____

No-load fund groups   *continued*

Families with 3 or more funds including one stock or bond fund
Arranged in alphabetical order by group and risk within group

| Fund group/fund | Objective | Total Net Assets $ Millions 12/31/94 | Annualized Total Return % with quintile ranks by obj | | | Post quintile ranks for your funds here | | |
			1994	3 years 1992-1994	5 years 1990-1994	1994	3 years ending 1994	5 years ending 1994
Galaxy TE Bond...	tax-free	31.3	-5.4[2]	5.0[2]	—			
Galaxy NY Muni...	tax-free	39.2	-7.2[4]	4.1[4]	—			
Galaxy MA Muni...	tax-free	14.1	-7.7[4]	—	—			
Galaxy Money Mkt...	money mkt	496.2	3.7[3]	3.3[2]	4.8[2]			
Galaxy TE MM...	money mkt TF	109.5	2.3[4]	2.2[4]	3.3[3]			
Galaxy Trsy MM...	money mkt gov	228.3	3.6[3]	3.2[2]	—			
Galaxy Gov MM...	money mkt gov	204.4	3.7[2]	3.4[1]	4.7[1]			
Your average...		2,160.7						
Gateway Funds...								
Gateway Sm Cap Idx SC...	agg gr	9.7	-6.0[4]	—	—			
Gateway MidCap Idx...	growth	6.6	-5.1[5]	—	—			
Gateway Cincinnati...	growth	3.2	—	—	—			
Gateway Idx Plus...	gr-inc	164.7	5.6[1]	6.0[3]	9.1[2]			
Your average...		184.2						
General Electric-Elfun Funds...								
GE Int'l Eqty...	int'l	0.7	—	—	—			
GE Elfun Trusts...	growth	900.6	0.2[3]	6.1[3]	8.1[3]			
GE S&S Prg: Mutual...	gr-inc	1,718.1	-1.8[4]	5.8[3]	8.3[2]			
GE US Equity...	gr-inc	16.7	-2.2[4]	—	—			
GE Global Eqty...	global	21.3	-1.9[2]	—	—			
GE Elfun Glob Inc...	global	126.1	-0.6[2]	11.6[1]	7.8[1]			
GE Elfun Div Inc...	gr-inc	57.8	-0.3[3]	6.0[3]	7.9[3]			
GE Strat Invest...	gr-inc	14.0	-1.8[4]	—	—			
GE Fixed Income...	fix-inc	15.0	-2.5[2]	—	—			
GE S&S Prg: LT Inst...	fix-inc	2,741.4	-2.5[2]	4.6[3]	7.7[2]			
GE Elfun Income...	fix-inc	184.8	-2.3[2]	4.5[3]	7.6[3]			
GE Elfun TE Inc...	tax-free	1,143.1	-5.8[2]	4.6[3]	6.3[3]			
GE TE Bond...	tax-free	6.0	-7.4[4]	—	—			
GE ST Gov...	fix-inc	1.1	—	—	—			
GE Money Mkt...	money mkt	45.9	—	—	—			
GE Elfun MM‡...	money mkt	107.1	4.2[1]	3.8[1]	—			
Your average...		7,099.7						
Gintel Funds...								
Gintel...	growth	88.3	-16.5[5]	2.0[5]	2.7[5]			
Gintel Erisa.‡...	gr-inc	30.1	-21.3[5]	-1.8[5]	0.4[5]			
UST Mstr Money Mkt*...	money mkt	733.5	3.9[2]	3.4[1]	4.9[1]			
UST Mstr Gov MM*...	money mkt gov	670.9	3.8[1]	3.4[1]	4.8[1]			
Your average...		118.4						
Government Investors Trust...								
GIT Special Gro SC...	agg gr	30.2	-3.9[4]	5.6[4]	4.5[5]			
GIT Select Gro...	growth	4.2	-5.2[5]	0.5[5]	4.1[5]			
GIT Wrldwd Growth...	global	3.9	-24.1[5]	—	—			
GIT Equity Inc...	gr-inc	3.2	-5.8[5]	2.1[5]	4.2[5]			

Families with 3 or more funds including one stock or bond fund
Arranged in alphabetical order by group and risk within group

Fund group/fund	Objective	Total Net Assets $ Millions 12/31/94	Annualized Total Return % with quintile ranks by obj 1994	3 years 1992-1994	5 years 1990-1994	Post quintile ranks for your funds here 1994	3 years ending 1994	5 years ending 1994
GIT Max Income	fix-inc	6.7	-2.6[2]	7.9[1]	7.8[2]			
GIT TF Nat	tax-free	31.7	-8.8[5]	3.3[5]	5.1[5]			
GIT Gov Port	fix-inc	7.5	-3.6[4]	3.7[4]	6.3[5]			
GIT TF AZ	tax-free	10.0	-8.7[5]	3.5[5]	5.3[5]			
GIT TF VA	tax-free	32.8	-8.3[4]	3.5[5]	5.2[5]			
GIT TF MO	tax-free	10.5	-8.5[5]	3.2[5]	4.9[5]			
GIT TF MD	tax-free	2.8	-8.9[5]	—	—			
GIT TF MM	money mkt TF	10.3	1.8[5]	1.8[5]	2.8[5]			
GIT MM Account	money mkt gov	75.7	3.1[5]	2.7[5]	4.1[5]			
Your average		229.5						
Goldman Sachs								
GS ST Gov Agency	fix-inc	160.0	0.4[2]	3.8[3]	6.0[4]			
Goldmn Sachs MM TE	money mkt TF	1,569.2	2.7[1]	—	—			
Goldmn Sachs MM Gov	money mkt gov	1,133.9	3.9[1]	3.5[1]	—			
Your average		2,863.1						
Government Street Funds								
Gov St Equity	growth	29.3	-2.2[4]	2.0[5]	—			
Gov St Bond	fix-inc	26.0	-2.7[3]	4.1[3]	—			
Gov St AL TF	tax-free	12.9	-3.1[1]	—	—			
Your average		68.2						
Gradison-McDonald Funds								
Gradison Oppty Value SC	agg gr	82.9	-2.2[3]	7.5[3]	8.0[4]			
Gradison Estab Value	growth	230.2	0.3[3]	10.1[2]	8.4[3]			
Gradison Gov MM	money mkt gov	1,033.8	3.5[4]	3.0[4]	4.3[5]			
Your average		1,346.9						
Harbor Capital								
Harbor Cap App	growth	239.1	3.4[1]	8.4[2]	14.1[1]			
Harbor Growth	growth	134.8	-11.4[5]	-0.6[5]	6.6[4]			
Harbor Int'l Gro	int'l	69.0	-7.7[4]	—	—			
Harbor Int'l‡	int'l	2,953.1	5.4[1]	15.2[1]	10.9[1]			
Harbor Value	gr-inc	56.9	0.7[2]	5.5[4]	6.1[4]			
Harbor Bond	fix-inc	167.0	-3.7[4]	5.7[1]	8.8[1]			
Harbor Short Dur	fix-inc	101.5	2.7[1]	3.9[3]	—			
Harbor Money Mkt	money mkt	74.0	3.9[2]	3.3[3]	4.7[2]			
Your average		3,795.4						
Heartland Advisors								
Heartland Value SC	agg gr	338.9	1.7[2]	19.8[1]	16.3[1]			
Heartland Val & Inc	gr-inc	9.9	-5.0[5]	—	—			
Heartland US Gov	fix-inc	64.8	-9.6[5]	5.4[1]	8.6[1]			
Heartland Nebraska TF	tax-free	12.5	-9.3[5]	—	—			
Heartland WI TF	tax-free	101.7	-6.6[3]	—	—			
Your average		527.8						

No-load fund groups   *continued*

Families with 3 or more funds including one stock or bond fund
Arranged in alphabetical order by group and risk within group

Fund group/fund	Objective	Total Net Assets $ Millions 12/31/94	1994	3 years 1992-1994	5 years 1990-1994	Post quintile ranks for your funds here 1994	3 years ending 1994	5 years ending 1994
Hercules Funds								
Hercules Pacific Bas..............................	int'l	39.4	-1.8[3]	—	—			
Hercules Latin Amer..............................	int'l	28.3	-18.1[5]	—	—			
Hercules European...	int'l	18.4	2.4[2]	—	—			
Hercules N Amer Gr&Inc...	global	15.9	-13.0[5]	—	—			
Hercules World Bond.............................	fix-inc	26.4	-6.2[4]	—	—			
Hercules Glob ST..................................	fix-inc	1.1	-0.4[3]	—	—			
Your average...		129.5						
Homestead Funds								
Homestead Value...................................	gr-inc	90.1	2.5[1]	10.8[1]	—			
Homestead ST Bond..............................	fix-inc	52.1	0.1[3]	4.3[2]	—			
Homestead Daily Inc..............................	money mkt	36.6	3.6[4]	3.3[3]	—			
Your average...		178.8						
Household Personal....................................								
Household Gro Eqty................................	growth	0.1	-4.5[4]	—	—			
Household Eqty Inc.................................	gr-inc	0.2	-5.5[5]	—	—			
Household Fix Inc...	fix-inc	0.1	-5.6[4]	—	—			
Household TE Inc...................................	tax-free	5.3	-3.1[1]	—	—			
Household ST Inc...................................	fix-inc	0.1	-1.8[4]	—	—			
Your average...		5.8						
Hotchkis & Wiley								
Htchks & Wly Sm Cap SC	agg gr	14.8	1.1[2]	9.0[2]	11.8[2]			
Htchks & Wly Int'l...	int'l	27.7	-3.0[4]	11.2[2]	—			
Htchks & Wly Eq Inc..............................	gr-inc	106.7	-3.5[4]	8.4[2]	7.0[3]			
Htchks & Wly Blncd................................	income	34.1	0.8[2]	7.5[2]	8.3[3]			
Htchks & Wly Low Dur............................	fix-inc	70.8	5.1[1]	—	—			
Htchks & Wly Tot Ret.............................	fix-inc	2.8	—	—	—			
Htchks & Wly ST Invest..........................	fix-inc	13.6	4.5[1]	—	—			
Your average...		270.5						
Investment Advisors, Inc								
IAI Emg Growth SC	agg gr	317.2	0.2[2]	12.1[1]	—			
IAI International...	int'l	149.1	0.5[3]	9.5[2]	5.9[2]			
IAI MidCap..	growth	84.8	5.7[1]	—	—			
IAI Growth...	growth	23.2	0.7[2]	—	—			
IAI Regional..	growth	514.0	0.7[2]	4.3[4]	8.9[3]			
IAI Value...	growth	34.6	-9.1[5]	7.5[3]	5.6[5]			
IAI Gro & Inc...	gr-inc	104.6	-4.8[5]	2.9[5]	5.2[5]			
IAI Balanced...	income	42.1	-1.4[3]	—	—			
IAI Bond...	fix-inc	80.4	-4.9[3]	4.5[3]	7.4[3]			
IAI Gov Bond...	fix-inc	39.1	-2.3[4]	3.9[3]	—			
IAI Reserve...	fix-inc	78.1	2.7[1]	3.1[4]	5.1[5]			
IAI MN TF...	tax-free	7.0	-8.4[4]	—	—			
IAI Money Mkt...	money mkt	27.2	3.7[3]	—	—			
Your average...		1,501.4						

Families with 3 or more funds including one stock or bond fund
Arranged in alphabetical order by group and risk within group

Fund group/fund	Objective	Total Net Assets $ Millions 12/31/94	Annualized Total Return % with quintile ranks by obj 1994	3 years 1992-1994	5 years 1990-1994	Post quintile ranks for your funds here 1994	3 years ending 1994	5 years ending 1994
Invesco Funds								
Invesco Strat Health...	sector	488.5	0.9³	-7.3⁵	14.0³	___	___	___
Invesco Strat Tech...	sector	310.1	5.3²	12.9³	22.5¹	___	___	___
Invesco Dynamics...	agg gr	338.9	-1.9³	9.7²	15.6¹	___	___	___
Invesco Emg Gro SC...	agg gr	179.3	-3.7⁴	14.3¹	—	___	___	___
Invesco Small Co SC...	agg gr	16.3	-1.0³	—	—	___	___	___
Invesco Strat Gold...	prec met	222.0	-27.9⁵	4.6⁵	-4.0⁵	___	___	___
Invesco Pacific Bas...	int'l	252.0	4.7²	8.9²	2.0⁴	___	___	___
Invesco Europe Sm Co...	int'l	—	—	—	—	___	___	___
Invesco Europe...	int'l	245.6	-3.0⁴	3.7⁵	3.9³	___	___	___
Invesco Int'l Gro...	int'l	108.7	0.6³	4.0⁵	0.6⁵	___	___	___
Invesco Wrld Cap Gds...	sector	3.5	—	—	—	___	___	___
Invesco Wrld Comm...	global	15.8	—	—	—	___	___	___
Invesco Strat Enrgy...	sector	46.9	-7.3⁴	-2.1⁵	-5.4⁵	___	___	___
Invesco Strat Fncl...	sector	236.4	-5.9⁴	12.2³	18.0¹	___	___	___
Invesco Strat Leisure...	sector	262.8	-5.0³	16.8²	16.7²	___	___	___
Invesco Strat Envrn...	sector	22.9	-11.4⁵	-11.8⁵	—	___	___	___
Invesco Value Eqty...	growth	108.1	4.0¹	6.4³	9.1³	___	___	___
Invesco Growth...	growth	444.5	-8.8⁵	3.4⁴	9.2³	___	___	___
Invesco Indust Inc...	gr-inc	3,695.5	-3.9⁴	4.2⁴	10.8¹	___	___	___
Invesco Total Ret...	income	293.7	2.5¹	8.2²	9.5²	___	___	___
Invesco Multi-Asst...	income	6.3	-2.0³	—	—	___	___	___
Invesco Balanced...	income	12.5	9.5¹	—	—	___	___	___
Invesco Strat Util...	sector	122.5	-9.9⁵	6.6⁴	6.9⁴	___	___	___
Invesco High Yld...	fix-inc	210.8	-5.1³	8.0¹	8.2²	___	___	___
Invesco Select Inc...	fix-inc	136.7	-1.2¹	6.7¹	8.6¹	___	___	___
Invesco TF Long...	tax-free	254.1	-7.5⁴	4.1⁴	6.3³	___	___	___
Invesco Gov Sec...	fix-inc	31.4	-7.2⁴	2.7⁵	6.0⁵	___	___	___
Invesco Inter Gov...	fix-inc	31.5	-1.7⁴	4.3¹	7.2¹	___	___	___
Invesco TF Inter...	tax-free	4.3	-4.4⁴	—	—	___	___	___
Invesco ST Bond...	fix-inc	8.6	-0.6³	—	—	___	___	___
Invesco Cash Res...	money mkt	745.5	3.7³	3.1⁴	4.5⁴	___	___	___
Invesco TF MM...	money mkt TF	76.5	2.2⁵	2.2⁴	3.1⁵	___	___	___
Invesco Gov MM...	money mkt gov	75.6	3.6³	3.0⁵	—	___	___	___
Your average...		9,007.8				___	___	___
Janus Capital								
Janus Twenty‡...	agg gr	2,504.3	-6.7⁴	-0.5⁵	10.9²	___	___	___
Janus Mercury...	agg gr	690.1	15.9¹	—	—	___	___	___
Janus Enterprise...	growth	354.1	8.9¹	—	—	___	___	___
Janus Venture SC.‡...	growth	1,496.1	5.5¹	7.3³	12.7¹	___	___	___
Janus Worldwide...	global	1,542.6	3.6¹	13.2¹	—	___	___	___
Janus Overseas...	int'l	65.4	—	—	—	___	___	___
Janus Fund...	growth	9,400.6	-1.1³	5.4⁴	10.7²	___	___	___
Janus Growth & Inc...	gr-inc	456.5	-4.9⁵	2.3⁵	—	___	___	___
Janus Balanced...	gr-inc	93.4	0.0²	—	—	___	___	___
Janus Flex Inc...	fix-inc	353.9	-2.9³	7.9¹	8.6¹	___	___	___

Families with 3 or more funds including one stock or bond fund
Arranged in alphabetical order by group and risk within group

Fund group/fund	Objective	Total Net Assets $ Millions 12/31/94	1994	3 years 1992-1994	5 years 1990-1994	Post quintile ranks for your funds here 1994	3 years ending 1994	5 years ending 1994
Janus Federal TE...	tax-free	24.2	-7.8[4]	—	—			
Janus Inter Gov...	fix-inc	35.0	-2.4[5]	1.6[5]	—			
Janus ST Bond...	fix-inc	45.5	0.4[2]	—	—			
Janus-MM...	money mkt	0.0	—	—	—			
Janus-TE MM...	money mkt TF	0.0	—	—	—			
Janus-Gov MM...	money mkt gov	0.0	—	—	—			
Your average...		17,061.7						
Jurika & Voyles								
Jurika & Vyls Mini Cap SC...	agg gr	2.9	—	—	—			
Jurika & Vyls Val & Gro...	gr-inc	1.6	—	—	—			
Jurika & Vyls Blncd...	income	32.2	-2.2[3]	—	—			
Your average...		36.7						
Legg Mason								
Legg Msn Spec Invest SC...	agg gr	605.7	-13.1[5]	7.6[3]	11.8[2]			
Legg Msn Total Ret...	growth	193.3	-7.2[5]	6.6[3]	7.3[4]			
Legg Msn Value...	growth	967.3	1.3[2]	7.9[2]	7.1[4]			
Legg Msn Amer Lead...	growth	56.1	-4.2[4]	—	—			
Legg Msn High Yld...	fix-inc	53.4	—	—	—			
Legg Msn Invest Grd...	fix-inc	66.0	-4.6[5]	4.3[3]	6.8[4]			
Legg Msn Glob Gov...	fix-inc	145.1	-1.6[1]	—	—			
Legg Msn Gov Inter...	fix-inc	235.0	-1.7[2]	3.7[4]	6.8[4]			
Legg Msn Cash Res...	money mkt	861.8	3.7[4]	3.3[2]	4.7[3]			
Legg Msn TE MM...	money mkt TF	222.5	2.3[4]	2.1[5]	3.1[5]			
Legg Msn Gov MM...	money mkt gov	214.5	3.7[2]	3.3[1]	4.7[2]			
Your average...		3,620.7						
Lexington Management								
Lexington Goldfund...	prec met	158.8	-7.3[2]	11.3[3]	0.5[4]			
Lexington World Emg...	int'l	288.5	-13.8[5]	13.5[1]	9.2[1]			
Lexington Int'l...	int'l	17.8	5.9[1]	—	—			
Lexington Global...	global	67.4	1.8[1]	9.0[2]	4.5[3]			
Lexington Corp Ldrs...	gr-inc	156.3	-0.8[3]	8.6[2]	7.9[3]			
Lexington Gro & Inc...	gr-inc	124.3	-3.1[4]	7.2[2]	6.7[4]			
Lexington Convert...	income	8.0	1.3[1]	6.2[3]	10.9[1]			
Lex-Ramrz Glob Inc...	fix-inc	—	—	—	—			
Lexington GNMA...	fix-inc	132.4	-2.1[2]	3.6[4]	6.9[3]			
Lexington TE Bond...	tax-free	10.6	-6.5[3]	3.4[5]	5.2[5]			
Lexington S-I Gov...	fix-inc	5.8	-0.2[3]	—	—			
Lexington MM...	money mkt	110.8	3.4[5]	2.9[5]	4.3[5]			
Lexington TF MM...	money mkt TF	37.5	2.0[5]	2.1[5]	3.2[4]			
Your average...		1,118.2						
Lindner Ryback Management								
Lindner Bulwark...	growth	83.1	—	—	—			
Lindner Small Cap SC...	growth	5.6	—	—	—			

No-load fund groups *continued*

Families with 3 or more funds including one stock or bond fund
Arranged in alphabetical order by group and risk within group

Fund group/fund	Objective	Total Net Assets $ Millions 12/31/94	Annualized Total Return % with quintile ranks by obj 1994	3 years 1992-1994	5 years 1990-1994	Post quintile ranks for your funds here 1994	3 years ending 1994	5 years ending 1994
Lindner Int'l	int'l	—	—					
Lindner Fund	growth	1,502.9	-0.7[3]	10.3[2]	8.0[4]			
Lindner Utility	income	43.4	-1.0[2]	—	—			
Lindner Dividend	income	1,605.2	-3.3[4]	10.4[1]	9.9[1]			
Your average		3,240.2						
Loomis Sayles								
Loomis Syls Sm Cap SC	agg gr	74.1	-8.3[5]	8.9[2]	—			
Loomis Syls Int'l Eq	int'l	71.6	-1.8[3]	8.9[2]	—			
Loomis Syls Growth	growth	36.9	-3.6[4]	3.0[4]	—			
Loomis Syls Gro & Inc	gr-inc	25.7	-0.9[3]	8.2[2]	—			
Loomis Syls Glob Bd	fix-inc	25.7	-8.7[5]	1.8[5]	—			
Loomis Syls Bond	fix-inc	82.5	-4.1[3]	10.2[1]	—			
Loomis Syls Muni	tax-free	7.3	-5.4[2]	4.9[2]	—			
Loomis Syls US Gov	fix-inc	17.3	-6.3[4]	5.7[2]	—			
Loomis Syls ST Bd	fix-inc	19.2	1.8[1]	—	—			
Your average		360.3						
Managers funds								
Managers Spec Eqty SC	agg gr	110.0	-2.0[3]	10.1[2]	10.9[2]			
Managers Cap App	agg gr	84.2	-1.5[3]	7.0[3]	9.7[3]			
Managers Int'l Eqty	int'l	86.5	2.0[2]	13.7[1]	9.4[1]			
Managers Glob Oppty	global	52.9	—	—	—			
Managers Balanced	gr-inc	1.5	-3.0[4]	2.6[5]	5.8[5]			
Managers Inc Eqty	income	47.6	1.0[1]	7.2[2]	7.0[4]			
Managers Glob Bd	fix-inc	10.0	—	—	—			
Managers Bond	fix-inc	30.2	-7.2[4]	3.7[4]	7.4[3]			
Managers Muni Bd	tax-free	20.0	-5.6[2]	4.0[4]	5.7[5]			
Managers Inter Mortg	fix-inc	56.6	-25.0[5]	-2.6[5]	3.8[5]			
Managers Sht & Int	fix-inc	30.8	-8.4[5]	3.5[4]	6.0[4]			
Managers ST Muni	tax-free	10.0	0.3[2]	2.8[5]	3.9[5]			
Managers ST Gov	fix-inc	13.8	-6.2[5]	0.4[5]	3.7[5]			
Managers Money Mkt	money mkt	18.0	3.6[4]	3.2[3]	4.5[4]			
Your average		572.1						
Marshall Funds								
Marshall Int'l Stk	int'l	74.8	—	—	—			
Marshall MidCap Stk	growth	69.3	-5.6[5]	—	—			
Marshall Stock	gr-inc	226.5	-5.8[5]	—	—			
Marshall Value Eqty	gr-inc	195.2	2.1[1]	—	—			
Marshall Eqty Inc	gr-inc	60.9	-1.6[4]	—	—			
Marshall Balanced	income	2.5	-5.7[5]	—	—			
Marshall Gov Inc	fix-inc	78.7	-2.7[2]	—	—			
Marshall Inter Bd	fix-inc	326.1	-3.1[3]	—	—			
Marshall Inter TF	tax-free	37.3	—	—	—			
Marshall ST Inc	fix-inc	92.7	1.8[1]	—	—			
Marshall ST TF	tax-free	24.8	—	—	—			

Families with 3 or more funds including one stock or bond fund
Arranged in alphabetical order by group and risk within group

Fund group/fund	Objective	Total Net Assets $ Millions 12/31/94	Annualized Total Return % with quintile ranks by obj 1994	3 years 1992-1994	5 years 1990-1994	Post quintile ranks for your funds here 1994	3 years ending 1994	5 years ending 1994
Marshall MM Trust...	money mkt	1,046.8	4.1[1]	—	—	___	___	___
Marshall MM Invest...	money mkt	17.9	3.8[3]	—	—	___	___	___
Your average...		2,253.5				___	___	___
Maxus Funds								
Maxus Laureate	agg gr	2.0	-3.2[4]	—	—	___	___	___
Maxus Equity...	gr-inc	17.0	1.1[2]	14.1[1]	10.7[1]	___	___	___
Maxus Income...	fix-inc	33.4	-4.5[3]	4.6[3]	6.7[4]	___	___	___
Your average...		52.4				___	___	___
Merriman Funds								
Merriman Levgd Gro...	agg gr	5.8	-0.1[2]	—	—	___	___	___
Merriman Cap App...	growth	23.8	-0.6[3]	2.4[5]	6.2[5]	___	___	___
Merriman Gro & Inc...	gr-inc	9.9	-0.2[3]	0.4[5]	4.6[5]	___	___	___
Merriman Asst All...	income	25.8	-2.9[4]	5.8[3]	6.1[5]	___	___	___
Merriman Flex Bd...	fix-inc	9.4	-1.7[2]	5.6[1]	7.2[2]	___	___	___
Portico Money Mkt*...	money mkt	158.0	3.8[2]	3.3[3]	4.7[2]	___	___	___
Portico TE MM*...	money mkt TF	67.4	2.5[2]	2.4[2]	3.4[2]	___	___	___
Portico Federal MM*...	money mkt gov	57.2	3.5[4]	3.1[4]	—	___	___	___
Portico Gov MM*...	money mkt gov	170.8	3.7[2]	3.2[2]	4.5[3]	___	___	___
Your average...		74.7				___	___	___
Mathematical Investing Systems								
MIM Stock Apprec...	agg gr	41.0	-10.4[5]	1.5[5]	14.3[1]	___	___	___
MIM Stock Growth...	growth	6.6	-11.7[5]	-4.0[5]	1.1[5]	___	___	___
MIM Stock Income...	gr-inc	5.4	-1.8[4]	0.8[5]	3.4[5]	___	___	___
MIM AFA Eqty Inc...	income	2.3	-6.0[5]	3.1[5]	—	___	___	___
MIM Bond Income...	fix-inc	1.9	-3.6[3]	2.0[5]	4.2[5]	___	___	___
MIM Money Mkt...	money mkt	3.9	3.2[5]	3.1[4]	4.5[4]	___	___	___
Your average...		61.1				___	___	___
Monetta Funds								
Monetta Fund‡...	growth	364.9	-6.2[5]	-0.2[5]	11.5[1]	___	___	___
Monetta MidCap Eqty...	growth	11.7	2.2[2]	—	—	___	___	___
Monetta Inter Bd...	fix-inc	3.0	-1.0[1]	—	—	___	___	___
Monetta Gov MM...	money mkt gov	3.3	4.0[1]	—	—	___	___	___
Your average...		382.9				___	___	___
Montgomery Asset Management								
Montgmry Emg Mkts...	int'l	878.0	-7.7[4]	—	—	___	___	___
Montgmry Micro Cap SC...	agg gr	0.1	—	—	—	___	___	___
Montgmry Sm Cap SC‡...	agg gr	202.5	-9.9[5]	7.1[3]	—	___	___	___
Montgmry Growth...	growth	592.7	20.9[1]	—	—	___	___	___
Montgmry Int'l Sm Cap...	int'l	29.3	-13.3[5]	—	—	___	___	___
Montgmry Glob Comm...	global	216.4	-13.4[5]	—	—	___	___	___
Montgmry Glob Oppty...	global	13.2	-8.5[4]	—	—	___	___	___
Montgmry Eqty Inc...	gr-inc	1.0	—	—	—	___	___	___

No-load fund groups *continued*

Families with 3 or more funds including one stock or bond fund
Arranged in alphabetical order by group and risk within group

Fund group/fund	Objective	Total Net Assets $ Millions 12/31/94	1994	3 years 1992-1994	5 years 1990-1994	1994	3 years ending 1994	5 years ending 1994
						Post quintile ranks for your funds here		
Montgmry Asst All...	income	9.5	—	—	—			
Montgmry CA TF S-I...	tax-free	8.3	0.0[3]	—	—			
Montgmry Short Gov...	fix-inc	19.0	1.1[2]	—	—			
Montgmry CA TF MM...	money mkt TF	47.2	—	—	—			
Montgmry Gov MM...	money mkt gov	235.5	3.8[2]	—	—			
Your average...		2,252.7						
Mutual Series								
Mutual Discovery SC‡...	growth	725.8	3.6[1]	—	—			
Mutual Beacon...	gr-inc	2,056.4	5.6[1]	16.8[1]	11.5[1]			
Mutual Qualified...	gr-inc	1,788.8	5.7[1]	16.7[1]	11.6[1]			
Mutual Shares...	gr-inc	3,745.3	4.5[1]	15.3[1]	10.8[1]			
Your average...		8,316.3						
Neuberger & Berman								
Nbrgr-Ber Genesis SC...	agg gr	108.0	-1.8[3]	8.9[3]	8.9[3]			
Nbrgr-Ber Manhtn...	growth	462.2	-3.6[4]	7.7[3]	8.5[3]			
Nbrgr-Ber Focus...	growth	603.1	0.9[2]	12.4[1]	10.8[2]			
Nbrgr-Ber Partners...	growth	1,245.2	-1.9[4]	10.3[2]	9.3[2]			
Nbrgr-Ber Guardian...	growth	2,423.8	0.6[2]	11.1[1]	11.9[1]			
Nbrgr-Ber Social Resp...	growth	4.0	—	—	—			
Nbrgr-Ber Int'l Eqty...	int'l	18.0	—	—	—			
Nbrgr-Ber Muni...	tax-free	40.6	-4.0[3]	4.0[5]	5.6[5]			
Nbrgr-Ber Gov Inc...	fix-inc	10.1	-3.3[3]	—	—			
Nbrgr-Ber NY Ins Inter...	tax-free	10.0	—	—	—			
Nbrgr-Ber Ltd Mat...	fix-inc	293.0	-0.3[3]	3.8[3]	6.4[3]			
Nbrgr-Ber Ultra Sht...	fix-inc	90.5	2.2[1]	3.0[4]	5.0[5]			
Nbrgr-Ber Cash Res...	money mkt	322.5	3.7[3]	3.2[3]	4.6[3]			
Nbrgr-Ber Muni MM...	money mkt TF	162.5	2.3[4]	2.2[5]	3.2[4]			
Nbrgr-Ber Gov MM...	money mkt gov	242.3	3.4[5]	3.1[4]	4.4[4]			
Your average...		6,035.8						
Nicholas Company								
Nicholas Ltd Edit SC...	growth	142.6	-3.0[4]	7.3[3]	11.7[1]			
Nicholas II SC...	growth	603.9	1.0[2]	5.5[4]	9.0[3]			
Nicholas Fund...	growth	2,820.2	-2.9[4]	5.0[4]	9.4[2]			
Nicholas Eqty Inc...	gr-inc	10.9	4.1[1]	—	—			
Nicholas Income...	fix-inc	140.9	-0.2[1]	7.5[1]	8.6[1]			
Nicholas Money Mkt...	money mkt	118.1	3.9[2]	3.3[2]	4.7[2]			
Your average...		3,836.6						
Northern Trust								
Northern Sm Cap SC...	agg gr	64.8	—	—	—			
Northern Growth Eq...	growth	95.5	—	—	—			
Northern Select Eq...	growth	10.5	—	—	—			
Northern Int'l Gro Eq...	int'l	101.9	—	—	—			
Northern Int'l Sel Eq...	int'l	77.6	—	—	—			

Families with 3 or more funds including one stock or bond fund
Arranged in alphabetical order by group and risk within group

Fund group/fund	Objective	Total Net Assets $ Millions 12/31/94	Annualized Total Return % with quintile ranks by obj 1994	3 years 1992-1994	5 years 1990-1994	Post quintile ranks for your funds here 1994	3 years ending 1994	5 years ending 1994
Northern Income Eq...	gr-inc	35.6	—	—	—			
Northern Int'l Fixed...	fix-inc	11.4	—	—	—			
Northern Fix Inc...	fix-inc	62.0	—	—	—			
Northern US Gov...	fix-inc	110.2	—	—	—			
Northern TE Bond...	tax-free	119.7	—	—	—			
Northern Inter TE...	tax-free	217.0	—	—	—			
Northern Money Mkt...	money mkt	—	—	—	—			
Northern CA MM...	money mkt TF	—	—	—	—			
Northern Muni MM...	money mkt TF	—	—	—	—			
Northern Gov MM...	money mkt gov	—	—	—	—			
Northern Gov Sel MM...	money mkt gov	—	—	—	—			
Your average...		906.2						
Northwest Funds (Saturna Capital) ...								
Northwest Growth...	growth	1.0	-11.4[5]	-1.3[5]	4.9[5]			
Amana Growth...	growth	1.7	—	—	—			
Amana Income...	income	10.0	-6.5[5]	2.1[5]	4.9[5]			
Northwest WA TE...	tax-free	1.5	-6.3[3]	—	—			
Northwest Idaho TE...	tax-free	6.9	-3.4[1]	3.8[5]	5.2[5]			
Your average...		21.1						
Pacifica Funds ...								
Pacifica Asset Pres...	fix-inc	78.9	2.4[1]	3.9[4]	—			
Pacifica ST CA TF...	tax-free	35.0	1.1[1]	—	—			
Pacifica Money Mkt...	money mkt	158.4	3.8[2]	—	—			
Pacifica Gov MM...	money mkt gov	140.2	3.7[2]	—	—			
Your average...		412.5						
Parnassus Funds ...								
Parnassus Balanced...	income	17.1	-5.3[4]	—	—			
Parnassus Fix Inc...	fix-inc	4.5	-6.8[4]	—	—			
Parnassus CA TF...	tax-free	3.9	-6.4[3]	—	—			
Your average...		25.5						
Pilgrim, Baxter ...								
PBHG Emg Growth SC‡...	agg gr	177.7	23.8[1]	—	—			
PBHG Growth‡...	agg gr	745.8	4.7[1]	25.4[1]	22.0[1]			
PBHG Int'l...	int'l	15.0	—	—	—			
Your average...		938.5						
Permanent Portfolio Funds ...								
Permanent Agg Growth† ...	agg gr	6.3	1.0[2]	13.9[1]	—			
Permanent Portfolio† ...	global	72.2	-2.9[3]	4.8[5]	3.6[5]			
Permanent Vers Bd† ..	fix-inc	23.9	2.6[1]	4.0[2]	—			
Permanent Treasy† ...	fix-inc	122.1	3.3[1]	2.8[5]	4.2[5]			
Your average...		224.5						

Families with 3 or more funds including one stock or bond fund
Arranged in alphabetical order by group and risk within group

Fund group/fund	Objective	Total Net Assets $ Millions 12/31/94	1994	Annualized Total Return % with quintile ranks by obj — 3 years 1992-1994	5 years 1990-1994	Post quintile ranks for your funds here — 1994	3 years ending 1994	5 years ending 1994
Pierpont Funds								
Pierpont Emg Mkts...	int'l	46.6	-7.0^4	—	—	____	____	____
Pierpont Cap App SC...	agg gr	171.1	-5.9^4	6.7^3	8.0^4	____	____	____
Pierpont US Stock...	growth	—				____	____	____
Pierpont Equity...	gr-inc	229.1	-0.6^3	6.3^3	10.3^1	____	____	____
Pierpont Int'l Eqty...	int'l	197.9	5.7^1	5.9^4	—	____	____	____
Pierpont Divsfd...	gr-inc	15.9	-0.6^3	—	—	____	____	____
Pierpont Bond...	fix-inc	110.5	-3.0^2	3.8^4	6.9^4	____	____	____
Pierpont TE Bond...	tax-free	330.6	-2.8^1	5.0^2	6.5^3	____	____	____
Pierpont ST Bond...	fix-inc	7.3	0.1^2	—	—	____	____	____
Pierpont Money Mkt...	money mkt	1,974.7	—	—	—	____	____	____
Pierpont TE MM...	money mkt TF	894.3	—	—	—	____	____	____
Pierpont Treas MM...	money mkt gov	213.0	—	—	—	____	____	____
Your average...		4,191.0				____	____	____
Pacific Investment Management								
PIMCO Tot Return‡...	fix-inc	6,554.8	-3.6^3	6.0^2	9.0^1	____	____	____
PIMCO Low Dur‡...	fix-inc	2,215.6	0.6^2	5.3^1	7.6^1	____	____	____
PIMCO Short-Term‡...	fix-inc	97.8	2.9^1	3.7^3	5.2^5	____	____	____
Your average...		8,868.2				____	____	____
Preferred Funds								
Preferred Growth...	growth	241.1	-1.1^3	—	—	____	____	____
Preferred Int'l...	int'l	107.6	3.3^2	—	—	____	____	____
Preferred Value...	gr-inc	148.6	0.5^2	—	—	____	____	____
Preferred Asst Allc...	gr-inc	61.0	-2.6^4	—	—	____	____	____
Preferred Fix Inc...	fix-inc	46.7	-2.4^2	—	—	____	____	____
Preferred ST Gov...	fix-inc	29.4	-0.7^3	—	—	____	____	____
Preferred Money Mkt...	money mkt	57.0	3.9^2	—	—	____	____	____
Your average...		691.4				____	____	____
T. Rowe Price Associates								
Price, Rowe SciTech...	sector	915.1	15.8^1	19.5^1	22.0^1	____	____	____
Price, Rowe Japan...	int'l	169.3	15.1^1	6.3^4	—	____	____	____
Price, Rowe Latin Amer...	int'l	163.8	-15.9^5	—	—	____	____	____
Price, Rowe Int'l Disc...	int'l	437.4	-7.6^4	8.0^3	4.1^3	____	____	____
Price, Rowe New Asia...	int'l	1,987.6	-19.2^5	17.1^1	—	____	____	____
Price, Rowe Europe...	int'l	366.5	4.1^2	7.7^4	—	____	____	____
Price, Rowe Int'l Stk...	int'l	5,786.9	-0.8^3	10.3^2	7.2^1	____	____	____
Price, Rowe New Horiz SC...	agg gr	1,648.4	0.3^2	10.6^2	13.2^2	____	____	____
Price, Rowe OTC SC...	agg gr	196.7	0.1^2	10.5^2	8.3^4	____	____	____
Price, Rowe New Amer...	agg gr	646.1	-7.4^5	6.1^3	11.2^2	____	____	____
Price, Rowe Cap Oppty...	agg gr	2.4	—	—	—	____	____	____
Price, Rowe Cap App...	growth	655.0	3.8^1	9.5^2	9.5^2	____	____	____
Price, Rowe New Era...	growth	979.5	5.2^1	7.4^3	5.3^5	____	____	____
Price, Rowe Sm Cap Val SC...	growth	408.4	-1.4^4	13.7^1	11.8^1	____	____	____

No-load fund groups *continued*

Families with 3 or more funds including one stock or bond fund
Arranged in alphabetical order by group and risk within group

| Fund group/fund | Objective | Total Net Assets $ Millions 12/31/94 | Annualized Total Return % with quintile ranks by obj | | | Post quintile ranks for your funds here | | |
			1994	3 years 1992-1994	5 years 1990-1994	1994	3 years ending 1994	5 years ending 1994
Price, Rowe Mid Cap...	growth	100.5	0.3[3]	—	—			
Price, Rowe Growth Stk...	growth	2,067.5	0.9[2]	7.3[3]	9.6[2]			
Price, Rowe Blue Chip...	growth	39.0	0.8[2]	—	—			
Price Pers Str-Gro...	growth	6.5	—	—	—			
Price, Rowe Spect-Gro...	growth	879.4	1.4[2]	9.6[2]	—			
Price, Rowe Eqty Idx...	gr-inc	270.2	1.0[2]	5.8[3]	—			
Price, Rowe Value...	gr-inc	8.6	—	—	—			
Price, Rowe Div Gro...	gr-inc	53.6	2.2[1]	—	—			
Price, Rowe Gro & Inc...	gr-inc	1,228.9	-0.1[3]	9.2[1]	8.7[2]			
Price Pers Str-Blncd...	gr-inc	8.3	—	—	—			
Price, Rowe Eqty Inc...	income	3,203.9	4.5[1]	11.1[1]	9.9[2]			
Price, Rowe Balanced...	income	392.0	-2.0[3]	5.7[4]	—			
Price Pers Str-Inc...	income	6.0	—	—	—			
Price, Rowe Emg Mkt Bond...	fix-inc	—	—	—	—			
Price, Rowe Int'l Bond...	fix-inc	738.1	-1.8[2]	6.4[1]	10.5[1]			
Price, Rowe High Yld...	fix-inc	1,040.4	-8.1[5]	8.7[1]	8.4[1]			
Price, Rowe Glob Gov...	fix-inc	36.5	-3.2[3]	3.7[4]	—			
Price, Rowe New Inc...	fix-inc	1,367.8	-2.2[2]	4.0[3]	7.1[3]			
Price, Rowe TF Hi Yld...	tax-free	802.2	-4.4[1]	5.8[1]	7.2[1]			
Price, Rowe CA TF...	tax-free	122.2	-5.7[2]	4.9[2]	6.5[3]			
Price, Rowe NY TF...	tax-free	110.8	-5.9[2]	5.6[1]	6.9[2]			
Price, Rowe NJ TF...	tax-free	53.3	-6.1[3]	5.5[1]	—			
Price, Rowe GA TF...	tax-free	20.9	-5.9[3]	—	—			
Price, Rowe VA TF...	tax-free	143.9	-5.1[2]	5.3[1]	—			
Price, Rowe MD TF...	tax-free	675.2	-5.0[1]	5.1[2]	6.5[2]			
Price Summit Muni Inc...	tax-free	7.3	-4.7[1]	—	—			
Price, Rowe TF Inc...	tax-free	1,253.9	-5.5[2]	5.3[2]	6.7[2]			
Price, Rowe Trsy Lng...	fix-inc	58.3	-5.7[4]	4.0[4]	6.9[4]			
Price, Rowe ST Glob...	fix-inc	56.4	-2.9[5]	—	—			
Price, Rowe Spect-Inc...	fix-inc	624.9	-1.9[2]	5.9[1]	—			
Price Summit GNMA...	fix-inc	16.3	-2.3[2]	—	—			
Price, Rowe GNMA...	fix-inc	752.2	-1.5[1]	3.6[4]	7.1[3]			
Price, Rowe Trsy Inter...	fix-inc	163.1	-2.2[4]	3.9[3]	7.0[2]			
Price Summit Muni Inter...	tax-free	16.2	-1.7[1]	—	—			
Price, Rowe TF Ins Inter...	tax-free	79.8	-2.6[2]	—	—			
Price, Rowe FL Ins Inter...	tax-free	51.7	-2.6[2]	—	—			
Price, Rowe MD ST TF...	tax-free	76.3	0.6[2]	—	—			
Price, Rowe TF S-I...	tax-free	451.1	0.3[3]	4.2[3]	5.3[3]			
Price Summit Ltd Trm...	fix-inc	17.3	-3.1[5]	—	—			
Price, Rowe ST Bond...	fix-inc	474.9	-2.9[5]	2.8[5]	5.7[5]			
Price, Rowe Adj Rate...	fix-inc	120.9	-0.6[3]	2.0[5]	—			
Price, Rowe Prime Res...	money mkt	3,891.2	3.7[3]	3.2[3]	4.6[3]			
Price Summit Cash Res...	money mkt	249.7	4.0[1]	—	—			
Price, Rowe NY MM...	money mkt TF	68.8	2.3[4]	2.2[4]	3.0[5]			
Price, Rowe CA MM...	money mkt TF	77.1	2.4[3]	2.2[4]	3.1[5]			
Price, Rowe TE MM...	money mkt TF	712.6	2.5[2]	2.3[3]	3.2[3]			

No-load fund groups *continued*

Families with 3 or more funds including one stock or bond fund
Arranged in alphabetical order by group and risk within group

| Fund group/fund | Objective | Total Net Assets $ Millions 12/31/94 | Annualized Total Return % with quintile ranks by obj | | | Post quintile ranks for your funds here | | |
			1994	3 years 1992-1994	5 years 1990-1994	1994	3 years ending 1994	5 years ending 1994
Price Summit Muni MM...	money mkt TF	61.0	2.6[2]	—	—	___	___	___
Price, Rowe Trsy MM...	money mkt gov	704.4	3.5[4]	3.1[4]	4.4[4]	___	___	___
Your average...		37,724.1				___	___	___
Primary Funds								
Primary Trend...	gr-inc	20.1	-0.2[3]	3.7[4]	5.5[5]	___	___	___
Primary Income...	income	3.8	-2.6[3]	4.8[4]	7.7[3]	___	___	___
Primary US Gov...	fix-inc	1.3	-3.1[3]	2.8[5]	6.2[5]	___	___	___
Your average...		25.2				___	___	___
Quantitative Advisors								
Quant Numeric SC...	agg gr	47.8	4.3[1]	—	—	___	___	___
Quant Numeric II...	agg gr	—	—	—	—	___	___	___
Quant Discp Gro...	growth	—	—	—	—	___	___	___
Quant Frgn Frntr...	int'l	5.0	—	—	—	___	___	___
Quant Int'l Eqty...	int'l	29.0	9.1[1]	7.6[4]	-0.3[5]	___	___	___
Quant Gro & Inc...	gr-inc	34.5	-0.7[3]	5.7[4]	8.3[2]	___	___	___
Your average...		116.3				___	___	___
Reich & Tang								
Reich & Tang Eqty...	growth	91.6	1.7[2]	10.4[1]	9.3[2]	___	___	___
Delafield Fund...	gr-inc	10.1	5.6[1]	—	—	___	___	___
Reich & Tang Gov...	fix-inc	18.6	-6.2[4]	3.7[4]	6.7[4]	___	___	___
Short Tm Inc-MM(R&T)...	money mkt	576.4	3.5[5]	3.2[4]	4.6[4]	___	___	___
Daily TF (R&T)...	money mkt TF	441.6	2.6[2]	2.5[2]	3.5[2]	___	___	___
CA Daily TF (R&T)...	money mkt TF	104.9	2.4[3]	2.3[3]	3.2[4]	___	___	___
CT Daily TF (R&T)...	money mkt TF	77.6	2.2[5]	2.0[5]	3.0[5]	___	___	___
FL Daily Muni (R&T)...	money mkt TF	53.0	—	—	—	___	___	___
MI Daily TF (R&T)...	money mkt TF	59.2	2.3[3]	2.2[4]	3.3[2]	___	___	___
NC Daily Muni (R&T)...	money mkt TF	136.7	2.2[5]	2.1[5]	—	___	___	___
NJ Daily Muni (R&T)...	money mkt TF	105.8	2.2[5]	2.3[3]	—	___	___	___
NY Daily TF Inc(R&T)...	money mkt TF	222.7	2.3[4]	2.3[3]	3.2[3]	___	___	___
PA Daily Muni (R&T)...	money mkt TF	40.6	2.6[2]	—	—	___	___	___
Short Tm Inc-Gov(R&T)...	money mkt gov	414.7	3.4[5]	3.1[4]	4.4[4]	___	___	___
Your average...		2,353.5				___	___	___
Retirement Systems Investors								
Retrmt Sys: Emg Gr SC...	agg gr	2.0	10.4[1]	17.4[1]	—	___	___	___
Retrmt Sys: Core Eq...	gr-inc	3.9	5.7[1]	8.8[1]	—	___	___	___
Retrmt Sys: Inter Fix...	fix-inc	4.3	-3.3[3]	4.2[3]	—	___	___	___
Retrmt Sys: MM‡...	money mkt	—	—	—	—	___	___	___
Your average...		10.2				___	___	___
Reynolds Capital Management								
Reynolds Opportunity...	growth	6.9	1.7[2]	—	—	___	___	___
Reynolds Blue Chip...	gr-inc	23.7	-0.6[3]	-1.9[5]	5.1[5]	___	___	___

Families with 3 or more funds including one stock or bond fund
Arranged in alphabetical order by group and risk within group

| Fund group/fund | Objective | Total Net Assets $ Millions 12/31/94 | Annualized Total Return % with quintile ranks by obj | | | Post quintile ranks for your funds here | | |
			1994	3 years 1992-1994	5 years 1990-1994	1994	3 years ending 1994	5 years ending 1994
Reynolds US Gov...	fix-inc	3.0	-5.5[5]	—	—			
Reynolds Money Mkt...	money mkt	—	—	—	—			
Your average...		33.6						
Robertson Stephens Funds...								
Robrtsn Stph Emg Mkts...	int'l	19.4	—	—	—			
Robrtsn Stph Emg Gro SC...	agg gr	176.1	8.0[1]	4.1[4]	14.4[1]			
Robrtsn Stph Contrn...	agg gr	485.7	-5.5[4]	—	—			
Robrtsn Stph Val Gro...	agg gr	132.5	23.1[1]	—	—			
Your average...		813.7						
Pennsylvania-Royce Funds...								
Royce Micro-Cap SC...	agg gr	26.8	3.6[1]	18.3[1]	—			
Royce Low Price Stk SC...	growth	1.9	3.0[2]	—	—			
Royce Penn Mutual SC...	growth	771.4	-0.7[3]	8.7[2]	8.4[3]			
Royce Premier SC...	growth	202.4	3.3[2]	12.4[1]	—			
Royce Value...	growth	166.9	-1.6[4]	8.1[2]	7.4[4]			
Royce Total Ret...	gr-inc	1.7	5.1[1]	—	—			
Royce Equity Inc...	income	77.1	-3.2[4]	9.3[1]	9.0[2]			
Your average...		1,248.2						
RSI Retirement Trust...								
RSI Tr-Emg Gro SC...	agg gr	51.6	3.5[1]	13.2[1]	14.8[1]			
RSI Tr-Int'l Eqty...	int'l	28.5	0.8[3]	7.5[4]	3.5[4]			
RSI Tr-Core Eqty...	gr-inc	144.3	1.3[2]	5.9[3]	6.9[4]			
RSI Tr-Value Eqty...	gr-inc	35.1	-1.1[3]	5.0[4]	5.5[5]			
RSI Tr-Act Mgd Bd...	fix-inc	131.4	-4.2[3]	4.4[3]	7.5[3]			
RSI Tr-Inter Bd...	fix-inc	85.8	-2.5[3]	3.6[4]	6.9[3]			
RSI Tr-ST Invest...	fix-inc	30.2	3.4[1]	3.0[5]	4.5[5]			
Your average...		506.9						
Rushmore Funds...								
Capp-Rush Gold...	prec met	6.2	—	—	—			
Capp-Rush Emg Gro SC...	agg gr	19.9	-6.9[5]	—	—			
Capp-Rush Growth...	growth	15.8	4.6[1]	—	—			
Rushmore Amer Gas Idx...	sector	176.2	-9.8[4]	5.4[4]	1.6[5]			
Capp-Rush Util...	income	19.6	-13.3[5]	—	—			
Rushmore VA TF...	tax-free	27.9	-5.0[1]	4.7[3]	5.9[4]			
Rushmore MD TF...	tax-free	44.4	-5.2[2]	4.6[3]	5.4[5]			
Rushmore Gov Long...	fix-inc	33.1	-9.9[5]	3.3[5]	6.1[5]			
Rushmore Gov Inter...	fix-inc	9.2	-7.3[5]	3.5[4]	6.6[4]			
Rushmore Money Mkt...	money mkt	—	—	—	—			
Rushmore TF MM...	money mkt TF	20.0	2.3[4]	2.1[5]	3.2[4]			
Rushmore Gov MM...	money mkt gov	532.0	3.6[3]	3.0[5]	4.3[5]			
Your average...		904.3						

Families with 3 or more funds including one stock or bond fund
Arranged in alphabetical order by group and risk within group

| Fund group/fund | Objective | Total Net Assets $ Millions 12/31/94 | Annualized Total Return % with quintile ranks by obj | | | Post quintile ranks for your funds here | | |
			1994	3 years 1992-1994	5 years 1990-1994	1994	3 years ending 1994	5 years ending 1994
Rydex Management								
Rydex Prec Met	prec met	28.4	-25.5[5]	—	—	___	___	___
Rydex OTC	agg gr	51.7	—	—	—	___	___	___
Rydex Ursa	agg gr	142.2	—	—	—	___	___	___
Rydex Nova	agg gr	58.4	-4.8[4]	—	—	___	___	___
Rydex Gov Bd	fix-inc	0.3	—	—	—	___	___	___
Rydex Gov MM	money mkt gov	104.4	3.6[3]	—	—	___	___	___
Your average		385.4				___	___	___
1784 Funds								
1784 Gro & Inc	gr-inc	193.1	-0.2[3]	—	—	___	___	___
1784 Asset Alloc	gr-inc	7.1	-0.7[3]	—	—	___	___	___
1784 MA TE Inc	tax-free	55.7	-5.5[2]	—	—	___	___	___
1784 Income	fix-inc	170.2	—	—	—	___	___	___
1784 TE Med Term	tax-free	90.9	-3.0[2]	—	—	___	___	___
1784 Gov Med	fix-inc	109.9	-3.7[4]	—	—	___	___	___
1784 ST Income	fix-inc	32.3	—	—	—	___	___	___
1784 TF MM	money mkt TF	416.4	2.7[1]	—	—	___	___	___
1784 Trsy MM	money mkt gov	270.3	4.0[1]	—	—	___	___	___
Your average		1,345.9				___	___	___
SAFECO Asset Management								
SAFECO Growth	agg gr	150.2	-1.6[3]	5.2[4]	10.0[3]	___	___	___
SAFECO Northwest Gro	growth	34.2	-1.6[4]	4.3[4]	—	___	___	___
SAFECO Equity	growth	449.1	9.9[1]	16.3[1]	13.0[1]	___	___	___
SAFECO Income	income	180.7	-1.1[2]	7.5[2]	6.4[4]	___	___	___
SAFECO Hi Yld Bd	fix-inc	25.5	-2.0[1]	9.3[1]	9.3[1]	___	___	___
SAFECO Muni Bd	tax-free	434.4	-8.2[4]	4.0[4]	6.4[3]	___	___	___
SAFECO CA TF	tax-free	58.1	-9.2[5]	3.6[5]	6.0[4]	___	___	___
SAFECO WA Muni	tax-free	5.9	-8.7[5]	—	—	___	___	___
SAFECO Insur Muni	tax-free	7.3	-10.4[5]	—	—	___	___	___
SAFECO GNMA	fix-inc	41.6	-4.3[4]	3.0[5]	6.4[5]	___	___	___
SAFECO Inter Trsy	fix-inc	12.6	-3.6[4]	4.4[2]	6.7[4]	___	___	___
SAFECO Inter Muni	tax-free	12.8	-5.6[5]	—	—	___	___	___
SAFECO Money Mkt	money mkt	186.0	3.5[4]	3.1[4]	4.6[3]	___	___	___
SAFECO TF MM	money mkt TF	85.6	2.5[2]	2.4[2]	3.4[2]	___	___	___
Your average		1,684.0				___	___	___
Salomon Brothers Asset Management								
Salomon Opportunity	agg gr	108.8	0.8[2]	9.0[2]	7.2[5]	___	___	___
Salomon Capital	agg gr	87.5	-14.2[5]	1.8[5]	5.1[5]	___	___	___
Salomon Investors	gr-inc	348.5	-1.3[4]	6.9[2]	8.1[3]	___	___	___
Salomon NY Muni	tax-free	3.7	-8.8[5]	—	—	___	___	___
Salomon Cash Mgmt	money mkt	18.1	3.9[2]	3.3[2]	—	___	___	___
Salomon NY MM	money mkt TF	270.7	2.7[1]	2.7[1]	—	___	___	___
Salomon Trsy MM	money mkt gov	28.6	3.6[2]	—	—	___	___	___
Your average		865.9				___	___	___

No-load fund groups *continued*

Families with 3 or more funds including one stock or bond fund
Arranged in alphabetical order by group and risk within group

| Fund group/fund | Objective | Total Net Assets $ Millions 12/31/94 | Annualized Total Return % with quintile ranks by obj | | | Post quintile ranks for your funds here | | |
			1994	3 years 1992-1994	5 years 1990-1994	1994	3 years ending 1994	5 years ending 1994
Spears, Benzak, Salomon, & Farrell								
SBSF Capital Gro...	growth	4.5	-4.5[4]	—	—	___	___	___
SBSF Fund...	growth	108.0	-5.6[5]	6.6[3]	7.0[4]	___	___	___
SBSF Convert...	income	57.9	-6.5[5]	7.7[2]	8.7[2]	___	___	___
SBSF Money Mkt...	money mkt gov	22.0	3.6[3]	3.2[3]	4.6[2]	___	___	___
Your average...		192.4				___	___	___
Schroder Funds								
Schroder Latin Amer...	int'l	—	—	—	—	___	___	___
Schroder US Sm Co SC...	agg gr	13.0	4.4[1]	—	—	___	___	___
Schroder US Eqty...	agg gr	17.7	-5.2[4]	7.1[3]	10.2[3]	___	___	___
Schroder Int'l Eqty...	int'l	174.6	0.2[3]	11.9[2]	5.4[2]	___	___	___
Your average...		205.3				___	___	___
Schwab Funds								
Schwab Sm Cap Idx...	agg gr	70.7	-3.1[4]	—	—	___	___	___
Schwab Int'l Idx...	int'l	138.1	3.8[2]	—	—	___	___	___
Schwab 1000...	gr-inc	554.0	-0.1[3]	5.9[3]	—	___	___	___
Schwab CA Long...	tax-free	87.2	-8.9[5]	—	—	___	___	___
Schwab LT TF...	tax-free	36.8	-7.0[4]	—	—	___	___	___
Schwab LT Gov...	fix-inc	8.0	-5.7[4]	—	—	___	___	___
Schwab CA S-I...	tax-free	40.2	-2.1[5]	—	—	___	___	___
Schwab S-I TF...	tax-free	55.9	-1.1[4]	—	—	___	___	___
Schwab S-I Gov...	fix-inc	160.0	-2.9[5]	3.6[4]	—	___	___	___
Schwab Money Mkt...	money mkt	11,227.3	3.7[4]	3.3[3]	—	___	___	___
Schwab Retirement MM...	money mkt	31.4	—	—	—	___	___	___
Schwab Value Adv MM...	money mkt	3,731.6	4.1[1]	—	—	___	___	___
Schwab TE MM...	money mkt TF	3,016.0	2.3[4]	2.2[4]	—	___	___	___
Schwab CA TF MM...	money mkt TF	1,293.9	2.2[5]	2.2[4]	—	___	___	___
Schwab Gov MM...	money mkt gov	1,897.3	3.6[3]	3.2[2]	—	___	___	___
Schwab Trsy MM...	money mkt gov	803.9	3.5[4]	—	—	___	___	___
Your average...		23,152.3				___	___	___
Scudder, Stevens, & Clark								
Scudder Development SC...	agg gr	601.9	-5.3[4]	0.4[5]	12.0[2]	___	___	___
Scudder Capital Gro...	agg gr	1,291.5	-9.9[5]	5.0[4]	6.6[5]	___	___	___
Scudder Gold...	prec met	129.9	-7.4[2]	10.3[4]	0.8[3]	___	___	___
Japan (Scudder)...	int'l	587.0	10.0[1]	4.2[5]	-0.5[5]	___	___	___
Scudder Latin Amer...	int'l	649.6	-9.4[5]	—	—	___	___	___
Scudder Pacific Opp...	int'l	422.3	-17.1[5]	—	—	___	___	___
Scudder Glob Sm Co...	global	235.3	-7.7[4]	8.4[3]	—	___	___	___
Scudder Int'l Stk...	int'l	2,271.8	-3.0[4]	8.9[2]	5.6[2]	___	___	___
Scudder Grt Europe...	int'l	16.0	—	—	—	___	___	___
Scudder Global...	global	1,117.7	-4.2[3]	9.5[2]	7.5[2]	___	___	___
Scudder Qual Growth...	growth	112.4	-1.3[4]	1.7[5]	—	___	___	___
Scudder Value...	growth	34.9	1.6[2]	—	—	___	___	___
Scudder Gro & Inc...	gr-inc	1,994.2	2.6[1]	9.1[1]	10.2[1]	___	___	___

No-load fund groups *continued*

Families with 3 or more funds including one stock or bond fund
Arranged in alphabetical order by group and risk within group

Fund group/fund	Objective	Total Net Assets $ Millions 12/31/94	Annualized Total Return % with quintile ranks by obj 1994	3 years 1992-1994	5 years 1990-1994	Post quintile ranks for your funds here 1994	3 years ending 1994	5 years ending 1994
Scudder Balanced...	gr-inc	66.1	-2.4[4]	—	—	___	___	___
Scudder US Zero 2000...	fix-inc	24.8	-7.9[5]	4.9[2]	7.7[3]	___	___	___
Scudder Emg Mkts Inc	fix-inc	89.6	-8.1[5]	—	—	___	___	___
Scudder Int'l Bond...	fix-inc	1,086.2	-8.6[5]	4.5[2]	11.0[1]	___	___	___
Scudder Income	fix-inc	464.1	-4.5[3]	4.7[3]	7.8[2]	___	___	___
Scudder Hi Yld TF	tax-free	259.8	-8.4[5]	5.0[2]	6.8[2]	___	___	___
Scudder NY TF...	tax-free	182.1	-7.2[4]	4.9[2]	6.6[2]	___	___	___
Scudder MA TF...	tax-free	277.5	-6.2[3]	5.9[1]	7.2[1]	___	___	___
Scudder CA TF...	tax-free	274.4	-7.3[4]	4.9[3]	6.7[2]	___	___	___
Scudder PA TF...	tax-free	67.8	-5.9[2]	5.1[2]	6.7[2]	___	___	___
Scudder OH TF...	tax-free	72.9	-5.5[2]	4.9[2]	6.6[2]	___	___	___
Scudder Mgd Muni...	tax-free	708.4	-6.0[3]	5.1[2]	6.8[2]	___	___	___
Scudder GNMA...	fix-inc	417.0	-3.1[3]	3.2[5]	6.8[3]	___	___	___
Scudder Medium TF	tax-free	703.1	-3.5[3]	5.3[1]	6.8[1]	___	___	___
Scudder ST Glob Inc	fix-inc	496.9	-1.1[4]	3.7[3]	—	___	___	___
Scudder ST Bond...	fix-inc	2,138.8	-2.9[5]	3.4[4]	6.8[2]	___	___	___
Scudder Ltd TF...	tax-free	96.1	—	—	—	___	___	___
Scudder MA Ltd TF...	tax-free	49.2	—	—	—	___	___	___
Scudder Cash Inv Tr...	money mkt	1,716.2	3.7[3]	3.3[3]	4.7[2]	___	___	___
Scudder CA TF MM...	money mkt TF	67.7	2.4[3]	2.3[3]	3.1[4]	___	___	___
Scudder NY TF MM...	money mkt TF	53.1	2.2[4]	2.2[4]	3.0[5]	___	___	___
Scudder TF MM...	money mkt TF	260.9	2.3[4]	2.2[4]	3.2[4]	___	___	___
Scudder Trsy MM...	money mkt gov	391.3	3.5[4]	3.1[3]	4.6[2]	___	___	___
Your average...		19,428.5				___	___	___
Seattle-First National Bank...						___	___	___
Seafirst Blue Chip...	growth	142.7	2.0[2]	6.8[3]	7.9[4]	___	___	___
Seafirst Asst Allc...	gr-inc	143.7	-0.2[3]	5.2[4]	7.5[3]	___	___	___
Seafirst Bond...	fix-inc	56.6	-2.3[2]	3.6[4]	6.6[4]	___	___	___
Your average...		343.0				___	___	___
Selected Venture Advisors...						___	___	___
Selected Spec Sh SC...	growth	45.1	-2.5[4]	5.4[4]	6.4[5]	___	___	___
Selected Amer Sh...	gr-inc	503.0	-3.2[4]	2.6[5]	8.7[2]	___	___	___
Selected US Gov...	fix-inc	10.2	-2.2[1]	3.5[4]	6.4[4]	___	___	___
Selected Daily Inc MM...	money mkt	—	—	—	—	___	___	___
Selected Daily Gov MM...	money mkt gov	125.6	3.5[4]	2.9[5]	4.3[5]	___	___	___
Your average...		683.9				___	___	___
Seven Seas Funds...						___	___	___
Seven Seas Emg Mkts...	int'l	30.8	—	—	—	___	___	___
Seven Seas Sm Cap SC...	agg gr	4.0	-1.0[3]	—	—	___	___	___
Seven Seas Matrix...	growth	138.3	-0.4[3]	—	—	___	___	___
Seven Seas S&P 500...	gr-inc	302.3	1.3[2]	—	—	___	___	___
Seven Seas Gro & Inc...	gr-inc	26.3	-0.3[3]	—	—	___	___	___
Seven Seas Yld Plus...	fix-inc	1,209.9	4.1[1]	—	—	___	___	___

Families with 3 or more funds including one stock or bond fund
Arranged in alphabetical order by group and risk within group

Fund group/fund	Objective	Total Net Assets $ Millions 12/31/94	Annualized Total Return % with quintile ranks by obj			Post quintile ranks for your funds here		
			1994	3 years 1992-1994	5 years 1990-1994	1994	3 years ending 1994	5 years ending 1994
Seven Seas Inter Fix..........	fix-inc	19.1	-4.4[5]	—	—			
Seven Seas ST Gov..........	fix-inc	9.1	0.2[2]	—	—			
Seven Seas MM...	money mkt	2,561.1	4.0[1]	—	—			
Seven Seas Gov MM..........	money mkt gov	606.9	3.9[1]	—	—			
Your average..........		4,907.8						
SIT Investment Associates..........								
SIT Develop Mkts...	int'l	3.8	—	—	—			
SIT Sm Cap Gr SC...	agg gr	4.5	—	—	—			
SIT Growth SC...	agg gr	303.1	-0.5[2]	1.9[5]	11.4[2]			
SIT Int'l Growth...	int'l	65.3	-3.0[4]	13.9[1]	—			
SIT Gro & Inc...	gr-inc	36.3	2.8[1]	3.6[4]	7.7[3]			
SIT Balanced...	income	1.5	-0.4[2]	—	—			
SIT Bond...	fix-inc	3.4	-1.3[1]	—	—			
SIT US Gov...	fix-inc	36.3	1.8[1]	4.8[3]	7.6[3]			
SIT TF Income...	tax-free	243.3	-0.6[1]	5.7[1]	6.7[2]			
SIT MN TF Inc...	tax-free	37.5	0.6[1]	—	—			
SIT Money Mkt...	money mkt	—	—	—	—			
Your average..........		735.0						
Smith Breeden..........								
Smith Brdn Mkt Track..........	gr-inc	1.8	1.8[2]	—	—			
Smith Brdn Inter Gov..........	fix-inc	33.3	-1.7[2]	—	—			
Smith Brdn ST Gov..........	fix-inc	224.9	4.2[1]	—	—			
Your average..........		260.0						
Smith Hayes Funds..........								
Smith Hayes Sm Cap SC...	agg gr	8.6	2.5[2]	—	—			
Smith Hayes Value...	growth	3.3	-12.4[5]	2.5[5]	2.6[5]			
Smith Hayes Asst Allc...	gr-inc	3.6	-4.2[5]	2.3[5]	6.6[4]			
Smith Hayes Convert..........	income	2.2	-8.0[5]	5.7[4]	7.4[4]			
Smith Hayes Blncd..........	income	4.7	-4.4[4]	3.4[5]	5.4[5]			
Smith Hayes Gov Qual..........	fix-inc	7.2	-3.3[3]	2.8[5]	5.8[5]			
Smith Hayes MM...	money mkt	5.7	3.4[5]	—	—			
Your average..........		35.3						
State Farm Investment Management..........								
State Farm Growth...	growth	796.1	6.0[1]	2.9[5]	10.0[2]			
State Farm Blncd..........	income	378.7	5.0[1]	4.6[4]	11.8[1]			
State Farm Interim...	fix-inc	93.2	-0.8[4]	4.1[2]	6.7[2]			
State Farm Muni Bd..........	tax-free	275.9	-2.5[1]	4.9[3]	6.5[2]			
Your average..........		1,543.9						
Steadman Funds..........								
Steadman Tech & Gro..........	agg gr	0.9	-37.1[5]	-18.1[5]	-17.0[5]			
Steadman Amer Indust...	agg gr	1.5	-37.2[5]	-13.8[5]	-14.9[5]			

No-load fund groups *continued*

Families with 3 or more funds including one stock or bond fund
Arranged in alphabetical order by group and risk within group

Fund group/fund	Objective	Total Net Assets $ Millions 12/31/94	1994	3 years 1992-1994	5 years 1990-1994	1994	3 years ending 1994	5 years ending 1994
				Annualized Total Return % with quintile ranks by obj		Post quintile ranks for your funds here		
Steadman Investment...	growth	2.2	-33.8[5]	-14.4[5]	-6.7[5]	___	___	___
Steadman Associated...	income	5.5	-20.5[5]	-2.4[5]	-2.8[5]	___	___	___
Your average...		10.1				___	___	___
SteinRoe & Farnham								
SteinRoe Cap Oppty...	agg gr	172.3	0.0[2]	9.3[2]	8.5[4]	___	___	___
SteinRoe Spec Venture SC...	agg gr	18.3	—	—	—	___	___	___
SteinRoe Stock...	agg gr	302.6	-3.8[4]	2.3[5]	9.6[3]	___	___	___
SteinRoe Special...	growth	1,167.7	-3.3[4]	9.9[2]	10.8[2]	___	___	___
SteinRoe Prime Eqty...	growth	121.5	-0.2[3]	7.4[3]	10.0[2]	___	___	___
SteinRoe Young Invest...	growth	12.0	—	—	—	___	___	___
SteinRoe Int'l...	int'l	74.0	—	—	—	___	___	___
SteinRoe Total Ret...	income	215.1	-4.1[4]	5.1[4]	8.1[3]	___	___	___
SteinRoe Income...	fix-inc	152.9	-4.1[4]	5.8[1]	8.0[1]	___	___	___
SteinRoe Hi Yld Muni...	tax-free	266.5	-4.2[1]	3.7[5]	5.7[5]	___	___	___
SteinRoe Mgd Muni...	tax-free	604.6	-5.5[2]	4.3[4]	6.3[3]	___	___	___
SteinRoe Inter Bd...	fix-inc	281.5	-2.8[3]	4.5[2]	7.1[3]	___	___	___
SteinRoe Inter Muni...	tax-free	215.5	-3.5[3]	4.9[2]	6.5[2]	___	___	___
SteinRoe Gov Inc...	fix-inc	44.4	-3.3[2]	3.2[5]	6.5[4]	___	___	___
SteinRoe Ltd Mat Inc...	fix-inc	26.6	0.0[3]	—	—	___	___	___
SteinRoe Cash Res...	money mkt	541.4	3.7[4]	3.2[3]	4.6[3]	___	___	___
SteinRoe Muni MM...	money mkt TF	174.1	2.3[4]	2.2[4]	3.2[4]	___	___	___
SteinRoe Gov Res...	money mkt gov	104.0	3.5[3]	3.1[3]	4.5[3]	___	___	___
Your average...		4,495.0				___	___	___
Stratton Management								
Stratton Sm Cap Yld SC...	growth	13.7	-2.7[4]	—	—	___	___	___
Stratton Growth...	gr-inc	26.6	7.1[1]	6.7[2]	6.7[4]	___	___	___
Stratton Month Div Sh...	income	121.9	-12.1[5]	1.1[5]	6.0[5]	___	___	___
Your average...		162.2				___	___	___
Stratus Funds (Union Bank & Trust)								
Stratus Cap Apprec...	agg gr	0.6	-6.3[4]	—	—	___	___	___
Stratus Eqty Inc...	gr-inc	11.2	0.6[2]	—	—	___	___	___
Stratus Gov Sec...	fix-inc	12.7	-3.3[2]	—	—	___	___	___
Stratus Inter Gov...	fix-inc	5.7	-2.8[3]	3.3[5]	—	___	___	___
Stratus Variable Rate...	fix-inc	—	—	—	—	___	___	___
Your average...		30.2				___	___	___
Strong Funds								
Strong Discovery SC...	agg gr	388.4	-5.7[4]	5.5[4]	13.8[1]	___	___	___
Strong Opportunity...	growth	805.7	3.2[2]	13.6[1]	11.4[1]	___	___	___
Strong Asia Pacific...	int'l	57.7	-5.3[4]	—	—	___	___	___
Strong Common Stk SC‡...	growth	790.1	-0.5[3]	14.6[1]	—	___	___	___
Strong Growth...	growth	106.0	17.3[1]	—	—	___	___	___
Strong Int'l Stk...	int'l	257.8	-1.6[3]	—	—	___	___	___

No-load fund groups *continued*

Families with 3 or more funds including one stock or bond fund
Arranged in alphabetical order by group and risk within group

Fund group/fund	Objective	Total Net Assets $ Millions 12/31/94	1994	3 years 1992-1994	5 years 1990-1994	1994	3 years ending 1994	5 years ending 1994
				Annualized Total Return % with quintile ranks by obj			**Post quintile ranks for your funds here**	
Strong Total Return...	gr-inc	606.8	-1.4[4]	6.7[2]	8.6[2]	_____	_____	_____
Strong Asst Allc...	income	248.6	-1.5[3]	5.2[4]	7.4[4]	_____	_____	_____
Strong Amer Util...	income	37.9	-2.6[3]	—	—	_____	_____	_____
Strong Int'l Bond...	fix-inc	10.0	—	—	—	_____	_____	_____
Strong Income...	fix-inc	123.3	-1.3[1]	8.0[1]	6.3[5]	_____	_____	_____
Strong Hi Yld Muni...	tax-free	107.6	0.0[1]	—	—	_____	_____	_____
Strong Muni Bond...	tax-free	279.8	-4.6[1]	6.2[1]	7.3[1]	_____	_____	_____
Strong Insur Muni...	tax-free	51.0	-6.5[3]	6.1[1]	—	_____	_____	_____
Strong Gov Sec...	fix-inc	276.8	-3.4[4]	5.9[1]	8.5[1]	_____	_____	_____
Strong ST Global...	fix-inc	20.0	—	—	—	_____	_____	_____
Strong ST Muni...	tax-free	161.2	-1.6[5]	—	—	_____	_____	_____
Strong ST Bond...	fix-inc	1,041.1	-1.6[4]	4.7[1]	6.7[3]	_____	_____	_____
Strong Advantage...	fix-inc	910.5	3.6[1]	6.6[1]	7.4[1]	_____	_____	_____
Strong Money Mkt...	money mkt	541.0	4.0[1]	3.6[1]	5.0[1]	_____	_____	_____
Strong Muni MM...	money mkt TF	1,260.6	2.9[1]	2.9[1]	4.0[1]	_____	_____	_____
Strong Trsy MM...	money mkt gov	67.5	3.9[1]	3.5[1]	—	_____	_____	_____
Your average...		8,149.4				_____	_____	_____
Trust Co of the West Dean Witter								
TCWDW Inc & Gro...	gr-inc	56.1	-3.3[4]	—	—	_____	_____	_____
TCWDW Balanced...	income	126.0	-9.7[5]	—	—	_____	_____	_____
TCWDW N Amer Gov...	fix-inc	880.9	-15.6[5]	—	—	_____	_____	_____
TCWDW N Amer Inter Inc...	fix-inc	4.6	—	—	—	_____	_____	_____
Dean Witter Liq Asst...	money mkt	8,906.6	3.8[3]	3.3[3]	4.7[3]	_____	_____	_____
Dean Witter TF MM...	money mkt TF	545.8	2.3[4]	2.2[4]	3.2[4]	_____	_____	_____
Dean Witter Gov MM...	money mkt gov	812.2	3.2[5]	2.8[5]	4.2[5]	_____	_____	_____
Your average...		11,332.2				_____	_____	_____
Thompson, Unger, & Plumb								
TU&P Growth...	growth	5.0	0.4[3]	—	—	_____	_____	_____
TU&P Balanced...	gr-inc	17.6	1.5[2]	2.7[5]	7.2[3]	_____	_____	_____
TU&P Bond...	fix-inc	10.4	-2.7[2]	—	—	_____	_____	_____
Your average...		33.0				_____	_____	_____
Twentieth Century Funds								
Twentieth Cent Int'l Emg...	int'l	111.9	—	—	—	_____	_____	_____
Twentieth Cent Ultra...	agg gr	9,850.8	-3.6[4]	5.9[4]	19.4[1]	_____	_____	_____
Twentieth Cent Giftrust...	agg gr	274.2	13.5[1]	20.7[1]	22.0[1]	_____	_____	_____
Twentieth Cent Vista...	agg gr	820.2	4.7[1]	2.6[5]	9.6[3]	_____	_____	_____
Twentieth Cent Growth...	agg gr	4,158.0	-1.5[3]	-0.7[5]	9.7[3]	_____	_____	_____
Twentieth Cent Int'l...	int'l	1,272.4	-4.8[4]	12.5[1]	—	_____	_____	_____
Twentieth Cent Select...	growth	3,995.2	-8.0[5]	0.3[5]	5.7[5]	_____	_____	_____
Twentieth Cent Heritage...	growth	851.6	-6.3[5]	7.5[3]	8.9[3]	_____	_____	_____
Twentieth Cent Value...	gr-inc	153.1	4.0[1]	—	—	_____	_____	_____
Twentieth Cent Strategic...	gr-inc	—	—	—	—	_____	_____	_____
Twentieth Cent Eqty Inc...	gr-inc	23.8	—	—	—	_____	_____	_____
Twentieth Cent Blncd...	gr-inc	689.3	-0.1[2]	0.2[5]	8.5[2]	_____	_____	_____

No-load fund groups *continued*

Families with 3 or more funds including one stock or bond fund
Arranged in alphabetical order by group and risk within group

Fund group/fund	Objective	Total Net Assets $ Millions 12/31/94	1994	Annualized Total Return % with quintile ranks by obj 3 years 1992-1994	5 years 1990-1994	Post quintile ranks for your funds here 1994	3 years ending 1994	5 years ending 1994
Twentieth Cent LT Bd...................	fix-inc	118.9	-4.5[5]	3.5[5]	6.6[4]	___	___	___
Twentieth Cent TE Long...............	tax-free	49.2	-5.6[2]	4.4[3]	6.3[3]	___	___	___
Twentieth Cent Inter Bd...............	fix-inc	5.0	—	—	—	___	___	___
Twentieth Cent Gov Inter.............	fix-inc	7.7	—	—	—	___	___	___
Twentieth Cent TE Inter...............	tax-free	77.0	-2.1[1]	4.6[3]	6.0[4]	___	___	___
Twentieth Cent Ltd Trm..............	fix-inc	4.6	—	—	—	___	___	___
Twentieth Cent Gov ST...............	fix-inc	382.6	-0.6[3]	2.6[5]	5.4[5]	___	___	___
Twentieth Cent TE Short.............	tax-free	61.2	2.4[1]	—	—	___	___	___
Twentieth Cent Cash...................	money mkt	1,363.9	3.7[4]	3.0[5]	4.5[4]	___	___	___
Your average...		24,270.6				___	___	___
United Missouri Bank								
Babson UMB Heartland SC...........	agg gr	28.0	0.7[2]	5.8[4]	5.0[5]	___	___	___
Babson UMB Stock....................	growth	120.9	2.8[2]	6.8[3]	8.2[3]	___	___	___
Babson UMB Worldwide..............	global	17.8	3.8[1]	—	—	___	___	___
Babson UMB Bond....................	fix-inc	75.2	-3.1[2]	3.8[4]	6.5[4]	___	___	___
Babson UMB Prime MM..............	money mkt	200.3	3.8[2]	3.3[2]	4.7[2]	___	___	___
Babson UMB TF MM..................	money mkt TF	101.1	2.4[3]	2.3[3]	3.3[3]	___	___	___
Babson UMB Fed MM.................	money mkt gov	185.8	3.8[2]	3.3[2]	4.7[2]	___	___	___
Your average...		729.1				___	___	___
United Services								
US Gold Shares........................	prec met	291.6	-2.7[1]	2.3[5]	-9.9[5]	___	___	___
US World Gold.........................	prec met	182.5	-16.9[5]	14.5[1]	0.9[2]	___	___	___
US Global Resrc.......................	growth	20.4	-9.7[5]	1.9[5]	-1.4[5]	___	___	___
US China Oppty.......................	int'l	20.9	—	—	—	___	___	___
Bonnel Growth........................	growth	2.6	—	—	—	___	___	___
US All-Amer Eqty.....................	gr-inc	9.2	-5.3[5]	3.2[5]	—	___	___	___
US Real Estate........................	sector	11.0	-11.6[5]	-2.3[5]	3.1[5]	___	___	___
US Income.............................	income	10.0	-10.3[5]	4.5[5]	3.6[5]	___	___	___
US Tax Free...........................	tax-free	16.1	-5.2[5]	4.3[4]	5.7[5]	___	___	___
US Inter Treas........................	fix-inc	4.2	-4.9[5]	—	—	___	___	___
US Spec Gov..........................	fix-inc	7.4	-1.6[1]	—	—	___	___	___
US Near Term TF......................	tax-free	9.2	-0.1[1]	—	—	___	___	___
US Gov MM............................	money mkt gov	579.4	4.0[1]	3.9[1]	—	___	___	___
US Trsy MM............................	money mkt gov	176.9	3.2[5]	2.9[5]	4.4[4]	___	___	___
Your average...		1,341.4				___	___	___
USAA Investment Management.......								
USAA Gold.............................	prec met	158.5	-9.4[3]	9.7[4]	-1.5[4]	___	___	___
USAA Emg Mkts.......................	int'l	10.9	—	—	—	___	___	___
USAA Agg Growth SC.................	agg gr	283.8	-0.8[3]	-0.6[5]	8.2[4]	___	___	___
USAA World Growth...................	global	185.3	0.6[2]	—	—	___	___	___
USAA International....................	int'l	337.8	2.7[2]	12.8[1]	8.1[1]	___	___	___
USAA Growth..........................	growth	677.2	3.4[1]	6.9[3]	9.3[3]	___	___	___

No-load fund groups *continued*

Families with 3 or more funds including one stock or bond fund
Arranged in alphabetical order by group and risk within group

| Fund group/fund | Objective | Total Net Assets $ Millions 12/31/94 | Annualized Total Return % with quintile ranks by obj | | | Post quintile ranks for your funds here | | |
			1994	3 years 1992-1994	5 years 1990-1994	1994	3 years ending 1994	5 years ending 1994
USAA Growth & Inc..........	gr-inc	150.5	1.3[2]	—	—			
USAA Cornerstone...	global	841.3	-1.1[2]	9.2[2]	6.6[3]			
USAA Income Stk...	income	1,171.7	-0.7[2]	6.1[3]	8.4[3]			
USAA Balanced...	income	124.7	-2.6[3]	5.2[4]	6.2[4]			
USAA TE Long...	tax-free	1,661.2	-7.9[4]	4.0[4]	6.1[4]			
USAA Income...	fix-inc	1,611.8	-5.2[5]	4.1[3]	7.7[1]			
USAA NY Bond...	tax-free	45.8	-9.0[5]	4.0[4]	—			
USAA CA Bond...	tax-free	335.2	-9.3[5]	3.4[5]	5.8[4]			
USAA FL TF...	tax-free	37.4	-10.0[5]	—	—			
USAA VA Bond...	tax-free	215.5	-6.3[3]	4.6[3]	—			
USAA Texas TF...	tax-free	4.7	—	—	—			
USAA GNMA...	fix-inc	244.9	0.0[1]	4.3[3]	—			
USAA ST Bond...	fix-inc	50.6	0.0[3]	—	—			
USAA TE Inter...	tax-free	1,416.1	-4.0[3]	5.1[1]	6.6[1]			
USAA TE Short...	tax-free	810.8	0.8[2]	4.1[3]	5.2[4]			
USAA Money Mkt...	money mkt	1,270.5	4.1[1]	3.6[1]	5.0[1]			
USAA FL MM...	money mkt TF	94.3	2.5[2]	—	—			
USAA CA MM...	money mkt TF	261.4	2.6[1]	2.6[1]	3.5[1]			
USAA NY MM...	money mkt TF	28.9	2.4[3]	2.4[2]	—			
USAA VA MM...	money mkt TF	97.5	2.6[2]	2.6[1]	—			
USAA TE MM...	money mkt TF	1,470.0	2.6[1]	2.7[1]	3.8[1]			
USAA Texas MM...	money mkt TF	—	—	—	—			
USAA Trsy MM...	money mkt gov	54.9	3.8[2]	3.4[1]	—			
Your average...		13,653.2						
Value Line Funds ...								
Value Line Lev Gro...	agg gr	264.8	-3.7[4]	3.0[4]	9.4[3]			
Value Line Spec Sit...	agg gr	90.2	1.0[2]	3.3[4]	7.5[4]			
Value Line Sm Cap...	agg gr	10.5	-0.6[3]	—	—			
Value Line Fund...	growth	272.8	-4.5[4]	2.2[5]	9.5[2]			
Value Line Income...	income	131.6	-4.3[4]	1.8[5]	6.7[4]			
Value Line Asst All...	income	22.4	3.4[1]	—	—			
Value Line Convert...	income	45.1	-5.2[4]	7.4[2]	8.9[2]			
Value Line Agg Inc...	fix-inc	30.1	-4.1[3]	8.6[1]	9.3[1]			
Value Line US Gov...	fix-inc	289.7	-10.6[5]	1.4[5]	6.0[5]			
Value Line Adj Rate Gov...	fix-inc	22.4	-9.9[5]	—	—			
Value Line TE Hi Yld...	tax-free	225.9	-6.9[3]	3.8[5]	5.9[4]			
Value Line NY TE...	tax-free	36.9	-7.7[4]	4.8[3]	6.6[2]			
Value Line Cash...	money mkt	341.6	3.7[3]	3.5[1]	4.8[1]			
Value Line TE MM...	money mkt TF	29.3	2.0[5]	2.0[5]	3.1[5]			
Your average...		1,813.3						
Vanguard Group ...								
Vangd Spec-Health...	sector	708.1	9.5[1]	6.4[4]	15.5[2]			
Vangd Spec-Gold...	prec met	639.2	-5.4[1]	13.8[2]	4.2[1]			
Vangd Spec-Energy...	sector	445.5	-1.6[3]	9.7[3]	5.4[5]			

Families with 3 or more funds including one stock or bond fund
Arranged in alphabetical order by group and risk within group

Fund group/fund	Objective	Total Net Assets $ Millions 12/31/94	Annualized Total Return % with quintile ranks by obj 1994	3 years 1992-1994	5 years 1990-1994	Post quintile ranks for your funds here 1994	3 years ending 1994	5 years ending 1994
Vangd Explorer SC	agg gr	1,121.6	0.5[2]	9.4[2]	12.8[2]	——	——	——
Vangd Idx Sm Cap SC	agg gr	605.4	-0.5[2]	11.7[1]	10.6[3]	——	——	——
Vangd Morgan	agg gr	1,074.8	-1.7[3]	4.9[4]	8.0[4]	——	——	——
Vangd Idx Pacific	int'l	697.1	12.9[1]	7.8[3]	—	——	——	——
Vangd Idx Emg Mkt	int'l	83.4	—	—	—	——	——	——
Vangd Idx Europe	int'l	715.0	1.9[2]	8.3[3]	—	——	——	——
Vangd Int'l Growth	int'l	2,927.7	0.7[3]	11.2[2]	4.8[3]	——	——	——
Vangd Trust Int'l	int'l	1,053.2	5.3[1]	7.8[3]	3.9[4]	——	——	——
Vangd Idx Extend Mkt	growth	967.3	-1.8[4]	8.1[2]	9.1[3]	——	——	——
Vangd Primecap‡	growth	1,553.7	11.4[1]	12.7[1]	13.1[1]	——	——	——
Vangd US Growth	growth	2,109.3	3.9[1]	1.7[5]	10.1[2]	——	——	——
Vangd Idx Total Mkt	growth	785.7	-0.1[3]	—	—	——	——	——
Vangd Star:Growth	growth	37.8	—	—	—	——	——	——
Vangd Tax Mgd:Cap App	growth	69.0	—	—	—	——	——	——
Vangd Quantitative	gr-inc	596.0	-0.6[3]	6.6[3]	9.0[2]	——	——	——
Vangd Idx Growth	gr-inc	86.2	2.9[1]	—	—	——	——	——
Vangd Idx 500	gr-inc	9,356.3	1.2[2]	6.1[3]	8.5[2]	——	——	——
Vangd Idx Value	gr-inc	296.9	-0.6[3]	—	—	——	——	——
Vangd Trust US	gr-inc	112.8	-3.9[5]	6.2[3]	6.8[4]	——	——	——
Vangd Windsor II	gr-inc	7,959.0	-1.2[4]	7.9[2]	7.7[3]	——	——	——
Vangd Windsor‡	gr-inc	10,672.9	-0.1[3]	11.5[1]	8.5[2]	——	——	——
Vangd Star:Star	gr-inc	3,766.2	-0.3[3]	6.9[2]	7.9[3]	——	——	——
Vangd Idx Balanced	gr-inc	402.9	-1.5[4]	—	—	——	——	——
Vangd Star:Mod Gr	gr-inc	34.8	—	—	—	——	——	——
Vangd Star:Cons Gro	gr-inc	41.3	—	—	—	——	——	——
Vangd Tax Mgd:Gro & Inc	gr-inc	31.0	—	—	—	——	——	——
Vangd Convert	income	170.7	-5.6[5]	8.4[1]	9.4[2]	——	——	——
Vangd Equity Inc	income	859.0	-1.5[3]	7.2[3]	6.3[4]	——	——	——
Vangd Wellington	income	8,809.4	-0.4[2]	6.8[3]	7.9[3]	——	——	——
Vangd Asset Alloc	income	1,125.6	-2.3[3]	6.0[3]	8.5[2]	——	——	——
Vangd Wellesley Inc	income	5,680.6	-4.4[4]	6.0[3]	8.4[3]	——	——	——
Vangd Spec-Util	income	560.5	-8.5[5]	—	—	——	——	——
Vangd Tax Mgd:Blncd	income	17.0	—	—	—	——	——	——
Vangd Star:Income	income	11.5	—	—	—	——	——	——
Vangd Hi Yld Corp	fix-inc	2,120.7	-1.7[1]	9.9[1]	10.0[1]	——	——	——
Vangd Muni Hi Yld	tax-free	1,572.6	-5.1[2]	5.5[1]	7.4[1]	——	——	——
Vangd LT Corp	fix-inc	2,552.3	-5.3[4]	6.0[2]	8.9[1]	——	——	——
Vangd-Adml Long	fix-inc	118.1	-6.8[4]	—	—	——	——	——
Vangd Bond Idx Long	fix-inc	8.6	—	—	—	——	——	——
Vangd Prefrd Stk	fix-inc	278.9	-7.9[5]	4.1[4]	7.7[2]	——	——	——
Vangd CA Insur LT	tax-free	830.2	-5.7[2]	5.2[2]	6.7[2]	——	——	——
Vangd PA Insur LT	tax-free	1,299.3	-4.5[1]	5.8[1]	7.3[1]	——	——	——
Vangd FL Insur	tax-free	328.1	-4.7[1]	—	—	——	——	——
Vangd OH Insur LT	tax-free	147.1	-5.1[2]	5.4[1]	—	——	——	——
Vangd NJ Insur LT	tax-free	653.9	-5.2[2]	5.5[1]	7.1[1]	——	——	——
Vangd Muni Long	tax-free	920.3	-5.8[2]	5.3[1]	7.2[1]	——	——	——
Vangd NY Insur	tax-free	699.0	-5.6[2]	5.4[1]	7.0[1]	——	——	——

No-load fund groups *continued*

Families with 3 or more funds including one stock or bond fund
Arranged in alphabetical order by group and risk within group

Fund group/fund	Objective	Total Net Assets $ Millions 12/31/94	1994	3 years 1992-1994	5 years 1990-1994	1994	3 years ending 1994	5 years ending 1994
Vangd LT Trsy...	fix-inc	644.2	-7.0[4]	5.2[2]	7.7[2]	___	___	___
Vangd Muni Insur LT...	tax-free	1,738.0	-5.6[2]	5.2[2]	7.0[1]	___	___	___
Vangd Bond Idx Total...	fix-inc	1,730.7	-2.7[3]	4.6[2]	7.4[2]	___	___	___
Vangd Inter Corp...	fix-inc	151.5	-4.2[4]	—	—	___	___	___
Vangd Bond Idx Inter...	fix-inc	71.4	—	—	—	___	___	___
Vangd GNMA...	fix-inc	5,777.8	-1.0[1]	3.9[3]	7.6[2]	___	___	___
Vangd-Adml Inter...	fix-inc	319.9	-4.2[4]	—	—	___	___	___
Vangd Inter Trsy...	fix-inc	844.2	-4.3[5]	4.7[2]	—	___	___	___
Vangd Muni Inter...	tax-free	4,585.0	-2.1[1]	5.9[1]	7.4[1]	___	___	___
Vangd CA Insur Inter...	tax-free	110.0	—	—	—	___	___	___
Vangd ST Corp...	fix-inc	2,905.8	-0.1[3]	4.7[1]	7.2[1]	___	___	___
Vangd Bond Idx Short...	fix-inc	77.0	—	—	—	___	___	___
Vangd Muni Ltd...	tax-free	1,629.5	0.1[3]	4.3[3]	5.8[1]	___	___	___
Vangd Muni Short...	tax-free	1,463.5	1.6[1]	3.4[4]	4.8[4]	___	___	___
Vangd-Adml Short...	fix-inc	311.1	-0.3[3]	—	—	___	___	___
Vangd ST Federal...	fix-inc	1,504.8	-0.9[4]	4.0[2]	6.7[3]	___	___	___
Vangd ST Trsy...	fix-inc	704.0	-0.5[3]	4.1[2]	—	___	___	___
Vangd MM Prime...	money mkt	15,321.2	4.1[1]	3.6[1]	5.0[1]	___	___	___
Vangd CA MM...	money mkt TF	1,094.9	2.7[1]	2.7[1]	3.6[1]	___	___	___
Vangd OH TF MM...	money mkt TF	158.6	2.7[1]	2.6[1]	—	___	___	___
Vangd PA TF MM...	money mkt TF	1,134.6	2.7[1]	2.6[1]	3.6[1]	___	___	___
Vangd Muni MM...	money mkt TF	4,248.2	2.8[1]	2.7[1]	3.7[1]	___	___	___
Vangd NJ TF MM...	money mkt TF	798.3	2.6[1]	2.6[1]	3.6[1]	___	___	___
Vangd-Adml MM...	money mkt gov	1,340.7	4.0[1]	—	—	___	___	___
Vangd MM Treas...	money mkt gov	2,108.8	3.8[2]	3.4[1]	4.8[1]	___	___	___
Vangd MM Federal...	money mkt gov	2,191.9	4.0[1]	3.6[1]	4.9[1]	___	___	___
Your average...		130,679.1				___	___	___
Vista Funds (Chase Manhattan)								
Vista Equity...	growth	48.4	0.2[3]	4.6[4]	—	___	___	___
Vista Bond...	fix-inc	50.9	-3.2[2]	4.6[3]	—	___	___	___
Vista ST Bond...	fix-inc	33.2	2.4[1]	4.0[2]	—	___	___	___
Vista Global MM...	money mkt	136.0	4.0[1]	—	—	___	___	___
Vista TF MM...	money mkt TF	132.1	2.2[5]	2.2[4]	—	___	___	___
Vista CA TF MM...	money mkt TF	58.3	2.5[2]	—	—	___	___	___
Vista NY TF MM...	money mkt TF	382.3	2.1[5]	2.0[5]	—	___	___	___
Vista Gov MM...	money mkt gov	320.9	3.6[3]	3.0[5]	—	___	___	___
Your average...		1,162.1				___	___	___
Vontobel Management								
Vontobel EuroPac...	int'l	138.6	-4.9[4]	8.8[3]	—	___	___	___
Vontobel US Value...	growth	30.4	0.3[3]	3.8[4]	—	___	___	___
Vontobel Int'l Bd...	fix-inc	10.2	—	—	—	___	___	___
Your average...		179.2				___	___	___

Post quintile ranks for your funds here

Annualized Total Return % with quintile ranks by obj

No-load fund groups   *continued*

Families with 3 or more funds including one stock or bond fund
Arranged in alphabetical order by group and risk within group

Fund group/fund	Objective	Total Net Assets $ Millions 12/31/94	Annualized Total Return % with quintile ranks by obj 1994	3 years 1992-1994	5 years 1990-1994	Post quintile ranks for your funds here 1994	3 years ending 1994	5 years ending 1994
Warburg, Pincus Counsellors								
Warbg Pincus Emg Mkts..................................	int'l	—	—	—	—	____	____	____
Warbg Pincus Emg Gro SC..............................	agg gr	222.8	-1.4^3	9.3^2	12.9^2	____	____	____
Warbg Pincus Japan OTC...	int'l	22.3	—	—	—	____	____	____
Warbg Pincus Cap App....	growth	145.3	-2.9^4	6.5^3	7.6^4	____	____	____
Warbg Pincus Int'l...	int'l	1,551.7	0.2^3	13.2^1	10.8^1	____	____	____
Warbg Pincus Gro & Inc	gr-inc	628.0	7.6^1	16.8^1	13.4^1	____	____	____
Warbg Pincus Balanced...	income	0.8	1.3^1	8.2^2	10.3^1	____	____	____
Warbg Pincus Glob Bd...	fix-inc	85.0	-5.5^5	4.9^1	—	____	____	____
Warbg Pincus NY Muni...	tax-free	76.9	-0.6^1	5.5^1	6.4^3	____	____	____
Warbg Pincus Fix Inc...	fix-inc	105.2	-0.8^1	5.6^1	7.2^2	____	____	____
Warbg Pincus Inter Gov....	fix-inc	44.1	-1.8^4	4.1^2	7.2^1	____	____	____
Warbg Pincus ST AfterTax...	fix-inc	1.0	—	—	—	____	____	____
Warbg Pincus NY MM...	money mkt TF	88.5	2.2^4	2.1^5	3.0^5	____	____	____
Warbg Pincus Cash Res...	money mkt gov	397.7	3.9^1	3.4^1	4.8^1	____	____	____
Your average...		3,369.3				____	____	____
Wasatch Advisors								
Wasatch Agg Eqty SC.....................................	agg gr	55.5	5.5^1	10.6^2	17.0^1	____	____	____
Wasatch Growth...	growth	8.5	2.7^2	6.1^3	13.2^1	____	____	____
Wasatch MidCap..	growth	1.2	8.1^1	—	—	____	____	____
Wasatch Income...	fix-inc	3.0	1.6^2	3.4^4	6.8^2	____	____	____
Your average...		68.2				____	____	____
Wayne Hummer Management								
Wayne Hummer Growth....................................	growth	87.7	-0.9^3	4.2^4	8.9^3	____	____	____
Wayne Hummer Income....................................	fix-inc	25.3	-2.5^2	—	—	____	____	____
Wayne Hummer MM..	money mkt	144.1	3.5^4	3.0^5	4.4^5	____	____	____
Your average...		257.1				____	____	____
Weitz Series Funds								
Weitz Hickory...	growth	3.2	-17.2^5	—	—	____	____	____
Weitz Prtnrs Value...	growth	51.3	-9.0^5	—	—	____	____	____
Weitz Value..	gr-inc	107.7	-9.8^5	7.1^2	8.3^2	____	____	____
Weitz Fix Inc...	fix-inc	18.5	-2.3^2	3.6^4	6.2^5	____	____	____
Weitz Gov MM...	money mkt gov	7.0	3.5^4	3.2^2	—	____	____	____
Your average...		187.7				____	____	____
Wertheim Schroeder....................................								
Wertheim Small Cap SC...................................	agg gr	24.8	—	—	—	____	____	____
Wertheim Eqty Value..	gr-inc	26.8	—	—	—	____	____	____
Wertheim High Yld...	fix-inc	17.7	—	—	—	____	____	____
Wertheim Invest Grd...	fix-inc	19.3	—	—	—	____	____	____
Wertheim ST Inv...	fix-inc	32.2	—	—	—	____	____	____
Your average...		120.8				____	____	____

Families with 3 or more funds including one stock or bond fund
Arranged in alphabetical order by group and risk within group

Fund group/fund	Objective	Total Net Assets $ Millions 12/31/94	Annualized Total Return % with quintile ranks by obj 1994	3 years 1992-1994	5 years 1990-1994	Post quintile ranks for your funds here 1994	3 years ending 1994	5 years ending 1994
Westwood Funds...............								
Westwood Equity...............	gr-inc	10.1	2.3[1]	8.3[2]	7.6[3]	____	____	____
Westwood Balanced...............	income	13.0	0.0[2]	7.4[2]	—	____	____	____
Westwood Inter Bd...............	fix-inc	4.6	-5.6[5]	3.4[5]	—	____	____	____
Your average...............		27.7				____	____	____
William Blair & Company...............								
Wm Blair Growth...............	growth	182.2	6.5[1]	9.8[2]	13.3[1]	____	____	____
Wm Blair Int'l Gro...	int'l	71.1	-0.1[3]	—	—	____	____	____
Wm Blair Income...............	fix-inc	149.5	-0.7[4]	4.7[1]	—	____	____	____
Wm Blair Ltd TF...............	tax-free	14.1	—	—	—	____	____	____
Wm Blair Ready Res...............	money mkt	517.7	3.5[5]	3.1[4]	—	____	____	____
Your average...............		934.6				____	____	____
Weiss, Peck, & Greer...............								
WPG Growth SC...............	agg gr	83.2	-14.0[5]	1.6[5]	7.4[4]	____	____	____
WPG Tudor...............	agg gr	143.8	-9.8[5]	2.4[5]	8.2[4]	____	____	____
WPG International...	int'l	17.1	-6.3[4]	6.7[4]	0.8[4]	____	____	____
WPG Quant Eqty...	growth	73.5	0.3[3]	—	—	____	____	____
WPG Growth & Inc...	gr-inc	61.2	-5.5[5]	5.6[4]	8.2[3]	____	____	____
WPG Inter Muni...	tax-free	14.1	-2.3[1]	—	—	____	____	____
WPG Gov Sec...	fix-inc	216.6	-8.7[5]	2.4[5]	5.9[5]	____	____	____
WPG TF MM...............	money mkt TF	152.3	2.6[1]	2.6[1]	3.6[1]	____	____	____
WPG Gov MM...............	money mkt gov	187.6	3.6[3]	3.1[4]	4.5[3]	____	____	____
Your average...............		949.4				____	____	____
Wright Investor's Service...............								
Wright Jr Blue Ch SC...............	agg gr	37.4	-2.7[3]	2.7[5]	5.8[5]	____	____	____
Wright Equi Japan...............	int'l	8.6	—	—	—	____	____	____
Wright Equi Mexico...	int'l	13.1	—	—	—	____	____	____
Wright Equi Hong Kong...	int'l	19.8	-37.0[5]	10.5[2]	—	____	____	____
Wright Equi Belg\Lux...	int'l	11.4	—	—	—	____	____	____
Wright Equi Nordic...	int'l	8.7	—	—	—	____	____	____
Wright Equi Swiss...............	int'l	3.8	—	—	—	____	____	____
Wright Equi Dutch...	int'l	4.0	11.7[1]	7.0[4]	—	____	____	____
Wright Equi Italy...	int'l	1.3	5.0[2]	-8.1[5]	—	____	____	____
Wright Equi Spain...	int'l	6.4	-9.5[5]	-9.6[5]	—	____	____	____
Wright Int'l Blue Ch...	int'l	201.1	-1.6[3]	6.6[4]	5.7[2]	____	____	____
Wright Qual Core Eqty...	gr-inc	51.1	-0.7[3]	2.7[5]	7.9[3]	____	____	____
Wright Sel Blue Ch...	gr-inc	187.7	-3.5[4]	1.0[5]	6.3[4]	____	____	____
Wright Curr Inc...	fix-inc	84.0	-3.3[2]	3.2[5]	6.9[4]	____	____	____
Wright Gov Oblig...	fix-inc	16.6	-8.7[5]	4.3[3]	7.2[3]	____	____	____
Wright Insur TF...	tax-free	15.0	-4.1[1]	4.4[3]	5.9[4]	____	____	____
Wright Total Ret...	fix-inc	143.8	-6.4[4]	3.6[4]	6.2[5]	____	____	____
Wright Near Term...	fix-inc	213.3	-3.1[5]	3.6[4]	6.3[3]	____	____	____
Wright Trsy MM...	money mkt gov	18.0	3.5[4]	3.1[3]	—	____	____	____
Your average...............		1,045.1				____	____	____

CHAPTER 8

No-load fund charts

■ It's often said a picture is worth a thousand words. And that's certainly true when it comes to getting a quick, easy fix on mutual fund performance. Charts show you a fund's volatility, resistance to downturns, and growth potential, all at a glance. A buy or sell point is often indicated when a fund's graph crosses its moving average.

The first two charts provide your key to making the greatest use of these valuable tools. These charts (for Crabbe Huson Special Fund and Price Capital Appreciation Funds) show the location of data for net assets, distributions, weekly highs, lows and closings, 13 and 39 week moving averages. All other

charts in this chapter are in alphabetical order. Charts for precious metals and international funds are grouped separately at the end.

All charts in this chapter were provided by *Mutual Fund Trends,* a publication of Growth Fund Research, a long-established and respected publisher of mutual fund data. *Mutual Fund Trends* shows all the funds included in this chapter, updated weekly. Trends regularly costs $139 per year for 12 monthly issues. A single copy of this fine publication is available to *Handbook* readers for $5 from Growth Fund Research. Their address is on the Price Capital Appreciation Fund chart.

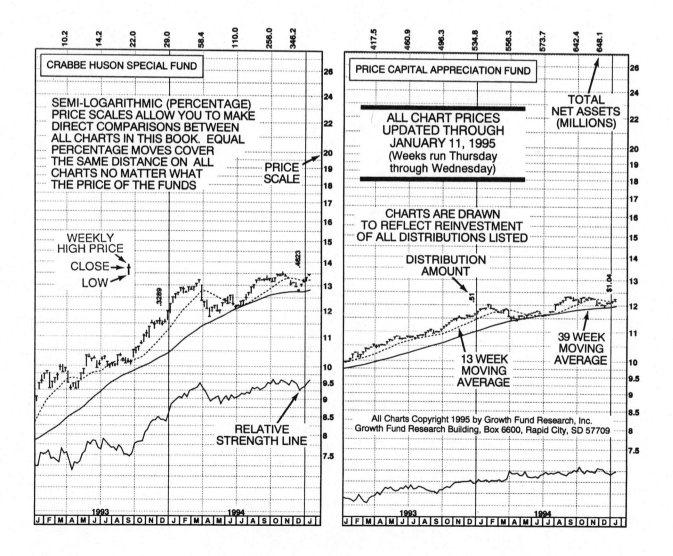

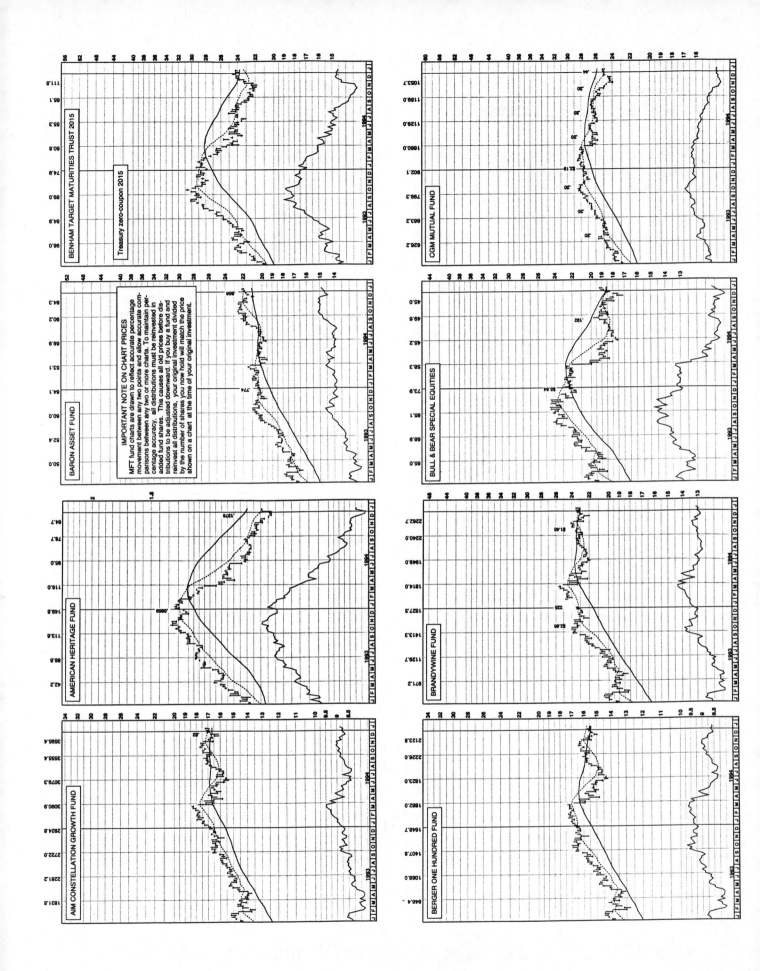

BENHAM TARGET MATURITIES TRUST 2015

Treasury zero-coupon 2015

BARON ASSET FUND

IMPORTANT NOTE ON CHART PRICES

MFT fund charts are drawn to reflect accurate percentage movement between any two points and allow accurate comparisons between any two or more charts. To maintain percentage accuracy, all distributions must be reinvested in added fund shares. This causes all old prices before distributions to be adjusted downward. If you buy a fund and reinvest all distributions, your original investment divided by the number of shares you now hold will match the price shown on a chart at the time of your original investment.

AMERICAN HERITAGE FUND

AIM CONSTELLATION GROWTH FUND

CGM MUTUAL FUND

BULL & BEAR SPECIAL EQUITIES

BRANDYWINE FUND

BERGER ONE HUNDRED FUND

148

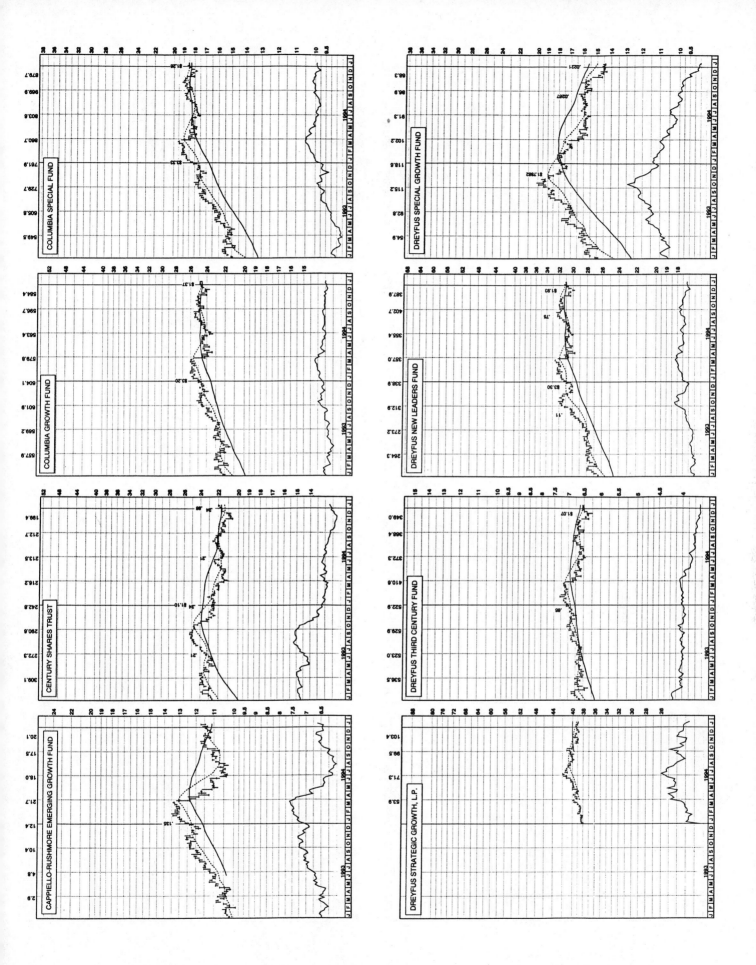

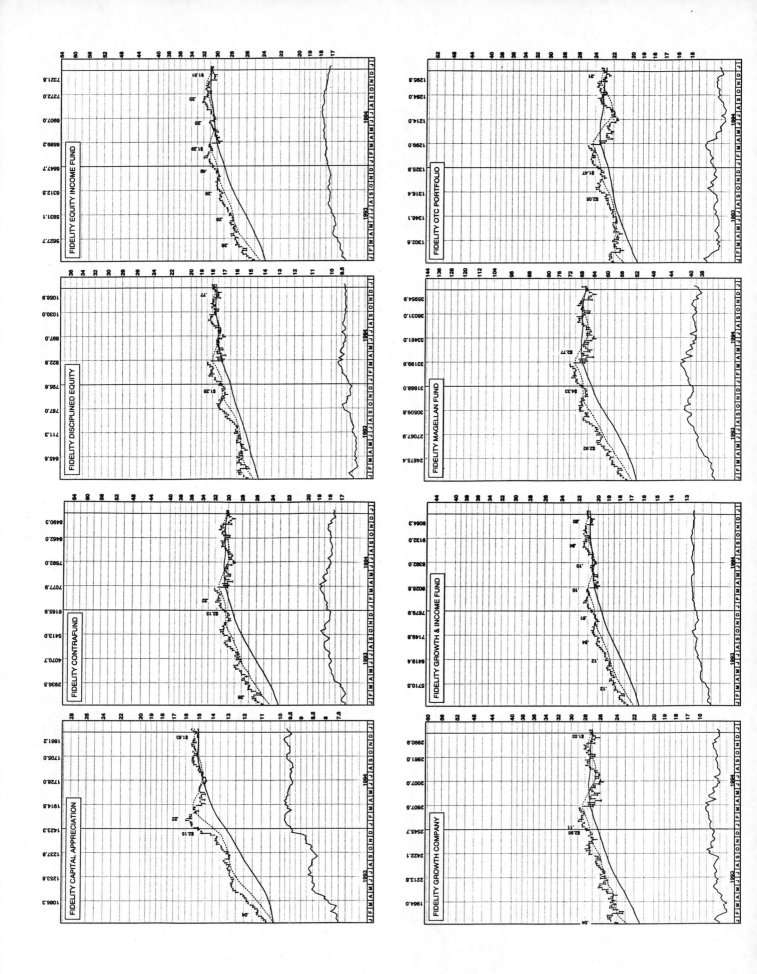

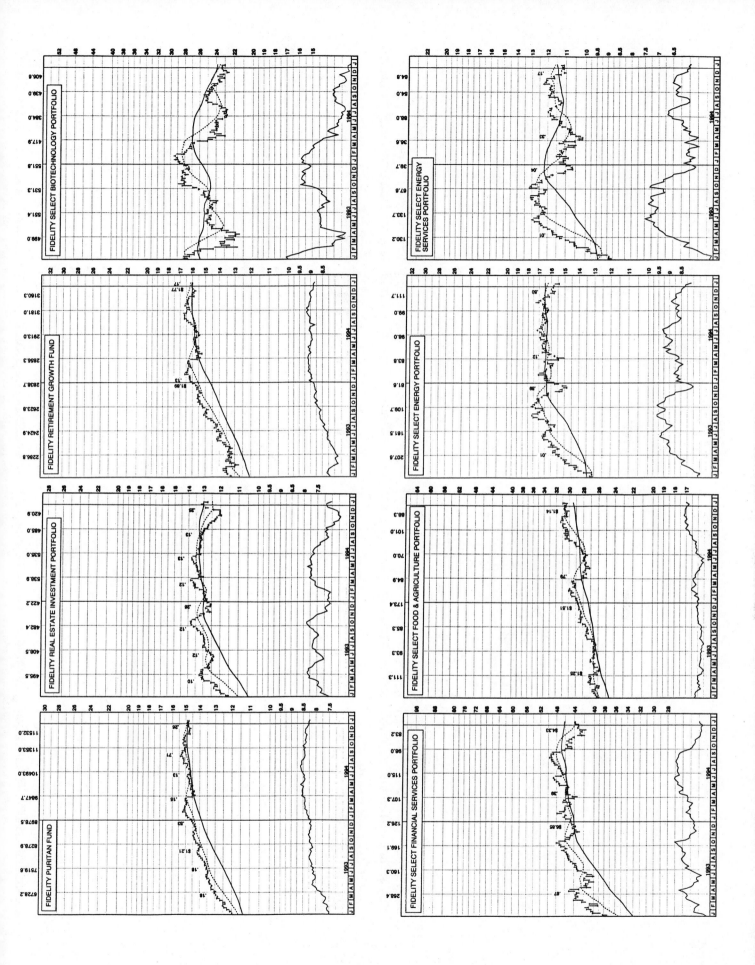

151

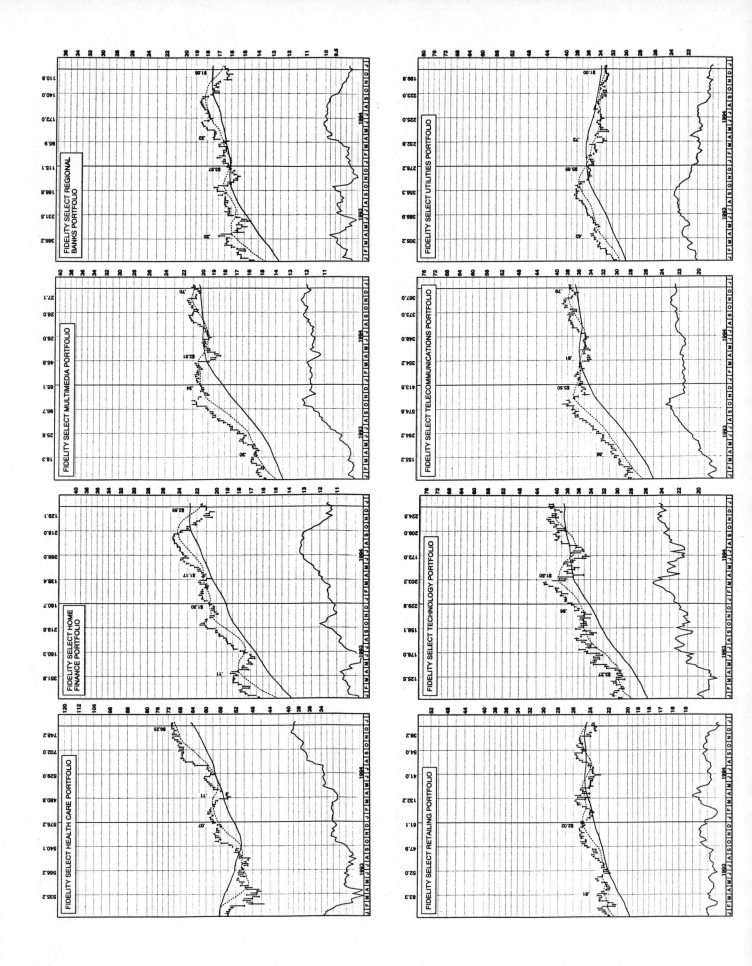

152

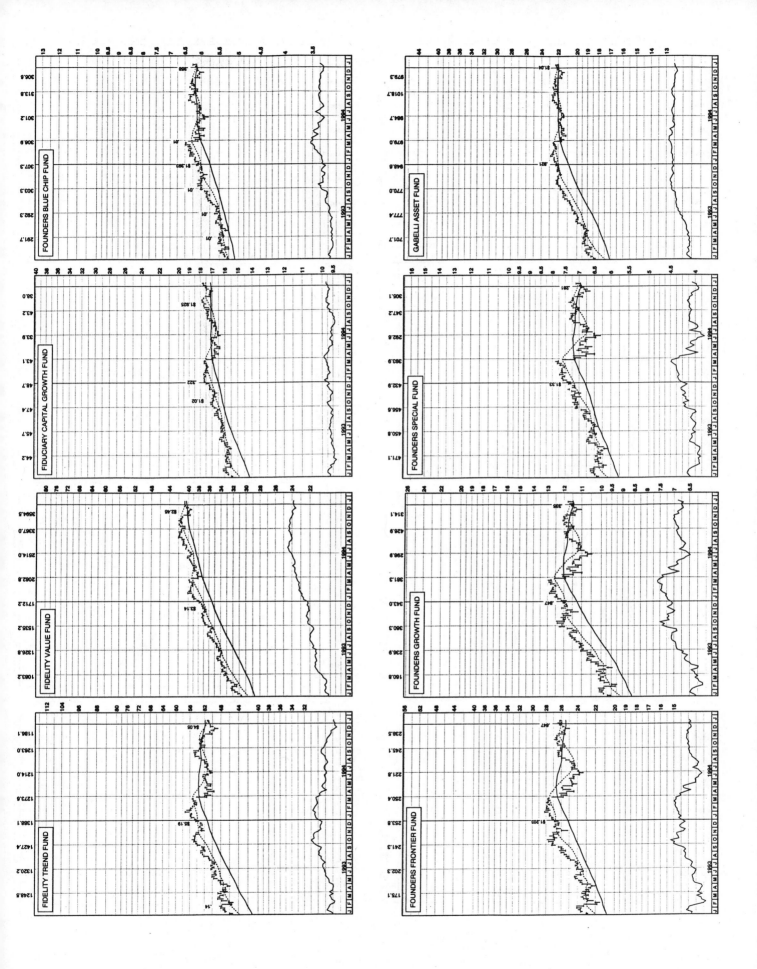

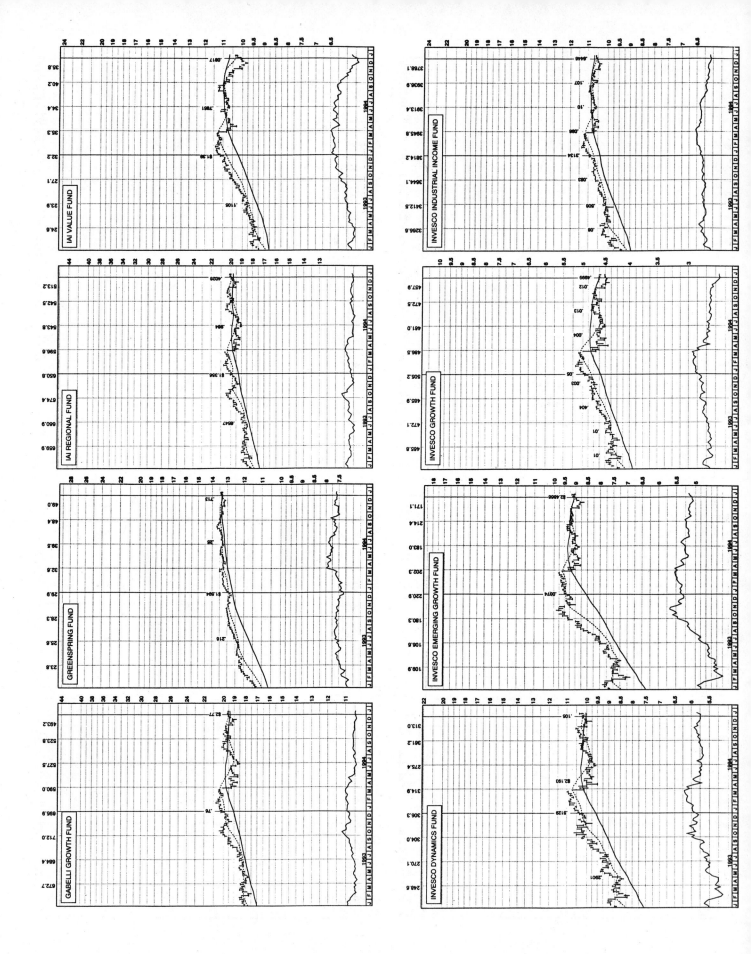

154

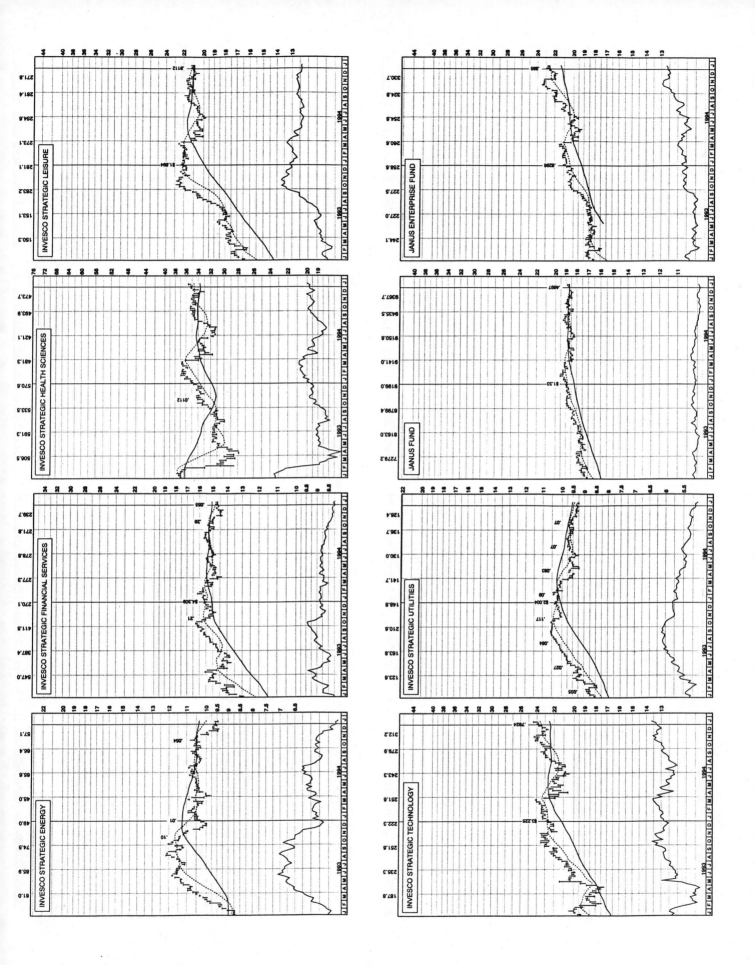

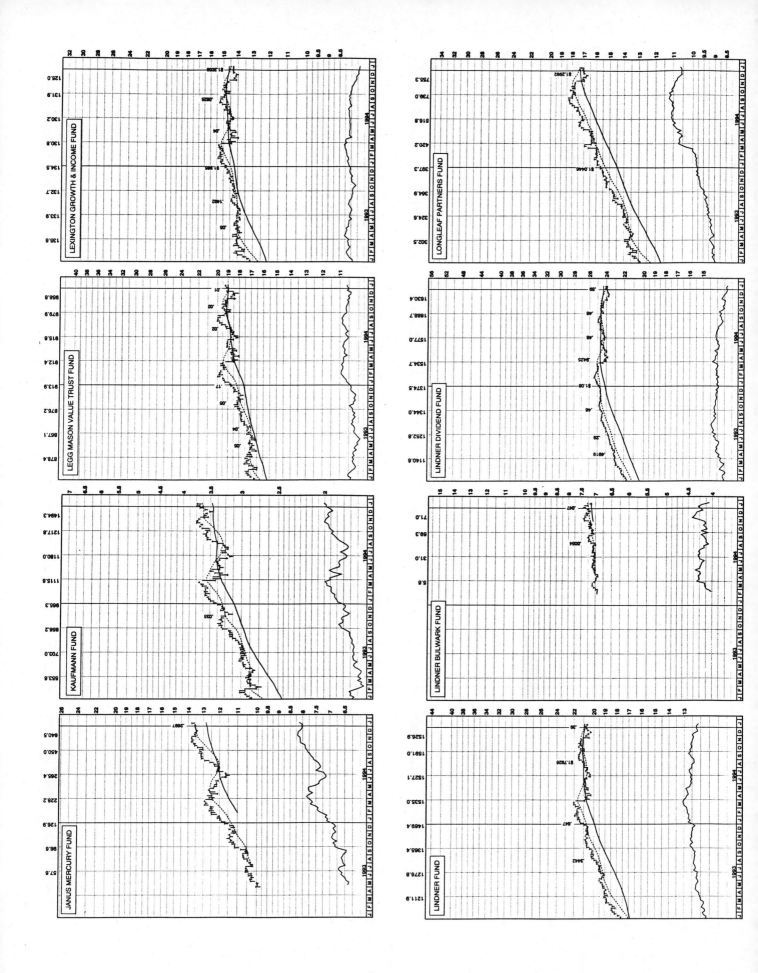

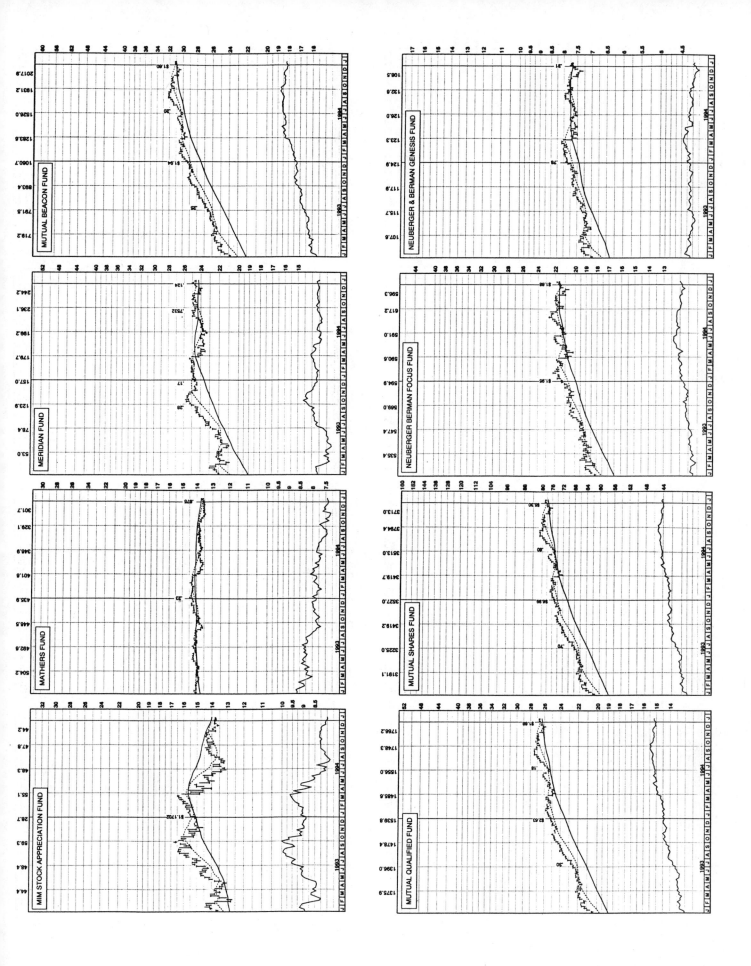

157

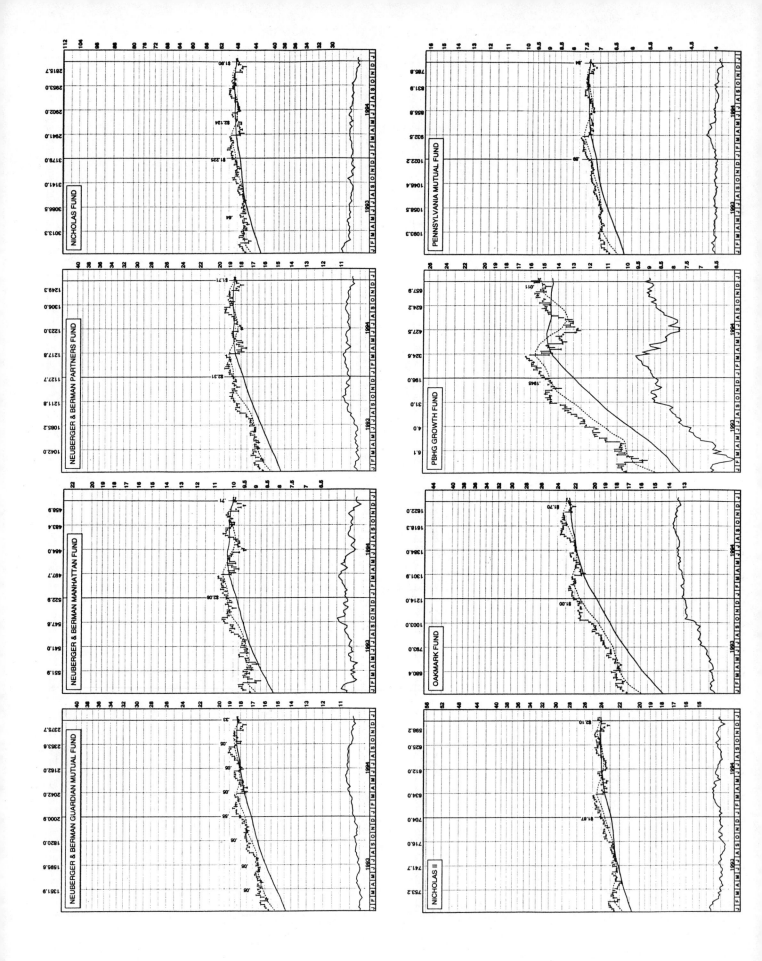

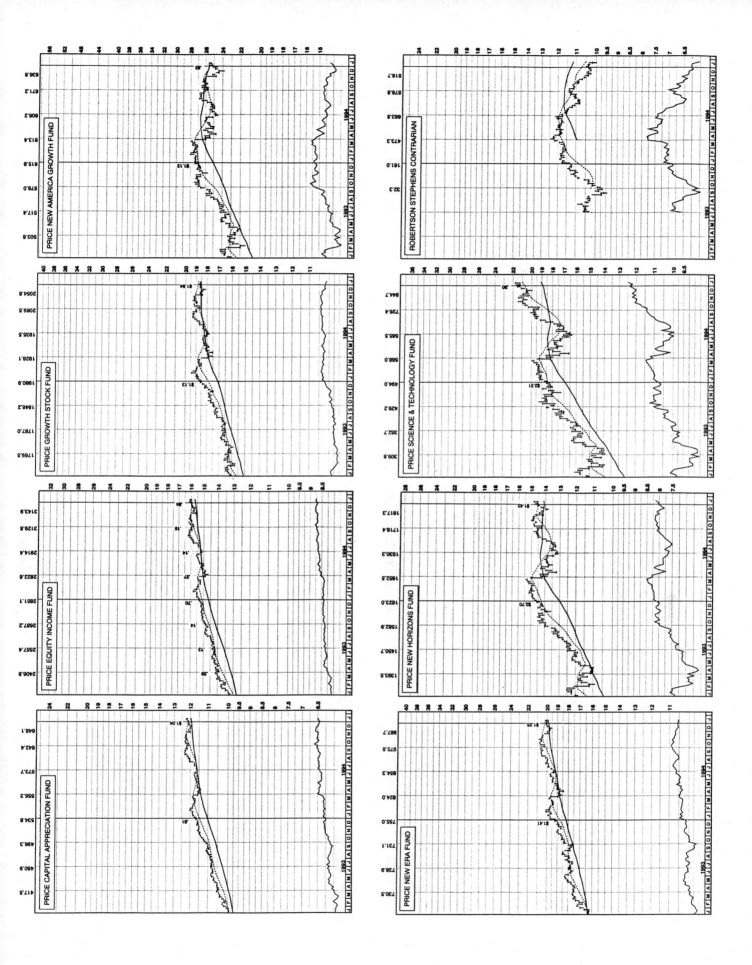

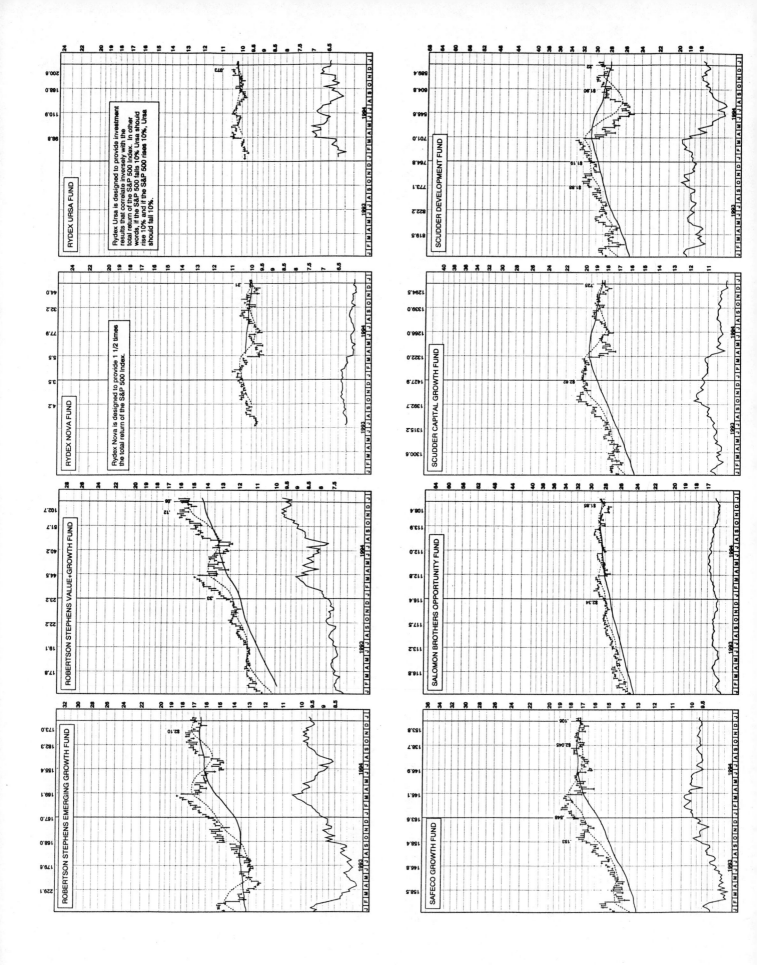

RYDEX URSA FUND

Rydex Ursa is designed to provide investment results that correlate inversely with the total return of the S&P 500 Index. In other words, if the S&P 500 falls 10% Ursa should rise 10% and if the S&P 500 rises 10%, Ursa should fall 10%.

RYDEX NOVA FUND

Rydex Nova is designed to provide 1 1/2 times the total return of the S&P 500 index.

ROBERTSON STEPHENS VALUE+GROWTH FUND

ROBERTSON STEPHENS EMERGING GROWTH FUND

SCUDDER DEVELOPMENT FUND

SCUDDER CAPITAL GROWTH FUND

SALOMON BROTHERS OPPORTUNITY FUND

SAFECO GROWTH FUND

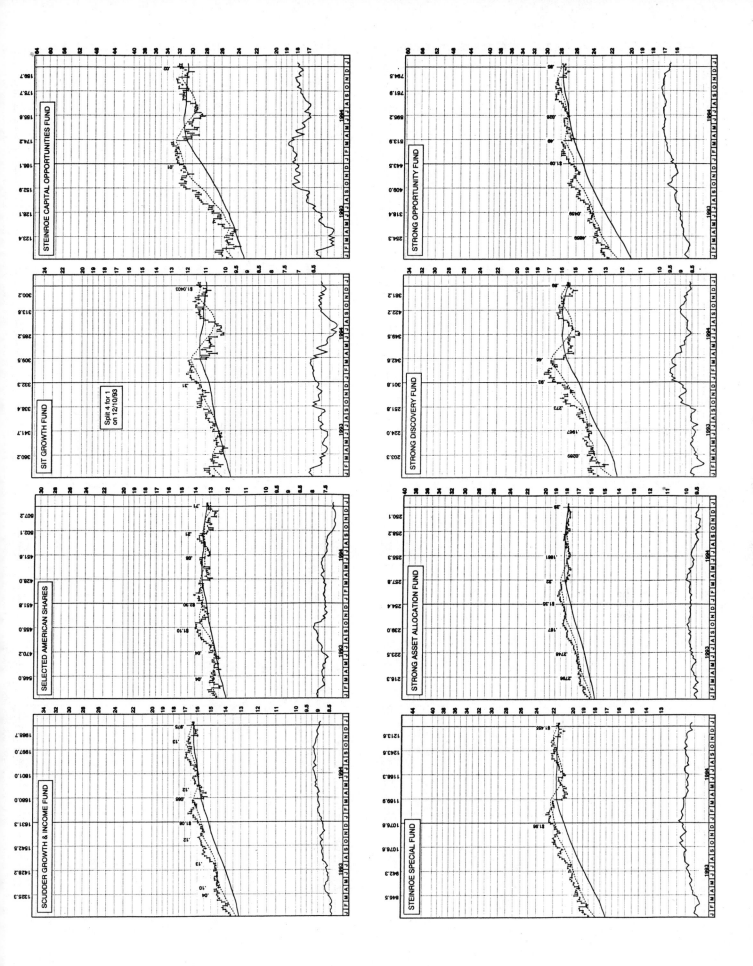

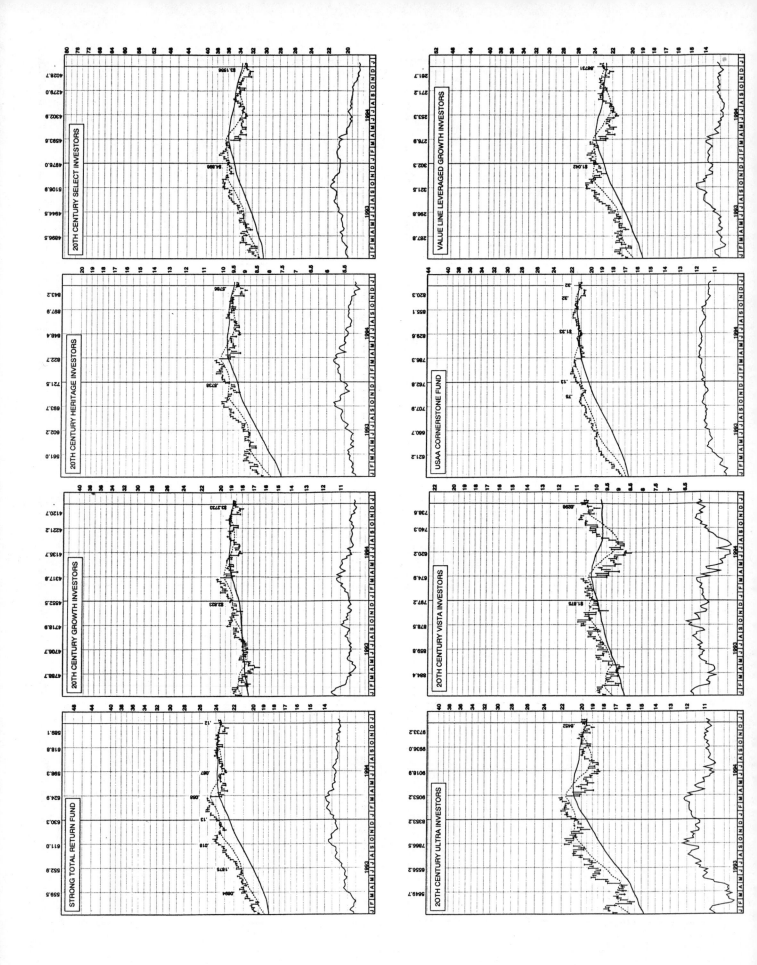

162

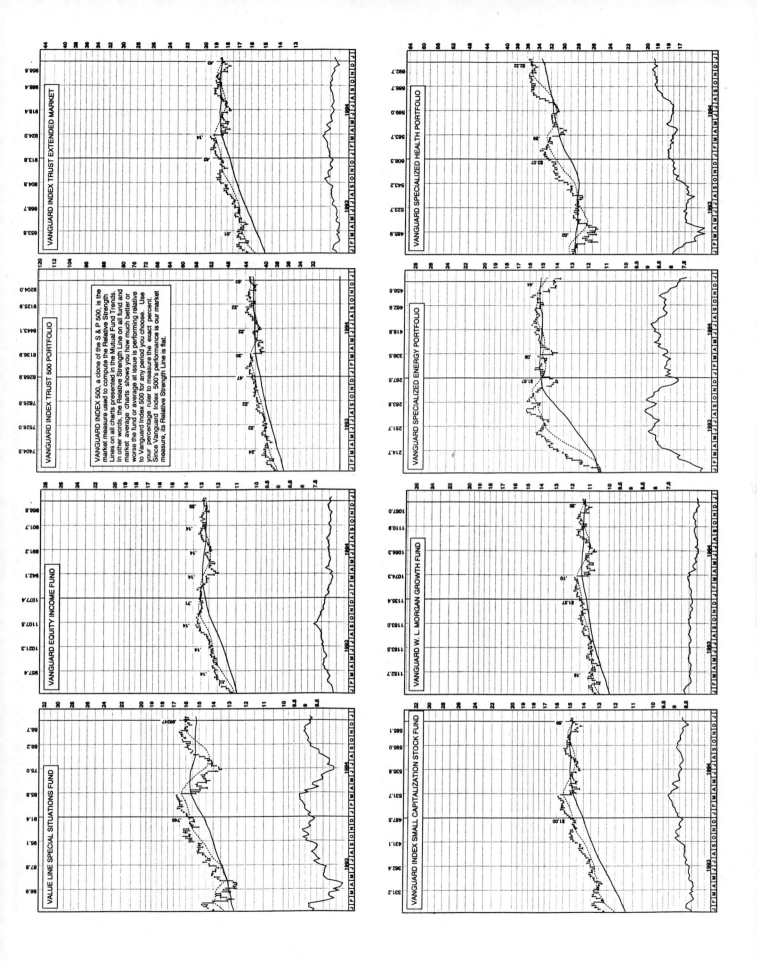

VANGUARD INDEX TRUST EXTENDED MARKET

VANGUARD INDEX TRUST 500 PORTFOLIO

VANGUARD INDEX 500, a clone of the S & P 500, is the market measure used to compute the Relative Strength Lines on all charts presented in the Mutual Fund Trends. In other words, the Relative Strength Line on all fund and market average charts shows you how much better or worse the fund or average at issue is performing relative to Vanguard Index 500 for any period you choose. Use your percentage ruler to measure the exact percent. Since Vanguard Index 500's performance is our market measure, its Relative Strength Line is flat.

VANGUARD SPECIALIZED HEALTH PORTFOLIO

VANGUARD SPECIALIZED ENERGY PORTFOLIO

VANGUARD EQUITY INCOME FUND

VANGUARD W. L. MORGAN GROWTH FUND

VALUE LINE SPECIAL SITUATIONS FUND

VANGUARD INDEX SMALL CAPITALIZATION STOCK FUND

163

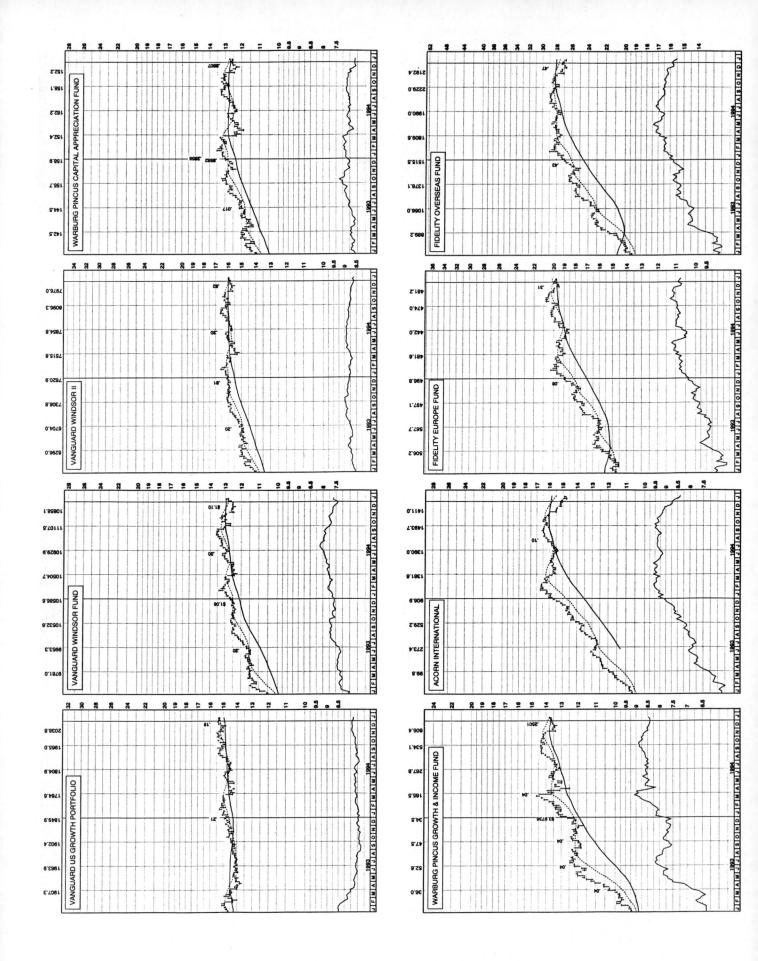

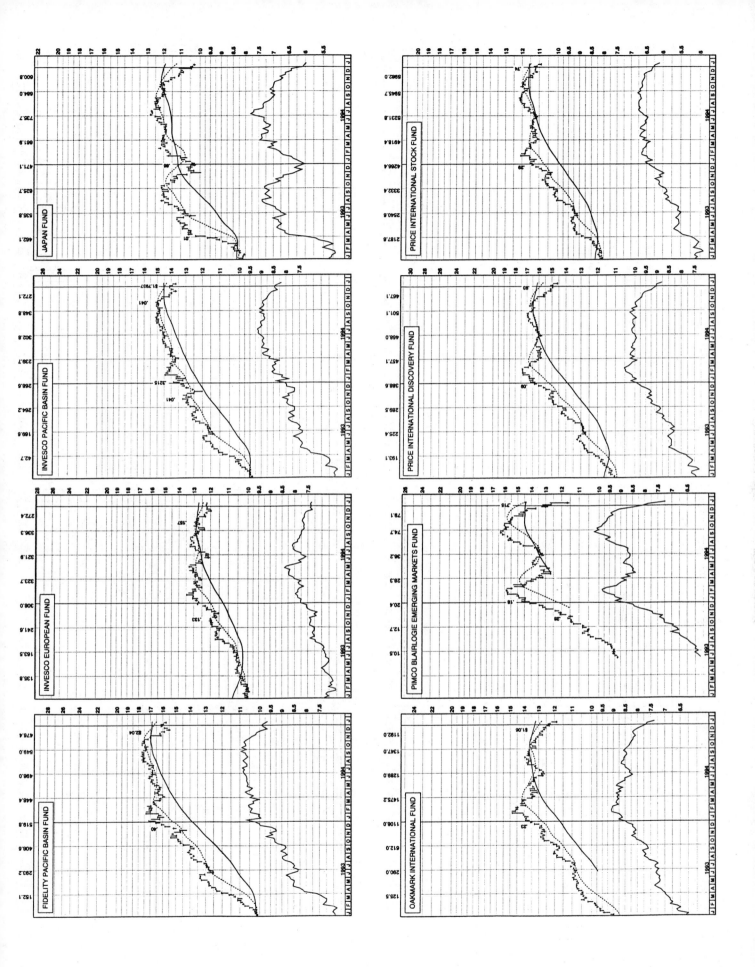

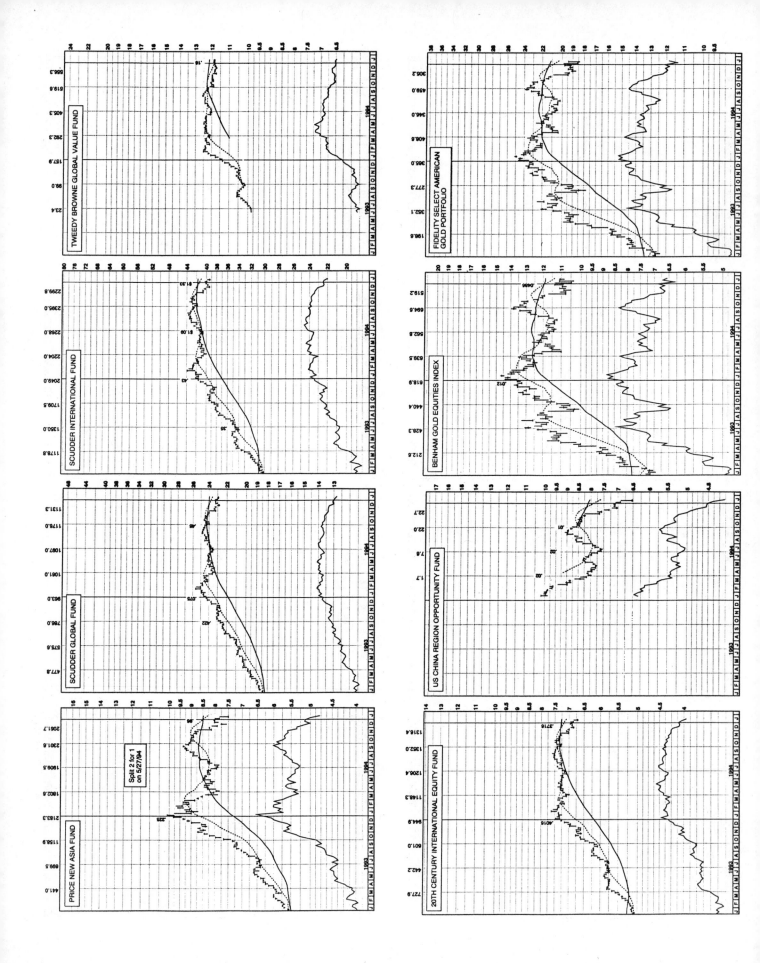

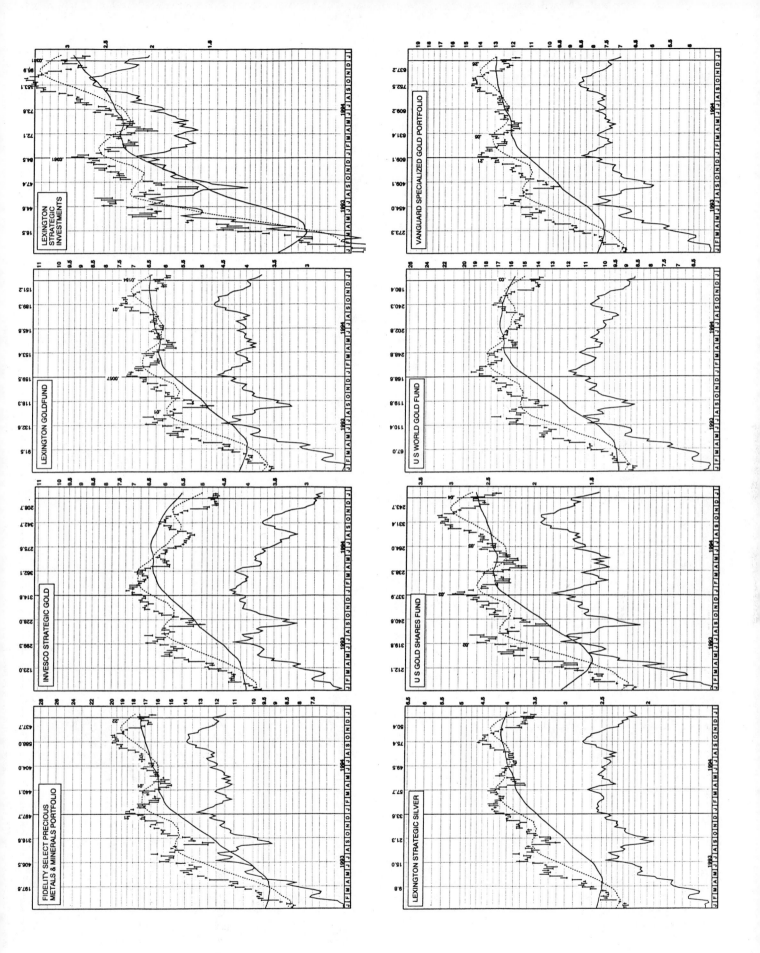

167

Money market funds
Arranged in alphabetical order within objective

No-Load Fund	Compound yield percent with quintile ranks by objective										Annualized	
	1985	1986	1987	1988	1989	1990	1991	1992	1993	1994	3 years	5 years
GENERAL MONEY MARKET FUNDS												
AARP Hi Qual MM	—	6.0[5]	5.4[5]	6.6[5]	8.4[5]	7.4[5]	5.9[2]	2.9[5]	2.1[5]	3.5[5]	2.8[5]	4.3[5]
Active Asst MM‡	8.1[1]	6.6[1]	6.2[2]	7.3[1]	9.1[1]	7.9[2]	5.8[3]	3.5[2]	2.8[2]	3.9[2]	3.4[2]	4.8[2]
Alliance Cap Res	7.4[5]	6.2[4]	6.0[4]	7.0[5]	8.7[5]	7.7[4]	5.6[4]	3.3[3]	2.5[5]	3.4[5]	3.0[4]	4.5[4]
Alliance Money Res	—	—	—	—	—	7.8[3]	5.7[4]	3.3[3]	2.5[5]	3.3[5]	3.0[4]	4.5[4]
Amcor Vntg Gov Obl MM	—	—	—	—	—	—	—	—	—	3.7[4]	—	—
Amer AAdv Mileage MM	—	—	—	—	—	—	—	3.8[1]	3.0[1]	3.9[2]	3.6[1]	—
API Money Mkt	—	—	—	—	—	—	—	—	—	—	—	—
Arbor OVB Prime Obl	—	—	—	—	—	—	—	—	—	—	—	—
Asset Mgmt Money Mkt	—	—	—	—	—	—	—	3.3	2.8	3.9[2]	3.3[2]	—
Babson Prime MM	7.6[5]	6.1[5]	5.8[5]	6.9[5]	8.7[5]	7.6[5]	5.4[5]	3.1[5]	2.3[5]	3.4[5]	3.0[5]	4.4[5]
Babson UMB Prime MM	7.9[2]	6.5[2]	6.4[1]	7.3[1]	9.1[2]	8.0[2]	5.8[3]	3.5[2]	2.8[3]	3.8[2]	3.3[2]	4.7[2]
Bartlett Cash Res	—	—	—	7.2[2]	8.7[4]	7.7[4]	5.7[3]	3.6[1]	2.7[3]	3.6[4]	3.3[3]	4.6[3]
Benham Prime MM	—	—	—	—	—	—	—	—	—	4.5[1]	—	—
Bull & Bear Dollar	7.5[5]	6.3[3]	5.9[5]	7.1[3]	8.5[5]	7.4[5]	5.4[5]	3.2[4]	2.4[5]	3.4[5]	3.0[5]	4.3[5]
Calvert Scl Inv MM	7.8[4]	6.2[4]	6.0[4]	7.1[4]	8.8[4]	7.7[4]	5.7[4]	3.3[4]	2.5[4]	3.6[4]	3.1[4]	4.5[4]
Cash Acct Tr-MM‡	—	—	—	—	—	—	5.4[5]	3.0[5]	2.4[5]	3.5[4]	3.0[5]	—
Cash Equiv-MM‡	7.9[2]	6.4[2]	6.1[3]	7.1[3]	8.8[4]	7.8[4]	5.6[4]	3.2[4]	2.5[4]	3.6[4]	3.1[4]	4.5[4]
CMA Money Mkt‡	8.1[1]	6.6[1]	6.3[1]	7.2[2]	9.0[2]	8.0[2]	6.0[1]	3.5[2]	2.9[2]	3.8[2]	3.4[1]	4.8[1]
Columbia Daily Inc	7.6[5]	6.2[4]	6.1[3]	7.1[4]	8.9[3]	7.8[3]	5.7[4]	3.3[4]	2.5[4]	3.7[4]	3.1[4]	4.6[4]
CT&T Money Mkt	—	—	—	—	—	—	—	—	—	3.9[2]	—	—
Dean Witter Liq Asst	8.1[1]	6.6[1]	6.2[2]	7.3[1]	9.1[1]	7.9[2]	5.7[3]	3.4[3]	2.7[3]	3.8[3]	3.3[3]	4.7[3]
Dreyfus BASIC MM	—	—	—	—	—	—	—	—	3.4[1]	4.3[1]	—	—
Dreyfus Liq Asst	8.1[1]	6.5[2]	6.1[3]	7.1[3]	9.1[1]	7.9[2]	5.9[2]	3.5[2]	2.6[4]	3.5[4]	3.2[3]	4.7[3]
Dreyfus MM Instr MM Ser	—	—	—	—	—	—	6.0[2]	3.5[2]	2.6[4]	3.4[5]	3.2[3]	—
Dreyfus Wrld Dollar	—	—	—	—	—	8.7[1]	6.4[1]	3.8[1]	2.7[3]	3.5[5]	3.3[2]	5.0[1]
Drey-General MM	7.9[2]	6.3[4]	5.9[5]	7.0[5]	8.8[4]	7.7[4]	5.8[2]	3.4[3]	2.6[4]	3.5[5]	3.2[4]	4.6[3]
Drey/Laurel Cash Mgmt	7.9[2]	6.3[5]	6.0[4]	7.0[4]	8.8[4]	7.7[4]	5.9[2]	3.3[3]	2.5[5]	—	—	—
Drey/Laurel Prime MM	—	—	—	—	—	—	—	3.6[1]	2.8[2]	3.9[2]	3.4[1]	—
Evergreen MM Tr	—	—	—	7.5[1]	9.4[1]	8.3[1]	6.3[1]	3.9[1]	3.2[1]	4.0[1]	3.7[1]	5.1[1]
59 Wall St MM	—	—	—	—	—	—	—	—	2.9[1]	—	—	—
Federated Prime MM	—	—	—	—	—	7.7[4]	5.5[5]	3.1[5]	2.4[5]	3.8[3]	3.1[4]	4.5[5]
FFB Lexcn Cash Mgt	—	—	—	—	—	—	—	3.5[2]	2.8[3]	3.7[3]	3.3[2]	—
Fidelity Cash MM	7.9[3]	6.5[2]	6.2[2]	7.3[2]	8.9[3]	7.8[3]	6.0[2]	3.8[1]	2.9[1]	4.0[2]	3.5[1]	4.9[1]
Fidelity Daily MM	8.0[1]	6.6[1]	6.1[3]	7.3[1]	8.9[3]	7.9[3]	5.8[3]	3.6[1]	2.8[2]	3.9[2]	3.4[1]	4.8[2]
Fidelity Select MM	—	6.4[3]	5.8[5]	7.1[3]	9.0[2]	7.8[4]	5.8[3]	3.5[2]	2.7[3]	3.7[3]	3.3[2]	4.7[2]
Fidelity Spart MM	—	—	—	—	—	8.4[1]	6.2[1]	4.0[1]	3.1[1]	4.1[1]	3.7[1]	5.2[1]
Flex-Fund MM	—	6.8[1]	6.4[1]	7.6[1]	9.4[1]	8.2[1]	6.1[1]	3.7[1]	3.0[1]	4.1[1]	3.6[1]	5.0[1]
Fortis Money Mkt	7.6[5]	6.1[5]	6.0[4]	6.9[5]	8.7[5]	7.7[4]	5.6[4]	3.1[5]	2.3[5]	3.5[5]	2.9[5]	4.4[5]
Founders Money Mkt	7.3[5]	6.0[5]	5.8[5]	6.9[5]	8.6[5]	7.5[5]	5.3[5]	2.9[5]	2.3[5]	3.5[5]	2.9[5]	4.3[5]
Fremont Money Mkt	—	—	—	—	8.9[3]	8.0[1]	6.0[1]	3.4[3]	2.6[4]	4.0[2]	3.3[3]	4.8[2]
FundTrust Money Mkt	—	—	—	—	—	—	5.6[4]	3.3[4]	2.8[2]	4.0[1]	3.3[3]	—
Galaxy Money Mkt	—	—	—	7.4[1]	8.9[3]	8.0[1]	5.9[2]	3.5[2]	2.7[3]	3.7[3]	3.3[2]	4.8[2]
GE Elfun MM‡	—	—	—	—	—	—	6.6[1]	3.9[1]	3.3[1]	4.2[1]	3.8[1]	—
GE Money Mkt	—	—	—	—	—	—	—	—	—	—	—	—
Green Cent MM	—	—	—	—	—	—	—	—	2.9[2]	3.8[3]	—	—
Harbor Money Mkt	—	—	—	7.1[4]	9.3[1]	8.0[2]	5.8[3]	3.2[4]	2.8[3]	3.9[2]	3.3[3]	4.7[2]
Highmark Dvsfd MM	—	—	—	—	8.7[5]	7.9[2]	5.8[3]	3.5[2]	2.6[4]	3.6[4]	3.2[3]	4.7[3]
Homestead Daily Inc	—	—	—	—	—	—	—	3.4[3]	2.9[2]	3.6[4]	3.3[3]	—
IAI Money Mkt	—	—	—	—	—	—	—	—	2.9[2]	3.7[3]	—	—
Invesco Cash Res	7.8[4]	6.2[4]	6.0[4]	7.1[3]	8.9[3]	7.8[3]	5.6[4]	3.1[4]	2.4[5]	3.7[3]	3.1[4]	4.5[4]
Kemper Money Mkt	8.1[1]	6.7[1]	6.3[1]	7.5[1]	9.2[1]	8.2[1]	6.0[1]	3.5[2]	2.9[2]	4.0[1]	3.5[1]	4.9[1]
Kidder Pbdy Cash Res‡	7.8[3]	6.4[3]	6.2[2]	7.2[2]	8.9[4]	7.8[3]	5.6[4]	3.2[4]	2.6[4]	3.6[4]	3.1[4]	4.5[4]
Legg Msn Cash Res	7.6[5]	6.1[5]	6.1[4]	7.0[4]	8.8[4]	7.7[4]	5.8[2]	3.5[2]	2.8[2]	3.7[4]	3.3[2]	4.7[3]
Lexington MM	8.0[1]	6.3[3]	6.1[3]	7.0[4]	8.6[5]	7.6[5]	5.5[5]	3.0[5]	2.3[5]	3.4[5]	2.9[5]	4.3[5]
Liquid Cap Inc MM	7.8[4]	6.1[5]	6.1[3]	7.1[3]	8.8[4]	7.6[5]	5.5[5]	3.0[5]	2.4[5]	3.5[5]	3.0[5]	4.4[5]
Managers Money Mkt	7.7[4]	6.4[3]	6.3[2]	7.3[2]	8.7[4]	7.7[5]	5.4[5]	3.1[5]	2.9[2]	3.6[4]	3.2[3]	4.5[4]
Marshall MM Invest	—	—	—	—	—	—	—	—	2.7[3]	3.8[3]	—	—
Marshall MM Trust	—	—	—	—	—	—	—	—	3.0[1]	4.1[1]	—	—
Merrill Lynch Rdy Asst	8.1[1]	6.5[2]	6.3[1]	7.2[3]	9.0[2]	8.0[1]	6.0[1]	3.5[2]	2.8[2]	3.7[3]	3.3[2]	4.8[1]

Money market funds *continued*
Arranged in alphabetical order within objective

Valuation Method	Total Net Assets $ Millions December 31 1993	1994	Avg. Maturity days 12/31/94	US Treas.	Other US	Repos	Time Deposits	Domestic Bank Oblig.	Foreign Bank Oblig.	Comm'l Paper 1st Tier	Comm'l Paper 2nd Tier	Floating Rate Notes	No-Load Fund
							GENERAL MONEY MARKET FUNDS						
4	259.3	375.2	37	—	—	1	—	17	—	41	—	41	AARP Hi Qual MM
4	3,688.7	4,759.6	53	14	22	—	—	4	—	60	—	—	Active Asst MM‡
3	2,181.3	2,319.7	65	2	5	—	—	9	7	70	—	7	Alliance Cap Res
3	1,735.8	1,808.5	69	3	3	—	10	6	70	—	8	—	Alliance Money Res
4	—	117.6	—	—	—	—	—	—	—	—	—	—	Amcor Vntg Gov Obl MM
4	36.2	64.7	36	—	9	15	13	—	6	21	6	30	Amer AAdv Mileage MM
—	—	—	—	—	—	—	—	—	—	—	—	—	API Money Mkt
4	—	0.7	—	—	—	—	—	—	—	—	—	—	Arbor OVB Prime Obl
4	33.2	35.1	39	41	59	—	—	—	—	—	—	—	Asset Mgmt Money Mkt
4	41.4	42.8	39	—	21	11	—	5	—	63	—	—	Babson Prime MM
4	197.7	200.3	41	—	—	9	—	—	—	91	—	—	Babson UMB Prime MM
4	77.9	76.8	19	—	—	1	—	—	—	98	—	1	Bartlett Cash Res
4	31.1	1.5	44	—	5	—	—	2	30	58	—	5	Benham Prime MM
3	68.1	67.7	10	7	93	—	—	—	—	—	—	—	Bull & Bear Dollar
4	139.2	144.4	35	—	13	—	—	11	—	61	—	15	Calvert Scl Inv MM
4	41.7	375.9	28	—	—	3	—	5	—	92	—	—	Cash Acct Tr-MM‡
4	3,402.5	3,420.3	27	—	—	6	2	10	1	81	—	—	Cash Equiv-MM‡
1	25,377.0	26,497.4	79	9	19	2	—	1	14	50	—	5	CMA Money Mkt‡
4	544.5	730.1	43	1	10	—	—	—	—	89	—	—	Columbia Daily Inc
4	91.1	97.1	25	—	12	14	3	—	—	46	20	5	CT&T Money Mkt
4	7,768.1	8,906.6	46	17	18	—	—	3	—	62	—	—	Dean Witter Liq Asst
4	1,139.5	1,719.2	34	7	—	2	—	—	40	51	—	—	Dreyfus BASIC MM
4	4,828.1	4,863.4	44	4	1	4	2	3	—	79	7	—	Dreyfus Liq Asst
4	207.4	170.4	35	—	12	—	—	1	47	27	8	5	Dreyfus MM Instr MM Ser
4	3,189.4	2,316.4	41	—	3	8	1	1	47	27	7	6	Dreyfus Wrld Dollar
4	621.3	575.6	28	—	3	—	5	—	49	36	—	7	Drey-General MM
4	130.9	—	—	—	—	—	—	—	—	—	—	—	Drey/Laurel Cash Mgmt
—	109.3	129.5	59	5	7	26	—	—	4	58	—	—	Drey/Laurel Prime MM
4	286.3	260.7	69	—	2	—	—	7	6	85	—	—	Evergreen MM Tr
4	1.2	—	—	—	—	—	—	—	—	—	—	—	59 Wall St MM
4	774.0	38.4	52	—	—	8	4	—	5	56	—	27	Federated Prime MM
4	557.7	402.2	43	—	7	—	50	43	—	—	—	—	FFB Lexcn Cash Mgt
1	10,179.3	15,215.8	57	—	8	3	3	3	38	36	4	5	Fidelity Cash MM
1	2,140.7	2,226.8	56	1	16	—	—	10	—	63	4	6	Fidelity Daily MM
4	457.5	669.0	58	1	12	6	—	2	—	72	4	3	Fidelity Select MM
4	4,194.6	7,531.9	57	—	6	—	1	1	43	40	4	5	Fidelity Spart MM
4	199.6	164.1	51	2	11	13	—	—	—	54	—	20	Flex-Fund MM
3	94.1	105.9	27	—	—	—	—	—	—	96	—	4	Fortis Money Mkt
4	142.9	203.5	17	—	—	—	—	—	—	100	—	—	Founders Money Mkt
4	25.0	241.4	39	—	—	—	—	—	—	95	—	5	Fremont Money Mkt
1	99.7	115.2	44	—	—	31	—	6	—	55	—	8	FundTrust Money Mkt
4	553.0	496.2	33	—	11	25	—	12	—	52	—	—	Galaxy Money Mkt
4	60.0	107.1	58	14	82	—	4	—	—	—	—	—	GE Elfun MM‡
4	1.0	45.9	54	12	84	—	4	—	—	—	—	—	GE Money Mkt
4	2.1	3.1	44	—	40	—	—	—	—	58	—	2	Green Cent MM
4	49.5	74.0	28	8	31	12	—	4	—	45	—	—	Harbor Money Mkt
4	315.1	225.9	56	—	—	10	—	5	—	78	—	7	Highmark Dvsfd MM
—	26.7	36.6	37	—	10	—	—	—	—	81	—	9	Homestead Daily Inc
—	8.0	27.2	14	—	60	—	—	—	—	40	—	—	IAI Money Mkt
4	521.2	745.5	25	12	—	—	—	—	—	88	—	—	Invesco Cash Res
4	4,139.7	4,019.4	27	—	—	6	1	10	—	83	—	—	Kemper Money Mkt
4	1,781.9	1,487.9	33	—	3	14	—	8	5	70	—	—	Kidder Pbdy Cash Res‡
4	741.3	861.8	57	2	19	1	—	11	1	19	—	47	Legg Msn Cash Res
4	94.8	110.8	42	12	7	—	—	—	4	69	—	8	Lexington MM
4	306.1	270.1	29	12	—	2	—	13	—	66	—	7	Liquid Cap Inc MM
—	12.8	18.0	23	—	—	11	5	—	—	84	—	—	Managers Money Mkt
4	2.4	17.9	49	—	—	—	—	—	—	—	—	—	Marshall MM Invest
4	907.2	1,046.8	52	—	—	—	—	—	—	—	—	—	Marshall MM Trust
1	6,522.7	6,258.7	81	5	16	3	—	—	9	63	—	4	Merrill Lynch Rdy Asst

| No-Load Fund | Compound yield percent with quintile ranks by objective | | | | | | | | | | Annualized | |
	1985	1986	1987	1988	1989	1990	1991	1992	1993	1994	3 years	5 years
Merrill Lynch Ret Res	—	—	—	—	—	—	6.1^{1}	3.5^{2}	2.9^{2}	3.9^{2}	3.4^{1}	—
MIM Money Mkt	—	—	—	6.2^{5}	7.3^{5}	7.8^{4}	5.7^{3}	3.1^{5}	2.9^{2}	3.2^{5}	3.1^{4}	4.5^{4}
Nbrgr-Ber Cash Res	—	—	—	—	9.0^{2}	7.8^{3}	5.7^{3}	3.4^{3}	2.7^{3}	3.7^{3}	3.2^{3}	4.6^{3}
New England MM	7.9^{2}	6.6^{1}	6.1^{4}	7.2^{3}	8.9^{2}	7.9^{2}	5.9^{2}	3.5^{2}	2.5^{4}	3.5^{5}	3.2^{4}	4.6^{3}
Nicholas Money Mkt	—	—	—	—	9.0^{2}	8.1^{1}	5.8^{3}	3.3^{3}	2.7^{3}	3.9^{2}	3.3^{2}	4.7^{2}
Northern Money Mkt	—	—	—	—	—	—	—	—	—	—	—	—
Pacific Hzn Prime MM	—	—	—	—	—	—	—	—	—	3.7^{3}	—	—
Pacifica Money Mkt	—	—	—	—	—	—	—	—	3.0^{1}	3.8^{2}	—	—
Paine Webber Cashfund	8.0^{2}	6.4^{2}	6.3^{1}	7.3^{1}	9.1^{2}	8.0^{2}	5.9^{2}	3.5^{2}	2.8^{3}	3.8^{3}	3.4^{2}	4.8^{2}
Pierpont Money Mkt	—	—	—	—	—	—	—	—	—	—	—	—
Portico Money Mkt	—	—	—	—	9.0^{2}	8.1^{1}	5.7^{3}	3.4^{3}	2.7^{3}	3.8^{2}	3.3^{3}	4.7^{2}
Preferred Money Mkt	—	—	—	—	—	—	—	—	2.6^{4}	3.9^{2}	—	—
Price, Rowe Prime Res	8.0^{2}	6.4^{3}	6.3^{2}	7.2^{3}	8.9^{3}	7.7^{4}	5.7^{3}	3.4^{3}	2.6^{4}	3.7^{3}	3.2^{3}	4.6^{3}
Price Summit Cash Res	—	—	—	—	—	—	—	—	2.5^{5}	4.0^{1}	—	—
Prudential Moneymart	7.9^{2}	6.2^{4}	6.1^{3}	7.2^{2}	9.0^{2}	7.9^{2}	6.0^{2}	3.6^{1}	2.7^{3}	3.8^{3}	3.3^{2}	4.8^{2}
Reserve Primary MM	8.1^{1}	6.4^{2}	6.0^{4}	7.2^{2}	8.8^{4}	7.6^{5}	5.4^{5}	3.1^{4}	2.4^{5}	4.0^{1}	3.2^{4}	4.5^{4}
Retrmt Sys: MM‡	—	—	—	—	—	—	—	3.4^{3}	2.8^{2}	—	—	—
Reynolds Money Mkt	—	—	—	—	—	—	—	3.2^{4}	2.8^{2}	—	—	—
RMA Money Mkt‡	7.8^{3}	6.3^{4}	6.4^{1}	7.2^{2}	9.1^{1}	8.0^{2}	5.9^{2}	3.6^{1}	2.8^{2}	3.8^{2}	3.4^{2}	4.8^{2}
Rushmore Money Mkt	—	6.0^{5}	5.9^{5}	7.0^{5}	8.8^{4}	7.7^{5}	5.4^{5}	3.0^{5}	2.4^{5}	—	—	—
SAFECO Money Mkt	7.8^{4}	6.2^{4}	6.1^{3}	7.0^{5}	9.1^{1}	8.0^{2}	5.7^{3}	3.3^{4}	2.5^{4}	3.5^{4}	3.1^{4}	4.6^{3}
Salomon Cash Mgmt	—	—	—	—	—	—	—	3.4^{3}	2.7^{3}	3.9^{2}	3.3^{2}	—
Schwab Money Mkt	—	—	—	—	—	—	5.7^{3}	3.5^{2}	2.7^{3}	3.7^{4}	3.3^{3}	—
Schwab Retirement MM	—	—	—	—	—	—	—	—	—	—	—	—
Schwab Value Adv MM	—	—	—	—	—	—	—	—	3.0^{1}	4.1^{1}	—	—
Scudder Cash Inv Tr	7.8^{4}	6.5^{1}	6.0^{4}	7.2^{2}	8.9^{3}	7.8^{3}	6.0^{1}	3.5^{2}	2.6^{4}	3.7^{3}	3.3^{3}	4.7^{2}
Selected Daily Inc MM	7.0^{5}	5.7^{5}	5.8^{5}	7.0^{4}	8.9^{2}	7.5^{5}	5.5^{5}	3.2^{4}	2.5^{4}	—	—	—
Seven Seas MM	—	—	—	—	—	—	—	—	—	4.0^{1}	—	—
Short Tm Inc-MM(R&T)	7.7^{4}	6.3^{4}	6.1^{3}	7.0^{4}	8.4^{4}	7.7^{4}	5.7^{4}	3.4^{2}	2.6^{4}	3.5^{5}	3.2^{4}	4.6^{4}
SIT Money Mkt	—	—	—	—	—	—	—	—	—	—	—	—
Smith Barney Cash MM	7.8^{3}	6.4^{3}	6.1^{3}	7.2^{3}	9.0^{2}	7.9^{3}	5.7^{4}	3.3^{4}	2.6^{4}	3.7^{3}	3.2^{4}	4.6^{3}
Smith Barney Ret MM	—	—	6.1^{2}	7.0^{4}	8.9^{3}	7.9^{3}	5.6^{4}	3.3^{4}	2.6^{4}	3.7^{4}	3.2^{4}	4.6^{4}
Smith Hayes MM	—	—	—	—	—	—	—	—	2.8^{3}	3.4^{5}	—	—
SteinRoe Cash Res	7.8^{4}	6.3^{4}	6.0^{4}	7.1^{3}	8.9^{3}	7.8^{4}	5.7^{3}	3.4^{3}	2.6^{4}	3.7^{4}	3.2^{3}	4.6^{3}
Strong Money Mkt	—	6.5^{2}	6.4^{1}	7.5^{1}	9.2^{1}	8.1^{1}	6.1^{1}	3.7^{1}	2.9^{1}	4.0^{1}	3.6^{1}	5.0^{1}
Twentieth Cent Cash	—	6.1^{5}	6.0^{5}	6.9^{5}	8.7^{5}	7.6^{5}	5.9^{2}	3.0^{5}	2.3^{5}	3.7^{4}	3.0^{5}	4.5^{4}
USAA Money Mkt	7.8^{4}	6.5^{1}	6.4^{1}	7.3^{2}	8.9^{2}	8.0^{2}	6.1^{1}	3.8^{1}	3.0^{1}	4.1^{1}	3.6^{1}	5.0^{1}
UST Mstr Money Mkt	—	6.8^{1}	6.0^{4}	7.4^{1}	8.7^{5}	8.1^{1}	6.0^{1}	3.6^{1}	2.8^{2}	3.9^{2}	3.4^{1}	4.9^{1}
Value Line Cash	7.9^{2}	6.5^{2}	6.5^{1}	7.4^{1}	9.1^{1}	7.9^{3}	5.9^{2}	3.7^{1}	3.1^{1}	3.7^{3}	3.5^{1}	4.8^{1}
Vangd MM Prime	8.1^{1}	6.6^{1}	6.7^{1}	7.6^{1}	9.4^{1}	8.3^{1}	6.1^{1}	3.7^{1}	3.0^{1}	4.1^{1}	3.6^{1}	5.0^{1}
Vista Global MM	—	—	—	—	—	—	—	—	2.9^{1}	4.0^{1}	—	—
Wayne Hummer MM	7.4^{5}	6.0^{5}	6.1^{3}	7.0^{5}	8.7^{5}	7.7^{4}	5.4^{5}	3.1^{5}	2.5^{5}	3.5^{4}	3.0^{5}	4.4^{5}
Wm Blair Ready Res	—	—	—	—	—	—	5.6^{4}	3.3^{4}	2.6^{3}	3.5^{5}	3.1^{4}	—
Wrkng Asst MM	7.6^{5}	6.1^{5}	5.9^{5}	6.7^{5}	8.4^{5}	7.5^{5}	5.5^{5}	3.0^{5}	2.2^{5}	3.2^{5}	2.8^{5}	4.3^{5}
GOVERNMENT MONEY MARKET FUNDS												
Active Asst Gov MM‡	7.7^{2}	6.2^{2}	5.8^{3}	6.9^{2}	8.7^{2}	7.6^{3}	5.5^{3}	3.3^{4}	2.6^{3}	3.6^{3}	3.1^{3}	4.5^{3}
Alliance Gov Res	7.2^{5}	6.0^{4}	5.9^{2}	6.9^{3}	8.5^{4}	7.5^{4}	5.4^{4}	3.2^{4}	2.4^{5}	3.3^{5}	2.9^{5}	4.3^{5}
Amer AAdv Trsy MM	—	—	—	—	—	—	—	—	—	3.8^{2}	—	—
Babson Fed MM	7.4^{4}	5.9^{4}	5.5^{4}	6.8^{4}	8.5^{4}	7.4^{4}	5.3^{5}	3.1^{5}	2.3^{5}	3.3^{5}	2.9^{5}	4.3^{5}
Babson UMB Fed MM	7.8^{1}	6.4^{1}	6.1^{1}	7.2^{1}	8.9^{1}	7.8^{1}	5.7^{2}	3.4^{2}	2.7^{2}	3.8^{2}	3.3^{2}	4.7^{2}
Benham Cap Presv II	7.4^{4}	6.1^{3}	5.7^{3}	6.8^{3}	8.8^{2}	7.8^{2}	5.3^{5}	2.9^{5}	2.4^{5}	3.5^{4}	2.9^{5}	4.3^{5}
Benham Cap Presv	7.5^{3}	6.1^{3}	5.7^{4}	6.5^{5}	8.4^{4}	7.7^{3}	5.6^{3}	3.3^{3}	2.7^{2}	3.6^{3}	3.2^{2}	4.6^{2}
Benham Gov Agcy MM	—	—	—	—	—	8.4^{1}	6.0^{1}	3.4^{3}	2.7^{2}	3.8^{2}	3.3^{2}	4.8^{1}
Blanchard Trsy MM	—	—	—	—	—	7.1^{5}	5.0^{5}	3.9^{1}	3.0^{1}	3.3^{5}	3.4^{1}	4.4^{4}
CA Inv Tr-Trsy MM	—	—	—	—	—	7.8^{2}	5.6^{3}	3.2^{4}	2.6^{3}	3.5^{4}	3.1^{3}	4.5^{3}
Cash Acct Tr-Gov MM‡	—	—	—	—	—	—	5.3^{5}	3.0^{5}	2.4^{5}	3.5^{4}	3.0^{5}	—
Cash Equiv-Gov MM‡	7.7^{2}	6.4^{2}	6.1^{1}	7.2^{1}	8.9^{1}	7.8^{2}	5.5^{3}	3.2^{4}	2.5^{4}	3.6^{3}	3.1^{4}	4.5^{3}
CMA Gov MM‡	7.7^{2}	6.4^{2}	6.0^{1}	6.8^{3}	8.9^{1}	7.8^{2}	5.9^{1}	3.5^{2}	2.8^{2}	3.7^{2}	3.3^{2}	4.7^{1}
CMA Trsy MM‡	—	—	—	—	—	—	—	3.3^{4}	2.7^{2}	3.5^{4}	3.1^{3}	—
Crabbe Hsn Gov MM	—	—	—	—	8.9^{3}	7.5^{5}	5.3^{5}	3.1^{5}	2.6^{3}	3.6^{3}	3.1^{4}	4.4^{4}

Money market funds   *continued*
Arranged in alphabetical order within objective

Valuation Method	Total Net Assets $ Millions December 31 1993	1994	Avg. Maturity days 12/31/94	US Treas.	Other US	Repos	Time Deposits	Domestic Bank Oblig.	Foreign Bank Oblig.	Comm'l Paper 1st Tier	Comm'l Paper 2nd Tier	Floating Rate Notes	No-Load Fund
1	7,122.7	7,304.5	75	7	11	1	—	—	15	56	—	10	Merrill Lynch Ret Res
4	5.3	3.9	40	—	57	—	—	—	—	43	—	—	MIM Money Mkt
4	262.4	322.5	34	1	9	—	—	23	—	54	—	13	Nbrgr-Ber Cash Res
3	702.7	640.6	71	—	—	—	—	13	25	62	—	—	New England MM
4	122.2	118.1	30	—	—	—	—	—	—	92	—	8	Nicholas Money Mkt
—	—	—	—	—	—	—	—	—	—	—	—	—	Northern Money Mkt
4	—	1,156.8	31	—	—	—	—	—	—	—	—	—	Pacific Hzn Prime MM
4	170.3	158.4	52	—	—	—	—	—	—	—	—	—	Pacifica Money Mkt
4	3,321.8	3,419.7	55	4	6	5	—	—	—	85	—	—	Paine Webber Cashfund
4	—	1,974.7	—	—	—	—	—	—	—	—	—	—	Pierpont Money Mkt
4	118.9	158.0	23	—	—	—	—	4	—	75	—	21	Portico Money Mkt
4	21.2	57.0	66	24	26	—	4	—	—	46	—	—	Preferred Money Mkt
4	3,360.8	3,891.2	34	—	—	—	—	2	8	69	—	21	Price, Rowe Prime Res
4	139.9	249.7	36	—	—	—	—	4	5	79	—	12	Price Summit Cash Res
1	7,318.6	6,544.9	60	1	—	1	1	7	21	56	—	13	Prudential Moneymart
4	1,371.4	1,362.2	45	—	—	19	7	42	16	12	—	4	Reserve Primary MM
—	1.9	—	—	—	—	—	—	—	—	—	—	—	Retrmt Sys: MM‡
—	8.7	—	—	—	—	—	—	—	—	—	—	—	Reynolds Money Mkt
4	4,091.3	4,331.5	57	4	—	3	—	—	12	81	—	—	RMA Money Mkt‡
1	34.2	—	—	—	—	—	—	—	—	—	—	—	Rushmore Money Mkt
4	147.1	186.0	30	5	30	—	—	—	—	63	—	2	SAFECO Money Mkt
4	14.4	18.1	76	23	—	33	—	—	—	10	—	34	Salomon Cash Mgmt
4	8,164.6	11,227.3	38	—	1	7	4	2	—	76	—	10	Schwab Money Mkt
4	—	31.4	44	—	3	5	6	—	—	86	—	—	Schwab Retirement MM
4	723.5	3,731.6	41	—	1	3	2	2	—	85	—	7	Schwab Value Adv MM
3	1,245.8	1,716.2	37	—	—	—	—	—	—	74	4	22	Scudder Cash Inv Tr
1	24.5	—	—	—	—	—	—	—	—	—	—	—	Selected Daily Inc MM
4	1.0	2,561.1	44	—	—	—	—	—	—	—	—	—	Seven Seas MM
3	778.9	576.4	31	6	11	3	21	24	3	32	—	—	Short Tm Inc-MM(R&T)
4	1.8	—	—	—	—	—	—	—	—	—	—	—	SIT Money Mkt
4	2,952.5	17,591.7	49	11	7	9	—	6	—	67	—	—	Smith Barney Cash MM
4	1,184.3	1,061.3	53	10	5	12	—	7	—	66	—	—	Smith Barney Ret MM
—	2.0	5.7	6	8	88	4	—	—	—	—	—	—	Smith Hayes MM
3	631.3	541.4	47	—	4	5	—	2	—	77	—	12	SteinRoe Cash Res
3	330.9	541.0	32	6	20	—	—	—	—	50	—	24	Strong Money Mkt
4	1,218.5	1,363.9	38	—	—	—	—	—	—	78	—	22	Twentieth Cent Cash
4	814.7	1,270.5	70	—	10	—	—	5	16	51	—	18	USAA Money Mkt
4	905.5	733.5	44	8	4	6	1	8	7	66	—	—	UST Mstr Money Mkt
1	345.8	341.6	56	—	68	—	—	—	—	20	—	12	Value Line Cash
3	12,267.3	15,321.2	39	—	13	—	—	—	—	87	—	—	Vangd MM Prime
4	344.7	136.0	47	—	—	—	—	—	—	—	—	—	Vista Global MM
1	156.5	144.1	30	—	12	—	—	21	—	54	—	13	Wayne Hummer MM
4	477.3	517.7	38	4	22	—	—	—	—	72	—	2	Wm Blair Ready Res
4	121.2	101.8	54	—	36	—	—	3	—	61	—	—	Wrkng Asst MM
				GOVERNMENT MONEY MARKET FUNDS									
4	500.0	542.8	48	13	80	7	—	—	—	—	—	—	Active Asst Gov MM‡
3	1,850.0	2,068.1	66	21	24	43	—	—	—	—	—	12	Alliance Gov Res
4	0.4	9.3	50	47	—	53	—	—	—	—	—	—	Amer AAdv Trsy MM
4	8.8	9.1	36	—	84	16	—	—	—	—	—	—	Babson Fed MM
4	360.4	185.8	44	—	—	22	—	—	—	78	—	—	Babson UMB Fed MM
4	280.1	261.0	4	—	—	100	—	—	—	—	—	—	Benham Cap Presv II
4	2,852.7	2,832.0	33	100	—	—	—	—	—	—	—	—	Benham Cap Presv
4	581.8	486.8	34	7	83	—	—	—	—	—	—	10	Benham Gov Agcy MM
4	162.7	184.2	53	100	—	—	—	—	—	—	—	—	Blanchard Trsy MM
4	63.0	65.0	63	100	—	—	—	—	—	—	—	—	CA Inv Tr-Trsy MM
4	28.5	117.6	21	—	28	72	—	—	—	—	—	—	Cash Acct Tr-Gov MM‡
4	1,680.4	1,552.5	23	—	40	60	—	—	—	—	—	—	Cash Equiv-Gov MM‡
1	3,474.7	3,007.3	65	16	—	84	—	—	—	—	—	—	CMA Gov MM
1	1,871.8	2,084.0	68	100	—	—	—	—	—	—	—	—	CMA Trsy MM‡
4	12.7	43.3	24	100	—	—	—	—	—	—	—	—	Crabbe Hsn Gov MM

| No-Load Fund | Compound yield percent with quintile ranks by objective ||||||||||| Annualized ||
	1985	1986	1987	1988	1989	1990	1991	1992	1993	1994	3 years	5 years
Dean Witter Gov MM	7.5[3]	6.1[3]	5.7[4]	6.8[3]	8.6[3]	7.3[5]	5.4[4]	3.0[5]	2.3[5]	3.2[5]	2.8[5]	4.2[5]
Dreyfus 100% US MM	—	—	—	6.9[2]	8.2[5]	7.9[1]	6.2[1]	3.6[1]	2.6[3]	3.4[5]	3.2[2]	4.7[1]
Dreyfus BASIC Gov MM	—	—	—	—	—	—	—	—	3.3[1]	4.2[1]	—	—
Dreyfus MM Instr Gov	8.3[1]	6.5[1]	5.9[2]	6.8[4]	8.7[2]	7.6[3]	5.7[2]	3.5[2]	2.5[4]	3.3[5]	3.1[4]	4.5[3]
Drey-General Gov MM	8.0[1]	6.0[4]	5.7[3]	6.8[3]	8.6[3]	7.5[4]	5.7[2]	3.5[2]	2.7[3]	3.7[2]	3.3[2]	4.6[2]
Drey/Laurel Gov MM	7.2[5]	5.6[5]	5.3[5]	6.4[5]	8.4[4]	7.3[5]	5.4[4]	3.4[3]	2.5[4]	3.6[3]	3.2[3]	4.4[4]
Drey/Laurel Trsy MM	—	—	—	—	—	—	—	3.4[2]	2.7[2]	3.7[2]	3.3[2]	—
59 Wall St Trsy MM	—	—	—	—	—	—	—	—	2.6[3]	3.5[4]	—	—
Federated Gov Cash	—	—	—	—	—	—	5.3[5]	3.0[5]	2.3[5]	3.4[5]	2.9[5]	—
Federated Trsy MM	—	—	—	—	—	—	5.2[5]	3.5[2]	2.3[5]	3.9[1]	3.2[2]	—
Fidelity Gov MM	7.8[2]	6.4[1]	5.9[2]	7.0[2]	8.7[2]	7.7[3]	5.7[3]	3.4[2]	2.6[3]	3.9[1]	3.3[2]	4.6[2]
Fidelity Spart Gov MM	—	—	—	—	—	—	6.1[1]	3.8[1]	2.8[1]	3.9[1]	3.5[1]	—
Fidelity Spart Trsy MM	—	—	—	—	8.3[5]	7.9[1]	6.1[1]	3.7[1]	2.7[2]	3.7[2]	3.4[1]	4.8[1]
First Omaha Gov MM	—	—	—	—	—	—	—	—	2.6[3]	3.6[3]	—	—
Forum Dly Asst Trsy	—	—	—	—	—	—	—	—	2.8[1]	3.8[2]	—	—
Gabelli Treas MM	—	—	—	—	—	—	—	—	2.8[2]	3.8[1]	—	—
Galaxy Gov MM	—	—	—	7.1[2]	9.1[1]	8.0[1]	5.8[2]	3.5[2]	2.9[1]	3.7[2]	3.4[1]	4.7[1]
Galaxy Trsy MM	—	—	—	—	—	—	—	3.4[3]	2.7[2]	3.6[3]	3.2[2]	—
GIT MM Account	7.5[4]	6.0[4]	5.8[3]	6.9[2]	8.6[3]	7.3[5]	5.1[5]	2.8[5]	2.1[5]	3.1[5]	2.7[5]	4.1[5]
Goldmn Sachs MM Gov	—	—	—	—	—	—	5.9[1]	3.7[1]	2.9[1]	3.9[1]	3.5[1]	—
Gradison Gov MM	7.3[5]	5.8[5]	5.3[5]	6.3[5]	8.4[5]	7.3[5]	5.3[5]	3.1[4]	2.5[4]	3.5[4]	3.0[4]	4.3[5]
Highmark Gov MM	—	—	—	—	8.5[4]	7.7[3]	5.5[3]	3.4[3]	2.6[4]	3.5[5]	3.1[3]	4.5[3]
Highmark Treas MM	—	—	—	—	8.4[4]	7.7[3]	5.5[3]	3.3[3]	2.5[4]	3.4[5]	3.0[4]	4.4[4]
Invesco Gov MM	—	—	—	—	—	—	4.0[5]	3.0[5]	2.4[5]	3.6[3]	3.0[5]	—
Kidder Pbdy Gov MM‡	7.6[3]	6.1[2]	6.0[1]	7.1[2]	8.6[3]	7.6[4]	5.4[4]	3.1[4]	2.5[4]	3.5[4]	3.1[4]	4.4[4]
Legg Msn Gov MM	—	—	—	—	—	7.6[4]	5.9[1]	3.5[2]	2.8[1]	3.7[2]	3.3[1]	4.7[2]
Merrill Lynch USA Gov	—	—	—	—	—	—	5.7[2]	3.3[4]	2.6[4]	3.4[5]	3.1[4]	—
Monetta Gov MM	—	—	—	—	—	—	—	—	—	4.0[1]	—	—
Montgmry Gov MM	—	—	—	—	—	—	—	—	2.7[2]	3.8[2]	—	—
Nbrgr-Ber Gov MM	7.4[4]	5.8[5]	5.2[5]	6.2[5]	7.9[5]	7.3[5]	5.5[4]	3.3[4]	2.5[4]	3.4[5]	3.1[4]	4.4[4]
New England Gov MM	7.9[1]	6.3[2]	5.6[4]	6.7[4]	8.5[4]	7.5[4]	5.7[2]	3.4[2]	2.5[4]	3.4[5]	3.1[4]	4.5[3]
Northern Gov MM	—	—	—	—	—	—	—	—	—	—	—	—
Northern Gov Sel MM	—	—	—	—	—	—	—	—	—	—	—	—
Pacifica Gov MM	—	—	—	—	—	—	—	—	2.7[2]	3.7[2]	—	—
Pierpont Treas MM	—	—	—	—	—	—	—	—	—	—	—	—
Portico Federal MM	—	—	—	—	—	—	—	3.2[4]	2.6[4]	3.5[4]	3.1[4]	—
Portico Gov MM	—	—	—	—	8.7[2]	7.7[3]	5.4[4]	3.3[4]	2.6[3]	3.7[2]	3.2[2]	4.5[3]
Price, Rowe Trsy MM	7.3[4]	5.7[5]	5.4[5]	6.5[5]	8.3[5]	7.4[5]	5.4[4]	3.2[4]	2.5[4]	3.5[4]	3.1[4]	4.4[4]
Prudential Gov MM	7.6[3]	6.2[2]	5.9[2]	7.1[2]	8.8[2]	7.8[2]	5.7[2]	3.4[2]	2.6[4]	3.5[4]	3.2[3]	4.6[2]
Reserve Gov MM	7.9[1]	6.1[3]	6.0[2]	7.2[1]	8.7[2]	7.5[4]	5.2[5]	3.1[5]	2.3[5]	3.4[5]	2.9[5]	4.3[5]
Reserve Treas MM	—	—	—	—	—	—	—	—	2.6[3]	4.0[1]	—	—
RMA Gov MM‡	7.4[4]	6.1[3]	5.9[3]	6.7[4]	8.5[3]	7.6[3]	5.6[3]	3.4[2]	2.6[3]	3.5[4]	3.2[3]	4.5[3]
Rushmore Gov MM	7.7[2]	6.0[4]	5.8[3]	6.7[4]	8.5[3]	7.4[5]	5.4[4]	3.0[5]	2.4[5]	3.6[3]	3.0[5]	4.3[5]
Rydex Gov MM	—	—	—	—	—	—	—	—	—	3.6[3]	—	—
1784 Trsy MM	—	—	—	—	—	—	—	—	3.0[1]	4.0[1]	—	—
Salomon Trsy MM	—	—	—	—	—	—	—	—	2.9[1]	3.6[2]	—	—
SBSF Money Mkt	—	—	—	—	8.9[1]	7.9[1]	5.8[2]	3.3[3]	2.6[3]	3.6[3]	3.2[3]	4.6[2]
Schwab Gov MM	—	—	—	—	—	—	5.3[5]	3.4[2]	2.7[2]	3.6[3]	3.2[2]	—
Schwab Trsy MM	—	—	—	—	—	—	—	—	2.5[4]	3.5[4]	—	—
Scudder Trsy MM	7.3[5]	5.9[4]	5.2[5]	6.3[5]	8.3[5]	7.8[2]	5.7[2]	3.4[3]	2.6[3]	3.5[4]	3.1[3]	4.6[2]
Selected Daily Gov MM	7.0[5]	5.3[5]	5.6[4]	7.0[2]	8.7[3]	7.4[5]	5.4[4]	3.0[5]	2.3[5]	3.5[4]	2.9[5]	4.3[5]
Seven Seas Gov MM	—	—	—	—	—	—	—	—	—	3.9[1]	—	—
Short Tm Inc-Gov(R&T)	7.5[3]	6.1[3]	5.7[4]	6.4[5]	8.2[5]	7.5[4]	5.5[4]	3.3[3]	2.5[4]	3.4[5]	3.1[4]	4.4[4]
Smith Barney Gov MM	—	—	5.9[2]	6.8[3]	8.6[3]	7.7[2]	5.6[3]	3.3[3]	2.6[4]	3.6[3]	3.2[3]	4.5[2]
SteinRoe Gov Res	7.1[5]	5.6[5]	5.3[5]	6.8[3]	8.7[2]	7.6[3]	5.6[3]	3.3[3]	2.6[3]	3.5[3]	3.1[3]	4.5[3]
Strong Trsy MM	—	—	—	—	—	—	5.8[2]	3.7[1]	2.9[1]	3.9[1]	3.5[1]	—
US Gov MM	—	—	—	—	—	—	6.3[1]	4.4[1]	3.4[1]	4.0[1]	3.9[1]	—
US Trsy MM	7.2[5]	5.4[5]	5.2[5]	6.8[4]	8.3[5]	7.5[4]	5.8[1]	3.1[4]	2.3[5]	3.2[5]	2.9[5]	4.4[4]
USAA Trsy MM	—	—	—	—	—	—	—	3.5[1]	2.8[1]	3.8[2]	3.4[1]	—
UST Mstr Gov MM	—	6.5[1]	5.9[2]	7.2[1]	8.6[3]	8.0[1]	5.8[1]	3.6[1]	2.8[2]	3.8[1]	3.4[1]	4.8[1]

Money market funds *continued*

Arranged in alphabetical order within objective

Valuation Method	Total Net Assets $ Millions December 31 1993	Total Net Assets $ Millions December 31 1994	Avg. Maturity days 12/31/94	US Treas.	Other US	Repos	Time Deposits	Domestic Bank Oblig.	Foreign Bank Oblig.	Comm'l Paper 1st Tier	Comm'l Paper 2nd Tier	Floating Rate Notes	No-Load Fund
4	861.6	812.2	46	9	82	9	—	—	—	—	—	—	Dean Witter Gov MM
4	1,917.9	1,450.6	64	100	—	—	—	—	—	—	—	—	Dreyfus 100% US MM
4	244.5	658.1	59	28	69	3	—	—	—	—	—	—	Dreyfus BASIC Gov MM
4	520.6	465.9	65	58	—	42	—	—	—	—	—	—	Dreyfus MM Instr Gov
4	532.2	490.0	58	31	68	1	—	—	—	—	—	—	Drey-General Gov MM
1	34.9	25.0	38	69	22	9	—	—	—	—	—	—	Drey/Laurel Gov MM
—	75.8	240.9	73	61	—	39	—	—	—	—	—	—	Drey/Laurel Trsy MM
4	1.5	5.0	54	—	—	—	—	—	—	—	—	—	59 Wall St Trsy MM
4	433.5	415.5	38	17	32	51	—	—	—	—	—	—	Federated Gov Cash
4	452.1	428.1	43	28	—	72	—	—	—	—	—	—	Federated Trsy MM
1	1,068.6	1,148.6	46	14	48	38	—	—	—	—	—	—	Fidelity Gov MM
4	764.7	737.8	50	16	52	32	—	—	—	—	—	—	Fidelity Spart Gov MM
4	1,656.5	1,771.2	70	100	—	—	—	—	—	—	—	—	Fidelity Spart Trsy MM
4	94.4	77.6	73	—	—	—	—	—	—	—	—	—	First Omaha Gov MM
4	27.3	31.2	35	42	58	—	—	—	—	—	—	—	Forum Dly Asst Trsy
4	183.2	204.9	43	100	—	—	—	—	—	—	—	—	Gabelli Treas MM
4	643.2	204.4	12	3	44	53	—	—	—	—	—	—	Galaxy Gov MM
4	480.8	228.3	54	71	29	—	—	—	—	—	—	—	Galaxy Trsy MM
3	81.9	75.7	19	—	84	16	—	—	—	—	—	—	GIT MM Account
4	1,578.8	1,133.9	56	39	9	52	—	—	—	—	—	—	Goldmn Sachs MM Gov
4	1,004.1	1,033.8	56	42	—	58	—	—	—	—	—	—	Gradison Gov MM
4	163.8	126.6	56	—	94	4	—	—	—	—	—	2	Highmark Gov MM
4	202.5	179.8	75	100	—	—	—	—	—	—	—	—	Highmark Treas MM
4	49.8	75.6	28	89	—	11	—	—	—	—	—	—	Invesco Gov MM
4	340.8	289.6	37	—	79	11	—	—	—	—	—	10	Kidder Pbdy Gov MM‡
4	172.5	214.5	24	—	85	15	—	—	—	—	—	—	Legg Msn Gov MM
1	552.3	518.8	54	31	—	69	—	—	—	—	—	—	Merrill Lynch USA Gov
4	1.0	3.3	76	96	4	—	—	—	—	—	—	—	Monetta Gov MM
4	138.2	235.5	35	11	59	30	—	—	—	—	—	—	Montgmry Gov MM
4	239.9	242.3	44	100	—	—	—	—	—	—	—	—	Nbrgr-Ber Gov MM
3	61.6	62.5	69	50	—	50	—	—	—	—	—	—	New England Gov MM
—	—	—	—	—	—	—	—	—	—	—	—	—	Northern Gov MM
—	—	—	—	—	—	—	—	—	—	—	—	—	Northern Gov Sel MM
4	178.9	140.2	53	—	—	—	—	—	—	—	—	—	Pacifica Gov MM
4	—	213.0	—	—	—	—	—	—	—	—	—	—	Pierpont Treas MM
4	47.0	57.2	17	—	91	—	—	—	—	—	—	9	Portico Federal MM
4	197.9	170.8	23	1	77	1	—	—	—	—	—	21	Portico Gov MM
4	599.0	704.4	35	100	—	—	—	—	—	—	—	—	Price, Rowe Trsy MM
4	638.1	796.0	53	17	37	46	—	—	—	—	—	—	Prudential Gov MM
4	736.5	669.5	28	13	—	87	—	—	—	—	—	—	Reserve Gov MM
4	2.3	83.3	30	100	—	—	—	—	—	—	—	—	Reserve Treas MM
4	895.1	767.0	57	54	—	46	—	—	—	—	—	—	RMA Gov MM‡
4	599.6	532.0	38	100	—	—	—	—	—	—	—	—	Rushmore Gov MM
4	1.0	104.4	55	100	—	—	—	—	—	—	—	—	Rydex Gov MM
4	291.2	270.3	42	—	—	—	—	—	—	—	—	—	1784 Trsy MM
4	33.9	28.6	81	100	—	—	—	—	—	—	—	—	Salomon Trsy MM
4	14.7	22.0	79	100	—	—	—	—	—	—	—	—	SBSF Money Mkt
4	1,744.6	1,897.3	42	2	61	20	—	—	—	—	—	17	Schwab Gov MM
4	378.1	803.9	55	100	—	—	—	—	—	—	—	—	Schwab Trsy MM
4	278.4	391.3	72	72	—	28	—	—	—	—	—	—	Scudder Trsy MM
1	8.7	125.6	10	100	—	—	—	—	—	—	—	—	Selected Daily Gov MM
4	1.0	606.9	48	—	—	—	—	—	—	—	—	—	Seven Seas Gov MM
3	411.2	414.7	35	94	6	—	—	—	—	—	—	—	Short Tm Inc-Gov(R&T)
4	635.8	3,730.0	50	63	—	37	—	—	—	—	—	—	Smith Barney Gov MM
3	105.1	104.0	39	14	76	10	—	—	—	—	—	—	SteinRoe Gov Res
—	41.9	67.5	72	100	—	—	—	—	—	—	—	—	Strong Trsy MM
—	540.3	579.4	6	—	99	—	1	—	—	—	—	—	US Gov MM
1	171.1	176.9	9	51	—	47	2	—	—	—	—	—	US Trsy MM
—	34.1	54.9	67	86	—	14	—	—	—	—	—	—	USAA Trsy MM
4	838.9	670.9	59	26	60	14	—	—	—	—	—	—	UST Mstr Gov MM

Money market funds *continued*
Arranged in alphabetical order within objective

| No-Load Fund | Compound yield percent with quintile ranks by objective | | | | | | | | | | Annualized | |
	1985	1986	1987	1988	1989	1990	1991	1992	1993	1994	3 years	5 years
Vangd MM Federal............................	7.9[1]	6.4[1]	6.4[1]	7.3[1]	9.2[1]	8.1[1]	6.0[1]	3.7[1]	3.0[1]	4.0[1]	3.6[1]	4.9[1]
Vangd MM Treas...	—	—	—	—	—	7.9[1]	5.7[2]	3.5[1]	2.9[1]	3.8[2]	3.4[1]	4.8[1]
Vangd-Adml MM................................	—	—	—	—	—	—	—	—	3.0[1]	4.0[1]	—	—
Vista Gov MM...................................	—	—	—	—	—	—	—	3.1[5]	2.4[5]	3.6[3]	3.0[5]	—
Warbg Pincus Cash Res...	7.8[2]	6.7[1]	6.5[1]	7.4[1]	9.2[1]	8.0[1]	5.9[1]	3.6[1]	2.8[2]	3.9[1]	3.4[1]	4.8[1]
Weitz Gov MM..................................	—	—	—	—	—	—	—	3.6[1]	2.6[3]	3.5[4]	3.2[2]	—
WPG Gov MM...................................	—	—	—	—	8.8[1]	7.7[2]	5.4[4]	2.9[5]	2.8[2]	3.6[3]	3.1[4]	4.5[3]
Wright Trsy MM................................	—	—	—	—	—	—	—	3.3[3]	2.6[3]	3.5[4]	3.1[3]	—

Valuation Method	Total Net Assets $ Millions		Avg. Maturity days 12/31/94	Portfolio holdings % 12/31/94									No-Load Fund
	December 31			US Treas.	Other US	Repos	Time Deposits	Domestic Bank Oblig.	Foreign Bank Oblig.	Comm'l Paper 1st Tier	Comm'l Paper 2nd Tier	Floating Rate Notes	
	1993	1994											
3	1,892.3	2,191.9	41	—	82	18	—	—	—	—	—	—	Vangd MM Federal
4	1,852.0	2,108.8	39	100	—	—	—	—	—	—	—	—	Vangd MM Treas
3	833.6	1,340.7	59	100	—	—	—	—	—	—	—	—	Vangd-Adml MM
4	339.8	320.9	30	4	42	52	—	—	—	—	—	2	Vista Gov MM
4	248.4	397.7	36	—	19	46	11	8	—	16	—	—	Warbg Pincus Cash Res
4	4.1	7.0	45	99	1	—	—	—	—	—	—	—	Weitz Gov MM
4	140.9	187.6	16	—	87	12	1	—	—	—	—	—	WPG Gov MM
4	15.8	18.0	53	99	1	—	—	—	—	—	—	—	Wright Trsy MM

No-Load Fund	Compound yield percent with quintile ranks by objective										Annualized	
---	1985	1986	1987	1988	1989	1990	1991	1992	1993	1994	3 years	5 years
TAX-FREE MONEY MARKET FUNDS												
AARP Hi Qual TF MM	—	—	—	—	—	—	—	2.1[5]	1.6[5]	2.0[5]	1.9[5]	—
Active Asst CA MM‡	—	—	—	—	—	—	—	—	1.7[5]	2.2[5]	—	—
Active Asst TF MM‡	5.0[2]	4.3[3]	4.2[2]	4.9[2]	6.0[2]	5.5[3]	4.1[4]	2.5[3]	2.0[3]	2.4[3]	2.3[3]	3.3[3]
Alliance Muni MM	4.9[3]	4.5[2]	4.2[2]	4.8[2]	6.0[2]	5.4[4]	4.0[4]	2.7[3]	1.8[4]	2.2[5]	2.2[4]	3.2[4]
Amer AAdv Muni Miles	—	—	—	—	—	—	—	—	—	2.4[3]	—	—
Babson TF MM	5.0[2]	4.5[1]	4.1[2]	5.0[1]	6.0[2]	5.5[3]	4.2[3]	2.7[2]	2.0[3]	2.4[3]	2.3[2]	3.3[2]
Babson UMB TF MM	4.9[3]	4.5[2]	4.1[3]	4.8[3]	5.9[3]	5.4[4]	4.0[4]	2.6[3]	2.0[3]	2.4[3]	2.3[3]	3.3[3]
Benham CA Muni MM	—	—	—	—	—	—	—	3.0[1]	2.1[2]	2.5[2]	2.5[2]	—
Benham CA TF MM	4.6[5]	4.1[5]	4.0[4]	4.6[4]	5.7[4]	5.2[5]	3.8[5]	2.5[4]	2.0[2]	2.4[3]	2.3[3]	3.2[4]
Benham FL TF MM	—	—	—	—	—	—	—	—	—	—	—	—
Benham Nat TF MM	5.3[1]	4.6[1]	4.3[1]	4.8[2]	6.1[2]	5.6[2]	4.2[3]	2.5[4]	1.9[4]	2.3[3]	2.2[4]	3.3[3]
CA Daily TF (R&T)	—	—	—	4.7[4]	5.8[4]	5.2[5]	3.8[5]	2.3[5]	2.2[2]	2.4[3]	2.3[3]	3.2[4]
CA Inv Tr-CA MM	—	4.5[2]	4.4[1]	5.0[1]	6.1[1]	5.6[2]	4.1[3]	2.7[2]	2.2[2]	2.5[2]	2.4[2]	3.4[2]
Cash Acct Tr-TF MM‡	—	—	—	—	—	—	3.9[4]	2.4[4]	1.8[4]	2.3[4]	2.2[4]	—
Cash Equiv-TE MM‡	4.9[4]	4.4[2]	4.1[3]	5.0[1]	6.0[2]	5.5[3]	4.1[3]	2.6[3]	2.0[3]	2.4[3]	2.3[3]	3.3[2]
CMA CA MM‡	—	—	—	—	5.8[4]	5.2[4]	3.9[5]	2.4[5]	1.9[3]	2.3[3]	2.2[4]	3.1[4]
CMA NY MM‡	—	—	—	—	5.5[5]	5.1[5]	3.8[5]	2.4[5]	1.8[5]	2.3[4]	2.1[5]	3.0[5]
CMA TE MM‡	4.9[3]	4.3[3]	4.2[1]	4.9[2]	6.1[2]	5.6[3]	4.2[2]	2.6[3]	2.0[3]	2.4[3]	2.3[3]	3.3[2]
CT Daily TF (R&T)	—	4.0[5]	3.9[5]	4.5[5]	5.6[5]	5.1[5]	3.7[5]	2.2[5]	1.7[5]	2.2[5]	2.0[5]	3.0[5]
Daily TF (R&T)	5.1[2]	4.3[3]	4.1[2]	5.0[1]	6.1[2]	5.5[3]	4.4[2]	2.7[2]	2.2[2]	2.6[2]	2.5[2]	3.5[2]
Dean Witter TF MM	5.1[1]	4.4[2]	4.1[3]	4.9[2]	6.0[2]	5.4[3]	4.0[4]	2.4[5]	1.9[4]	2.3[4]	2.2[4]	3.2[4]
Dreyfus BASIC Muni MM	—	—	—	—	—	—	—	—	2.6[1]	2.9[1]	—	—
Dreyfus CA TF MM	—	—	4.1[2]	4.7[3]	5.8[4]	5.2[4]	4.0[4]	2.6[3]	2.0[3]	2.3[4]	2.3[3]	3.2[4]
Dreyfus CT TF MM	—	—	—	—	—	—	4.4[2]	2.9[2]	2.2[1]	2.6[2]	2.6[1]	—
Dreyfus MA MM	—	—	—	—	—	—	—	2.9[1]	2.1[2]	2.6[1]	2.5[1]	—
Dreyfus MI MM	—	—	—	—	—	—	4.7[1]	2.7[2]	2.1[2]	2.5[2]	2.4[2]	—
Dreyfus Muni MM	5.0[2]	4.4[2]	4.1[3]	4.8[3]	6.0[3]	5.6[2]	4.1[4]	2.5[4]	2.0[2]	2.4[3]	2.3[3]	3.3[3]
Dreyfus NJ MM	—	—	—	—	6.4[1]	5.9[1]	4.4[1]	2.8[2]	2.1[2]	2.5[2]	2.4[2]	3.5[1]
Dreyfus NY MM	—	—	—	4.5[5]	5.5[5]	5.2[4]	3.8[5]	2.3[5]	1.6[5]	2.1[5]	2.0[5]	3.0[5]
Dreyfus OH MM	—	—	—	—	—	—	—	3.2[1]	2.4[1]	2.8[1]	2.8[1]	—
Dreyfus PA MM	—	—	—	—	—	—	4.7[1]	3.0[1]	2.4[1]	2.8[1]	2.7[1]	—
Drey-General CA MM	—	—	—	4.8[3]	5.8[4]	5.9[1]	4.7[1]	2.9[1]	2.3[1]	2.6[2]	2.6[1]	3.7[1]
Drey-General Muni MM	5.0[3]	4.5[1]	4.0[4]	4.8[3]	5.9[3]	5.5[3]	4.2[3]	2.6[3]	2.1[2]	2.4[3]	2.4[2]	3.3[2]
Drey-General NY MM	4.8[4]	4.0[5]	3.7[5]	4.4[5]	5.4[5]	5.8[1]	4.3[2]	2.6[3]	2.0[3]	2.5[2]	2.4[2]	3.4[2]
Drey/Laurel CA MM	—	—	—	—	6.2[1]	5.7[1]	4.5[1]	3.0[1]	2.4[1]	2.5[2]	2.6[1]	3.6[1]
Drey/Laurel MA MM	4.9[3]	4.4[3]	4.1[3]	4.8[3]	6.0[2]	5.7[1]	4.4[2]	2.5[4]	1.8[5]	2.3[4]	2.2[5]	3.3[3]
Drey/Laurel NY MM	—	—	—	—	5.9[3]	5.5[3]	4.5[1]	2.9[1]	2.1[2]	2.2[5]	2.4[2]	3.4[2]
Drey/Laurel TxEx MM	—	—	—	—	—	—	—	2.7[2]	2.1[2]	2.5[2]	2.4[2]	—
Drey/Laurel TxFr MM	4.9[3]	4.1[5]	4.0[4]	4.6[4]	5.9[3]	5.6[2]	4.1[3]	2.5[4]	1.9[3]	2.5[2]	2.3[3]	3.3[3]
Evergreen TE MM	—	—	—	—	6.6[1]	5.6[2]	4.9[1]	3.2[1]	2.5[1]	2.8[1]	2.8[1]	3.8[1]
Federated Muni Cash	—	—	—	—	—	5.7[2]	4.3[2]	2.5[4]	1.9[4]	2.2[5]	2.2[4]	3.3[3]
Federated OH Cash	—	—	—	—	—	—	—	2.6[3]	2.0[3]	2.3[4]	2.3[3]	—
Fidelity CA TF MM	—	—	4.1[3]	4.8[3]	5.8[4]	5.2[5]	4.0[4]	2.6[3]	2.0[3]	2.4[3]	2.3[3]	3.2[3]
Fidelity CT TF MM	—	—	—	—	—	5.7[1]	4.4[2]	2.6[3]	1.9[4]	2.3[4]	2.2[3]	3.4[2]
Fidelity MA TF MM	4.7[4]	4.2[4]	4.0[4]	4.6[4]	5.9[3]	5.3[4]	4.0[4]	2.2[5]	1.7[5]	2.2[5]	2.0[5]	3.1[5]
Fidelity MI Muni MM	—	—	—	—	—	—	4.5[1]	2.7[2]	2.0[3]	2.4[3]	2.4[2]	—
Fidelity NJ TF MM	—	—	—	—	6.4[1]	5.7[2]	4.1[3]	2.7[2]	1.9[4]	2.3[3]	2.3[3]	3.3[2]
Fidelity NY TF MM	—	4.2[5]	3.8[5]	4.5[5]	5.5[5]	5.1[5]	3.9[5]	2.5[4]	1.9[4]	2.3[3]	2.2[4]	3.1[5]
Fidelity OH Muni MM	—	—	—	—	—	5.9[1]	4.5[1]	2.8[2]	2.1[2]	2.5[2]	2.5[2]	3.6[1]
Fidelity Spart AZ MM	—	—	—	—	—	—	—	—	—	—	—	—
Fidelity Spart CA MM	—	—	—	—	—	5.9[1]	4.6[1]	3.0[1]	2.4[1]	2.8[1]	2.7[1]	3.7[1]
Fidelity Spart CT MM	—	—	—	—	—	—	—	3.0[1]	2.2[2]	2.4[3]	2.5[2]	—
Fidelity Spart FL MM	—	—	—	—	—	—	—	—	2.3[1]	2.6[1]	—	—
Fidelity Spart MA MM	—	—	—	—	—	—	—	2.7[2]	2.0[3]	2.3[3]	2.3[2]	—
Fidelity Spart Muni MM	—	—	—	—	—	—	—	3.3[1]	2.5[1]	2.8[1]	2.9[1]	—
Fidelity Spart NJ MM	—	—	—	—	—	—	4.6[1]	3.0[1]	1.9[4]	2.7[1]	2.5[2]	—
Fidelity Spart NY MM	—	—	—	—	—	—	4.3[2]	2.7[2]	2.0[2]	2.5[2]	2.4[2]	—
Fidelity Spart PA MM	—	—	4.3[1]	5.1[1]	6.3[1]	6.1[1]	4.6[1]	2.9[1]	2.2[1]	2.6[1]	2.6[1]	3.7[1]
Fidelity TE MM	5.2[1]	4.5[1]	4.2[2]	4.9[2]	6.0[2]	5.6[2]	4.4[2]	2.9[2]	2.2[2]	2.5[2]	2.5[2]	3.5[1]

Money market funds *continued*
Arranged in alphabetical order within objective

Valuation Method	Total Net Assets $ Millions December 31 1993	Total Net Assets $ Millions December 31 1994	Avg. Maturity days 12/31/94	Demand Notes Rated	Demand Notes Unrated	Gen Mkt Notes Rated	Gen Mkt Notes Unrated	Comm'l Paper	Put Bonds Under 6 Mo.	Put Bonds Over 6 Mo.	Other	AMT Paper	No-Load Fund
	TAX-FREE MONEY MARKET FUNDS

Valuation Method	1993	1994	Avg. Maturity days 12/31/94	Demand Notes Rated	Demand Notes Unrated	Gen Mkt Notes Rated	Gen Mkt Notes Unrated	Comm'l Paper	Put Bonds Under 6 Mo.	Put Bonds Over 6 Mo.	Other	AMT Paper	No-Load Fund
4	133.6	131.4	45	62	—	23	—	7	8	—	—	—	AARP Hi Qual TF MM
4	260.8	281.4	46	49	1	10	—	30	10	—	—	14	Active Asst CA MM‡
4	1,433.0	1,437.4	50	53	4	13	—	15	15	—	—	18	Active Asst TF MM‡
4	1,070.1	1,061.2	79	64	—	15	—	—	3	17	1	54	Alliance Muni MM
4	1.3	10.9	27	68	—	—	—	32	—	—	—	54	Amer AAdv Muni Miles
4	10.0	10.5	50	11	—	30	—	3	16	—	40	—	Babson TF MM
3	85.0	101.1	31	—	—	—	—	—	—	—	—	—	Babson UMB TF MM
4	246.6	211.4	39	68	—	8	—	19	5	—	—	—	Benham CA Muni MM
4	366.3	376.9	43	66	—	11	—	15	7	—	1	—	Benham CA TF MM
4	—	47.6	31	54	—	—	—	15	—	12	—	19	Benham FL TF MM
4	108.3	94.2	35	64	—	4	—	14	8	—	10	—	Benham Nat TF MM
4	117.3	104.9	45	55	—	21	—	18	6	—	—	25	CA Daily TF (R&T)
4	66.5	90.0	75	79	—	—	—	13	11	—	3	—	CA Inv Tr-CA MM
4	12.2	68.2	35	53	—	5	—	41	1	—	—	—	Cash Acct Tr-TF MM‡
4	1,177.2	1,015.4	39	50	—	7	—	35	8	—	—	—	Cash Equiv-TE MM‡
1	1,159.0	1,101.4	74	34	14	30	—	18	4	—	—	22	CMA CA MM‡
1	687.3	811.3	73	37	8	25	9	8	7	6	—	21	CMA NY MM‡
1	7,062.5	6,615.2	55	55	3	20	6	8	6	2	—	14	CMA TE MM‡
4	120.3	77.6	72	61	—	12	—	6	11	10	—	18	CT Daily TF (R&T)
4	561.6	441.6	59	68	—	17	—	4	1	10	—	—	Daily TF (R&T)
4	566.3	545.8	50	54	3	11	1	12	18	1	—	—	Dean Witter TF MM
4	725.9	1,045.0	42	74	—	7	1	2	15	1	—	55	Dreyfus BASIC Muni MM
4	307.7	298.6	61	71	—	26	—	1	2	—	—	13	Dreyfus CA TF MM
4	274.1	262.0	53	58	—	28	5	3	5	1	—	10	Dreyfus CT TF MM
4	99.0	141.2	74	50	1	7	16	4	18	4	—	9	Dreyfus MA MM
4	77.2	60.7	48	61	—	11	—	17	7	4	—	47	Dreyfus MI MM
4	1,174.4	1,002.5	70	60	1	14	—	2	16	7	—	36	Dreyfus Muni MM
4	789.9	763.5	61	61	4	15	9	5	4	2	—	13	Dreyfus NJ MM
4	350.0	323.7	43	65	—	16	8	2	4	5	—	14	Dreyfus NY MM
4	63.6	58.7	41	72	—	7	2	4	7	8	—	42	Dreyfus OH MM
4	140.3	159.9	43	53	—	6	—	17	19	5	—	55	Dreyfus PA MM
4	700.6	523.0	55	71	1	27	—	—	1	—	—	32	Drey-General CA MM
4	325.6	283.3	48	61	—	19	—	1	15	4	—	53	Drey-General Muni MM
4	588.6	680.7	33	63	—	18	6	4	5	4	—	24	Drey-General NY MM
4	14.7	13.0	60	46	—	21	—	15	18	—	—	—	Drey/Laurel CA MM
4	68.6	103.0	43	46	—	17	13	20	4	—	—	—	Drey/Laurel MA MM
4	9.9	6.3	37	41	—	51	—	—	8	—	—	—	Drey/Laurel NY MM
4	215.7	197.0	50	58	—	24	—	9	8	1	—	—	Drey/Laurel TxEx MM
4	20.5	—	40	40	—	38	—	16	—	6	—	—	Drey/Laurel TxFr MM
4	410.3	385.0	58	52	5	16	—	3	15	9	—	—	Evergreen TE MM
4	582.4	490.2	57	49	—	10	13	11	17	—	—	62	Federated Muni Cash
4	132.7	144.6	53	56	—	4	17	15	8	—	—	41	Federated OH Cash
4	578.2	687.0	55	54	1	27	—	11	5	1	1	17	Fidelity CA TF MM
4	289.5	312.8	56	37	12	5	16	19	3	—	8	24	Fidelity CT TF MM
4	615.0	729.1	39	58	3	17	4	7	5	—	6	11	Fidelity MA TF MM
4	174.4	220.2	40	55	2	12	12	11	1	—	7	47	Fidelity MI Muni MM
4	374.8	413.3	68	39	9	17	26	6	—	1	2	14	Fidelity NJ TF MM
4	598.7	715.4	53	38	9	13	8	13	11	2	6	20	Fidelity NY TF MM
4	262.7	298.2	58	47	5	11	13	10	7	—	7	40	Fidelity OH Muni MM
4	—	—	—	—	—	—	—	—	—	—	—	—	Fidelity Spart AZ MM
4	1,024.9	1,163.7	55	57	1	28	—	8	4	1	1	48	Fidelity Spart CA MM
4	155.5	162.5	49	46	6	4	14	20	—	3	7	19	Fidelity Spart CT MM
4	547.0	627.4	51	54	—	16	—	28	1	—	1	—	Fidelity Spart FL MM
4	352.0	390.2	46	49	5	10	3	14	9	—	10	5	Fidelity Spart MA MM
4	1,797.4	2,133.7	48	52	4	8	1	10	21	3	1	92	Fidelity Spart Muni MM
4	374.8	407.5	71	41	6	16	29	4	1	—	3	19	Fidelity Spart NJ MM
4	453.5	545.6	57	31	14	15	9	12	11	2	6	35	Fidelity Spart NY MM
4	238.7	254.9	53	49	4	9	—	15	—	19	4	55	Fidelity Spart PA MM
4	3,024.9	3,584.4	46	48	6	24	4	10	6	1	1	—	Fidelity TE MM

No-Load Fund	— Compound yield percent with quintile ranks by objective										Annualized 3 years	5 years
	1985	1986	1987	1988	1989	1990	1991	1992	1993	1994	3 years	5 years
FL Daily Muni (R&T)...	—	—	—	—	—	—	—	—	—	—	—	—
Fundamental TF MM...	—	—	—	4.5[5]	5.5[5]	5.1[5]	4.8[1]	2.8[2]	1.4[5]	1.7[5]	2.0[5]	3.2[4]
Galaxy TE MM...	—	—	—	—	5.9[3]	5.5[3]	4.2[3]	2.5[4]	2.0[2]	2.3[4]	2.2[4]	3.3[3]
GIT TF MM...	4.6[5]	4.3[4]	3.9[5]	4.4[5]	5.8[4]	5.3[4]	3.5[5]	2.2[5]	1.4[5]	1.8[5]	1.8[5]	2.8[5]
Goldmn Sachs MM TE...	—	—	—	—	—	—	—	—	—	2.7[1]	—	—
Highmark CA TF MM...	—	—	—	—	5.6[5]	5.2[4]	4.0[4]	2.5[4]	2.0[3]	2.4[3]	2.3[3]	3.2[3]
Highmark TF MM...	—	—	—	—	5.7[4]	5.6[2]	4.3[2]	2.7[2]	1.9[3]	2.3[4]	2.3[3]	3.3[2]
Hough FL TF MM...	—	—	—	—	—	—	—	—	—	3.1[1]	—	—
Invesco TF MM...	5.5[1]	4.7[1]	3.9[5]	4.7[4]	5.7[4]	5.3[4]	3.7[5]	2.4[5]	1.9[4]	2.2[5]	2.2[4]	3.1[5]
Kidder Pbdy CA TF MM‡...	—	—	—	—	5.7[4]	5.0[5]	3.6[5]	2.5[4]	1.7[5]	2.1[5]	2.1[5]	3.0[5]
Kidder Pbdy TE MM‡...	5.0[2]	4.4[2]	4.2[2]	4.9[2]	5.9[3]	5.5[3]	4.1[3]	2.4[5]	1.8[4]	2.2[4]	2.2[4]	3.2[4]
Legg Msn TE MM...	4.6[5]	4.1[5]	3.9[5]	4.6[4]	5.9[3]	5.3[4]	3.9[4]	2.3[5]	1.8[5]	2.3[4]	2.1[5]	3.1[5]
Lexington TF MM...	5.1[1]	4.5[2]	4.2[2]	4.8[3]	5.7[4]	5.4[4]	4.2[3]	2.5[4]	1.8[5]	2.0[5]	2.1[5]	3.2[4]
MI Daily TF (R&T)...	—	—	—	4.7[4]	6.3[1]	5.9[1]	4.1[3]	2.4[4]	1.9[4]	2.3[3]	2.2[4]	3.3[2]
Montgmry CA TF MM...	—	—	—	—	—	—	—	—	—	—	—	—
Nbrgr-Ber Muni MM...	5.0[3]	4.3[3]	4.1[3]	5.0[1]	6.1[2]	5.5[3]	4.1[3]	2.4[5]	1.8[4]	2.3[4]	2.2[5]	3.2[4]
NC Daily Muni (R&T)...	—	—	—	—	—	—	—	2.5[4]	1.8[5]	2.2[5]	2.1[5]	—
New England TE MM...	5.1[1]	4.3[3]	4.0[4]	4.8[2]	5.8[3]	5.5[3]	4.2[3]	2.6[3]	2.0[3]	2.5[2]	2.4[2]	3.3[2]
NJ Daily Muni (R&T)...	—	—	—	—	—	—	4.4[2]	2.7[2]	1.9[3]	2.2[5]	2.3[3]	—
Northern CA MM...	—	—	—	—	—	—	—	—	—	—	—	—
Northern Muni MM...	—	—	—	—	—	—	—	—	—	—	—	—
Nuveen TF Res...	4.9[3]	4.2[4]	4.2[2]	4.8[3]	6.0[2]	5.6[2]	4.2[2]	2.6[3]	1.9[4]	2.3[4]	2.2[4]	3.3[3]
NY Daily TF Inc(R&T)...	4.8[4]	4.0[5]	3.8[5]	4.5[5]	5.6[5]	5.1[5]	4.2[2]	2.6[3]	1.9[4]	2.3[4]	2.3[3]	3.2[3]
PA Daily Muni (R&T)...	—	—	—	—	—	—	—	—	2.3	2.6[2]	—	—
Pierpont TE MM...	—	—	—	—	—	—	—	—	—	—	—	—
Portico TE MM...	—	—	—	—	6.0[2]	5.5[3]	4.2[3]	2.6[3]	2.1[2]	2.5[2]	2.4[2]	3.4[2]
Price, Rowe CA MM...	—	—	4.1[3]	4.6[4]	5.5[5]	4.9[5]	3.7[5]	2.5[4]	1.9[3]	2.4[3]	2.2[4]	3.1[5]
Price, Rowe NY MM...	—	—	3.7[5]	4.3[5]	5.3[5]	4.9[5]	3.8[5]	2.4[5]	1.8[4]	2.3[4]	2.2[4]	3.0[5]
Price, Rowe TE MM...	5.0[2]	4.6[1]	4.4[1]	4.9[1]	6.0[3]	5.4[4]	3.9[4]	2.5[4]	2.0[2]	2.5[2]	2.3[3]	3.2[3]
Price Summit Muni MM...	—	—	—	—	—	—	—	—	—	2.6[2]	—	—
Prudential TF MM...	4.9[3]	4.5[1]	5.0[1]	4.8[2]	5.8[4]	5.4[4]	4.2[2]	2.6[3]	1.9[4]	2.3[4]	2.3[3]	3.3[3]
Reserve CA TE MM...	—	—	—	—	—	—	—	—	—	—	—	—
Reserve CT TE MM...	—	4.2[4]	3.8[5]	4.5[5]	5.6[5]	5.1[5]	3.6[5]	2.2[5]	1.6[5]	2.0[5]	2.0[5]	2.9[5]
Reserve MA TE MM...	—	—	—	—	—	—	4.1[3]	2.4[4]	1.8[4]	2.0[5]	2.1[5]	—
Reserve NJ TE MM...	—	—	—	—	—	—	—	—	—	—	—	—
Reserve NY TE MM...	4.7[5]	3.9[5]	3.5[5]	4.4[5]	5.4[5]	5.0[5]	3.7[5]	2.2[5]	1.5[5]	2.0[5]	1.9[5]	2.9[5]
Reserve TE Interstate...	5.1[2]	4.2[4]	3.9[4]	4.9[2]	5.9[3]	5.4[4]	4.1[4]	2.6[3]	1.7[5]	2.0[5]	2.1[5]	3.1[4]
RMA TF MM‡...	4.7[5]	4.1[5]	4.0[4]	4.8[3]	5.8[4]	5.4[4]	4.0[4]	2.6[3]	1.9[4]	2.3[4]	2.2[4]	3.2[3]
Rushmore TF MM...	4.7[5]	4.2[4]	3.9[4]	4.6[4]	5.8[4]	5.6[2]	4.0[4]	2.3[5]	1.7[5]	2.3[4]	2.1[5]	3.2[4]
1784 TF MM...	—	—	—	—	—	—	—	—	—	2.7[1]	—	—
SAFECO TF MM...	4.6[5]	4.2[4]	4.0[4]	4.8[3]	6.1[1]	5.6[2]	4.3[2]	2.7[2]	2.0[2]	2.5[2]	2.4[2]	3.4[2]
Salomon NY MM...	—	—	—	—	—	—	—	3.1[1]	2.3[1]	2.7[1]	2.7[1]	—
Schwab CA TF MM...	—	—	—	—	—	—	3.8[5]	2.4[5]	1.9[3]	2.2[5]	2.2[4]	—
Schwab TE MM...	—	—	—	—	—	—	4.0[4]	2.5[4]	1.9[3]	2.3[4]	2.2[4]	—
Scudder CA TF MM...	—	—	—	4.7[4]	5.6[5]	5.0[5]	3.9[4]	2.5[3]	2.0[3]	2.4[3]	2.3[3]	3.1[4]
Scudder NY TF MM...	—	—	—	4.5[5]	5.4[5]	5.0[5]	3.7[5]	2.5[4]	1.8[5]	2.2[4]	2.2[4]	3.0[5]
Scudder TF MM...	4.6[5]	4.3[3]	4.0[4]	4.7[4]	5.8[4]	5.4[3]	3.8[5]	2.5[3]	1.9[4]	2.3[4]	2.2[4]	3.2[4]
Smith Barney TF MM...	4.9[4]	4.3[3]	4.1[3]	4.8[2]	6.0[2]	5.6[2]	4.1[3]	2.5[4]	1.9[4]	2.3[4]	2.2[4]	3.2[4]
SteinRoe Muni MM...	4.8[4]	4.2[4]	4.1[3]	4.8[3]	5.9[3]	5.4[3]	3.9[4]	2.4[5]	1.9[4]	2.3[4]	2.2[4]	3.2[4]
Strong Muni MM...	—	—	4.7[1]	5.2[1]	6.1[1]	6.1[1]	5.2[1]	3.4[1]	2.5[1]	2.9[1]	2.9[1]	4.0[1]
USAA CA MM...	—	—	—	—	—	5.6[2]	4.4[2]	2.9[1]	2.3[1]	2.6[1]	2.6[1]	3.5[1]
USAA FL MM...	—	—	—	—	—	—	—	—	—	2.5[2]	—	—
USAA NY MM...	—	—	—	—	—	—	4.2[3]	2.8[2]	2.0[2]	2.4[3]	2.4[2]	—
USAA TE MM...	5.3[1]	4.9[1]	4.6[1]	5.2[1]	6.3[1]	6.1[1]	4.8[1]	3.1[1]	2.4[1]	2.6[1]	2.7[1]	3.8[1]
USAA Texas MM...	—	—	—	—	—	—	—	—	—	—	—	—
USAA VA MM...	—	—	—	—	—	—	4.5[1]	2.9[1]	2.2[2]	2.6[2]	2.6[1]	—
Value Line TE MM...	4.7[4]	4.3[3]	4.2[2]	4.6[4]	5.9[3]	5.4[3]	4.1[4]	2.5[4]	1.6[5]	2.0[5]	2.0[5]	3.1[5]
Vangd CA MM...	—	—	—	5.1[1]	6.2[1]	5.6[2]	4.3[2]	2.9[2]	2.4[1]	2.7[1]	2.7[1]	3.6[1]
Vangd Muni MM...	5.2[1]	4.7[1]	4.6[1]	5.2[1]	6.3[1]	5.8[1]	4.6[1]	3.0[1]	2.4[1]	2.8[1]	2.7[1]	3.7[1]
Vangd NJ TF MM...	—	—	—	—	6.3[1]	5.8[1]	4.4[2]	2.9[1]	2.3[1]	2.6[1]	2.6[1]	3.6[1]

Arranged in alphabetical order within objective

Valuation Method	Total Net Assets $ Millions December 31 1993	1994	Avg. Maturity days 12/31/94	Demand Notes Rated	Demand Notes Unrated	Gen Mkt Notes Rated	Gen Mkt Notes Unrated	Comm'l Paper	Put Bonds Under 6 Mo.	Put Bonds Over 6 Mo.	Other	AMT Paper	No-Load Fund
4	—	53.0	26	67	—	7	—	25	1	—	—	14	FL Daily Muni (R&T)
4	5.7	9.5	42	73	—	18	—	—	1	—	8	—	Fundamental TF MM
4	261.9	109.5	37	23	—	30	—	47	—	—	—	—	Galaxy TE MM
3	13.9	10.3	41	63	—	33	—	—	—	4	—	5	GIT TF MM
4	—	1,569.2	—	—	—	—	—	—	—	—	—	—	Goldmn Sachs MM TE
4	39.1	31.0	54	29	—	29	—	42	—	—	—	18	Highmark CA TF MM
4	33.0	34.3	54	14	—	12	—	59	7	8	—	20	Highmark TF MM
4	—	120.5	79	47	2	36	1	11	2	1	—	15	Hough FL TF MM
4	66.2	76.5	56	—	—	—	—	—	—	—	100	—	Invesco TF MM
4	198.7	145.3	51	45	5	11	—	12	27	—	—	—	Kidder Pbdy CA TF MM‡
4	662.2	454.8	68	33	6	11	3	17	23	7	—	—	Kidder Pbdy TE MM‡
4	237.6	222.5	39	41	—	9	—	42	4	1	3	—	Legg Msn TE MM
3	41.2	37.5	53	48	—	28	—	17	4	2	1	—	Lexington TF MM
4	64.3	59.2	40	65	—	22	—	6	—	7	1	19	MI Daily TF (R&T)
4	—	47.2	37	68	—	16	—	16	—	—	—	—	Montgmry CA TF MM
4	156.9	162.5	55	54	—	15	—	11	14	6	—	52	Nbrgr-Ber Muni MM
4	109.1	136.7	43	55	—	21	—	17	3	4	—	29	NC Daily Muni (R&T)
4	56.8	74.0	47	50	—	21	—	23	4	2	—	—	New England TE MM
4	87.9	105.8	73	54	—	33	—	12	—	1	—	—	NJ Daily Muni (R&T)
—	—	—	—	—	—	—	—	—	—	—	—	—	Northern CA MM
—	—	—	—	—	—	—	—	—	—	—	—	—	Northern Muni MM
4	397.9	336.2	35	51	9	15	—	15	9	1	—	—	Nuveen TF Res
4	207.7	222.7	59	68	—	23	—	—	—	10	—	16	NY Daily TF Inc(R&T)
4	32.6	40.6	64	—	—	19	—	—	7	—	7	67	PA Daily Muni (R&T)
4	—	894.3	—	—	—	—	—	—	—	—	—	—	Pierpont TE MM
4	70.4	67.4	54	65	—	2	—	1	20	12	—	—	Portico TE MM
4	69.3	77.1	31	56	4	20	—	20	—	—	—	—	Price, Rowe CA MM
4	53.0	68.8	36	46	—	30	2	22	—	—	—	—	Price, Rowe NY MM
4	680.3	712.6	34	48	2	17	—	27	6	—	—	—	Price, Rowe TE MM
4	5.1	61.0	55	47	2	25	—	19	6	1	—	—	Price Summit Muni MM
4	601.6	487.3	49	38	4	13	—	7	37	1	—	—	Prudential TF MM
4	—	8.1	42	—	—	—	—	7	31	—	62	—	Reserve CA TE MM
4	133.2	32.4	58	—	—	—	—	—	38	—	62	—	Reserve CT TE MM
4	12.1	13.6	47	—	—	—	—	7	19	16	58	—	Reserve MA TE MM
4	—	16.9	59	—	—	—	—	6	43	—	15	36	Reserve NJ TE MM
4	152.5	141.2	66	—	—	—	—	—	49	—	51	—	Reserve NY TE MM
4	386.5	315.5	58	—	—	—	—	5	30	15	50	—	Reserve TE Interstate
4	1,309.6	1,399.1	62	35	—	21	—	26	15	3	—	—	RMA TF MM‡
4	23.3	20.0	66	78	—	9	—	3	6	4	—	12	Rushmore TF MM
4	273.0	416.4	68	50	—	12	1	2	29	6	—	15	1784 TF MM
4	83.7	85.6	55	64	—	1	—	6	24	5	—	—	SAFECO TF MM
4	261.0	270.7	55	51	—	42	—	2	2	3	—	37	Salomon NY MM
4	1,062.0	1,293.9	40	11	62	4	—	20	1	—	2	—	Schwab CA TF MM
4	2,423.3	3,016.0	40	10	8	63	—	10	8	—	1	—	Schwab TE MM
4	56.1	67.7	61	47	—	32	—	16	5	—	—	—	Scudder CA TF MM
4	41.3	53.1	64	57	—	31	—	7	5	—	—	—	Scudder NY TF MM
4	220.5	260.9	46	58	—	31	—	7	4	—	—	—	Scudder TF MM
4	998.1	4,413.6	43	48	—	8	—	26	14	4	—	—	Smith Barney TF MM
4	208.2	174.1	46	63	—	—	—	17	5	—	16	—	SteinRoe Muni MM
3	1,172.6	1,260.6	63	55	—	9	—	—	20	16	—	—	Strong Muni MM
4	229.6	261.4	51	57	—	21	—	10	10	2	—	—	USAA CA MM
4	56.7	94.3	52	33	—	40	—	25	—	2	—	—	USAA FL MM
4	19.8	28.9	59	72	—	14	—	—	7	7	—	—	USAA NY MM
4	1,395.6	1,470.0	65	48	—	15	—	6	18	13	—	—	USAA TE MM
4	—	—	—	—	—	—	—	—	—	—	—	—	USAA Texas MM
4	79.5	97.5	41	70	—	6	—	—	20	4	—	—	USAA VA MM
4	31.5	29.3	82	51	—	9	—	5	15	20	—	—	Value Line TE MM
4	1,027.5	1,094.9	51	36	—	37	—	25	—	2	—	—	Vangd CA MM
4	3,878.6	4,248.2	76	37	—	35	—	21	—	7	—	—	Vangd Muni MM
4	757.6	798.3	47	37	—	60	—	1	—	2	—	12	Vangd NJ TF MM

Money market funds *continued*
Arranged in alphabetical order within objective

No-Load Fund	Compound yield percent with quintile ranks by objective										Annualized	
	1985	1986	1987	1988	1989	1990	1991	1992	1993	1994	3 years	5 years
Vangd OH TF MM	—	—	—	—	—	—	—	2.9[1]	2.3[1]	2.7[1]	2.6[1]	—
Vangd PA TF MM	—	—	—	—	6.4[1]	5.9[1]	4.4[1]	2.8[2]	2.4[1]	2.7[1]	2.6[1]	3.6[1]
Vista CA TF MM	—	—	—	—	—	—	—	—	2.2[1]	2.5[2]	—	—
Vista NY TF MM	—	—	—	—	—	—	—	2.3[5]	1.7[5]	2.1[5]	2.0[5]	—
Vista TF MM	—	—	—	—	—	—	—	2.5[4]	1.8[4]	2.2[5]	2.2[4]	—
Warbg Pincus NY MM	—	—	4.0[4]	4.5[5]	5.6[5]	5.2[5]	3.6[5]	2.4[5]	1.8[5]	2.2[4]	2.1[5]	3.0[5]
WPG TF MM	—	—	—	—	6.3[1]	5.7[1]	4.6[1]	3.0[1]	2.3[1]	2.6[1]	2.6[1]	3.6[1]

Money market funds   *continued*
Arranged in alphabetical order within objective

Valuation Method	Total Net Assets $ Millions December 31 1993	Total Net Assets $ Millions December 31 1994	Avg. Maturity days 12/31/94	Demand Notes Rated	Demand Notes Unrated	Gen Mkt Notes Rated	Gen Mkt Notes Unrated	Comm'l Paper	Put Bonds Under 6 Mo.	Put Bonds Over 6 Mo.	Other	AMT Paper	No-Load Fund
4	132.1	158.6	46	48	—	47	—	—	—	5	—	—	Vangd OH TF MM
4	952.2	1,134.6	39	53	—	23	—	14	—	10	—	—	Vangd PA TF MM
4	51.4	58.3	—	40	9	36	2	—	11	2	—	8	Vista CA TF MM
4	322.7	382.3	63	48	2	24	19	—	2	5	—	21	Vista NY TF MM
4	144.5	132.1	66	39	2	24	6	2	24	3	—	19	Vista TF MM
4	59.4	88.5	35	71	—	7	—	17	5	—	—	—	Warbg Pincus NY MM
4	136.9	152.3	59	57	—	16	—	—	27	—	—	—	WPG TF MM

Money market funds – ranked within objective
By 1994 performance

No-Load Fund	Total return percent with quintile ranks by objective		
	1994	Annualized 3 years	5 years
GENERAL MONEY MARKET FUNDS			
Benham Prime MM	4.5[1]	—	—
Dreyfus BASIC MM	4.3[1]	—	—
GE Elfun MM‡	4.2[1]	3.8[1]	—
Fidelity Spart MM	4.1[1]	3.7[1]	5.2[1]
Flex-Fund MM	4.1[1]	3.6[1]	5.0[1]
Schwab Value Adv MM	4.1[1]	—	—
Vangd MM Prime	4.1[1]	3.6[1]	5.0[1]
USAA Money Mkt	4.1[1]	3.6[1]	5.0[1]
Marshall MM Trust	4.1[1]	—	—
Price Summit Cash Res	4.0[1]	—	—
Strong Money Mkt	4.0[1]	3.6[1]	5.0[1]
Reserve Primary MM	4.0[1]	3.2[4]	4.5[4]
Kemper Money Mkt	4.0[1]	3.5[1]	4.9[1]
Seven Seas MM	4.0[1]	—	—
Evergreen MM Tr.	4.0[1]	3.7[1]	5.1[1]
FundTrust Money Mkt	4.0[1]	3.3[2]	—
Vista Global MM	4.0[1]	—	—
Fremont Money Mkt	4.0[2]	3.3[2]	4.8[2]
Fidelity Cash MM	4.0[2]	3.5[1]	4.9[1]
Asset Mgmt Money Mkt	3.9[2]	3.3[2]	—
Harbor Money Mkt	3.9[2]	3.3[3]	4.7[2]
Preferred Money Mkt	3.9[2]	—	—
UST Mstr Money Mkt	3.9[2]	3.4[1]	4.9[1]
Amer AAdv Mileage MM	3.9[2]	3.6[1]	—
CT&T Money Mkt	3.9[2]	—	—
Nicholas Money Mkt	3.9[2]	3.3[2]	4.7[2]
Fidelity Daily MM	3.9[2]	3.4[1]	4.8[2]
Salomon Cash Mgmt	3.9[2]	3.3[2]	—
Active Asst MM‡	3.9[2]	3.4[2]	4.8[2]
Drey/Laurel Prime MM	3.9[2]	3.4[1]	—
Merrill Lynch Ret Res	3.9[2]	3.4[1]	—
Pacifica Money Mkt	3.8[2]	—	—
Portico Money Mkt	3.8[2]	3.3[3]	4.7[2]
CMA Money Mkt‡	3.8[2]	3.4[1]	4.8[1]
Babson UMB Prime MM	3.8[2]	3.3[2]	4.7[2]
RMA Money Mkt‡	3.8[2]	3.4[2]	4.8[2]
Dean Witter Liq Asst	3.8[3]	3.3[3]	4.7[3]
Paine Webber Cashfund	3.8[3]	3.4[2]	4.8[2]
Federated Prime MM	3.8[3]	3.1[4]	4.5[5]
Green Cent MM	3.8[3]	—	—
Marshall MM Invest	3.8[3]	—	—
Prudential Moneymart	3.8[3]	3.3[2]	4.8[2]
Fidelity Select MM	3.7[1]	3.3[2]	4.7[2]
Price, Rowe Prime Res	3.7[3]	3.2[3]	4.6[3]
Merrill Lynch Rdy Asst	3.7[3]	3.3[2]	4.8[1]
IAI Money Mkt	3.7[3]	—	—
Nbrgr-Ber Cash Res	3.7[3]	3.2[3]	4.6[3]
Smith Barney Cash MM	3.7[3]	3.2[3]	4.6[3]
FFB Lexcn Cash Mgt	3.7[3]	3.3[2]	—
Invesco Cash Res	3.7[3]	3.1[4]	4.5[4]
Pacific Hzn Prime MM	3.7[3]	—	—
Scudder Cash Inv Tr	3.7[3]	3.3[3]	4.7[2]
Columbia Daily Inc	3.7[4]	3.1[4]	4.6[4]
Value Line Cash	3.7[3]	3.5[1]	4.8[1]
Amcor Vntg Gov Obl MM	3.7[4]	—	—
SteinRoe Cash Res	3.7[4]	3.2[3]	4.6[3]
Galaxy Money Mkt	3.7[4]	3.3[2]	4.8[2]
Schwab Money Mkt	3.7[4]	3.3[3]	—
Smith Barney Ret MM	3.7[4]	3.2[4]	4.6[4]

No-Load Fund	Total return percent with quintile ranks by objective		
	1994	Annualized 3 years	5 years
Twentieth Cent Cash	3.7[4]	3.0[5]	4.5[4]
Legg Msn Cash Res	3.7[4]	3.3[2]	4.7[3]
Kidder Pbdy Cash Res‡	3.6[4]	3.1[4]	4.5[4]
Calvert Scl Inv MM	3.6[4]	3.1[4]	4.5[4]
Homestead Daily Inc	3.6[4]	3.3[3]	—
Bartlett Cash Res	3.6[4]	3.3[3]	4.6[3]
Highmark Dvsfd MM	3.6[4]	3.2[3]	4.7[3]
Cash Equiv-MM‡	3.6[4]	3.1[4]	4.5[4]
Managers Money Mkt	3.6[4]	3.2[3]	4.5[4]
Dreyfus Liq Asst	3.5[4]	3.2[3]	4.7[3]
SAFECO Money Mkt	3.5[4]	3.1[4]	4.6[3]
Wayne Hummer MM	3.5[4]	3.0[5]	4.4[5]
Cash Acct Tr-MM‡	3.5[4]	3.0[5]	—
Drey-General MM	3.5[5]	3.2[4]	4.6[3]
New England MM	3.5[5]	3.2[4]	4.6[3]
Liquid Cap Inc MM	3.5[5]	3.0[5]	4.4[5]
Wm Blair Ready Res	3.5[5]	3.1[4]	—
Founders Money Mkt	3.5[5]	2.9[5]	4.3[5]
AARP Hi Qual MM	3.5[5]	2.8[5]	4.3[5]
Fortis Money Mkt	3.5[5]	2.9[5]	4.4[5]
Dreyfus Wrld Dollar	3.5[5]	3.3[2]	5.0[1]
Short Tm Inc-MM(R&T)	3.5[5]	3.2[4]	4.6[4]
Dreyfus MM Instr MM Ser	3.4[5]	3.2[3]	—
Babson Prime MM	3.4[5]	3.0[5]	4.4[5]
Smith Hayes MM	3.4[5]	—	—
Bull & Bear Dollar	3.4[5]	3.0[5]	4.3[5]
Alliance Cap Res	3.4[5]	3.0[4]	4.5[4]
Lexington MM	3.4[5]	2.9[5]	4.3[5]
Alliance Money Res	3.3[5]	3.0[4]	4.5[4]
Wrkng Asst MM	3.2[5]	2.8[5]	4.3[5]
MIM Money Mkt	3.2[5]	3.1[4]	4.5[4]
GOVERNMENT MONEY MARKET FUNDS			
Dreyfus BASIC Gov MM	4.2[1]	—	—
Monetta Gov MM	4.0[1]	—	—
1784 Trsy MM	4.0[1]	—	—
Vangd MM Federal	4.0[1]	3.6[1]	4.9[1]
US Gov MM	4.0[1]	3.9[1]	—
Reserve Treas MM	4.0[1]	—	—
Vangd-Adml MM	4.0[1]	—	—
Goldmn Sachs MM Gov	3.9[1]	3.5[1]	—
Seven Seas Gov MM	3.9[1]	—	—
Fidelity Spart Gov MM	3.9[1]	3.5[1]	—
Federated Trsy MM	3.9[1]	3.2[2]	—
Warbg Pincus Cash Res	3.9[1]	3.4[1]	4.8[1]
Strong Trsy MM	3.9[1]	3.5[1]	—
Fidelity Gov MM	3.9[1]	3.3[2]	4.6[2]
Gabelli Treas MM	3.8[1]	—	—
UST Mstr Gov MM	3.8[1]	3.4[1]	4.8[1]
Vangd MM Treas	3.8[2]	3.4[1]	4.8[1]
Forum Dly Asst Trsy	3.8[2]	—	—
USAA Trsy MM	3.8[2]	3.4[1]	—
Amer AAdv Trsy MM	3.8[2]	—	—
Montgmry Gov MM	3.8[2]	—	—
Benham Gov Agcy MM	3.8[2]	3.3[2]	4.8[1]
Babson UMB Fed MM	3.8[2]	3.3[2]	4.7[2]
Galaxy Gov MM	3.7[2]	3.4[1]	4.7[1]
Portico Gov MM	3.7[2]	3.2[2]	4.5[3]
Fidelity Spart Trsy MM	3.7[2]	3.4[1]	4.8[1]
Drey/Laurel Trsy MM	3.7[2]	3.3[2]	—
Drey-General Gov MM	3.7[2]	3.3[2]	4.6[2]

Money market funds – ranked within objective *continued*
By 1994 performance

No-Load Fund	1994	Annualized 3 years	Annualized 5 years	No-Load Fund	1994	Annualized 3 years	Annualized 5 years
CMA Gov MM‡	3.7[2]	3.3[2]	4.7[1]	Evergreen TE MM	2.8[1]	2.8[1]	3.8[1]
Legg Msn Gov MM	3.7[2]	3.3[1]	4.7[2]	Vangd Muni MM	2.8[1]	2.7[1]	3.7[1]
Pacifica Gov MM	3.7[2]	—	—	Vangd CA MM	2.7[1]	2.7[1]	3.6[1]
Salomon Trsy MM	3.6[2]	—	—	Vangd OH TF MM	2.7[1]	2.6[1]	—
Smith Barney Gov MM	3.6[3]	3.2[3]	4.5[2]	1784 TF MM	2.7[1]	—	—
Benham Cap Presv	3.6[3]	3.2[2]	4.6[2]	Vangd PA TF MM	2.7[1]	2.6[1]	3.6[1]
Active Asst Gov MM‡	3.6[3]	3.1[3]	4.5[3]	Goldmn Sachs MM TE	2.7[1]	—	—
Schwab Gov MM	3.6[3]	3.2[2]	—	Salomon NY MM	2.7[1]	2.7[1]	—
Invesco Gov MM	3.6[3]	3.0[5]	—	Fidelity Spart NJ MM	2.7[1]	2.5[2]	—
Rydex Gov MM	3.6[3]	—	—	USAA TE MM	2.6[1]	2.7[1]	3.8[1]
Crabbe Hsn Gov MM	3.6[3]	3.1[4]	4.4[5]	Vangd NJ TF MM	2.6[1]	2.6[1]	3.6[1]
Rushmore Gov MM	3.6[3]	3.0[5]	4.3[5]	Fidelity Spart PA MM	2.6[1]	2.6[1]	3.7[1]
Drey/Laurel Gov MM	3.6[3]	3.2[3]	4.4[4]	WPG TF MM	2.6[1]	2.6[1]	3.6[1]
Galaxy Trsy MM	3.6[3]	3.2[2]	—	Dreyfus MA MM	2.6[1]	2.5[1]	—
Vista Gov MM	3.6[3]	3.0[5]	—	USAA CA MM	2.6[1]	2.6[1]	3.5[1]
Cash Equiv-Gov MM‡	3.6[3]	3.1[4]	4.5[3]	Fidelity Spart FL MM	2.6[1]	—	—
WPG Gov MM	3.6[3]	3.1[4]	4.5[3]	Dreyfus CT TF MM	2.6[2]	2.6[1]	—
First Omaha Gov MM	3.6[3]	—	—	Price Summit Muni MM	2.6[2]	—	—
SBSF Money Mkt	3.6[3]	3.2[3]	4.6[2]	Drey-General CA MM	2.6[2]	2.6[1]	3.7[1]
Prudential Gov MM	3.5[4]	3.2[3]	4.6[2]	Daily TF (R&T)	2.6[2]	2.5[2]	3.5[2]
Portico Federal MM	3.5[4]	3.1[4]	—	PA Daily Muni (R&T)	2.6[2]	—	—
Kidder Pbdy Gov MM‡	3.5[4]	3.1[4]	4.4[4]	USAA VA MM	2.6[2]	2.6[1]	—
SteinRoe Gov Res	3.5[3]	3.1[3]	4.5[3]	Dreyfus MI MM	2.5[2]	2.4[2]	—
Price, Rowe Trsy MM	3.5[4]	3.1[4]	4.4[4]	Fidelity TE MM	2.5[2]	2.5[2]	3.5[1]
RMA Gov MM‡	3.5[4]	3.2[3]	4.5[3]	New England TE MM	2.5[2]	2.4[2]	3.3[2]
Schwab Trsy MM	3.5[4]	—	—	Vista CA TF MM	2.5[2]	—	—
Selected Daily Gov MM	3.5[4]	2.9[5]	4.3[5]	Fidelity OH Muni MM	2.5[2]	2.5[2]	3.6[1]
CMA Trsy MM‡	3.5[4]	3.1[3]	—	Drey/Laurel TxFr MM	2.5[2]	2.3[3]	3.3[3]
Scudder Trsy MM	3.5[4]	3.1[3]	4.6[2]	Drey/Laurel TxEx MM	2.5[2]	2.4[2]	—
Cash Acct Tr-Gov MM‡	3.5[4]	3.0[5]	—	USAA FL MM	2.5[2]	—	—
Wright Trsy MM	3.5[4]	3.1[3]	—	Benham CA Muni MM	2.5[2]	2.5[2]	—
Benham Cap Presv II	3.5[4]	2.9[5]	4.3[5]	CA Inv Tr-CA MM	2.5[2]	2.4[2]	3.4[2]
Weitz Gov MM	3.5[4]	3.2[2]	—	Portico TE MM	2.5[2]	2.4[2]	3.4[2]
59 Wall St Trsy MM	3.5[4]	—	—	Price, Rowe TE MM	2.5[2]	2.3[3]	3.2[3]
CA Inv Tr-Trsy MM	3.5[4]	3.1[3]	4.5[3]	Dreyfus NJ MM	2.5[2]	2.4[2]	3.5[1]
Gradison Gov MM	3.5[4]	3.0[4]	4.3[5]	Drey-General NY MM	2.5[2]	2.4[2]	3.4[2]
Highmark Gov MM	3.5[5]	3.1[3]	4.5[3]	SAFECO TF MM	2.5[2]	2.4[2]	3.4[2]
Merrill Lynch USA Gov	3.4[5]	3.1[4]	—	Fidelity Spart NY MM	2.5[2]	2.4[2]	—
Short Tm Inc-Gov(R&T)	3.4[5]	3.1[4]	4.4[4]	Drey/Laurel CA MM	2.5[2]	2.6[1]	3.6[1]
Nbrgr-Ber Gov MM	3.4[5]	3.1[4]	4.4[4]	Fidelity MI Muni MM	2.4[3]	2.4[2]	—
Dreyfus 100% US MM	3.4[5]	3.2[2]	4.7[1]	CA Daily TF (R&T)	2.4[3]	2.3[3]	3.2[4]
New England Gov MM	3.4[5]	3.1[4]	4.5[3]	Benham CA TF MM	2.4[3]	2.3[3]	3.2[4]
Federated Gov Cash	3.4[5]	2.9[5]	—	Cash Equiv-TE MM‡	2.4[3]	2.3[3]	3.3[2]
Highmark Treas MM	3.4[5]	3.0[4]	4.4[4]	CMA TE MM‡	2.4[3]	2.3[3]	3.3[2]
Reserve Gov MM	3.4[5]	2.9[5]	4.3[5]	Fidelity Spart CT MM	2.4[3]	2.5[2]	—
Babson Fed MM	3.3[5]	2.9[5]	4.3[5]	Drey-General Muni MM	2.4[3]	2.4[2]	3.3[2]
Dreyfus MM Instr Gov	3.3[5]	3.1[4]	4.5[3]	Babson UMB TF MM	2.4[3]	2.3[3]	3.3[3]
Blanchard Trsy MM	3.3[5]	3.4[1]	4.4[4]	USAA NY MM	2.4[3]	2.4[2]	—
Alliance Gov Res	3.3[5]	2.9[5]	4.3[5]	Active Asst TF MM‡	2.4[3]	2.3[3]	3.3[3]
Dean Witter Gov MM	3.2[5]	2.8[5]	4.2[5]	Dreyfus Muni MM	2.4[3]	2.3[3]	3.3[3]
US Trsy MM	3.2[5]	2.9[5]	4.4[4]	Amer AAdv Muni Miles	2.4[3]	—	—
GIT MM Account	3.1[5]	2.7[5]	4.1[5]	Fidelity CA TF MM	2.4[3]	2.3[3]	3.2[3]
TAX-FREE MONEY MARKET FUNDS				Babson TF MM	2.4[3]	2.3[2]	3.3[2]
Hough FL TF MM	3.1[1]	—	—	Highmark CA TF MM	2.4[3]	2.3[3]	3.2[3]
Dreyfus BASIC Muni MM	2.9[1]	—	—	Scudder CA TF MM	2.4[3]	2.3[3]	3.1[4]
Strong Muni MM	2.9[1]	2.9[1]	4.0[1]	Smith Barney TF MM	2.4[3]	2.3[3]	3.3[3]
Dreyfus PA MM	2.8[1]	2.7[1]	—	Price, Rowe CA MM	2.4[3]	2.2[4]	3.1[5]
Dreyfus OH MM	2.8[1]	2.8[1]	—	CMA CA MM‡	2.3[3]	2.2[4]	3.1[4]
Fidelity Spart CA MM	2.8[1]	2.7[1]	3.7[1]	MI Daily TF (R&T)	2.3[3]	2.2[4]	3.3[2]
Fidelity Spart Muni MM	2.8[1]	2.9[1]	—	Fidelity Spart MA MM	2.3[3]	2.3[2]	—

Money market funds – ranked within objective   *continued*
By 1994 performance

No-Load Fund	Total return percent with quintile ranks by objective			No-Load Fund	Total return percent with quintile ranks by objective		
		Annualized				Annualized	
	1994	3 years	5 years		1994	3 years	5 years
Fidelity NY TF MM	**2.3**[3]	2.2[4]	3.1[5]	Warbg Pincus NY MM	**2.2**[4]	2.1[5]	3.0[5]
Fidelity NJ TF MM	**2.3**[3]	2.3[3]	3.3[2]	Invesco TF MM	**2.2**[5]	2.2[4]	3.1[5]
Fidelity CT TF MM	**2.3**[4]	2.2[3]	3.4[2]	Schwab CA TF MM	**2.2**[5]	2.2[4]	—
Benham Nat TF MM	**2.3**[3]	2.2[4]	3.3[3]	NJ Daily Muni (R&T)	**2.2**[5]	2.3[3]	—
Prudential TF MM	**2.3**[4]	2.3[3]	3.3[3]	Federated Muni Cash	**2.2**[5]	2.2[4]	3.3[3]
Schwab TE MM	**2.3**[4]	2.2[4]	—	Active Asst CA MM‡	**2.2**[5]	—	—
Dreyfus CA TF MM	**2.3**[4]	2.3[3]	3.2[4]	Drey/Laurel NY MM	**2.2**[5]	2.4[2]	3.4[2]
RMA TF MM‡	**2.3**[4]	2.2[4]	3.2[3]	Fidelity MA TF MM	**2.2**[5]	2.0[5]	3.1[5]
Rushmore TF MM	**2.3**[4]	2.1[5]	3.2[4]	CT Daily TF (R&T)	**2.2**[5]	2.0[5]	3.0[5]
Federated OH Cash	**2.3**[4]	2.3[3]	—	NC Daily Muni (R&T)	**2.2**[5]	2.1[5]	—
Cash Acct Tr-TF MM‡	**2.3**[4]	2.2[4]	—	Alliance Muni MM	**2.2**[5]	2.2[4]	3.2[4]
Price, Rowe NY MM	**2.3**[4]	2.2[4]	3.0[5]	Vista TF MM	**2.2**[5]	2.2[4]	—
Nbrgr-Ber Muni MM	**2.3**[4]	2.2[5]	3.2[4]	Kidder Pbdy CA TF MM‡	**2.1**[5]	2.1[5]	3.0[5]
Nuveen TF Res	**2.3**[4]	2.2[4]	3.3[3]	Dreyfus NY MM	**2.1**[5]	2.0[5]	3.0[5]
NY Daily TF Inc(R&T)	**2.3**[4]	2.3[3]	3.2[3]	Vista NY TF MM	**2.1**[5]	2.0[5]	—
Galaxy TE MM	**2.3**[4]	2.2[4]	3.3[3]	AARP Hi Qual TF MM	**2.0**[5]	1.9[5]	—
Highmark TF MM	**2.3**[4]	2.3[3]	3.3[2]	Value Line TE MM	**2.0**[5]	2.0[5]	3.1[5]
SteinRoe Muni MM	**2.3**[4]	2.2[4]	3.2[4]	Lexington TF MM	**2.0**[5]	2.1[5]	3.2[4]
Scudder TF MM	**2.3**[4]	2.2[4]	3.2[4]	Reserve TE Interstate	**2.0**[5]	2.1[5]	3.1[4]
Dean Witter TF MM	**2.3**[4]	2.2[4]	3.2[4]	Reserve NY TE MM	**2.0**[5]	1.9[5]	2.9[5]
CMA NY MM‡	**2.3**[4]	2.1[5]	3.0[5]	Reserve MA TE MM	**2.0**[5]	2.1[5]	—
Legg Msn TE MM	**2.3**[4]	2.1[5]	3.1[5]	Reserve CT TE MM	**2.0**[5]	2.0[5]	2.9[5]
Drey/Laurel MA MM	**2.3**[4]	2.2[5]	3.3[3]	GIT TF MM	**1.8**[5]	1.8[5]	2.8[5]
Scudder NY TF MM	**2.2**[4]	2.2[4]	3.0[5]	Fundamental TF MM	**1.7**[5]	2.0[5]	3.2[4]
Kidder Pbdy TE MM‡	**2.2**[4]	2.2[4]	3.2[4]				

Money market funds – ranked within objective

By 1992-1994 performance

No-Load Fund	Total return percent with quintile ranks by objective		
	1994	Annualized 3 years	Annualized 5 years
GENERAL MONEY MARKET FUNDS			
GE Elfun MM‡	4.2[1]	**3.8[1]**	—
Fidelity Spart MM	4.1[1]	**3.7[1]**	5.2[1]
Evergreen MM Tr	4.0[1]	**3.7[1]**	5.1[1]
USAA Money Mkt	4.1[1]	**3.6[1]**	5.0[1]
Vangd MM Prime	4.1[1]	**3.6[1]**	5.0[1]
Flex-Fund MM	4.1[1]	**3.6[1]**	5.0[1]
Amer AAdv Mileage MM	3.9[2]	**3.6[1]**	—
Strong Money Mkt	4.0[1]	**3.6[1]**	5.0[1]
Fidelity Cash MM	4.0[2]	**3.5[1]**	4.9[1]
Value Line Cash	3.7[3]	**3.5[1]**	4.8[1]
Kemper Money Mkt	4.0[1]	**3.5[1]**	4.9[1]
UST Mstr Money Mkt	3.9[2]	**3.4[1]**	4.9[1]
Fidelity Daily MM	3.9[2]	**3.4[1]**	4.8[2]
Drey/Laurel Prime MM	3.9[2]	**3.4[1]**	—
CMA Money Mkt‡	3.8[2]	**3.4[1]**	4.8[1]
Merrill Lynch Ret Res	3.9[2]	**3.4[1]**	—
RMA Money Mkt‡	3.8[2]	**3.4[2]**	4.8[2]
Active Asst MM‡	3.9[2]	**3.4[2]**	4.8[2]
Paine Webber Cashfund	3.8[3]	**3.4[2]**	4.8[2]
Asset Mgmt Money Mkt	3.9[2]	**3.3[2]**	—
FundTrust Money Mkt	4.0[1]	**3.3[2]**	—
Prudential Moneymart	3.8[3]	**3.3[2]**	4.8[2]
FFB Lexcn Cash Mgt	3.7[3]	**3.3[2]**	—
Babson UMB Prime MM	3.8[2]	**3.3[2]**	4.7[2]
Merrill Lynch Rdy Asst	3.7[3]	**3.3[2]**	4.8[1]
Salomon Cash Mgmt	3.9[2]	**3.3[2]**	—
Fremont Money Mkt	4.0[2]	**3.3[2]**	4.8[2]
Galaxy Money Mkt	3.7[3]	**3.3[2]**	4.8[2]
Fidelity Select MM	3.7[3]	**3.3[2]**	4.7[2]
Dreyfus Wrld Dollar	3.5[5]	**3.3[2]**	5.0[1]
Nicholas Money Mkt	3.9[2]	**3.3[2]**	4.7[2]
Legg Msn Cash Res	3.7[4]	**3.3[2]**	4.7[3]
Homestead Daily Inc	3.6[4]	**3.3[3]**	—
Harbor Money Mkt	3.9[2]	**3.3[3]**	4.7[2]
Bartlett Cash Res	3.6[4]	**3.3[3]**	4.6[3]
Portico Money Mkt	3.8[2]	**3.3[3]**	4.7[2]
Schwab Money Mkt	3.7[4]	**3.3[3]**	—
Dean Witter Liq Asst	3.8[3]	**3.3[3]**	4.7[3]
Scudder Cash Inv Tr	3.7[3]	**3.3[3]**	4.7[2]
Nbrgr-Ber Cash Res	3.7[3]	**3.2[3]**	4.6[3]
Highmark Dvsfd MM	3.6[4]	**3.2[3]**	4.7[3]
Price, Rowe Prime Res	3.7[3]	**3.2[3]**	4.6[3]
SteinRoe Cash Res	3.7[4]	**3.2[3]**	4.6[3]
Smith Barney Cash MM	3.7[3]	**3.2[3]**	4.6[3]
Dreyfus Liq Asst	3.5[4]	**3.2[3]**	4.7[3]
Dreyfus MM Instr MM Ser	3.4[5]	**3.2[3]**	—
Managers Money Mkt	3.6[4]	**3.2[3]**	4.5[4]
Smith Barney Ret MM	3.7[4]	**3.2[4]**	4.6[4]
Short Tm Inc-MM(R&T)	3.5[5]	**3.2[4]**	4.6[4]
New England MM	3.5[5]	**3.2[4]**	4.6[3]
Drey-General MM	3.5[5]	**3.2[4]**	4.6[3]
Reserve Primary MM	4.0[1]	**3.2[4]**	4.5[4]
Calvert Scl Inv MM	3.6[4]	**3.1[4]**	4.5[4]
Columbia Daily Inc	3.7[4]	**3.1[4]**	4.6[4]
Wm Blair Ready Res	3.5[5]	**3.1[4]**	—
Kidder Pbdy Cash Res‡	3.6[4]	**3.1[4]**	4.5[4]
SAFECO Money Mkt	3.5[4]	**3.1[4]**	4.6[3]
Cash Equiv-MM‡	3.6[4]	**3.1[4]**	4.5[4]
Invesco Cash Res	3.7[3]	**3.1[4]**	4.5[4]

No-Load Fund	Total return percent with quintile ranks by objective		
	1994	Annualized 3 years	Annualized 5 years
Federated Prime MM	3.8[3]	**3.1[4]**	4.5[5]
MIM Money Mkt	3.2[5]	**3.1[4]**	4.5[4]
Alliance Cap Res	3.4[5]	**3.0[4]**	4.5[4]
Alliance Money Res	3.3[5]	**3.0[4]**	4.5[4]
Wayne Hummer MM	3.5[4]	**3.0[5]**	4.4[5]
Bull & Bear Dollar	3.4[5]	**3.0[5]**	4.3[5]
Twentieth Cent Cash	3.7[4]	**3.0[5]**	4.5[4]
Cash Acct Tr-MM‡	3.5[4]	**3.0[5]**	—
Liquid Cap Inc MM	3.5[5]	**3.0[5]**	4.4[5]
Babson Prime MM	3.4[5]	**3.0[5]**	4.4[5]
Fortis Money Mkt	3.5[5]	**2.9[5]**	4.4[5]
Lexington MM	3.4[5]	**2.9[5]**	4.3[5]
Founders Money Mkt	3.5[5]	**2.9[5]**	4.3[5]
AARP Hi Qual MM	3.5[5]	**2.8[5]**	4.3[5]
Wrkng Asst MM	3.2[5]	**2.8[5]**	4.3[5]
GOVERNMENT MONEY MARKET FUNDS			
US Gov MM	4.0[1]	**3.9[1]**	—
Vangd MM Federal	4.0[1]	**3.6[1]**	4.9[1]
Goldmn Sachs MM Gov	3.9[1]	**3.5[1]**	—
Fidelity Spart Gov MM	3.9[1]	**3.5[1]**	—
Strong Trsy MM	3.9[1]	**3.5[1]**	—
Warbg Pincus Cash Res	3.9[1]	**3.4[1]**	4.8[1]
Vangd MM Treas	3.8[2]	**3.4[1]**	4.8[1]
UST Mstr Gov MM	3.8[1]	**3.4[1]**	4.8[1]
USAA Trsy MM	3.8[2]	**3.4[1]**	—
Blanchard Trsy MM	3.3[5]	**3.4[1]**	4.4[4]
Fidelity Spart Trsy MM	3.7[2]	**3.4[1]**	4.8[1]
Galaxy Gov MM	3.7[2]	**3.4[1]**	4.7[1]
Legg Msn Gov MM	3.7[2]	**3.3[1]**	4.7[2]
Babson UMB Fed MM	3.8[2]	**3.3[2]**	4.7[2]
CMA Gov MM‡	3.7[2]	**3.3[2]**	4.7[1]
Drey/Laurel Trsy MM	3.7[2]	**3.3[2]**	—
Drey-General Gov MM	3.7[2]	**3.3[2]**	4.6[2]
Fidelity Gov MM	3.9[1]	**3.3[2]**	4.6[2]
Benham Gov Agcy MM	3.8[2]	**3.3[2]**	4.8[1]
Schwab Gov MM	3.6[3]	**3.2[2]**	—
Galaxy Trsy MM	3.6[3]	**3.2[2]**	—
Weitz Gov MM	3.5[4]	**3.2[2]**	—
Portico Gov MM	3.7[2]	**3.2[2]**	4.5[3]
Federated Trsy MM	3.9[1]	**3.2[2]**	—
Dreyfus 100% US MM	3.4[5]	**3.2[2]**	4.7[1]
Benham Cap Presv	3.6[3]	**3.2[2]**	4.6[2]
RMA Gov MM‡	3.5[4]	**3.2[3]**	4.5[3]
Prudential Gov MM	3.5[4]	**3.2[3]**	4.6[2]
SBSF Money Mkt	3.6[3]	**3.2[3]**	4.6[2]
Smith Barney Gov MM	3.6[3]	**3.2[3]**	4.5[2]
Drey/Laurel Gov MM	3.6[3]	**3.2[3]**	4.4[4]
CMA Trsy MM‡	3.5[4]	**3.1[3]**	—
SteinRoe Gov Res	3.5[3]	**3.1[3]**	4.5[3]
Scudder Trsy MM	3.5[4]	**3.1[3]**	4.6[2]
Active Asst Gov MM‡	3.6[3]	**3.1[3]**	4.5[3]
Wright Trsy MM	3.5[4]	**3.1[3]**	—
Highmark Gov MM	3.5[5]	**3.1[3]**	4.5[3]
CA Inv Tr-Trsy MM	3.5[4]	**3.1[3]**	4.5[3]
WPG Gov MM	3.6[3]	**3.1[4]**	4.5[3]
New England Gov MM	3.4[5]	**3.1[4]**	4.5[3]
Cash Equiv-Gov MM‡	3.6[3]	**3.1[4]**	4.5[3]
Portico Federal MM	3.5[4]	**3.1[4]**	—
Price, Rowe Trsy MM	3.5[4]	**3.1[4]**	4.4[4]
Merrill Lynch USA Gov	3.4[5]	**3.1[4]**	—

Money market funds – ranked within objective continued

By 1992-1994 performance

No-Load Fund	Total return percent with quintile ranks by objective			No-Load Fund	Total return percent with quintile ranks by objective		
	1994	Annualized 3 years	5 years		1994	Annualized 3 years	5 years
Crabbe Hsn Gov MM	3.6[3]	**3.1[4]**	4.4[4]	Drey-General NY MM	2.5[2]	**2.4[2]**	3.4[2]
Dreyfus MM Instr Gov	3.3[5]	**3.1[4]**	4.5[3]	Fidelity Spart MA MM	2.3[3]	**2.3[2]**	—
Kidder Pbdy Gov MM‡	3.5[4]	**3.1[4]**	4.4[4]	Babson TF MM	2.4[3]	**2.3[2]**	3.3[2]
Nbrgr-Ber Gov MM	3.4[5]	**3.1[4]**	4.4[4]	Price, Rowe TE MM	2.5[2]	**2.3[3]**	3.2[3]
Short Tm Inc-Gov(R&T)	3.4[5]	**3.1[4]**	4.4[4]	Cash Equiv-TE MM‡	2.4[3]	**2.3[3]**	3.3[2]
Highmark Treas MM	3.4[5]	**3.0[4]**	4.4[4]	CMA TE MM‡	2.4[3]	**2.3[3]**	3.3[2]
Gradison Gov MM	3.5[4]	**3.0[4]**	4.3[5]	Benham CA TF MM	2.4[3]	**2.3[3]**	3.2[3]
Vista Gov MM	3.6[3]	**3.0[5]**	—	Babson UMB TF MM	2.4[3]	**2.3[3]**	3.3[3]
Rushmore Gov MM	3.6[3]	**3.0[5]**	4.3[5]	Fidelity CA TF MM	2.4[3]	**2.3[3]**	3.2[3]
Cash Acct Tr-Gov MM‡	3.5[4]	**3.0[5]**	—	Highmark TF MM	2.3[4]	**2.3[3]**	3.3[2]
Invesco Gov MM	3.6[3]	**3.0[5]**	—	CA Daily TF (R&T)	2.4[3]	**2.3[3]**	3.2[4]
Alliance Gov Res	3.3[5]	**2.9[5]**	4.3[5]	Dreyfus Muni MM	2.4[3]	**2.3[3]**	3.3[3]
Selected Daily Gov MM	3.5[4]	**2.9[5]**	4.3[5]	Active Asst TF MM‡	2.4[3]	**2.3[3]**	3.3[3]
Benham Cap Presv II	3.5[4]	**2.9[5]**	4.3[5]	Drey/Laurel TxFr MM	2.5[2]	**2.3[3]**	3.3[3]
Babson Fed MM	3.3[5]	**2.9[5]**	4.3[5]	Federated OH Cash	2.3[4]	**2.3[3]**	—
Federated Gov Cash	3.4[5]	**2.9[5]**	—	Fidelity NJ TF MM	2.3[3]	**2.3[3]**	3.3[2]
Reserve Gov MM	3.4[5]	**2.9[5]**	4.3[5]	Highmark CA TF MM	2.4[3]	**2.3[3]**	3.2[3]
US Trsy MM	3.2[5]	**2.9[5]**	4.4[4]	Dreyfus CA TF MM	2.3[4]	**2.3[3]**	3.2[4]
Dean Witter Gov MM	3.2[5]	**2.8[5]**	4.2[5]	Scudder CA TF MM	2.4[3]	**2.3[3]**	3.1[4]
GIT MM Account	3.1[5]	**2.7[5]**	4.1[5]	NJ Daily Muni (R&T)	2.2[5]	**2.3[3]**	—
TAX-FREE MONEY MARKET FUNDS				Prudential TF MM	2.3[4]	**2.3[3]**	3.3[3]
Strong Muni MM	2.9[1]	**2.9[1]**	4.0[1]	Smith Barney TF MM	2.4[3]	**2.3[3]**	3.3[3]
Fidelity Spart Muni MM	2.8[1]	**2.9[1]**	—	NY Daily TF Inc(R&T)	2.3[4]	**2.3[3]**	3.2[3]
Evergreen TE MM	2.8[1]	**2.8[1]**	3.8[1]	Fidelity CT TF MM	2.3[4]	**2.2[3]**	3.4[2]
Dreyfus OH MM	2.8[1]	**2.8[1]**	—	Schwab TE MM	2.3[4]	**2.2[4]**	—
Fidelity Spart CA MM	2.8[1]	**2.7[1]**	3.7[1]	Galaxy TE MM	2.3[4]	**2.2[4]**	3.3[3]
Vangd Muni MM	2.8[1]	**2.7[1]**	3.7[1]	RMA TF MM‡	2.3[4]	**2.2[4]**	3.2[3]
Dreyfus PA MM	2.8[1]	**2.7[1]**	—	Price, Rowe CA MM	2.4[3]	**2.2[4]**	3.1[5]
USAA TE MM	2.6[1]	**2.7[1]**	3.8[1]	Nuveen TF Res	2.3[4]	**2.2[4]**	3.3[3]
Salomon NY MM	2.7[1]	**2.7[1]**	—	CMA CA MM‡	2.3[3]	**2.2[4]**	3.1[4]
Vangd CA MM	2.7[1]	**2.7[1]**	3.6[1]	Benham Nat TF MM	2.3[3]	**2.2[4]**	3.3[3]
Vangd OH TF MM	2.7[1]	**2.6[1]**	—	MI Daily TF (R&T)	2.3[3]	**2.2[4]**	3.3[2]
Vangd PA TF MM	2.7[1]	**2.6[1]**	3.6[1]	Scudder TF MM	2.3[4]	**2.2[4]**	3.2[4]
WPG TF MM	2.6[1]	**2.6[1]**	3.6[1]	Fidelity NY TF MM	2.3[3]	**2.2[4]**	3.1[5]
Vangd NJ TF MM	2.6[1]	**2.6[1]**	3.6[1]	Alliance Muni MM	2.2[5]	**2.2[4]**	3.2[4]
Drey-General CA MM	2.6[2]	**2.6[1]**	3.7[1]	Federated Muni Cash	2.2[5]	**2.2[4]**	3.3[3]
Drey/Laurel CA MM	2.5[2]	**2.6[1]**	3.6[1]	Cash Acct Tr-TF MM‡	2.3[4]	**2.2[4]**	—
USAA CA MM	2.6[1]	**2.6[1]**	3.5[1]	Invesco TF MM	2.2[5]	**2.2[4]**	3.1[5]
Fidelity Spart PA MM	2.6[1]	**2.6[1]**	3.7[1]	Price, Rowe NY MM	2.3[4]	**2.2[4]**	3.0[5]
Dreyfus CT TF MM	2.6[2]	**2.6[1]**	—	SteinRoe Muni MM	2.3[4]	**2.2[4]**	3.2[4]
USAA VA MM	2.6[2]	**2.6[1]**	—	Scudder NY TF MM	2.2[4]	**2.2[4]**	3.0[5]
Dreyfus MA MM	2.6[1]	**2.5[1]**	—	Dean Witter TF MM	2.3[4]	**2.2[4]**	3.2[4]
Fidelity TE MM	2.5[2]	**2.5[2]**	3.5[1]	Schwab CA TF MM	2.2[5]	**2.2[4]**	—
Benham CA Muni MM	2.5[2]	**2.5[2]**	—	Vista TF MM	2.2[5]	**2.2[4]**	—
Fidelity Spart CT MM	2.4[3]	**2.5[2]**	—	Kidder Pbdy TE MM‡	2.2[4]	**2.2[4]**	3.2[4]
Fidelity Spart NJ MM	2.7[1]	**2.5[2]**	—	Nbrgr-Ber Muni MM	2.3[4]	**2.2[5]**	3.2[4]
Daily TF (R&T)	2.6[2]	**2.5[2]**	3.5[2]	Drey/Laurel MA MM	2.3[4]	**2.2[5]**	3.3[3]
Fidelity OH Muni MM	2.5[2]	**2.5[2]**	3.6[1]	NC Daily Muni (R&T)	2.2[5]	**2.1[5]**	—
Dreyfus NJ MM	2.5[2]	**2.4[2]**	3.5[1]	CMA NY MM‡	2.3[4]	**2.1[5]**	3.0[5]
CA Inv Tr-CA MM	2.5[2]	**2.4[2]**	3.4[2]	Kidder Pbdy CA TF MM‡	2.1[5]	**2.1[5]**	3.0[5]
Dreyfus MI MM	2.5[2]	**2.4[2]**	—	Warbg Pincus NY MM	2.2[4]	**2.1[5]**	3.0[5]
Drey/Laurel NY MM	2.2[5]	**2.4[2]**	3.4[2]	Legg Msn TE MM	2.3[4]	**2.1[5]**	3.1[5]
Drey/Laurel TxEx MM	2.5[2]	**2.4[2]**	—	Lexington TF MM	2.0[5]	**2.1[5]**	3.2[4]
SAFECO TF MM	2.5[2]	**2.4[2]**	3.4[2]	Reserve TE Interstate	2.0[5]	**2.1[5]**	3.1[4]
Portico TE MM	2.5[2]	**2.4[2]**	3.4[2]	Reserve MA TE MM	2.0[5]	**2.1[5]**	—
USAA NY MM	2.4[3]	**2.4[2]**	—	Rushmore TF MM	2.3[4]	**2.1[5]**	3.2[4]
Fidelity Spart NY MM	2.5[2]	**2.4[2]**	—	Value Line TE MM	2.0[5]	**2.0[5]**	3.1[5]
New England TE MM	2.5[2]	**2.4[2]**	3.3[2]	Fidelity MA TF MM	2.2[5]	**2.0[5]**	3.1[5]
Fidelity MI Muni MM	2.4[3]	**2.4[2]**	—	CT Daily TF (R&T)	2.2[5]	**2.0[5]**	3.0[5]
Drey-General Muni MM	2.4[3]	**2.4[2]**	3.3[2]	Dreyfus NY MM	2.1[5]	**2.0[5]**	3.0[5]

Money market funds – ranked within objective   *continued*

By 1992-1994 performance

| No-Load Fund | Total return percent with quintile ranks by objective | | | No-Load Fund | Total return percent with quintile ranks by objective | | |
	1994	Annualized 3 years	5 years		1994	Annualized 3 years	5 years
Vista NY TF MM...	2.1[5]	**2.0[5]**	—	AARP Hi Qual TF MM...	2.0[5]	**1.9[5]**	—
Fundamental TF MM...	1.7[5]	**2.0[5]**	3.2[4]	Reserve NY TE MM...	2.0[5]	**1.9[5]**	2.9[5]
Reserve CT TE MM...	2.0[5]	**2.0[5]**	2.9[5]	GIT TF MM...	1.8[5]	**1.8[5]**	2.8[5]

Money market funds – ranked within objective

By 1990-1994 performance

No-Load Fund	Total return percent with quintile ranks by objective			No-Load Fund	Total return percent with quintile ranks by objective		
	1994	Annualized 3 years	5 years		1994	Annualized 3 years	5 years
GENERAL MONEY MARKET FUNDS				Founders Money Mkt...	3.5[5]	2.9[5]	**4.3[5]**
Fidelity Spart MM...	4.1[1]	3.7[1]	**5.2[1]**	Wrkng Asst MM...	3.2[5]	2.8[5]	**4.3[5]**
Evergreen MM Tr...	4.0[1]	3.7[1]	**5.1[1]**	**GOVERNMENT MONEY MARKET FUNDS**			
Vangd MM Prime...	4.1[1]	3.6[1]	**5.0[1]**	Vangd MM Federal...	4.0[1]	3.6[1]	**4.9[1]**
Flex-Fund MM...	4.1[1]	3.6[1]	**5.0[1]**	Fidelity Spart Trsy MM...	3.7[2]	3.4[1]	**4.8[1]**
Dreyfus Wrld Dollar...	3.5[5]	3.3[2]	**5.0[1]**	Warbg Pincus Cash Res...	3.9[1]	3.4[1]	**4.8[1]**
USAA Money Mkt...	4.1[1]	3.6[1]	**5.0[1]**	Benham Gov Agcy MM...	3.8[2]	3.3[2]	**4.8[1]**
Strong Money Mkt...	4.0[1]	3.6[1]	**5.0[1]**	UST Mstr Gov MM...	3.8[1]	3.4[1]	**4.8[1]**
Kemper Money Mkt...	4.0[1]	3.5[1]	**4.9[1]**	Vangd MM Treas...	3.8[2]	3.4[1]	**4.8[1]**
Fidelity Cash MM...	4.0[2]	3.5[1]	**4.9[1]**	Galaxy Gov MM...	3.7[2]	3.4[1]	**4.7[1]**
UST Mstr Money Mkt...	3.9[2]	3.4[1]	**4.9[1]**	Dreyfus 100% US MM...	3.4[5]	3.2[2]	**4.7[1]**
Value Line Cash...	3.7[3]	3.5[1]	**4.8[1]**	CMA Gov MM‡...	3.7[2]	3.3[2]	**4.7[1]**
CMA Money Mkt‡...	3.8[2]	3.4[1]	**4.8[1]**	Babson UMB Fed MM...	3.8[2]	3.3[2]	**4.7[2]**
Merrill Lynch Rdy Asst...	3.7[3]	3.3[2]	**4.8[1]**	Legg Msn Gov MM...	3.7[2]	3.3[1]	**4.7[2]**
RMA Money Mkt‡...	3.8[2]	3.4[1]	**4.8[2]**	Fidelity Gov MM...	3.9[1]	3.3[2]	**4.6[2]**
Fremont Money Mkt...	4.0[2]	3.3[2]	**4.8[2]**	SBSF Money Mkt...	3.6[3]	3.2[3]	**4.6[2]**
Fidelity Daily MM...	3.9[2]	3.4[1]	**4.8[2]**	Drey-General Gov MM...	3.7[2]	3.3[2]	**4.6[2]**
Paine Webber Cashfund...	3.8[3]	3.4[2]	**4.8[2]**	Prudential Gov MM...	3.5[4]	3.2[3]	**4.6[2]**
Galaxy Money Mkt...	3.7[3]	3.3[2]	**4.8[2]**	Scudder Trsy MM...	3.5[4]	3.1[3]	**4.6[2]**
Active Asst MM‡...	3.9[2]	3.4[2]	**4.8[2]**	Benham Cap Presv...	3.6[3]	3.2[2]	**4.6[2]**
Prudential Moneymart...	3.8[3]	3.3[2]	**4.8[2]**	Smith Barney Gov MM...	3.6[3]	3.2[3]	**4.5[3]**
Nicholas Money Mkt...	3.9[2]	3.3[2]	**4.7[2]**	RMA Gov MM‡...	3.5[4]	3.2[3]	**4.5[3]**
Babson UMB Prime MM...	3.8[2]	3.3[2]	**4.7[2]**	Portico Gov MM...	3.7[2]	3.2[2]	**4.5[3]**
Harbor Money Mkt...	3.9[2]	3.3[3]	**4.7[2]**	CA Inv Tr-Trsy MM...	3.5[4]	3.1[3]	**4.5[3]**
Portico Money Mkt...	3.8[2]	3.3[3]	**4.7[2]**	SteinRoe Gov Res...	3.5[3]	3.1[3]	**4.5[3]**
Scudder Cash Inv Tr...	3.7[3]	3.3[3]	**4.7[2]**	Cash Equiv-Gov MM‡...	3.6[3]	3.1[4]	**4.5[3]**
Fidelity Select MM...	3.7[3]	3.3[2]	**4.7[2]**	Active Asst Gov MM‡...	3.6[3]	3.1[3]	**4.5[3]**
Legg Msn Cash Res...	3.7[4]	3.3[2]	**4.7[3]**	Highmark Gov MM...	3.5[5]	3.1[3]	**4.5[3]**
Dean Witter Liq Asst...	3.8[3]	3.3[3]	**4.7[3]**	New England Gov MM...	3.4[5]	3.1[4]	**4.5[3]**
Dreyfus Liq Asst...	3.5[4]	3.2[3]	**4.7[3]**	Dreyfus MM Instr Gov...	3.3[5]	3.1[4]	**4.5[3]**
Highmark Dvsfd MM...	3.6[4]	3.2[3]	**4.7[3]**	WPG Gov MM...	3.6[3]	3.1[4]	**4.5[3]**
New England MM...	3.5[5]	3.2[4]	**4.6[3]**	Highmark Treas MM...	3.4[5]	3.0[4]	**4.4[4]**
Nbrgr-Ber Cash Res...	3.7[3]	3.2[3]	**4.6[3]**	Blanchard Trsy MM...	3.3[5]	3.4[1]	**4.4[4]**
Bartlett Cash Res...	3.6[4]	3.3[3]	**4.6[3]**	Drey/Laurel Gov MM...	3.6[3]	3.2[3]	**4.4[4]**
Smith Barney Cash MM...	3.7[3]	3.2[3]	**4.6[3]**	Kidder Pbdy Gov MM‡...	3.5[4]	3.1[4]	**4.4[4]**
SteinRoe Cash Res...	3.7[4]	3.2[3]	**4.6[3]**	Short Tm Inc-Gov(R&T)...	3.4[5]	3.1[4]	**4.4[4]**
Price, Rowe Prime Res...	3.7[3]	3.2[3]	**4.6[3]**	Price, Rowe Trsy MM...	3.5[4]	3.1[4]	**4.4[4]**
Drey-General MM...	3.5[5]	3.2[4]	**4.6[3]**	Crabbe Hsn Gov MM...	3.6[3]	3.1[4]	**4.4[4]**
SAFECO Money Mkt...	3.5[4]	3.1[4]	**4.6[3]**	Nbrgr-Ber Gov MM...	3.4[5]	3.1[4]	**4.4[4]**
Columbia Daily Inc...	3.7[4]	3.1[4]	**4.6[4]**	US Trsy MM...	3.2[5]	2.9[5]	**4.4[4]**
Smith Barney Ret MM...	3.7[4]	3.2[4]	**4.6[4]**	Benham Cap Presv II...	3.5[4]	2.9[5]	**4.3[5]**
Short Tm Inc-MM(R&T)...	3.5[5]	3.2[4]	**4.6[4]**	Rushmore Gov MM...	3.6[3]	3.0[5]	**4.3[5]**
Kidder Pbdy Cash Res‡...	3.6[4]	3.1[4]	**4.5[4]**	Alliance Gov Res...	3.3[5]	2.9[5]	**4.3[5]**
Calvert Scl Inv MM...	3.6[4]	3.1[4]	**4.5[4]**	Gradison Gov MM...	3.5[4]	3.0[4]	**4.3[5]**
Cash Equiv-MM‡...	3.6[4]	3.1[4]	**4.5[4]**	Selected Daily Gov MM...	3.5[4]	2.9[5]	**4.3[5]**
MIM Money Mkt...	3.2[5]	3.1[4]	**4.5[4]**	Babson Fed MM...	3.3[5]	2.9[5]	**4.3[5]**
Invesco Cash Res...	3.7[3]	3.1[4]	**4.5[4]**	Reserve Gov MM...	3.4[5]	2.9[5]	**4.3[5]**
Alliance Money Res...	3.3[5]	3.0[4]	**4.5[4]**	Dean Witter Gov MM...	3.2[5]	2.8[5]	**4.2[5]**
Managers Money Mkt...	3.6[4]	3.2[3]	**4.5[4]**	GIT MM Account...	3.1[5]	2.7[5]	**4.1[5]**
Reserve Primary MM...	4.0[1]	3.2[4]	**4.5[4]**	**TAX-FREE MONEY MARKET FUNDS**			
Twentieth Cent Cash...	3.7[4]	3.0[5]	**4.5[4]**	Strong Muni MM...	2.9[1]	2.9[1]	**4.0[1]**
Alliance Cap Res...	3.4[5]	3.0[5]	**4.5[4]**	USAA TE MM...	2.6[1]	2.7[1]	**3.8[1]**
Federated Prime MM...	3.8[3]	3.1[4]	**4.5[5]**	Evergreen TE MM...	2.8[1]	2.8[1]	**3.8[1]**
Wayne Hummer MM...	3.5[4]	3.0[5]	**4.4[5]**	Fidelity Spart CA MM...	2.8[1]	2.7[1]	**3.7[1]**
Fortis Money Mkt...	3.5[5]	2.9[5]	**4.4[5]**	Vangd Muni MM...	2.8[1]	2.7[1]	**3.7[1]**
Liquid Cap Inc MM...	3.5[5]	3.0[5]	**4.4[5]**	Drey-General CA MM...	2.6[2]	2.6[1]	**3.7[1]**
Babson Prime MM...	3.4[5]	3.0[5]	**4.4[5]**	Fidelity Spart PA MM...	2.6[1]	2.6[1]	**3.7[1]**
AARP Hi Qual MM...	3.5[5]	2.8[5]	**4.3[5]**	WPG TF MM...	2.6[1]	2.6[1]	**3.6[1]**
Lexington MM...	3.4[5]	2.9[5]	**4.3[5]**	Vangd PA TF MM...	2.7[1]	2.6[1]	**3.6[1]**
Bull & Bear Dollar...	3.4[5]	3.0[5]	**4.3[5]**	Drey/Laurel CA MM...	2.5[2]	2.6[1]	**3.6[1]**

Money market funds – ranked within objective   *continued*

By 1990-1994 performance

No-Load Fund	Total return percent with quintile ranks by objective			No-Load Fund	Total return percent with quintile ranks by objective		
	1994	Annualized 3 years	5 years		1994	Annualized 3 years	5 years
Vangd NJ TF MM...	2.6[1]	2.6[1]	**3.6[1]**	Fidelity CA TF MM...	2.4[3]	2.3[3]	**3.2[3]**
Vangd CA MM...	2.7[1]	2.7[1]	**3.6[1]**	RMA TF MM‡...	2.3[4]	2.2[4]	**3.2[3]**
Fidelity OH Muni MM...	2.5[2]	2.5[2]	**3.6[1]**	Highmark CA TF MM...	2.4[3]	2.3[3]	**3.2[3]**
USAA CA MM...	2.6[1]	2.6[1]	**3.5[1]**	Kidder Pbdy TE MM‡...	2.2[4]	2.2[4]	**3.2[4]**
Dreyfus NJ MM...	2.5[2]	2.4[2]	**3.5[1]**	Nbrgr-Ber Muni MM...	2.3[4]	2.2[5]	**3.2[4]**
Fidelity TE MM...	2.5[2]	2.5[2]	**3.5[1]**	Dreyfus CA TF MM...	2.3[4]	2.3[3]	**3.2[4]**
Daily TF (R&T)...	2.6[2]	2.5[2]	**3.5[2]**	Alliance Muni MM...	2.2[5]	2.2[4]	**3.2[4]**
Drey/Laurel NY MM...	2.2[5]	2.4[2]	**3.4[2]**	Dean Witter TF MM...	2.3[4]	2.2[4]	**3.2[4]**
SAFECO TF MM...	2.5[2]	2.4[2]	**3.4[2]**	CA Daily TF (R&T)...	2.4[3]	2.3[3]	**3.2[4]**
Drey-General NY MM...	2.5[2]	2.4[2]	**3.4[2]**	Benham CA TF MM...	2.4[3]	2.3[3]	**3.2[4]**
CA Inv Tr-CA MM...	2.5[2]	2.4[2]	**3.4[2]**	SteinRoe Muni MM...	2.3[4]	2.2[4]	**3.2[4]**
Fidelity CT TF MM...	2.3[4]	2.2[3]	**3.4[2]**	Scudder TF MM...	2.3[4]	2.2[4]	**3.2[4]**
Portico TE MM...	2.5[2]	2.4[2]	**3.4[2]**	Lexington TF MM...	2.0[5]	2.1[5]	**3.2[4]**
Drey-General Muni MM...	2.4[3]	2.4[2]	**3.3[2]**	Rushmore TF MM...	2.3[4]	2.1[5]	**3.2[4]**
New England TE MM...	2.5[2]	2.4[2]	**3.3[2]**	Fundamental TF MM...	1.7[5]	2.0[5]	**3.2[4]**
Highmark TF MM...	2.3[4]	2.3[3]	**3.3[2]**	CMA CA MM‡...	2.3[3]	2.2[4]	**3.1[4]**
CMA TE MM‡...	2.4[3]	2.3[3]	**3.3[2]**	Scudder CA TF MM...	2.4[3]	2.3[3]	**3.1[4]**
Fidelity NJ TF MM...	2.3[3]	2.3[3]	**3.3[2]**	Reserve TE Interstate...	2.0[5]	2.1[5]	**3.1[4]**
MI Daily TF (R&T)...	2.3[3]	2.2[4]	**3.3[2]**	Value Line TE MM...	2.0[5]	2.0[5]	**3.1[5]**
Babson TF MM...	2.4[3]	2.3[2]	**3.3[2]**	Fidelity NY TF MM...	2.3[3]	2.2[4]	**3.1[5]**
Cash Equiv-TE MM‡...	2.4[3]	2.3[3]	**3.3[2]**	Legg Msn TE MM...	2.3[4]	2.1[5]	**3.1[5]**
Drey/Laurel TxFr MM...	2.5[2]	2.3[3]	**3.3[3]**	Invesco TF MM...	2.2[5]	2.2[4]	**3.1[5]**
Federated Muni Cash...	2.2[5]	2.2[4]	**3.3[3]**	Fidelity MA TF MM...	2.2[5]	2.0[5]	**3.1[5]**
Dreyfus Muni MM...	2.4[3]	2.3[3]	**3.3[3]**	Price, Rowe CA MM...	2.4[3]	2.2[4]	**3.1[5]**
Drey/Laurel MA MM...	2.3[4]	2.2[5]	**3.3[3]**	CMA NY MM‡...	2.3[4]	2.1[5]	**3.0[5]**
Nuveen TF Res...	2.3[4]	2.2[4]	**3.3[3]**	Price, Rowe NY MM...	2.3[4]	2.2[4]	**3.0[5]**
Benham Nat TF MM...	2.3[3]	2.2[4]	**3.3[3]**	Scudder NY TF MM...	2.2[4]	2.2[4]	**3.0[5]**
Active Asst TF MM‡...	2.4[3]	2.3[3]	**3.3[3]**	Warbg Pincus NY MM...	2.2[4]	2.1[5]	**3.0[5]**
Smith Barney TF MM...	2.4[3]	2.3[3]	**3.3[3]**	Dreyfus NY MM...	2.1[5]	2.0[5]	**3.0[5]**
Prudential TF MM...	2.3[4]	2.3[3]	**3.3[3]**	Kidder Pbdy CA TF MM‡...	2.1[5]	2.1[5]	**3.0[5]**
Galaxy TE MM...	2.3[4]	2.2[4]	**3.3[3]**	CT Daily TF (R&T)...	2.2[5]	2.0[5]	**3.0[5]**
Babson UMB TF MM...	2.4[3]	2.3[3]	**3.3[3]**	Reserve NY TE MM...	2.0[5]	1.9[5]	**2.9[5]**
Price, Rowe TE MM...	2.5[2]	2.3[3]	**3.2[3]**	Reserve CT TE MM...	2.0[5]	2.0[5]	**2.9[5]**
NY Daily TF Inc(R&T)...	2.3[4]	2.3[3]	**3.2[3]**	GIT TF MM...	1.8[5]	1.8[5]	**2.8[5]**

CHAPTER 10

Additional funds available no-load through discount brokers

Arranged in alphabetical order

No-Load Fund	Objective	\multicolumn{10}{c}{Total return percent}										Annualized	
		1985	1986	1987	1988	1989	1990	1991	1992	1993	1994	3 yrs.	5 yrs.
Accessor Growth...	growth	—	—	—	—	—	—	—	—	14.2	4.0	—	—
Accessor Inter Fix Inc...	fix-inc	—	—	—	—	—	—	—	—	9.5	-5.2	—	—
Accessor Int'l Eqty...	int'l	—	—	—	—	—	—	—	—	—	—	—	—
Accessor Int'l Fix Inc...	fix-inc	—	—	—	—	—	—	—	—	—	—	—	—
Accessor Mrtg Sec...	fix-inc	—	—	—	—	—	—	—	—	7.3	-1.6	—	—
Accessor Muni Inter...	tax-free	—	—	—	—	—	—	—	—	—	—	—	—
Accessor Sm Cap SC...	agg gr	—	—	—	—	—	—	—	—	14.4	-4.1	—	—
Accessor S-I Fix Inc...	fix-inc	—	—	—	—	—	—	—	—	5.6	-1.4	—	—
Accessor Val and Inc...	gr-inc	—	—	—	—	—	—	—	—	14.7	-1.9	—	—
Alger Balanced...	income	—	—	—	—	—	—	—	—	7.7	-6.6	—	—
Alger Growth...	growth	—	—	-0.4	6.4	35.1	2.2	43.2	11.1	20.3	-1.6	9.6	14.0
Alger Inc & Gro...	gr-inc	—	—	0.5	16.0	25.3	-7.8	23.1	7.1	7.6	-8.1	1.9	3.8
Alger Lvgd AllCap...	agg gr	—	—	—	—	—	—	—	—	—	-2.2	—	—
Alger MidCap Gro...	growth	—	—	—	—	—	—	—	—	—	0.6	—	—
Alger Sm Cap SC...	agg gr	—	—	-1.5	17.5	64.5	6.7	54.5	4.0	12.8	-4.6	3.8	13.0
BT Inv Eqty App...	growth	—	—	—	—	—	—	—	—	—	3.5	—	—
BT Inv Glob Hi Yld...	fix-inc	—	—	—	—	—	—	—	—	—	-3.1	—	—
BT Inv Latin Amer...	int'l	—	—	—	—	—	—	—	—	—	-10.8	—	—
BT Inv Lifecycle Lng...	growth	—	—	—	—	—	—	—	—	—	-2.9	—	—
BT Inv Lifecycle Mid...	gr-inc	—	—	—	—	—	—	—	—	—	-3.4	—	—
BT Inv Lifecycle Sht...	income	—	—	—	—	—	—	—	—	—	-2.8	—	—
BT Inv Pacific Bas...	int'l	—	—	—	—	—	—	—	—	—	16.9	—	—
BT Inv Sm Cap SC...	agg gr	—	—	—	—	—	—	—	—	—	19.3	—	—
Burnham Fund...	gr-inc	32.1	21.8	6.7	11.9	22.8	-1.8	18.0	7.7	9.3	-1.8	5.0	6.0
Calvert AZ Inter...	tax-free	—	—	—	—	—	—	—	—	—	—	—	—
Calvert CA Inter...	tax-free	—	—	—	—	—	—	—	—	8.9	-2.6	—	—
Calvert FL Inter...	tax-free	—	—	—	—	—	—	—	—	—	—	—	—
Calvert Income...	fix-inc	24.0	11.2	1.9	10.3	15.1	4.4	18.2	7.4	12.3	-6.2	4.2	6.9
Calvert MD Inter...	tax-free	—	—	—	—	—	—	—	—	—	-3.0	—	—
Calvert MI Inter...	tax-free	—	—	—	—	—	—	—	—	—	-2.5	—	—
Calvert Nat Muni Inter...	tax-free	—	—	—	—	—	—	—	—	9.5	-1.2	—	—
Calvert NY Inter...	tax-free	—	—	—	—	—	—	—	—	—	-2.3	—	—
Calvert PA Inter...	tax-free	—	—	—	—	—	—	—	—	—	—	—	—
Calvert Scl Inv Bd...	fix-inc	—	—	—	8.0	13.5	8.3	15.8	6.7	11.8	-5.3	4.1	7.2
Calvert Scl Inv Eqty...	growth	—	—	—	14.8	27.4	-4.9	21.9	8.4	2.1	-12.1	-0.9	2.5
Calvert Scl Inv Mgd Gro...	growth	26.9	18.1	5.0	10.7	18.7	1.8	17.8	7.5	5.9	-4.7	2.7	5.4
Calvert Strat Gro...	growth	—	—	—	—	—	—	—	—	—	—	—	—
Calvert TF Rsv Ltd...	tax-free	8.5	8.5	3.5	6.8	7.1	6.5	6.6	5.0	4.0	2.4	3.8	4.9
Calvert TF Rsv LT...	tax-free	18.4	17.4	-3.0	10.3	9.8	4.8	11.8	7.6	11.1	-2.3	5.3	6.5
Calvert TF VT ...	tax-free	—	—	—	—	—	—	—	7.6	10.9	-2.9	5.1	—
Calvert US Gov...	fix-inc	—	—	1.7	8.1	13.8	7.9	12.7	5.4	8.7	-5.1	2.8	5.7
Calvert VA Inter...	tax-free	—	—	—	—	—	—	—	—	—	-2.1	—	—
Calvert Wrld Glob Eq...	global	—	—	—	—	—	—	—	—	25.8	-2.7	—	—
Cowen Inc & Gro...	growth	—	—	-4.6	17.5	23.6	-8.6	26.5	12.3	9.3	-6.3	4.7	5.8
Cowen Opportunity...	agg gr	—	—	—	—	16.4	6.1	45.8	4.9	31.6	3.9	12.8	17.3
Delwre Decatur Inc...	income	26.4	21.7	3.3	19.9	21.5	-12.3	21.8	8.8	15.4	-0.8	7.6	5.9
Delwre Decatur Tot Ret...	gr-inc	—	—	-4.0	25.8	26.6	-8.3	20.4	8.2	14.9	-0.5	7.3	6.4
Delwre Delcap...	agg gr	—	—	17.1	17.8	33.9	-3.5	42.3	1.9	11.9	-5.3	2.6	8.2
Delwre Int'l Eqty...	int'l	—	—	—	—	—	—	—	-1.5	27.8	1.6	8.6	—
Delwre Trend SC...	agg gr	28.0	5.3	-7.8	26.8	49.7	-24.6	74.5	22.4	22.4	-10.0	10.5	12.1

Additional funds available no-load through discount brokers _continued_

Arranged in alphabetical order

No-Load Fund	Objective	Total return percent										Annualized	
		1985	1986	1987	1988	1989	1990	1991	1992	1993	1994	3 yrs.	5 yrs.
Enterprise Cap App	agg gr	—	—	—	5.9	34.3	3.9	59.0	5.8	5.7	-3.5	2.6	12.3
Enterprise Gov Sec	fix-inc	—	—	—	4.5	10.0	9.3	12.7	9.9	9.3	-7.8	3.5	6.4
Enterprise Gro & Inc	gr-inc	—	—	—	13.6	17.6	-8.2	23.6	8.5	13.5	-0.5	7.0	6.8
Enterprise Growth	growth	25.1	12.6	11.5	12.3	23.0	-2.3	41.8	6.5	10.6	-1.0	5.2	10.1
Enterprise Hi Yld Bd	fix-inc	—	—	—	12.1	-0.7	-11.6	33.0	16.7	17.6	0.0	11.1	10.0
Enterprise Int'l Gro	int'l	—	—	—	7.6	17.2	-15.1	12.9	-0.9	36.1	-2.8	9.4	4.7
Enterprise Sm Co SC	agg gr	—	—	—	—	—	—	—	—	—	0.3	—	—
Enterprise TE Inc	tax-free	—	—	—	10.9	8.7	5.8	11.0	7.9	10.8	-5.7	4.1	5.8
Federated MI Inter	tax-free	—	—	—	—	—	—	—	8.0	11.9	-4.7	4.8	—
Federated PA Muni	tax-free	—	—	—	—	—	—	11.4	9.2	12.3	-6.5	4.7	—
Fortress Adj Rate Gov	fix-inc	—	—	—	—	—	—	—	4.6	3.5	-0.3	2.6	—
Fortress Bond	fix-inc	—	—	—	9.1	1.3	-9.6	44.7	15.9	16.3	-3.3	9.2	11.3
Fortress CA Muni Inc	tax-free	—	—	—	—	—	—	—	—	14.9	-10.4	—	—
Fortress Muni Inc	tax-free	—	—	—	12.2	10.8	6.6	10.9	8.0	11.1	-5.8	4.2	6.0
Fortress NY Inc	tax-free	—	—	—	—	—	—	—	—	14.0	-9.9	—	—
Fortress OH Inc	tax-free	—	—	—	—	—	—	11.2	8.4	13.3	-6.4	4.7	—
Fortress Utility	income	—	—	—	13.7	26.1	0.9	25.9	8.9	15.2	-8.0	4.9	8.0
FPA Capital	growth	28.9	12.6	11.0	18.1	25.3	-13.8	64.5	21.6	16.7	10.4	16.1	17.3
FPA New Income	fix-inc	21.3	11.4	7.7	8.5	12.2	8.4	18.7	11.2	10.2	1.5	7.5	9.8
FPA Perennial	gr-inc	20.4	10.2	-1.1	19.9	25.8	1.0	21.7	13.1	4.6	0.0	5.8	7.8
Frank/Temp German Gov	fix-inc	—	—	—	—	—	—	—	—	5.6	9.6	—	—
Frank/Temp Glob Curr	fix-inc	—	—	22.6	2.8	5.0	13.8	6.7	3.6	6.0	8.1	5.9	7.6
Frank/Temp Hard Curr	fix-inc	—	—	—	—	—	19.4	7.4	2.2	4.6	15.1	7.2	9.6
Frank/Temp Hi Inc Curr	fix-inc	—	—	—	—	—	18.0	10.8	-2.9	-2.6	10.2	1.4	6.4
GAM Europe	int'l	—	—	—	—	—	—	-0.7	-4.9	22.6	-3.1	4.2	—
GAM Global	global	—	—	-2.5	25.0	24.2	-11.3	10.6	-4.4	74.7	-16.2	11.9	6.6
GAM International	int'l	—	47.5	12.1	21.5	22.5	-7.3	15.6	3.1	80.0	-10.2	18.5	12.3
GAM Japan Capital	int'l	—	—	—	—	—	—	—	—	—	—	—	—
GAM North America	growth	—	—	—	—	—	—	30.7	2.4	-2.1	3.0	1.1	—
GAM Pacific Basin	int'l	—	—	—	23.2	43.3	-8.2	16.7	-0.6	53.3	7.5	17.9	11.9
Govett Dvlp Mkts Bd	fix-inc	—	—	—	—	—	—	—	—	—	-14.5	—	—
Govett Emg Mkts	int'l	—	—	—	—	—	—	—	—	79.7	-12.7	—	—
Govett Glob Gov	fix-inc	—	—	—	—	—	—	—	—	16.8	-9.2	—	—
Govett Int'l Eqty	int'l	—	—	—	—	—	—	—	—	54.5	-8.4	—	—
Govett Latin Amer	int'l	—	—	—	—	—	—	—	—	—	—	—	—
Govett Pacific Strat	int'l	—	—	—	—	—	—	—	—	—	—	—	—
Govett Small Co SC	agg gr	—	—	—	—	—	—	—	—	58.5	28.7	—	—
Hanover Blue Chip	growth	—	—	—	—	—	—	—	—	—	-3.9	—	—
Hanover Small Cap SC	agg gr	—	—	—	—	—	—	—	—	—	-9.4	—	—
Hanover ST US Gov	fix-inc	—	—	—	—	—	—	—	—	—	0.1	—	—
Hanover US Gov	fix-inc	—	—	—	—	—	—	—	—	—	-4.1	—	—
Israel Growth	int'l	—	—	—	—	—	—	—	—	—	—	—	—
Ivy Int'l	int'l	—	—	19.6	29.7	28.3	-13.0	16.9	0.1	48.3	3.9	15.5	9.4
JPM Adv Asia Gro	int'l	—	—	—	—	—	—	—	—	—	—	—	—
JPM Adv Emg Mkts	int'l	—	—	—	—	—	—	—	—	—	—	—	—
JPM Adv Europe	int'l	—	—	—	—	—	—	—	—	—	—	—	—
JPM Adv Int'l Eq	int'l	—	—	—	—	—	—	—	—	—	—	—	—
JPM Adv Int'l Fixed	fix-inc	—	—	—	—	—	—	—	—	—	—	—	—
JPM Adv Japan	int'l	—	—	—	—	—	—	—	—	—	—	—	—
JPM Adv US Eqty	growth	—	—	—	—	—	—	—	—	—	—	—	—

No-Load Fund	Objective	Total return percent										Annualized	
		1985	1986	1987	1988	1989	1990	1991	1992	1993	1994	3 yrs.	5 yrs.
JPM Adv US Fixed...	fix-inc	—	—	—	—	—	—	—	—	—	—	—	—
JPM Adv US Sm Co...	agg gr	—	—	—	—	—	—	—	—	—	—	—	—
Keeley Sm Cap Val SC...	growth	—	—	—	—	—	—	—	—	—	-8.7	—	—
Laidlaw Covenant...	gr-inc	—	—	—	—	—	—	—	—	—	3.0	—	—
Lexington Strat Invest...	prec met	-29.8	28.5	23.6	-43.0	61.2	-42.4	-18.9	-60.7	269.8	11.3	17.4	-5.5
Lexington Strat Silver...	prec met	-12.4	-9.7	16.2	-15.9	16.1	-32.1	-14.5	-11.5	76.5	-8.4	12.7	-3.6
Liberty Equity Inc...	gr-inc	—	—	-9.2	36.1	8.4	-12.5	42.2	9.8	20.2	-3.8	8.3	9.6
Liberty High Inc...	fix-inc	21.7	12.5	0.0	15.1	-0.4	-12.7	60.6	17.2	17.2	-1.7	10.5	13.6
Liberty Muni Sec...	tax-free	18.3	20.4	-0.1	11.3	10.5	5.8	12.5	8.3	10.2	-3.8	4.7	6.5
Liberty Utility...	income	—	—	—	15.1	23.6	2.0	25.8	9.1	15.1	-8.0	5.0	8.2
MAS Equity...	growth	30.9	21.1	3.6	13.1	28.3	-0.1	40.0	7.7	6.7	0.5	4.9	10.1
MAS Fix Inc...	fix-inc	23.6	16.3	3.4	8.8	11.1	7.2	21.0	8.6	13.8	-5.4	5.4	8.7
MAS Ltd Dur...	fix-inc	—	—	—	—	—	—	—	—	—	-0.1	—	—
MAS Sm Cap Val ...	growth	—	—	-18.4	21.3	17.6	-16.6	63.5	22.7	21.1	2.2	15.0	15.7
MAS Value...	gr-inc	29.3	23.8	-5.0	22.2	20.7	-6.1	36.1	14.7	14.3	3.5	10.7	11.6
Monitrend Gaming/Leis...	sector	—	—	—	—	—	—	—	—	—	—	—	—
Monitrend Gold...	prec met	—	—	—	—	14.5	-13.9	-7.0	-29.1	20.7	-50.3	-24.8	-19.4
Monitrend Gov Inc...	fix-inc	—	—	0.9	2.0	8.4	4.2	9.5	-2.6	12.3	-3.4	1.9	3.8
Monitrend Growth...	growth	—	—	—	—	—	—	—	—	3.2	-19.9	—	—
Monitrend PIA Adj Rate...	fix-inc	—	—	—	—	—	—	—	—	—	—	—	—
Monitrend Summtn Idx...	gr-inc	—	—	—	—	14.7	-1.9	9.1	-8.2	-5.3	-2.0	-5.2	-1.8
Monitrend Technology...	sector	—	—	—	—	—	—	—	—	—	-3.5	—	—
Newport Tiger...	int'l	—	—	—	—	—	-15.1	26.0	22.0	75.4	-12.0	23.5	15.0
Pacific Adv Balanced...	income	—	—	—	—	—	—	—	—	—	-2.4	—	—
Pacific Adv Gov Sec...	fix-inc	—	—	—	—	—	—	—	—	—	-0.2	—	—
Pacific Hzn Agg Gro...	agg gr	37.6	20.1	11.9	0.4	37.2	5.1	70.8	-2.0	7.3	-11.5	-2.4	10.8
Pacific Hzn CA TE...	tax-free	18.4	18.4	-1.4	8.6	9.3	6.2	11.1	8.6	12.5	-6.1	4.7	6.2
Pacific Hzn Cap Inc...	income	—	—	—	15.2	27.9	-4.3	38.3	21.3	22.7	-5.9	11.9	13.1
Pacific Hzn US Gov...	fix-inc	—	—	—	—	12.8	10.3	15.1	7.7	6.9	-3.9	3.4	7.0
Parnassus ...	growth	—	2.4	-8.0	42.4	2.8	-21.2	52.6	36.8	17.3	12.0	21.6	16.7
PIMCO Balanced...	gr-inc	—	—	—	—	—	—	—	—	5.7	-1.0	—	—
PIMCO Blair Emg Mkts...	int'l	—	—	—	—	—	—	—	—	—	-7.8	—	—
PIMCO Blair Int'l Act...	int'l	—	—	—	—	—	—	—	—	—	7.1	—	—
PIMCO Cadnc Cap App...	agg gr	—	—	—	—	—	—	—	7.5	17.6	-4.3	6.6	—
PIMCO Cadnc Micro Cap SC...	agg gr	—	—	—	—	—	—	—	—	—	1.0	—	—
PIMCO Cadnc MidCap...	growth	—	—	—	—	—	—	—	9.2	15.8	-2.4	7.3	—
PIMCO Cadnc Sm Cap SC...	agg gr	—	—	—	—	—	—	—	16.7	24.4	1.0	13.6	—
PIMCO Foreign Bd...	fix-inc	—	—	—	—	—	—	—	—	16.1	-7.3	—	—
PIMCO Global Bd...	fix-inc	—	—	—	—	—	—	—	—	—	-1.6	—	—
PIMCO Growth Stk...	agg gr	—	—	—	12.3	25.7	-0.3	36.9	3.9	6.0	1.5	3.8	8.8
PIMCO Hi Yld Bd...	fix-inc	—	—	—	—	—	—	—	—	18.7	2.4	—	—
PIMCO Low Dur II...	fix-inc	—	—	—	—	—	—	—	6.2	6.7	0.3	4.4	—
PIMCO LT US Gov...	fix-inc	—	—	—	—	—	—	—	11.9	18.6	-7.4	7.1	—
PIMCO Mgd Bd & Inc...	fix-inc	—	—	—	—	—	—	—	9.4	10.9	-2.2	5.9	—
PIMCO NFJ Div Low P/E...	gr-inc	—	—	—	—	—	—	—	13.1	16.4	-4.1	8.1	—
PIMCO NFJ Eqty Inc...	gr-inc	—	—	—	—	—	—	—	14.6	8.5	-1.6	6.9	—
PIMCO NFJ Sm Cap Val SC...	growth	—	—	—	—	—	—	—	18.7	13.8	-3.7	9.2	—
PIMCO Prmtrc Enhncd Eq...	gr-inc	—	—	—	—	—	—	—	6.6	3.8	-0.5	3.2	—
PIMCO Prmtrc Int'l Eq...	int'l	—	—	—	—	—	—	10.4	-14.2	30.6	5.5	5.7	—
PIMCO Stock Plus...	gr-inc	—	—	—	—	—	—	—	—	—	3.0	—	—

No-Load Fund	Objective	Total return percent										Annualized	
		1985	1986	1987	1988	1989	1990	1991	1992	1993	1994	3 yrs.	5 yrs.
PIMCO Tot Ret III...	fix-inc	—	—	—	—	—	—	—	8.7	13.1	-3.4	5.9	—
PIMCO Util Stock...	income	—	—	—	—	—	—	—	—	—	—	—	—
Progressive Value...	growth	—	—	—	—	—	—	—	—	—	-11.3	—	—
Rainier Blncd...	income	—	—	—	—	—	—	—	—	—	—	—	—
Rainier Core Eqty...	growth	—	—	—	—	—	—	—	—	—	—	—	—
Rainier Inter Fix Inc...	fix-inc	—	—	—	—	—	—	—	—	—	—	—	—
Rainier Sm/Mid Cap...	agg gr	—	—	—	—	—	—	—	—	—	—	—	—
Rea-Graham Blncd...	global	29.6	10.4	-0.3	11.0	7.9	-5.7	14.7	4.2	0.2	-5.3	-0.3	1.4
Regis Acdn Emg Mkts...	int'l	—	—	—	—	—	—	—	—	—	-2.7	—	—
Regis Acdn Int'l Eqty...	int'l	—	—	—	—	—	—	—	—	—	6.8	—	—
Regis ICM Equity...	gr-inc	—	—	—	—	—	—	—	—	—	0.6	—	—
Regis Sirach Fix Inc...	fix-inc	—	—	—	—	—	—	—	—	—	-3.9	—	—
Regis Sirach Growth...	growth	—	—	—	—	—	—	—	—	—	-7.5	—	—
Regis Sirach ST Res...	fix-inc	—	—	—	—	—	—	—	—	—	3.8	—	—
Regis Sirach Str Blncd...	income	—	—	—	—	—	—	—	—	—	-6.9	—	—
Regis TS&W Eqty...	gr-inc	—	—	—	—	—	—	—	—	12.8	-0.6	—	—
Regis TS&W Fix Inc...	fix-inc	—	—	—	—	—	—	—	—	9.2	-4.2	—	—
Regis TS&W Int'l Eqty...	int'l	—	—	—	—	—	—	—	—	32.7	-0.8	—	—
SEI Bond...	fix-inc	—	—	—	12.6	17.5	5.5	17.4	7.7	15.1	-6.3	5.1	7.5
SEI Cash GNMA ...	fix-inc	—	—	—	8.0	14.0	10.4	15.9	7.3	6.6	-3.4	3.4	7.2
SEI Cash Inter Gov...	fix-inc	—	—	—	5.4	11.5	9.5	13.7	6.4	7.2	-2.7	3.5	6.7
SEI Cash ST Gov...	fix-inc	—	—	—	5.8	9.9	9.1	11.2	5.4	4.8	0.3	3.5	6.1
SEI Eqty Cap App...	growth	—	—	—	—	35.5	0.0	35.1	7.7	9.2	-7.5	2.8	8.0
SEI Eqty Inc ...	gr-inc	—	—	—	—	25.1	-8.9	30.6	10.0	13.2	-0.2	7.5	8.1
SEI Eqty Sm Cap SC...	agg gr	—	—	—	—	—	—	—	—	13.3	1.7	—	—
SEI Index:Bond...	fix-inc	—	—	1.4	7.0	13.9	8.3	13.5	7.1	9.3	-3.2	4.3	6.9
SEI Index:S&P 500...	gr-inc	—	18.0	4.1	15.3	31.6	-3.2	29.9	7.4	9.8	1.0	6.0	8.4
SEI Inter Fixed...	fix-inc	—	—	—	7.1	11.5	7.3	15.2	6.0	8.8	-4.9	3.1	6.3
SEI Inter Muni...	tax-free	—	—	—	—	—	6.9	8.7	7.3	9.2	-3.0	4.3	5.7
SEI Int'l Tr ...	int'l	—	—	—	—	—	-13.5	10.0	-2.9	22.8	0.0	6.0	2.5
SEI Lrg Cap Val...	gr-inc	—	—	—	22.4	19.3	-5.3	26.8	7.3	2.5	-3.8	1.9	4.9
SEI MidCap Gr...	agg gr	—	—	—	—	—	—	—	—	—	-10.8	—	—
SEI PA Muni ...	tax-free	—	—	—	—	—	6.1	10.5	7.1	8.5	-2.0	4.4	5.9
SoGen Gold...	prec met	—	—	—	—	—	—	—	—	—	-0.8	—	—
SoGen Int'l ...	int'l	32.8	25.1	13.8	14.2	17.2	-1.3	17.7	8.4	26.2	2.5	11.9	10.3
SoGen Overseas...	int'l	—	—	—	—	—	—	—	—	—	7.8	—	—
Solon SDGF 1 Yr...	fix-inc	—	—	—	—	—	—	—	—	—	—	—	—
Solon SDGF 3 Yr...	fix-inc	—	—	—	—	—	—	—	—	—	—	—	—
Stagecoach Asst Allc...	gr-inc	—	—	8.5	9.8	11.8	7.7	15.2	13.4	14.9	-2.8	8.2	9.5
Stagecoach Lfpth 2000...	income	—	—	—	—	—	—	—	—	—	—	—	—
Stagecoach Lfpth 2010...	gr-inc	—	—	—	—	—	—	—	—	—	—	—	—
Stagecoach Lfpth 2020...	growth	—	—	—	—	—	—	—	—	—	—	—	—
Stagecoach Lfpth 2030...	growth	—	—	—	—	—	—	—	—	—	—	—	—
Stagecoach Lfpth 2040...	growth	—	—	—	—	—	—	—	—	—	—	—	—
UST Mstr Age/Amer...	growth	—	—	—	—	—	—	—	—	6.4	-2.9	—	—
UST Mstr Bus/Indust...	growth	—	—	—	—	—	—	—	—	40.0	2.6	—	—
UST Mstr Comm/Enter...	growth	—	—	—	—	—	—	—	—	38.2	0.9	—	—
UST Mstr Early Life...	agg gr	—	—	—	—	—	—	—	—	27.9	5.3	—	—
UST Mstr Emg Amer...	agg gr	—	—	—	—	—	—	—	—	39.7	-10.6	—	—
UST Mstr Environment...	sector	—	—	—	—	—	—	—	—	-7.2	-6.4	—	—

No-Load Fund	Objective	Total return percent										Annualized	
		1985	1986	1987	1988	1989	1990	1991	1992	1993	1994	3 yrs.	5 yrs.
UST Mstr Equity...	growth	—	17.5	-4.9	19.0	27.8	-12.3	34.5	16.6	16.3	0.2	10.8	9.9
UST Mstr Glob Comp...	global	—	—	—	—	—	—	—	—	16.4	-1.6	—	—
UST Mstr Inc & Gro...	gr-inc	—	—	—	24.0	22.4	-18.2	26.4	20.4	19.4	-4.3	11.2	7.3
UST Mstr Inter Mgd Inc...	fix-inc	—	—	—	—	—	—	—	—	8.4	-3.7	—	—
UST Mstr Inter TE...	tax-free	—	—	7.1	9.0	15.8	8.6	16.7	5.8	12.6	-5.5	4.0	7.4
UST Mstr Int'l...	int'l	—	17.8	4.6	7.0	8.7	6.4	10.2	8.5	10.8	-4.2	4.8	6.2
UST Mstr LT Energy...	sector	—	—	—	13.8	23.0	-9.4	5.9	-9.4	36.5	-2.0	6.6	3.1
UST Mstr LT TE...	tax-free	—	—	—	—	—	—	—	—	14.7	-2.7	—	—
UST Mstr Mgd Inc...	fix-inc	—	—	9.4	12.8	11.8	6.9	12.7	10.0	15.8	-5.8	6.3	7.7
UST Mstr NY Inter TE...	tax-free	—	—	—	—	—	9.1	6.5	9.3	-4.2	3.7	—
UST Mstr Pac/Asia...	int'l	—	—	—	—	—	—	—	—	66.3	-14.7	—	—
UST Mstr Pan Europe...	int'l	—	—	—	—	—	—	—	—	17.3	0.0	—	—
UST Mstr Productivity...	growth	—	—	—	—	—	—	—	—	10.3	0.7	—	—
UST Mstr ST Gov...	fix-inc	—	—	—	—	—	—	—	—	4.3	1.1	—	—
UST Mstr ST TE...	tax-free	—	—	—	—	—	—	—	—	5.5	-0.3	—	—
Van Eck Asia Dynasty...	int'l	—	—	—	—	—	—	—	—	—	-18.7	—	—
Van Eck Asia Infra...	int'l	—	—	—	—	—	—	—	—	—	-24.1	—	—
Van Eck Glob Blncd...	global	—	—	—	—	—	—	—	—	—	-3.2	—	—
Van Eck Glob Hard Asst...	global	—	—	—	—	—	—	—	—	—	—	—	—
Van Eck Glob Income...	global	—	—	—	11.2	11.4	16.7	18.6	-3.5	4.9	-2.8	-0.5	6.4
Van Eck Glob Sm Cap...	global	—	—	—	—	—	—	—	—	—	—	—	—
Van Eck Gold/Res...	prec met	—	—	47.2	-21.3	18.9	-26.4	-4.1	-4.5	78.1	-15.6	12.8	0.3
Van Eck Int'l Inv Gold...	prec met	-2.0	34.0	34.8	-22.0	51.3	-27.0	2.6	-29.1	113.4	-1.0	14.4	2.3
Van Eck World Trends...	global	—	40.5	7.9	6.1	13.3	-7.9	12.5	-8.5	22.3	2.3	4.6	3.5
Vista Balanced...	income	—	—	—	—	—	—	—	—	12.7	0.2	—	—
Vista CA Inter...	tax-free	—	—	—	—	—	—	—	—	—	-3.2	—	—
Vista Capital Gro...	agg gr	—	—	—	23.2	44.4	-6.0	70.7	12.9	20.2	-1.3	10.3	16.6
Vista Eqty Inc...	income	—	—	—	—	—	—	—	—	—	-3.8	—	—
Vista Glob Fix Inc...	fix-inc	—	—	—	—	—	—	—	—	—	-1.5	—	—
Vista Gro & Inc...	gr-inc	—	—	—	40.1	56.9	0.2	59.1	15.1	13.0	-3.4	7.9	14.9
Vista Int'l Eqty...	int'l	—	—	—	—	—	—	—	—	21.4	-4.3	—	—
Vista NY TF...	tax-free	—	—	—	9.5	10.6	5.8	13.2	10.3	13.8	-6.1	5.6	7.1
Vista TF Inc...	tax-free	—	—	—	10.4	10.1	7.2	14.0	12.8	15.0	-7.6	6.2	7.9
Vista US Gov Inc...	fix-inc	—	—	—	7.0	14.4	8.5	14.8	5.9	10.3	-4.5	3.7	6.8
Wrkng Asst Ctzn Blncd...	income	—	—	—	—	—	—	—	—	4.3	-2.3	—	—
Wrkng Asst Ctzn Emg Gr...	int'l	—	—	—	—	—	—	—	—	—	—	—	—
Wrkng Asst Ctzn Glob...	global	—	—	—	—	—	—	—	—	—	—	—	—
Wrkng Asst Ctzn Gro...	growth	—	—	—	—	—	—	—	—	0.0	-0.7	—	—
Wrkng Asst Ctzn Inc...	fix-inc	—	—	—	—	—	—	—	—	10.0	-3.1	—	—

Section III

Directory of No-Load Funds

Explanation of directory data

Fund name: An ◆ after the fund name indicates the fund is a pure no-load. This is defined as a fund without any front- or back-end sales charges or 12b-1 fees. Funds with front- or back-end fees payable to the *fund* and funds with redemption fees of 2% or less, in force for no more than 90 days, are considered pure no-loads. An ! after the initial group listing indicates all the group's funds are pure no-load.

Addresses: The *Handbook* usually shows the fund's address. In some cases the fund's custodial bank is shown if investments must be made there.

Phone numbers: The local phone number is given first, 800 number for out-of-state callers next, then 800 number for in-state callers. If only one 800 number is shown, it is usually valid in-state. If it isn't, use the regular number. TDD phone numbers are "Telecommunications Device for the Deaf." Funds without 800 numbers may accept collect calls.

Americans are a mobile people, and mutual funds are no exception. Consequently, addresses and phone numbers can change without warning. If the phone listed in our Directory section is out of date, call the regular area code or the toll-free information operator (800-555-1212) for the new number.

Hours of service: Full service means all services including transactions handled by a live representative. Other service generally means live service but omitting some service, typically transactions. After hours service, either on tape or computerized, is generally available at all other times.

Newspaper listing: Identifies funds in cases where the abbreviation used in the paper may be unclear. The lack of an entry in the Directory does not mean the fund is not listed in the paper.

Portfolio manager: The date after the portfolio manager's name indicates the year he or she began managing the fund. Portfolio managers are listed alphabetically in a separate table in Chapter 14. Use this table to find out what fund the manager runs.

Investment objective and policies: Growth or income is an objective. A policy explains how the objective is achieved. E.g. the fund buys gold stocks to achieve a growth objective. If a fund leverages or sells short, it is noted in this section.

Year organized: In most cases, the year that the fund was first offered to the public is shown.

Minimum investments: If there is no special listing for IRAs or Keoghs, the regular minimum investments apply.

Telephone orders accepted: *Yes* means you get end-of-day NAV with payment mailed later.

Wire orders accepted: *Yes* means you get end-of-day NAV. In some cases, pre-notification by phone may be necessary.

Deadline for same day wire purchase: Shown in Eastern Standard Time.

Discount broker availability: Fund trading through five brokers is shown: Charles Schwab & Co. (Schwab), Jack White & Co. (White), Waterhouse Securities (Waterhouse), Fidelity Brokerage (Fidelity) and Muriel Siebert (Siebert). Funds traded without brokerage fees are asterisked. See Chapter 13 for more details.

Telephone redemptions: This means that the fund will sell your shares at that day's price with the proceeds wired or mailed to you, or occasionally to your bank. This is different from telephone switch, which may be available even if the fund does not redeem directly by phone.

Portfolio turnover: The turnover rate for the last three fiscal years is shown, with the most recent year shown first. The period covered generally ends on the same date as is shown for the expense ratio.

Shareholder services: Generally describes retirement, withdrawal options, and systematic investment plans. A number of funds that do not have Keogh or IRA plans will accept tax-sheltered accounts from investors with their own plans. Since tax-free mutual funds are inappropriate for tax-sheltered accounts, their availability, or unavailability, is not noted.

Dividends paid: The *Handbook* shows the specific months by date of record (not pay date). Capital gains are paid only if realized.

Management fee: Percentage of the fund's average daily net assets. M equals millions, B equals billions. Where there are several breakpoints at different asset levels, only the first and last are shown.

12b-1 distribution fee: Percentage of the fund's average daily net assets, paid annually unless otherwise indicated. Where the listing states, "up to   %", the fund pays only the amounts actually expended for the allowed purposes. Expenditures can be, and often are, considerably less than the maximum. Actual expenditures are shown where available. See Chapter 3 for a detailed discussion of 12b-1 plans. We note whether the fund or the advisor is paying the fee.

Expense ratio: Ratio of expenses to average net assets. When fiscal period is less than one year, annualized data are shown. The **Turnover ratio** is shown for the same fiscal period as the expense ratio. The **Largest holding** is from the most recent report available.

No information listed: If specific purchase or redemption services are not listed, that generally means they are unavailable. Missing data for group funds may often be found in the first generic listing for the group.

Qualified for sale in: States where the fund is registered to sell its shares. N.A (Not available) means the fund failed to furnish data. The *Handbook* uses official two-letter postal abbreviations for the states. These are:

Alabama	AL	Montana	MT
Alaska	AK	Nebraska	NE
Arizona	AZ	Nevada	NV
Arkansas	AR	New Hampshire	NH
California	CA	New Jersey	NJ
Colorado	CO	New Mexico	NM
Connecticut	CT	New York	NY
Delaware	DE	North Carolina	NC
Dist. of Col.	DC	North Dakota	ND
Florida	FL	Ohio	OH
Georgia	GA	Oklahoma	OK
Hawaii	HI	Oregon	OR
Idaho	ID	Pennsylvania	PA
Illinois	IL	Puerto Rico	PR
Indiana	IN	Rhode Island	RI
Iowa	IA	South Carolina	SC
Kansas	KS	South Dakota	SD
Kentucky	KY	Tennessee	TN
Louisiana	LA	Texas	TX
Maine	ME	Utah	UT
Maryland	MD	Vermont	VT
Massachusetts	MA	Virginia	VA
Michigan	MI	Washington	WA
Minnesota	MN	West Virginia	WV
Mississippi	MS	Wisconsin	WI
Missouri	MO	Wyoming	WY

CHAPTER 11

Directory of no-load mutual funds

AARP FUNDS ◆
(Data common to all AARP funds are shown below. See subsequent listings for data specific to individual funds.)

160 Federal Street
Boston, MA 02110
617-439-4640, 800-253-2277
prices/yields 800-631-4636
TDD 800-634-9454, fax 800-821-6234

Shareholder service hours: Full service: M-F 8 A.M.-6 P.M. EST; After hours service: prices, yields, balances, last transaction
Adviser: Scudder, Stevens & Clark
Custodian: State Street Bank & Trust Co.
Transfer agent: Scudder Service Corporation
Special sales restrictions: Designed for members of the American Association of Retired Persons but open to all investors
Minimum purchase: Initial: $500 ($2,500 for High Quality Tax Free Money Fund), Subsequent: None; IRA/Keogh: Initial: $250
Telephone orders accepted: Yes, subsequent only, $100 minimum
Wire orders accepted: Yes
Deadline for same day wire purchase: 4 P.M.
Qualified for sale in: All states
Telephone redemptions: Yes
Wire redemptions: Yes, $5 fee
Letter redemptions: Signature guarantee required over $50,000
Telephone switching: With other AARP Funds
Number of switches permitted: 4 round trips per year
Shareholder services: Keogh, IRA, automatic investment plan—minimum $50/month, withdrawal plan min. req. $10,000, electronic funds transfer
IRA/Keogh fees: None

AARP BALANCED STOCK AND BOND FUND ◆
(See first AARP listing for data common to all AARP funds)

Portfolio managers: Robert T. Hoffman (1994), William T. Hutchinson (1994), Kathleen T. Millard (1994)
Investment objective and policies: Long-term capital growth and quarterly income consistent with stability of principal. Invests in common stocks (maximum 70% of assets), fixed-income securities and cash equivalents. Allocation of assets will vary depending on economic and market conditions. At least 30% of assets will be in investment-grade debt securities and cash equivalents. May invest in foreign securities and use currency exchange contracts, futures and options to hedge.
Year organized: 1994
Ticker symbol: ABSBX
Discount broker availability: White
Dividends paid: Income - March, June, September, December; Capital gains - December
Portfolio turnover (1 yr): 49%
Largest holding: U.S. Treasury Note 6.875% due 7/31/99 (3.6%)
Management fee: 0.19% + group fee of 0.35% first $2B to 0.24% over $14B
Expense ratio: 1.31% (8 months ending 9/30/94)

AARP CAPITAL GROWTH FUND ◆
(See first AARP listing for data common to all AARP funds)

Portfolio managers: William F. Gadsden (1989), Bruce F. Beaty (1994)
Investment objective and policies: Long-term capital growth. Invests in common stocks and securities convertible into common stocks. Securities may be "undervalued" and may have above-average stock market risk. May invest in foreign securities without limit and use currency exchange contracts, futures and options to hedge. Fund seeks to keep value of its shares more stable than other growth mutual funds.
Year organized: 1984
Ticker symbol: ACGFX
Discount broker availability: White
Dividends paid: Income - December; Capital gains - December
Portfolio turnover (3 yrs): 80%, 101%, 89%
Largest holding: Tele-Communications, Inc "A" (5.0%)
Management fee: 0.32% + group fee of 0.35% first $2B to 0.24% over $14B
Expense ratio: 0.97% (year ending 9/30/94)

AARP GNMA AND U.S. TREASURY FUND ◆
(See first AARP listing for data common to all AARP funds)

Portfolio managers: David H. Glen (1984), Robert E. Pruyne (1984)
Investment objective and policies: High income consistent with a more stable price than that of a long-term bond. Invests primarily in GNMA securities and U.S. Treasury obligations. May use futures contracts and covered call options on up to 25% of assets.
Year organized: 1984
Ticker symbol: AGNMX
Discount broker availability: White
Dividends paid: Income - declared daily, paid monthly; Capital gains - December
Portfolio turnover (3 yrs): 115%, 105%, 74%
Management fee: 0.12% + group fee of 0.35% first $2B to 0.24% over $14B
Expense ratio: 0.66% (year ending 9/30/94)

AARP GROWTH AND INCOME FUND ◆
(See first AARP listing for data common to all AARP funds)

Portfolio managers: Robert T. Hoffman (1990), Kathleen T. Millard (1992), Benjamin W. Thorndike (1986)
Investment objective and policies: Long-term growth of capital, current income and growth of income. Invests primarily in dividend-paying common stocks and securities convertible into common stocks. May also invest in preferred stocks and foreign securities without limit. May use currency exchange contracts, covered call options and options on stock indices to hedge. Fund seeks to keep value of its shares more stable than other growth and income mutual funds.
Year organized: 1984
Ticker symbol: AGIFX
Discount broker availability: White
Dividends paid: Income - March, June, September, December; Capital gains - December
Portfolio turnover (3 yrs): 32%, 17%, 36%
Largest holding: United Technologies Corp. (2.3%)
Management fee: 0.19% + group fee of 0.35% first $2B to 0.24% over $14B
Expense ratio: 0.76% (year ending 9/30/94)

AARP HIGH QUALITY BOND FUND ◆
(See first AARP listing for data common to all AARP funds)

Portfolio managers: William T. Hutchinson (1987), Stephen Wohler (1994)
Investment objective and policies: High income. Invests primarily in U.S. Government, corporate, and other notes and bonds in the 3 highest rating categories with at least 80% of assets in the top 2 categories. May invest in foreign debt securities and use futures contracts and covered call options on up to 25% of assets. Fund seeks to keep value of its shares more stable than a long-term bond.
Year organized: 1984 (formerly AARP General Bond Fund)
Ticker symbol: AGBFX
Discount broker availability: White
Dividends paid: Income - declared daily, paid monthly; Capital gains - December
Portfolio turnover (3 yrs): 64%, 101%, 63%
Management fee: 0.19% + group fee of 0.35% first $2B to 0.24% over $14B
Expense ratio: 0.95% (year ending 9/30/94)

AARP HIGH QUALITY MONEY FUND ◆
(See first AARP listing for data common to all AARP funds)

Portfolio managers: Robert T. Neff (1985), Jeanette A. Kelly (1990)
Investment objective and policies: Current income and liquidity consistent with maintaining stability and safety of capital. Invests in money market obligations which are issued, guaranteed or insured by the U.S. Government, its agencies or instrumentalities, and repurchase agreements.
Year organized: 1985 (name changed from AARP Money Fund in Mar. 1991)
Ticker symbol: ARPXX
Check redemptions: No minimum
Confirmations mailed: After each purchase and each check, mail or wire redemption
Checks returned: Monthly
Periodic account statements mailed: Monthly (IRAs quarterly)
Dividends paid: Income - declared daily, paid monthly
Management fee: 0.10% + group fee of 0.35% first $2B to 0.24% over $14B
Expense ratio: 1.13% (year ending 9/30/94)

AARP HIGH QUALITY TAX FREE MONEY FUND ◆
(See first AARP listing for data common to all AARP funds)

Portfolio managers: K. Sue Cote (1991), Donald C. Carleton (1989)
Investment objective and policies: Current income exempt from federal income taxes and liquidity consistent with stability and safety of principal. Invests in high quality municipal money market securities.
Year organized: 1984 (formerly AARP Insured Short Term TF Bond Fund. Name and objectives changed on 9/30/91.)
Ticker symbol: AHTXX
Check redemptions: No minimum
Confirmations mailed: After each purchase and each check, mail or wire redemption
Checks returned: Monthly
Periodic account statements mailed: Monthly (IRAs quarterly)
Dividends paid: Income - declared daily, paid monthly
Management fee: 0.10% + group fee of 0.35% first $2B to 0.24% over $14B
Expense ratio: 0.90% (year ending 9/30/94)

AARP INSURED TAX FREE GENERAL BOND FUND ◆

(See first AARP listing for data common to all AARP funds)

Portfolio managers: Donald C. Carleton (1988), Philip Condon (1989)
Investment objective and policies: High income exempt from federal income tax. Invests primarily in long-term municipal securities that are insured against default by private insurers. May use futures contracts and covered call options on up to 25% of assets. Fund seeks to keep value of its shares more stable than a long-term municipal bond.
Year organized: 1984
Ticker symbol: AITGX
Discount broker availability: White
Dividends paid: Income - declared daily, paid monthly; Capital gains - December
Portfolio turnover (3 yrs): 38%, 48%, 62%
Management fee: 0.19% + group fee of 0.35% first $2B to 0.24% over $14B
Expense ratio: 0.68% (year ending 9/30/94)

ACORN FUND ◆

227 West Monroe St., Suite 3000
Chicago, IL 60606
312-634-9200, 800-922-6769
fax 312-634-0016

Shareholder service hours: Full service: M-F 8 A.M.-5 P.M. CST. After hours service: prices, prospectuses, total returns
Adviser: Wanger Asset Management, L.P.
Portfolio manager: Ralph L. Wanger, Jr. (1970)
Custodian and transfer agent: State Street Bank & Trust Co.
Investment objective and policies: Capital growth. Seeks areas of economy that will benefit from favorable trends for a number of years. Emphasizes common stocks of smaller companies with market capitalizations under $800M. Up to 33% of assets may be in foreign securities.
Year organized: 1970 (split 5 for 1 on 12/15/93)
Ticker symbol: ACRNX
Minimum purchase: Initial: $1,000, Subsequent: $100; IRA: Initial: $200, Subsequent: $200
Special sales restriction: Fund has been closed to new shareholders since 7/27/90 (except via telephone switch with Acorn International
Telephone orders accepted: Yes, $1,000 minimum
Wire orders accepted: No
Discount broker availability: White, Waterhouse, Fidelity, Siebert
Qualified for sale in: All states and PR
Telephone redemptions: Yes, $1,000 minimum
Wire redemptions: Yes, $1,000 minimum, $5 fee
Letter redemptions: Signature guarantee required
Redemption fee: 2% for shares held less than 60 days, payable to the fund, including telephone switch
Telephone switching: With Acorn International and Reich & Tang Money Market Funds
Number of switches permitted: Unlimited
Dividends paid: Income - July, December; Capital gains - July, December
Portfolio turnover (3 yrs): 18%, 20%, 25%
Largest holding: Tele-Communications (4.2%)
Shareholder services: IRA, SEP-IRA, corporate retirement plans, automatic investment plan—minimum $100/month, withdrawal plan min. req. $25,000
Management fee: 0.75% first $100M to 0.4% over $1.5B
Expense ratio: 0.62% (year ending 12/31/94)
IRA fees: Annual $10, Initial $5, Closing $10

ACORN INTERNATIONAL ◆

227 West Monroe St., Suite 3000
Chicago, IL 60606
312-634-9200, 800-922-6769
fax 312-634-0016

Shareholder service hours: Full service: M-F 8 A.M.-5 P.M. CST. After hours service: prices, prospectuses, total returns
Adviser: Wanger Asset Management, L.P.
Portfolio manager: Ralph L. Wanger, Jr. (1992)
Custodian and transfer agent: State Street Bank & Trust Co.
Investment objective and policies: Long term capital growth. Normally invests at least 75% of assets in equity securities of small and medium size non-U.S. companies in mature and emerging markets. May invest in ADRs, EDRs or other securities representing shares of foreign issuers. May invest up to 20% of assets in debt securities, including junk bonds, and use futures and options to hedge.
Year organized: 1992
Ticker symbol: ACINX
Minimum purchase: Initial: $1,000, Subsequent: $100; IRA: Initial: $200 Subsequent: $200
Special sales restriction: Fund closed to new shareholders on 2/11/94 (except via telephone switch with Acorn).
Telephone orders accepted: No
Wire orders accepted: No
Discount broker availability: Schwab, White, Waterhouse, Fidelity, Siebert
Qualified for sale in: All states and PR
Telephone redemptions: Yes, $1,000 minimum
Wire redemptions: Yes, $1,000 minimum, $5 fee
Letter redemptions: Signature guarantee required
Redemption fee: 2% for shares held less than 60 days, payable to the fund, including telephone switch
Telephone switching: With Acorn Fund and Reich & Tang Money Market Funds
Number of switches permitted: Unlimited
Dividends paid: Income - July, December; Capital gains - July, December
Shareholder services: IRA, SEP-IRA, corporate retirement plans, automatic investment plan—minimum $100/month, withdrawal plan min. req. $25,000
Portfolio turnover (2 yrs.) 20%, 19%
Largest holding: Secom (1.4%)
Management fee: 1.25% first $100M to 0.8% over $500M
Expense ratio: 1.20% (year ending 12/31/94) (includes waiver)
IRA fees: Annual $10, Initial $5, Closing $10

ACTIVE ASSETS TRUSTS

(Data common to all Active Assets Trusts are shown below. See subsequent listings for data specific to individual Active Assets Trusts.)

Two World Trade Center
New York, NY 10048
212-392-5000, 800-869-3326

Adviser: Dean Witter InterCapital, Inc.
Custodian: Bank of New York
Transfer agent: Dean Witter Trust Company
Special sales restrictions: Available only to Dean Witter Reynolds clients as part of "Active Assets Account Program"
Minimum purchase for Active Assets program participants: $10,000 cash and securities, Subsequent: None
Minimum purchase for other Dean Witter clients: Initial: $5,000, Subsequent: $1,000
Qualified for sale in: All states
Wire redemptions: Yes, through broker
Letter redemptions: Signature guarantee not required
Service fee: $80 per year for Active Assets program participants
Dividends paid: Income - declared daily, paid monthly
Check redemptions: No minimum
Checks returned: On request
Periodic account statements mailed: Monthly
Shareholder services: Fund is part of central assets account
Management fee: 0.5% first $500M to 0.25% over $3B
12b-1 distribution fee: 0.10%

ACTIVE ASSETS CALIFORNIA TAX-FREE TRUST

(See first Active Assets listing for data common to all Active Assets Trusts)

Investment objective and policies: High current income exempt from federal and California personal income taxes consistent with preservation of capital and liquidity. Invests primarily in California municipal money market instruments. Up to 20% of assets may be exempt from federal taxes but subject to California taxes.
Year organized: 1991
Ticker symbol: AACXX
Expense ratio: 0.68% (year ending 6/30/94)

ACTIVE ASSETS GOVERNMENT SECURITIES TRUST

(See first Active Assets listing for data common to all Active Assets Trusts)

Investment objective and policies: High current income consistent with preservation of capital and liquidity. Invests in money market instruments issued or guaranteed by the U.S. Government or its agencies or instrumentalities.
Year organized: 1981
Ticker symbol: AAGXX
Expense ratio: 0.66% (year ending 6/30/94)

ACTIVE ASSETS MONEY TRUST

(See first Active Assets listing for data common to all Active Assets Trusts)

Investment objective and policies: High current income consistent with preservation of capital and liquidity. Invests in money market instruments.
Year organized: 1981
Ticker symbol: AAMXX
Expense ratio: 0.51% (year ending 6/30/94)

ACTIVE ASSETS TAX-FREE TRUST

(See first Active Assets listing for data common to all Active Assets Trusts)

Investment objective and policies: High current income exempt from federal income tax consistent with preservation of capital and liquidity. Invests in municipal money market securities.
Year organized: 1981
Ticker symbol: AATXX
Expense ratio: 0.56% (year ending 6/30/94)

ADVANCE CAPITAL I FUNDS

(Data common to all Advance Capital I funds are shown below. See subsequent listings for data specific to individual Advance Capital I funds.)

One Towne Square, Suite 444
Southfield, MI 48076
810-350-8543, 800-345-4783
fax 810-350-0115

Adviser: Advance Capital Management, Inc.
Custodian: Huntington Banks of Michigan
Transfer agent: Advance Capital Group, Inc.
Minimum purchase: Initial: $10,000 (aggregate total for all funds, $1,000 for individual fund), Subsequent: None; IRA: Initial: $2,000
Telephone orders accepted: No
Wire orders accepted: Yes
Deadline for same day wire purchase: 4 P.M.
Qualified for sale in: FL, IL, IN, MI, MO, NJ, OH, PA, TX
Telephone redemptions: Yes, $25,000 maximum
Letter redemptions: Signature guarantee required over $25,000
Telephone switching: With other Advance Capital I funds
Number of switches permitted: Unlimited
Shareholder services: IRA
IRA fees: Closing $50

ADVANCE CAPITAL I
BALANCED FUND
(See first Advance Capital I listing for data common to all Advance Capital I funds.)

Sub-adviser: T. Rowe Price Associates, Inc.
Portfolio managers: John C. Shoemaker (1987), Robert J. Cappelli (1991), Richard T. Whitney (1993)
Investment objective and policies: Capital growth, current income and preservation of capital. Normally invests 60% (but at least 25%) of assets in common stocks of companies expected to outperform the S&P 500 over a 3 to 5 year horizon, and remaining 40% (range 25-75%) in investment-grade debt securities. Allocation of assets adjusted to changes in market conditions. Fund may hedge.
Year organized: 1987
Ticker symbol: ADBAX
Dividends paid: Income - declared daily, paid monthly; Capital gains - December
Portfolio turnover (3 yrs): 101%, 42%, 51%
Largest holding: Mobil Corp. (1.3%)
Management fee: 0.70%
12b-1 distribution fee: 0.25%
Expense ratio: 1.08% (year ending 12/31/93) (1.09% without waiver)

ADVANCE CAPITAL I BOND FUND ◆
(See first Advance Capital I listing for data common to all Advance Capital I funds.)

Portfolio manager: John C. Shoemaker (1987)
Investment objective and policies: High current income consistent with relative stability of principal and liquidity. Invests at least 65% of assets in investment-grade corporate debt securities and U.S. Government bonds. Remainder may be in preferred stocks, U.S. Government agency securities, U.S. Government obligations and money market instruments. Fund maintains a weighted average maturity of 3 to 10 years.
Year organized: 1987
Dividends paid: Income - declared daily, paid monthly; Capital gains - December
Portfolio turnover (3 yrs): 36%, 38%, 2%
Management fee: 0.40%
12b-1 distribution fee: 0.25% (not currently imposed)
Expense ratio: 0.61% (year ending 12/31/93) (0.62% without waiver)

ADVANCE CAPITAL I EQUITY
GROWTH FUND
(See first Advance Capital I listing for data common to all Advance Capital I funds.)

Sub-adviser: T. Rowe Price Associates, Inc.
Portfolio manager: Richard T. Whitney (1993)
Investment objective and policies: Long-term capital growth. Invests primarily in common stocks of small, rapidly growing companies. May also invest in convertible securities, preferred stocks and restricted securities. Fund may hedge.
Year organized: 1987 (name changed from Equity Universe fund in 1994)
Dividends paid: Income - December; Capital gains - December
Portfolio turnover (3 yrs): 135%, 96%, 86%
Largest holding: Microsoft Corp. (1.8%)
Management fee: 0.70%
12b-1 distribution fee: 0.25%
Expense ratio: 1.16% (year ending 12/31/93)

ADVANCE CAPITAL I
LONG TERM INCOME FUND ◆
(See first Advance Capital I listing for data common to all Advance Capital I funds.)

Portfolio managers: John C. Shoemaker (1992), Robert J. Cappelli (1992)
Investment objective and policies: High current income consistent with relative stability of principal and liquidity. Invests at least 65% of assets in investment-grade corporate debt securities and U.S. Government bonds. Remainder may be in preferred

stocks, U.S. Government agency securities, U.S. Government obligations and money market instruments. Fund maintains a weighted average maturity of 15 to 30 years.
Year organized: 1992
Dividends paid: Income - declared daily, paid monthly; Capital gains - December
Portfolio turnover (1 yr): 76%
Management fee: 0.40%
12b-1 distribution fee: 0.25% (not currently imposed)
Expense ratio: 0.64% (year ended 12/31/93) (0.75% without waiver)

ADVANCE CAPITAL I RETIREMENT
INCOME FUND
(See first Advance Capital I listing for data common to all Advance Capital I funds.)

Portfolio managers: John C. Shoemaker (1992), Robert J. Cappelli (1992)
Investment objective and policies: High income without undue risk of principal. Invests at least 50% of assets in investment-grade corporate debt securities and U.S. Government bonds. Remainder may be in preferred stocks, U.S. Government agency securities, U.S. Government obligations and money market instruments. Up to 33% of assets may be in junk bonds. Fund maintains a weighted average maturity of 5 to 22 years.
Year organized: 1992
Ticker symbol: ADRIX
Dividends paid: Income - declared daily, paid monthly; Capital gains - December
Portfolio turnover (1 yr): 38%
Management fee: 0.50%
12b-1 distribution fee: 0.25%
Expense ratio: 0.88% (year ending 12/31/93) (0.89% without waiver)

ADVISORS' INNER CIRCLE FUNDS ◆
(Data common to all Advisors' Inner Circle funds are shown below. See subsequent listings for data specific to individual Advisors' Inner Circle funds.)

Supervised Service Company
811 Main Street
Kansas City, MO 64105
Administrator 800-932-7781
800-808-4921, fax 816-292-6790

Administrator: SEI Financial Management Corp.
Custodian: CoreStates Bank, N.A.
Transfer agent: Supervised Service Company, Inc.
Telephone orders accepted: No
Wire orders accepted: Yes
Deadline for same day wire purchase: 4 P.M.
Telephone redemptions: Yes
Wire redemptions: Yes, $10 fee
Letter redemptions: Signature guarantee required
Shareholder services: IRA, automatic investment plan—minimum $100/month ($500 for Clover funds), withdrawal plan min. req. $25,000 ($50,000 for Clover funds)
IRA fees: Annual $25

ADVISORS' INNER CIRCLE FUND -
CLOVER CAPITAL EQUITY
VALUE FUND ◆
(See first Advisors' Inner Circle listing for data common to all Advisors' Inner Circle funds)

716-385-6090

Adviser: Clover Capital Management, Inc.
Portfolio manager: Paul W. Spindler (1991)
Investment objective and policies: Long-term total return. Invests at least 70% of assets in equity securities, including common stocks, debt securities, convertible preferred stocks and ADRs (up to 20%). Up to 15% of assets may be in non-convertible fixed-income securities and 30% in money market instruments.
Year organized: 1991
Ticker symbol: CCEVX
Minimum purchase: Initial: $2,000, Subsequent: $1,000

Qualified for sale in: AZ, CO, CT, DC, FL, GA, HI, IL, ME, MI, MO, MT, NH, NJ, NY, NC, OH, PA, WY
Telephone switching: With Clover Capital Fixed Income Fund
Number of switches permitted: Unlimited
Dividends paid: Income - March, June, September, December; Capital gains - December
Portfolio turnover (3 yrs): 58%, 83%, 31%
Largest holding: Policy Management Systems (4.5%)
Management fee: 0.74%
Administration fee: 0.20%
Expense ratio: 1.14% (year ending 10/31/94) (1.30% without waiver)

ADVISORS' INNER CIRCLE FUND -
CLOVER CAPITAL
FIXED INCOME FUND ◆
(See first Advisors' Inner Circle listing for data common to all Advisors' Inner Circle funds)

716-385-6090

Adviser: Clover Capital Management, Inc.
Portfolio manager: Richard J. Huxley (1991)
Investment objective and policies: High income consistent with reasonable risk to capital. Invests at least 70% of assets in fixed-income securities consisting of U.S. Government and government agency and instrumentality obligations, investment-grade corporate bonds and debentures and high-rated mortgage backed securities with a weighted average maturity of 5 to 10 years. Up to 10% of assets may be in dollar denominated fixed-income securities of foreign issuers.
Year organized: 1991
Minimum purchase: Initial: $2,000, Subsequent: $1,000
Qualified for sale in: AZ, CO, CT, DC, FL, GA, HI, IL, ME, MT, NJ, NY, NC, OH, PA, WY
Telephone switching: With Clover Capital Equity Value Fund
Number of switches permitted: Unlimited
Dividends paid: Income - declared daily, paid monthly; Capital gains - December
Portfolio turnover (3 yrs): 11%, 69%, 113%
Management fee: 0.45%
Administration fee: 0.20%
Expense ratio: 0.80% (year ending 10/31/94) (1.46% without waiver)

ADVISORS' INNER CIRCLE FUND -
JURIKA & VOYLES BALANCED FUND
(See Jurika & Voyles Balanced Fund in Discount Broker Funds section)

ADVISORS' INNER CIRCLE FUND -
PIN OAK AGGRESSIVE STOCK FUND ◆
(See first Advisors' Inner Circle listing for data common to all Advisors' Inner Circle funds)

216-668-1234

Adviser: Oak Associates
Portfolio manager: James D. Oelschlager (1992)
Investment objective and policies: Long-term capital growth. Invests as fully as practicable in a diversified portfolio of common stocks of companies with market capitalizations between $100M and $1B. May also invest in warrants and rights, debt securities, convertible preferred stocks and ADRs.
Year organized: 1992
Minimum purchase: Initial: $25,000, Subsequent: $5,000: IRA: Initial: None, Subsequent: None
Qualified for sale in: AL, CA, CO, CT, FL, GA, ID, IL, IN, KS, KY, MI, MN, MO, NY, NC, OH, PA, TN, TX, WY
Telephone switching: With White Oak Growth Stock Fund
Number of switches permitted: Unlimited
Dividends paid: Income - quarterly; Capital gains - October
Portfolio turnover (2 yrs): 49%, 68%
Largest holding: Intuit Software (7.3%)
Management fee: 0.74%

Administration fee: 0.2%
Expense ratio: 0.96% (year ending 10/31/94) (1.74% without waiver)

ADVISORS' INNER CIRCLE FUND - ROULSTON GOVERNMENT SECURITIES FUND ◆
(See first Advisors' Inner Circle listing for data common to all Advisors' Inner Circle funds)

216-431-3000

Adviser: Roulston & Company, Inc.
Portfolio managers: Joseph A. Harrison (1993), D. Keith Lockyer (1993)
Investment objective and policies: Current income consistent with preservation of capital. Invests at least 65% of assets in U.S. Government and government agency and instrumentality securities. Remainder of assets may be in corporate debt securities, short-term bank obligations, and U.S. dollar denominated debt securities of foreign government issuers. Fund maintains a weighted average maturity of 3 to 10 years. May use options to hedge.
Year organized: 1993
Ticker symbol: RGVSX
Minimum purchase: Initial: $5,000, Subsequent: $1,000; IRA: Initial: $1,000, Subsequent: $100
Discount broker availability: Schwab, *White
Qualified for sale in: CA, CO, FL, GA, IL, IN, MI, MT, NM, NY, NC, OH, PA, VA, WV, WI, WY
Telephone switching: With other Roulston funds
Number of switches permitted: Unlimited
Dividends paid: Income - quarterly; Capital gains - October
Portfolio turnover (2 yrs): 24%, 25%
Management fee: 0.5% first $100M to 0.25% over $200M
Administration fee: 0.2%
Expense ratio: 0.90% (year ending 10/31/94) (1.80% without waiver)

ADVISORS' INNER CIRCLE FUND - ROULSTON GROWTH AND INCOME FUND ◆
(See first Advisors' Inner Circle listing for data common to all Advisors' Inner Circle funds)

216-431-3000

Adviser: Roulston & Company, Inc.
Portfolio manager: Joseph A. Harrison (1993)
Investment objective and policies: Capital appreciation and current income. Invests primarily in common stocks of U.S. issuers but may also invest in warrants, rights and debt securities and convertible preferred stocks and U.S. dollar denominated securities of foreign issuers, including ADRs. May use options to hedge.
Year organized: 1993
Ticker symbol: RGINX
Minimum purchase: Initial: $5,000, Subsequent: $1,000; IRA: Initial: $1,000, Subsequent: $100
Discount broker availability: Schwab, *White
Qualified for sale in: CA, CO, FL, GA, IL, IN, MI, MT, NM, NY, NC, OH, PA, VA, WV, WI, WY
Telephone switching: With other Roulston funds
Number of switches permitted: Unlimited
Dividends paid: Income - October; Capital gains - October
Portfolio turnover (2 yrs): 35%, 4%
Largest holding: Sara Lee (3.2%)
Management fee: 1.0% first $100M, 0.75% over $100M
Administration fee: 0.2%
Expense ratio: 1.50% (year ending 10/31/94) (1.72% without waiver)

ADVISORS' INNER CIRCLE FUND - ROULSTON MIDWEST GROWTH FUND ◆
(See first Advisors' Inner Circle listing for data common to all Advisors' Inner Circle funds)

216-431-3000

Adviser: Roulston & Company, Inc.
Portfolio manager: Norman F. Klopp (1993)

Investment objective and policies: Long-term capital appreciation. Invests at least 65% of assets in common stocks of companies headquartered or maintaining a substantial operating presence in the states or areas bordering the Great Lakes. May also invest in warrants, rights and debt securities and convertible preferred stocks and use options to hedge.
Year organized: 1993
Ticker symbol: RMGRX
Minimum purchase: Initial: $5,000, Subsequent: $1,000; IRA: Initial: $1,000, Subsequent: $100
Discount broker availability: Schwab, *White
Qualified for sale in: CA, CO, FL, GA, IL, IN, MI, MT, NM, NY, NC, OH, PA, VA, WV, WY
Telephone switching: With other Roulston funds
Number of switches permitted: Unlimited
Dividends paid: Income - October; Capital gains - October
Portfolio turnover (2 yrs): 78%, 0%
Largest holding: Invacare (3.6%)
Management fee: 1.0% first $100M, 0.75% over $100M
Administration fee: 0.2%
Expense ratio: 1.45% (year ending 10/31/94) (1.54% without waiver)

ADVISORS' INNER CIRCLE FUND - WHITE OAK GROWTH STOCK FUND ◆
(See first Advisors' Inner Circle listing for data common to all Advisors' Inner Circle funds)

216-668-1234

Adviser: Oak Associates
Portfolio manager: James D. Oelschlager (1992)
Investment objective and policies: Long-term Capital growth. Invests as fully as practicable in a diversified portfolio of common stocks of companies with market capitalizations of more than $1B. May also invest in warrants and rights, debt securities, convertible preferred stocks and ADRs.
Year organized: 1992
Minimum purchase: Initial: $25,000, Subsequent: $5,000; IRA: Initial: None, Subsequent: None
Qualified for sale in: AL, CA, CO, CT, FL, GA, ID, IL, IN, KS, KY, MI, MN, MO, NY, NC, OH, PA, TN, TX, WY
Telephone switching: With Pin Oak Aggressive Stock Fund
Number of switches permitted: Unlimited
Dividends paid: Income - quarterly; Capital gains - October
Portfolio turnover (2 yrs): 37%, 27%
Largest holding: Microsoft Corp. (8.7%)
Management fee: 0.74%
Administration fee: 0.2%
Expense ratio: 0.97% (year ending 10/31/94) (2.24% without waiver)

THE ALABAMA TAX FREE BOND FUND ◆
(See Government Street Alabama Tax Free Bond Fund)

ALLIANCE FUNDS
(Data common to all Alliance funds are shown below. See subsequent listings for data specific to individual Alliance funds.)

1345 Avenue of Americas
New York, NY 10105
212-969-1000, 800-221-5672
yields 800-221-9513, 800-251-0539
TDD 800-367-1684

Adviser: Alliance Capital Management L.P. (a wholly-owned subsidiary of The Equitable Life Assurance Society of the United States)
Custodian: State Street Bank & Trust Co.
Transfer agent: Alliance Fund Services, Inc.
Wire orders accepted: Yes
Deadline for same day wire purchase: 4 P.M.
Qualified for sale in: All states
Wire redemptions: Yes, $1,000 minimum
Letter redemptions: Signature guarantee required over $25,000

Telephone switching: With other Alliance funds
Number of switches permitted: Unlimited
Check redemptions: $100 minimum (not available for World Income Trust)
Checks returned: Quarterly
Periodic account statements mailed: Monthly
Dividends paid: Income - declared daily, paid monthly
Shareholder services: Keogh, IRA, SEP-IRA, 403(b), corporate retirement plans, automatic investment plan, electronic funds transfer, withdrawal plan
IRA/Keogh fees: Annual $10, Initial $5

ALLIANCE CAPITAL RESERVES
(See first Alliance listing for data common to all Alliance funds)

Portfolio manager: Pamela F. Richardson (1990)
Investment objective and policies: Income, safety of principal and liquidity. Invests in short-term money market securities of the highest quality.
Year organized: 1978
Ticker symbol: ACRXX
Minimum purchase: Initial: $1,000, Subsequent: $100
Management fee: 0.5% first $1.25B to 0.45% over $3B
12b-1 distribution fee: 0.25%
Expense ratio: 1.00% (year ending 6/30/94) (1.03% without waiver)

ALLIANCE GOVERNMENT RESERVES
(See first Alliance listing for data common to all Alliance funds)

Portfolio manager: Pamela F. Richardson (1990)
Investment objective and policies: Current income, safety of principal and liquidity. Invests in U.S. Government money market instruments, including U.S. Treasury bills, notes and other obligations issued or guaranteed by the U.S. Government, its agencies or instrumentalities, and repurchase agreements pertaining to these securities.
Year organized: 1979
Ticker symbol: AGRXX
Minimum purchase: Initial: $1,000, Subsequent: $100
Management fee: 0.5% first $1.25B to 0.45% over $3B
12b-1 distribution fee: 0.23%
Expense ratio: 1.00% (year ending 6/30/94) (1.04% without waiver)

ALLIANCE MONEY RESERVES
(See first Alliance listing for data common to all Alliance funds)

Portfolio manager: Pamela F. Richardson (1989)
Investment objective and policies: Maximum current income consistent with safety of principal and liquidity. Invests in money market securities of the highest quality.
Year organized: 1978
Ticker symbol: ACMXX
Minimum purchase: Initial: $1,000, Subsequent: $100
Management fee: 0.5% first $1.25B to 0.45% over $3B
12b-1 distribution fee: 0.21%
Expense ratio: 1.00% (year ending 6/30/94) (1.09% without waiver)

ALLIANCE MUNICIPAL TRUST - GENERAL PORTFOLIO
(See first Alliance listing for data common to all Alliance funds)

Portfolio manager: Stella Lou (1989)
Investment objective and policies: Safety of principal, liquidity, and maximum current income exempt from federal income taxes. Invests in high grade municipal money market securities.

Year organized: 1982 (name changed from Alliance Tax-Exempt Reserves in 1992)
Ticker symbol: ALLXX
Minimum purchase: Initial: $1,000, Subsequent: $100
Management fee: 0.5% first $1.25B to 0.45% over $3B
12b-1 distribution fee: 0.23%
Expense ratio: 0.92% (year ending 6/30/94) (0.94% without waiver)

ALLIANCE WORLD INCOME TRUST
(See first Alliance listing for data common to all Alliance funds)

Portfolio managers: Robert Sinche (1990), Douglas Peebles (1992)
Investment objective and policies: High current income consistent with prudent investment risk. Invests in high quality debt securities denominated in the U.S. dollar and selected foreign currencies with remaining maturities of 1 year or less. At least 35% of assets denominated in U.S. dollar and 35% in currencies of countries participating in European Monetary System. May use futures and options. Fund seeks higher yields than money market funds with less fluctuation than longer-term bond funds.
Year organized: 1990
Ticker symbol: AWITX
Minimum purchase: Initial: $10,000, Subsequent: $1,000
Discount broker availability: Schwab, White, Fidelity, Siebert
Management fee: 0.65%
12b-1 distribution fee: 0.68%
Expense ratio: 1.70% (year ending 10/31/94) (2.08% without waiver)

AMANA GROWTH FUND ◆
P.O. Box 2838
Bellingham, WA 98227
206-360-734-9900, 800-728-8762
fax 206-734-0755

Adviser: Saturna Capital Corp.
Portfolio manager: Nicholas Kaiser (1994)
Custodian: National City Bank, Indiana
Transfer agent: Saturna Capital Corp.
Investment objective and policies: Long-term capital growth. In accordance with Islamic principles the fund will not make any investments which pay interest. Fund invests primarily in common stocks believed to have potential for above average increases in earnings and share price. May purchase preferred stocks and write covered options.
Year organized: 1994 (a portfolio of Amana Mutual Funds Trust)
Special sales restrictions: Fund is designed to meet the special needs of Muslims by investing in accordance with Islamic principles, but is open to all investors.
Minimum purchase: Initial: $100, Subsequent: $25
Telephone orders accepted: No
Wire orders accepted: Yes, $100 initial minimum; $25, subsequently
Deadline for same day wire purchase: 4 P.M.
Qualified for sale in: AZ, CA, CO, DC, FL, GA, HI, IA, ID, IL, IN, KS, KY, MA, MD, MI, MO, NC, NJ, NY, OR, PA, TN, TX, UT, VA, WA, WI
Telephone redemptions: Yes
Wire redemptions: Yes, $1,000 minimum, $15 fee
Letter redemptions: Signature guarantee not required
Check redemptions: $300 minimum
Telephone switching: With Amana Income Fund, Alliance funds and Northwest Investors Trust funds
Number of switches permitted: Unlimited
Dividends paid: Income - May, December; Capital gains - May, December
Largest holding: Motorola (4.3%)
Shareholder services: IRA, automatic investment plan, electronic funds transfer
Management fee: 0.95%
Expense ratio: 0.62% (3 months ending 5/31/94) (0.89% without waiver)
IRA fees: None

AMANA INCOME FUND ◆
P.O. Box 2838
Bellingham, WA 98227
206-360-734-9900, 800-728-8762
fax 206-734-0755

Adviser: Saturna Capital Corp.
Portfolio manager: Nicholas Kaiser (1986)
Custodian: National City Bank, Indiana
Transfer agent: Saturna Capital Corp.
Investment objective and policies: High current income and preservation of capital. In accordance with Islamic principles the fund will not make any investments which pay interest. Fund invests primarily in income-producing securities such as common stock. May purchase preferred stocks and write covered options.
Year organized: 1984 (a portfolio of Amana Mutual Funds Trust)
Ticker symbol: AMANX
Special sales restrictions: Fund is designed to meet the special needs of Muslims by investing in accordance with Islamic principles, but is open to all investors.
Minimum purchase: Initial: $100, Subsequent: $25; IRA: Initial: $25
Telephone orders accepted: No
Wire orders accepted: Yes, $100 minimum
Deadline for same day wire purchase: 4 P.M.
Qualified for sale in: AZ, CA, CO, DC, FL, GA, HI, IA, ID, IL, IN, KS, KY, MA, MD, MI, MO, NC, NJ, NY, OR, PA, TN, TX, UT, VA, WA, WI
Telephone redemptions: Yes
Wire redemptions: Yes, $1,000 minimum
Letter redemptions: Signature guarantee not required
Check redemptions: Yes, $300 minimum
Telephone switching: With Amana Growth Fund, Alliance funds and Northwest Investors Trust funds
Number of switches permitted: Unlimited
Dividends paid: Income - May, December; Capital gains - May, December
Portfolio turnover (3 yrs): 21%, 29%, 19%
Largest holding: H & R Block (3.7%)
Shareholder services: IRA, automatic investment plan, electronic funds transfer
Management fee: 0.95%
Expense ratio: 1.58% (year ending 5/31/94)
IRA fees: None

AMCORE VINTAGE MUTUAL FUNDS ◆
(Data common to all Amcore Vintage funds are shown below. See subsequent listings for data specific to individual Amcore funds.)

1900 E. Dublin-Granville Road
Columbus, OH 43229
800-438-6375
fax 614-899-1257

Adviser: Amcore Capital Management, Inc.
Custodian: First National Bank of Chicago
Transfer agent: Winsbury Service Corp.
Minimum purchase: Initial: $1000, Subsequent: $50; IRA: Subsequent: None
Telephone orders accepted: No
Wire orders accepted: Yes, $1,000 minimum
Deadline for same day wire purchase: 4 P.M.
Qualified for sale in: CA, CO, DC, FL, GA, HI, IL, IN, MD, NJ, NY, OH, WI
Telephone redemptions: Yes
Wire redemptions: Yes
Letter redemptions: Signature guarantee required
Telephone switching: With other Amcore funds
Number of switches permitted: Unlimited, $1,000 minimum
Deadline for same day switch: 4 P.M. (12 NN for U.S. Government Obligations)
Shareholder services: IRA, automatic investment plan - minimum $25/month ($250 initial minimum), withdrawal plan
IRA fees: Annual $15

AMCORE VINTAGE EQUITY FUND ◆
(See first Amcore Vintage listing for data common to all Amcore Vintage funds)

Portfolio manager: Darrell C. Thompson (1992)
Investment objective and policies: Long term capital appreciation. Invests primarily in equity securities of large capitalization companies with strong earnings potential, striving for high overall return while minimizing risk through the selection of quality dividend-paying securities. May invest in ADRs of foreign issuers, other mutual funds, U.S. government obligations and repurchase agreements and use call options.
Year organized: 1992
Ticker symbol: AVEQX
Dividends paid: Income - March, June, September, December; Capital gains - December
Portfolio turnover (1 yr): 4%
Largest holding: Motorola, Inc. (1.4%)
Management fee: 0.75%
Expense ratio: 0.54% (year ending 3/31/94) (1.37% without waiver)

AMCORE VINTAGE FIXED INCOME FUND ◆
(See first Amcore Vintage listing for data common to all Amcore Vintage funds)

Portfolio manager: Dean C. Countryman (1992)
Investment objective and policies: Total return consistent with current income and preservation of capital. Invests primarily in fixed income corporate and government securities with a weighted average maturity of 3 to 7 years. May invest in dollar-denominated fixed income foreign securities.
Year organized: 1992
Ticker symbol: AVINX
Dividends paid: Income - declared and paid monthly; Capital gains - December
Portfolio turnover (1 yr): 32%
Management fee: 0.60%
Expense ratio: 0.51% (year ending 3/31/94) (1.24% without waiver)

AMCORE VINTAGE INTERMEDIATE TAX-FREE FUND ◆
(See first Amcore Vintage listing for data common to all Amcore Vintage funds)

Portfolio manager: Dean C. Countryman (1993)
Investment objective and policies: Current income exempt from federal income taxes consistent with preservation of capital. Invests primarily in municipal securities with a weighted average maturity of 5 to 9 years. Up to 20% of assets may be in AMT securities and 15% in illiquid securities.
Year organized: 1993
Ticker symbol: AVTFX
Dividends paid: Income - declared and paid monthly; Capital gains - December
Portfolio turnover (1 yr): 13%
Management fee: 0.60%
Expense ratio: 0.57% (year ending 3/31/94)

AMCORE VINTAGE U.S. GOVERNMENT OBLIGATIONS FUND ◆
(See first Amcore Vintage listing for data common to all Amcore Vintage funds)

Portfolio manager: Dean C. Countryman (1992)
Investment objective and policies: Current income consistent with liquidity and stability of principal. Invests exclusively in U.S. Government money market instruments.
Year organized: 1992
Ticker symbol: AVGXX
Check redemptions: $250 minimum
Dividends paid: Income - declared daily, paid monthly
Portfolio turnover (1 yr): 2%
Management fee: 0.40%
Expense ratio: 0.56% (year ending 3/31/94) (1.02% without waiver)

AMERICAN AADVANTAGE FUNDS

(Data common to all American Aadvantage funds are shown below. See subsequent listings for data specific to individual American Aadvantage funds.)

P.O. Box 4580
Chicago, IL 60680
800-231-4252, fax 312-655-4489

Fund manager: AMR Investment Services, Inc. (a wholly owned subsidiary of AMR Corporation)
Adviser: AMR Investment Services, Inc.
Custodian: NationsBank of Texas N.A., Dallas
Transfer agent: Goldman, Sachs & Co.
Sales restrictions: Funds have 3 classes of shares - Mileage Class, PlanAhead Class, and Institutional - with the first two available to individual investors. Mileage Class shares are only for taxable accounts. PlanAhead Class shares are primarily for tax-deferred accounts (but are available for taxable accounts) and are also offered through discount brokerage firms. Each shareholder of Mileage Class is credited with mileage in the American Airlines Aadvantage Travel Awards Program at the annual rate of one mile for every $10 invested on an annualized basis. There are no mileage credits for PlanAhead class shares. Mileage Class shares have 12b-1 distribution fees while PlanAhead shares do not.
Minimum purchase: Initial: $10,000, Subsequent: $250
Telephone orders accepted: No
Wire orders accepted: Yes, $1,000 subsequent minimum
Deadline for same day wire purchase: 4 P.M. (except money market funds)
Qualified for sale in: All states except LA
Telephone redemptions: Yes
Wire redemptions: Yes, 1,000 minimum, $12 fee
Letter redemptions: Signature guarantee required over $25,000
Telephone switching: With other American Aadvantage Mileage Class and PlanAhead Class funds, $1,000 minimum
Number of switches permitted: Unlimited, 15 day hold
Deadline for same day switch: 4 P.M. (3 P.M. for money market funds)
Shareholder services: Keogh, IRA & SEP-IRA (for PlanAhead Class shares only), automatic investment plan, electronic funds transfer (purchase only), withdrawal plan
12b-1 distribution fee: Maximum of 0.25% (for Mileage Class shares; not currently imposed for PlanAhead shares)
IRA/Keogh fees: Annual $12 total for all funds (for PlanAhead Class shares only)

AMERICAN AADVANTAGE BALANCED FUND

(See first American Aadvantage listing for data common to all American Aadvantage funds)

Portfolio manager: Dennis M. O'Hara (1989)
Investment objective and policies: Income and capital growth. Normally invests 50-65% of assets in equity securities and 35-50% in investment-grade fixed-income securities. May invest in convertible securities and ADRs of foreign issuers. Up to 15% of assets may be in illiquid securities.
Year organized: 1987 (1994 for Mileage and PlanAhead classes)
Discount broker availability: *White, *Waterhouse, Fidelity, Siebert
Dividends paid: Income - December; Capital gains - December
Portfolio turnover (3 yrs): 48%, 83%, 80%
Largest holding: American Express Co. (1.7%)
Management fee: 0.30%
12b-1 distribution fee: 0.13% (Mileage Class)
Expense ratio: 0.96% (year ending 10/31/94) (1.05% without waiver) - Mileage Class

AMERICAN AADVANTAGE GROWTH AND INCOME FUND

(See first American Aadvantage listing for data common to all American Aadvantage funds)

Portfolio manager: Dennis M. O'Hara (1989)
Investment objective and policies: Long-term capital growth and current income. Invests primarily in common stocks, preferred stocks, convertible securities and ADRs of foreign issuers. Up to 15% of assets may be in illiquid securities.
Year organized: 1987 (1994 for Mileage and PlanAhead classes. Name changed from Equity Fund in 1994)
Discount broker availability: *White, *Waterhouse, Fidelity, Siebert
Dividends paid: Income - December; Capital gains - December
Portfolio turnover (3 yrs): 23%, 30%, 35%
Largest holding: Philip Morris Companies, Inc. (3.3%)
Management fee: 0.30%
12b-1 distribution fee: 0.13% (Mileage Class)
Expense ratio: 0.96% (year ending 10/31/94) (1.06% without waiver) - Mileage Class

AMERICAN AADVANTAGE INTERNATIONAL EQUITY FUND

(See first American Aadvantage listing for data common to all American Aadvantage funds)

Portfolio manager: Dennis M. O'Hara (1989)
Investment objective and policies: Long-term capital growth. Invests primarily in common stocks and convertible securities of foreign issuers. May use forward foreign currency contracts and futures to hedge. Up to 15% of assets may be in illiquid securities.
Year organized: 1991 (1994 for Mileage and PlanAhead classes. Name changed from Equity Fund in 1994)
Discount broker availability: *White, *Waterhouse, Fidelity, Siebert
Dividends paid: Income - December; Capital gains - December
Portfolio turnover (3 yrs): 37%, 61%, 21%
Largest holding: Fuji Photo Film Corp. (1.7%)
Management fee: 0.43%
12b-1 distribution fee: 0.25% (Mileage Class)
Expense ratio: 1.31% (year ending 10/31/94) - Mileage Class

AMERICAN AADVANTAGE LIMITED-TERM INCOME FUND

(See first American Aadvantage listing for data common to all American Aadvantage funds)

Portfolio managers: Michael W. Fields (1987), David P. Gurun (1994)
Investment objective and policies: Income and capital growth. Invests primarily in investment-grade fixed-income government and corporate securities with a weighted average maturity of 1 to 5 years. May invest in asset- and mortgage-backed securities and YankeeDollar and EuroDollar bonds and notes. Up to 15% of assets may be in illiquid securities.
Year organized: 1987 (1994 for Mileage and PlanAhead classes)
Discount broker availability: *White, *Waterhouse, Fidelity, Siebert
Dividends paid: Income - declared daily, paid monthly; Capital gains - December
Portfolio turnover (3 yrs): 94%, 176%, 133%
Management fee: 0.20%
12b-1 distribution fee: 0.04% (Mileage Class)
Expense ratio: 0.82% (year ending 10/31/94) (1.02% without waiver) - Mileage Class

AMERICAN AADVANTAGE MONEY MARKET FUND

(See first American Aadvantage listing for data common to all American Aadvantage funds)

Portfolio manager: Michael W. Fields (1991)
Investment objective and policies: Current income consistent with stability of principal and liquidity. Invests in money market instruments.
Year organized: 1991 - Mileage Class, 1994 - PlanAhead Class
Deadline for same day wire purchase: 3 P.M.
Check redemptions: $100 minimum
Confirmations mailed: After each purchase and each check, mail or wire redemption
Checks returned: Not returned
Periodic statements mailed: Monthly
Dividends paid: Income - declared daily, paid monthly
Management fee: 0.15%
12b-1 distribution fee: 0.17% (Mileage Class)
Expense ratio: 0.51% (year ending 10/31/94) - Mileage Class

AMERICAN AADVANTAGE MUNICIPAL MONEY MARKET FUND

(See first American Aadvantage listing for data common to all American Aadvantage funds)

Portfolio manager: Michael W. Fields (1993)
Investment objective and policies: Current income exempt from federal income tax consistent with stability of principal and liquidity. Invests in municipal money market instruments.
Year organized: 1993 - Mileage Class, 1994 - PlanAhead Class
Deadline for same day wire purchase: 12 NN
Check redemptions: $100 minimum
Confirmations mailed: After each purchase and each check, mail or wire redemption
Checks returned: Not returned
Periodic statements mailed: Monthly
Dividends paid: Income - declared daily, paid monthly
Management fee: 0.15%
12b-1 distribution fee: 0.25% (Mileage Class)
Expense ratio: 0.63% (year ending 10/31/94) (0.83% without waiver) - Mileage Class

AMERICAN AADVANTAGE U.S. TREASURY MONEY MARKET FUND

(See first American Aadvantage listing for data common to all American Aadvantage funds)

Portfolio manager: Michael W. Fields (1992)
Investment objective and policies: Current income consistent with stability of principal and liquidity. Invests exclusively in short-term U.S. Treasury money market instruments.
Year organized: 1992 - Mileage Class, 1994 - PlanAhead Class
Deadline for same day wire purchase: 3 P.M.
Check redemptions: $100 minimum
Confirmations mailed: After each purchase and each check, mail or wire redemption
Checks returned: Not returned
Periodic statements mailed: Monthly
Dividends paid: Income - declared daily, paid monthly
Management fee: 0.15%
12b-1 distribution fee: 0.25%
Expense ratio: 0.57% (year ending 10/31/94) - Mileage Class

THE AMERICAN HERITAGE FUND, INC. ◆

1370 Avenue of the Americas
New York, NY 10019
212-397-3900, 800-828-5050
fax 212-397-4036

Shareholder service hours: Full service: M-F 9 A.M.-6 P.M. EST. After hours service: prices, messages, prospectuses
Newspaper listing: A Heritg
Adviser: American Heritage Management Corp.
Portfolio manager: Heiko Thieme (1990)
Custodian: Star Bank, Cincinnati, OH
Transfer agent: American Data Services, Inc.
Investment objective and policies: Growth of capital. Invests primarily in common stocks and securities convertible into common stocks. Normally invests approximately 50% in large capitalization companies. May sell short (up to 35% of assets), leverage, hedge, invest overseas and purchase restricted securities (15% of assets). Fund is non-diversified.
Year organized: 1951 (Present management 1990, Industry Fund of America was merged into Fund in June, 1988)
Ticker symbol: AHERX

Minimum purchase: Initial: $5,000, Subsequent: $1,000; IRA/Keogh: Initial: $2,000, Subsequent: None
Telephone orders accepted: No
Wire orders accepted: No
Discount broker availability: Schwab, *White, *Fidelity, *Siebert
Qualified for sale in all states except: AR, NE, NH, WI
Letter redemptions: Signature guarantee required
Dividends paid: Income - December; Capital gains - December
Portfolio turnover (3 yrs): 434%, 278%, 776%
Largest holding: Kouri Capital Group, Inc. (7.3%)
Shareholder services: Keogh, IRA, withdrawal plan min. req. $50,000
Management fee: 1.25% first $100M, 1.0% over $100M
Expense ratio: 2.41% (year ending 5/31/94)
IRA/Keogh fees: Annual $13, Closing $10

AMERICAN HERITAGE GROWTH FUND, INC. ◆
1370 Avenue of the Americas
New York, NY 10019
212-397-3900, 800-828-5050
fax 212-397-4036

Collect phone calls accepted: Yes
Adviser: American Heritage Management Corp.
Portfolio Manager: Heiko Thieme (1994)
Custodian: Star Bank, Cincinnati, OH
Transfer agent: American Data Services, Inc.
Investment objectives and policies: Capital growth. Invests at least 80% of assets in common stocks and securities convertible into common stocks. Up to 35% of assets may be in securities of foreign issuers. May write covered call options to hedge.
Year organized: 1994
Ticker symbol: AHEGX
Minimum purchase: Initial: $5,000, Subsequent: $1,000; IRA/Keogh: Initial: $2,000, Subsequent: None
Telephone orders accepted: No
Wire orders accepted: No
Discount broker availability: *White, *Fidelity, *Siebert
Qualified for sale in: All states except HI, MO, NE, NH
Letter redemptions: Signature guarantee required
Dividends paid: Income - December; Capital gains - December
Shareholder services: Keogh, IRA, withdrawal plan min. req. $50,000
IRA/Keogh fees: Annual $13, Closing $10

AMERICA'S UTILITY FUND ◆
901 East Byrd Street
P.O. Box 26501
Richmond, VA 23261
804-649-1315, 800-487-3863
fax 804-775-5866

Adviser: Lord, Abbett & Co.
Portfolio manager: Julie M. Cannell (1992)
Custodian: Bank of New York
Transfer agent: America's Utility Fund Service Co.
Investment objective and policies: Current income and moderate capital growth. Invests at least 65% of assets in common stocks of electric utility companies, electric utility holding companies, electric and gas combination utility companies and local and long distance telephone companies.
Year organized: 1992
Ticker symbol: AMUTX
Minimum purchase: Initial: $1,000, Subsequent: $250
Telephone orders accepted: No
Wire orders accepted: No
Qualified for sale in: All states except AK, AR, DE, ID, IA, ME, MT, NE, NV, NH, NM, ND, RI, SD, UT, VT
Letter redemptions: Signature guarantee required over $25,000
Dividends paid: Income - March, June, September, December; Capital gains - December
Portfolio turnover (2 yrs): 21%, 24%

Largest holding: Public Service Co. of Colorado (4.1%)
Shareholder services: IRA, SEP-IRA, installment investment plan monthly min. req. $20
Management fee: 0.75% first $5M to 0.1% over $300M
Expense ratio: 1.21% (year ending 12/31/93) (1.41% without waiver)
IRA fees: Annual $10

AMTRUST VALUE FUND ◆
P.O. Box 3467
Victoria, TX 77903
512-578-7778, 800-532-1146
fax 512-575-5097

Adviser: AmTrust Capital Resources, Inc.
Portfolio manager: James Edward Baker (1993)
Custodian: First Victoria National Bank
Transfer agent: AmTrust Capital Resources, Inc.
Investment objective and policies: Long-term growth of capital. Invests primarily in common stocks of small to mid-size domestic companies (market capitalization less than $1 billion) listed on a national securities exchange or NASDAQ. May invest in U.S. Government securities and other short-term interest-bearing securities for defensive purposes.
Year organized: 1993
Minimum purchase: Initial: $250, Subsequent: $50
Telephone orders accepted: Yes
Wire orders accepted: Yes
Qualified for sale in: TX
Telephone redemptions: Yes, $30,000 maximum
Letter redemptions: Signature guarantee required over $30,000
Dividends paid: Income - December; Capital gains - December
Shareholder services: Keogh, IRA, SEP-IRA, 403(b)
Portfolio turnover (1 yr): 49%
Largest holding: Triconex (4.2%)
Management fee: 1.0%
Expense ratio: 0.80% (10 months ending 6/30/94) (includes waiver)
IRA/Keogh fees: Annual $12

ANALYSTS FIXED INCOME FUND ◆
9200 Montgomery Road
Bldg D, Suite 13A
Cincinnati, OH 45242
513-984-3377, fax 513-984-2411

Adviser: Equity Analysts, Inc.
Portfolio manager: David Lee Manzler, Jr. (1993)
Custodian: Star Bank, N.A. of Cincinnati
Transfer agent: Analysts Investment Trust
Investment objective and policies: High income over the long term consistent with preservation of capital. Invests primarily in investment-grade fixed-income securities - U.S. Government obligations, securities of foreign governments, domestic and foreign corporate debt securities, convertible bonds and repurchase agreements. Up to 50% of assets may be in securities of foreign issuers. Fund may use futures and options to hedge.
Year organized: 1993
Minimum purchase: Initial: $1,000, Subsequent: $25; IRA/Keogh: Initial: None, Subsequent: None
Telephone orders accepted: No
Wire orders accepted: Yes
Deadline for same day wire purchase: 3:30 P.M.
Qualified for sale in: OH, KY
Telephone redemptions: Yes
Wire redemptions: Yes, $1,000 minimum, $11 fee
Letter redemptions: Signature guarantee required over $25,000
Telephone switching: With Analysts Stock Fund and Cash Account Trust money market funds
Number of switches permitted: Unlimited
Dividends paid: Income - March, June, September, December; Capital gains - December
Portfolio turnover (1 yr): 23%
Shareholder services: Keogh, IRA, SEP-IRA, 401(k), 403(b), corporate retirement plans, automatic investment plan—minimum $25/month (waives initial minimum), withdrawal plan min. req. $10,000

Management fee: 1.5% first $20M to 0.75% over $100M
Expense ratio: 1.50% (11 months ending 7/31/94)
IRA/Keogh fees: None

ANALYSTS STOCK INCOME FUND ◆
9200 Montgomery Road
Bldg D, Suite 13A
Cincinnati, OH 45242
513-984-3377, fax 513-984-2411

Adviser: Equity Analysts, Inc.
Portfolio manager: David Lee Manzler, Jr. (1993)
Custodian: Star Bank, N.A. of Cincinnati
Transfer agent: Analysts Investment Trust
Investment objective and policies: Long-term capital appreciation. Invests primarily in common stocks of companies in 3 capitalization groups - over $1B, $500M to $1B, and under $500M - with maximum of 50% of assets in any single group. Up to 50% of assets may be in securities of foreign issuers. Fund may use futures and options to hedge.
Year organized: 1993
Minimum purchase: Initial: $1,000, Subsequent: $25; IRA/Keogh: Initial: None, Subsequent: None
Telephone orders accepted: No
Wire orders accepted: Yes
Deadline for same day wire purchase: 3:30 P.M.
Qualified for sale in: OH, KY
Telephone redemptions: Yes
Wire redemptions: Yes, $1,000 minimum, $11 fee
Letter redemptions: Signature guarantee required over $25,000
Telephone switching: With Analysts Fixed Income Fund and Cash Account Trust money market funds
Number of switches permitted: Unlimited
Dividends paid: Income - March, June, September, December; Capital gains - December
Portfolio turnover (1 yr): 5%
Largest holding: Norsk Hydro A S ADR (2.0%)
Shareholder services: Keogh, IRA, SEP-IRA, 401(k), 403(b), corporate retirement plans, automatic investment plan—minimum $25/month (waives initial minimum), withdrawal plan min. req. $10,000
Management fee: 2.0% first $20M to 0.75% over $100M
Expense ratio: 2.0% (11 months ending 7/31/94)
IRA/Keogh fees: None

ANALYTIC FUNDS ◆
(Data common to all Analytic funds are shown below. See subsequent listings for data specific to individual Analytic funds.)

2222 Martin Street, Suite 230
Irvine, CA 92715
714-833-0294, 800-374-2633
fax 714-833-8049

Shareholder service hours: Full service: M-F 8 A.M.-5 ; p.m. PST
Adviser: Analytic Investment Management, Inc.
Custodian: Bank of California, N.A.
Transfer agent: Analytic Investment Management, Inc.
Minimum purchase: Initial: $5,000, Subsequent: None; IRA/Keogh: Initial: None
Telephone orders accepted: No
Wire orders accepted: Yes
Deadline for same day wire purchase: 4 P.M.
Wire redemptions: Yes
Letter redemptions: Signature guarantee required
Telephone switching: With other Analytic Series funds
Number of switches permitted: Unlimited
Shareholder services: IRA, SEP-IRA, corporate retirement plans, withdrawal plan
IRA fees: None

ANALYTIC SERIES FUND - ENHANCED EQUITY PORTFOLIO ◆
(See first Analytic listing for data common to all Analytic funds)

Portfolio manager: Steven N. Huntsinger (1992)
Investment objective and policies: Above-average total return. Invests primarily in domestic common

stocks and options and futures that relate to such stocks.
Year organized: 1992
Qualified for sale in: CA, CT, IL, MD, MS, MO, NJ, NY, OH, PA, TN, TX
Dividends paid: Income - March, June, September, December; Capital gains - December
Portfolio turnover (1 yr): 76%
Largest holding: Exxon Corp. (1.8%)
Management fee: 0.60%
Expense ratio: 0.57% (year ending 12/31/93) (1.04% without waiver)

ANALYTIC SERIES FUND - MASTER FIXED INCOME PORTFOLIO ◆
(See first Analytic listing for data common to all Analytic funds)

Portfolio manager: John A. Flom (1994)
Investment objective and policies: Above-average total return. Normally invests in high grade U.S. Government, corporate, and mortgage-related fixed-income securities with a weighted average maturity of 3 to 10 years.
Year organized: 1992
Qualified for sale in: CA, CT, IL, MD, MS, MO, NJ, NY, OH, PA, TN, TX
Dividends paid: Income - monthly; Capital gains - December
Portfolio turnover (1 yr): 105%
Largest holding: Sunamerica PERCS (2.3%)
Management fee: 0.45%
Expense ratio: 0.60% (year ending 12/31/93) (1.04% without waiver)

ANALYTIC OPTIONED EQUITY FUND ◆
(See first Analytic listing for data common to all Analytic funds)

Newspaper listing: Analyt
Portfolio manager: Charles L. Dobson (1978)
Investment objective and policies: Greater long-term total return and smaller fluctuations in quarterly total return from a hedged common stock portfolio. Invests primarily in dividend-paying common stocks on which options are traded on national securities exchanges and in securities convertible into common stocks by selling covered call options and secured put options and by entering into closing purchase transactions.
Year organized: 1978
Ticker symbol: ANALX
Discount broker availability: Schwab, White, Waterhouse
Qualified for sale in: All states except ND, VT
Dividends paid: Income - March, June, September, December; Capital gains - December
Portfolio turnover (3 yrs): 49%, 36%, 82%
Largest holding: General Electric Co. (02.4%)
Management fee: 0.75%
Expense ratio: 1.10% (year ending 12/31/94)

ANALYTIC SERIES FUND - SHORT-TERM GOVERNMENT PORTFOLIO ◆
(See first Analytic listing for data common to all Analytic funds)

Portfolio manager: John A. Flom (1993)
Investment objective and policies: High current income consistent with stability of market value and low credit risk. Normally invests at least 80% of assets in high grade U.S. Government securities with a weighted average maturity of 1 to 3 years.
Year organized: 1993
Ticker symbol: ANSGX
Qualified for sale in: CA, CT, IL, MD, MO, NJ, NY, OH, PA, TN, TX
Dividends paid: Income - declared daily, paid monthly; Capital gains - December
Portfolio turnover (1 yr): 86%
Management fee: 0.30%
Expense ratio: 0.45% (year ending 12/31/93) (0.75% without waiver)

ANTHEM FUNDS ◆
(Data common to all Anthem funds are shown below. See subsequent listings for data specific to individual Anthem funds)

1000 Market Tower
10 West Market Street
Indianapolis, IN 46204
317-692-3900, 800-273-3936
fax 317-692-3940

Adviser: Anthem Capital Management, Inc.
Administrator/Distributor: Sunstone Financial Group, Inc.
Custodian and transfer agent: Firstar Trust Co.
Minimum purchase: Initial: $1,000, Subsequent: $250; IRA: Initial: $500, Subsequent: $50
Telephone orders accepted: Yes
Wire orders accepted: Yes
Deadline for same day wire purchase: 4 P.M.
Telephone redemptions: Yes, $1,000 minimum, $10,000 maximum
Telephone redemptions: Yes, $1,000 minimum, $7.50 fee
Letter redemptions: Signature guarantee required over $10,000
Telephone switching: With other Anthem funds, Federated International Equity and International Income funds and Portico Money Market funds
Number of switches permitted: Unlimited, $5 fee
Shareholder services: IRA, 401(k), 403(b), automatic investment plan (minimum $50/month), withdrawal plan min. req. $10,000

ANTHEM AGGRESSIVE GROWTH FUND ◆
(See first Anthem listing for data common to all Anthem funds)

Portfolio manager: Thomas P. Lynch (1994)
Investment objective and policies: Capital growth. Invests at least 75% of assets in equity securities of small- (under $200M) to mid-capitalization ($200M to $2B) companies believed to possess superior growth potential. May engage in active short-term trading and participate in initial public offerings.
Year organized: 1994
Qualified for sale in: AL, DC, FL, HI, IL, IN, KY, MI, NJ, OH
Dividends paid: Income - March, June, September, December; Capital gains - December
Largest holding: Eli Lilly & Co. (2.2%)
Management fee: 0.75%
Expense ratio: 1.35% (4 months ending 10/31/94) (3.31% without waiver)

ANTHEM BALANCED FUND ◆
(See first Anthem listing for data common to all Anthem funds)

Portfolio managers: Gregory C. Donaldson (1991), Steven W. Voss (1994)
Investment objective and policies: Capital appreciation and current income. Invests primarily in stocks and debt securities of mid- to large-capitalization companies or taxable municipal obligations of issuers. No more than 65% of assets invested in equity securities and at least 25% invested in fixed income senior securities. May also invest in convertible securities.
Year organized: 1991 (name changed from Sagamore Total Return Fund in 1994)
Qualified for sale in: AL, AZ, CO, FL, IL, IN, KY, MI, NC, NJ, OH, TX, VA
Dividends paid: Income - March, June, September, December; Capital gains - December
Portfolio turnover (3 yrs): 91%, 64%, 46%
Largest holding: U.S. Treasury Note 7.25% due 5/15/04 (6.3%)
Management fee: 0.625%
Expense ratio: 1.42% (year ending 10/31/94) (1.93% without waiver)

ANTHEM EQUITY INCOME FUND ◆
(See first Anthem listing for data common to all Anthem funds)

Portfolio manager: Gregory C. Donaldson (1994)
Investment objective and policies: Current yield higher than S&P 500 Index plus dividend income with long-term capital appreciation secondary. Invests primarily in common stocks of mid- to large-capitalization companies with a demonstrated record of rising earnings and dividends, but may also invest in the preferred stocks of such companies. May invest up to 35% of assets in convertible securities and investment grade debt securities.
Year organized: 1994
Qualified for sale in: DC, FL, HI, IN, KY, MI, NJ, OH
Dividends paid: Income - March, June, September, December; Capital gains - December
Largest holding: Schering-Plough Corp. (3.7%)
Management fee: 0.65%
Expense ratio: 1.25% (4 months ending 10/31/94) (3.13% without waiver)

ANTHEM GOVERNMENT SECURITIES FUND ◆
(See first Anthem listing for data common to all Anthem funds)

Portfolio manager: Gregory C. Donaldson (1991)
Investment objective and policies: Current income and preservation of capital. Invests primarily in U.S. government securities but up to 35% of assets may be in non-governmental securities rated A of better by S&P or Moody's. Adjusts weighted average maturity to changes in interest rate climate.
Year organized: 1991 (formerly Sagamore Bond Fund)
Qualified for sale in: AZ, CO, FL, IL, IN, KY, MI, NC, NJ, OH, VA
Dividends paid: Income - monthly; Capital gains - December
Portfolio turnover (3 yrs): 69%, 39%, 66%
Management fee: 0.50%
Expense ratio: 1.18% (year ending 10/31/94) (2.81% without waiver)

ANTHEM GROWTH & INCOME FUND ◆
(See first Anthem listing for data common to all Anthem funds)

Portfolio manager: Thomas P. Lynch (1991)
Investment objective and policies: Capital appreciation and income. Invests primarily in common stocks of mid- to large-capitalization companies with records of rising earnings and dividends. May also invest in small-capitalization companies and companies under restructuring if they appear undervalued. Up to 25% of assets may be invested in preferred stock, convertible securities or investment grade debt securities.
Year organized: 1991 (formerly Sagamore Growth Fund)
Ticker symbol: SGGRX
Qualified for sale in: CO, FL, IL, IN, KY, NC, OH, VA
Dividends paid: Income - March, June, September, December; Capital gains - December
Portfolio turnover (3 yrs): 184%, 211%, 53%
Largest holding: Dow Chemical Co. (4.2%)
Management fee: 0.625%
Expense ratio: 1.55% (year ending 10/31/94) (1.99% without waiver)

ANTHEM INCOME FUND ◆
(See first Anthem listing for data common to all Anthem funds)

Portfolio manager: Stephen L. Tufts (1994)
Investment objective and policies: Maximum current income. Invests at least 65% of assets in income-producing securities such as investment grade corporate and government securities, high-

yield securities consisting of lower-rated corporate bonds, convertible securities, preferred stock, dividend-paying common stocks and U.S. dollar denominated foreign securities. Up to 35% may be in junk bonds.
Year organized: 1994
Dividends paid: Income - monthly; Capital gains - December
Largest holding: U.S. Treasury Bond 10.75% due 5/15/03 (9.6%)
Management fee: 0.65%
Expense ratio: 1.25% (4 months ending 10/31/94) (3.36% without waiver)

ANTHEM INTERMEDIATE U.S. GOVERNMENT SECURITIES FUND ◆
(See first Anthem for data common to all Anthem funds)

Portfolio manager: Stephen L. Tufts (1994)
Investment objective and policies: Current income and preservation of capital. Invests substantially all assets in intermediate-term securities with weighted average maturity of 3 to 10 years issued or backed by the U.S. government or its agencies or instrumentalities.
Year organized: 1994
Dividends paid: Income - Monthly; Capital gains - December
Management fee: 0.55%
Expense ratio: 1.10% (4 months ending 10/31/94) (4.14% without waiver)

ANTHEM MUNICIPAL SECURITIES FUND ◆
(See first Anthem listing for data common to all Anthem funds)

Portfolio managers: Thomas P. Lynch (1994), Gregory C. Donaldson (1994)
Investment objective and policies: Current income exempt from federal income tax. Invests in investment grade municipal securities with at least 80% of assets in "general obligation" and "revenue" securities. May invest up to 25% of assets in AMT securities.
Year organized: 1994
Dividends paid: Income - Monthly; Capital gains - December
Management fee: 0.45%
Expense ratio: 0.90% (4 months ending 10/31/94) (2.22% without waiver)

ANTHEM VALUE FUND ◆
(See first Anthem listing for data common to all Anthem funds)

Portfolio manager: Steven W. Voss (1994)
Investment objective and policies: Capital growth. Invests at least 75% of assets in equity securities of mid- to large-capitalization companies judged to be undervalued compare to market of historical valuations.
Year organized: 1994
Dividends paid: Income - March, June, September, December; Capital gains - December
Largest holding: Chevron Corp. (1.9%)
Management fee: 0.65%
Expense ratio: 1.25% (4 months ending 10/31/94) (3.08% without waiver)

API TRUST FUNDS
(Data common to all API Trust funds are shown below. See subsequent listings for data specific to individual API Trust funds.)

P.O. Box 2529
Yorktown Avenue
Lynchburg, VA 24501
804-846-1361, 800-544-6060
fax 804-846-1837

Adviser: Yorktown Management and Research Co., Inc.
Custodian: Piedmont Trust Bank, Lynchburg, VA
Transfer agent: Fund Services, Inc.

Minimum purchase: Initial: $500, Subsequent: $100
Telephone orders accepted: No
Wire orders accepted: Yes
Deadline for same day wire purchase: 4 P.M.
Qualified for sale in: All states except IA, WI
Wire redemptions: Yes, $100 minimum, $10 fee
Letter redemptions: Signature guarantee required over $10,000
Telephone switching: With other API Trust funds and the Government Cash Series money market fund
Number of switches permitted: Unlimited
Shareholder services: IRA, Keogh, 401(k), 403(b), automatic investment plan (waives initial minimum), withdrawal plan min. req. $10,000, electronic funds transfer
IRA fee: Annual $10

API TRUST CAPITAL INCOME FUND
(See first API Trust listing for data common to all API Trust funds)

Portfolio manager: David D. Basten (1988)
Investment objective and policies: High current income with growth of capital and income secondary. Invests at least 65% of assets in shares of underlying funds that seek to achieve an objective of high current income by investing in equity securities, including dividend-paying common stocks and convertible securities, long- or short-term bonds and other fixed-income securities. May invest up to 25% of assets in underlying funds that leverage.
Year organized: 1988 (Income Fund prior to 2/22/91, which invested in individual securities; formerly Investment Grade Securities Fund)
Ticker symbol: APIGX
Dividends paid: Income - December; Capital gains - December
Portfolio turnover (3 yrs): 17%, 29%, 55%
Management fee: 0.6%
12b-1 distribution fee: 0.50%
Expense ratio: 2.12% (year ending 5/31/94) (2.72% without waiver)

API TRUST GROWTH FUND
(See first API Trust listing for data common to all API Trust funds)

Portfolio manager: David D. Basten (1985)
Investment objective and policies: Capital growth. Invests primarily in shares of underlying funds that seek long-term capital growth or appreciation by investing in common stock or securities convertible into or exchangeable for common stock. May also invest in funds that invest in long- or short-term bonds and other fixed-income securities. Up to 25% of assets may be in funds that leverage.
Year organized: 1985 (invested in individual securities prior to 2/22/91)
Ticker symbol: APITX
Dividends paid: Income - December; Capital gains - December
Portfolio turnover (3 yrs): 90%, 157%, 99%
Management fee: 1.0% first $100M, 0.75% over $100M
12b-1 distribution fee: 1.0%
Expense ratio: 2.24% (year ending 5/31/94) (2.56% without waiver)

API TRUST SPECIAL MARKETS TRUST
(See first API Trust listing for data common to all API Trust funds)

Portfolio manager: David D. Basten (1988)
Investment objective and policies: Maximum total return from capital growth and income. Invests primarily in shares of funds whose portfolios mirror those of market securities indices such as the S&P 500 and NYSE. Leverages up to one-third of net assets. May invest up to 10% of assets in illiquid securities.
Year organized: 1988 (Precious Resources Fund

prior to 2/22/91, which invested in individual securities. Name and objective changed from Natural Resources Fund in 1992.)
Ticker symbol: APIPX
Dividends paid: Income - December; Capital gains - December
Portfolio turnover (3 yrs): 279%, 332%, 242%
Management fee: 1.0% first 100M, 0.75% over $100M
12b-1 distribution fee: 0.25%
Expense ratio: 5.22% (year ending 5/21/94) (6.98% without waiver)

API TRUST T-1 TREASURY TRUST
(See first API Trust listing for data common to all API Trust funds)

Portfolio manager: David D. Basten (1988)
Investment objective and policies: Current income with limited credit risk. Invests primarily in U.S. Treasury securities with remaining maturities of 1 year or less. Fund is not operated as a money market fund and does not maintain a stable NAV.
Year organized: 1988 (U.S. Government Intermediate Fund prior to 2/22/91, which invested in individual securities. Name and objective changed from Global Income Fund in November 1994. Prior performance may be misleading.)
Dividends paid: Income - March, June, September, December; Capital gains - December
Portfolio turnover (3 yrs): 127%, 308%, 391%
Management fee: 0.6%
12b-1 distribution fee: 0.25%
Expense ratio: 1.57% (year ending 5/31/94) (2.16% without waiver)

API TRUST TOTAL RETURN FUND
(See first API Trust listing for data common to all API Trust funds)

Portfolio manager: David D. Basten (1988)
Investment objective and policies: Maximum total return, capital growth and income. Invests in a broad range of underlying funds, allocating assets among aggressive growth, growth, growth and income, fixed-income and money market funds with composition adjusted to reflect changes in market and economic conditions. Up to 25% of assets may be in funds that leverage.
Year organized: 1988 (Balanced Fund prior to 2/22/91, which invested in individual securities)
Ticker symbol: APIBX
Dividends paid: Income - December; Capital gains - December
Portfolio turnover (3 yrs): 30%, 121%, 140%
Management fee: 1.0% first $100M, 0.75% over $100M
12b-1 distribution fee: 1.0%
Expense ratio: 2.19% (year ending 5/31/94) (3.19% without waiver)

AQUINAS FUNDS ◆
(Data common to all Aquinas funds are shown below. See subsequent listings for data specific to individual Aquinas funds.)

5310 Harvest Hill Road, Suite 248
Dallas, TX 75230
214-233-6655, 800-423-6369

Adviser: Aquinas Investment Advisers, Inc. (a wholly-owned subsidiary of The Catholic Foundation)
Administrator: Sunstone Financial Group, Inc.
Custodian: United Missouri Bank, N.A.
Transfer agent: Supervised Service Company, Inc.
Minimum purchase: Initial: $1,000, Subsequent: $250; IRA: Initial: $500, Subsequent: $50
Telephone orders accepted: No
Wire orders accepted: No
Qualified for sale in: CA, IL, LA, MT, NY, OR, PA, SD, TX
Telephone redemptions: Yes, $1,000 minimum
Wire redemptions: Yes, $1,000 minimum, $9 fee

Letter redemptions: Signature guarantee required over $25,000
Telephone switching: With other Aquinas funds, $1,000 minimum
Number of switches permitted: Unlimited
Shareholder services: IRA, 403(b), automatic investment plan—minimum $50/month, withdrawal plan min. req. $10,000
Administrator fee: 0.23% first $50M to 0.075% over $250M (for combined assets of all funds)
IRA fees: Annual $12

AQUINAS BALANCED FUND ◆
(See first Aquinas listing for data common to all Aquinas funds)

Sub-advisers: Team composed of sub-advisers of other Aquinas funds
Portfolio managers: Team composed of portfolio managers of other Aquinas funds
Investment objective and policies: Long-term capital growth consistent with reasonable risk. Invests in common stocks of established companies (40-70% of assets), investment-grade bonds (25-40%) and cash equivalents. Allocation will vary depending on market and economic conditions. May invest up to 20% of assets in securities of foreign issuers and use futures and options to hedge.
Year organized: 1994
Ticker symbol: AQBLX
Dividends paid: Income - March, June, September, December; Capital gains - December
Management fee: 1.0%

AQUINAS EQUITY GROWTH FUND ◆
(See first Aquinas listing for data common to all Aquinas funds)

Sub-advisers: John McStay Investment Counsel, Sirach Capital Management, Inc.
Portfolio manager: Team composed of portfolio managers of other Aquinas funds (1994)
Investment objective and policies: Capital appreciation. Invests primarily in common stocks of companies believed to have above average growth potential. May also invest in preferred stocks, convertible securities and warrants. May invest up to 20% of assets in securities of foreign issuers and use futures and options to hedge.
Year organized: 1994
Dividends paid: Income - March, June, September, December; Capital gains - December
Management fee: 1.0%

AQUINAS EQUITY INCOME FUND ◆
(See first Aquinas listing for data common to all Aquinas funds)

Sub-adviser: Spare, Tengler, Kaplan & Bischel, Inc.
Portfolio managers: Team composed of portfolio managers of other Aquinas funds (1994)
Investment objective and policies: Growth of capital and high current income. Invests at least 85% of assets in dividend-paying common stocks of large conservative companies with market capitalizations of $2B or more. May invest up to 20% of assets in securities of foreign issuers and use futures and options to hedge.
Year organized: 1994
Ticker symbol: AQEIX
Dividends paid: Income - March, June, September, December; Capital gains - December
Management fee: 1.0%

AQUINAS FIXED INCOME FUND ◆
(See first Aquinas listing for data common to all Aquinas funds)

Sub-advisers: Atlantic Asset Management Partners, Inc.; Income Research & Management, Inc.
Portfolio managers: Team composed of portfolio managers of other Aquinas funds (1994)
Investment objective and policies: High current

income with reasonable opportunity for capital appreciation. Invests primarily in investment-grade debt securities of government and corporate issuers and in mortgage-backed securities. May invest up to 25% of assets in junk bonds, 20% in securities of foreign issuers and use futures and options to hedge.
Year organized: 1994
Ticker symbol: AQFIX
Dividends paid: Income - declared and paid monthly; Capital gains - December
Management fee: 0.6%

ARBOR FUND - OVB PORTFOLIOS
(Data common to all Arbor Fund OVB portfolios are shown below. See subsequent listings for data specific to individual Arbor Fund OVB portfolios)

680 E. Swedesford Road
Wayne, PA 19087
304-348-7094, 800-545-6331

Adviser: One Valley Bank, N.A.
Administrator: SEI Financial Management Corp.
Custodian: CoreStates Bank, N.A.
Transfer agent: Supervised Service Company
Minimum purchase: Initial $1,000, Subsequent $50; IRA/Keogh: Initial: $500
Telephone orders accepted: No
Wire orders accepted: Yes
Deadline for same day wire purchase: 4 P.M.
Qualified for sale in: CA, FL, KY, MD, NC, OH, PA, VA, WV, WY
Telephone redemptions: Yes
Wire redemptions: Yes, $500 minimum, $10 fee
Letter redemptions: Signature guarantee required over $5,000
Telephone switching: With other Arbor Fund OVB portfolios
Number of switches permitted: Unlimited
Shareholder services: Keogh, IRA, 401(k), corporate retirement plans, automatic investment plan—minimum $100/month, electronic funds transfer (purchase only), withdrawal plan min. req. $10,000
IRA/Keogh fees: D.N.A.

ARBOR FUND - OVB CAPITAL APPRECIATION PORTFOLIO
(See first Arbor OVB listing for data common to all Arbor OVB portfolios)

Portfolio manager: David Nolan (1993)
Investment objective and policies: Long-term capital growth. Invests primarily in equity securities of undervalued companies with established records of growth and market capitalizations of more than $1B and the potential to achieve above average returns. May invest in securities of foreign issuers traded in the U.S. or Canada without limit and have up to 15% of assets in illiquid securities.
Year organized: 1993
Dividends paid: Income - March, June, September, December; Capital gains - December
Largest holding: General Instrument Corp. (3.1%)
Management fee: 0.95%
12b-1 distribution fee: 0.25%

ARBOR FUND - OVB EMERGING GROWTH PORTFOLIO
(See first Arbor OVB listing for data common to all Arbor OVB portfolios)

Portfolio manager: David Nolan (1993)
Investment objective and policies: Long-term capital growth. Invests primarily in equity securities of undervalued companies with market capitalizations of less than $1B and the potential to achieve above average returns. May invest in securities of foreign issuers traded in the U.S. or Canada without limit and have up to 15% of assets in illiquid securities.
Year organized: 1993
Dividends paid: Income - March, June, September, December; Capital gains - December
Largest holding: Hollywood Entertainment (3.7%)
Management fee: 0.95%
12b-1 distribution fee: 0.25%

ARBOR FUND - OVB GOVERNMENT SECURITIES PORTFOLIO
(See first Arbor OVB listing for data common to all Arbor OVB portfolios)

Portfolio manager: Jay Thomas (1993)
Investment objective and policies: Current income consistent with preservation of capital. Invests primarily in debt obligations guaranteed as to principal and interest by the U.S. government or its agencies and instrumentalities with a weighted average maturity of 3 to 10 years. May also invest in investment-grade corporate debt securities and mortgage- and asset-backed securities. Up to 20% of assets may be in common and preferred stocks of utility companies. May use futures and options to hedge.
Year organized: 1993
Dividends paid: Income - declared daily, paid monthly; Capital gains - December
Management fee: 0.75%
12b-1 distribution fee: 0.25%

ARBOR FUND - OVB PRIME OBLIGATIONS PORTFOLIO
(See first Arbor OVB listing for data common to all Arbor OVB portfolios)

Sub-adviser: Wellington Management Corp.
Portfolio manager: Tim Smith (1993)
Investment objective and policies: Current income consistent with preservation of capital and liquidity. Invests in high quality money market instruments.
Year organized: 1993
Dividends paid: Income - declared daily, paid monthly
Management fee: 0.25%
12b-1 distribution fee: 0.25%

ARBOR FUND - OVB WEST VIRGINIA TAX-EXEMPT INCOME PORTFOLIO
(See first Arbor OVB listing for data common to all Arbor OVB portfolios)

Portfolio manager: Jay Thomas (1993)
Investment objective and policies: Current income exempt from federal and West Virginia personal income taxes consistent with preservation of capital. Invests primarily in high quality municipal securities exempt from federal and West Virginia personal income taxes. Up to 20% of assets may be in AMT securities. May use futures and options to hedge.
Year organized: 1993
Dividends paid: Income - declared daily, paid monthly; Capital gains - December
Management fee: 0.45%
12b-1 distribution fee: 0.25%

ARIEL APPRECIATION FUND
307 North Michigan Avenue, Suite 500
Chicago, IL 60601
312-726-0140, 800-292-7435
fax 312-726-7473

Adviser: Ariel Capital Management, Inc.
Portfolio manager: Eric McKissack (1989)
Custodian and transfer agent: Investors Fiduciary Trust Company
Investment objective and policies: Long-term capital appreciation. Invests primarily in equity securities of undervalued companies with market capitalizations of $200M to $5B and the potential to achieve above average returns. May invest up to 20% of assets in bonds and other debt obligations or fixed income obligations. Investments are environmentally and socially screened; avoids companies with poor environmental records or engaged in weapons manufacturing, nuclear energy production or doing business in South Africa.

Year organized: 1989 (name changed from Calvert-Ariel Appreciation fund in 1994)
Ticker symbol: CAAPX
Minimum purchase: Initial $1,000, Subsequent $50; IRA/Keogh: Initial $250
Telephone orders accepted: No
Wire orders accepted: Yes, $1,000 minimum
Deadline for same day wire purchase: 4 P.M.
Discount broker availability: *Schwab, *White, Waterhouse, Fidelity, Siebert
Qualified for sale in: All states
Telephone redemptions: Yes, $1,000 minimum
Wire redemptions: Yes, $1,000 minimum, $10 fee
Letter redemptions: Signature guarantee required over $25,000
Telephone switching: With Ariel Growth Fund and Cash Resource money market funds
Number of switches permitted: May be limited to 5 per year
Dividends paid: Income - December; Capital gains - December
Portfolio turnover (3 yrs): 12%, 56%, 2%
Largest holding: Interco, Inc. (4.0%)
Shareholder services: IRA, SEP-IRA, 401(k), 403(b), corporate retirement plans, automatic investment plan, electronic funds transfer (purchase only), withdrawal plan min. req. $10,000
Management fee: 0.75%
12b-1 distribution fee: 0.25%
Expense ratio: 1.35% (year ending 9/30/94) (1.40% without waiver)
IRA/Keogh fees: Annual $25

ARIEL GROWTH FUND
307 North Michigan Avenue, Suite 500
Chicago, IL 60601
312-726-0140, 800-292-7435
fax 312-726-7473

Adviser: Ariel Capital Management, Inc.
Portfolio manager: John W. Rogers, Jr. (1986)
Custodian and transfer agent: Investors Fiduciary Trust Company
Investment objective and policies: Long-term capital appreciation. Invests primarily in equity securities of undervalued companies with market capitalizations under $1.5B with high growth potential and the ability to achieve a high annual return on equity. May invest up to 20% of assets in bonds and other debt or fixed income obligation. Investments are environmentally and socially screened; avoids investing in companies with poor environmental records or engaged in weapons manufacturing, nuclear energy production or doing business in South Africa.
Year organized: 1986 (name changed from Calvert-Ariel Growth Fund in 1994)
Ticker symbol: ARGFX
Minimum purchase: Initial $1,000, Subsequent $50; IRA/Keogh: Initial $250
Special sales restriction: Fund closed to new shareholders since 4/30/90
Telephone orders accepted: No
Wire orders accepted: Yes, $1,000 minimum
Deadline for same day wire purchase: 4 P.M.
Discount broker availability: *Schwab, *White
Qualified for sale in: All states
Telephone redemptions: Yes, $1,000 minimum
Wire redemptions: Yes, $1,000 minimum, $10 fee
Letter redemptions: Signature guarantee required over $25,000
Telephone switching: With Ariel Appreciation Fund and Cash Resource money market funds
Number of switches permitted: May be limited to 5 per year
Dividends paid: Income - December; Capital gains - December
Portfolio turnover (3 yrs): 9%, 13%, 19%
Largest holding: Longs Drug Stores, Inc. (4.6%)
Shareholder services: IRA, SEP-IRA, 401(k), 403(b), corporate retirement plans, automatic investment plan, electronic funds transfer (purchase only), withdrawal plan min. req. $10,000
Management fee: 0.65%
12b-1 distribution fee: 0.25%
Expense ratio: 1.25% (year ending 9/30/94)
IRA/Keogh fees: Annual $25

ARK FUNDS
(Data common to all Ark funds are shown below. See subsequent listings for data specific to individual Ark funds.

First Maryland Brokerage Corp.
25 South Charles Street
P.O. Box 1596
Baltimore, MD 21203
800-842-2265, fax 410-347-6612

Adviser: First National Bank of Maryland
Custodian: U.S. Trust Company of New York
Transfer agent: Mutual Funds Service Company
Minimum purchase: Initial $1,000, Subsequent $100
Telephone orders accepted: No
Wire orders accepted: Yes, $1,000 minimum
Deadline for same day wire purchase: 4 P.M.
Qualified for sale in: CA, CT, DC, DE, FL, GA, MD, NC, NJ, NY, SC, TX, VA, WV
Telephone redemptions: Yes
Letter redemptions: Signature guarantee required over $25,000
Telephone switching: With other Ark funds
Number of switches permitted: Unlimited
Shareholder services: Keogh, IRA, SEP-IRA, corporate retirement plans, automatic investment plan
IRA/Keogh fees: Annual $25

ARK CAPITAL GROWTH PORTFOLIO
(See first Ark listing for data common to all Ark funds)

Portfolio manager: James D. McCall (1993)
Investment objective and policies: Long-term capital appreciation. Invests primarily in common stocks and securities convertible into common stock of companies of all sizes with above average growth prospects. May invest up to 35% of assets in bonds and other debt or fixed income obligations and 25% in ADRs and EDRs of foreign issuers. May use futures and options and sell short "against the box."
Year organized: 1993
Discount broker availability: Fidelity, Siebert
Dividends paid: Income - December; Capital gains - December
Portfolio turnover (1 yr): 41%
Largest holding: Sensormatics Electronics Corp. (2.8%)
Management fee: 0.60%
12b-1 distribution fee: 0.55%
Expense ratio: 1.92% (9 months ending 3/40/94) (30.78% without waiver)

ARK GROWTH AND INCOME PORTFOLIO
(See first Ark listing for data common to all Ark funds)
Portfolio manager: Charles E. Knudsen III (1993)
Investment objective and policies: Long-term total return - capital appreciation and current income. Invests in a broad range of common stocks, bonds and cash equivalents. May invest up to 25% of assets ADRs and EDRs of foreign issuers. May use futures and options and sell short "against the box."
Year organized: 1993
Discount broker availability: Fidelity, Siebert
Dividends paid: Income - March, June, September, December; Capital gains - December
Portfolio turnover (1 yr): 37%
Largest holding: Triton Energy Corp. (2.6%)
Management fee: 0.55%
12b-1 distribution fee: 0.55%
Expense ratio: 1.86% (9 months ending 4/30/94) (15.08% without waiver)

ARK INCOME PORTFOLIO
(See first Ark listing for data common to all Ark funds)

Portfolio managers: Susan S. Schnaars (1993), Marcia Z. Myers (1993)

Investment objective and policies: High current income with capital appreciation secondary, consistent with reasonable risk. Invests primarily in investment-grade fixed-income securities including bonds, notes, mortgage- and asset-backed securities, government obligations and convertible securities. May invest up to 25% of assets ADRs and EDRs of foreign issuers. May use futures and options and sell short "against the box."
Year organized: 1993
Discount broker availability: Fidelity, Siebert
Dividends paid: Income - monthly; Capital gains - December
Portfolio turnover (1 yr): 20%
Management fee: 0.50%
12b-1 distribution fee: 0.45%
Expense ratio: 1.72% (9 months ending 4/30/94) (55.35% without waiver)

ARK MONEY MARKET PORTFOLIO
(See first Ark listing for data common to all Ark funds)

Portfolio manager: James M. Hannan (1993)
Investment objective and policies: High current income consistent with preservation of principal and liquidity. Invests primarily in investment-grade money market instruments.
Year organized: 1993
Dividends paid: Income - declared daily, paid monthly
Management fee: 0.25%
12b-1 distribution fee: 0.40%
Expense ratio: 1.16% (9 months ending 4/30/94) (592.55% without waiver)

ARK TAX-FREE MONEY MARKET PORTFOLIO
(See first Ark listing for data common to all Ark funds)

Portfolio manager: James M. Hannan (1993)
Investment objective and policies: High current income exempt from federal income tax consistent with preservation of principal and liquidity. Invests primarily in investment-grade municipal money market instruments.
Year organized: 1993
Dividends paid: Income - declared daily, paid monthly
Management fee: 0.25%
12b-1 distribution fee: 0.40%
Expense ratio: 1.25% (9 months ending 4/30/94) (32.17% without waiver)

ARK U.S. GOVERNMENT MONEY MARKET PORTFOLIO
(See first Ark listing for data common to all Ark funds)

Portfolio manager: James M. Hannan (1993)
Investment objective and policies: High current income consistent with preservation of principal and liquidity. Invests exclusively in money market instruments guaranteed as to principal and interest by the U.S. Government, its agencies or instrumentalities.
Year organized: 1993
Dividends paid: Income - declared daily, paid monthly
Management fee: 0.25%
12b-1 distribution fee: 0.40%
Expense ratio: 0.35% (9 months ending 4/30/94) (0.62% without waiver)

ARK U.S. TREASURY MONEY MARKET PORTFOLIO
(See first Ark listing for data common to all Ark funds)

Portfolio manager: James M. Hannan (1993)
Investment objective and policies: High current

income consistent with preservation of principal and liquidity. Invests exclusively in money market instruments guaranteed as to principal and interest by the U.S. Government with interest exempt from state and local income taxes.
Year organized: 1993
Dividends paid: Income - declared daily, paid monthly
Management fee: 0.25%
12b-1 distribution fee: 0.40%
Expense ratio: 0.43% (9 months ending 4/30/94) (0.51% without waiver)

ARMSTRONG ASSOCIATES ◆
750 North St. Paul, LB 13
Suite 1300
Dallas, TX 75201
214-720-9101, fax 214-871-8948

Adviser: Portfolios, Inc.
Portfolio manager: C. K. Lawson (1967)
Custodian: The Bank of California, N.A.
Transfer agent: Portfolios, Inc.
Investment objective and policies: Capital growth. Invests primarily in common stocks which offer prospects for earnings growth or capital growth over a 1 to 3 year period, but may also invest in convertible securities and, in volatile markets, short-term debt instruments. Up to 15% of assets may be in illiquid securities.
Year organized: 1967
Ticker symbol: AP.MSX
Minimum purchase: Initial: $250, Subsequent: $25
Telephone orders accepted: No
Wire orders accepted: No
Discount broker availability: White
Qualified for sale in: TX
Letter redemptions: Signature guarantee required
Dividends paid: Income - December; Capital gains - December
Portfolio turnover (3 yrs): 15%, 17%, 35%
Largest holding: Motorola, Inc. (9.4%)
Shareholder services: Keogh, IRA, corporate retirement plans, automatic investment plan, withdrawal plan
Management fee: 0.8%
Expense ratio: 1.79% (year ending 6/30/94)
IRA/Keogh fees: Annual $12, Closing $7

ASM FUND ◆
14538 N. Florida Ave. #107
Tampa, FL 33613
813-963-3150, 800-445-2763
fax 813-968-4074

Adviser: Vector Index Advisors, Inc.
Portfolio managers: Steven H. Adler (1991)
Custodian and transfer agent: Star Bank, N.A.
Investment objective and policies: Total return - capital appreciation and current income. Invests in common stocks of large well-established companies, principally the 30 companies that comprise the Dow Jones Industrial Average (DJIA). Although the fund may invest in other companies, it is effectively an index fund that mirrors the performance of the DJIA.
Year organized: 1991
Ticker symbol: ASMUX
Minimum purchase: Initial: $1,000, Subsequent: $100; IRA/Keogh: Initial: $500
Telephone orders accepted: Yes, subsequent only
Wire orders accepted: Yes
Deadline for same day wire purchase: 4 P.M.
Discount broker availability: *White, *Waterhouse, Fidelity, Siebert
Qualified for sale in: All states except ND, SD
Wire redemptions: Yes, $1,000 minimum
Letter redemptions: Signature guarantee not required
Redemption fee: 0.75% if shareholder redeems shares more than 6 times per year
Telephone switching: With Flex-Fund Money Market fund
Number of switches permitted: Unlimited

Dividends paid: Income - March, June, September, December; Capital gains - December
Portfolio turnover (3 yrs): 1193%, 642%, 405%
Largest holding: Aluminum Company of America (5.3%)
Shareholder services: Keogh, IRA, automatic investment plan
Management fee: 0.60%
Expense ratio: 0.75% (year ending 10/31/94) (3.07% without waiver)
IRA/Keogh fees: Annual $8, Closing $7

ASSET MANAGEMENT FUND, INC.
(Data common to all Asset Management Fund portfolios are shown below. See subsequent listings for data specific to individual Asset Management portfolios.)

111 East Wacker Drive
Chicago, IL 60601
800-527-3713, fax 312-938-2548

Adviser: Shay Assets Management Co.
Portfolio manager: Edward E. Sammons, Jr.
Custodian: PNC Bank, Philadelphia
Transfer agent: PFPC, Inc.
Special sales restrictions: Designed for institutional investors but available to individual investors in specific states
Minimum purchase: Initial: $10,000, Subsequent: None
Telephone orders accepted: No
Wire orders accepted: Yes
Deadline for same day wire purchase: 4 P.M.
Telephone redemptions: Yes
Wire redemptions: Yes
Letter redemptions: Signature guarantee required
Telephone switching: With other Asset Management Fund portfolios
Number of switches permitted: Unlimited
Deadline for same day switch: 12 NN
Dividends paid: Income - monthly; Capital gains - December

ASSET MANAGEMENT FUND, INC. - ADJUSTABLE RATE MORTGAGE PORTFOLIO
(See first Asset Management listing for data common to all Asset Management portfolios)

Investment objective and policies: High level of current income consistent with preservation of capital and liquidity. Invests at least 65% of assets in Adjustable Rate Mortgage Securities with remainder in U.S. Government or agency securities, private fixed rate mortgage-related securities, certificates of deposit, bankers acceptances with remaining maturities of 9 months or less and repurchase agreements. Fund maintains a weighted average maturity of one year or less.
Year organized: 1991
Ticker symbol: ASARX
Qualified for sale in: CO, CT, DC, FL, GA, HI, IL, IN, LA, MS, NJ, NY, PA, TN, VA, WI, WY
Portfolio turnover (3 yrs): 65%, 30%, 43%
Management fee: 0.45% first $3B to 0.25% over $5B
12b-1 distribution fee: 0.25%
Expense ratio: 0.47% (year ending 10/31/94) (0.76% without waiver)

ASSET MANAGEMENT FUND, INC. - INTERMEDIATE MORTGAGE SECURITIES PORTFOLIO
(See first Asset Management listing for data common to all Asset Management portfolios)

Investment objective and policies: High level of current income consistent with preservation of capital and liquidity. Invests at least 65% of assets in mortgage-related securities paying fixed or adjustable rates of interest with a weighted average maturity of 2 to 7 years.

Year organized: 1986 (name changed from Corporate Bond Portfolio on 6/2/92. Prior to name change Portfolio was invested primarily in investment-grade corporate bonds.)
Ticker symbol: ASCPX
Qualified for sale in: CO, DC, FL, GA, HI, IL, IN, NJ, PA, VA, TN, WY
Portfolio turnover (3 yrs): 358%, 106%, 226%
Management fee: 0.35% first $500M to 0.10% over $1.5B
12b-1 distribution fee: 0.15%
Expense ratio: 0.39% (year ending 10/31/94) (0.59% without waiver)

ASSET MANAGEMENT FUND - MONEY MARKET PORTFOLIO
(See first Asset Management listing for data common to all Asset Management portfolios)

Investment objective and policies: High level of current income consistent with preservation of capital and liquidity. Invests in high quality money market instruments.
Year organized: 1982 (name changed from Short-Term Liquidity Portfolio in 10/94)
Ticker symbol: ASLXX
Qualified for sale in: CO, DC, FL, GA, HI, IL, IN, NJ, NY, PA, TN, VA, WY
Management fee: 0.15% first $500M to 0.10% over $1B
12b-1 distribution fee: 0.15%
Expense ratio: 0.40% (year ending 10/31/94) (0.42% without waiver)

ASSET MANAGEMENT FUND, INC. - SHORT U.S. GOVERNMENT SECURITIES PORTFOLIO
(See first Asset Management listing for data common to all Asset Management portfolios)

Investment objective and policies: High level of current income consistent with preservation of capital and liquidity. Invests in obligations issued by or fully guaranteed as to principal and interest by U.S. Government agencies or instrumentalities, certificates of deposit and other time deposits, bankers' acceptances with remaining maturities of 9 months or less and repurchase agreements. The fund does not invest in securities with remaining maturities in excess of 5 years.
Year organized: 1982 (name changed from Intermediate-Term Liquidity Portfolio on 10/3/94)
Ticker symbol: ASITX
Qualified for sale in: CO, CT, DC, FL, GA, HI, IL, IN, NJ, NY, PA, TN, VA, WY
Portfolio turnover (3 yrs): 195%, 110%, 43%
Management fee: 0.25% first $500M to 0.10% over $1.5B
12b-1 distribution fee: 0.15%
Expense ratio: 0.47% (year ending 10/31/94)

ASSET MANAGEMENT FUND, INC. - U.S. GOVERNMENT MORTGAGE SECURITIES PORTFOLIO
(See first Asset Management listing for data common to all Asset Management portfolios)

Investment objective and policies: High level of current income consistent with preservation of capital and liquidity. Invests at least 65% of assets in mortgage-related securities with remainder in U.S. Government or agency securities, certificates of deposit or other time deposits, repurchase agreements and interest rate futures contracts and options.
Year organized: 1984 (name changed from Mortgage Securities Performance Portfolio on 10/3/94)
Ticker symbol: ASMTX
Qualified for sale in: CO, DC, FL, GA, HI, IL, IN, NJ, NY, PA, TN, VA, WI, WY

Portfolio turnover (3 yrs): 187%, 64%, 43%
Management fee: 0.25% first $500M to 0.10% over $1.5B
12b-1 distribution fee: 0.15%
Expense ratio: 0.51% (year ending 10/31/94)

AUSTIN GLOBAL EQUITY FUND ◆
P.O. Box 446
Portland, ME 04112
207-879-0001, 800-216-8463
fax 207-879-6050

Adviser: Austin Investment Management, Inc.
Portfolio manager: Peter Austin Vlachos (1993)
Custodian: First National Bank of Boston
Transfer agent: Forum Financial Corp.
Investment objective and policies: Capital appreciation. Invests primarily in common stocks and securities convertible into common stocks of issuers based in the U.S., Europe, Japan and the Pacific Basin with above average growth potential or attractive valuations. May invest in foreign securities directly and through use of ADRs. Up to 35% of assets may be in convertible securities. May use futures and options to hedge up to 25% of assets.
Year organized: 1993
Minimum purchase: Initial: $10,000, Subsequent: $2,500; IRA: Initial: $2,000, Subsequent: $1,000
Telephone orders accepted: No
Wire orders accepted: Yes
Deadline for same day wire purchase: 4 P.M.
Qualified for sale in: CA, CT, DC, FL, IL, MN, NH, NJ, NY, OH, PA, TX, VA, VT, WY
Telephone redemptions: Yes
Wire redemptions: Yes, $10,000 minimum
Letter redemptions: Signature guarantee required
Dividends paid: Income - December; Capital gains - December
Portfolio turnover (1 yr): 2%
Largest holding: Liberty Property Trust (2.6%)
Shareholder services: IRA
Management fee: 1.5%
12b-1 distribution fee: 0.25%
Expense ratio: 2.36% (7 months ending 6/30/94) (4.18% without waiver)
IRA fees: Annual $25

AVONDALE TOTAL RETURN FUND ◆
1105 Holliday
Wichita Falls, TX 76301
817-761-3777

Adviser: Herbert R. Smith, Inc.
Portfolio manager: Herbert R. Smith (1988)
Custodian and transfer agent: Provident Bank of Cincinnati
Investment objective and policies: Income and capital growth generating maximum total return consistent with reasonable risk. Invests primarily in higher quality fixed-income obligations (minimum 15% of assets) and equity securities - common stocks, securities convertible into common stocks and preferred stocks. Up to 15% of assets may be in securities of foreign issuers.
Year organized: 1988
Minimum purchase: Initial: $1,000, Subsequent: $250; IRA/Keogh: Initial: $500, Subsequent $100
Telephone orders accepted: No
Wire orders accepted: Yes
Deadline for same day wire purchase: 4 P.M.
Qualified for sale in: AR, CO, CT, DC, FL, GA, HI, IL, IN, MN, MO, NC, OK, PA, TX, VA, WV, WY
Telephone redemptions: Yes
Wire redemptions: Yes, $1,000 minimum
Letter redemptions: Signature guarantee required
Dividends paid: Income - March, June, September, December; Capital gains - December
Portfolio turnover (3 yrs): 74%, 158%, 60%
Largest holding: FHLB, 8.00% due 5/16/01 (7.3%)
Shareholder services: IRA, automatic investment plan—minimum $500/month, withdrawal plan min. req. $10,000, electronic funds transfer (purchase only)

Management fee: 0.7% first $200M to 0.5% over $500M
Expense ratio: 1.83% (year ending 3/31/94)
IRA fees: Annual $10

BABSON FUNDS ◆
(Data common to all Babson funds are shown below. See subsequent listings for data specific to individual Babson funds.)

Three Crown Center
2440 Pershing Road
Kansas City, MO 64108
816-471-5200, 800-422-2766
fax 816-471-7826

Shareholder service hours: Full service: M-F 8 A.M.-4:30 P.M. CST; After hours service: prices, yields, news and views, messages, DJIA, prospectuses
Adviser: Jones & Babson, Inc. (a wholly-owned subsidiary of Business Men's Assurance Company of America, itself a wholly-owned subsidiary of Assicurazioni Generali S.p.A., an insurance organization founded in 1831 based in Trieste, Italy)
Custodian: United Missouri Bank of Kansas City (except Babson-Stewart Ivory International)
Transfer agent: Each fund serves as its own transfer agent
Telephone orders accepted: Yes, subsequent only
Wire orders accepted: Yes
Deadline for same day wire purchase: 4 P.M. (1 P.M. for money market funds)
Qualified for sale in: All states
Telephone redemptions: Money market funds only, $1,000 minimum
Wire redemptions: Money market funds only, $1,000 minimum
Letter redemptions: Signature guarantee required over $10,000
Telephone switching: With other Babson funds, $1,000 minimum
Number of switches permitted: 30 day hold
Shareholder services: Keogh, IRA, SEP-IRA, corporate retirement plans, automatic investment plan—minimum $100/month (waives initial minimum); withdrawal plan min. req. $10,000
IRA fees: Annual $10, Closing $10
Keogh fees: Annual $15, Closing $15

D. L. BABSON BOND TRUST - PORTFOLIO L ◆
(See first Babson listing for data common to all Babson funds)

Portfolio manager: Edward L. Martin (1984)
Investment objective and policies: Maximum current income and reasonable stability of principal. Normally invests at least 80% of assets in corporate bonds and U.S. Government or government guaranteed obligations with a weighted average maturity of more than 5 years. Up to 20% of assets may be in U.S. dollar-denominated Canadian Government or corporate debt securities.
Year organized: 1944 (formerly Babson Income Trust)
Ticker symbol: BABIX
Minimum purchase: Initial: $500, Subsequent: $50; IRA: Initial: $250; Keogh: Initial: $100
Discount broker availability: Schwab, *White, *Waterhouse, *Fidelity, *Siebert
Dividends paid: Income - declared daily, paid monthly; Capital gains - December
Portfolio turnover (3 yrs): 40%, 80%, 54%
Management fee: 0.95%
Expense ratio: 0.97% (year ending 11/30/94)

D. L. BABSON BOND TRUST - PORTFOLIO S ◆
(See first Babson listing for data common to all Babson funds)

Portfolio manager: Edward L. Martin (1988)
Investment objective and policies: Maximum current income and reasonable stability of principal. Normally invests at least 80% of assets in corporate bonds and U.S. Government or government guaranteed obligations with a weighted average maturity

of 2 to 5 years. Up to 20% of assets may be in U.S. dollar-denominated Canadian Government or corporate debt securities.
Year organized: 1988
Ticker symbol: BBDSX
Minimum purchase: Initial: $500, Subsequent: $50; IRA: Initial: $250; Keogh: Initial: $100
Discount broker availability: *White, *Waterhouse, *Fidelity, *Siebert
Dividends paid: Income - declared daily, paid monthly; Capital gains - December
Portfolio turnover (3 yrs): 42%, 147%, 47%
Management fee: 0.95%
Expense ratio: 0.67% (year ending 11/30/94) (0.95% without waiver)

BABSON BUFFALO BALANCED FUND ◆
(See first Babson fund for data common to all Babson funds)

Portfolio manager: Kent W. Gasaway (1994)
Investment objective and policies: Long-term capital growth and high current income. Invests primarily in common stocks of large capitalization ($1B +) companies listed on the NYSE and secondarily in convertible bonds and convertible preferred stock. May write covered put and call options and invest in issues of the U.S. government subject to repurchase agreements.
Year organized: 1994
Ticker symbol: BUFBX
Minimum purchase: Initial: $2,500, Subsequent: $100; IRA: Initial: $250
Dividends paid: Income - March, June September, December; Capital gains - December
Management fee: 1.0%

BABSON ENTERPRISE FUND ◆
(See first Babson listing for data common to all Babson funds)

Portfolio manager: Peter C. Schliemann (1983)
Investment objective and policies: Long-term growth of capital. Invests primarily in common stocks of smaller, faster growing companies which at time of purchase are considered to be realistically valued in the smaller company sector of the market. Capitalizations range from $15 million to $300 million.
Year organized: 1983
Ticker symbol: BABEX
Special sales restrictions: Fund closed to new shareholders on 2/1/92.
Minimum purchase: Initial: $1,000, Subsequent: $100; IRA/Keogh: Initial: $250, Subsequent: $50
Discount broker availability: Schwab, *White, *Waterhouse
Dividends paid: Income - December; Capital gains - December
Portfolio turnover (3 yrs): 15%, 17%, 28%
Largest holding: Anthony Industries (2.4%)
Management fee: 1.08%
Expense ratio: 1.08% (year ending 11/30/94)

BABSON ENTERPRISE FUND II ◆
(See first Babson listing for data common to all Babson funds)

Portfolio managers: Peter Schliemann (1991), Lance F. James (1991)
Investment objective and policies: Long-term growth of capital. Invests primarily in common stocks of smaller ($250M-$1B capitalization), faster growing companies which at time of purchase are considered to be realistically valued in the smaller company sector of the market. May also invest in U.S. government agency issues subject to repurchase agreements.
Year organized: 1991
Ticker symbol: BAETX
Minimum purchase: Initial: $1,000, Subsequent: $100; IRA: Initial: $250, Subsequent: $50; Keogh: Initial: $100, Subsequent: $50
Discount broker availability: Schwab, *White, *Waterhouse, *Fidelity, *Siebert

Dividends paid: Income - December; Capital gains
- December
Portfolio turnover (3 yrs): 9%, 18%, 14%
Largest holding: Baldor Electric Co. (3.4%)
Management fee: 1.5%
Expense ratio: 1.50% (year ending 11/30/94)

DAVID. L. BABSON GROWTH FUND ◆
(See first Babson listing for data common to all
Babson funds)

Portfolio manager: David G. Kirk (1985)
Investment objective and policies: Above-average
total return over longer periods of time through the
growth of both capital and dividend income.
Current yield is secondary. Invests in common
stocks of progressive, well-managed companies in
growing industries. Fund tends to remain fully
invested.
Year organized: 1959 (formerly D. L. Babson
Investment Fund)
Ticker symbol: BABSX
Minimum purchase: Initial: $500, Subsequent:
$50; IRA: Initial $250; Keogh: Initial: $100
Discount broker availability: Schwab, *White,
*Waterhouse, *Fidelity, *Siebert
Dividends paid: Income - June, December; Capital
gains - June, December
Portfolio turnover (3 yrs): 10%, 13%, 12%
Largest holding: Computer Sciences Corp. (2.7%)
Management fee: 0.85%
Expense ratio: 0.86% (year ending 6/30/94)

D. L. BABSON MONEY MARKET
FUND - FEDERAL PORTFOLIO ◆
(See first Babson listing for data common to all
Babson funds)

Portfolio manager: Brian F. Reynolds (1985)
Investment objective and policies: High income,
safety of principal and liquidity. Invests in short
term high quality debt instruments. U.S.
Government obligations issued by the Treasury,
Government agencies and instrumentalities, and
repurchase agreements.
Year organized: 1982
Minimum purchase: Initial: $1,000, Subsequent:
$100; IRA: Initial: $250, Subsequent: $100; Keogh:
Initial: $50, Subsequent: $50
Check redemptions: $500 minimum
Confirmations mailed: After each purchase and
each check, mail or wire redemption
Checks returned: As clear
Periodic account statements mailed: Monthly
Dividends paid: Income - declared daily, paid
monthly
Management fee: 0.85%
Expense ratio: 0.91% (year ending 6/30/94)

D. L. BABSON MONEY MARKET
FUND - PRIME PORTFOLIO ◆
(See first Babson listing for data common to all
Babson funds)

Portfolio manager: Brian F. Reynolds (1986)
Investment objective and policies: High income,
safety of principal and liquidity. Invests in short
term high quality money market instruments.
Year organized: 1980
Ticker symbol: BMMXX
Minimum purchase: Initial: $1,000, Subsequent:
$100; IRA: Initial: $250, Subsequent: $50; Keogh:
Initial: $100, Subsequent: $50
Check redemptions: $500 minimum
Confirmations mailed: After each purchase and
each check, mail or wire redemption
Checks returned: As clear
Periodic account statements mailed: Monthly
Dividends paid: Income - declared daily, paid
monthly
Management fee: 0.85%
Expense ratio: 0.92% (year ending 6/30/94)

BABSON SHADOW STOCK FUND ◆
(See first Babson listing for data common to all
Babson funds)

Sub-adviser: Analytic Systems, Inc.
Portfolio managers: Peter Schliemann (1987),
Roland W. Whitridge (1987)
Investment objective and policies: Long-term capital growth. Invests in small company stocks called
"Shadow stocks". These are stocks that combine the
characteristics of small stocks (as ranked by market
capitalization - under $110M - and other factors)
and neglected stocks (those least held by institu-
tions and least covered by analysts). Portfolio can
be exposed to above average risk in anticipation of
greater rewards.
Year organized: 1987
Ticker symbol: SHSTX
Minimum purchase: Initial: $2,500, Subsequent:
$100; IRA: Initial: $250, Subsequent: $50; Keogh:
Initial: $100, Subsequent: $50
Discount broker availability: Schwab, *White,
*Waterhouse, *Fidelity, *Siebert
Dividends paid: Income - June & December;
Capital gains - June, December
Portfolio turnover (3 yrs): 43%, 15%, 23%
Largest holding: Philadelphia Suburban Corp.
(1.3%)
Management fee: 1.00%
Expense ratio: 1.28% (year ending 6/30/94)

BABSON-STEWART IVORY
INTERNATIONAL FUND ◆
(See first Babson listing for data common to all
Babson funds)

Investment Counsel: Babson-Stewart Ivory
International
Portfolio manager: John G. L. Wright (1987)
Custodian: State Street Bank & Trust Co.
Investment objective and policies: Seeks a favorable total return from market appreciation and current income. Invests primarily in a diversified portfolio of equity securities of established companies
whose primary business is carried on outside the
U.S. May purchase ADRs, EDRs, IDRs, and foreign
stocks directly on foreign securities markets. May
use forward foreign currency exchange contracts to
protect against exchange rate fluctuations. Up to
20% of assets may be in companies located in
developing countries.
Year organized: 1987
Ticker symbol: BAINX
Minimum purchase: Initial: $2,500, Subsequent:
$100; IRA: Initial: $250, Subsequent: $50; Keogh:
Initial: $100, Subsequent: $50
Discount broker availability: Schwab, *White,
*Waterhouse, *Fidelity, *Siebert
Dividends paid: Income - June & December;
Capital gains - December
Portfolio turnover (3 yrs): 60%, 49%, 44%
Largest holding: Kato Denki (1.8%)
Management fee: 0.95%
Expense ratio: 1.57% (year ending 6/30/94)

D. L. BABSON TAX-FREE
INCOME FUND - PORTFOLIO L ◆
(See first Babson listing for data common to all
Babson funds)

Portfolio manager: Joel M. Vernick (1986)
Investment objective and policies: High income
exempt from federal income tax consistent with
preservation of capital. Invests primarily in invest-
ment-grade municipal securities with a weighted
average maturity of 10 to 25 years. Up to 20% of
assets may be in AMT securities.
Year organized: 1980
Ticker symbol: BALTX
Minimum purchase: Initial: $1,000, Subsequent:
$100
Discount broker availability: *White, *Waterhouse,
*Fidelity, *Siebert
Dividends paid: Income - declared daily, paid
monthly; Capital gains - June, December
Portfolio turnover (3 yrs): 53%, 126%, 128%
Management fee: 0.95%
Expense ratio: 1.02% (year ending 6/30/94)

D. L. BABSON TAX-FREE
INCOME FUND - PORTFOLIO MM ◆
(See first Babson listing for data common to all
Babson funds)

Portfolio manager: Joanne E. Keers (1989)
Investment objective and policies: High income
exempt from federal income tax consistent with
preservation of capital and liquidity. Invests in invest-
ment-grade municipal money market instruments. Up
to 20% of assets may be in AMT securities.
Year organized: 1981
Minimum purchase: Initial: $1,000, Subsequent:
$100
Check redemptions: $500 minimum
Confirmations mailed: After each purchase and
each check, mail or wire redemption
Checks returned: As clear
Periodic account statements mailed: Monthly
Dividends paid: Income - declared daily, paid
monthly
Management fee: 0.5%
Expense ratio: 0.57% (year ending 6/30/94)

D. L. BABSON TAX-FREE
INCOME FUND - PORTFOLIO S ◆
(See first Babson listing for data common to all
Babson funds)

Portfolio manager: Joel M. Vernick (1987)
Investment objective and policies: High income
exempt from federal income tax consistent with
preservation of capital. Invests in investment-grade
municipal securities with a weighted average matu-
rity of 2 to 5 years. Up to 20% of assets may be in
AMT securities.
Year organized: 1980
Ticker symbol: BASTX
Minimum purchase: Initial: $1,000, Subsequent:
$100
Discount broker availability: *White, *Waterhouse,
*Fidelity, *Siebert
Dividends paid: Income - declared daily, paid
monthly; Capital gains - June
Portfolio turnover (3 yrs): 21%, 47%, 81%
Management fee: 0.95%
Expense ratio: 1.02% (year ending 6/30/94)

BABSON VALUE FUND ◆
(See first Babson listing for data common to all
Babson funds)

Portfolio manager: Roland W. Whitridge (1984)
Investment objective and policies: Long-term
growth of capital and dividend income. Invests in
common stocks which are considered undervalued
in relation to earnings, dividends and assets.
Includes stocks that are unpopular and out of favor
with general investors.
Year organized: 1984
Ticker symbol: BVALX
Minimum purchase: Initial: $1,000, Subsequent:
$100; IRA: Initial: $250; Subsequent: $50; Keogh:
Initial: $100, Subsequent: $50
Discount broker availability: Schwab, *White,
*Waterhouse, *Fidelity, *Siebert
Dividends paid: Income - December; Capital gains
- December
Portfolio turnover (3 yrs): 14%, 26%, 17%
Largest holding: Shared Medical Systems Corp.
(2.6%)
Management fee: 0.95%
Expense ratio: 0.99% (year ending 11/30/94)

BABSON-UMB FUNDS ◆
(Data common to all Babson-UMB funds are
shown below. See subsequent listings for date specific to individual Babson-UMB funds.)

Three Crown Center
2440 Pershing Road
Kansas City, MO 64108
816-471-5200, 800-422-2766
fax 816-471-7826

Shareholder service hours: Full service: M-F 8 A.M.-
4:30 P.M. CST; After hours service: prices, messages,
DJIA

Adviser: United Missouri Bank, N.A. Kansas City (David L. Babson & Co., Inc. for money market funds)
Custodian: United Missouri Bank of Kansas City
Transfer agent: Jones & Babson, Inc.
Special sales restrictions: Designed for the benefit of customers of affiliated banks of United Missouri Bancshares, Inc. (UMB)
Minimum purchase: Initial: $1,000, Subsequent: $100; IRA: Initial: $250, Subsequent: $50; Keogh: Initial: $100, Subsequent: $50
Telephone orders accepted: No
Wire orders accepted: Yes, $500 subsequent minimum
Deadline for same day wire purchase: 4 P.M. (1 P.M. for money market funds)
Qualified for sale in: AR, AZ, CA, CO, DC, FL, HI, IL, IN, IA, KS, KY, MA, MN, MO, MT, NE, NJ, OH, OK, PA, SD, TX, TN, WY
Letter redemptions: Signature guarantee required over $10,000
Telephone switching: With other UMB funds, $1,000 minimum
Number of switches permitted: 15 day hold
Shareholder services: Keogh, IRA, corporate retirement plans, automatic investment plan—minimum $100/month (waives initial minimum), withdrawal plan min. req. $10,000
IRA fees: Annual $10, Closing $10
Keogh fees: Annual $15, Closing $15

BABSON-UMB BOND FUND ◆
(See first BABSON-UMB listing for data common to all Babson-UMB funds)

Portfolio manager: George W. Root (1982)
Investment objective and policies: Maximum current income consistent with quality and maturity standards. Normally invests at least 80% of assets in investment-grade government and corporate bonds with remaining individual maturities of 20 years or less.
Year organized: 1982
Ticker symbol: UMBBX
Discount broker availability: Fidelity, Siebert
Dividends paid: Income - declared daily, paid monthly; Capital gains - December
Portfolio turnover (3 yrs): 9%, 19%, 24%
Management fee: 0.85%
Expense ratio: 0.87% (year ending 6/30/94)

BABSON-UMB HEARTLAND FUND ◆
(See first Babson-UMB listing for data common to all Babson-UMB funds)

Portfolio manager: David B. Anderson (1986)
Investment objective and policies: Long-term growth of both capital and dividend income with current yield secondary. Invests at least 80% of assets in common stocks of smaller regional companies (with capitalizations under 1B) doing a substantial portion of their business in MO, KS, IA, NE, AR, OK, IL and CO, selected for their long-term growth potential.
Year organized: 1986 (formerly UMB Qualified Dividend Fund. Name and objectives changed in 1991)
Ticker symbol: UMBHX
Discount broker availability: Fidelity, Siebert
Dividends paid: Income - June, December; Capital gains - December
Portfolio turnover (3 yrs): 17%, 7%, 7%
Largest holding: VICROP Restaurants, Inc. (1.7%)
Management fee: 0.85%
Expense ratio: 0.92% (year ending 12/31/93)

BABSON-UMB MONEY MARKET FUND - FEDERAL PORTFOLIO ◆
(See first Babson-UMB listing for data common to all Babson-UMB funds)

Portfolio manager: Brian F. Reynolds (1985)
Investment objective and policies: Maximum income consistent with safety of principal and liquidity by investing in high quality short-term U.S. Government obligations.
Year organized: 1982

Ticker symbol: UMFXX
Check redemptions: $500 minimum
Confirmations mailed: After each purchase and each check, mail or wire redemption
Checks returned: As clear
Periodic account statements mailed: Monthly
Dividends paid: Income - declared daily, paid monthly
Management fee: 0.50%
Expense ratio: 0.50% (year ending 6/30/94)

BABSON-UMB MONEY MARKET FUND - PRIME PORTFOLIO ◆
(See first Babson-UMB listing for data common to all Babson-UMB funds)

Portfolio manager: Brian F. Reynolds (1985)
Investment objective and policies: Maximum income consistent with safety of principal and liquidity by investing in government and corporate high quality short-term debt obligations.
Year organized: 1982
Ticker symbol: UMPXX
Check redemptions: $500 minimum
Confirmations mailed: After each purchase and each check, mail or wire redemption
Checks returned: As clear
Periodic account statements mailed: Monthly
Dividends paid: Income - declared daily, paid monthly
Management fee: 0.50%
Expense ratio: 0.51% (year ending 6/30/94)

BABSON-UMB STOCK FUND ◆
(See first Babson-UMB listing for data common to all Babson-UMB funds)

Portfolio manager: David B. Anderson (1982)
Investment objective and policies: Long-term growth of both capital and dividend income with current yield secondary. Invests at least 80% of assets in common stocks selected for earning power, dividend-paying ability and assets within industries that have demonstrated both a consistent and an above-average ability to increase their earnings and dividends and which have favorable prospects of sustaining such growth.
Year organized: 1982
Ticker symbol: UMBSX
Discount broker availability: Fidelity, Siebert
Dividends paid: Income - June, December; Capital gains - June, December
Portfolio turnover (3 yrs): 22%, 21%, 12%
Largest holding: IBM Corp. (1.1%)
Management fee: 0.85%
Expense ratio: 0.87% (year ending 6/30/94)

BABSON-UMB TAX-FREE MONEY MARKET FUND ◆
(See first Babson-UMB listing for data common to all Babson-UMB funds)

Adviser: David L. Babson & Co.
Portfolio manager: Joanne E. Keers (1989)
Investment objective and policies: Highest level of income exempt from federal income taxes consistent with safety of principal and liquidity. Invests in high quality short-term municipal obligations.
Year organized: 1982
Ticker symbol: UMTXX
Check redemptions: $500 minimum
Confirmations mailed: After each purchase and each check, mail or wire redemption
Checks returned: As clear
Periodic account statements mailed: Monthly
Dividends paid: Income - declared daily, paid monthly
Management fee: 0.50%
Expense ratio: 0.53% (year ending 6/30/94)

BABSON-UMB WORLDWIDE FUND ◆
(See first Babson-UMB listing for data common to all Babson-UMB funds)

Portfolio manager: James L. Moffett (1993)
Investment objective and policies: Long-term growth of capital and income. Invests in equity securities of established foreign and domestic companies. Normally invests at least 65% of assets in equity securities of foreign issuers primarily through ADRs. May also invest in EDRs, IDRs and directly in foreign securities. Up to 20% of assets may be in companies located in developing countries.
Year organized: 1993
Ticker symbol: UMBWX
Discount broker availability: Fidelity, Siebert
Dividends paid: Income - June, December; Capital gains - December
Largest holding: Vodafone Group (3.0%)
Management fee: 0.85%

BAILARD, BIEHL & KAISER FUNDS ◆
(Data common to all Bailard, Biehl & Kaiser funds are shown below. See subsequent listings for data specific to individual Bailard, Biehl & Kaiser funds.)

2755 Campus Drive
San Mateo, CA 94403
415-571-5800, 800-882-8383
fax 415-578-9434

Adviser: Bailard, Biehl & Kaiser, Inc.
Custodian: U.S. Trust Company of New York
Transfer agent: Mutual Funds Service Co.
Minimum purchase: Initial: $5,000, Subsequent: $100
Telephone orders accepted: No
Wire orders accepted: Yes
Deadline for same day wire purchase: 4 P.M.
Qualified for sale in: CA, CO, CT, HI, MD, NV, NY
Telephone redemptions: Yes, $1,000
Wire redemptions: Yes, $1,000 minimum, $10 fee
Letter redemptions: Signature guarantee required over $50,000
Telephone switching: With other Bailard, Biehl & Kaiser funds
Number of switches permitted: Unlimited
Shareholder services: IRA, withdrawal plan min. req. $10,000
IRA fees: Annual $10, Initial $10

BAILARD, BIEHL & KAISER DIVERSA FUND ◆
(See first Bailard, Biehl & Kaiser listing for data common to all Bailard, Biehl & Kaiser funds)

Portfolio manager: Arthur Micheletti (1991)
Investment objective and policies: Above average total return with below average risk through multiple asset allocation. Invests in up to nine classes of securities - stocks (U.S. and foreign), bonds (U.S. and foreign), cash equivalents (U.S. and foreign), real estate securities, precious metal-related securities and precious metals. Allocation varies with changing market conditions. May use forward currency transaction, futures contracts and options. Fund hedges.
Year organized: 1986
Ticker symbol: DVERX
Discount broker availability: Schwab
Qualified for sale in: CA, CO, CT, GA, HI, MA, NV, NJ, NM, NY, VA, WI
Dividends paid: Income - March, June, September, December; Capital gains - December
Portfolio turnover (3 yrs): 137%, 96%, 94%
Largest holding: U.S. Treasury Bond (9.3%)
Management fee: 0.95% first $75M to 0.65% over $150M
Expense ratio: 1.82% (year ending 9/30/94)

BAILARD, BIEHL & KAISER INTERNATIONAL EQUITY FUND ◆
(See first Bailard, Biehl & Kaiser listing for data common to all Bailard, Biehl & Kaiser funds)

Portfolio manager: Richard Holbrook (1993)
Investment objective and policies: Long-term capital appreciation. Invests primarily in equity securities of foreign issuers, including U.S. companies whose assets are primarily located or whose operations are primarily conducted outside the U.S. May

use forward currency contracts, options, futures contracts and options on futures contracts for hedging purposes.
Year organized: 1979 (name changed from The International Fund on 7/31/90)
Ticker symbol: BBIEX
Discount broker availability: Schwab
Qualified for sale in: CA, CO, CT, HI, MD, NV, NY
Dividends paid: Income - December; Capital gains - December
Portfolio turnover (3 yrs): 176%, 131%, 77%
Largest holding: Keyence Corp. (1.8%)
Management fee: 0.95%
Expense ratio: 1.39% (year ending 9/30/94)

BAILARD, BIEHL & KAISER INTERNATIONAL FIXED INCOME FUND ◆
(See first Bailard, Biehl & Kaiser listing for data common to all Bailard, Biehl & Kaiser funds)

Portfolio manager: Arthur A. Micheletti (1991)
Investment objective and policies: Total return - long-term growth of capital and income. Invests primarily in fixed-income securities of foreign issuers, including corporations, governments, supranational entities and U.S. issuers whose assets are primarily located or whose operations are primarily conducted outside the U.S. or whose securities are denominated in foreign currencies. May use forward currency contracts, options, futures contracts, options on futures contracts and swaps relating to debt securities and foreign currencies for hedging purposes.
Year organized: 1990
Ticker symbol: BBIFX
Discount broker availability: Schwab
Qualified for sale in: CA, CO, CT, HI, MD, NV, NY
Dividends paid: Income - March, June, September, December; Capital gains - December
Portfolio turnover (3 yrs): 319%, 157%, 140%
Management fee: 0.75%
Expense ratio: 1.12 (year ending 9/30/94)

BARON ASSET FUND
450 Park Avenue, Suite 2800
New York, NY 10022
212-759-7700, 800-992-2766
fax 212-759-7529

Adviser: BAMCO, Inc.
Portfolio manager: Ronald S. Baron (1987)
Custodian: Bank of New York
Transfer agent: Supervised Service Company, Inc.
Investment objective and policies: Capital appreciation. Invests in equity and convertible securities of small cap (size $100M-$500M) and medium-sized companies ($500M-$1B) with undervalued assets or favorable growth prospects. Fund may use options and hedge.
Year organized: 1987
Ticker symbol: BARAX
Minimum purchase: Initial: $2,000, Subsequent: None
Telephone orders accepted: No
Wire orders accepted: Yes
Deadline for same day wire purchase: 4 P.M.
Discount broker availability: *Schwab, *White, *Waterhouse, *Fidelity, *Siebert
Qualified for sale in: All states
Letter redemptions: Signature guarantee required over $10,000
Dividends paid: Income - December; Capital gains - December
Portfolio turnover (3 yrs): 56%, 108%, 96%
Largest holding: Robert Half International, Inc. (7.4%)
Shareholder services: IRA, automatic investment plan—minimum $50/month ($500 initial minimum)
Management fee: 1.0%
12b-1 distribution fee: Maximum of 0.25%
Expense ratio: 1.6% (year ending 9/30/94)
IRA fees: Annual $10, Initial $10, Closing $10

BARON GROWTH & INCOME FUND
450 Park Avenue, Suite 2800
New York, NY 10022
212-759-7700, 800-992-2766
fax 212-759-7529

Adviser: BAMCO, Inc.
Portfolio manager: Ronald S. Baron (1995)
Custodian: Bank of New York
Transfer agent: Supervised Service Company, Inc.
Investment objective and policies: Capital appreciation with income secondary. Invests in equity and convertible securities of small (market capitalization $100M-$500M) and medium-sized companies ($500M-$1B) with undervalued assets or favorable growth prospects and in corporate and government debt obligations. Up to 35% of assets may be in junk bonds and 15% in illiquid securities. May use options to increase income and hedge and sell short against the box.
Year organized: 1995
Minimum purchase: Initial: $2,000, Subsequent: None
Telephone orders accepted: No
Wire orders accepted: Yes
Deadline for same day wire purchase: 4 P.M.
Discount broker availability: *Fidelity, *Siebert
Qualified for sale in: All states
Letter redemptions: Signature guarantee required over $10,000
Dividends paid: Income - December; Capital gains - December
Shareholder services: IRA, automatic investment plan—minimum $50/month ($500 initial minimum)
Management fee: 1.0%
12b-1 distribution fee: Maximum of 0.25%
IRA fees: Annual $10, Initial $10, Closing $10

BARTLETT FUNDS ◆
(Data common to all Bartlett funds are shown below. See subsequent listings for data specific to individual Bartlett funds.)

36 East Fourth Street
Cincinnati, OH 45202
513-621-4612, 800-800-4612
fax 513-621-6462

Shareholder service hours: Full service: M-F 8:15 A.M.-5:30 P.M. EST; After hours services: messages, prospectuses
Adviser: Bartlett & Co.
Custodian: Provident Bank, OH (except Bartlett Value Int'l Fund)
Transfer agent: Bartlett & Co.
Minimum purchase: Initial: $5,000, Subsequent: $100; IRA: Initial $250
Telephone orders accepted: No
Wire orders accepted: Yes, with advance notification
Deadline for same day wire purchase: 4 P.M.
Telephone redemptions: Yes, $1,000 minimum
Letter redemptions: Signature guarantee may be required over $5,000
Telephone switching: With other Bartlett funds
Deadline for same day switch: 4 P.M.
Number of switches permitted: 12 per year
Shareholder services: IRA
IRA fees: Annual $10

BARTLETT BASIC VALUE FUND ◆
(See first Bartlett listing for data common to all Bartlett funds)

Portfolio managers: James A. Miller (1983), Woodrow H. Uible (1993)
Investment objective and policies: Capital appreciation with current income secondary. Invests in securities believed to be attractive relative to their intrinsic value, with particular emphasis given to price/earnings, dividend yield, and price/book value. May invest in foreign securities, use options, futures contracts and options thereon and sell short. May hedge all or a portion of its investments.
Year organized: 1983 (a portfolio of Bartlett Capital Trust, formerly Midwest Group Capital Trust/Bartlett Basic Value)

Ticker symbol: MBBVX
Discount broker availability: Schwab, *White, Waterhouse
Qualified for sale in: All states except AK
Dividends paid: Income - March, June, September, December; Capital gains - March, June, September, December
Portfolio turnover (3 yrs): 33%, 43%, 49%
Largest holding: Martin Marietta Corp. (3.3%)
Management fee: 2.0% first $10M to 1.0% over $30M (adviser pays all expenses except brokerage, taxes, interest, and extraordinary expenses)
Expense ratio: 1.20% (year ending 3/31/94)

BARTLETT CASH RESERVES ◆
(See first Bartlett listing for data common to all Bartlett funds)

Portfolio manager: Dale H. Rabiner (1988)
Investment objective and policies: Highest level of current income consistent with stability of principal and liquidity. Invests in money market instruments.
Year organized: 1988 (a portfolio of Bartlett Management Trust; formerly Bartlett Enhanced Reserves, name changed August 1991)
Ticker symbol: BCTXX
Qualified for sale in: All states except AK
Check redemptions: $500 minimum
Dividends paid: Income - declared daily, paid monthly
Confirmations mailed: Not mailed
Checks returned: Monthly
Periodic account statements mailed: Monthly
Management fee: 0.9% first $500M, 0.75% over $500M
Expense ratio: 0.77% (year ending 3/31/94) (0.88% without waiver)

BARTLETT FIXED INCOME FUND ◆
(See first Bartlett listing for data common to all Bartlett funds)

Portfolio manager: Dale H. Rabiner (1986)
Investment objective and policies: Current income with capital appreciation secondary. Invests in fixed-income securities including U.S. and foreign government and corporate debt securities, municipal obligations, mortgage-related securities, financial service industry obligations, preferred stock and repurchase agreements. May use options, futures contracts and options thereon and sell short. May hedge all or a portion of its investments.
Year organized: 1986 (a portfolio of Bartlett Capital Trust)
Ticker symbol: BFXFX
Discount broker availability: *White
Qualified for sale in: All states except AK
Dividends paid: Income - declared daily, paid monthly; Capital gains - March
Portfolio turnover (3 yrs): 163%, 175%, 126%
Management fee: 2.0% first $10M to 1.0% over $30M (adviser pays all expenses except brokerage, taxes, interest, and extraordinary expenses)
Expense ratio: 1.00% (year ending 3/31/94) (includes waiver)

BARTLETT SHORT TERM BOND FUND ◆
(See first Bartlett listing for data common to all Bartlett funds)

Portfolio manager: Dale H. Rabiner (1994)
Investment objective and policies: High current income consistent with preservation of capital. Invests primarily in high quality fixed-income securities with a weighted average maturity of 1 to 3 years. May invest in domestic and foreign government and corporate debt securities, municipal obligations, mortgage-related securities and financial service industry obligations. May use options, futures contracts and options thereon and sell short. May hedge all or a portion of its investments.
Year organized: 1994 (a portfolio of Bartlett Capital Trust)
Ticker symbol: BLSTX
Discount broker availability: *White
Qualified for sale in: All states except AK

Check redemptions: $1,000 minimum
Dividends paid: Income - declared daily, paid monthly; Capital gains - March
Management fee: 0.85%

BARTLETT VALUE INTERNATIONAL FUND ◆
(See first Bartlett listing for data common to all Bartlett funds)

Portfolio manager: Madelynn M. Matlock (1989)
Custodian: Mitsubishi Global Custody (a division of The Bank of California)
Investment objective and policies: Capital appreciation with income secondary. Normally invests at least 65% of assets in foreign equity securities believed undervalued from issuers domiciled in at least 3 different countries. May also invest in debt securities of foreign companies, governments, governmental agencies and international organizations. May use options, futures contracts, forward currency contracts and options thereon. May hedge all or a portion of its investments.
Year organized: 1989 (a portfolio of Bartlett Capital Trust)
Ticker symbol: BVLIX
Discount broker availability: Schwab, *White, Waterhouse
Qualified for sale in: All states except AK
Dividends paid: Income - March, June, September, December; Capital gains - March
Portfolio turnover (3 yrs): 19%, 19%, 27%
Largest holding: George Fischer, Bearer (3.1%)
Management fee: 2.0% first $50M to 1.25% over $200M (adviser pays all expenses except brokerage, taxes, interest, and extraordinary expenses)
Expense ratio: 1.88% (year ending 3/31/94)

BASCOM HILL BALANCED FUND, INC. ◆
6411 Mineral Point Road
Madison, WI 53705
608-274-2020, 800-767-0300
fax 608-274-7905

Adviser: Madison Investment Advisors, Inc.
Portfolio managers: Jay R. Sekelsky (1990), Frank Burgess (1986)
Custodian and transfer agent: Firstar Trust Co.
Investment objective and policies: Current income and long-term growth of capital and income. Invests in a mix of equity securities, bonds and money market instruments and adjusts the allocation to reflect changes in economic and market conditions.
Year organized: 1986 (fund carried a 3.0% sales charge until 9/12/94)
Ticker symbol: BHBFX
Minimum purchase: Initial: $1,000, Subsequent: $100
Telephone orders accepted: No
Wire orders accepted: Yes
Deadline for same day wire purchase: 4 P.M.
Qualified for sale in: AK, CO, GA, IL, IA, MI, MN, NY, NC, TX, WI
Wire redemptions: Yes
Letter redemptions: Signature guarantee required
Dividends paid: Income - April, July, October, December; Capital gains - December
Portfolio turnover (3 yrs): 76%, 72%, 65%
Largest holding: Federal Home Loan Mortgage Corp. (4.8%)
Shareholder services: IRA
Management fee: 0.85% first $100M, 0.75% over $100M
Expense ratio: 1.24% (year ending 12/31/93)
IRA fees: Annual $12.50

BASCOM HILL INVESTORS ◆
6411 Mineral Point Road
Madison, WI 53705
608-274-2020, 800-767-0300
fax 608-274-7905

Adviser: Madison Investment Advisors, Inc.
Portfolio managers: Jay R. Sekelsky (1990), Frank Burgess (1978)
Custodian and transfer agent: Firstar Trust Co.

Investment objective and policies: Capital growth, with income as a secondary but important consideration. Invests primarily in common stocks but will move into bonds and money market instruments for defensive purposes.
Year organized: 1978
Minimum purchase: Initial: $1,000, Subsequent: $100
Telephone orders accepted: No
Wire orders accepted: Yes
Deadline for same day wire purchase: 4 P.M.
Qualified for sale in: CA, IL, MN, WI
Wire redemptions: Yes
Letter redemptions: Signature guarantee required
Dividends paid: Income - July, December; Capital gains - December
Portfolio turnover (3 yrs): 80%, 69%, 71%
Largest holding: Federal Home Loan Mortgage Corp. (6.7%)
Shareholder services: IRA
Management fee: 0.80% first $50M, 0.75% over $50M
Expense ratio: 1.20% (year ending 12/31/93)
IRA fees: Annual $12.50

BEACON HILL MUTUAL FUND ◆
75 Federal Street
Boston, MA 02110
617-482-0795

Adviser: Beacon Hill Management, Inc.
Portfolio manager: David L. Stone (1964)
Custodian and transfer agent: State Street Bank & Trust Co.
Investment objective and policies: Long-term growth of capital with income secondary. Invests primarily in common stocks (including bonds and convertible preferred stocks) of well-established companies.
Year organized: 1964
Ticker symbol: BEHMX
Minimum purchase: Initial: None, Subsequent: None
Telephone orders accepted: No
Wire orders accepted: Yes, subsequent only
Deadline for same day wire purchase: 4 P.M.
Qualified for sale in: All states
Letter redemptions: Signature guarantee required
Dividends paid: Income - June; Capital gains - June
Portfolio turnover (3 yrs): 0%, 3%, 6%
Largest holding: Harcourt General, Inc. (8.3%)
Shareholder services: Keogh, IRA, corporate retirement plans, withdrawal plan min. req. $10,000
Management fee: 1.0%
Expense ratio: 2.7% (year ending 6/30/94)
IRA/Keogh fees: Annual $10

BENHAM FUNDS ◆
(Data common to all Benham funds are shown below. See subsequent listings for individual funds.)

1665 Charleston Road
Mountain View, CA 94043
415-965-4222, 800-321-8321
TDD 800-624-6338, fax 415-965-4975

Shareholder service hours: Full service: M-F 6 A.M.-5 P.M. PST; After hours service: prices, yields, orders, balances, total returns
Adviser: Benham Management Corp.
Custodian: State Street Bank & Trust Co. (exceptions noted)
Transfer agent: Benham Financial Services
Minimum purchase: Initial: $1,000, Subsequent: $100 (except Capital Manager Fund)
Telephone orders accepted: No
Wire orders accepted: Yes, $25,000 initial minimum
Deadline for same day wire purchase: 4 P.M.
Qualified for sale in: All states (exceptions noted)
Telephone redemptions: Yes
Wire redemptions: Yes, $1,000 minimum, $5 fee under $5,000
Letter redemptions: Signature guarantee required over $5,000
Telephone switching: With other Benham Capital

Management Group Funds
Number of switches permitted: 6 per year (unlimited for money market funds)
Shareholder services: Keogh, IRA & corporate retirement plans, automatic investment plan—minimum $25/month, directed dividends, withdrawal plan no min. req., electronic funds transfer
Management fee: 0.5% first $100M to 0.19% over $6.5B (exceptions noted)
IRA fees: None
Keogh fees: Annual $10
Note: At press time Benham was in the process of merging with Twentieth Century Funds

BENHAM ADJUSTABLE RATE GOVERNMENT SECURITIES FUND ◆
(See first Benham listing for data common to all Benham funds)

Portfolio manager: Randall Merk (1991), Newlin Ranklin (1994)
Custodian: Morgan Guaranty Trust Co.
Investment objective and policies: High level of current income consistent with stability of principal. Normally invests at least 65% of assets in adjustable rate mortgage securities (ARMs) issued or guaranteed by the U.S. Government, its agencies or instrumentalities and other mortgage-backed securities. Remainder of assets may be in U.S. Treasury bills, notes, and bonds and in other securities issued or guaranteed by the U.S. government or its agencies or instrumentalities.
Year organized: 1991
Ticker symbol: BARGX
Discount broker availability: *Schwab, *White, Waterhouse, *Fidelity, *Siebert
Check redemptions: $100 minimum
Dividends paid: Income - declared daily, paid monthly; Capital gains - December
Portfolio turnover (3 yrs): 92%, 83%, 82%
Expense ratio: 0.51% (year ending 3/31/94)

BENHAM ARIZONA MUNICIPAL INTERMEDIATE-TERM FUND ◆
(See first Benham listing for data common to all Benham funds)

Portfolio manager: G. David MacEwen (1994)
Investment objective and policies: High level of current income exempt from Arizona and federal income taxes consistent with preservation of capital. Invests primarily in intermediate-term Arizona municipal obligations with a weighted average maturity of 5 to 10 years. May also invest in other municipal obligations. Up to 100% of assets may be in AMT securities.
Year organized: 1994
Discount broker availability: *Schwab, *White, *Fidelity, *Siebert
Qualified for sale in: AZ, CA, CO, NV, OR, TX, WA
Dividends paid: Income - declared daily, paid monthly; Capital gains - December

BENHAM CALIFORNIA MUNICIPAL HIGH-YIELD FUND ◆
(See first Benham listing for data common to all Benham funds)

Newspaper listing: CatfH
Portfolio manager: Steven Permut (1988)
Investment objective and policies: High level of current income exempt from federal and California income taxes consistent with its investment policies, which permit investment in lower-rated and unrated municipal securities. Invests in high yielding, long- and intermediate-term medium to lower grade California municipal securities with a weighted average maturity of more than 10 years. May invest in AMT securities.
Year organized: 1986
Ticker symbol: BCHYX
Discount broker availability: *Schwab, *White, Waterhouse, *Fidelity, *Siebert
Dividends paid: Income - declared daily, paid monthly; Capital gains - December
Portfolio turnover (3 yrs): 43%, 27%, 33%
Expense Ratio: 0.51% (year ending 8/31/94)

BENHAM CALIFORNIA MUNICIPAL MONEY MARKET FUND ◆
(See first Benham listing for data common to all Benham funds)

Portfolio manager: G. David MacEwen (1991)
Investment objective and policies: High level of interest income exempt from federal and California income taxes consistent with prudent investment management and conservation of capital. Invests in money market instruments with at least Aa ratings and with a weighted average maturity of less than 60 days. Fund will normally invest 60-80% in obligations subject to alternative minimum tax (AMT), but may invest up to 100% in these instruments. Fund designed for individuals not subject to AMT taxes.
Year organized: 1991
Ticker symbol: BNCXX
Check redemptions: $100 minimum
Confirmations mailed: After each purchase and each check, mail or wire redemption
Checks returned: On request
Periodic account statements mailed: Monthly (dividends paid out) or quarterly (dividends reinvested)
Dividends paid: Income - declared daily, paid monthly
Expense Ratio: 0.51% (year ending 8/31/94)

BENHAM CALIFORNIA TAX-FREE INSURED FUND ◆
(See first Benham listing for data common to all Benham funds)

Newspaper listing: CatfIn
Portfolio manager: G. David MacEwen (1991)
Investment objective and policies: High level of interest income exempt from federal and California income taxes consistent with safety of principal. Invests in long-term California municipal securities covered by insurance guaranteeing the timely payment of principal and interest with a weighted average maturity of more than 10 years.
Year organized: 1986
Ticker symbol: BCINX
Discount broker availability: *Schwab, *White, Waterhouse, *Fidelity, *Siebert
Dividends paid: Income - declared daily, paid monthly; Capital gains - December
Portfolio turnover (3 yrs): 47%, 61%, 54%
Expense Ratio: 0.52% (year ending 8/31/94)

BENHAM CALIFORNIA TAX-FREE INTERMEDIATE-TERM FUND ◆
(See first Benham listing for data common to all Benham funds)

Newspaper listing: CaTFI
Portfolio manager: G. David MacEwen (1991)
Investment objective and policies: High level of interest income exempt from federal and California income taxes consistent with prudent investment management and conservation of capital. Invests in California municipal securities of the 3 highest grades with a weighted average maturity of 5 to 10 years.
Year organized: 1983
Ticker symbol: BCITX
Discount broker availability: *Schwab, *White, Waterhouse, *Fidelity, *Siebert
Dividends paid: Income - declared daily, paid monthly; Capital gains - December
Portfolio turnover (3 yrs): 44%, 27%, 49%
Expense Ratio: 0.48% (year ending 8/31/94)

BENHAM CALIFORNIA TAX-FREE LONG-TERM FUND ◆
(See first Benham listing for data common to all Benham funds)

Newspaper listing: CatfL
Portfolio manager: David MacEwen (1991)
Investment objective and policies: High level of interest income exempt from federal and California income taxes consistent with prudent investment management and conservation of capital. Invests in

California municipal securities of the 3 highest grades with a weighted average maturity of 10 years or longer.
Year organized: 1983
Ticker symbol: BCLTX
Discount broker availability: *Schwab, *White, Waterhouse, *Fidelity, *Siebert
Dividends paid: Income - declared daily, paid monthly; Capital gains - December
Portfolio turnover (3 yrs): 62%, 55%, 72%
Expense Ratio: 0.48% (year ending 8/31/94)

BENHAM CALIFORNIA TAX-FREE MONEY MARKET FUND ◆
(See first Benham listing for data common to all Benham funds)

Portfolio manager: G. David MacEwen (1991)
Investment objective and policies: High level of interest income exempt from federal and California income taxes consistent with conservation of capital. Invests in California municipal money market instruments.
Year organized: 1983
Ticker symbol: BCTXX
Check redemptions: $100 minimum
Confirmations mailed: After each purchase and each check, mail or wire redemption
Checks returned: On request
Periodic account statements mailed: Monthly (dividends paid out) or quarterly (dividends reinvested)
Dividends paid: Income - declared daily, paid monthly
Expense Ratio: 0.50% (year ending 8/31/94)

BENHAM CALIFORNIA TAX-FREE SHORT-TERM FUND ◆
(See first Benham listing for data common to all Benham funds)

Newspaper listing: CaTFS
Portfolio manager: Dave MacEwen (1992)
Investment objective and policies: High level of interest income exempt from federal and California income taxes consistent with prudent investment management and conservation of capital. Invests in California municipal securities of the 3 highest grades with a weighted average maturity of 1 to 5 years.
Year organized: 1992
Ticker symbol: BCSTX
Discount broker availability: *Schwab, *White, *Fidelity, *Siebert
Dividends paid: Income - declared daily, paid monthly; Capital gains - December
Portfolio turnover (2 yrs): 66%, 54%
Expense ratio: 0.51% (year ending 8/31/94)

BENHAM CAPITAL MANAGER FUND ◆
(See first Benham listing for data common to all Benham funds)

Portfolio manager: Jeffrey R. Tyler (1994)
Investment objective and policies: Maximum total return consistent with prudent investment risk. Normally invests 35% of assets in U.S. equity securities (range 25-45%), 35% in U.S. fixed income securities (25-45%), 15% in money market securities (10-25%), 12% in foreign securities (5-25%) and 3% in gold & natural resource companies (0-10%). Allocation of assets will depend on market conditions. May use options and futures to hedge up to 20% of assets.
Year organized: 1994
Minimum purchase: Initial: $2,500, Subsequent: $100; IRA/Keogh: Initial $1,000
Discount broker availability: *Schwab, *White, *Fidelity, *Siebert
Dividends paid: Income - March, June, September, December; Capital gains - December
Management fee: 0.65% first $100M to 0.27% over $6.5B

BENHAM CAPITAL PRESERVATION FUND ◆
(See first Benham listing for data common to all Benham funds)

Portfolio manager: Jeffrey Tyler (1987)
Investment objective and policies: High current income consistent with safety and liquidity. Invests exclusively in U.S. Treasury money market instruments guaranteed by the full faith and credit of the U.S. government with a weighted average maturity of 60 days or less.
Year organized: 1972
Ticker symbol: CPFXX
Check redemptions: $100 minimum
Confirmations mailed: After each purchase and each check, mail or wire redemption
Checks returned: On request
Periodic account statements mailed: Monthly (dividends paid out) or quarterly (dividends reinvested)
Dividends paid: Income - declared daily, paid monthly
Expense ratio: 0.51% (year ending 3/31/94)

BENHAM CAPITAL PRESERVATION FUND II ◆
(See first Benham listing for data common to all Benham funds)

Portfolio manager: Amy O'Donnell (1988)
Investment objective and policies: High return consistent with maximum safety and liquidity. Invests primarily in repurchase agreements backed by the full faith and credit of the U.S. government consisting of U.S. Treasury securities with portfolio maturities of 7 days or less.
Year organized: 1980
Ticker symbol: CAPXX
Check redemptions: $100 minimum
Confirmations mailed: After each purchase and each check, mail or wire redemption
Checks returned: On request
Periodic account statements mailed: Monthly (dividends paid out) or quarterly (dividends reinvested)
Dividends paid: Income - declared daily, paid monthly
Expense ratio: 0.75% (year ending 3/31/94) (0.78% without waiver)

BENHAM EQUITY GROWTH FUND ◆
(See first Benham listing for data common to all Benham funds)

Portfolio manager: Steven Colton (1991)
Investment objective and policies: Long term capital appreciation. Invests in large and small cap common stocks to deliver total return in excess of that of the S&P 500. May invest in securities of foreign issuers and use options and futures to hedge up to 20% of assets.
Year organized: 1991 (a portfolio of Benham Equity Funds)
Ticker symbol: BEQGX
Discount broker availability: *Schwab, *White, Waterhouse, *Fidelity, *Siebert
Dividends paid: Income - March, June, September, December; Capital gains - December
Portfolio turnover (3 yrs): 97%, 114%, 89%
Largest holding: Abbott Labs (4.0%)
Expense Ratio: 0.75% (year ending 12/31/93) (0.83% without waiver)

BENHAM EUROPEAN GOVERNMENT BOND FUND ◆
(See first Benham listing for data common to all Benham funds)

Sub-adviser: J.P. Morgan Investment Management
Portfolio managers: Jeffrey Tyler (1992), John Graham (1992)
Custodian: Morgan Guaranty Trust Co.
Investment objective and policies: High long-term total return - interest income, capital appreciation and currency gains - consistent with investment in the highest-quality European government debt securities. Invests primarily in AAA-rated bonds

denominated in European currencies and issued by European governments and government agencies and by supranational organizations. Under normal circumstances at least 25% of assets will be in German government debt securities.
Year organized: 1992
Ticker symbol: BEGBX
Discount broker availability: *Schwab, *White, Waterhouse, *Fidelity, *Siebert
Dividends paid: Income - March, June, September, December; Capital gains - December
Portfolio turnover (2 yrs): 310%, 252%
Expense ratio: 0.85% (year ending 12/31/93)

BENHAM FLORIDA MUNICIPAL INTERMEDIATE-TERM FUND ◆
(See first Benham listing for data common to all Benham funds)

Portfolio manager: G. David MacEwen (1994)
Investment objective and policies: High level of current income exempt from federal income tax and the Florida intangible personal property tax. Invests primarily in intermediate-term Florida municipal obligations for which the interest is a tax preference item for purposes of the AMT. The weighted average portfolio maturity is 5 to 10 years.
Year organized: 1994
Discount broker availability: *Schwab, *White, *Fidelity, *Siebert
Dividends paid: Income - declared daily, paid monthly; Capital gains - December

BENHAM FLORIDA MUNICIPAL MONEY MARKET FUND ◆
(See first Benham listing for data common to all Benham funds)

Portfolio manager: G. David MacEwen (1994)
Investment objective and policies: High level of current income exempt from regular federal income tax and the Florida intangible personal property tax. Invests primarily in high-quality municipal money market instruments for which the interest is a tax preference item for purposes of the AMT.
Check redemptions: $100 minimum
Confirmations mailed: After each purchase and each check, mail or wire redemption
Checks returned: On request
Periodic account statements mailed: Monthly (dividends paid out) or quarterly (dividends reinvested)
Dividends paid: Income - declared daily, paid monthly

BENHAM GLOBAL NATURAL RESOURCES INDEX FUND ◆
(See first Benham listing for data common to all Benham funds)

Portfolio manager: William Martin (1994)
Investment objective and policies: Capital growth and dividends. Invests primarily in the securities of companies engaged in the energy or basic materials industries that are part of the Dow Jones World Stock Index. Under normal market conditions, assets will be invested in the securities of at least three different countries. May hedge and invest in illiquid securities, ADRs and EDRs.
Year organized: 1994
Ticker symbol: BGRIX
Discount broker availability: *Schwab, *White, *Fidelity, *Siebert
Dividends paid: Income - June, December; Capital gains - December

BENHAM GNMA INCOME FUND ◆
(See first Benham listing for data common to all Benham funds)

Portfolio manager: Randall Merk (1987)
Custodian: Morgan Guaranty Trust Co.
Investment objective and policies: High level of current income consistent with safety of principal and maintenance of liquidity. Invests primarily in

mortgage-backed GNMA certificates endorsed by the Government National Mortgage Association.
Year organized: 1985
Ticker symbol: BGNMX
Discount broker availability: *Schwab, *White, Waterhouse, *Fidelity, *Siebert
Dividends paid: Income - declared daily, paid monthly; Capital gains - December
Portfolio turnover (3 yrs): 49%, 71%, 97%
Expense ratio: 0.54% (year ending 3/31/94)

BENHAM GOLD EQUITIES INDEX FUND ◆
(See first Benham listing for data common to all Benham funds)

Sub-adviser: State Street Bank & Trust Co.
Portfolio manager: William Martin (1992)
Investment objective and policies: Total return that corresponds to the total return of an index constructed by Benham and comprising the equity securities of 30 North American companies, principally engaged in mining, fabricating, processing, or otherwise dealing in gold, with an aggregate market value of $20 billion. Invests primarily in the equity securities represented in the Index. Fund may also invest directly in gold, gold coins, certificates of ownership of gold and gold futures (limited to 10% of assets).
Year organized: 1988
Ticker symbol: BGEIX
Discount broker availability: *Schwab, *White, Waterhouse, *Fidelity, *Siebert
Dividends paid: Income - June, December; Capital gains - December
Portfolio turnover (3 yrs): 28%, 53%, 56%
Largest holding: American Barrick Resources Corp. (20.7%)
Expense ratio: 0.72% (year ending 12/31/93)

BENHAM GOVERNMENT AGENCY FUND ◆
(See first Benham listing for data common to all Benham funds)

Portfolio manager: Amy O'Donnell (1992)
Investment objective and policies: High level of current income exempt from state income taxes, consistent with safety of principal and maintenance of liquidity. Normally invests at least 65% of assets in money market securities issued by U.S. government agencies and instrumentalities.
Year organized: 1990
Ticker symbol: BGAXX
Check redemptions: $100 minimum
Confirmations mailed: After each purchase and each check, mail or wire redemption
Checks returned: On request
Periodic account statements mailed: Monthly (dividends paid out) or quarterly (dividends reinvested)
Dividends paid: Income - declared daily, paid monthly
Expense Ratio: 0.50% (year ending 3/31/94) (0.58% without waiver)

BENHAM INCOME & GROWTH FUND ◆
(See first Benham listing for data common to all Benham funds)

Portfolio manager: Steven Colton (1990)
Investment objective and policies: Dividend growth, current income and capital appreciation. Invests in dividend paying common stocks with total return approximating that of the S&P 500.
Year organized: 1990
Ticker symbol: BIGRX
Discount broker availability: *Schwab, *White, Waterhouse, *Fidelity, *Siebert
Dividends paid: Income - monthly; Capital gains - December
Portfolio turnover (3 yrs): 31%, 63%, 140%
Largest holding: General Electric Co. (3.9%)
Expense ratio: 0.75% (year ending 12/31/93) (0.81% without waiver)

BENHAM LONG-TERM TREASURY AND AGENCY FUND ◆
(See first Benham listing for data common to all Benham funds)

Portfolio manager: David Schroeder (1992)
Custodian: Morgan Guaranty Trust Co.
Investment objective and policies: Consistent and high level of current income exempt from state taxes. Invests exclusively in securities issued or guaranteed by the U.S. Treasury and agencies or instrumentalities of the U.S. government with maturities of 10 years or more and a weighted average maturity of 20-30 years.
Year organized: 1992
Ticker symbol: BLAGX
Discount broker availability: *Schwab, *White, *Fidelity, *Siebert
Dividends paid: Income - declared daily, paid monthly; Capital gains - December
Portfolio turnover (2 yrs): 201%, 57%
Expense ratio: 0.57% (year ending 3/31/94) (0.79% without waiver)

BENHAM NATIONAL TAX-FREE INTERMEDIATE-TERM FUND ◆
(See first Benham listing for data common to all Benham funds)

Newspaper listing: NITFI
Portfolio manager: G. David MacEwen (1991)
Investment objective and policies: High level of interest income exempt from federal income tax consistent with prudent investment management and conservation of capital. Invests in municipal securities of the 3 highest grades with a weighted average maturity of 4 to 10 years.
Year organized: 1984
Ticker symbol: BNTIX
Discount broker availability: *Schwab, *White, Waterhouse, *Fidelity, *Siebert
Dividends paid: Income - declared daily, paid monthly; Capital gains - December
Portfolio turnover (3 yrs): 46%, 36%, 85%
Expense ratio: 0.67% (year ending 5/31/94) (0.76% without waiver)

BENHAM NATIONAL TAX-FREE LONG-TERM FUND ◆
(See first Benham listing for data common to all Benham funds)

Newspaper listing: NITFL
Portfolio manager: G. David MacEwen (1991)
Investment objective and policies: High level of interest income exempt from federal income tax consistent with prudent investment management and conservation of capital. Invests in municipal securities of the 3 highest grades with a weighted average maturity of 10 years or longer.
Year organized: 1984
Ticker symbol: BTFLX
Discount broker availability: *Schwab, *White, Waterhouse, *Fidelity, *Siebert
Dividends paid: Income - declared daily, paid monthly; Capital gains - December
Portfolio turnover (3 yrs): 39%, 105%, 148%
Expense ratio: 0.67% (year ending 5/31/94) (0.77% without waiver)

BENHAM NATIONAL TAX-FREE MONEY MARKET FUND ◆
(See first Benham listing for data common to all Benham funds)

Portfolio manager: G. David MacEwen (1991)
Investment objective and policies: High interest income exempt from federal income tax consistent with conservation of capital. Invests in municipal money market instruments.
Year organized: 1984
Ticker symbol: BNTXX
Check redemptions: $100 minimum
Confirmations mailed: After each purchase and each check, mail or wire redemption

Checks returned: On request
Periodic account statements mailed: Monthly (dividends paid out) or quarterly (dividends reinvested)
Dividends paid: Income - declared daily, paid monthly
Expense ratio: 0.67% (year ending 5/31/94) (0.77% without waiver)

BENHAM PRIME MONEY MARKET FUND ◆
(See first Benham listing for data common to all Benham funds)

Portfolio manager: Amy O'Donnell (1993)
Investment objective and policies: High current income consistent with preservation of capital. Invests in high quality U.S. dollar-denominated money market instruments of domestic and foreign issuers.
Year organized: 1993
Ticker symbol: BPRXX
Check redemptions: $100 minimum
Confirmations mailed: After each purchase and each check, mail or wire redemption
Checks returned: On request
Periodic account statements mailed: Monthly (dividends paid out) or quarterly (dividends reinvested)
Dividends paid: Income - declared daily, paid monthly

BENHAM SHORT-TERM TREASURY AND AGENCY FUND ◆
(See first Benham listing for data common to all Benham funds)

Portfolio manager: David Schroeder (1992)
Custodian: Morgan Guaranty Trust Co.
Investment objective and policies: Highest level of current income exempt from state taxes consistent with preservation of capital. Invests exclusively in securities issued or guaranteed by the U.S. Treasury and agencies or instrumentalities of the U.S. government with maturities of 3 years or less and a weighted average maturity of 13 months to 3 years.
Year organized: 1992
Ticker symbol: BSTAX
Discount broker availability: *Schwab, *White, *Fidelity, *Siebert
Dividends paid: Income - declared daily, paid monthly; Capital gains - December
Portfolio turnover (2 yrs): 262%, 158%
Expense ratio: 0.58% (year ending 3/31/94) (0.79% without waiver)

BENHAM TARGET MATURITIES TRUST ◆
(See first Benham listing for data common to all Benham funds)

Newspaper listings: Tg1995, Tg2000, etc.
Portfolio manager: David Schroeder (1990)
Investment objective and policies: Highest attainable investment return consistent with the creditworthiness of U.S. Treasury securities and the professional management of reinvestment and market risk. Invests in zero coupon U.S. Treasury securities and in Treasury bills, notes and bonds placed in separate portfolios, each maturing in a specified target maturity year.
Portfolios/maturity: 1995, 2000, 2005, 2010, 2015, 2020
Year organized: 1985, Target 2020 Portfolio in 1990
Ticker symbol: BTMFX (1995), BTMTX (2000), BTFIX (2005), BTTNX (2010), BTFTX (2015), BTTTX (2020)
Deadline for same day wire purchase: 3 P.M.
Discount broker availability: *Schwab, *White, Waterhouse, *Fidelity, *Siebert
Dividends paid: Income - December; Capital gains - December (Fund declares a reverse split for the value of the distributions at the same time to reflect the non-cash taxable distribution.)
Portfolio turnover (3 yrs): T1995 - 177%, 134%, 140%; T2000 - 89%, 77%, 93%; T2005 - 68%, 50%, 64%; T2010 - 35%, 132%, 95%; T2015 - 65%, 138%, 103%; T2020 - 116%, 179%, 144%

Management fee: 0.35% first $750M to 0.19% over $6.5B (for each portfolio)
Expense ratio: T1995 - 0.61%; T2000- 0.59%; T2005 - 0.64%; T2010- 0.68%; T2015 - 0.68%; T2020 - 0.70% (year ending 9/30/94)

BENHAM TREASURY NOTE FUND ◆
(See first Benham listing for data common to all Benham funds)

Portfolio manager: Dave Schroeder (1990)
Investment objective and policies: High current income consistent with conservation of assets and safety. Invests primarily in U.S. Treasury notes, U.S. Treasury bills and repurchase agreements secured by U.S. Treasury securities with a weighted average maturity of 13 months to 10 years. Dividends are tax-free in many states.
Year organized: 1980 (formerly Capital Preservation Treasury Note Trust)
Ticker symbol: CPTNX
Discount broker availability: *Schwab, *White, Waterhouse, *Fidelity, *Siebert
Dividends paid: Income - declared daily, paid monthly; Capital gains - December
Portfolio turnover (3 yrs): 213%, 299%, 149%
Expense ratio: 0.51% (year ending 3/31/94)

BENHAM UTILITIES INCOME FUND ◆
(See first Benham listing for data common to all Benham funds)

Portfolio manager: Steven Colton (1993)
Investment objective and policies: Current income and long-term growth of capital and income. Normally invests at least 75% of assets in equity securities of companies engaged in the utilities industry - providing electricity, natural gas, telecommunications services, pay television, water or sanitary services. Up to 25% may be in fixed-income securities, with 10-20% in utility bonds.
Year organized: 1993
Ticker symbol: BULIX
Discount broker availability: *Schwab, *White, Waterhouse, *Fidelity, *Siebert
Dividends paid: Income - declared daily, paid monthly; Capital gains - December
Portfolio turnover (1 yr): 39%
Largest holding: Southwestern Bell Co. (4.4%)
Expense ratio: 0.50% (10 months ending 12/31/93) (0.94% without waiver)

THE BERGER FUNDS
(Data common to all Berger funds are shown below. See subsequent listings for data specific to individual Berger funds.)

210 University Blvd., Suite 900
Denver, CO 80206
303-329-0200, 800-333-1001
fax 303-329-8719

Shareholder service hours: Full service: M-F 7:30 A.M.-6 P.M. CST. After hours service: prices, yield, balances, last transaction, prospectuses
Adviser: Berger Associates, Inc.
Custodian: United Missouri Bank
Transfer agent: Investors Fiduciary Trust Co.
Sub-transfer agent: DST Systems, Inc.
Minimum purchase: Initial: $250, Subsequent: $50
Telephone orders accepted: Subsequent only
Wire orders accepted: Subsequent only
Deadline for same day wire purchase: 4 P.M.
Telephone redemptions: Yes, $25,000 maximum
Wire redemptions: Yes, $1,000 minimum, $25,000 maximum, $10 fee
Letter redemptions: Signature guarantee required over $25,000
Telephone switching: With other Berger funds and Cash Account Trust money funds
Number of switches permitted: 4 round trips per year
Shareholder services: Keogh, IRA, 403(b), corporate retirement plans, automatic investment plan—

minimum $50/month (waives initial minimum), withdrawal plan min. req. $5,000
IRA/Keogh fees: Annual $12

THE BERGER ONE HUNDRED FUND
(See first Berger listing for data common to all Berger funds)

Portfolio manager: Rodney L. Linafelter (1991)
Investment objective and policies: Long-term capital appreciation. Invests primarily in common stocks with emphasis on established growth companies. May invest in securities convertible into common stock, government securities, preferred stocks and other senior securities. Fund may invest in securities of foreign issuers and purchase options for hedging purposes.
Year organized: 1966 (formerly the 100 Fund) (3 for 1 split on 12/15/89)
Ticker symbol: BEONX
Discount broker availability: *Schwab, *White, *Waterhouse, *Fidelity, *Siebert
Qualified for sale in: All states
Dividends paid: Capital gains - November
Portfolio turnover (3 yrs): 64%, 74%, 51%
Largest holding: Oracle Systems Corp. (1.7%)
Management fee: 0.75%
12b-1 distribution fee: 0.25%
Expense ratio: 1.70% (year ending 9/30/94)

THE BERGER ONE HUNDRED AND ONE FUND
(See first Berger listing for data common to all Berger funds)

Portfolio manager: Rodney L. Linafelter (1991)
Investment objective and policies: Capital appreciation with moderate level of current income secondary. Invests primarily in common stocks of companies with favorable growth prospects that also provide current income. Fund also invests in government and municipal securities, corporate bonds, convertible securities and preferred stocks. Fund may invest in securities of foreign issuers and purchase options for hedging purposes.
Year organized: 1966 (formerly the 101 Fund, then Berger 101 Fund to 6/19/90) (2 for 1 split on 12/15/89)
Ticker symbol: BEOOX
Discount broker availability: *Schwab, *White, *Waterhouse, *Fidelity, *Siebert
Qualified for sale in: All states
Dividends paid: Income - April, July, November, December; Capital gains - November
Portfolio turnover (3 yrs): 23%, 62%, 42%
Largest holding: Nokia Corp. (1.8%)
Management fee: 0.75%
12b-1 distribution fee: 0.25%
Expense ratio: 1.81% (year ending 9/30/94)

THE BERGER SMALL COMPANY GROWTH FUND
(See first Berger listing for data common to all Berger funds)

Portfolio manager: William R. Keithler (1993)
Investment objective and policies: Capital appreciation. Invests at least 65% in equity securities of growth companies with market capitalizations under $1B. May invest securities of both domestic and foreign issuers and purchase options for hedging purposes. Up to 15% of assets may be in illiquid securities.
Year organized: 1993
Ticker symbol: BESCX
Discount broker availability: *Schwab, *White, *Waterhouse, *Fidelity, *Siebert
Qualified for sale in: All states
Dividends paid: Income - November; Capital gains - November
Portfolio turnover (1 yr): 108%
Largest holding: Level One Communications Inc. (1.3%)
Management fee: 0.9%
12b-1 distribution fee: 0.25%
Expense ratio : 2.05% (9 months ending 9/30/94)

SANFORD C. BERNSTEIN FUND, INC. ◆
(Data common to all Bernstein portfolios are shown below. See subsequent listings for data specific to individual Bernstein portfolios.)

767 Fifth Avenue
New York, NY 10153
212-756-4097, fax 212-756-4404

Shareholder service hours: Full service: M-F 9 A.M.-5 P.M. EST
Adviser: Sanford C. Bernstein & Co., Inc.
Custodian and transfer agent: State Street Bank & Trust Co.
Minimum purchase: Initial: $25,000, Subsequent: $5,000
Telephone orders accepted: No
Wire orders accepted: Yes
Deadline for same day wire purchase: 4 P.M.
Wire redemptions: Yes
Letter redemptions: Signature guarantee required
Telephone switching: With other Bernstein Fund portfolios, $5,000 minimum
Number of switches permitted: Unlimited
Dividends paid: Income - declared daily, paid monthly (except International Value); Capital gains - December
Shareholders services: IRA, Keogh, withdrawal plan min. req. $25,000
Management fee: 0.5% (1.0% for International Value Portfolio)
IRA fees: Annual $40
Keogh fees: Annual $60

BERNSTEIN CALIFORNIA MUNICIPAL PORTFOLIO ◆
(See first Bernstein listing for data common to all Bernstein portfolios)

Portfolio manager: Francis H. Trainer, Jr. (1990)
Investment objective and policies: Maximum return after federal and California state income taxes. At least 80% of assets in municipals, at least 65% in California obligations. May use non-municipal securities if after-tax return (maximum federal and California) increased. Average effective duration will vary from 3 to 6 years. May invest up to 10% in foreign securities, buy options, write covered options, and use futures contracts and options thereon.
Year organized: 1990
Ticker symbol: SNCAX
Qualified for sale in: CA, CO, DC, FL, GA, HI, IL, IN, KY, LA, NE, NC, OK, OR, PA, UT, WY
Portfolio turnover (3 yrs): 25%, 24%, 53%
Expense ratio: 0.70% (year ending 9/30/94)

BERNSTEIN DIVERSIFIED MUNICIPAL PORTFOLIO ◆
(See first Bernstein listing for data common to all Bernstein portfolios)

Portfolio manager: Francis H. Trainer, Jr. (1988)
Investment objective and policies: Maximum total return after federal tax. Invests primarily in municipal securities with average weighted portfolio duration of 3 to 6 years. Adviser uses a variety of internally developed, quantitatively based valuation techniques. Fund may invest up to 10% in foreign securities, buy options, write covered options, and use futures contracts and options thereon.
Year organized: 1988
Ticker symbol: SNDPX
Qualified for sale in: All states except AR, MS
Portfolio turnover (3 yrs): 34%, 35%, 48%
Expense ratio: 0.67% (year ending 9/30/94)

BERNSTEIN GOVERNMENT SHORT DURATION PORTFOLIO ◆
(See first Bernstein listing for data common to all Bernstein portfolios)

Portfolio manager: Francis H. Trainer, Jr. (1988)
Investment objective and policies: Higher return than money market funds and inflation, and limit state and local taxes. Invests primarily in securities of the U.S. Government and its agencies rated A or

better, with an effective portfolio duration of 1 to 3 years. Fund may invest up to 10% in foreign securities, buy options, write covered options, and use futures contracts and options thereon.
Year organized: 1988
Ticker symbol: SNGSX
Qualified for sale in: All states except AK, AR, DE, ID, IA, KS, NV, NH, NM, ND, MS, TN, WA
Portfolio turnover (3 yrs): 213%, 130%, 221%
Expense ratio: 0.68% (year ending 9/30/94)

BERNSTEIN INTERMEDIATE DURATION PORTFOLIO ◆
(See first Bernstein listing for data common to all Bernstein portfolios)

Portfolio manager: Francis H. Trainer, Jr. (1988)
Investment objective and policies: Current income consistent with a prudent level of credit risk. Invests at least 65% of assets in securities rated AA or higher, with an effective portfolio duration of 3 to 6 years. Fund may invest up to 10% in foreign securities, buy options, write covered options, and use futures contracts and options thereon.
Year organized: 1988
Ticker symbol: SNIDX
Discount broker availability: Schwab
Qualified for sale in: All states except MS, ND, TN
Portfolio turnover (3 yrs): 204%, 61%, 150%
Expense ratio: 0.65% (year ending 9/30/94)

BERNSTEIN INTERNATIONAL VALUE PORTFOLIO ◆
(See first Bernstein listing for data common to all Bernstein portfolios)

Portfolio manager: Paul Bagnoli (1992)
Investment objective and policies: Long-term capital appreciation and total return. Invests in equity securities of the 19 nations of the Morgan Stanley Capital International EAFE Index and Canada. Invests in 12 countries at a time on average (with a minimum of 3 countries), weighting each in proportion to the size of its economy. Stocks selected based on value characteristics for expected return. Fund hedges its current exposure to offset changes in foreign exchange rates.
Year organized: 1992
Ticker symbol: SNIVX
Qualified for sale in: All states except MS
Dividends paid: Income - December; Capital gains - December
Portfolio turnover (2 yrs): 24%, 21%
Largest holding: Hitachi, Ltd. (2.5%)
Expense ratio: 1.39% (year ending 9/30/94)

BERNSTEIN NEW YORK MUNICIPAL PORTFOLIO ◆
(See first Bernstein listing for data common to all Bernstein portfolios)

Portfolio manager: Francis H. Trainer, Jr. (1988)
Investment objective and policies: Maximum after-tax total return for taxable residents of New York State. Invests at least 65% of assets in securities issued by New York State and its political subdivisions, instrumentalities, and agencies with an effective portfolio duration of 3 to 6 years. Fund may invest up to 10% in foreign securities, buy options, write covered options, and use futures contracts and options thereon.
Year organized: 1988
Ticker symbol: SNNYX
Qualified for sale in: CA, CO, CT, DC, FL, HI, IL, KY, LA, MN, NE, NJ, NY, NC, OK, OR, TX, UT, WY
Portfolio turnover (3 yrs): 22%, 35%, 43%
Expense ratio: 0.67% (year ending 9/30/94)

BERNSTEIN SHORT DURATION CALIFORNIA MUNICIPAL PORTFOLIO ◆
(See first Bernstein listing for data common to all Bernstein portfolios)

Investment objective and policies: Maximum after-tax total return for taxable residents of California. Invests at least 65% of assets in securities issued by

California State and its political subdivisions, instrumentalities, and agencies with a weighted average maturity of 6 to 30 months.
Year organized: 1994
Ticker symbol: SDCMX
Qualified for sale in: CA, CO, DC, FL, GA, HI, IL, IN, KY, MN, NJ, NC, OH, OK, OR, PA, UT, VA, WV

BERNSTEIN SHORT DURATION DIVERSIFIED MUNICIPAL PORTFOLIO ◆
(See first Bernstein listing for data common to all Bernstein portfolios)

Investment objective and policies: Maximum after-tax total return consistent with prudent level of credit risk. Invests no more than 25% of total assets in any one state. Portfolio maintains a weighted average maturity of 6 to 30 months.
Year organized: 1994
Ticker symbol: SDDMX
Qualified for sale in: All states except AK, AR, ID, LA, NE, NM, MS, VT, WY

BERNSTEIN SHORT DURATION NEW YORK MUNICIPAL PORTFOLIO ◆
(See first Bernstein listing for data common to all Bernstein portfolios)

Investment objective and policies: Maximum after-tax total return for taxable residents of New York. Invests at least 65% of assets in securities issued by New York State and its political subdivisions, instrumentalities, and agencies with a weighted average maturity of 6 to 30 months.
Year organized: 1994
Ticker symbol: SDNYX
Qualified for sale in: CA, CO, DC, FL, GA, HI, IL, IN, KY, MN, NJ, NY, NC, OH, OK, OR, PA, UT, VA, WV

BERNSTEIN SHORT DURATION PLUS PORTFOLIO ◆
(See first Bernstein listing for data common to all Bernstein portfolios)

Portfolio manager: Francis H. Trainer, Jr. (1988)
Investment objective and policies: Exceed the total return of both money market funds and inflation. Invests in a diverse group of high-quality fixed-income securities with an effective portfolio duration of 1 to 3 years. Differs from Short Duration by investing in highest pre-tax return obligations without regard to tax considerations of shareholders. Fund may invest up to 10% in foreign securities, buy options, write covered options, and use futures contracts and options thereon.
Year organized: 1988
Ticker symbol: SNSDX
Qualified for sale in: All states except ID, MS
Dividends paid: Income - declared daily, paid monthly; Capital gains - December
Portfolio turnover (3 yrs): 286%, 113%, 170%
Expense ratio: 0.65% (year ending 9/30/94)

THE BERWYN FUND
1189 Lancaster Avenue
Berwyn, PA 19312
302-324-0200, 800-824-2249
fax 302-324-0213

Adviser: The Killen Group, Inc.
Portfolio manager: Robert E. Killen (1984)
Custodian: National Westminster Bank NJ
Transfer agent: Fund/Plan Services, Inc.
Investment objective and policies: Long-term capital appreciation with current income secondary. Normally invests at least 80% of assets in common stocks believed undervalued. Fund may invest up to 20% of assets in fixed-income securities with potential for long-term capital appreciation, 10% in

illiquid securities, and in real estate investment trusts. Fund is non-diversified.
Year organized: 1983
Ticker symbol: BERWX
Minimum purchase: Initial: $10,000, Subsequent: $1,000; IRA: Initial: $1,000, Subsequent: $250; Keogh: None
Telephone orders accepted: No
Wire orders accepted: Yes
Deadline for same day wire purchase: 12 NN
Discount broker availability: Schwab, Fidelity, Siebert
Qualified for sale in: All states except AR, MS, NM, ND, SD, WV
Telephone redemptions: Yes, $5,000 maximum
Wire redemptions: Yes, $1,000 minimum, $9 fee
Letter redemptions: Signature guarantee not required
Redemption fee: 1% if held for less than 1 year
Telephone switching: With Berwyn Income Fund, $1,000 minimum
Number of switches permitted: 2 per year
Deadline for same day switches: 4 P.M.
Dividends paid: Income - December; Capital gains - December
Portfolio turnover (3 yrs): 24%, 45%, 33%
Shareholder services: IRA, Keogh, corporate retirement plans, automatic investment plan—minimum $50/month (initial minimum waived), withdrawal plan
Management fee: 1.0%
Expense ratio: 1.37% (year ending 12/31/93)
IRA fees: Annual $12
Keogh fees: None

THE BERWYN INCOME FUND ◆
1189 Lancaster Avenue
Berwyn, PA 19312
302-324-2249, 800-824-2249
fax 302-324-0213

Adviser: The Killen Group, Inc.
Portfolio manager: Edward A. Killen (1994)
Custodian: National Westminster Bank NJ
Transfer agent: Fund/Plan Services, Inc.
Investment objective and policies: Current income with preservation of capital. Invests primarily in fixed-income corporate securities, preferred stocks, securities of the U.S. Government, its agencies and instrumentalities and common stocks paying cash dividends. May invest up to 50% of assets in junk bonds.
Year organized: 1987
Ticker symbol: BERIX
Minimum purchase: Initial: $10,000 (waived on request), Subsequent: $250; IRA: Initial: $1,000, Subsequent: $250; Keogh: None
Telephone orders accepted: No
Wire orders accepted: Yes
Deadline for same day wire purchase: 12 NN
Discount broker availability: Schwab, White, Fidelity, Siebert
Qualified for sale in: All states except MS, ND, SD, WY
Telephone redemptions: Yes, $5,000 maximum
Wire redemptions: Yes, $1,000 minimum, $9 fee
Letter redemptions: Signature guarantee not required
Telephone switching: With Berwyn Fund, $1,000 minimum
Number of switches permitted: 2 per year
Deadline for same day switches: 4 P.M.
Dividends paid: Income - April, July, October, December; Capital gains - December
Portfolio turnover (3 yrs): 83%, 46%, 14%
Shareholder services: IRA, Keogh, corporate retirement plans, automatic investment plan—minimum $50/month (initial minimum waived), withdrawal plan
Management fee: 0.5%
Expense ratio: 1.07% (year ending 12/31/93)
IRA fees: Annual $12
Keogh fees: None

BLANCHARD FUNDS
(Data common to all Blanchard funds are shown below. See subsequent listings for data specific to individual Blanchard funds.)

41 Madison Ave., 24th Floor
New York, NY 10010
212-779-7979, 800-922-7771
fax 212-725-8223

Shareholder service hours: Full service: M-F 9 A.M.-5:30 P.M. EST. After hours service: prices, yields, prospectuses
Adviser: Sheffield Management Co.
Custodian and transfer agent: U.S. Trust Co. of New York
Minimum purchase: Initial: $3,000, Subsequent: $200; IRA/Keogh: Initial: $2,000 (except 100% Treasury Money Market Fund)
Telephone orders accepted: No
Wire orders accepted: Yes
Deadline for same day wire purchase: 4 P.M.
Qualified for sale in: All states (exceptions noted)
Telephone redemptions: Yes, $250 minimum
Wire redemptions: Yes, $1,000 minimum, $8 fee
Letter redemptions: Signature guarantee required over $25,000
Telephone switching: With other Blanchard funds, $1,000 minimum
Number of switches permitted: Unlimited
Shareholder services: IRA, SEP-IRA, Keogh, 403(b), corporate retirement plans, automatic investment plan—minimum $100/month (waives initial minimum), electronic funds transfer, withdrawal plan min. req. $10,000
IRA/Keogh fees: Annual $10, Initial $10, Closing $10

BLANCHARD AMERICAN EQUITY FUND
(See first Blanchard listing for data common to all Blanchard funds)

Sub-adviser: Provident Investment Counsel, Inc.
Portfolio manager: Jeffrey Miller (1992)
Investment objective and policies: Long-term capital growth. Invests at least 65% of assets (normally at least 80%) in common stocks and securities convertible into common stocks of domestic companies with above average rates of earnings growth. Fund is non-diversified.
Year organized: 1992
Ticker symbol: BLAEX
Discount broker availability: *Schwab, *White, *Waterhouse, *Fidelity, *Siebert
Account opening fee: $75
Dividends paid: Income - December; Capital gains - December
Portfolio turnover (2 yrs): 97%, 49%
Largest holding: Motorola, Inc. (5.5%)
Management fee: 1.1%
12b-1 distribution fee: 0.5%
Expense ratio: 3.00% (year ending 4/30/94)

BLANCHARD CAPITAL GROWTH FUND
(See first Blanchard listing for data common to all Blanchard funds)

Portfolio managers: Mark A. Tincher (1994), David Klassen (1994)
Investment objective and policies: Long-term capital growth. Invests at least 80% of assets in common stocks of issuers believed likely to benefit from changes or trends caused by social, economic, demographic and legislative developments. May have up to 20% of assets in securities of foreign issuers and use futures and options to hedge.
Year organized: 1994
Initial registration fee: $75
Discount broker availability: *Fidelity, *Siebert
Qualified for sale in: All states except MS
Dividends paid: Income - June, December; Capital gains - June, December
Management fee: 1.1%
12b-1 distribution fee: 0.5%

BLANCHARD FLEXIBLE INCOME FUND
(See first Blanchard listing for data common to all Blanchard funds)

Sub-adviser: Offitbank
Portfolio manager: Jack D. Burks (1992)
Investment objective and policies: High current income with some capital appreciation. Invests primarily in a mix of U.S. Government securities, investment-grade fixed-income securities, junk bonds (up to 35% of assets), and international fixed-income securities. Up to 25% of assets may be in debt obligations of issuers in emerging markets countries. May use cross currency hedges, futures and related options transactions, and forward currency contracts and futures and options transactions to hedge. Fund is non-diversified.
Year organized: 1992
Ticker symbol: BLFIX
Discount broker availability: *Schwab, *White, *Waterhouse, *Fidelity, *Siebert
Account opening fee: $75
Check redemptions: $250 minimum
Dividends paid: Income - declared daily, paid monthly; Capital gains - December
Portfolio turnover (2 yrs): 346%, 129%
Management fee: 0.75%
12b-1 distribution fee: 0.25%
Expense ratio: 1.30% (year ending 4/30/94)

BLANCHARD FLEXIBLE TAX-FREE BOND FUND
(See first Blanchard listing for data common to all Blanchard funds)

Sub-adviser: U.S. Trust Co. of New York
Portfolio manager: Kenneth J. McAlley (1993)
Investment objective and policies: High current income exempt from federal income tax consistent with preservation of principal. Normally invests at least 80% of assets in tax-exempt obligations with at least 65% in investment-grade municipal bonds with weighted average maturity ranging from very short to very long, depending on the market environment. Up to 20% of assets may be in AMT securities. Fund may use cross currency hedges, futures and related options transactions, and forward currency contracts and futures and options transactions to hedge. Fund is non-diversified.
Year organized: 1993
Ticker symbol: BTFBX
Discount broker availability: *Schwab, *White, *Waterhouse, *Fidelity, *Siebert
Check redemptions: $250 minimum
Dividends paid: Income - declared daily, paid monthly; Capital gains - December
Portfolio turnover (1 yr): 190%
Management fee: 0.75%
12b-1 distribution fee: 0.25%
Expense ratio: 0.00% (9 months ending 4/30/94) (2.22% without waiver)

BLANCHARD GLOBAL GROWTH FUND
(See first Blanchard listing for data common to all Blanchard funds)

Allocation Strategist: Jeremy H. Biggs, Fiduciary Trust Co. Int'l (1992)
Portfolio managers: Precious metals - Peter Cavelti (1986), Foreign equities - Stephen Butt (1986), U.S. equities - Robert Weiss (1986), U.S. fixed-income - Larry R. Hill (1986), International fixed-income - Stuart Hochberger (1992), Emerging markets - Madav Dhar (1992)
Investment objective and policies: Long-term capital growth. Assets will be flexibly invested within various investment sectors: U.S. equity securities, foreign securities, precious metals securities and bullion, domestic bonds, international bonds and emerging markets. Percentages allocated to any one sector will range from 0% to 65% (0% to 15% for emerging markets) depending on economic and investment conditions.
Year organized: 1986 (formerly Blanchard Strategic Growth)

Ticker symbol: BGGFX
Discount broker availability: *Schwab, *White, *Waterhouse, *Fidelity, *Siebert
Account opening fee: $75
Dividends paid: Income - December; Capital gains - December
Portfolio turnover (3 yrs): 166%, 138%, 109%
Largest holding: U.S. Treasury Bond 8.125% due 8/5/19 (3.2%)
Management fee: 1.00% first $150M to 0.75% over $300M
12b-1 distribution fee: 0.75%
Expense ratio: 2.61% (year ending 4/30/94)

BLANCHARD GROWTH & INCOME FUND

(See first Blanchard listing for data common to all Blanchard funds)

Portfolio managers: Mark A. Tincher (1994), David Klassen (1994)
Investment objective and policies: Long-term capital growth with current income secondary. Invests at least 80% of assets in common stocks of issuers with market capitalizations under $3B currently out of favor with investors in the stock market. May have up to 20% of assets in securities of foreign issuers and use futures and options to hedge.
Year organized: 1994
Account opening fee: $75
Discount broker availability: *Fidelity, *Siebert
Qualified for sale in: All states except MS
Dividends paid: Income - March, June, September, December; Capital gains - December
Management fee: 1.1%
12b-1 distribution fee: 0.5%

BLANCHARD 100% TREASURY MONEY MARKET FUND ◆

(See first Blanchard listing for data common to all Blanchard funds)

Sub-adviser: HSBC Asset Management Americas, Inc
Portfolio manager: Edward J. Merkele (1989)
Investment objective and policies: High current income consistent with preservation of capital and liquidity. Invests exclusively in short-term direct obligations of the U.S. Treasury and in repurchase agreements collateralized by U.S. Treasury securities.
Year organized: 1989 (name changed from Blanchard Government Money Market Fund on 12/1/91)
Ticker symbol: BGMXX
Minimum purchase: Initial: $1,000, Subsequent: $200; IRA/Keogh: Initial $500
Check redemptions: $250 minimum
Confirmations mailed: After each purchase and each check, mail or wire redemption
Checks returned: Monthly
Periodic account statements mailed: Quarterly
Dividends paid: Income - declared daily, paid monthly
Management fee: 0.50% first $500M to 0.45% over $1B
Expense ratio: 0.41% (year ended 4/30/94) (includes waiver)

BLANCHARD PRECIOUS METALS FUND

(See first Blanchard listing for data common to all Blanchard funds)

Sub-adviser: Cavelti Capital Management, Ltd.
Portfolio managers: Peter Cavelti (1988), Kevin MacLean (1988)
Investment objective and policies: Long-term capital growth and preservation of capital. Invests in precious metals (up to 49% of assets) and securities of companies involved with precious metals. In order to reduce volatility and risk of capital loss assets may be moved to short-term instruments and government securities when the manager believes the precious metals markets may experience declines.

Year organized: 1988 (acquired National Precious Metals Fund 2/23/90)
Ticker symbol: BLPMX
Discount broker availability: *Schwab, *White, *Waterhouse, *Fidelity, *Siebert
Qualified for sale in: All states except WI
Account opening fee: $75
Dividends paid: Income - December; Capital gains - December
Portfolio turnover (3 yrs): 174%, 66%, 62%
Largest holding: Santa Fe Pacific Gold Corp. (9.7%)
Management fee: 1.0% first $150M to 0.75% over $300M
12b-1 distribution fee: 0.75%
Expense ratio: 2.46% (year ending 4/30/94)

BLANCHARD SHORT-TERM BOND FUND

(See first Blanchard listing for data common to all Blanchard funds)

Sub-adviser: Offitbank
Portfolio manager: Jack D. Burks (1993)
Investment objective and policies: High current income consistent with preservation of capital. Invests at least 65% of assets in short-term investment-grade debt securities with a weighted average maturity of less than three years. May invest up to 20% of assets in non-US debt securities when they offer attractive returns. Fund may use currency hedges, futures and options on futures contracts and forward currency transactions.
Year organized: 1993
Ticker symbol: BSTBX
Discount broker availability: *Schwab, *White, *Fidelity, *Siebert
Check redemptions: $250 minimum
Dividends paid: Income - declared daily, paid monthly; Capital gains - December
Portfolio turnover (1 yr): 212%
Management fee: 0.75%
12b-1 distribution fee: 0.25%
Expense ratio: 0.63% (year ending 4/30/94) (2.05% without waiver)

BLANCHARD SHORT-TERM GLOBAL INCOME FUND

(See first Blanchard listing for data common to all Blanchard funds)

Sub-adviser: Lombard Odier International Portfolio Management Ltd.
Portfolio manager: Robert McHenry (1991)
Investment objective and policies: High current income consistent with minimum risk of principal and relative stability of NAV. Invests primarily in high quality debt obligations denominated in the U.S. dollar and foreign currencies from at least 3 countries with a weighted average maturity of 3 years or less. No country other than U.S. may have more than 25% of assets. Fund may use currency hedges, futures and options on futures contracts and forward currency transactions.
Year organized: 1991
Ticker symbol: BSGIX
Discount broker availability: *Schwab, *White, *Waterhouse, *Fidelity, *Siebert
Account opening fee: $75
Check redemptions: $250 minimum
Dividends paid: Income - declared daily, paid monthly; Capital gains - December
Portfolio turnover (3 yrs): 327%, 610%, 412%
Management fee: 0.75%
12b-1 distribution fee: 0.25%
Expense ratio: 1.44% (year ending 4/30/94)

BLANCHARD WORLD WIDE EMERGING MARKETS FUND

(See first Blanchard listing for data common to all Blanchard funds)

Sub-advisers: Martin Currie Inc. (equities), Offitbank (income)
Portfolio managers: Equities - James Fairweather (1994), Income- Richard M. Johnston (1994)

Investment objective and policies: Capital appreciation and current income. Invests in equity and fixed-income securities in emerging markets around the world - primarily in Latin America, Eastern Europe, and the Pacific Rim. Normally invests at least 65% of assets in equity and equity-related securities. May use foreign currency futures and options.
Year organized: 1994 (name changed from Emerging Markets Growth & Income in December 1994)
Ticker symbol: BEGIX
Account opening fee: $75
Discount broker availability: *Schwab, *White, *Waterhouse, *Fidelity, *Siebert
Qualified for sale in: All states except VT
Dividends paid: Income - December; Capital gains - December
Largest holding: Korea Electric Power Corp. (3.3%)
Management fee: 1.25%
12b-1 distribution fee: 0.50%

BONNEL GROWTH FUND

P.O. Box 781234
San Antonio, TX 78278
210-308-1234, 800-426-6635
TDD 800-677-1212, fax 210-308-1217

Adviser: United Services Advisors, Inc.
Sub-adviser: Bonnel, Inc.
Portfolio manager: Arthur J. Bonnel (1994)
Custodian: Bankers Trust Co.
Transfer agent: United Shareholder Services, Inc.
Investment objective and policies: Long-term capital growth. Invests primarily in common stocks chosen for their appreciation potential on both fundamental and technical bases. Fund intends to stay fully invested. Up to 25% of assets may be in equity securities of foreign issuers listed on domestic or foreign exchanges. May use options to hedge.
Year organized: 1994
Minimum purchase: Initial: $5,000, Subsequent: $50; IRA/Keogh: None
Telephone orders accepted: Subsequent only, up to 10 times account balance (except money market funds)
Wire orders accepted: Yes
Deadline for same day wire purchase: 4 P.M.
Qualified for sale in: All states
Wire redemptions: Yes, $10 fee
Letter redemptions: Signature guarantee required over $15,000
Redemption fee: 0.10% for shares held less than 14 days
Account closing fee: $10
Telephone switching: With United Services funds and Pauze/Swanson U.S. Government Total Return Bond Fund
Number of switches permitted: Unlimited, $5 fee
Dividends paid: Income - June, December; Capital gains - December
Shareholder services: Keogh, IRA, SEP-IRA, 403(b), 401(k), corporate retirement plans, automatic investment plan—minimum $30/mo. ($100 initial minimum), withdrawal plan min. req. $5,000, electronic funds transfer (purchase only)
Management fee: 1.0%
12b-1 distribution fee: 0.25%
Expense ratio: 1.50% (6 months ending 6/30/94) (3.30% without waiver)
IRA fees: Annual $10, Closing $10
Keogh fees: Closing $10

BRAMWELL GROWTH FUND ◆

745 Fifth Avenue
New York NY 10151
800-272-6227

Adviser: Bramwell Capital Management, Inc.
Portfolio manager: Elizabeth Bramwell (1994)
Custodian and transfer agent: Firstar Trust Company
Investment objective and policies: Long-term capital growth with current income secondary. Invests in equity securities of companies with above-average growth prospects, primarily common stock and

high-grade securities convertible into common stock. May also hold cash or cash equivalents and invest in U.S. government obligations (no limit), warrants or rights (up to 5% of assets), illiquid or restricted securities (no more than 15%) and securities of foreign issuers (up to 25%). May write covered put and call options and purchase put and call options on securities indices that are traded on U.S. and foreign exchanges or in over-the-counter markets. May sell short (up to 5%).
Year organized: 1994
Ticker symbol: BRGRX
Minimum purchase: Initial: $1,000, Subsequent: $100; IRA: Initial: $500
Telephone orders accepted: Yes, $100 minimum
Wire orders accepted: Yes, $1,000 minimum
Deadline for same day wire purchase: 4 P.M.
Discount broker availability: *Schwab, *White, *Fidelity, *Siebert
Qualified for sale in: All states
Letter redemptions: Signature guarantee required over $25,000
Telephone switching: With Portico Money Market Fund
Number of switches permitted: Unlimited, but reserves the right to limit
Dividends paid: Income - December; Capital gains - December
Shareholder services: IRA, SEP-IRA, automatic investment plan
Management fee: 1.0%
12b-1 distribution fee: 0.25%
IRA fees: Annual $12.50

BRANDYWINE FUND ◆
3908 Kennett Pike
Greenville, DE 19807
302-656-6200, 800-656-3017

Adviser: Friess Associates, Inc.
Portfolio manager: Foster S. Friess (1985)
Custodian and transfer agent: Firstar Trust Co.
Investment Objective and policies: Long-term capital appreciation with current income secondary. Invests primarily in common stocks of well-financed issuers with records of profitability and strong earnings momentum. May invest 10% of assets in securities or ADRs of foreign issuers.
Year organized: 1985
Ticker symbol: BRWIX
Minimum purchase: Initial: $25,000; Subsequent: $1,000
Telephone orders accepted: No
Wire orders accepted: Yes
Deadline for same day wire purchase: 4 P.M.
Discount broker availability: Schwab, White, Waterhouse
Qualified for sale in: All states
Telephone redemptions: Yes
Wire redemptions: Yes, $7.50 fee
Letter redemptions: Signature guarantee not required
Dividends paid: Income - October, December; Capital gains - October, December
Portfolio turnover (3 yrs): 190%, 150%, 189%
Largest holding: LSI Logic Corp. (3.3%)
Shareholder services: IRA, withdrawal plan min. req. $25,000
Management fee: 1.0%
Expense ratio: 1.10% (year ending 9/30/94)
IRA fees: Annual $12.50

BRANDYWINE BLUE FUND ◆
3908 Kennett Pike
P.O. Box 4166
Greenville, DE 19807
302-656-6200
account info 800-338-1579 (Firstar)

Adviser: Friess Associates, Inc.
Portfolio manager: Foster S. Friess (1991)
Custodian and transfer agent: Firstar Trust Co.
Investment Objective and policies: Long-term capital appreciation with income secondary. Invests primarily in common stocks of companies with market capitalization of more than $500M. Uses same

selection process as Brandywine fund but restricted to large companies.
Special sales restrictions: Designed for Institutions only, available to individual investors only in the states of DE and PA.
Year organized: 1991
Ticker symbol: BLUEX
Minimum purchase: Initial: $100,000; Subsequent: $1,000
Telephone orders accepted: No
Wire orders accepted: Yes
Deadline for same day wire purchase: 4 P.M.
Qualified for sale in: All states for institutions; only DE and PA for individuals
Telephone redemptions: Yes
Wire redemptions: Yes, $7.50 fee
Letter redemptions: Signature guarantee not required
Dividends paid: Income - October, December; Capital gains - October, December
Portfolio turnover (3 yrs): 220%, 144%, 192%
Largest holding: LSI Logic Corp. (3.4%)
Shareholder services: IRA, Withdrawal plan min. req. $100,000
Management fee: 1.0%
Expense ratio: 1.90% (year ending 9/30/94)
IRA fees: Annual $12.50

BRIDGES INVESTMENT FUND ◆
8401 West Dodge Road, Suite 256
Omaha, NE 68114
402-397-4700, fax 402-397-8617

Adviser: Bridges Investment Counsel, Inc.
Portfolio manager: Edson L. Bridges, II (1963)
Custodian: FirsTier Bank, Omaha
Transfer agent: Bridges Investor Services
Investment objective and policies: Long-term capital growth with a modest amount of current income secondary. Invests at least 60% of assets in common stocks and securities convertible into common stocks. May invest up to 40% of assets in non-convertible fixed-income government and corporate securities and 10% in securities of foreign issuers.
Year organized: 1963
Minimum purchase: Initial: $800, Subsequent: $200
Telephone orders accepted: No
Wire orders accepted: No
Qualified for sale in: NE
Letter redemptions: Signature guarantee required
Dividends paid: Income - April, July, October, December; Capital gains - December
Portfolio turnover (3 yrs): 11%, 7%, 28%
Largest holding: Philip Morris Companies, Inc. (3.3%)
Shareholder services: Keogh, IRA, 401(k), corporate retirement plans
Management fee: 0.5%
Expense ratio: 0.90% (year ending 12/31/93)
IRA/Keogh fees: Annual $8, Initial $5, Closing $6

BRIDGEWAY FUNDS ◆
(Data common to all Bridgeway funds are shown below. See subsequent listings for data specific to individual Bridgeway funds.)

5650 Kirby Drive, Suite 141
Houston, TX 77005
713-661-3500, 800-661-3550
fax 713-661-3587

Adviser: Bridgeway Capital Management, Inc.
Custodian: River Oaks Trust Co.
Transfer agent: Bridgeway Fund, Inc.
Minimum purchase: Initial: $2,000, Subsequent: $500
Telephone orders accepted: No
Wire orders accepted: Yes
Deadline for same day wire purchase: 3 P.M.
Qualified for sale in: CA, GA, HI, MI, PA, TX, VA
Telephone redemptions: Yes
Wire redemptions: Yes, $15 fee
Letter redemptions: Signature guarantee required
Telephone switching: With other Bridgeway funds
Number of switches permitted: 4 per year

Deadline for same day switch: 3 P.M.
Dividends paid: Income - December; Capital gains - December
Shareholder services: IRA, automatic investment plan—minimum $100/mo. (waives initial minimum), electronic funds transfer, withdrawal plan
IRA fees: Annual $20

BRIDGEWAY AGGRESSIVE GROWTH FUND ◆
(See first Bridgeway listing for data common to all Bridgeway funds)

Portfolio manager: John N.R. Montgomery (1994)
Investment objective and policies: Total return - capital growth and income - exceeding the broad stock market at a level of total risk roughly equal to that of the stock market over periods greater than three years. Normally invests in common stocks and uses leverage to increase potential return. Uses futures and options on indexes and stocks to increase return and hedge.
Year organized: 1994
Management fee: 0.90% (+/- up to 0.7% depending on performance relative to the S&P 500 Index over 60 months)

BRIDGEWAY SOCIAL RESPONSIBILITY PORTFOLIO ◆
(See first Bridgeway listing for data common to all Bridgeway funds)

Portfolio manager: John N.R. Montgomery (1994)
Investment objective and policies: Total return - capital growth and income - exceeding the broad stock market at a level of total risk roughly equal to that of the stock market over periods greater than three years. Invests in equities of companies with social criteria measured by the Council on Economic Priorities including environmental record, charitable giving, workplace issues, military contracts and animal testing. May leverage and use index futures and options to hedge.
Year organized: 1994
Management fee: 0.90% (+/- up to 0.7% depending on performance relative to the S&P 500 Index over 60 months)

BRIDGEWAY ULTRA-SMALL COMPANY PORTFOLIO ◆
(See first Bridgeway listing for data common to all Bridgeway funds)

Portfolio manager: John N.R. Montgomery (1994)
Investment objective and policies: Capital appreciation plus income. Invests primarily in equities of very small companies (market capitalizations less than $73M).
Year organized: 1994
Special sales restrictions: Will close to new shareholders when assets reach $55M.
Management fee: 0.90%

BRINSON FUNDS ◆
(Data common to all Brinson funds are shown below. See subsequent listings for data specific to individual Brinson funds.)

209 South LaSalle St.
Chicago, IL 60604
800-448-2430

Adviser: Brinson Partners, Inc.
Custodian: Bankers Trust Co., Jersey City, NJ
Transfer agent: Fund/Plan Services, Inc.
Minimum purchase: Initial: $100,000; Subsequent: $2,500
Telephone orders accepted: Yes, $100,000 initial minimum
Wire orders accepted: Yes
Deadline for same day wire purchase: 4 P.M.
Qualified for sale in: All states
Letter redemptions: Signature guarantee required
Telephone switching: With other Brinson funds
Number of switches permitted: Unlimited

BRINSON GLOBAL BOND FUND ◆
(See first Brinson listing for data common to all Brinson funds)

Portfolio managers: Team managed (1993)
Investment objective and policies: Maximum total return - capital appreciation and current income. Invests at least 65% of assets in debt securities of issuers from at least 3 different countries, one of which may be the U.S. May use futures and options to increase return and hedge. Up to 15% of assets may be in illiquid securities.
Year organized: 1993
Ticker symbol: BPGBX
Dividends paid: Income - June, September; Capital Gains - December
Portfolio turnover (1 yr): 189%
Management fee: 0.75%
Expense ratio: 0.90% (Year ended 4/30/94) (1.78% without waiver)

BRINSON GLOBAL EQUITY FUND ◆
(See first Brinson listing for data common to all Brinson funds)

Portfolio managers: Team managed (1994)
Investment objective and policies: Maximum total return - capital appreciation and current income. Invests at least 65% of assets in equity securities of issuers from at least 3 different countries, one of which may be the U.S. May use futures and options to increase return and hedge. Up to 15% of assets may be in illiquid securities.
Year organized: 1994
Dividends paid: Income - June, December; Capital Gains - December
Portfolio turnover (1 yr): 21%
Largest holding: Stone Container Corp. (1.6%)
Management fee: 0.8%
Expense ratio: 1.00% (5 months ending 6/30/94) (2.65% without waiver)

BRINSON GLOBAL FUND ◆
(See first Brinson listing for data common to all Brinson funds)

Portfolio managers: Team managed (1992)
Investment objective and policies: Maximum total return - capital appreciation and current income. Invests at least 65% of assets in equity and debt securities of issuers from at least 3 different countries, one of which may be the U.S., using an active asset allocation strategy. May use futures and options to increase return and hedge. Up to 15% of assets may be in illiquid securities.
Year organized: 1992
Ticker symbol: BPGLX
Discount broker availability: Schwab
Dividends paid: Income - June, December; Capital Gains - December
Portfolio turnover (2 yrs): 231%, 149%
Largest holding: U.S. Treasury Note due 4/15/98 (3.4%)
Management fee: 0.8%
Expense ratio: 1.10% (year ended 6/30/94) (1.14% without waiver)

BRINSON NON-U.S. EQUITY FUND ◆
(See first Brinson listing for data common to all Brinson funds)

Portfolio managers: Team managed (1993)
Investment objective and policies: Maximum total return - capital appreciation and current income. Invests at least 65% of assets in equity securities of issuers from at least 3 different countries other than the U.S. May use futures and options to increase return and hedge. Up to 15% of assets may be in illiquid securities.
Year organized: 1993
Ticker symbol: BNUEX
Dividends paid: Income - June, December; Capital Gains - December

Portfolio turnover (1 yr): 12%
Largest holding: Royal Dutch Petroleum (2.3%)
Management fee: 0.8%
Expense ratio: 1.00% (10 months ended 6/30/94) (1.60% without waiver)

BRINSON U.S. BALANCED FUND ◆
(See first Brinson listing for data common to all Brinson funds)

Portfolio managers: Team managed (1995)
Investment objective and policies: Maximum total return - capital appreciation and current income. Invests at least 65% of assets in equity and debt securities of domestic issuers using an active asset allocation strategy. May use futures and options to increase return and hedge. Up to 15% of assets may be in illiquid securities.
Year organized: 1995
Dividends paid: Income - June, December; Capital Gains - December
Management fee: 0.7%

BRINSON U.S. EQUITY FUND ◆
(See first Brinson listing for data common to all Brinson funds)

Portfolio managers: Team managed (1994)
Investment objective and policies: Maximum total return - capital appreciation and current income. Invests at least 65% of assets in equity securities of U.S. companies. May use futures and options to increase return and hedge. Up to 15% of assets may be in illiquid securities.
Year organized: 1994
Ticker symbol: BPEQX
Dividends paid: Income - June, December; Capital Gains - December
Largest holding: Citicorp (4.2%)
Management fee: 0.7%

BROWN CAPITAL MANAGEMENT FUNDS ◆
(Data common to all Brown Capital Management funds are shown below. See subsequent listings for data specific to individual Brown Capital Management funds.)

105 North Washington Street
P.O. Drawer 69
Rocky Mount, NC 27802
800-525-3863

Adviser: Brown Capital Management, Inc.
Administrator: The Nottingham Company
Custodian: Wachovia Bank of North Carolina, N.A.
Transfer agent: The Nottingham Company
Year organized: 1992
Minimum purchase: Initial: $10,000, Subsequent: $500; IRA/Keogh: Initial: $2,000
Telephone orders accepted: No
Wire orders accepted: Yes, with advance notification
Deadline for same day wire purchase: 4 P.M.
Qualified for sale in: CA, CO, FL, GA, IL, IN, LA, MD, NC, OR, PA, TX, VA, WY
Telephone redemptions: Yes
Wire redemptions: Yes, $5,000 minimum
Letter redemptions: Signature guarantee required over $50,000
Telephone switching: With other Brown Capital Management funds
Number of switches permitted: Unlimited
Dividends paid: Income - March, June, September, December; Capital Gains - December
Shareholder services: IRA, automatic investment plan—minimum $100/month, withdrawal plan min. req. $10,000
Administration fee: 0.25% first $10M to 0.175% over $100M
12b-1 distribution fee: Maximum of 0.20% (not currently imposed)
IRA fees: Annual $15

BROWN CAPITAL MANAGEMENT BALANCED FUND ◆
(See first Brown Capital Management listing for data common to all Brown Capital Management funds)

Investment objective and policies: Maximum total return - capital growth and income with current income secondary. Invests in equity, fixed-income securities and money market instruments with allocation adjusted to reflect changing market conditions. At least 25% (maximum of 75%) of assets are in fixed-income and money market securities. May invest in ADRs of foreign issuers and have up to 15% of assets in junk bonds.
Portfolio turnover (2 yrs): 29%, 21%
Largest holding: Philip Morris Companies, Inc. (3.4%)
Management fee: 0.65% first $25M, 0.50% over $25M
Expense ratio: 2.00% (year ending 3/31/94) (6.44% without waiver)

BROWN CAPITAL MANAGEMENT EQUITY FUND ◆
(See first Brown Capital Management listing for data common to all Brown Capital Management funds)

Investment objective and policies: Capital growth with current income secondary. Invests primarily in common and preferred stocks and securities convertible into common stocks of companies believed undervalued with remainder in money market instruments. May invest in ADRs of foreign issuers and have up to 10% of assets in small capitalization companies.
Portfolio turnover (2 yrs): 48%, 3%
Largest holding: Aflac, Inc. (4.2%)
Management fee: 0.65% first $25M, 0.50% over $25M
Expense ratio: 2.00% (year ending 3/31/94) (11.86% without waiver)

BROWN CAPITAL MANAGEMENT SMALL COMPANY FUND ◆
(See first Brown Capital Management listing for data common to all Brown Capital Management funds)

Investment objective and policies: Capital growth with current income secondary. Invests primarily in common stocks of companies with market capitalizations under $250M believed undervalued with remainder in money market instruments. May invest in ADRs of foreign issuers.
Portfolio turnover (2 yrs): 23%, 4%
Largest holding: T. Rowe Price Associates (4.5%)
Management fee: 1.00%
Expense ratio: 2.00% (year ending 3/31/94) (4.73% without waiver)

BRUCE FUND ◆
20 N. Wacker Drive, Suite 2414
Chicago, IL 60606
312-236-9160, 800-872-7823
fax 312-236-9161

Adviser: Bruce and Co.
Portfolio manager: Robert B. Bruce (1983)
Custodian: Fifth Third Bank, Cincinnati
Transfer agent: Unified Management Corp.
Investment objective and policies: Long-term capital growth with income secondary. Invests primarily in common stocks and bonds, but may also invest in convertible securities, preferred stocks, and other debt instruments and warrants.
Year organized: 1968 (formerly Herold Fund)
Ticker symbol: BRUFX
Minimum purchase: Initial: $1,000, Subsequent: $500
Telephone orders accepted: No
Wire orders accepted: Yes
Deadline for same day wire purchase: 4 P.M.
Qualified for sale in: All states except AL, AK, ID, IA, MS, MO, NE, NV, ND, RI, SD, UT

Letter redemptions: Signature guarantee required over $5,000
Dividends paid: Income - December; Capital Gains - December
Portfolio turnover (3 yrs): 2%, 14%, 4%
Largest holding: U.S. Treasury "STRIPS" Bond (59.1%)
Shareholder services: IRA
Management fee: 1.0%
Expense ratio: 1.90% (year ending 6/30/94)
IRA fees: Annual $10

BRUNDAGE, STORY AND ROSE GROWTH & INCOME FUND
312 Walnut Street, 21st Floor
Cincinnati, OH 45202
513-629-2000, 800-543-8721
prices 800-852-4052, fax 513-629-2901

Adviser: Brundage, Story and Rose
Administrator: MGF Service Corp.
Portfolio manager: Charles G. Watson (1992)
Custodian: Fifth Third Bank, Cincinnati
Transfer agent: MGF Service Corp.
Investment objective and policies: Protection and enhancement of capital, current income and growth of income. Invests primarily in dividend-paying common stocks and securities convertible into common stock. May invest in securities of foreign issuers.
Year organized: 1991
Minimum purchase: Initial: $1,000; Subsequent: None; IRA/Keogh: Initial: $250
Telephone orders accepted: No
Wire orders accepted: Yes
Deadline for same day wire purchase: 4 P.M.
Discount broker availability: Schwab
Qualified for sale in: All states except AL, AK, ID, IA, MS, MO, MT, NE, NV, ND, RI, SD, UT
Telephone redemptions: Yes
Wire redemptions: Yes, $1,000 minimum, $8 fee
Letter redemptions: Signature guarantee required over $5,000
Telephone switching: With Brundage, Story and Rose Short/Intermediate Term Fixed-Income Fund, Midwest Group Tax Free Trust - Tax-Free Money Fund and Midwest Income Trust - Short Term Government Fund
Number of switches permitted: Unlimited
Dividends paid: Income - March, June, September, December; Capital gains - December
Portfolio turnover (3 yrs): 44%, 45%, 44%
Largest holding: Pepsico (2.8%)
Shareholder services: Keogh, IRA, 401(k), 403(b), corporate retirement plans, automatic investment plan—minimum $50/month, electronic funds transfer, withdrawal plan min. req. $5,000
Management fee: 0.65%
Administrative fee: $39,600 + 0.2% first $50M to 0.15% over $100M
12b-1 distribution fee: 0.01%
Expense ratio: 1.50% (year ending 11/30/94)
IRA fees: Annual $10
Keogh fees: Annual $35

BRUNDAGE, STORY AND ROSE SHORT/INTERMEDIATE TERM FIXED-INCOME FUND
312 Walnut Street, 21st Floor
Cincinnati, OH 45202
513-629-2000, 800-543-8721
prices 800-852-4052, fax 513-629-2901

Adviser: Brundage, Story and Rose
Administrator: MGF Service Corp.
Portfolio manager: H. Dean Benner (1991)
Custodian: Fifth Third Bank, Cincinnati
Transfer agent: MGF Service Corp.
Investment Objective and policies: High current income consistent with stability of principal. Invests primarily in investment-grade short and intermediate-term debt securities with a weighted average maturity of 2 to 5 years. May invest in U.S. Government obligations (up to 35%), corporate debt securities, bank debt instruments, mortgage-backed and asset-backed securities, U.S. dollar-denominated debt securities of foreign issuers and

money market instruments. May use futures and options to hedge up to 25% of total assets.
Year organized: 1991
Ticker symbol: BRSFX
Minimum purchase: Initial: $1,000; Subsequent: None; IRA/Keogh: Initial: $250
Telephone orders accepted: No
Wire orders accepted: Yes
Deadline for same day wire purchase: 4 P.M.
Discount broker availability: Schwab
Qualified for sale in: All states except AL, AK, ID, IA, MS, MO, MT, NE, NV, ND, RI, SD, UT
Telephone redemptions: Yes
Wire redemptions: Yes, $1,000 minimum, $8 fee
Letter redemptions: Signature guarantee required over $5,000
Check redemptions: No minimum, $0.50 fee
Telephone switching: With Brundage, Story and Rose Growth & Income Fund, Midwest Group Tax Free Trust - Tax-Free Money Fund and Midwest Income Trust - Short Term Government Fund
Number of switches permitted: Unlimited
Dividends paid: Income - declared and paid monthly; Capital gains - December
Portfolio turnover (3 yrs): 57%, 29%, 24%
Shareholder services: Keogh, IRA, 401(k), 403(b), corporate retirement plans, automatic investment plan—minimum $50/month, electronic funds transfer, withdrawal plan min. req. $5,000
Management fee: 0.50%
Administrative fee: $43,200 + 0.2% first $50M to 0.15% over $100M
12b-1 distribution fee: 0.01%
Expense ratio: 0.50% (year ending 11/30/94) (1.06% without waiver)
IRA fees: Annual $10
Keogh fees: Annual $35

BULL & BEAR FUNDS
(Data common to all Bull & Bear funds are shown below. See subsequent listings for data specific to individual Bull & Bear funds.)

11 Hanover Square
New York, NY 10005
212-363-1100, 800-847-4200
fax 212-363-1103

Shareholder service hours: Full service: M-F 9 A.M.-5 P.M.; After hours service: prices, news, messages, DJIA, prospectuses
Adviser: Bull & Bear Advisors, Inc.
Custodian: Investors Bank & Trust Co.
Transfer agent: Fund/Plan Services, Inc.
Minimum purchase: Initial: $1,000, Subsequent: $100; IRA: Initial: $500; Keogh: Initial: $100
Telephone orders accepted: Subsequent only, $500 minimum, exceptions noted
Wire orders accepted: Yes
Deadline for same day wire purchases: 4 P.M. (11 A.M. for Dollar Reserves)
Qualified for sale in: All states
Telephone redemptions: Yes, $1,000 minimum
Wire redemptions: Yes, $1,000 minimum
Letter redemptions: Signature guarantee may be required
Telephone switching: With other Bull & Bear funds, $500 minimum
Deadline for close of day switch: 3 P.M.
Number of switches permitted: Unlimited
Shareholder services: Keogh, IRA, SEP-IRA, & 403(b), corporate retirement plans, automatic investment plan (waives initial minimum), directed dividends, withdrawal plan min. req. $10,000, electronic funds transfer (purchase only)
IRA fees: Annual $10
Keogh fees: None
Maintenance fee: $2 per month ($5 for Special Equities fund) for accounts with balances under $500

BULL & BEAR DOLLAR RESERVES ◆
(See first Bull & Bear listing for data common to all Bull & Bear funds)

Portfolio manager: G. Clifford McCarthy, Jr. (1990)
Investment objective and policies: Maximum cur-

rent income consistent with preservation of capital and liquidity. Invests only in money market instruments issued or guaranteed as to principal and interest by the U.S. Government or its agencies or instrumentalities.
Year organized: 1977 (as Bear Fund); name and objective change 1980
Ticker symbol: BBDXX
Check redemptions: $250 minimum
Confirmations mailed: After each purchase and each check, mail or wire redemption
Checks returned: Monthly
Periodic account statements mailed: Quarterly
Dividends paid: Income - declared daily, paid monthly
Management fee: 0.5% first $250M to 0.4% over $500M
12b-1 distribution fee: Yes (not currently imposed)
Expense ratio: 0.89% (year ending 6/30/94) (1.14% without waiver)

BULL & BEAR GLOBAL INCOME FUND
(See first Bull & Bear listing for data common to all Bull & Bear funds)

Portfolio manager: G. Clifford McCarthy, Jr. (1990)
Investment objective and policies: High current income with growth of capital secondary. Invests at least 65% of assets in a global portfolio of investment-grade fixed-income securities. Maturities can be long, short, intermediate, or any combination thereof. Fund generally invests in securities of at least 3 countries and may invest 35% of assets in junk bonds. Fund hedges.
Year organized: 1983 (formerly Bull & Bear High Yield Fund. Name and objective changed on 10/29/92)
Ticker symbol: BBGLX
Discount broker availability: Schwab, *White, *Waterhouse, *Fidelity, *Siebert
Check redemptions: $250 minimum
Dividends paid: Income - declared and paid monthly, Capital gains - December
Portfolio turnover (3 yrs): 223%, 172%, 206%
Management fee: 0.7% first $250M to 0.5% over $500M
12b-1 distribution fee: 0.50%
Expense ratio: 1.98% (year ending 6/30/94)

BULL & BEAR GOLD INVESTORS LTD.
(See first Bull & Bear listing for data common to all Bull & Bear funds)

Portfolio manager: Bassett S. Winmill (1994)
Investment objective and policies: Long-term capital appreciation with income secondary. Invests at least 65% of assets in gold, platinum and silver bullion and a global portfolio of securities of companies involved directly or indirectly in mining, processing or dealing in gold or other precious metals. May also invest in companies who own or develop natural resources and other basic commodities, growth companies, and U.S. Government securities. May use futures and options to hedge.
Year organized: 1974 (formerly Golconda Investors)
Ticker symbol: BBGIX
Special share purchases: Fund will exchange shares for investors round lots in acceptable individual securities.
Discount broker availability: Schwab, *White, *Waterhouse, *Fidelity, *Siebert
Dividends paid: Income - December; Capital gains - December
Portfolio turnover (3 yrs): 156%, 97%, 95%
Largest holding: Newcrest Mining Ltd. (5.4%)
Management fee: 0.91%
12b-1 distribution fee: 1.00%
Expense ratio: 2.57% (year ending 6/30/94)

BULL & BEAR MUNICIPAL INCOME FUND
(See first Bull & Bear listing for data common to all Bull & Bear funds)

Portfolio manager: G. Clifford McCarthy, Jr. (1990)
Investment objective and policies: High income exempt from federal income taxes consistent with the preservation of principal. Invests in municipal securities with maturities that can be long, short, intermediate, or any combination thereof with a weighted average maturity of 5 to more than 25 years. May invest in AMT securities.
Year organized: 1984 (name changed from Bull & Bear Tax-Free Income Fund on 12/1/92)
Ticker symbol: BBMIX
Discount broker availability: Schwab, *White, *Waterhouse, *Fidelity, *Siebert
Dividends paid: Income - declared daily, paid monthly; Capital gains - December
Portfolio turnover (3 yrs): 74%, 320%, 511%
Management fee: 0.59% (0.60% without waiver)
12b-1 distribution fee: 0.35%
Expense ratio: 1.61% (year ending 12/31/93)

BULL & BEAR QUALITY GROWTH FUND
(See first Bull & Bear listing for data common to all Bull & Bear funds)

Portfolio manager: Thomas B. Winmill (1994)
Investment objective and policies: Capital growth with income secondary. Invests primarily in common stocks of large, quality companies with potential for significant growth of earnings and dividends. Up to 35% of assets may be in preferred stocks, fixed-income securities, convertible securities and securities of foreign issuers. Up to 15% of assets may be in illiquid securities. Fund may use future and options.
Year organized: 1993
Ticker symbol: BBQGX
Discount broker availability: *White, *Waterhouse, *Fidelity, *Siebert
Dividends paid: Income - December; Capital gains - December
Largest holding: Allied Signal Inc. (4.8%)
Management fee: 0.76%
12b-1 distribution fee: 1.00%

BULL & BEAR SPECIAL EQUITIES FUND
(See first Bull & Bear listing for data common to all Bull & Bear funds)

Portfolio manager: Brett B. Sneed (1988)
Investment objective and policies: Capital appreciation. Engages in such speculative activities as special situations, purchasing or writing put and call options, warrants, short selling and short-term trading. Investments may be in established and new and unseasoned companies. At least 65% of the fund will consist of equity securities of U.S. and foreign issuers. Up to 35% may be in corporate bonds, debentures or preferred stocks, both convertible and non-convertible, and U.S. Government or municipal securities. Up to 15% of assets may be in illiquid securities. Fund leverages and sells short.
Year organized: 1986
Ticker symbol: BBSEX
Special share purchases: Fund will exchange shares for investors' round lots in acceptable individual securities.
Discount broker availability: Schwab, *White, *Waterhouse, *Fidelity, *Siebert
Portfolio turnover (3 yrs): 256%, 261%, 384%
Largest holding: Americredit Corp. (7.2%)
Management fee: 0.82%
12b-1 distribution fee: 1.0%
Expense Ratio: 2.74% (year ending 12/31/93)

BULL & BEAR U.S. & OVERSEAS FUND
(See first Bull & Bear listing for data common to all Bull & Bear funds)

Sub-adviser: Banque Worms Management Corp.
Portfolio manager: Brett B. Sneed (1994)
Investment objective and policies: Total return -

long term growth of capital and income. Invests in equity and debt securities of U.S. and overseas issuers. There is no limitation on the percent of assets which may be invested for growth or income and the emphasis can be changed at any point in time. May use futures and options to hedge.
Year organized: 1987 (name changed from Bull & Bear Overseas Fund on 2/26/92 and fund split 2 for 1 on 2/25/92)
Ticker symbol: BBOSX
Special share purchases: Fund will exchange shares for investors' round lots in acceptable individual securities.
Discount broker availability: Schwab, *White, *Waterhouse, *Fidelity, *Siebert
Dividends paid: Income - December, Capital gains - December
Portfolio turnover (3 yrs): 182%, 175%, 208%
Largest holding: Nokia Corp. ADR (4.5%)
Management fee: 1.0% first $10M to 0.5% over $500M
12b-1 distribution fee: 1.0%
Expense ratio: 3.55% (year ending 12/31/93) (3.69% without waiver)

BULL & BEAR U.S. GOVERNMENT SECURITIES FUND
(See first Bull & Bear listing for data common to all Bull & Bear funds)

Newspaper listing: GovtSc
Portfolio manager: G. Clifford McCarthy, Jr. (1990)
Investment objective and policies: High level of current income, liquidity and safety of principal. Invests primarily in fixed-income securities backed by the full faith and credit of the United States.
Year organized: 1986
Ticker symbol: BBUSX
Discount broker availability: Schwab, *White, *Waterhouse, *Fidelity, *Siebert
Dividends paid: Income - declared daily, paid monthly; Capital Gains - December
Portfolio turnover (3 yrs): 261%, 176%, 140%
Management fee: 0.70%
12b-1 distribution fee: 0.25%
Expense ratio: 1.85% (year ending 6/30/94)

CALDWELL FUNDS ◆
(Data common to all Caldwell funds are shown below. See subsequent listings for data specific to individual Caldwell funds.)

P.O. Box 622
Venice, FL 34284
813-488-6772, 800-338-9477
fax 813-496-4661

Adviser: Omnivest Research Corp.
Custodian: Caldwell Trust Company
Transfer agent: Caldwell Fund, Inc.
Minimum purchase: Initial: None, Subsequent: None
Telephone orders accepted: No
Wire orders accepted: No
Qualified for sale in: FL
Telephone redemptions: Yes
Letter redemptions: Signature guarantee not required
Shareholder services: IRA, SEP-IRA
IRA fees: None

CALDWELL FUND ◆
(See first Caldwell listing for data common to all Caldwell funds)

Investment objective and policies: Current income with some capital growth. Invests in equity securities - common stocks, convertible preferred stocks and convertible bonds - and fixed-income securities with allocation varying depending on economic or market conditions. Securities will most commonly be traded on the NYSE.
Year organized: 1985
Dividends paid: Income - June, December; Capital gains - December

Portfolio turnover (3 yrs): 52%, 93%, 42%
Largest holding: U.S. Treasury 8.000% notes due May 2001 (16.2%)
Management fee: 1.0%
Expense ratio: 1.89% (year ending 12/31/93) (includes waiver)

CALDWELL GOVERNMENT FUND ◆
(See first Caldwell listing for data common to all Caldwell funds)

Portfolio manager: Roland G. Caldwell (1992)
Investment objective and policies: Higher interest rate returns than are available from government-only money market mutual funds. Invests exclusively in U.S. Treasury issues or in obligations issued by agencies of the U.S. government with remaining maturities of 2 to 10 years.
Year organized: 1992
Dividends paid: Income - declared and paid daily; Capital gains - December
Portfolio turnover (1 yr): 124%
Management fee: 0.5%
Expense ratio: 0.93% (year ending 12/31/93) (includes waiver)

CALDWELL GROWTH STOCK FUND ◆
(See first Caldwell listing for data common to all Caldwell funds)

Portfolio manager: Roland G. Caldwell (1992)
Investment objective and policies: Maximum capital appreciation. Invests primarily in common stocks or equivalents of companies believed to have above average growth prospects regardless of the capitalizations of the companies or their annual sales volumes.
Year organized: 1992
Dividends paid: Income - June, December; Capital gains - December
Portfolio turnover (1 yr): 20%
Largest holding: S&P 500 Depository Receipt (16.2%)
Management fee: 1.0%
Expense ratio: 1.60% (year ending 12/31/93) (includes waiver)

CALDWELL TAX-FREE FUND ◆
(See first Caldwell listing for data common to all Caldwell funds)

Portfolio manager: Roland G. Caldwell (1992)
Investment objective and policies: High interest income exempt from federal income taxes. Invests in securities issued by states, municipalities and other governmental jurisdictions exempt from federal income tax with remaining maturities of 12 years or less.
Year organized: 1992
Dividends paid: Income - declared and paid daily; Capital gains - December
Portfolio turnover (1 yr): 86%
Management fee: 0.5%
Expense ratio: 0.88% (year ending 12/31/93) (includes waiver)

THE CALDWELL & ORKIN AGGRESSIVE GROWTH FUND ◆
2050 Tower Place
3340 Peachtree Road
Atlanta, GA 30326
404-239-0707, 800-237-7073
fax 404-237-8603

Adviser: C&O Funds Advisor, Inc.
Portfolio managers: Michael B. Orkin (1992), P. Ivan Faulkenberry (1992)
Custodian: Bank One Ohio Trust Co., N.A.
Transfer agent: Mutual + Shareholder Services Corp.
Investment objective and policies: Capital growth and capital preservation through investment selection and asset allocation and to outperform the NASDAQ Composite. Invests at least 80% of assets in common stocks of small companies with poten-

tial for capital growth and up to 20% in bonds and cash. Up to 25% of assets may be in equity securities of foreign issuers. May hedge investments to realize additional gains through short sales.
Year organized: 1991
Ticker symbol: COAGX
Minimum purchase: Initial: $10,000, Subsequent $1,000; IRA/Keogh: Initial $2,000
Telephone orders accepted: No
Wire orders accepted: No
Discount broker availability: Schwab
Qualified for sale: AL, AZ, CA, DC, FL, GA, KY, MD, MI, MS, NV, NC, NJ, NY, OH, OR, SC, TN, TX, WA
Letter redemptions: Signature guarantee required
Dividends paid: Income - December; Capital gains - December
Portfolio turnover (3 yrs): 292%, 223%, 50%
Largest holding: Revco Drug Stores, Inc. (3.6%)
Shareholder services: IRA, Keogh, withdrawal plan
Management fee: 0.9% first $100M to 0.5% over $500M
Expense ratio: 1.21% (year ending 4/30/94) (1.77% without waiver)

CALIFORNIA DAILY TAX FREE INCOME FUND ◆
600 Fifth Avenue - 8th Floor
New York, NY 10020
212-676-5200, 800-676-6779
prices/yields 212-830-5225
fax 212-830-5476

Adviser: Reich & Tang Asset Management L.P.
Portfolio manager: Molly Flewharty (1987)
Custodian: Investors Fiduciary Trust Co.
Transfer agent: Fundtech Services L.P.
Investment objective and policies: High current interest income exempt from federal income taxes and, to the extent possible, from California income taxes, consistent with preservation of capital and liquidity. Invests primarily in California municipal money market instruments.
Year organized: 1987
Ticker symbol: CFDXX
Minimum purchase: Initial: $5,000, Subsequent: $100
Wire orders accepted: Yes
Deadline for same day wire purchase: 12 NN
Qualified for sale in: AZ, CA, CO, NY
Telephone redemptions: Yes
Wire redemptions: Yes, $1,000 minimum
Letter redemptions: Signature guarantee required
Telephone switching: With other Reich & Tang Money Market funds, R & T Equity and R & T Government Securities Trust
Number of switches permitted: Unlimited, $1,000 minimum
Deadline for same day switch: 12 NN
Check redemptions: $250 minimum
Confirmations mailed: After each purchase and each check, mail or wire redemption
Checks returned: As clear
Periodic account statements mailed: Monthly
Dividends paid: Income - declared daily, paid monthly
Shareholder services: Withdrawal plan
Management fee: 0.50%
12b-1 distribution fee: 0.20% (not currently imposed)
Expense ratio: 0.35% (year ending 12/31/93) (0.89% without waiver)

CALIFORNIA INVESTMENT TRUST FUND GROUP ◆
(Data common to all California Investment Trust funds are shown below. See subsequent listings for data specific to individual California Investment Trust funds.)

44 Montgomery St., Suite 2100
San Francisco, CA 94104
415-398-2727, 800-225-8778
fax 415-421-2019

Shareholder service hours: Full service: M-F 8 A.M.-5 P.M. PST
Adviser: CCM Partners

Custodian: Firstar Trust Co.
Transfer agent: Fund/Plan Services Inc.
Minimum purchase: Initial: $10,000 ($5,000 for S&P funds), Subsequent: $250; IRA/Keogh: Initial: None; Subsequent: None
Telephone orders accepted: No
Wire orders accepted: Yes
Deadline for same day wire purchase: 4 P.M.
Qualified for sale in: CA, HI, NV
Wire redemptions: Yes, $1,000 minimum, $7.50 fee
Letter redemptions: Signature guarantee required
Telephone switching: With other California Investment Trust funds
Number of switches permitted: Unlimited
Check redemptions: $500 minimum (none for S&P funds)
Confirmations mailed: After each purchase and each check, mail or wire redemption
Checks returned: Monthly
Periodic account statements mailed: Monthly
Shareholders services: IRA, Keogh, corporate retirement plans, automatic investment plan, withdrawal plan min. req. $10,000
IRA/Keogh fees: Annual $12.50

CALIFORNIA INVESTMENT TRUST: CALIFORNIA INSURED TAX-FREE INCOME FUND ◆
(See first California Investment Trust listing for data common to all California Investment Trust funds)

Portfolio manager: Phillip W. McClanahan (1992)
Investment objective and policies: High income exempt from federal and California personal income taxes consistent with prudent investment risk and safety of capital. Invests primarily in intermediate and long-term California municipal securities that are covered by insurance guaranteeing the timely payment of principal and interest.
Year organized: 1992
Ticker symbol: CATFX
Dividends paid: Income - declared daily, paid monthly; Capital gains - December
Portfolio turnover (2 yrs): 9%, 0%
Management fee: 0.5% first $100M to 0.4% over $500M
Expense ratio: 0.46% (year ending 10/31/94) (0.88% without waiver)

CALIFORNIA INVESTMENT TRUST: CALIFORNIA TAX-FREE INCOME FUND ◆
(See first California Investment Trust listing for data common to all California Investment Trust funds)

Newspaper listing: CalInc
Portfolio manager: Phillip W. McClanahan (1985)
Investment objective and policies: High income exempt from federal and California personal income taxes. Invests primarily in intermediate and long-term California municipal securities rated within the 4 highest categories by S&P, Moody's or Fitch's with a weighted average maturity of 5 years or more. Up to 20% of assets may be in securities rated as low as Baa.
Year organized: 1985
Ticker symbol: CFNTX
Discount broker availability: Schwab, *White
Dividends paid: Income - declared daily, paid monthly; Capital gains - December
Portfolio turnover (3 yrs): 31%, 25%, 45%
Management fee: 0.5% first $100M to 0.4% over $500M
Expense ratio: 0.60% (year ending 8/31/94)

CALIFORNIA INVESTMENT TRUST: CALIFORNIA TAX-FREE MONEY MARKET FUND ◆
(See first California Investment Trust listing for data common to all California Investment Trust funds)

Portfolio manager: Phillip W. McClanahan (1985)
Investment objective and policies: High current

income exempt from federal and California personal income taxes. Invests in all types of high quality California municipal obligations, primarily in money market instruments.
Year organized: 1985
Ticker symbol: CAXXX
Dividends paid: Income - declared daily; paid monthly
Management fee: 0.5% first $100M to 0.4% over $500M
Expense ratio: 0.35% (year ending 8/31/94) (0.68% without waiver)

CALIFORNIA INVESTMENT TRUST: S&P 500 INDEX FUND ◆
(See first California Investment Trust listing for data common to all California Investment Trust funds)

Sub-adviser: Bank of America
Investment objective and policies: Investment results that correspond to the total return of the common stocks comprising the S&P 500 Composite Stock Price Index. Invests in a sub-set of the stocks included in the index, weighted to match their representation in the Index.
Year organized: 1992
Ticker symbol: SPFIX
Discount broker availability: *White
Dividends paid: Income - March, June, September, December; Capital gains - December
Portfolio turnover (2 yrs): 1%, 8%
Largest holding: General Electric Co. (1.7%)
Management fee: 0.25%
Expense ratio: 0.20% (year ending 8/31/94) (1.01% without waiver)

CALIFORNIA INVESTMENT TRUST: S&P MIDCAP INDEX FUND ◆
(See first California Investment Trust listing for data common to all California Investment Trust funds)

Sub-adviser: Bank of America
Investment objective and policies: Investment results that correspond to the total return of the common stocks comprising the S&P MidCap 400 Composite Stock Price Index. Invests in a sub-set of the stocks included in the index, weighted to match their representation in the Index.
Year organized: 1992
Ticker symbol: SPMIX
Dividends paid: Income - March, June, September, December; Capital gains - December
Portfolio turnover (2 yrs): 15%, 8%
Largest holding: General Motors Corp. Class E (1.6%)
Management fee: 0.4%
Expense ratio: 0.40% (year ending 8/31/94) (0.97% without waiver)

CALIFORNIA INVESTMENT TRUST: U.S. GOVERNMENT SECURITIES FUND ◆
(See first California Investment Trust listing for data common to all California Investment Trust funds)

Newspaper listing: CalUS
Portfolio manager: Philip W. McClanahan (1985)
Investment objective and policies: High income consistent with preservation of capital and liquidity. Invests in full faith and credit obligations of the U.S. Government and its agencies or instrumentalities, primarily GNMA certificates.
Year organized: 1985
Ticker symbol: CAUSX
Discount broker availability: Schwab, *White
Dividends paid: Income - declared daily, paid monthly: Capital gains - December
Portfolio turnover (3 yrs): 129%, 52%, 122%
Management fee: 0.5% first $100M to 0.4% over $500M
Expense ratio: 0.62% (year ending 8/31/94) (0.73% without waiver)

CALIFORNIA INVESTMENT TRUST: THE UNITED STATES TREASURY TRUST ◆

(See first California Investment Trust listing for data common to all California Investment Trust funds)

Portfolio manager: Philip W. McClanahan (1989)
Investment objective and policies: High current income exempt from state income taxes, consistent with preservation of capital & liquidity. Invests exclusively in short-term U.S. Treasury money market securities.
Year organized: 1989
Ticker symbol: UTSXX
Dividends paid: Income - declared daily, paid monthly
Management fee: 0.5% first $100M to 0.4% over $500M
Expense ratio: 0.52% (year ending 8/31/94) (0.75% without waiver)

CALVERT SOCIAL INVESTMENT FUND - MONEY MARKET PORTFOLIO ◆

4550 Montgomery Avenue - Suite 1000N
Bethesda, MD 20814
301-951-4800, 800-368-2748
800-368-2745, TDD 800-541-1524

Adviser: Calvert Asset Management Company, Inc.
Portfolio managers: Colleen Trosko (1988)
Custodian: Riggs National Bank of Washington, D. C.
Transfer agent: Calvert Shareholder Services, Inc.
Investment objective and policies: High current income consistent with liquidity, safety and stability of capital. Invests in U.S. Government agency securities and other money market instruments, as well as repurchase agreements, selected in accordance with the fund's social criteria.
Year organized: 1982
Ticker symbol: CSIXX
Minimum purchase: Initial: $1,000, Subsequent: $250
Wire orders accepted: Yes
Deadline for same day wire purchase: 12:30 P.M.
Qualified for sale in: All states
Telephone redemptions: Yes
Wire redemptions: Yes, $5 fee under $1,000
Letter redemptions: Signature guarantee required
Telephone switching: With other Calvert funds all of which have loads
Number of switches permitted: Unlimited
Deadline for same day switch: 5 P.M. to money market funds, 4 P.M. to stock and bond funds
Check redemptions: $250 minimum
Confirmations mailed: After each purchase and each check, mail or wire redemption
Checks returned: Quarterly
Periodic account statements mailed: Quarterly
Dividends paid: Income - declared and paid daily
Shareholder services: Keogh, IRA, SEP-IRA, 403(b), 401(k), withdrawal plan min. req. $10,000, electronic funds transfer
Management fee: 0.5%
12b-1 distribution fee: Maximum of 0.25% (not currently imposed)
Expense ratio: 0.87% (year ending 9/30/93) (includes waiver)
IRA fees: Annual $15
Keogh fees: Annual $25

CAMCO FUNDS

(Data common to all Camco funds are shown below. See subsequent listings for data specific to individual Camco funds.)

555 North Lane - Suite 6160
Conshohocken, PA 19428
800-352-7507, fax 610-832-1067

Adviser: Consistent Asset Management Company, Inc.
Portfolio manager: Daryl L. Hudson (1992)

Custodian: CoreStates Bank, N.A., Philadelphia, PA
Transfer agent: Declaration Service Co.
Year organized: 1992
Minimum purchase: Initial: $10,000, Subsequent $100; IRA: Initial: $2,000, Subsequent: $100
Telephone orders accepted: No
Wire orders accepted: Yes
Deadline for same day wire purchase: 11 A.M.
Qualified for sale in: AL, CA, CT, DC, DE, FL, GA, MI, MO, NC, NJ, NY, PA, TX
Telephone redemptions: Yes, $5,000 minimum
Wire redemptions: Yes, $5,000 minimum, $12 fee
Letter redemptions: Signature guarantee required over $5,000
Telephone switching: With other Camco funds
Dividends paid: Income - monthly; Capital gains - December
Shareholder services: IRA, automatic investment plan—minimum $100, electronic funds transfer
IRA fees: None

CAMCO 100% U.S. TREASURY INTERMEDIATE-TERM FUND

(See first Camco listing for data common to all Camco funds)

Investment objective and policies: High total return (income plus capital gains) consistent with preservation of capital and liquidity. Invests in U.S. Treasury securities with individual maturities of 1 day to 10 years and a weighted average maturity of 3 to 6 years. May use interest rate futures and options to hedge.
Portfolio turnover (2 yrs): 1107%, 490%
Management fee: 0.20%
12b-1 distribution fee: 0.20%
Expense ratio: 0.75% (year ending 12/31/93) (includes waiver)

CAMCO 100% U.S. TREASURY SHORT-TERM FUND

(See first Camco listing for data common to all Camco funds)

Investment objective and policies: High total return (income plus capital gains) consistent with preservation of capital and liquidity. Invests in U.S. Treasury securities with individual maturities of 1 day to 10 years and a weighted average maturity of 1 to 3 years. May use interest rate futures and options to hedge.
Check redemptions: No minimum, $5 fee
Portfolio turnover (2 yrs): 1339%, 859%
Management fee: 0.15%
12b-1 distribution fee: 0.15%
Expense ratio: 0.60% (year ending 12/31/93) (includes waiver)

CAMCO 100% U.S. TREASURY TOTAL RETURN FUND

(See first Camco listing for data common to all Camco funds)

Investment objective and policies: High total return (income plus capital gains) consistent with preservation of capital and liquidity. Invests in U.S. Treasury securities with individual maturities of 1 day to 30 years and a weighted average maturity of 6 to 15 years. May use interest rate futures and options to hedge.
Portfolio turnover (2 yrs): 925%, 483%
Management fee: 0.20%
12b-1 distribution fee: 0.20%
Expense ratio: 0.75% (year ending 12/31/93) (includes waiver)

CAPPIELLO-RUSHMORE FUNDS ◆

(Data common to all Cappiello-Rushmore funds are shown below. See subsequent listings for data specific to individual Cappiello-Rushmore funds.)

4922 Fairmont Avenue
Bethesda, MD 20814
301-657-1500, 800-343-3355
prices 800-451-2234, fax 301-657-1520

Adviser: McCullough, Andrews & Cappiello, Inc.
Custodian: Rushmore Trust and Savings Bank, FSB

Transfer agent: Money Management Associates
Minimum purchase: Initial: $2,500 (total among all funds, $500 minimum per fund), Subsequent: None; IRA/Keogh: Initial: $500
Telephone orders accepted: No
Wire orders accepted: Yes
Deadline for same day wire purchase: 3:30 P.M.
Qualified for sale in: All states except AK, DE, ME, MS, ND, SD, UT, WV (except Gold Fund)
Telephone redemptions: Yes
Wire redemptions: Yes, $5,000 minimum
Letter redemptions: Signature guarantee may be required
Telephone switching: With other Cappiello-Rushmore funds and Rushmore funds
Number of switches permitted: Unlimited
Deadline for same day switch: 3:30 P.M.
Shareholder services: Keogh, IRA, 401(k), 403(b) & corporate retirement plans
IRA/Keogh fees: Annual $10, Closing $10

CAPPIELLO-RUSHMORE EMERGING GROWTH FUND ◆

(See first Cappiello-Rushmore listing for data common to all Cappiello-Rushmore funds)

Portfolio manager: Frank A. Cappiello (1992)
Investment objective and policies: Capital appreciation. Invests primarily in common stocks, securities convertible into common stocks and warrants to purchase common stocks of companies with market capitalization of $750M or less. May invest 35% of assets in debt securities, 25% in larger-capitalization stocks and 20% in securities of foreign issuers. May sell short.
Year organized: 1992
Ticker symbol: CREGX
Discount broker availability: *Schwab, *White, *Waterhouse, *Fidelity, *Siebert
Dividends paid: Income - December; Capital gains - December
Portfolio turnover (2 yrs): 128%, 68%
Largest holding: Bradlees, Inc. (5.7%)
Management fee: 0.50%
Expense ratio: 1.50% (year ending 6/30/94)

CAPPIELLO-RUSHMORE GOLD FUND ◆

(See first Cappiello-Rushmore listing for data common to all Cappiello-Rushmore funds)

Portfolio manager: Frank A. Cappiello (1994)
Investment objective and policies: Capital appreciation. Invests primarily in equity securities of companies engaged in the mining, exploration, fabrication, processing, marketing and distribution of gold and companies that finance, manage, control or operate companies engaged in these activities. Fund also invests directly in gold bullion and in companies engaged in the foregoing activities with respect to silver, platinum and other precious metals and in diamonds and other precious minerals. May use futures and options and sell short.
Year organized: 1994
Ticker symbol: CRGDX
Discount broker availability: *Schwab, *White, *Waterhouse, *Fidelity, *Siebert
Qualified for sale in: CA, CO, DC, FL, HI, IL, MD, MN, NJ, NY, OH, TX, VA
Dividends paid: Income - December; Capital gains - December
Largest holding: American Barrick Resources Corp. (9.3%)
Management fee: 0.70%

CAPPIELLO-RUSHMORE GROWTH FUND ◆

(See first Cappiello-Rushmore listing for data common to all Cappiello-Rushmore funds)

Portfolio manager: Frank A. Cappiello (1992)
Investment objective and policies: Capital appreciation. Invests primarily in common stocks, securities convertible into common stocks and warrants to purchase common stock. May invest 20% of assets in securities of foreign issuers. Fund may use

options to hedge and sell short against the box.
Year organized: 1992
Ticker symbol: CRGRX
Discount broker availability: *Schwab, *White, *Waterhouse, *Fidelity, *Siebert
Dividends paid: Income - December; Capital gains - December
Portfolio turnover (2 yrs): 119%, 21%
Largest holding: AT&T Corp. (7.6%)
Management fee: 0.50%
Expense ratio: 1.50% (year ending 6/30/94)

CAPPIELLO-RUSHMORE UTILITY INCOME FUND ◆

(See first Cappiello-Rushmore listing for data common to all Cappiello-Rushmore funds)

Portfolio manager: Frank A. Cappiello (1992)
Investment objective and policies: Current income with an opportunity for capital appreciation. Invests at least 65% of assets in securities of public utility companies. May invest 20% of assets in securities of foreign issuers. Fund may use options to hedge and sell short against the box.
Year organized: 1992
Ticker symbol: CRUTX
Discount broker availability: *Schwab, *White, *Waterhouse, *Fidelity, *Siebert
Dividends paid: Income - March, June, September December; Capital gains - December
Portfolio turnover (2 yrs): 26%, 16%
Largest holding: Pacific Telesis Group (5.1%)
Management fee: 0.35%
Expense ratio: 1.05% (year ending 6/30/94)

CAPSTONE GOVERNMENT INCOME FUND

5847 San Felipe, Suite 4100
Houston, TX 77057
713-260-9015, 800-262-6631
fax 713-260-9030

Adviser: Capstone Asset Planning Company
Sub-adviser: New Castle Advisers, Inc.
Portfolio managers: Howard S. Potter (1991)
Custodian: Fifth Third Bank, Cincinnati
Transfer agent: Fund/Plan Services, Inc.
Investment objective and policies: High total return consistent with safety of principal. Invests primarily in debt obligations issued or guaranteed by the U.S. Government, its agencies or instrumentalities with remaining maturities of 3 years or less. Fund may hedge.
Year organized: 1968 (formerly Investors Income Fund, Inc. Name and objective changed on 1/8/91.)
Ticker symbol: CGVIX
Minimum purchase: Initial: $10,000, Subsequent: None; IRA: Initial: None
Telephone orders accepted: Yes, $1,000 subsequent minimum
Wire orders accepted: Yes
Deadline for same day wire purchase: 4 P.M.
Discount broker availability: Fidelity, Siebert
Qualified for sale in: All states
Telephone redemptions: Yes
Wire redemptions: Yes
Letter redemptions: Signature guarantee not required
Telephone switching: With other Capstone funds (which have loads)
Number of switches permitted: 1 per month
Dividends paid: Income - December; Capital gains - December
Shareholder services: IRA, SEP-IRA, automatic investment plan—minimum $25/month, withdrawal plan min. req. $5,000, electronic funds transfer
Portfolio turnover (3 yrs): 596%, 633%, 754%
Management fee: 0.50%
12b-1 distribution fee: 0.20%
Expense ratio: 0.93% (year ending 12/31/93)
IRA fees: Annual $12

CASH ACCOUNT TRUST PORTFOLIOS

(Data common to all Cash Account Trust portfolios are shown below. See subsequent listings for data specific to individual Cash Account Trust portfolios.)

120 S. LaSalle Street
Chicago, IL 60603
312-781-1121, 312-332-6472
800-231-8568, yields 800-621-9268

Adviser: Kemper Financial Services
Custodian and transfer agent: Investors Fiduciary Trust Company
Sub-custodian: United Missouri Bank of Kansas City
Minimum purchase: Initial: $1,000, Subsequent: $100; IRA/Keogh: Initial: $250
Wire orders accepted: Yes
Deadline for same day wire purchase: 2 P.M. (12 NN for Tax-Exempt Portfolio)
Qualified for sale in: All states
Telephone redemptions: Yes
Wire redemptions: Yes, $1,000 minimum
Letter redemptions: Signature guarantee required over $25,000
Telephone switching: With Kemper Funds and Berger funds
Number of switches permitted: Unlimited
Check redemptions: $250 minimum
Confirmations mailed: After each purchase and each mail or wire redemption
Checks returned: Monthly
Periodic account statements mailed: Monthly
Dividends paid: Income - declared daily, paid monthly
Shareholder services: IRA, SEP-IRA, 401(k), 403(b), corporate retirement plans, withdrawal plan min. req. $5,000, electronic funds transfer
Management fee: 0.22% first $500M to 0.15% over $3B (for all portfolios combined)
IRA fees: Annual $12, $24 maximum per social security number

CASH ACCOUNT TRUST - GOVERNMENT SECURITIES PORTFOLIO

(See first Cash Account Trust listing for data common to all Cash Account Trust portfolios)

Portfolio manager: Frank J. Rachwalski (1990)
Investment objective and policies: Maximum current income consistent with stability of capital. Invests exclusively in money market obligations issued or guaranteed by the U.S. Government, its agencies or its instrumentalities.
Year organized: 1990
Ticker symbol: CAGXX
12b-1 distribution fee: 0.60%
Expense ratio: 0.84% (year ending 4/30/94) (1.22% without waiver)

CASH ACCOUNT TRUST - MONEY MARKET PORTFOLIO

(See first Cash Account listing for data common to all Cash Account Trust portfolios)

Portfolio manager: John Stuebe (1990)
Investment objective and policies: Maximum current income consistent with stability of capital. Invests in high quality money market instruments.
Year organized: 1990
Ticker symbol: CSAXX
12b-1 distribution fee: 0.60%
Expense ratio: 0.93% (year ending 4/30/94) (1.20% without waiver)

CASH ACCOUNT TRUST - TAX-EXEMPT PORTFOLIO

(See first Cash Account Trust listing for data common to all Cash Account Trust portfolios)

Portfolio manager: Frank J. Rachwalski (1990)
Investment objective and policies: Maximum current income exempt from federal income taxes to the extent consistent with stability of capital.

Invests in a diversified portfolio of municipal money market instruments.
Year organized: 1990
12b-1 distribution fee: 0.50%
Expense ratio: 0.74% (year ending 4/30/94) (1.20% without waiver)

CASH EQUIVALENT FUND PORTFOLIOS

(Data common to all Cash Equivalent portfolios are shown below. See subsequent listings for data specific to individual Cash Equivalent Fund portfolios.)

120 S. LaSalle Street
Chicago, IL 60603
312-781-1121, 800-231-8568
prices/yields 800-621-0322

Adviser: Kemper Financial Services
Custodian and transfer agent: Investors Fiduciary Trust Company
Sub-custodian: United Missouri Bank of Kansas City
Special sales restrictions: Sold through selected broker-dealer and financial services firms
Minimum purchase: Initial: $1,000, Subsequent: $100; IRA/Keogh: Initial: $250
Wire orders accepted: Yes
Deadline for same day wire purchase: 2 P.M. (12 NN for Tax-Exempt Portfolio)
Qualified for sale in: All states
Telephone redemptions: Yes
Wire redemptions: Yes, $1,000 minimum
Letter redemptions: Signature guarantee required over $25,000
Telephone switching: With Kemper Funds all of which have loads
Check redemptions: $250 minimum
Confirmations mailed: After each purchase and each mail or wire redemption
Checks returned: Monthly
Periodic account statements mailed: Monthly
Dividends paid: Income - declared daily, paid monthly
Shareholder services: IRA, SEP-IRA, 401(k), 403(b), corporate retirement plans, withdrawal plan min. req. $5,000, electronic funds transfer
IRA fees: Annual $12, $24 maximum per social security number

CASH EQUIVALENT FUND - GOVERNMENT PORTFOLIO

(See first Cash Equivalent listing for data common to all Cash Equivalent Fund portfolios)

Portfolio manager: Frank J. Rachwalski (1982)
Investment objective and policies: Maximum current income consistent with stability of capital. Invests exclusively in money market obligations issued or guaranteed by the U.S. Government, its agencies or its instrumentalities.
Year organized: 1981
Ticker symbol: CQGXX
Management fee: 0.22% first $500M to 0.15% over $3B (Government & Money Market portfolios combined)
12b-1 distribution fee: 0.38%
Expense ratio: 0.81% (year ending 7/31/94)

CASH EQUIVALENT FUND - MONEY MARKET PORTFOLIO

(See first Cash Equivalent listing for data common to all Cash Equivalent Fund portfolios)

Portfolio manager: John W. Stuebe (1982)
Investment objective and policies: Maximum current income consistent with stability of capital. Invests in high quality money market instruments.
Year organized: 1979
Ticker symbol: CQMXX
Management fee: 0.22% first $500M to 0.15% over $3B (Government & Money Market portfolios combined)
12b-1 distribution fee: 0.38%
Expense ratio: 0.88% (year ending 7/31/94)

CASH EQUIVALENT FUND - TAX-EXEMPT PORTFOLIO
(See first Cash Equivalent listing for data common to all Cash Equivalent Fund portfolios)

Portfolio manager: Frank J. Rachwalski (1985)
Investment objective and policies: Maximum current income exempt from federal income taxes to the extent consistent with stability of capital. Invests in a diversified portfolio of municipal money market instruments.
Year organized: 1982 (formerly Tax-Exempt Money Market Fund, Inc.)
Ticker symbol: TEMXX
Management fee: 0.22% first $500M to 0.15% over $3B
12b-1 distribution plan: 0.33%
Expense ratio: 0.68% (year ending 7/31/94)

CENTURY SHARES TRUST ◆
One Liberty Square
Boston, MA 02109
617-482-3060, 800-321-1928

Newspaper listing: Cnt Shs
Adviser: Century Capital Management, Inc.
Portfolio manager: Allan W. Fulkerson (1976)
Custodian: State Street Bank & Trust Co.
Transfer agent: Boston Financial Data Services, Inc.
Investment objective and policies: Long-term growth of principal and income. Invests in common stocks, or securities convertible into common stocks, of insurance companies and banks, insurance brokers and other companies providing services to, or closely related to, insurance companies and banks.
Year organized: 1928
Ticker symbol: CENSX
Minimum purchase: Initial $500, Subsequent $25; IRA: Initial $500, Subsequent $25
Telephone orders accepted: Subsequent only
Wire orders accepted: Yes
Deadline for same day wire purchase: 4 P.M.
Discount broker availability: Schwab, White, Waterhouse
Qualified for sale in: All states
Letter redemptions: Signature guarantee required over $10,000
Dividends paid: Income - June, December; Capital gains - December
Portfolio turnover (3 yrs): 19%, 5%, 0%
Largest holding: General Re Corp. (6.1%)
Shareholder services: IRA
Management fee: 0.70% first $250M, 0.60 over $250M
Expense ratio: 0.82% (year ending 12/31/93)
IRA fees: Annual $10, Closing $10

CGM FUNDS ◆
(Data common to all CGM funds are shown below. See subsequent listings for data specific to individual CGM funds.)

One International Place
Boston, MA 02110
617-859-7714, 800-345-4048
prices/yields 800-343-5678

Adviser: Capital Growth Management Limited Partnership
Custodian and transfer agent: State Street Bank & Trust Co.
Minimum purchase: Initial: $2,500, Subsequent: $50; IRA/Keogh: Initial: $1,000
Telephone orders accepted: No
Wire orders accepted: Yes, subsequent only
Deadline for same day wire purchase: 2 P.M.
Qualified for sale in: All states (except Realty Fund)
Telephone redemptions: Yes, $25,000 maximum
Wire redemptions: Yes, $1,000 minimum, $5 fee
Letter redemptions: Signature guarantee required over $25,000
Telephone switching: With other CGM funds and New England money market funds

Number of switches permitted: 4 per year, $1,000 minimum
Shareholder services: Keogh, IRA, SEP-IRA, 403(b), corporate retirement plans, automatic investment plan, withdrawal plan min. req. $10,000, electronic funds transfer
IRA/Keogh fees: Annual $10, Initial $5

CGM AMERICAN TAX FREE FUND ◆
(See first CGM listing for data common to all CGM funds)

Portfolio manager: Janice Saul (1993)
Investment objective and policies: High current income exempt from federal income tax with capital appreciation. Invests primarily in investment-grade tax-exempt general obligation bonds, revenue bonds and notes. Up to 25% of assets may be in securities rated below investment grade.
Year organized: 1993
Ticker symbol: CGMAX
Dividends paid: Income - declared and paid monthly; Capital gains - December
Portfolio turnover (1 yr): 231%
Management fee: 0.60% first $500M to 0.45% over $1B
Expense ratio: 0.00% (6 months ending 6/30/94) (2.28% without waiver)

CGM CAPITAL DEVELOPMENT FUND ◆
(See first CGM listing for data common to all CGM funds)

Portfolio manager: G. Kenneth Heebner (1976)
Investment objective and policies: Long-term capital appreciation. Normally is fully invested in common stocks and securities convertible into common stocks of both established and new, smaller companies.
Special sales restriction: Available only to existing shareholders, CGM employees and clients, employees and agents of New England Life Insurance Co. and other specialized categories. Fund closed to new shareholders in 1968.
Year organized: 1960 (formerly Loomis-Sayles Capital Development Fund)
Ticker symbol: LOMCX
Discount broker availability: Waterhouse
Dividends paid: Income - December; Capital gains - December
Portfolio turnover (3 yrs): 143%, 163%, 272%
Largest holding: Stone Container Corp. (8.1%)
Management fee: 0.75% first $200M to 0.65% over $500M
Expense ratio: 0.85% (year ending 12/31/93)

CGM FIXED INCOME FUND ◆
(See first CGM listing for data common to all CGM funds)

Portfolio managers: G. Kenneth Heebner (1992), Janice Saul (1993)
Investment objective and policies: Maximum total return. Invests in debt securities and preferred stocks that provide current income, capital appreciation, or a combination of both. May invest up to 20% of assets in foreign securities, 10% in illiquid securities, and 35% in junk bonds.
Year organized: 1992
Ticker symbol: CFXIX
Dividends paid: Income - declared and paid monthly; Capital gains - December
Portfolio turnover (2 yrs): 149%, 212%
Management fee: 0.55% first $200M to 0.35% over $500M
Expense ratio: 0.85% (year ending 12/31/93) (2.02% without waiver)

CGM MUTUAL FUND ◆
(See first CGM listing for data common to all CGM funds)

Portfolio manager: G. Kenneth Heebner (1981)
Investment objective and policies: Long-term capital appreciation with a prudent approach to protection of capital from undue risks. Current income is a secondary objective. Invests in equity securities (common stocks, securities convertible into common stocks and REITs) and fixed-income securities (notes, bonds, preferred stock and money market instruments) with allocation of assets adjusted to changes in market conditions.
Year organized: 1929 (formerly Loomis-Sayles Mutual Fund)
Ticker symbol: LOMMX
Discount broker availability: White, Waterhouse
Dividends paid: Income - April, July, October, December; Capital gains - December
Portfolio turnover (3 yrs): 97%, 121%, 201%
Largest holding: Telefonos de Mexico S.A. ADR (5.4%)
Management fee: 0.75% first $200M to 0.65% over $500M
Expense ratio: 0.93% (year ending 12/31/93)

CGM REALTY FUND ◆
(See first CGM listing for data common to all CGM funds)

Portfolio manager: G. Kenneth Heebner (1994)
Investment objective and policies: Above-average income and long-term capital growth. Invests at least 65% of assets in equities of companies engaged in the real estate industry, including REITs and companies with significant real estate holdings. Securities include common stock, preferred stock and securities convertible into common stock. Up to 25% may be in junk bonds.
Year organized: 1994
Ticker symbol: CGMRX
Discount broker availability: White, Waterhouse
Qualified for sale in: All states except SD, WI
Dividends paid: Income - April, July, October, December; Capital gains - December
Largest holding: Felcor Suite Hotels, Inc. (6.3%)
Management fee: 0.85% first $500M, 0.75% over $500M

CHARTERCAPITAL BLUE CHIP FUND ◆
Charter Capital Management
4920 W. Vliet Street
Milwaukee, WI 53208
414-257-1842, fax 414-257-0917

Adviser: Charter Capital Management, Inc.
Portfolio manager: Lauren E. Toll (1990)
Custodian and transfer agent: Firstar Trust Co.
Investment objective and policies: Long-term capital growth with current income secondary. Invests at least 65% of assets in blue chip companies with market capitalization of $250M or more. Companies chosen on the basis of projected above-average long-term earnings growth. Up to 25% of assets may be in ADRs of foreign issuers.
Year organized: 1984 (formerly Adtek Fund)
Ticker symbol: CCBGX
Minimum purchase: Initial: $50, Subsequent: $50, IRA/Keogh: Initial: $250
Telephone orders accepted: No
Wire orders accepted: Yes, $1,000 minimum
Deadline for same day wire purchase: 4 P.M.
Qualified for sale in: CA, FL, IL, MD, MN, NJ, OH, PA, WI
Telephone redemptions: Yes, $15,000 maximum
Wire redemptions: Yes, $1,000 minimum, $7.50 fee
Letter redemptions: Signature guarantee required over $25,000
Dividends paid: Income - November; Capital gains - November
Portfolio turnover (3 yrs): 295%, 166%, 112%
Largest holding: Bell Atlantic Corp. (3.6%)
Shareholder services: Keogh, IRA, 401(k), 403(b), corporate retirement plans, automatic investment

plan, withdrawal plan min. req. $10,000, electronic funds transfer
Management fee: 1.50% first $25M to 0.75% over $50M
Expense ratio: 2.18% (year ending 12/31/93)
IRA fees: Annual $12.50, Closing $15

CLIPPER FUND ◆
9601 Wilshire Blvd., Suite 800
Beverly Hills, CA 90210
310-247-3940, 800-776-5033
prices 800-432-2504, fax 310-273-0514

Adviser: Pacific Financial Research
Portfolio managers: James H. Gipson (1984), Michael C. Sandler (1994)
Custodian: State Street Bank & Trust Co.
Transfer agent: National Financial Data Services
Investment objective and policies: Long-term growth of capital. Invests in common stocks, convertible long-term corporate debt, and convertible preferred stocks believed undervalued as determined by fundamental considerations. Fund may invest up to 25% of assets in junk bonds, 15% in securities of foreign issuers and/or 10% in special situations.
Year organized: 1984
Ticker symbol: CFIMX
Minimum purchase: Initial: $5,000, Subsequent: $1,000; IRA: Initial: $2,000, Subsequent: $200
Telephone orders accepted: No
Wire orders accepted: Yes
Deadline for same day wire purchase: 4 P.M.
Discount broker availability: Schwab, White, Waterhouse
Qualified for sale in: All states
Telephone redemptions: Yes
Wire redemptions: Yes
Letter redemptions: Signature guarantee required
Dividends paid: Income - December; Capital gains - December
Portfolio turnover (3 yrs): 45%, 64%, 46%
Largest holding: Philip Morris Companies, Inc. (10.1%)
Shareholder services: IRA, automatic investment plan—minimum $150/month
Management fee: 1.0%
Expense ratio: 1.11% (year ending 12/31/94)
IRA fees: Annual $10

CMA FUNDS
(Data common to all CMA funds are shown below. See subsequent listing for data specific to individual CMA funds.)

800 Scudders Mill Road
Plainsboro, NJ 08536
609-282-2800, 800-262-4636
yields 800-262-3276

Adviser: Fund Asset Management, Inc. (a subsidiary of Merrill Lynch Asset Management, Inc.)
Custodian: State Street Bank & Trust Co.
Transfer agent: Financial Data Services, Inc.
Special sales restrictions: Available to Merrill Lynch customers only
Minimum purchase: Initial: $20,000 in cash or securities, Subsequent: $1,000
Qualified for sale in: All states
Check redemptions: No minimum
Checks returned: Not returned
Periodic account statements mailed: Monthly
Service fee: $100 per year
Dividends paid: Income - declared and paid daily
Shareholders services: Fund is part of a central assets account
Management fee: 0.5% first $500M to 0.375% over $1B
12b-1 distribution fee: 0.125%

CMA CALIFORNIA
MUNICIPAL MONEY FUND
(See first CMA listing for data common to all CMA funds)

Portfolio manager: Helen Marie Sheehan (1988)
Investment objective and policies: Current income exempt from federal and California personal

income taxes consistent with preservation of capital and liquidity. Invests in short-term high quality municipal money market instruments, the interest on which is exempt from federal and California personal income taxes.
Year organized: 1988
Expense ratio: 0.62% (year ending 3/31/94)

CMA GOVERNMENT
SECURITIES FUND
(See first CMA listing for data common to all CMA funds)

Portfolio manager: Donaldo S. Benito (1988)
Investment objective and policies: Preservation of capital, liquidity and current income. Invests in short-term marketable money market securities which are direct obligations of the U.S. Government and repurchase agreements pertaining to such securities.
Year organized: 1981
Ticker symbol: CMGXX
Expense ratio: 0.56% (year ending 3/31/94)

CMA MONEY FUND
(See first CMA listing for data common to all CMA funds)

Portfolio manager: Joseph T. Monagle (1985)
Investment objective and policies: Current income, preservation of capital and liquidity. Invests in short-term money market securities.
Year organized: 1977
Ticker symbol: CMEXX
Expense ratio: 0.55% (year ending 3/31/94)

CMA NEW YORK MUNICIPAL
MONEY FUND
(See first CMA listing for data common to all CMA funds)

Portfolio manager: Peter J. Hayes (1989)
Investment objective and policies: Current income exempt from federal, New York State and New York City personal income taxes consistent with preservation of capital and liquidity. Invests in short-term money market instruments, the interest on which is exempt from Federal, New York State and New York City personal income taxes.
Year organized: 1989
Expense ratio: 0.67% (year ending 3/31/94)

CMA TAX-EXEMPT FUND
(See first CMA listing for data common to all CMA funds)

Portfolio manager: Peters J. Hayes (1988)
Investment objective and policies: Current income exempt from federal income taxes consistent with preservation of capital and liquidity. Invests in short-term high quality municipal money market instruments with remaining maturities of one year or less.
Year organized: 1980
Ticker symbol: CMAXX
Expense ratio: 0.55% (year ending 3/31/94)

CMA TREASURY FUND
(See first CMA listing for data common to all CMA funds)

Portfolio manager: Alex V. Bouzakis (1991)
Investment objective and policies: Preservation of capital, liquidity and current income. Invests in short-term marketable securities which are direct obligations of the U.S. Treasury.
Year organized: 1991
Expense ratio: 0.61% (year ending 3/31/94)

COHEN & STEERS
REALTY SHARES ◆
757 Third Avenue
New York, NY 10017
212-832-3232, 800-437-9912
fax 212-832-3622

Newspaper listing: C&S Rlty
Adviser: Cohen & Steers Capital Management, Inc.
Portfolio managers: Martin Cohen (1991), Robert H. Steers (1991)
Custodian: U.S. Trust Company of New York
Transfer agent: Mutual Funds Service Company
Investment objective and policies: Total return - current income and capital appreciation. Invests substantially all its assets in the equity securities of real estate companies, including common and preferred stocks and convertible debt securities. May invest in REITs without limit. Fund is non-diversified.
Year organized: 1991
Ticker symbol: CSRSX
Minimum purchase: Initial: $10,000, Subsequent: $500
Telephone orders accepted: No
Wire orders accepted: Yes
Deadline for same day wire purchase: 4 P.M.
Discount broker availability: *Schwab, *White, *Waterhouse, *Fidelity, *Siebert
Qualified for sale in: All states
Telephone redemptions: Yes
Wire redemptions: Yes
Letter redemptions: Signature guarantee required
Dividends paid: Income - March, June, September, December; Capital gains - December
Portfolio turnover (3 yrs): 65%, 15%, 57%
Largest holding: Kimco Realty Corp. (4.7%)
Management fee: 0.85%
Expense ratio: 1.25% (year ending 12/31/93) (1.35% without waiver)

COLUMBIA FUNDS ◆
(Data common to all Columbia funds are shown below. See subsequent listings for data specific to individual Columbia funds.)

1301 S.W. 5th Ave.
P.O. Box 1350
Portland, OR 97207
503-222-3606, 800-547-1707
prices 800-547-2170

Shareholder service hours: Full service: M-F 7:30 A.M.-5 P.M. PST; After hours service: prices, yields, messages, prospectuses
Adviser: Columbia Funds Management Co.
Custodian: United States National Bank of Oregon (except International Stock Fund)
Transfer agent: Columbia Trust Co.
Minimum purchase: Initial: $1,000 ($2,000 for Columbia Special Fund), Subsequent: $100
Telephone orders accepted: No
Wire orders accepted: Yes
Deadline for same day wire purchase: 4 P.M.
Telephone redemptions: Yes
Wire redemptions: Yes, $1,000 minimum, $5 fee
Letter redemptions: Signature guarantee required over $50,000
Telephone switching: With other Columbia Funds
Number of switches permitted: 4 round trips per year
Shareholder services: Keogh, IRA, SEP-IRA, automatic investment plan, withdrawal plan min. req. $5,000, electronic funds transfer
IRA fees: Annual $25, Initial $25
Keogh fees: Annual $50, Initial $100

COLUMBIA BALANCED FUND ◆
(See first Columbia Funds listing for data common to all Columbia funds)

Portfolio manager: Michael W. Powers (1991)
Investment objective and policies: High total return (capital growth and income). Invests in common stocks (35-65% of assets) and fixed-income securities (35-65%) with mix based on expected relative

returns as investment environment changes. At least 25% of assets always in non-convertible fixed-income securities with cash equivalents normally less than 10%. May invest up to 33% of assets in securities of foreign issuers and use futures and options to hedge up to 25% of assets.
Year organized: 1991
Ticker symbol: CBALX
Discount broker availability: Schwab, White, Fidelity, Siebert
Qualified for sale in: All states except NH
Dividends paid: Income - March, June, September, December; Capital gains - December
Portfolio turnover (2 yrs): 108%, 138%
Largest holding: U.S. Treasury Notes 5.125% due 2/28/98 (3.8%)
Management fee: 0.5%
Expense ratio: 0.73% (year ending 12/31/93)

COLUMBIA COMMON STOCK FUND ◆
(See first Columbia Funds listing for data common to all Columbia funds)

Portfolio manager: Terry L. Chambers (1991)
Investment objective and policies: Capital growth and dividend income. Invests primarily in common stocks which management believes will increase in value in current economic environment. May invest up to 33% of assets in securities of foreign issuers and use futures and options to hedge up to 25% of assets.
Year organized: 1991
Ticker symbol: CMSTX
Discount broker availability: Schwab, White, Fidelity, Siebert
Qualified for sale in: All states except NH
Dividends paid: Income - March, June, September, December; Capital gains - December
Portfolio turnover (2 yrs): 91%, 68%
Largest holding: Federal National Mortgage Association (3.0%)
Management fee: 0.6%
Expense ratio: 0.84% (year ending 12/31/93)

COLUMBIA DAILY INCOME CO. ◆
(See first Columbia Funds listing for data common to all Columbia funds)

Portfolio manager: Thomas L. Thomsen (1983)
Investment objective and policies: High current income consistent with maintenance of liquidity and preservation of capital. Invests in money market instruments.
Year organized: 1974
Ticker symbol: CDIXX
Qualified for sale in: All states except NH
Check redemptions: $500 minimum
Confirmations mailed: After each purchase and each check, mail or wire redemption
Checks returned: Monthly
Periodic account statements mailed: Monthly
Dividends paid: Income - declared and paid daily
Management fee: 0.5% first $500M to 0.4% over $1B
Expense ratio: 0.75% (year ending 12/31/93)

COLUMBIA FIXED INCOME SECURITIES FUND ◆
(See first Columbia Funds listing for data common to all Columbia funds)

Portfolio manager: Thomas L. Thomsen (1983)
Investment objective and policies: High level of current income, consistent with conservation of capital. Invests at least 95% of assets in investment-grade fixed-income securities such as bonds, debentures, government securities, GNMAs and repurchase agreements.
Year organized: 1983
Ticker symbol: CFISX
Discount broker availability: Schwab, White, Waterhouse, Fidelity, Siebert
Qualified for sale in: All states except NH
Dividends paid: Income - declared daily, paid monthly; Capital gains - December

Portfolio turnover (3 yrs): 119%, 196%, 159%
Management fee: 0.5%
Expense ratio: 0.66% (year ending 12/31/93)

COLUMBIA GROWTH FUND ◆
(See first Columbia Funds listing for data common to all Columbia funds)

Portfolio manager: Alexander S. Macmillan (1992)
Investment objective and policies: Capital growth. Invests primarily in common stocks believed undervalued. Up to 10% of assets may be in securities of foreign issuers. May use futures and options to hedge up to 25% of assets.
Year organized: 1967
Ticker symbol: CLMBX
Discount broker availability: Schwab, White, Waterhouse, Fidelity, Siebert
Qualified for sale in: All states except NH
Dividends paid: Income - December; Capital gains - December
Portfolio turnover (3 yrs): 106%, 116%, 164%
Largest holding: Federal National Mortgage Association (2.9%)
Management fee: 0.75% first $200M to 0.5% over $500M
Expense ratio: 0.82% (year ending 12/31/93)

COLUMBIA HIGH YIELD FUND ◆
(See first Columbia Funds listing for data common to all Columbia funds)

Portfolio manager: Jeffrey L. Rippey (1993)
Investment objective and policies: High current income with capital appreciation secondary. Invests primarily in lower-rated fixed-income securities such as bonds, debentures, government securities, GNMAs and repurchase agreements. Normally invests at least 65% of assets in junk bonds. May invest 10% of assets in fixed-income securities of foreign issuers and use options to hedge up to 25% of assets.
Year organized: 1993
Ticker symbol: CMHYX
Discount broker availability: White
Redemption fee: 1% for shares held less than 1 year, payable to the fund
Qualified for sale in: All states except AL, AR, DE, IN, KS, LA, ME, MA, MS, NH, ND, RI, SC, TN, VT, WV, WI
Dividends paid: Income - declared daily, paid monthly; Capital gains - December
Management fee: 0.6%

COLUMBIA INTERNATIONAL STOCK FUND ◆
(See first Columbia Funds listing for data common to all Columbia funds)

Portfolio manager: James M. McAlear (1992)
Custodian: Morgan Company Trust Co.
Investment objective and policies: Long-term capital growth. Invests primarily in equity securities of companies based outside the U.S. - common stocks, preferred stocks and convertible securities - of issuers from at least 3 countries other than the U.S. Up to 35% of assets may be in securities of U.S. issuers. May use futures and options to hedge.
Year organized: 1992
Ticker symbol: CMISX
Discount broker availability: Schwab, White, Fidelity, Siebert
Qualified for sale in: All states except NH
Dividends paid: Income - December; Capital gains - December
Portfolio turnover (2 yrs): 145%, 26%
Largest holding: Canon, Inc. (2.6%)
Management fee: 1.0%
Expense ratio: 1.71% (year ending 12/31/93)

COLUMBIA MUNICIPAL BOND FUND ◆
(See first Columbia Funds listing for data common to all Columbia funds)

Portfolio manager: Thomas L. Thomsen (1984)
Investment objective and policies: High current income exempt from federal and State of Oregon income taxes consistent with conservation of capital. Invests in municipal securities of which at least 60% are expected to be exempt from Oregon income taxes, primarily those issued by the state of Oregon or other Oregon issuers. Fund normally has a weighted average maturity of 10 years or more.
Year organized: 1984
Ticker symbol: CMBFX
Discount broker availability: Schwab, White, Waterhouse, Fidelity, Siebert
Qualified for sale in: CO, DC, HI, ID, KY, NE, NV, NJ, NM, OK, OR, PA, SD, UT, WA
Dividends paid: Income - declared daily, paid monthly; Capital gains - December
Portfolio turnover (3 yrs): 10%, 18%, 15%
Management fee: 0.5%
Expense ratio: 0.58% (year ending 12/31/93)

COLUMBIA REAL ESTATE EQUITY FUND ◆
(See first Columbia Funds listing for data common to all Columbia funds)

Portfolio manager: David W. Jellison (1994)
Investment objective and policies: Above-average current income and capital growth. Invests primarily in equity securities of companies in the real estate industry - that own, construct, manage or sell residential, commercial or industrial real estate. May invest in real estate investment trusts (REITs) without limit and have up to 35% of assets in non-real estate companies and 20% in securities of foreign issuers. May use futures and options to hedge.
Year organized: 1994
Ticker symbol: CREEX
Discount broker availability: White
Qualified for sale in: All states except AL, AR, DE, IN, KS, LA, ME, MA, MS, NH, ND, RI, SC, TN, VT, WV, WI
Dividends paid: Income - December; Capital gains - December
Largest holding: Horizon Outlet Centers, Inc. (4.8%)
Management fee: 0.75%

COLUMBIA SPECIAL FUND ◆
(See first Columbia Funds listing for data common to all Columbia funds)

Portfolio manager: Robert A. Unger (1994)
Investment objective and policies: Capital appreciation. Invests primarily in common stocks of smaller companies believed to have growth potential higher than the overall market (as measured by the S&P 500) albeit with a higher degree of risk. May invest in special situations such as new issues, companies undergoing management or technology changes, tender offers, leveraged buyouts, or mergers. May invest up to 33% of assets in securities of foreign issuers and use futures and options to hedge up to 25% of assets.
Year organized: 1985 (3 for 1 split on 2/1/92)
Ticker symbol: CLSPX
Discount broker availability: Schwab, White, Waterhouse, Fidelity, Siebert
Qualified for sale in: All states except NH
Dividends paid: Income - December; Capital gains - December
Portfolio turnover (3 yrs): 155%, 117%, 115%
Largest holding: CBS, Inc. (2.2%)
Management fee: 1.00% first $500M, 0.75% over $500M
Expense ratio: 1.12% (year ending 12/31/93)

COLUMBIA U.S. GOVERNMENT SECURITIES FUND ◆

(See first Columbia Funds listing for data common to all Columbia funds)

Portfolio manager: Thomas L. Thomsen (1986)
Investment objective and policies: Preservation of capital and a high level of income. Invests substantial all its assets in U.S. Government obligations with remaining individual maturities of 3 years or less.
Year organized: 1986 (formerly U.S. Government Guaranteed Securities Fund)
Ticker symbol: CUGGX
Discount broker availability: White, Waterhouse, Fidelity, Siebert
Qualified for sale in: All states except AL, AR, DE, IN, KS, LA, ME, MA, MS, NH, ND, RI, SC, TN, VT, WV, WI
Dividends paid: Income - declared daily, paid monthly; Capital gains - December
Portfolio turnover (3 yrs): 255%, 289%, 309%
Management fee: 0.5%
Expense ratio: 0.75% (year ending 12/31/93)

CONCORDE VALUE FUND ◆

5430 LBJ Freeway, #1500
Dallas, TX 75240
214-387-8258, 800-338-1579
fax 214-701-0530

Adviser: Concorde Financial Corp.
Portfolio manager: Gary B. Wood (1987)
Custodian and transfer agent: Firstar Trust Co.
Investment objective and policies: Long term growth of capital without exposing capital to undue risk. Invests primarily in out-of-favor common stocks, focusing on "value" approach characterized by low relative price/earnings or price/book value, high dividend yield, less than $500M capitalization and/or low analyst coverage. Up to 20% of assets may be in ADRs of foreign issuers and 20% in foreign securities.
Year organized: 1987
Minimum purchase: Initial: $500, Subsequent: $100
Telephone orders accepted: No
Wire orders accepted: Yes, $500 subsequent minimum
Deadline for same day wire purchase: 3 P.M.
Discount broker availability: Schwab
Qualified for sale: FL, GA, MD, MO, NY, NC, TX, VA, WI
Telephone redemptions: Yes, $1,000 minimum
Wire redemptions: Yes, $1,000 minimum, $7.50 fee
Letter redemptions: Signature guarantee required
Dividends paid: Income - December; Capital gains - December
Portfolio turnover (3 yrs): 75%, 72%, 52%
Largest holding: Magna International, Inc., Class A (3.1%)
Shareholder services: IRA, SEP-IRA, Keogh, 401(k), 403(b), corporate retirement plans
Management fee: 0.9%
Expense ratio: 1.69% (year ending 9/30/94)
IRA/Keogh fees: Annual $12.50

CONNECTICUT DAILY TAX FREE INCOME FUND

600 Fifth Avenue - 8th Floor
New York, NY 10020
212-830-5200, 800-676-6779
prices/yields 212-830-5225
fax 212-830-5476

Adviser: Reich & Tang Asset Management L.P.
Portfolio manager: Molly Flewharty (1985)
Custodian and transfer agent: Investors Fiduciary Trust Co.
Investment objective and policies: High current interest income exempt from federal income taxes and, to the extent possible, from Connecticut income taxes, consistent with preservation of capital and liquidity. Invests primarily in Connecticut municipal money market instruments.
Year organized: 1985

Ticker symbol: CTIXX
Minimum purchase: Initial: $5,000, Subsequent: $100
Wire orders accepted: Yes
Deadline for same day wire purchase: 12 NN
Qualified for sale in: CT, MA, NJ, NY
Telephone redemptions: Yes
Wire redemptions: Yes, $1,000 minimum
Letter redemptions: Signature guarantee required
Telephone switching: With other Reich & Tang Money Markets, R & T Equity, and R & T Government Securities Trust
Number of switches permitted: Unlimited, $1,000 minimum
Deadline for same day switch: 4 P.M.
Check redemptions: $250 minimum
Confirmations mailed: After each purchase and each check, mail or wire redemption
Checks returned: As clear
Periodic account statements mailed: Monthly
Dividends paid: Income - declared daily, paid monthly
Shareholder services: Withdrawal plan
Management fee: 0.30%
Administration fee: 0.20%
12b-1 distribution fee: 0.20%
Expense ratio: 0.87% (year ending 1/31/94)

COPLEY FUND ◆

P.O. Box 3287
Fall River, MA 02722
508-674-8459, fax 508-672-9348

Adviser: Copley Financial Services Corp.
Portfolio manager: Irving Levine (1978)
Custodian: Fleet Investment Services
Transfer agent: Steadman Security Corp.
Investment objective and policies: Tax-advantaged accumulation of dividend income utilizing the Fund's 70% deduction from federal income taxes for dividends received. Long-term capital growth is secondary. Invests in securities with high, and increasing, dividend income. May invest in bonds or money market instruments for defensive purposes.
Year organized: 1976 (Formerly Copley Tax-Managed Fund) (1 for 3 reverse split in 1983)
Ticker symbol: COPLX
Minimum purchase: Initial: $1,000, Subsequent: $100; IRA/Keogh: Initial: $100
Telephone orders accepted: No
Wire orders accepted: No
Qualified for sale: All states
Letter redemptions: Signature guarantee required
Dividends paid: No distributions by policy - retained in NAV.
Portfolio turnover (3 yrs): 58%, 5%, 7%
Largest holding: Texas Utilities Co. (3.0%)
Shareholder services: Keogh, IRA, withdrawal plan min. req. $10,000
Management fee: 1.00% first $25M to 0.50% over $40M
Expense ratio: 1.51% (year ending 2/28/94) (1.56% without waiver)
IRA/Keogh fees: Annual $25

CORNERSTONE GROWTH FUND ◆

1500 Forest Ave. - Suite 223
Richmond VA 23229
804-285-8211, 800-527-9525
800-527-9500, fax 804-285-8252

Shareholder service hours: Full service: M-F 9 A.M.-7 P.M. EST; After hours service: prices, yields, balances
Adviser: Cornerstone Capital Corp.
Portfolio manager: Thomas E. Quinn (1992)
Custodian: Wachovia Bank of N.C.
Transfer agent: Fund Services Inc.
Investment objective and policies: Long-term capital appreciation with income secondary. Invests primarily in common stocks, preferred stocks and securities convertible to common stocks, selected from among 1500 issues ranked according to fundamental factors. Up to 20% of assets may be in securities of foreign issuers. May sell short, use futures and options and, for defensive purposes, invest in short-term debt instruments.

Year organized: 1986 (as Wealth Monitors Fund - name/management change to Sunshine Growth Trust on 8/13/90; name/management changed to current on 12/10/92)
Ticker symbol: CGRFX
Minimum purchase: Initial: $2,000, Subsequent: $250
Telephone orders accepted: No
Wire orders accepted: Yes
Deadline for same day wire purchase: 4 P.M.
Discount broker availability: Schwab
Qualified for sale in: All states except AK, CT, ID, ME, MA, MT, NE, NV, NM, ND, OK, RI, SD, UT, VT, WY
Letter redemptions: Signature guarantee not required
Dividends paid: Income - April, December; Capital gains - December
Portfolio turnover (3 yrs): 36%, 83%, 92%
Largest holding: Furon Company (3.0%)
Shareholder services: IRA, automatic investment plan—minimum $250/month (waives initial minimum), withdrawal plan min. req. $10,000
Management fee: 1.0%
12b-1 distribution fee: Maximum of 0.25% (not currently imposed)
Expense ratio: 2.00% (year ending 3/31/94) (3.00% without waiver)
IRA fees: Annual $10

COUNTDOWN TO RETIREMENT - RETIRE 2010 FUND ◆

1807 S. Washington Ave., Suite 106
Naperville, IL 60565
708-778-0373, 800-398-2299
fax 708-778-0613

Adviser: Countdown Management Corp.
Portfolio manager: Gregory L. Bruno (1994)
Custodian: Star Bank, N.A., Cincinnati
Transfer agent: American Data Services, Inc.
Investment objective and policies: Maximum total return until the target retirement year of 2010, with maximum current income and preservation of capital thereafter. Initially invests primarily in domestic and international growth and value stocks, bonds and high-quality fixed-income securities (at least 50% in U.S. Government securities). Gradually, more assets will be in dividend-paying stocks, bonds, and fixed-income securities. At target date, assets will be in income-producing stocks, bonds and short-term securities.
Year organized: 1994
Minimum purchase: Initial: $2,000, Subsequent: $200; IRA: Initial: $1,000
Telephone orders accepted: No
Wire orders accepted: Yes, subsequent only
Deadline for same day wire purchase: 3 P.M.
Qualified for sale in: CT, FL, IL, IN, NY, NJ, PA, TX, WI
Letter redemptions: Signature guarantee required
Dividends paid: Income - December; Capital gains - December
Shareholder services: IRA, SEP-IRA, automatic investment plan, withdrawal plan min. req. $10,000
Management fee: 1.75% (covers all expenses)
IRA fees: Annual $12, Initial $12, Closing $15

COUNTDOWN TO RETIREMENT - RETIRE 2020 FUND ◆

1807 S. Washington Ave., Suite 106
Naperville, IL 60565
708-778-0373, 800-398-2299
fax 708-778-0613

Adviser: Countdown Management Corp.
Portfolio manager: Gregory L. Bruno (1994)
Custodian: Star Bank, N.A., Cincinnati
Transfer agent: American Data Services, Inc.
Investment objective and policies: Maximum total return until the target retirement year of 2020 with maximum current income and preservation of capital thereafter. Initially invests primarily in domestic and international growth and value stocks, bonds and high-quality fixed-income securities (at least 50% in U.S. Government securities). Gradually, more assets will be put in dividend-paying stocks,

bonds, and fixed-income securities. At target date, assets will be in income-producing stocks, bonds and short-term securities.
Year organized: 1994
Minimum purchase: Initial: $2,000, Subsequent: $200; IRA: Initial $1,000
Telephone orders accepted: No
Wire orders accepted: Yes, subsequent only
Deadline for same day wire purchase: 3 P.M.
Qualified for sale in: CT, FL, IL, IN, NY, NJ, PA, TX, WI
Letter redemptions: Signature guarantee required
Dividends paid: Income - December; Capital gains - December
Shareholder services: IRA, SEP-IRA, automatic investment plan, withdrawal plan min. req. $10,000
Management fee: 1.75% (covers all expenses)
IRA fees: Annual $12, Initial $12, Closing $15
Keogh fees: None

THE CRABBE HUSON FUNDS
(Data common to all Crabbe Huson funds are shown below. See subsequent listings for data specific to individual Crabbe Huson funds.)

121 S.W. Morrison, Suite 1400
Portland, OR 97204
503-295-0919, 800-541-9732
fax 503-295-2939

Shareholder service hours: Full service: M-F 7 A.M.-5 P.M. PST; After hours service: prices, yields, prospectuses
Adviser: Prudential Direct Advisers, L.P. (since 1995)
Sub-adviser: The Crabbe Huson Group, Inc.
Custodian: First Interstate Bank of Oregon
Transfer agent: Pacific Northwest Trust Co.
Minimum purchase: Initial: $2,000, Subsequent: $500
Telephone orders accepted: No
Wire orders accepted: No
Qualified for sale: All states except AL, AR, IA, ME, MA, MN, MO, NH, TN, WI (except Oregon Municipal Bond)
Telephone redemptions: Yes
Wire redemptions: Yes, $1,000 minimum
Letter redemptions: Signature guarantee required
Telephone switching: With other Crabbe Huson funds
Number of switches permitted: 10 per year
Shareholder services: Keogh, IRA, 401(k), corporate retirement plans, automatic investment plan—minimum $100/month, withdrawal plan min. req. $5,000
IRA fees: Annual $25
Keogh fees: None

THE CRABBE HUSON ASSET ALLOCATION FUND, INC.
(See first Crabbe Huson listing for data common to all Crabbe Huson funds)

Portfolio manager: Richard S. Huson (1989)
Investment objective and policies: Capital appreciation and income consistent with preservation of capital. Invests in a variable mix of stocks, fixed-income securities, cash, and cash equivalents. Stock portion of portfolio will normally range from 20% to 75% depending on market conditions.
Year organized: 1988
Ticker symbol: CHAAX
Discount broker availability: *Schwab, *White, Fidelity, Siebert
Dividends paid: Income - March, June, September, December; Capital gains - December
Portfolio turnover (3 yrs): 149%, 116%, 155%
Largest holding: U.S. Treasury Note 8.000% due 01/15/97 (5.1%)
Management fee: 1.0% first $100M to 0.60% over $500M
12b-1 distribution fee: 0.24%
Expense ratio: 1.44% (year ending 10/31/94) (1.52% without waiver)

THE CRABBE HUSON EQUITY FUND, INC.
(See first Crabbe Huson listing for data common to all Crabbe Huson funds)

Portfolio manager: Richard S. Huson (1989)
Investment objective and policies: Long-term capital appreciation. Invests at least 65% of assets in common stocks. Fund employs a basic value, contrarian approach in selecting stocks and focuses on large capitalization companies. May invest up to 35% of assets in foreign securities. Fund may hedge.
Year organized: 1988
Ticker symbol: CHEYX
Discount broker availability: *Schwab, *White, Fidelity, Siebert
Dividends paid: Income - December; Capital gains - December
Portfolio turnover (3 yrs): 106%, 114%, 181%
Largest holding: Equitable Companies (2.9%)
Management fee: 1.0% first $100M to 0.60% over $500M
12b-1 distribution fee: 0.19%
Expense ratio: 1.45% (year ending 10/31/94) (1.56% without waiver)

THE CRABBE HUSON INCOME FUND, INC.
(See first Crabbe Huson listing for data common to all Crabbe Huson funds)

Portfolio manager: Jay L. Willoughby (1989)
Investment objective and policies: Current income consistent with preservation of capital. Invests in a diversified portfolio of high quality fixed-income securities and preferred or convertible preferred stock. Up to 35% of assets may be in foreign securities.
Year organized: 1988
Discount broker availability: *Schwab, *White, Fidelity, Siebert
Dividends paid: Income - declared daily, paid monthly; Capital gains - December
Portfolio turnover (3 yrs): 307%, 260%, 227%
Management fee: 0.75% first $100M to 0.50% over $500M
12b-1 distribution fee: 0.18%
Expense ratio: 0.80% (year ending 10/31/94) (2.16% without waiver)

THE CRABBE HUSON OREGON MUNICIPAL BOND FUND
(See first Crabbe Huson listing for data common to all Crabbe Huson funds)

Portfolio manager: Jay L. Willoughby
Investment objective and policies: High income exempt from federal and Oregon income taxes consistent with preservation of capital. Invests at least 80% of assets in tax-exempt municipal bonds issued by the state of Oregon and its political subdivisions.
Year organized: 1983
Ticker symbol: ORBFX
Discount broker availability: *Schwab, Fidelity, Siebert
Qualified for sale in: OR
Dividends paid: Income - declared and paid monthly; Capital gains - December
Portfolio turnover (3 yrs): 21%, 12%, 25%
Management fee: 0.50% first $500M to 0.40% over $1B
12b-1 distribution fee: 0.20%
Expense ratio: 0.98% (year ending 10/31/94) (1.08% without waiver)

THE CRABBE HUSON REAL ESTATE INVESTMENT FUND, INC.
(See first Crabbe Huson listing for data common to all Crabbe Huson funds)

Portfolio managers: Jay L. Willoughby (1994), Richard S. Huson (1994)
Investment objective and policies: Capital appreciation and current income. Invests primarily in equi-

ty securities of real estate investment trusts (REITs) and other companies involved in real estate. May invest up to 25% in debt securities of real estate companies, mortgage-backed securities and short-term investments and use futures and options to hedge.
Year organized: 1994
Discount broker availability: *Schwab, *White, Fidelity, Siebert
Dividends paid: Income - March, June, September, December; Capital gains - December
Management fee: 1.00% first $100M to 0.60% over $500M
12b-1 distribution fee: Maximum of 0.25%

THE CRABBE HUSON SPECIAL FUND, INC.
(See first Crabbe Huson listing for data common to all Crabbe Huson funds)

Portfolio manager: James E. Crabbe (1987)
Investment objective and policies: Long-term capital appreciation with current income secondary. Normally invests at least 75% of assets in stocks of sound domestic and foreign companies with short term difficulties that have temporarily depressed the price of their securities. May also invest in preferred stocks and bonds. Fund may leverage and sell short.
Year organized: 1987 (name changed from Crabbe Huson Growth in March 1993)
Ticker symbol: CHSPX
Discount broker availability: *Schwab, *White, Fidelity, Siebert
Dividends paid: Income - December; Capital gains - December
Portfolio turnover (3 yrs): 146%, 73%, 102%
Largest holding: Rollins Environmental Services (4.0%)
Management fee: 1.0% first $100M to 0.60% over $500M
12b-1 distribution fee: 0.12%
Expense ratio: 1.44% (year ending 10/31/94) (1.54% without waiver)

THE CRABBE HUSON U.S. GOVERNMENT INCOME FUND, INC.
(See first Crabbe Huson listing for data common to all Crabbe Huson funds)

Portfolio manager: Jay L. Willoughby (1989)
Investment objective and policies: High current income consistent with safety of principal. Invests substantially all assets in direct or indirect debt obligations of the U.S. Government, its agencies and instrumentalities. Up to 10% of assets may be in repurchase agreements covering direct obligations of the U.S. Government.
Year organized: 1988
Discount broker availability: *Schwab, Fidelity, Siebert
Dividends paid: Income - monthly; Capital gains - December
Portfolio turnover (3 yrs): 76%, 82%, 106%
Management fee: 0.50% first $500M to 0.40% over $1B
12b-1 distribution fee: 0.16%
Expense ratio: 0.75% (year ending 10/31/94) (1.47% without waiver)

THE CRABBE HUSON U.S. GOVERNMENT MONEY MARKET FUND, INC.
(See first Crabbe Huson listing for data common to all Crabbe Huson funds)

Portfolio manager: Jay L. Willoughby (1989)
Investment objective and policies: Current income consistent with preservation of capital and liquidity. Invests in U.S. Government money market instruments.
Year organized: 1988 (name and objective changed from Crabbe Huson Money Market Fund on 2/23/93)
Ticker symbol: CHGXX
Dividends paid: Income - declared daily, paid monthly

Management fee: 0.50% first $500M to 0.40% over $1B
12b-1 distribution fee: 0.11%
Expense ratio: 0.70% (year ending 10/31/94) (2.81% without waiver)

CRESCENT FUND ◆
P.O. Box 14967
Cincinnati, OH 45250
310-789-5099, 800-424-2295
fax 310-789-5090

Adviser: Crescent Management & Research
Custodian and transfer agent: The Provident Bank, Cincinnati
Investment objective and policies: Total return - income and capital appreciation. Invests primarily in equity securities believed to offer superior investment value and fixed-income obligations such as securities issued by the U.S. government and investment grade corporate debt securities. Up to 15% of assets may be in illiquid securities and 20% in securities of foreign issuers. May use futures and options to hedge.
Year organized: 1993
Minimum purchase: Initial: $5,000, Subsequent: $500; IRA/Keogh: Initial: $2,000, Subsequent: $200
Telephone orders accepted: No
Wire orders accepted: Yes
Deadline for same day wire purchase: 3 P.M.
Qualified for sale in: CA, CO, FL, GA, HI, IL, IN, MN, NJ, NY, NC, PA, TX, VA, WV, WY
Telephone redemptions: Yes
Wire redemptions: Yes, $1,000 minimum, $10 fee
Letter redemptions: Signature guarantee required
Dividends paid: Income - June, December; Capital gains - June, December
Portfolio turnover (1 yr): 89%
Largest holding: Sunrise Medical, Inc. (3.8%)
Shareholder services: IRA, electronic funds transfer, automatic investment plan, withdrawal plan min. req. $10,000
Management fee: 1.0%
Expense ratio: 1.85% (10 months ending 3/31/94) (1.86% without waiver)
IRA fees: Annual $10, Initial $25

THE CROWLEY PORTFOLIOS ◆
(Data common to all Crowley Portfolios are shown below. See subsequent listings for data specific to individual Crowley portfolios.)

1813 Marsh Road, Suite H
Wilmington, DE 19810
302-529-1717, fax 302-529-1718

Adviser: Crowley & Crowley Corp.
Custodian: Wilmington Trust Co.
Custodian and transfer agent: The Crowley Financial Group, Inc.
Minimum purchase: Initial: $5,000, Subsequent: $1,000; IRA/Keogh: Initial: $1,000
Telephone orders accepted: No
Wire orders accepted: No
Qualified for sale in: DE, MD, NJ, PA
Letter redemptions: Signature guarantee required over $5,000
Dividends paid: Income - December; Capital gains - December
Shareholder services: Keogh, IRA, 401(k), 403(b), withdrawal plan
IRA fees: D.N.A.

THE CROWLEY DIVERSIFIED MANAGEMENT PORTFOLIO ◆
(See first Crowley listing for data common to all Crowley portfolios)

Portfolio manager: Robert A. Crowley (1995)
Investment objective and policies: High total return consistent with reasonable risk. Invests primarily in shares of other mutual funds - including funds that impose sales charges and/or invest in foreign securities. May use futures and options to hedge.
Year organized: 1995
Management fee: 1.0%

THE CROWLEY GROWTH PORTFOLIO ◆
(See first Crowley listing for data common to all Crowley portfolios)

Portfolio manager: Robert A. Crowley (1989)
Investment objective and policies: Long-term capital growth with current income secondary. Invests primarily in dividend-paying common stocks and other equity securities with potential for earnings growth. May use futures and options to hedge.
Year organized: 1989
Portfolio turnover (3 yrs): 107%, 244%, 179%
Largest holding: U.S. Treasury Note 6.750% due 2/28/97 (17.9%)
Management fee: 1.0%
Expense ratio: 1.85% (year ending 11/30/94)

THE CROWLEY INCOME PORTFOLIO ◆
(See first Crowley listing for data common to all Crowley portfolios)

Portfolio manager: Robert A. Crowley (1989)
Investment objective and policies: Maximum current income consistent with prudent risk. Invests primarily in investment-grade in debt securities of domestic corporate and government issuers, dividend-paying common stocks and dollar-denominated debt obligations of foreign issuers. Debt obligations will generally have remaining maturities of 7 years or less. May use futures and options to hedge.
Year organized: 1989
Portfolio turnover (3 yrs): 14%, 19%, 45%
Management fee: 0.6%
Expense ratio: 1.37% (year ending 11/30/94)

CT & T FUNDS
(Data common to all CT & T funds are shown below. See subsequent listings for data specific to individual CT & T funds.)

171 North Clark Street
Chicago, IL 60601
610-834-3692, 800-992-8151
fax 610-834-3591

Adviser: Chicago Title and Trust Co. (except Montag & Caldwell Growth fund and Montag & Caldwell Balanced fund)
Custodian: National Westminster Bank NJ
Transfer agent: Fund/Plan Services, Inc.
Minimum purchase: Initial: $500 ($1,000 for Money Market fund), Subsequent: $250 ($500 for Money Market fund); IRA: Initial: $250
Telephone orders accepted: No
Wire orders accepted: Yes
Deadline for same day wire purchase: 4 P.M. (1 P.M. for Money Market Fund)
Qualified for sale: All states except AK, AR, CO, ID, IA, KY, LA, ME, MD, MA, MS, MT, NV, NH, ND, OK, RI, UT, VT, WV
Telephone redemptions: Yes
Wire redemptions: Yes, $20 fee
Letter redemptions: Signature guarantee required over $10,000
Telephone switching: With other CT & T funds
Number of switches permitted: Reserves right to limit on 60 days notice
Shareholder services: IRA, automatic investment plan—minimum $50/month (waives initial minimum for shareholders with any open CT & T fund account), withdrawal plan min. req. $50,000
IRA fees: Annual $15

CT & T GROWTH & INCOME FUND
(See first CT & T listing for data common to all CT & T funds)

Portfolio manager: Jerold Stodden (1993)
Investment objective and policies: Long-term total return - capital growth and current income. Invests primarily in common stocks, preferred stocks, securities convertible into common stocks and fixed income securities. Up to 20% of assets may be in

ADRs & EDRs of foreign issuers and 15% in illiquid securities. May use futures and options to hedge.
Year organized: 1993
Dividends paid: Income - March, June, September, December; Capital gains - December
Portfolio turnover (1 yr): 37%
Largest holding: Proctor & Gamble Co. (3.1%)
Management fee: 0.70%
12b-1 distribution fee: 0.25%
Expense ratio: 1.20% (11 months ending 10/31/94) (2.21% without waiver)

CT & T INTERMEDIATE FIXED INCOME FUND
(See first CT & T listing for data common to all CT & T funds)

Portfolio managers: Thomas Marthaler (1993), Chris Mika (1993)
Investment objective and policies: High current income consistent with prudent risk of capital. Invests primarily in bonds and other fixed income securities with a weighted average maturity of 3 to 10 years. Up to 20% of assets may be in junk bonds. May use futures and options to hedge.
Year organized: 1993
Dividends paid: Income - declared and paid monthly; Capital gains - December
Portfolio turnover (1 yr): 21%
Management fee: 0.55%
12b-1 distribution fee: 0.25%
Expense ratio: 0.80% (11 months ending 10/31/94) (2.02% without waiver)

CT & T INTERMEDIATE MUNICIPAL BOND FUND
(See first CT & T listing for data common to all CT & T funds)

Portfolio managers: Lois Pasquale (1993), Chris Mika (1993)
Investment objective and policies: High current income exempt from federal income taxes consistent with preservation of capital. Invests substantially all assets in domestic municipal debt obligations with a weighted average maturity of 3 to 10 years. Up to 20% of assets may be in AMT securities and 20% in junk bonds.
Year organized: 1993
Dividends paid: Income - declared and paid monthly; Capital gains - December
Portfolio turnover (1 yr): 15%
Management fee: 0.60%
12b-1 distribution fee: 0.25%
Expense ratio: 0.90% (11 months ending 10/31/94) (2.09% without waiver)

CT & T MONEY MARKET FUND ◆
(See first CT & T listing for data common to all CT & T funds)

Portfolio managers: Fred Senft (1993), Joan Konecki (1993)
Investment objective and policies: High current income consistent with liquidity and stability of principal. Invests in money market instruments.
Year organized: 1993
Check redemptions: $500 minimum
Confirmations mailed: After each purchase and each check, mail or wire redemption
Checks returned: On request
Periodic account statements mailed: Monthly
Dividends paid: Income - declared daily, paid monthly
Management fee: 0.40%
Expense ratio: 0.40% (11 months ending 10/31/94) (0.64% without waiver)

CT & T FUNDS - MONTAG & CALDWELL BALANCED FUND
(See first CT & T listing for data common to all CT & T funds)

Adviser: Montag & Caldwell, Inc.
Portfolio managers: Ronald E. Canakaris (1994), David F. Seng (1994)

Investment objective and policies: Long-term total return through capital appreciation and current income. Invests primarily in common stocks, preferred stock and debt securities, including those convertible into common stock. Up to 30% of assets may be in ADRs or EDRs, at least 25% will be in fixed-income securities with weighted average maturities normally ranging from 3 to 10 years and up to 15% may be in illiquid securities. May use futures and options to hedge.
Year organized: 1994
Dividends paid: Income - March, June, September, December; Capital gains - December
Management fee: 0.75%
12b-1 distribution fee: 0.25%

CT & T FUNDS - MONTAG & CALDWELL GROWTH FUND
(See first CT & T listing for data common to all CT & T funds)

Adviser: Montag & Caldwell, Inc.
Portfolio managers: Ronald E. Canakaris (1994), David F. Seng (1994)
Investment objective and policies: Long-term capital appreciation with income secondary. Invests primarily in equity securities of companies of varied capitalization levels with strong growth potential. Up to 30% of assets may be in ADRs and EDRs and up to 15% in illiquid securities. May use futures and options to hedge.
Year organized: 1994
Dividends paid: Income - March, June, September, December; Capital gains - December
Management fee: 0.80%
12b-1 distribution fee: 0.25%

CT & T TALON FUND
(See first CT & T listing for data common to all CT & T funds)

Sub-adviser: Talon Asset Management, Inc.
Portfolio manager: Terrance Diamond (1994)
Investment objective and policies: Long-term total return through capital appreciation. Invests primarily in stocks of companies of varied capitalization levels with good growth prospects. May also invest preferred stock and debt securities. Up to 30% of assets may be in ADRs & EDRs of foreign issuers, 20% in junk bonds and 15% in illiquid securities. May use covered call options to hedge.
Year organized: 1994
Dividends paid: Income - March, June, September, December; Capital gains - December
Largest holding: Fruit of the Loom (4.3%)
Management fee: 0.80%
12b-1 distribution fee: 0.25%

DAILY TAX FREE INCOME FUND ◆
600 Fifth Avenue - 8th Floor
New York, NY 10020
212-676-5200, 800-676-6779
prices/yields 212-830-5225
fax 212-830-5476

Adviser: Reich & Tang L. P.
Portfolio manager: Molly Flewharty (1983)
Custodian: Investors Fiduciary Trust Co.
Transfer agent: Fundtech Services L.P.
Investment objective and policies: High current interest income exempt from federal income taxes consistent with preservation of capital and liquidity. Invests in money market instruments issued by state & municipal governments and other tax-exempt issuers.
Year organized: 1982
Ticker symbol: DTIXX
Minimum purchase: Initial: $5,000, Subsequent: $100; IRA: Initial: $250, Subsequent: None
Wire orders accepted: Yes
Deadline for same day wire purchase: 12 NN
Qualified for sale in: All states
Telephone redemptions: Yes
Wire redemptions: Yes, $1,000 minimum

Letter redemptions: Signature guarantee required
Telephone switching: With other Reich & Tang funds
Number of switches permitted: Unlimited, $1,000 minimum
Deadline for same day switch: 12 NN
Check redemptions: $250 minimum
Confirmations mailed: After each purchase and each check, mail or wire redemption
Checks returned: As clear
Periodic account statements mailed: Monthly
Dividends paid: Income - declared daily, paid monthly
Shareholder services: IRA, withdrawal plan
Management fee: 0.525% first $750M to 0.48% over $1.5B
Expense ratio: 0.63% (year ending 10/31/94)

DEAN WITTER FUNDS
(Data common to all Dean Witter funds are shown below. See subsequent listings for data specific to individual Dean Witter funds.)

Two World Trade Center
New York, NY 10048
212-392-2550, 800-869-3863
800-676-0460
prices/yields 800-869-7283

Adviser: InterCapital Division of Dean Witter Reynolds
Custodian: Bank of New York
Transfer agent: Dean Witter Trust Company
Wire orders accepted: Yes
Deadline for same day wire purchase: 4 P.M. (12 NN for money market funds)
Qualified for sale in: All states
Telephone redemptions: Yes
Wire redemptions: Yes, $1,000 minimum
Letter redemptions: Signature guarantee not required
Shareholder services: Keogh, IRA, 403(b), corporate retirement plans, automatic investment plan, withdrawal plan min. req. $5,000
IRA/Keogh fees: Annual $30

DEAN WITTER LIQUID ASSET FUND
(See first Dean Witter listing for data common to all Dean Witter funds)

Investment objective and policies: Income, preservation of capital and liquidity. Invests in money market instruments.
Year organized: 1975 (formerly InterCapital Liquid Asset Fund)
Ticker symbol: DWLXX
Minimum purchase: Initial $5,000, Subsequent $100; IRA/Keogh: Initial: $1,000
Check redemptions: $500 minimum
Confirmations mailed: After each purchase and each check, mail or wire redemption
Checks returned: On request
Periodic account statements mailed: Monthly
Dividends paid: Income - declared daily, paid monthly
Management fee: 0.5% first $500M to 0.248% over $17.5B
12b-1 distribution fee: 0.10%
Expense ratio: 0.70% (year ending 8/31/94)

DEAN WITTER SHORT-TERM BOND FUND ◆
(See first Dean Witter listing for data common to all Dean Witter funds)

Portfolio manager: Rochelle Siegel (1994)
Investment objective and policies: High current income consistent with preservation of capital. Invests in short-term fixed-income securities with a weighted average maturity of less than 3 years. May invest in investment-grade corporate and government fixed-income securities, mortgage- and asset-backed securities and in preferred stocks. Up

to 25% of assets may be in securities of foreign issuers.
Year organized: 1994
Ticker symbol: DWSBX
Minimum purchase: Initial $1,000, Subsequent $100
Dividends paid: Income - declared daily, paid monthly; Capital gains - December
Portfolio turnover (1 yr): 9%
Management fee: 0.7%
Expense ratio: 0.00% (4 months ending 4/30/94) (1.55% without waiver)

DEAN WITTER SHORT-TERM U.S. TREASURY TRUST
(See first Dean Witter listing for data common to all Dean Witter funds)

Portfolio manager: Rajesh K. Gupta (1991)
Investment objective and policies: High current income consistent with preservation of capital and liquidity. Invests exclusively in short-term fixed-income U.S. Treasury securities with a weighted average maturity of less than 3 years.
Year organized: 1991
Ticker symbol: DWSHX
Minimum purchase: Initial $10,000, Subsequent $100
Dividends paid: Income - declared daily, paid monthly; Capital gains - December
Portfolio turnover (3 yrs): 49%, 21%, 12%
Management fee: 0.35%
12b-1 distribution fee: 0.35%
Expense ratio: 0.79% (year ending 5/31/94)

DEAN WITTER TAX-FREE DAILY INCOME FUND
(See first Dean Witter listing for data common to all Dean Witter funds)

Investment objective and policies: High current income exempt from federal income taxes consistent with stability of principal and liquidity. Invests in high quality tax-exempt securities with short term maturities.
Year organized: 1981
Ticker symbol: DSTXX
Minimum purchase: Initial: $5,000, Subsequent: $100
Check redemptions: $500 minimum
Confirmations mailed: After each purchase and each check, mail or wire redemption
Checks returned: On request
Periodic account statements mailed: Monthly
Dividends paid: Income - declared daily, paid monthly
Management fee: 0.5% first $500M to 0.25% over $3B
12b-1 distribution fee: 0.10%
Expense ratio: 0.68% (year ending 12/31/93)

DEAN WITTER U.S. GOVERNMENT MONEY MARKET TRUST
(See first Dean Witter listing for data common to all Dean Witter funds)

Investment objective and policies: Security of principal, high income and liquidity. Invests in money market instruments issued or guaranteed by the U.S. Government or its agencies or instrumentalities.
Year organized: 1982
Ticker symbol: DWGXX
Minimum purchase: Initial: $1,000, Subsequent: $50
Check redemptions: $500 minimum
Confirmations mailed: After each purchase and each check, mail or wire redemption
Checks returned: On request
Periodic account statements mailed: Monthly
Dividends paid: Income - declared daily, paid monthly
Management fee: 0.5% first $500M to 0.25% over $3B
12b-1 distribution fee: 0.09%
Expense ratio: 1.00% (year ending 1/31/94)

DELAFIELD FUND, INC.
600 Fifth Avenue - 8th Floor
New York, NY 10020
212-676-5200, 800-676-6779
prices/yields 212-830-5225
fax 212-830-5476

Adviser: Reich & Tang L.P.
Portfolio manager: J. Dennis Delafield (1993)
Custodian and transfer agent: Investors Fiduciary Trust Co.
Investment objective and policies: Growth of capital consistent with preservation of capital. Invests at least 65% of assets in equity securities of domestic companies believed undervalued or undergoing change that might cause their market value to grow faster than the overall economy. May invest in debt securities and preferred stocks offering opportunity for price appreciation. Up to 15% of assets may be in foreign securities and 10% in restricted securities. May sell short.
Year organized: 1993
Minimum purchase: Initial: $5,000, Subsequent: None, IRA: Initial: $250
Telephone orders accepted: No
Wire orders accepted: Yes
Deadline for same day wire purchases: 4 P.M.
Qualified for sale in: All states
Wire redemptions: Yes, $1,000 minimum
Letter redemptions: Signature guarantee required
Telephone switching: Other Reich & Tang managed funds, $1,000 minimum
Number of switches permitted: Unlimited
Dividends paid: Income - June, December; Capital gains - December
Portfolio turnover (1 yr): 43%
Largest holding: Univar Corp. (3.3%)
Shareholder services: IRA, withdrawal plan min. req. $10,000, electronic funds transfer
Management fee: 1.0%
12b-1 distribution fee: 0.25%
Expense ratio: 1.78% (10 months ending 9/30/94) (2.90% without waiver)
IRA fees: None

DODGE & COX FUNDS ◆
(Data common to all Dodge & Cox funds are shown below. See subsequent listing for data specific to individual Dodge & Cox funds.)

One Sansome St - 35th Floor
San Francisco, CA 94104
415-434-0311
for shareholders only 800-338-1579
prices 415-981-1710

Shareholder service hours: Full service: M-F 9 A.M.-8 P.M. EST; After hours service: prices, account balances, last transaction, messages, prospectuses
Adviser: Dodge & Cox
Portfolio managers: Group of 4
Custodian and transfer agent: Firstar Trust Co.
Minimum purchase: Initial: $2,500, Subsequent: $100; IRA: Initial: $1,000
Telephone orders accepted: No
Wire orders accepted: Yes
Deadline for same day wire purchase: 1 P.M.
Qualified for sale in: All states
Letter redemptions: Signature guarantee not required
Dividends paid: Income - March, June, September, December; Capital gains - March, December
Shareholder services: IRA, automatic investment plan, withdrawal plan min. req. $10,000
IRA fees: Annual $12.50

DODGE & COX BALANCED FUND ◆
(See first Dodge & Cox listing for data common to all Dodge & Cox funds)

Investment objective and policies: Income, conservation of principal and long-term growth of capital. Invests in common stocks (up to 75% of assets), preferred stocks, and fixed-income securities. Allocation of assets varies depending on market and economic conditions.
Year organized: 1931

Ticker symbol: DODBX
Discount broker availability: Schwab, White, Waterhouse
Portfolio turnover (3 yrs): 20%, 15%, 6%
Largest holding: Federal National Mortgage Association 6 1/2% due in 2023 (2.0%)
Management fee: 0.5%
Expense ratio: 0.58% (year ending 12/31/94)

DODGE & COX INCOME FUND ◆
(See first Dodge & Cox listing for data common to all Dodge & Cox funds)

Investment objective and policies: High current income consistent with preservation of capital with capital appreciation secondary. Invests in a diversified portfolio of high-quality bonds and other fixed-income securities. Up to 25% of assets may be in dollar-denominated securities of foreign issuers and 20% in junk bonds.
Year organized: 1988
Ticker symbol: DODIX
Discount broker availability: Schwab, White, Waterhouse
Portfolio turnover (3 yrs): 55%, 26%, 12%
Management fee: 0.5% first $100M, 0.4% over $100M
Expense ratio: 0.54% (year ending 12/31/94)

DODGE & COX STOCK FUND ◆
(See first Dodge & Cox listing for data common to all Dodge & Cox funds)

Investment objective and policies: Long-term growth of principal and income, with reasonable current income secondary. Invests primarily in high grade common stocks and securities convertible into common stock. Up to 15% of assets may be in illiquid securities.
Year organized: 1965
Ticker symbol: DODGX
Discount broker availability: Schwab, White, Waterhouse
Portfolio turnover (3 yrs): 7%, 15%, 7%
Largest holding: Dayton-Hudson Corp. (2.7%)
Management fee: 0.5%
Expense ratio: 0.61% (year ending 12/31/94)

DOMINI SOCIAL EQUITY FUND ◆
6 St. James Avenue, 9th Floor
Boston, MA 02116
617-423-0800, 800-762-6814
fax 617-542-5815

Adviser: Kinder, Lydenberg, Domini & Co., Inc.
Administrator: Signature Broker-Dealer Services, Inc.
Portfolio manager: Amy L. Domini (1990)
Custodian and transfer agent: Investors Bank & Trust Company
Investment objective and policies: Long-term total return which corresponds to the total return performance of the Domini Social Index, a capitalization weighted index of 400 stocks drawn from the S&P 500 (about 50%) and other domestic and foreign (ADRs) companies selected to exclude those with involvement in military weapons, tobacco and alcohol, gambling and nuclear power production or construction. Inclusion will also be determined by a company's product quality, consumer awareness, environmental performance, corporate citizenship and employee relations. The Trust will have at least 80% of its assets in securities comprising the Index and attempt to be fully invested at all times.
Year organized: 1990 (name changed from Domini Social Index Trust in 1993)
Ticker symbol: DSEFX
Minimum purchase: Initial: $1,000, Subsequent: None; IRA: Initial: $250
Telephone orders accepted: No
Wire orders accepted: Yes
Deadline for same day wire purchase: 4 P.M.
Discount broker availability: Schwab, *White
Qualified for sale in: All states
Telephone redemptions: Yes

Wire redemptions: Yes
Letter redemptions: Signature guarantee not required
Dividends paid: Income - June, December; Capital gains - December
Portfolio turnover: N.A.
Largest holding: Coca Cola Co. (3.5%)
Shareholder services: IRA, automatic investment plan—minimum $25/month, withdrawal plan min. req. $10,000
Management fee: 0.10% first $50M, 0.30% $50M-$100M to 0.15% over $500M
Administration fee: 0.15%
12b-1 distribution fee: Maximum of 0.25% (not currently imposed)
Expense ratio: 0.75% (year ending 7/31/94) (1.39% without waiver)
IRA fees: Annual $10, Initial $10

DREMAN FUNDS ◆
(Data common to all Dreman funds are shown below. See subsequent listings for data specific to individual Dreman funds.)

10 Exchange Place, Suite 2050
Jersey City, NJ 07302
201-332-8228, 800-533-1608
fax 201-434-2862

Shareholder service hours: Full service: M-F 8:30 A.M.-5:30 P.M. EST; After hours service: prices, prospectuses
Investment adviser: Dreman Value Management, L.P.
Custodian: Bank of New York
Transfer agent: Fund/Plan Services, Inc.
Minimum purchase: Initial: $1,000 Subsequent: $100
Telephone orders accepted: Yes, Subsequent only, maximum equal to current fund balance
Wire orders accepted: Yes
Deadline for same day wire purchase: 4 P.M.
Qualified for sale in: All states except AK, AR, IA, KS, MS, MT, NE, ND, OK, RI, SC, SD, WY
Telephone redemptions: Yes, $1,000 minimum
Wire redemptions: Yes $1,000 minimum
Letter redemptions: Signature guarantee required over $5,000
Telephone switching: With other Dreman funds and Government Cash Series, Municipal Cash Series, Prime Cash Series & Treasury Cash series
Number of switches permitted: Unlimited
Dividends paid: Income - March, June, September, December; Capital gains - December
Shareholder services: IRA, SEP-IRA, automatic investment plan—minimum $50/month ($100 initial minimum), withdrawal plan
IRA fees: Annual $12

DREMAN CONTRARIAN PORTFOLIO ◆
(See first Dreman listing for data common to all Dreman funds)

Portfolio manager: David N. Dreman (1988)
Investment objective and policies: Long term capital appreciation with current income secondary. Contrarian investing entails the acquisition of stocks of sound companies believed to be undervalued in the securities markets and out of favor. Invests primarily in common stocks of larger companies listed on the NYSE. May buy ADRs of foreign issuers and use futures and options to enhance return and hedge.
Year organized: 1988
Ticker symbol: DRCPX
Discount broker availability: Schwab, *White, *Fidelity, *Siebert
Portfolio turnover (3 yrs): 16%, 28%, 36%
Largest holding: Federal Home Loan Mortgage Corp. (6.3%)
Management fee: 1.00% first $1B, 0.75% over $1B
Expense ratio: 1.25% (year ending 12/31/93) (1.54% without waiver)

DREMAN FIXED INCOME PORTFOLIO ◆
(See first Dreman listing for data common to all Dreman funds)

Portfolio manager: William F. Coughlin (1988)
Investment objective and policies: Current income consistent with preservation of principal. Invests up to 50% of assets in securities issued or guaranteed as to principal and interest by the US Government, its agencies or instrumentalities. Remainder of assets are in high grade corporate obligations, bank certificates of deposit and high grade commercial paper.
Year organized: 1988 (name changed from Bond Portfolio on 6/18/92)
Discount broker availability: Schwab, *White, *Fidelity, *Siebert
Portfolio turnover (3 yrs): 18%, 58%, 39%
Management fee: 0.50%
Expense ratio: 0.75% (year ending 12/31/93) (1.60% without waiver)

DREMAN HIGH RETURN PORTFOLIO ◆
(See first Dreman listing for data common to all Dreman funds)

Portfolio manager: David N. Dreman (1988)
Investment objective and policies: High rate of total return. Invests primarily in stocks which pay relatively high dividends, and have the same investment characteristics as those acquired by Dreman Contrarian. Holdings are targeted toward an opportunistic mix between income and capital appreciation. May purchase ADRs of foreign issuers and use futures and options to enhance return and hedge.
Year organized: 1988
Ticker symbol: DRHRX
Discount broker availability: Schwab, *White, *Fidelity, *Siebert
Portfolio turnover (3 yrs): 14%, 13%, 37%
Largest holding: Federal Home Loan Mortgage Corp. (5.9%)
Management fee: 1.00% first $1B, 0.75% over $1B
Expense ratio: 1.25% (year ending 12/31/93) (1.56% without waiver)

DREMAN SMALL CAP VALUE PORTFOLIO ◆
(See first Dreman listing for data common to all Dreman funds)

Portfolio manager: Jeffrey E. Schuss (1994)
Investment objective and policies: Long term capital appreciation. Invests in equity securities of companies with market capitalization of $100M to $1B using the contrarian approach of acquiring securities of sound companies believed to be undervalued in the securities markets. Invests primarily in common stocks. May purchase ADRs of foreign issuers and use futures and options to enhance return and hedge.
Year organized: 1992
Ticker symbol: DRSCX
Discount broker availability: *White, *Fidelity, *Siebert
Portfolio turnover (1 yr): 79%
Largest holding: Blount Incorporated - Class A (6.0%)
Management fee: 1.00% first $1B, 0.75% over $1B
Expense ratio: 1.25% (year ending 12/31/93) (2.09% without waiver)

DREYFUS FUNDS
(Data common to all Dreyfus funds are show below. See subsequent listings for data specific to individual Dreyfus funds.)

EAB Plaza
144 Glenn Curtis Boulevard, Plaza Level
Uniondale, NY 11556
718-895-1206, 516-794-5200
800-829-3733
prices/yields 800-645-6561

Shareholder service hours: Full service: Sun-Sat 24 hours

Adviser: The Dreyfus Corporation (a wholly-owned subsidiary of Mellon Bank, N.A.)
Custodian: Bank of New York (exceptions noted); Dreyfus Trust Company (for all retirement accounts)
Transfer agent: The Shareholder Services Group, Inc. (exceptions noted)
Minimum purchase: Initial: $2,500, Subsequent: $100; IRA/Keogh: Initial: $750, Subsequent: None (exceptions noted)
Telephone orders accepted: No
Wire orders accepted: Yes
Deadline for same day wire purchase: 4 P.M. (exceptions noted)
Qualified for sale in: All states (exceptions noted)
Telephone redemptions: Yes
Wire redemptions: Yes, $1,000 minimum
Letter redemptions: Signature guarantee required over $100,000
Telephone switching: With other Dreyfus funds (except index funds and Wilshire funds), $500 minimum
Number of switches permitted: Unlimited (exceptions noted)
Shareholder services: Keogh, IRA, SEP-IRA, 403(b), 401(k), & corporate retirement plans, automatic investment plan, directed dividends, withdrawal plan min. req. $5,000, electronic funds transfer
IRA/Keogh fees: Annual $10 (maximum $25 per individual) (none for Dreyfus Growth & Income Fund)
Note: For information on the former Laurel funds, please see listings under Dreyfus/Laurel following the listings for the regular Dreyfus funds.

DREYFUS A BONDS PLUS ◆
(See first Dreyfus listing for data common to all Dreyfus funds)

Portfolio manager: Garitt Kono (1994)
Investment objective and policies: High current income consistent with preservation of capital and liquidity. Invests primarily in debt obligations of corporations and the U.S. Government and its agencies and instrumentalities and major banking institutions. At least 80% of assets will be corporate obligations rated A or better and government guaranteed issues. Up to 15% of assets may be in illiquid securities and 10% in securities of foreign issuers.
Year organized: 1976
Ticker symbol: DRBDX
Discount broker availability: *Schwab, *White, *Waterhouse, *Fidelity, *Siebert
Check redemptions: $500 minimum
Dividends paid: Income - declared and paid monthly; Capital gains - December
Portfolio turnover (3 yrs): 94%, 81%, 67%
Management fee: 0.65%
Expense ratio: 0.90% (year ending 3/31/94)

DREYFUS APPRECIATION FUND
(See first Dreyfus listing for data common to all Dreyfus funds)

Sub-adviser: Fayez Sarofim & Co.
Portfolio manager: Fayez Sarofim (1990)
Investment objective and policies: Long-term capital growth consistent with preservation of capital and current income secondary. Invests primarily in common stocks of companies with market capitalizations over $500M believed undervalued. Fund looks for new or innovative products, services or processes, economic or political changes, and corporate restructurings. May invest up to 10% of assets in foreign securities, 15% in illiquid securities and use currency exchange contracts. Fund may write covered calls on up to 20% of assets.
Year organized: 1984 (name changed from General Aggressive Growth Fund on 12/30/91) (split 2 for 1 on 3/9/92)
Ticker symbol: DGAGX
Discount broker availability: *Schwab, *White, Waterhouse, *Fidelity, *Siebert
Dividends paid: Income - annually; Capital gains - annually

Portfolio turnover (3 yrs): 10%, 3%, 13%
Largest holding: Philip Morris Companies (6.1%)
Management fee: 0.44% first $25M to 0.275% over $300M
12b-1 distribution fee: 0.25%
Expense ratio: 1.07% (year ending 12/31/93)

DREYFUS ASSET ALLOCATION FUND - GROWTH PORTFOLIO
(See first Dreyfus listing for data common to all Dreyfus funds)

Portfolio manager: Ernest Wiggins (1994)
Investment objective and policies: Maximum total return - capital growth and current income. Fund follows an asset allocation strategy that reapportions holdings, possibly with high frequency, among common stocks included in the S&P 500 Index (normally 80% of assets; range 65-95%) and US Treasury Notes and Bonds and short-term money market instruments (20%; 5-35%). Fund may leverage, sell short, and write covered options on up to 20% of assets.
Year organized: 1994
Dividends paid: Income - annually, Capital gains - annually
Management fee: 0.75%
12b-1 distribution fee: 0.50%

DREYFUS ASSET ALLOCATION FUND - INCOME PORTFOLIO
(See first Dreyfus listing for data common to all Dreyfus funds)

Portfolio manager: Ernest Wiggins (1994)
Investment objective and policies: Maximum total return - capital growth and current income. Fund follows an asset allocation strategy that reapportions holdings, possibly with high frequency, among common stocks included in the S&P 500 Index (normally 35% of assets; range 25-45%), US Treasury Notes and Bonds (55%; 45-70%), and short-term money market instruments (10%; 0-15%). Fund may leverage, sell short, and write covered options on up to 20% of assets.
Year organized: 1994
Dividends paid: Income - quarterly, Capital gains - annually
Management fee: 0.75%
12b-1 distribution fee: 0.50%

DREYFUS ASSET ALLOCATION FUND - TOTAL RETURN PORTFOLIO
(See first Dreyfus listing for data common to all Dreyfus funds)

Portfolio manager: Ernest Wiggins (1994)
Investment objective and policies: Maximum total return - capital growth and current income. Fund follows an asset allocation strategy that reapportions holdings, possibly with high frequency, among common stocks included in the S&P 500 Index (normally 55% of assets; range 40-70%), US Treasury Notes and Bonds (35%; 25-50%), and short-term money market instruments (10%; 0-15%). Fund may leverage, sell short, and write covered options on up to 20% of assets.
Year organized: 1993 (name changed from Dreyfus Asset Allocation Fund in 1994)
Ticker symbol: DRAAX
Discount broker availability: Schwab
Dividends paid: Income - annually, Capital gains - annually
Largest holding: U.S. Treasury Note 8.50% due 11/15/00 (10.7%)
Management fee: 0.75%
12b-1 distribution fee: 0.50%
Expense ratio: 0.16% (10 months ending 4/30/94) (1.74% without waiver)

DREYFUS BALANCED FUND ◆
(See first Dreyfus listing for data common to all Dreyfus funds)

Portfolio manager: Peter A. Santoriello (1992)
Investment objective and policies: Long-term capi-

tal growth and current income consistent with reasonable investment risk. Normally invests 50% of assets in equity securities and remainder in debt securities with at least 25% of assets in fixed-income senior securities. Equity securities include common and preferred stocks, convertible securities and warrants. Debt securities must be of investment grade with a weighted average maturity of 2 to 10 years. Fund is non-diversified and may leverage.
Year organized: 1992
Ticker symbol: DRBAX
Discount broker availability: *Schwab, *White, *Fidelity, *Siebert
Dividends paid: Income - annually, Capital gains - annually
Portfolio turnover (2 yrs): 58%, 46%
Largest holding: U.S. Treasury Bonds 7 1/4% due 5/15/16 (5.5%)
Management fee: 0.60%
Expense ratio: 0.69% (year ending 8/31/94) (1.10% without waiver)

DREYFUS BASIC INTERMEDIATE MUNICIPAL BOND FUND ◆
(See first Dreyfus listing for data common to all Dreyfus funds)

Portfolio manager: Joseph Darcy (1994)
Investment objective and policies: High current income exempt from federal income taxes consistent with preservation of capital. Invests primarily in high quality municipal obligations with a weighted average maturity of 3 to 10 years. Up to 35% of assets may be in obligations rated below investment grade. May use futures and options and sell short. Designed to deliver extra high yields for long-term buy and hold investors by maintaining a lower than average expense ratio.
Year organized: 1994
Ticker symbol: DBIMX
Minimum purchase: Initial: $10,000, Subsequent: $1,000
Wire orders accepted: Yes, $5 fee
Deadline for same day wire purchase: 4 P.M.
Wire redemptions: Yes, $5,000 minimum, $5 fee
Account closeout fee: $5
Number of switches permitted: 4 outbound per year, $5 fee
Check redemptions $1,000 minimum, $2 fee
Dividends paid: Income - declared daily, paid monthly; Capital gains - annually
Management fee: 0.6%
Expense ratio: 0.00% (4 months ending 8/31/94) (1.54% without waiver)

DREYFUS BASIC MONEY MARKET FUND ◆
(See first Dreyfus listing for data common to all Dreyfus funds)

Portfolio manager: Patricia A. Larkin (1994)
Investment objective and policies: High current income consistent with preservation of capital and liquidity. Invests in high quality short-term money market obligations. Designed to deliver extra high yields for long-term buy and hold investors by maintaining a lower than average expense ratio.
Year organized: 1992
Ticker symbol: DBAXX
Minimum purchase: Initial: $25,000, Subsequent: $1,000
Wire orders accepted: Yes, $5 fee
Wire redemptions: Yes, $5,000 minimum, $5 fee
Account closeout fee: $5
Number of switches permitted: 4 outbound per year, $5 fee:
Check redemptions $1,000 minimum, $2 fee
Confirmations mailed: After each purchase and each check, mail or wire redemption
Checks returned: Monthly
Periodic account statements mailed: Quarterly
Dividends paid: Income - declared daily, paid monthly
Management fee: 0.5%
Expense ratio: 0.10% (year ending 2/28/94) (0.65% without waiver)

DREYFUS BASIC MUNICIPAL BOND FUND ◆
(See first Dreyfus listing for data common to all Dreyfus funds)

Portfolio manager: Joseph Darcy (1994)
Investment objective and policies: High current income exempt from federal income taxes consistent with preservation of capital. Invests primarily in high quality municipal obligations with no limit on maturity. Up to 35% of assets may be in obligations rated below investment grade. May use futures and options and sell short. Designed to deliver extra high yields for long-term buy and hold investors by maintaining a lower than average expense ratio.
Year organized: 1994
Minimum purchase: Initial: $10,000, Subsequent: $1,000
Wire orders accepted: Yes, $5 fee
Deadline for same day wire purchase: 4 P.M.
Wire redemptions: Yes, $5,000 minimum, $5 fee
Account closeout fee: $5
Number of switches permitted: 4 outbound per year, $5 fee
Check redemptions $1,000 minimum, $2 fee
Dividends paid: Income - declared daily, paid monthly; Capital gains - annually
Management fee: 0.6%
Expense ratio: 0.00% (4 months ending 8/31/94) (2.06% without waiver)

DREYFUS BASIC MUNICIPAL MONEY MARKET FUND ◆
(See first Dreyfus listing for data common to all Dreyfus funds)

Portfolio manager: Karen M. Hand (1991)
Investment objective and policies: High current income exempt from federal income taxes consistent with preservation of capital and liquidity. Invests in high quality municipal money market obligations. Designed to deliver extra high yields for long-term buy and hold investors by maintaining a lower than average expense ratio.
Year organized: 1991 (name changed from Dreyfus Investors Municipal Money Market Fund on 4/23/92)
Ticker symbol: DBMXX
Minimum purchase: Initial: $25,000, Subsequent: $1,000
Wire orders accepted: Yes, $5 fee
Deadline for same day wire purchase: 12 NN
Wire redemptions: Yes, $5,000 minimum, $5 fee
Account closeout fee: $5
Number of switches permitted: 4 outbound per year, $5 fee
Check redemptions $1,000 minimum, $2 fee
Confirmations mailed: After each purchase and each check, mail or wire redemption
Checks returned: Monthly
Periodic account statements mailed: Quarterly
Dividends paid: Income - declared daily, paid monthly
Management fee: 0.5%
Expense ratio: 0.09% (year ending 8/31/94) (0.59% without waiver)

DREYFUS BASIC U.S. GOVERNMENT MONEY MARKET FUND ◆
(See first Dreyfus listing for data common to all Dreyfus funds)

Portfolio manager: Patricia A. Larkin (1994)
Investment objective and policies: High current income consistent with preservation of capital and liquidity. Invests in high quality short-term U.S. Government securities and repurchase agreements. Designed to deliver extra high yields for long-term buy and hold investors by maintaining a lower than average expense ratio.
Year organized: 1992
Ticker symbol: DBGXX
Minimum purchase: Initial: $25,000, Subsequent: $1,000
Wire orders accepted: Yes, $5 fee
Wire redemptions: Yes, $5,000 minimum, $5 fee

Account closeout fee: $5
Number of switches permitted: 4 outbound per year, $5 fee
Check redemptions $1,000 minimum, $2 fee
Confirmations mailed: After each purchase and each check, mail or wire redemption
Checks returned: Monthly
Periodic account statements mailed: Quarterly
Dividends paid: Income - declared daily, paid monthly
Management fee: 0.5%
Expense ratio: 0.02% (year ending 2/28/94) (0.66% without waiver)

DREYFUS CALIFORNIA INTERMEDIATE MUNICIPAL BOND FUND ◆
(See first Dreyfus listing for data common to all Dreyfus funds)

Newspaper listing: CalMun
Portfolio manager: L. Lawrence Troutman (1992)
Investment objective and policies: High current income exempt from federal and California state income taxes consistent with preservation of capital. Invests primarily in California municipal bonds with at least 80% rated BBB or better and a weighted average maturity of 3 to 10 years. Up to 15% of assets may be in illiquid securities. May use futures and options and sell short.
Year organized: 1992
Ticker symbol: DCIMX
Discount broker availability: *Schwab, White, *Fidelity, *Siebert
Qualified for sale in: AZ, CA, DC, HI, MI, NV, NJ, NY, OR, WA, WY
Check redemptions: $500 minimum
Dividends paid: Income - declared daily, paid monthly; Capital gains - annually
Portfolio turnover (2 yrs): 6%, 7%
Management fee: 0.60%
Expense ratio: 0.04% (year ending 3/31/94) (0.82% without waiver)

DREYFUS CALIFORNIA TAX EXEMPT BOND FUND ◆
(See first Dreyfus listing for data common to all Dreyfus funds)

Newspaper listing: CalTx
Portfolio manager: L. Lawrence Troutman (1986)
Investment objective and policies: High current income exempt from federal and California state income taxes consistent with preservation of capital. Invests primarily in California municipal bonds with at least 80% rated BBB or better. Up to 15% of assets may be in illiquid securities.
Year organized: 1983
Ticker symbol: DRCAX
Discount broker availability: *Schwab, *White, Waterhouse, *Fidelity, *Siebert
Check redemptions: $500 minimum
Dividends paid: Income - declared daily, paid monthly; Capital gains - annually
Portfolio turnover (3 yrs): 28%, 41%, 46%
Management fee: 0.60%
Expense ratio: 0.70% (year ending 5/31/94)

DREYFUS CALIFORNIA TAX EXEMPT MONEY MARKET FUND ◆
(See first Dreyfus listing for data common to all Dreyfus funds)

Portfolio manager: Jill C. Shaffro (1993)
Investment objective and policies: High current income exempt from federal and California state income taxes consistent with preservation of capital and liquidity. Invests in California money market instruments.
Year organized: 1986
Ticker symbol: DCTXX
Deadline for same day wire purchase: 12 NN
Qualified for sale in: AK, AZ, CA, CO, DC, FL, HI, ID, IL, LA, MD, MA, MI, MN, MS, NE, NV, NJ, NM, NY, OH, OR, TX, VA, WA, WY
Check redemptions: $500 minimum

Confirmations mailed: After each purchase and each check, mail or wire redemption
Checks returned: Monthly
Periodic account statements mailed: Quarterly
Dividends paid: Income - declared daily, paid monthly
Management fee: 0.50%
Expense ratio: 0.65% (year ending 3/31/93)

DREYFUS CAPITAL GROWTH FUND
(See first Dreyfus listing for data common to all Dreyfus funds)

Portfolio manager: Howard Stein (1968)
Investment objective and policies: Maximum capital growth. Invests primarily in common stocks and securities convertible into common stocks. May invest up to 30% of assets in foreign securities and use foreign currency exchange contracts, futures and options thereon. Fund may use debt securities rated as low as Caa and zero coupon U.S. Treasuries, and invest up to 15% of assets in illiquid securities. Fund may sell short up to 25% of total assets, leverage up to 20% of net assets, and use futures and options transactions on indices, securities and interest rates.
Year organized: 1968 (name changed from Dreyfus Leverage Fund on 7/21/92)
Ticker symbol: DRLEX
Sales charges: 3%, reduced for volume purchases
Discount broker availability: Fidelity, Siebert
Dividends paid: Income - annually; Capital gains - annually
Portfolio turnover (3 yrs): 158%, 102%, 142%
Management fee: 0.75%
Expense ratio: 1.12% (year ending 9/30/94)

DREYFUS CONNECTICUT INTERMEDIATE MUNICIPAL BOND FUND ◆
(See first Dreyfus listing for data common to all Dreyfus funds)

Portfolio manager: Stephen Kris (1992)
Investment objective and policies: High current income exempt from federal and Connecticut income taxes consistent with preservation of capital. Invests primarily in debt securities of the state of Connecticut, its political subdivisions, authorities and corporations, with at least 80% rated BBB or better and a weighted average maturity of 3 to 10 years. Up to 15% of assets may be in illiquid securities. May use futures and options and sell short against the box.
Year organized: 1992
Ticker symbol: DCTIX
Discount broker availability: *Schwab, *White, *Fidelity, *Siebert
Qualified for sale in: CT, DC, FL, HI, NJ, NY, WY
Check redemptions: $500 minimum
Dividends paid: Income - declared daily, paid monthly; Capital gains - annually
Portfolio turnover (2 yrs): 11%, 38%
Management fee: 0.60%
Expense ratio: 0.01% (year ending 3/31/94) (0.85% without waiver)

DREYFUS CONNECTICUT MUNICIPAL MONEY MARKET FUND ◆
(See first Dreyfus listing for data common to all Dreyfus funds)

Portfolio manager: Jill C. Shaffro (1993)
Investment objective and policies: High current income exempt from federal and State of Connecticut income taxes consistent with preservation of capital liquidity. Invests in Connecticut money market instruments.
Year organized: 1990
Ticker symbol: DRCXX
Deadline for same day wire purchase: 12 NN
Qualified for sale in: CT, DC, FL, HI, NJ, NY, WY
Check redemptions: $500 minimum
Confirmations mailed: After each purchase and each check, mail or wire redemption
Checks returned: Monthly

Periodic account statements mailed: Quarterly
Dividends paid: Income - declared daily, paid monthly
Management fee: 0.50%
Expense ratio: 0.22% (year ending 9/30/94) (0.64% without waiver)

DREYFUS EDISON ELECTRIC INDEX FUND ◆
(See first Dreyfus listing for data common to all Dreyfus funds)

Portfolio manager: Wells Fargo Nikko Investment Advisors
Investment objective and policies: Provide investment results that correspond to the price and yield performance of common stocks of companies engaged in the generation, transmission or distribution of electric energy as represented by an index comprising the common stocks of companies that are members of the Edison Electric Institute. Invests in the stocks that comprise the index.
Year organized: 1991
Ticker symbol: DEEIX
Discount broker availability: *White, Waterhouse
Dividends paid: Income - quarterly; Capital gains - annually
Portfolio turnover (3 yrs): 9%, 14%, 3%
Largest holding: Southern (6.0%)
Management fee: 0.1%
Expense ratio: 0.74% (year ending 10/31/94)

DREYFUS FLORIDA INTERMEDIATE BOND FUND ◆
(See first Dreyfus listing for data common to all Dreyfus funds)

Portfolio manager: Steven Kris (1992)
Investment objective and policies: High current income exempt from federal income tax and Florida intangible personal property tax consistent with preservation of capital. Invests at least 80% in high quality municipal obligations (rated A or better), primarily issued by the state of Florida and its political subdivisions, agencies and authorities, with a weighted average maturity of 3 to 10 years. Up to 15% of assets may be in illiquid securities. May use futures and options and sell short.
Year organized: 1992
Ticker symbol: DFLIX
Discount broker availability: *Schwab, White, *Fidelity, *Siebert
Qualified for sale in: DC, FL, HI, NJ, NY, WY
Check redemptions: $500 minimum
Dividends paid: Income - declared daily, paid monthly; Capital gains - annually
Portfolio turnover (2 yrs): 13%, 13%
Management fee: 0.60%
Expense ratio: 0.20% (year ending 12/31/93) (0.84% without waiver)

DREYFUS FLORIDA MUNICIPAL MONEY MARKET FUND ◆
(See first Dreyfus listing for data common to all Dreyfus funds)

Portfolio manager: Jill C. Shaffro (1993)
Investment objective and policies: High current income exempt from federal income tax and Florida intangible personal property tax consistent with preservation of capital liquidity. Invests in Florida money market instruments.
Year organized: 1993
Ticker symbol: DFMXX
Deadline for same day wire purchase: 12 NN
Qualified for sale in: DC, FL, HI, NJ, NY, WY
Check redemptions: $500 minimum
Confirmations mailed: After each purchase and each check, mail or wire redemption
Checks returned: Monthly
Periodic account statements mailed: Quarterly
Dividends paid: Income - declared daily, paid monthly
Management fee: 0.50%
Expense ratio: 0.00% (8 months ending 6/30/94) (0.79% without waiver)

DREYFUS FOCUS FUND - LARGE COMPANY GROWTH PORTFOLIO
(See first Dreyfus listing for data common to all Dreyfus funds)

Portfolio manager: Howard Stein (1993)
Investment objective and policies: Capital growth. Invests primarily in equity securities of domestic and foreign issuers with market capitalizations of $900M to $90B with above average earnings or sales growth, retention of earnings and higher P/E ratios. Up to 15% of assets may be in illiquid securities. May use futures and options and foreign currency transactions. May leverage, hedge up to 20% of total assets and sell short up to 25% of total assets
Year organized: 1993
Dividends paid: Income - annually; Capital gains - annually
Portfolio turnover (1 yr) 12%
Largest holding: Motorola Corp. (3.1%)
Management fee: 0.75%
12b-1 distribution fee: 0.50%
Expense ratio: 0.00% (10 months ending 10/31/94) (1.97% without waiver)

DREYFUS FOCUS FUND - LARGE COMPANY VALUE PORTFOLIO
(See first Dreyfus listing for data common to all Dreyfus funds)

Portfolio manager: Ernest Wiggins (1993)
Investment objective and policies: Capital growth. Invests primarily in equity securities of domestic and foreign issuers with market capitalizations of $900M to $90B with low price to book ratios, lower P/E ratios and higher than average dividend rates. Up to 15% of assets may be in illiquid securities. May use futures and options and foreign currency transactions. May leverage, hedge up to 20% of total assets and sell short up to 25% of total assets
Year organized: 1993
Dividends paid: Income - annually; Capital gains - annually
Portfolio turnover (1 yr) 48%
Largest holding: American Express (2.8%)
Management fee: 0.75%
12b-1 distribution fee: 0.50%
Expense ratio: 0.00% (10 months ending 10/31/94) (2.01% without waiver)

DREYFUS FOCUS FUND - SMALL COMPANY GROWTH PORTFOLIO
(See first Dreyfus listing for data common to all Dreyfus funds)

Portfolio manager: Howard Stein (1993)
Investment objective and policies: Capital growth. Invests primarily in equity securities of domestic and foreign issuers with market capitalizations of $90M to $900M with above average earnings or sales growth, retention of earnings and higher P/E ratios. Up to 15% of assets may be in illiquid securities. May use futures and options and foreign currency transactions. May leverage, hedge up to 20% of total assets and sell short up to 25% of total assets
Year organized: 1993
Dividends paid: Income - annually; Capital gains - annually
Portfolio turnover (1 yr) 26%
Largest holding: Tellabs (5.2%)
Management fee: 0.75%
12b-1 distribution fee: 0.50%
Expense ratio: 0.00% (10 months ending 10/31/94) (1.96% without waiver)

DREYFUS FOCUS FUND - SMALL COMPANY VALUE PORTFOLIO
(See first Dreyfus listing for data common to all Dreyfus funds)

Portfolio manager: Ernest Wiggins (1993)
Investment objective and policies: Capital growth. Invests primarily in equity securities of domestic

and foreign issuers with market capitalizations of $90M to $900M with low price to book ratios, lower P/E ratios and higher than average dividend rates. Up to 15% of assets may be in illiquid securities. May use futures and options and foreign currency transactions. May leverage, hedge up to 20% of total assets and sell short up to 25% of total assets
Year organized: 1993
Dividends paid: Income - annually; Capital gains - annually
Portfolio turnover (1 yr) 220%
Largest holding: QMS (2.0%)
Management fee: 0.75%
12b-1 distribution fee: 0.50%
Expense ratio: 0.00% (10 months ending 10/31/94) (2.07% without waiver)

THE DREYFUS FUND ◆
(See first Dreyfus listing for data common to all Dreyfus funds)

Portfolio manager: Wolodymr Wronskyj (1989)
Investment objective and policies: Long-term capital appreciation with income a secondary, though important, consideration. Fund leans toward full investment in common stocks of seasoned companies, but may invest in fixed-income securities. Up to 20% of assets may be in foreign securities. May use foreign currency exchange transactions.
Year organized: 1951
Ticker symbol: DREVX
Discount broker availability: *Schwab, *White, Waterhouse, *Fidelity, *Siebert
Dividends paid: Income - March, June, September, December; Capital gains - December
Portfolio turnover (3 yrs): 39%, 55%, 80%
Largest holding: Chrysler Corp. (2.8%)
Shareholder services: Waives initial minimum for automatic investment plan
Management fee: 0.65% first $1.5B to 0.55% over $2.5B
Expense ratio: 0.74% (year ending 12/31/93)

DREYFUS - GENERAL CALIFORNIA MUNICIPAL BOND FUND ◆
(See first Dreyfus listing for data common to all Dreyfus funds)

Newspaper listing: GnCA
Portfolio manager: A. Paul Disdier (1989)
Investment objective and policies: Maximum current income exempt from federal and California state income taxes consistent with preservation of capital. Invests at least 65% of assets in California municipal obligations rated Baa or better. Fund may use securities rated as low as C and invest in AMT securities without limit. May use financial futures and options thereon to hedge.
Year organized: 1989
Ticker symbol: GCABX
Discount broker availability: *Schwab, *White, *Waterhouse, *Fidelity, *Siebert
Qualified for sale in: AK, AZ, CA, CO, CT, DC, FL, HI, ID, IL, LA, MD, MA, MI, MN, MS, NE, NV, NJ, NM, NY, OH, OR, PA, TX, VA, WA, WY
Check redemptions: $500 minimum
Dividends paid: Income - declared daily, paid monthly; Capital gains - annually
Portfolio turnover (3 yrs): 30%, 30%, 24%
Management fee: 0.60%
12b-1 distribution fee: 0.25% (not currently imposed)
Expense ratio: 0.76% (year ending 9/30/94)

DREYFUS - GENERAL CALIFORNIA MUNICIPAL MONEY MARKET FUND ◆
(See first Dreyfus listing for data common to all Dreyfus funds)

Portfolio manager: Jill C. Shaffro (1993)
Investment objective and policies: Maximum income exempt from federal and California state income taxes consistent with preservation of capital and liquidity. Invests primarily in money market debt securities of the state of California and its

political subdivisions, authorities and corporations.
Year organized: 1986 (Formerly General California Tax-Exempt Money Market Fund)
Ticker symbol: GCAXX
Deadline for same day wire purchase: 12 NN
Qualified for sale in: AZ, CA, DC, HI, ID, NV, NJ, NM, NY, OR, UT, WA, WY
Check redemptions: $500 minimum
Confirmations mailed: After each purchase and each check, mail or wire redemption
Checks returned: Monthly
Periodic account statements mailed: Quarterly
Dividends paid: Income - declared daily, paid monthly
Management fee: 0.50%
12b-1 distribution fee: 0.005% with $100,000 maximum (not currently imposed)
Expense ratio: 0.33% (year ending 7/31/94) (0.61% without waiver)

DREYFUS - GENERAL GOVERNMENT SECURITIES MONEY MARKET FUND
(See first Dreyfus listing for data common to all Dreyfus funds)

Portfolio manager: Patricia A. Larkin (1989)
Investment objective and policies: Current income consistent with preservation of capital and liquidity. Invests in money market securities issued or guaranteed by the U.S. Government and repurchase agreements on such securities.
Year organized: 1983
Ticker symbol: GGSXX
Deadline for same day wire purchase: 12 NN
Check redemptions: $500 minimum
Confirmations mailed: After each purchase and each check, mail or wire redemption
Checks returned: Monthly
Periodic account statements mailed: Quarterly
Dividends paid: Income - declared daily, paid monthly
Management fee: 0.5%
12b-1 distribution fee: 0.20%
Expense ratio: 0.81% (year ending 1/31/94)

DREYFUS - GENERAL MONEY MARKET FUND
(See first Dreyfus listing for data common to all Dreyfus funds)

Portfolio manager: Patricia A. Larkin (1989)
Investment objective and policies: High current income consistent with preservation of capital and liquidity. Invests in money market securities issued or guaranteed by the U.S. Government, bank obligations, repurchase agreements and commercial paper. May invest in securities of foreign issuers.
Year organized: 1982
Ticker symbol: GMMXX
Deadline for same day wire purchase: 12 NN
Check redemptions: $500 minimum
Confirmations mailed: After each purchase and each check, mail or wire redemption
Checks returned: Monthly
Periodic account statements mailed: Quarterly
Dividends paid: Income - declared daily, paid monthly
Shareholder services: No electronic funds transfer
Management fee: 0.50%
12b-1 distribution fee: 0.20%
Expense ratio: 0.94% (year ending 1/31/94) (0.96% without waiver)

DREYFUS - GENERAL MUNICIPAL BOND FUND
(See first Dreyfus listing for data common to all Dreyfus funds)

Newspaper listing: GMBd
Portfolio manager: A. Paul Disdier (1988)
Investment objective and policies: Maximum current interest income consistent with the preservation of capital. Invests in municipal obligations, at least 65% of which must be rated Baa or better, and invest in AMT securities without limit. Up to 15% of assets may be in illiquid securities. May use futures and options.

Year organized: 1984 (Formerly General Tax-Exempt Bond Fund)
Ticker symbol: GMBDX
Discount broker availability: *Schwab, *White, *Waterhouse, *Fidelity, *Siebert
Dividends paid: Income - declared daily, paid monthly; Capital gains - February
Portfolio turnover (3 yrs): 59%, 65%, 38%
Management fee: 0.55%
12b-1 distribution fee: 0.20%
Expense ratio: 0.82% (year ending 2/28/94) (0.85% without waiver)

DREYFUS - GENERAL MUNICIPAL MONEY MARKET FUND ◆
(See first Dreyfus listing for data common to all Dreyfus funds)

Portfolio manager: Karen M. Hand (1987)
Investment objective and policies: Maximum income exempt from federal income tax consistent with preservation of capital and liquidity. Invests in municipal money market obligations.
Year organized: 1983 (formerly General Tax Exempt Money Market Fund)
Ticker symbol: GTMXX
Deadline for same day wire purchase: 12 NN
Check redemptions: $500 minimum
Confirmations mailed: After each purchase and each check, mail or wire redemption
Checks returned: Monthly
Periodic account statements mailed: Quarterly
Dividends paid: Income - declared daily, paid monthly
Shareholder services: No electronic funds transfer
Management fee: 0.50%
Expense ratio: 0.64% (year ending 11/30/94)

DREYFUS - GENERAL NEW YORK MUNICIPAL BOND FUND
(See first Dreyfus listing for data common to all Dreyfus funds)

Newspaper listing: GNY
Portfolio manager: Monica S. Wieboldt (1988)
Investment objective and policies: High current income exempt from federal, New York State and City income taxes consistent with preservation of capital. Invests at least 65% of assets in investment-grade New York municipal obligations and invest in AMT securities without limit. Up to 15% of assets may be in illiquid securities. May use futures and options.
Year organized: 1984 (formerly General New York Tax Exempt Intermediate Bond Fund)
Ticker symbol: GNYMX
Discount broker availability: *Schwab, *White, *Waterhouse, *Fidelity, *Siebert
Qualified for sale in: CT, DC, FL, HI, NV, NJ, NY, WY
Check redemptions: $500 minimum
Dividends paid: Income - declared daily, paid monthly
Portfolio turnover (3 yrs): 25%, 23%, 43%
Management fee: 0.60%
12b-1 distribution fee: 0.20%
Expense ratio: 0.76% (year ending 10/31/94) (0.88% without waiver)

DREYFUS - GENERAL NEW YORK MUNICIPAL MONEY MARKET FUND ◆
(See first Dreyfus listing for data common to all Dreyfus funds)

Portfolio manager: Karen M. Hand (1987)
Investment objective and policies: Maximum income exempt from federal, New York State and City income taxes consistent with preservation of capital and liquidity. Invests primarily in money market securities issued by New York State and City and its political subdivisions, authorities and corporations.
Year organized: 1984 (formerly Park Avenue New York Tax Exempt Money Market Fund and General New York Tax Exempt Money Market Fund)

Ticker symbol: GNMXX
Deadline for same day wire purchase: 12 NN
Qualified for sale in: CT, DC, HI, MA, NV, NH, NJ, NY, PA, RI, VT, WY
Check redemptions: $500 minimum
Confirmations mailed: After each purchase and each check, mail or wire redemption
Checks returned: Monthly
Periodic account statements mailed: Quarterly
Dividends paid: Income - declared daily, paid monthly
Management fee: 0.50%
12b-1 distribution fee: 0.005% with maximum of $100,000 (not currently imposed)
Expense ratio: 0.34% (year ending 11/30/94) (0.66% without waiver)

DREYFUS GLOBAL BOND FUND
(See first Dreyfus listing for data common to all Dreyfus funds)

Sub-adviser: M&G Investment Management, Ltd.
Portfolio manager: Paul D.A. Nix (1994)
Investment objective and policies: Total return - capital growth and income. Invests primarily in bonds and debentures of corporate, government and supranational issuers located throughout the world. Up to 35% of assets may be in junk bonds, 35% in securities of issuers in emerging markets and 15% in illiquid securities. May sell short up to 25% of total assets, leverage up to 1/3 of net assets, and use futures and options transactions on indices, securities and interest rates.
Year organized: 1994
Dividends paid: Income - declared and paid monthly; Capital gains - annually
Portfolio turnover (1 yr): 416%
Management fee: 0.70%
12b-1 distribution fee: 0.26%
Expense ratio: 0.00% (8 months ending 11/30/94) (2.49% without waiver)

DREYFUS GLOBAL GROWTH, L.P.
(See first Dreyfus listing for data common to all Dreyfus funds)

Portfolio manager: Kelly McDermott (1993)
Investment objective and policies: Capital growth. Invests primarily in common stocks of foreign and domestic issuers. May invest in common stocks of foreign companies which are not publicly traded in the U.S. and the debt securities of foreign governments. Up to 35% of assets may be in junk bonds and 15% in illiquid securities. Fund may sell short up to 25% of total assets, leverage up to 1/3 of net assets, and use futures and options transactions on indices, securities and interest rates.
Year organized: 1987 (name changed from Dreyfus Strategic World Investing, L.P. on 1/1/94)
Ticker symbol: DSWIX
Minimum purchase: Subsequent: $500
Retirement accounts: Not offered
Sales charges: 3%, reduced for volume purchases
Number of switches permitted: 2 outbound per year
Dividends paid: Income - December; Capital gains - December
Portfolio turnover (3 yrs): 187%, 439%, 420%
Largest holding: Mitsubishi Heavy Industries (1.8%)
Management fee: 0.75%
12b-1 distribution fee: 0.28%
Expense ratio: 1.50% (year ending 12/31/93)

DREYFUS GNMA FUND
(See first Dreyfus listing for data common to all Dreyfus funds)

Newspaper listing: GNM
Portfolio manager: Garitt Kono (1993)
Investment objective and policies: High current income consistent with preservation of capital. Invests at least 65% of assets in GNMA certificates backed by the full faith and credit of the United States. May purchase other securities issued or guaranteed by the U.S. Government, its agencies or

instrumentalities. May write covered calls on 20% of assets.
Year organized: 1985
Ticker symbol: DRGMX
Discount broker availability: *Schwab, *White, *Waterhouse, *Fidelity, *Siebert
Check redemptions: $500 minimum
Dividends paid: Income - declared and paid monthly; Capital gains - annually
Portfolio turnover (3 yrs): 211%, 156%, 61%
Management fee: 0.60%
12b-1 distribution fee: 0.20%
Expense ratio: 0.95% (year ending 4/30/94)

DREYFUS GROWTH AND INCOME FUND ◆
(See first Dreyfus listing for data common to all Dreyfus funds)

Portfolio manager: Richard B. Hoey (1992)
Investment objective and policies: Long-term capital growth, current income and growth of income, consistent with reasonable investment risk. Invests in equity and investment-grade debt securities and money market instruments of domestic and foreign issuers. Equity securities include common stocks, preferred stocks and convertible securities, as well as ADRs, EDRs and warrants. Up to 15% of assets may be in illiquid securities. Fund may leverage, sell short, use futures and options and take advantage of international currency fluctuations.
Year organized: 1991
Ticker symbol: DGRIX
Discount broker availability: *Schwab, *White, Waterhouse, *Fidelity, *Siebert
Dividends paid: Income - quarterly; Capital gains - annually
Portfolio turnover (3 yrs): 97%, 85%, 127%
Largest holding: AT&T (3.2%)
Management fee: 0.75%
Expense ratio: 1.14% (year ending 10/31/94)

DREYFUS GROWTH OPPORTUNITY FUND ◆
(See first Dreyfus listing for data common to all Dreyfus funds)

Portfolio manager: Ernest Wiggins (1994)
Investment objective and policies: Long-term capital growth consistent with preservation of capital. Invests primarily in common stocks of small companies considered undervalued. Up to 15% of assets may be in illiquid securities and 25% in securities of foreign governments and companies not publicly traded in the U.S. May write covered call options on up to 20% of assets and use foreign currency exchange contracts.
Year organized: 1972 (formerly Dreyfus Number Nine)
Ticker symbol: DREQX
Discount broker availability: *Schwab, *White, Waterhouse, *Fidelity, *Siebert
Dividends paid: Income - annually; Capital gains - annually
Portfolio turnover (3 yrs): 195%, 90%, 57%
Largest holding: Schlumberger (3.6%)
Management fee: 0.75%
Expense ratio: 1.09% (year ending 2/28/94)

DREYFUS INSURED MUNICIPAL BOND FUND
(See first Dreyfus listing for data common to all Dreyfus funds)

Portfolio manager: L. Lawrence Troutman (1985)
Investment objective and policies: High current income exempt from federal income taxes consistent with preservation of capital. Invests primarily in municipal obligations that are insured as to timely payment of principal and interest. May invest in AMT securities without limit and have up to 15% of assets in illiquid securities.
Year organized: 1985 (formerly Dreyfus Insured Tax Exempt Bond Fund)
Ticker symbol: DTBDX
Discount broker availability: *Schwab, *White,

*Waterhouse, *Fidelity, *Siebert
Check redemptions: $500 minimum
Dividends paid: Income - declared daily, paid monthly; Capital gains - annually
Portfolio turnover (3 yrs): 35%, 81%, 51%
Management fee: 0.60%
12b-1 distribution fee: 0.20%
Expense ratio: 0.93% (year ending 4/30/94)

DREYFUS INTERMEDIATE MUNICIPAL BOND FUND ◆
(See first Dreyfus listing for data common to all Dreyfus funds)

Portfolio manager: Monica S. Wieboldt (1985)
Investment objective and policies: High current income exempt from federal income taxes consistent with preservation of capital. Invests at least 80% of assets in high quality municipal obligations (rated A or better) with a weighted average maturity of 3 to 10 years. May invest in AMT securities without limit and have up to 15% of assets in illiquid securities.
Year organized: 1983 (formerly Dreyfus Intermediate Tax Exempt Bond Fund)
Ticker symbol: DITEX
Discount broker availability: *Schwab, *White, Waterhouse, *Fidelity, *Siebert
Check redemptions: $500 minimum
Dividends paid: Income - declared daily, paid monthly; Capital gains - September
Portfolio turnover (3 yrs): 36%, 60%, 48%
Management fee: 0.60%
Expense ratio: 0.70% (year ending 5/31/94)

DREYFUS INTERNATIONAL EQUITY FUND
(See first Dreyfus listing for data common to all Dreyfus funds)

Sub-adviser: M&G Investment Management Ltd.
Portfolio manager: Paul D.A. Nix (1993)
Investment objective and policies: Long-term capital growth. Normally invests at least 65% of assets in equity securities - common stocks, convertible securities and preferred stocks - of non-US issuers located throughout the world. May invest in debt securities of foreign issuers believed to offer opportunities for capital growth. Up to 15% of assets may be in illiquid securities. May write options on up to 20% of assets, use foreign currency exchange contracts, and use stock index futures and interest rate futures contracts and options thereon.
Year organized: 1993
Ticker symbol: DITFX
Discount broker availability: Schwab, *White, *Fidelity, *Siebert
Dividends paid: Income - annually; Capital gains - annually
Portfolio turnover (1 yr): 51%
Largest holding: South African Breweries (1.3%)
Management fee: 0.75%
12b-1 distribution fee: 0.50%
Expense ratio: 1.71% (11 months ending 5/31/94) (1.87% without waiver)

DREYFUS INVESTORS GNMA FUND, L.P. ◆
(See first Dreyfus listing for data common to all Dreyfus funds)

Portfolio manager: Garitt Kono (1993)
Investment objective and policies: High current income consistent with preservation of capital. Invests at least 65% of assets in GNMA certificates backed by the full faith and credit of the United States. May purchase CMOs and other securities issued or guaranteed by the U.S. Government, its agencies or instrumentalities. Fund may leverage and use futures and options. May write covered calls on 20% of assets and sell short on 15% of assets.
Year organized: 1987 (formerly Dreyfus Foreign Investors GNMA Fund, L.P. Name and objectives changed on 8/23/91.)
Ticker symbol: DIGFX

Check redemptions: $500 minimum
Dividends paid: Income - declared daily, paid monthly; Capital gains - annually
Portfolio turnover (3 yrs): 34%, 31%, 40%
Management fee: 0.60%
Expense ratio: 0.00% (year ending 12/31/93) (1.28% without waiver)

DREYFUS LIQUID ASSETS ◆
(See first Dreyfus listing for data common to all Dreyfus funds)

Portfolio manager: Patricia A. Larkin (1995)
Investment objective and policies: High current income consistent with preservation of capital. Invests in money market obligations. At least 25% of assets will be in bank time deposits, CDs and bankers acceptances.
Year organized: 1974
Ticker symbol: DLAXX
Check redemptions: $500 minimum
Confirmations mailed: After each purchase and each check, mail or wire redemption
Checks returned: Monthly
Periodic account statements mailed: Quarterly
Dividends paid: Income - declared and paid daily
Management fee: 0.5% first $1.5B to 0.45% over $2.5B
Expense ratio: 0.77% (year ending 12/31/93)

DREYFUS MASSACHUSETTS INTERMEDIATE MUNICIPAL BOND FUND ◆
(See first Dreyfus listing for data common to all Dreyfus funds)

Portfolio manager: L. Lawrence Troutman (1992)
Investment objective and policies: High current income exempt from federal and Massachusetts income taxes consistent with preservation of capital. Invests in debt securities of the state of Massachusetts, its political subdivisions, authorities and corporations, with at least 80% rated BBB or better, with weighted average maturity of 3 to 10 years. May invest in AMT securities without limit and have up to 15% of assets in illiquid securities. May use futures and options and sell short.
Year organized: 1992
Ticker symbol: DMAIX
Discount broker availability: *Schwab, *White
Qualified for sale in: DC, FL, HI, MA, NH, NJ, NY, RI, WY
Check redemptions: $500 minimum
Dividends paid: Income - declared daily, paid monthly; Capital gains - annually
Portfolio turnover (2 yrs): 5%, 10%
Management fee: 0.60%
Expense ratio: 0.06% (year ending 3/31/94) (0.98% without waiver)

DREYFUS MASSACHUSETTS MUNICIPAL MONEY MARKET FUND ◆
(See first Dreyfus listing for data common to all Dreyfus funds)

Portfolio manager: Jill C. Shaffro (1993)
Investment objective and policies: High current income exempt from federal and Massachusetts income taxes, consistent with preservation of capital and liquidity. Invests primarily in Massachusetts municipal money market instruments.
Year organized: 1991
Ticker symbol: DMAXX
Deadline for same day wire purchase: 12 NN
Qualified for sale in: DC, FL, HI, MA, NJ, NY, WY
Check redemptions: $500 minimum
Confirmations mailed: After each purchase and each check, mail or wire redemption
Checks returned: Monthly
Periodic account statements mailed: Quarterly
Dividends paid: Income - declared daily, paid monthly; Capital gains - annually
Management fee: 0.50%
Expense ratio: 0.28% (year ending 1/31/94) (0.81% without waiver)

DREYFUS MASSACHUSETTS TAX EXEMPT BOND FUND ◆
(See first Dreyfus listing for data common to all Dreyfus funds)

Portfolio manager: L. Lawrence Troutman (1986)
Investment objective and policies: High current income exempt from federal and Massachusetts income taxes consistent with preservation of capital. Invests primarily in the debt securities of the Commonwealth of Massachusetts and its political subdivisions, rated Baa or better. May invest in AMT securities without limit and have up to 15% of assets in illiquid securities.
Year organized: 1985
Ticker symbol: DMEBX
Discount broker availability: *Schwab, *White, Waterhouse, *Fidelity, *Siebert
Qualified for sale in: AL, AR, AZ, CA, CT, DE, DC, FL, HI, IN, KY, ME, MD, MA, MN, NV, NH, NJ, NY, NC, OH, OR, PA, RI, SC, TN, TX, VT, VA, WY
Check redemptions: $500 minimum
Dividends paid: Income - declared daily, paid monthly; Capital gains - annually
Portfolio turnover (3 yrs): 30%, 85%, 68%
Management fee: 0.60%
Expense ratio: 0.80% (year ending 5/31/94)

DREYFUS MICHIGAN MUNICIPAL MONEY MARKET FUND ◆
(See first Dreyfus listing for data common to all Dreyfus funds)

Portfolio manager: Jill C. Shaffro (1991)
Investment objective and policies: High current income exempt from federal and Michigan income taxes consistent with preservation of capital and liquidity. Invests in municipal money market instruments, principally of State of Michigan and its subdivisions.
Year organized: 1990
Ticker symbol: DRIXX
Deadline for same day wire purchase: 12 NN
Qualified for sale in: DC, FL, HI, MI, NJ, NY, WY
Check redemptions: $500 minimum
Confirmations mailed: After each purchase and each check, mail or wire redemption
Checks returned: Monthly
Periodic account statements mailed: Quarterly
Dividends paid: Income - declared daily, paid monthly; Capital gains - annually
Management fee: 0.50%
Expense ratio: 0.53% (year ending 9/30/94) (0.73% without waiver)

DREYFUS MONEY MARKET INSTRUMENTS - GOVERNMENT SECURITIES SERIES ◆
(See first Dreyfus listing for data common to all Dreyfus funds)

Portfolio manager: Patricia A. Larkin (1994)
Investment objective and policies: High current income consistent with the preservation of capital and liquidity. Invests only in short-term securities issued or guaranteed by the U.S. Government.
Year organized: 1979
Ticker symbol: DMMXX
Deadline for same day wire purchase: 12 NN
Check redemptions: $500 minimum
Confirmations mailed: After each purchase and each check, mail or wire redemption
Checks returned: Monthly
Periodic account statements mailed: Quarterly
Dividends paid: Income - declared daily, paid monthly
Management fee: 0.5%
Expense ratio: 0.80% (year ending 12/31/93)

DREYFUS MONEY MARKET INSTRUMENTS - MONEY MARKET SERIES ◆
(See first Dreyfus listing for data common to all Dreyfus funds)

Portfolio manager: Patricia A. Larkin (1994)
Investment objective and policies: High current

income consistent with the preservation of capital and liquidity. Invests in short-term money market instruments.
Year organized: 1975
Ticker symbol: DMIXX
Minimum purchase: Initial: $50,000
Deadline for same day wire purchase: 12 NN
Check redemptions: $500 minimum
Confirmations mailed: After each purchase and each check, mail or wire redemption
Checks returned: Monthly
Periodic account statements mailed: Quarterly
Dividends paid: Income - declared daily, paid monthly
Management fee: 0.5%
Expense ratio: 0.83% (year ending 12/31/93)

DREYFUS MUNICIPAL BOND FUND ◆
(See first Dreyfus listing for data common to all Dreyfus funds)

Portfolio manager: Richard Moynihan (1976)
Investment objective and policies: High current income exempt from federal income tax consistent with preservation of capital. Invests at least 75% of assets in municipal bonds rated A or better, but may invest in securities rated as low as C. May invest in AMT securities without limit and have up to 15% of assets in illiquid securities.
Year organized: 1976 (name changed from Dreyfus Tax-Exempt Bond Fund on 4/20/92)
Ticker symbol: DRTAX
Discount broker availability: *Schwab, Waterhouse, *Fidelity, *Siebert
Check redemptions: $500 minimum
Dividends paid: Income - declared daily, paid monthly; Capital gains - September
Portfolio turnover (3 yrs): 36%, 45%, 68%
Management fee: 0.6%
Expense ratio: 0.68% (year ending 8/31/94)

DREYFUS MUNICIPAL MONEY MARKET FUND ◆
(See first Dreyfus listing for data common to all Dreyfus funds)

Portfolio manager: Karen M. Hand (1987)
Investment objective and policies: High current income exempt from federal taxes consistent with preservation of capital and liquidity. Invests in high quality short-term municipal money market obligations.
Year organized: 1980 (name changed from Dreyfus Tax Exempt Money Market Fund, Inc. on 5/29/91)
Ticker symbol: DTEXX
Deadline for same day wire purchase: 12 NN
Check redemptions $500 minimum
Confirmations mailed: After each purchase and each check, mail or wire redemption
Checks returned: Monthly
Periodic account statements mailed: Quarterly
Dividends paid: Income - declared daily, paid monthly
Management fee: 0.50%
Expense ratio: 0.62% (year ending 5/31/94)

DREYFUS NEW JERSEY INTERMEDIATE MUNICIPAL BOND FUND ◆
(See first Dreyfus listing for data common to all Dreyfus funds)

Portfolio manager: Stephen Kris (1992)
Investment objective and policies: High current income exempt from federal and New Jersey income taxes consistent with preservation of capital. Invests in debt securities of the state of New Jersey, its political subdivisions, authorities and corporations, with at least 80% rated BBB or better and a weighted average maturity of 3 to 10 years. May invest in AMT securities without limit and have up to 15% of assets in illiquid securities. May use futures and options and sell short against the box.
Year organized: 1992
Ticker symbol: DNJIX

Discount broker availability: *Schwab, *White, Waterhouse, *Fidelity, *Siebert
Qualified for sale in: DC, FL, HI, NJ, NY, WY
Check redemptions: $500 minimum
Dividends paid: Income - declared daily, paid monthly; Capital gains - annually
Portfolio turnover (2 yrs): 6%, 33%
Management fee: 0.60%
Expense ratio: 0.06% (year ending 3/31/94) (0.89% without waiver)

DREYFUS NEW JERSEY MUNICIPAL BOND FUND
(See first Dreyfus listing for data common to all Dreyfus funds)

Newspaper listing: NJ Mun
Portfolio manager: Samuel Weinstock (1987)
Investment objective and policies: High current income exempt from federal and New Jersey income taxes, consistent with preservation of capital. Invests in municipal bonds, with at least 80% rated BBB or better, principally of State of New Jersey and its subdivisions with average weighted maturity of more than 10 years. May invest in AMT securities without limit and have up to 15% of assets in illiquid securities.
Year organized: 1987 (originally Dreyfus New Jersey Tax Exempt Bond Fund, L.P., then Dreyfus New Jersey Tax Exempt Bond Fund, Inc.)
Ticker symbol: DRNJX
Discount broker availability: *Schwab, *White, *Waterhouse, *Fidelity, *Siebert
Qualified for sale in: CT, DC, FL, HI, MA, NH, NJ, NY, PA, RI, VT, WY
Check redemptions: $500 minimum
Dividends paid: Income - declared daily, paid monthly; Capital gains - December
Portfolio turnover (3 yrs): 6%, 34%, 23%
Management fee: 0.60%
12b-1 distribution fee: 0.25%
Expense ratio: 0.72% (year ending 12/31/93) (0.97% without waiver)

DREYFUS NEW JERSEY MUNICIPAL MONEY MARKET FUND ◆
(See first Dreyfus listing for data common to all Dreyfus funds)

Portfolio manager: Karen M. Hand (1988)
Investment objective and policies: High current income exempt from federal and New Jersey income taxes consistent with preservation of capital and liquidity. Invests in municipal money market instruments, principally of State of New Jersey and its subdivisions.
Year organized: 1988 (formerly Dreyfus New Jersey Tax Exempt Money Market Fund)
Ticker symbol: DNJXX
Deadline for same day wire purchase: 12 NN
Qualified for sale in: CT, DC, FL, HI, MA, NH, NJ, NY, PA, RI, VT, WY
Check redemptions: $500 minimum
Confirmations mailed: After each purchase and each check, mail or wire redemption
Checks returned: Monthly
Periodic account statements mailed: Quarterly
Dividends paid: Income - declared daily, paid monthly; Capital gains - September
Management fee: 0.50%
Expense ratio: 0.35% (year ending 1/31/94) (0.65% without waiver)

DREYFUS NEW LEADERS FUND
(See first Dreyfus listing for data common to all Dreyfus funds)

Portfolio manager: Thomas A. Frank (1985)
Investment objective and policies: Maximum capital appreciation. Invests primarily in common stocks of domestic and foreign companies with market capitalizations under $750M and significant growth potential. Companies will have new or innovative products, services or processes. Fund also looks for economic or political changes and corporate restructurings, mergers and acquisitions.

Up to 25% of assets may be in foreign securities. May use currency exchange contracts, futures and options, sell short and hedge on up to 20% of total assets.
Year organized: 1985
Ticker symbol: DNLDX
Redemption fee: 1% for shares held less than 6 months
Discount broker availability: *Schwab, *White, Waterhouse, Fidelity, Siebert
Dividends paid: Income - annually; Capital gains - annually
Portfolio turnover (3 yrs): 128%, 119%, 108%
Largest holding: NovaCare (1.6%)
Shareholder services: Waives initial minimum for automatic investment plan
Management fee: 0.75%
12b-1 distribution fee: 0.26%
Expense ratio: 1.22% (year ending 12/31/93) (1.26% without waiver)

DREYFUS NEW YORK INSURED TAX EXEMPT BOND FUND
(See first Dreyfus listing for data common to all Dreyfus funds)

Newspaper listing: NYIn
Portfolio manager: L. Lawrence Troutman (1986)
Investment objective and policies: High current income exempt from federal, New York State and City income taxes, consistent with preservation of capital. Invests primarily in New York municipal obligations rated Baa or higher that are insured as to the timely payment of principal and interest. Up to 20% of assets may be in AMT securities and 15% in illiquid securities.
Year organized: 1986
Ticker symbol: DNYBX
Discount broker availability: *Schwab, *White, *Waterhouse, *Fidelity, *Siebert
Qualified for sale in: CT, DC, FL, HI, MA, MO, NV, NH, NJ, NY, PA, RI, VT, WY
Check redemptions: $500 minimum
Dividends paid: Income - declared daily, paid monthly; Capital gains - annually
Portfolio turnover (3 yrs): 20%, 16%, 16%
Management fee: 0.60%
12b-1 distribution fee: 0.26%
Expense Ratio: 0.96% (year ending 12/31/93) (0.98% without waiver)

DREYFUS NEW YORK TAX EXEMPT BOND FUND ◆
(See first Dreyfus listing for data common to all Dreyfus funds)

Newspaper listing: NY Tax
Portfolio manager: Monica S. Wieboldt (1985)
Investment objective and policies: High current income exempt from federal and New York State and City income taxes consistent with preservation of capital. Invests at least 80% of assets in municipal bonds, principally of New York State and its subdivisions rated Baa or better. Up to 20% of assets may be in AMT securities and 15% in illiquid securities. May use futures and options and sell short against the box.
Year organized: 1983
Ticker symbol: DRNYX
Discount broker availability: *Schwab, *White, Waterhouse, *Fidelity, *Siebert
Check redemptions: $500 minimum
Dividends paid: Income - declared daily, paid monthly; Capital gains - September
Portfolio turnover (3 yrs): 36%, 51%, 40%
Management fee: 0.6%
Expense ratio: 0.71% (year ending 5/31/94)

DREYFUS NEW YORK TAX EXEMPT INTERMEDIATE BOND FUND
(See first Dreyfus listing for data common to all Dreyfus funds)

Newspaper listing: NYTE
Portfolio manager: Monica S. Wieboldt (1987)
Investment objective and policies: High current

income exempt from federal and New York State and City income taxes consistent with preservation of capital. Invests at least 80% of assets in municipal bonds, principally of New York State and its subdivisions, rated Baa or better with a weighted average maturity of 3 to 10 years. Up to 20% of assets may be in AMT securities and 15% in illiquid securities. May use futures and options and sell short against the box.
Year organized: 1987
Ticker symbol: DRNIX
Discount broker availability: *Schwab, *White, *Waterhouse, *Fidelity, *Siebert
Qualified for sale in: CT, DC, FL, HI, MA, NV, NH, NJ, NY, PA, RI, VT, WY
Check redemptions: $500 minimum
Dividends paid: Income - declared daily, paid monthly; Capital gains - annually
Portfolio turnover (3 yrs): 20%, 17%, 29%
Management fee: 0.60%
12b-1 distribution fee: 0.25%
Expense ratio: 0.89% (year ending 5/31/94) (0.97% without waiver)

DREYFUS NEW YORK TAX EXEMPT MONEY MARKET FUND ◆
(See first Dreyfus listing for data common to all Dreyfus funds)

Portfolio manager: Karen M. Hand (1987)
Investment objective and policies: Current income exempt from federal, New York State, and New York City income taxes consistent with the preservation of capital and liquidity. Invests in short-term money market securities issued by the State of New York and its subdivisions.
Year organized: 1987
Ticker symbol: DNYXX
Deadline for same day wire purchase: 12 NN
Qualified for sale in: CT, DC, FL, HI, MA, NH, NJ, NY, NV, PA, RI, VT, WY
Check redemptions: $500 minimum
Confirmations mailed: After each purchase and each check, mail or wire redemption
Checks returned: Monthly
Periodic account statements mailed: Quarterly
Dividends paid: Income - declared daily, paid monthly
Management fee: 0.5%
12b-1 distribution fee: Yes (not currently imposed)
Expense ratio: 0.68% (year ending 5/31/94)

DREYFUS OHIO MUNICIPAL MONEY MARKET FUND ◆
(See first Dreyfus listing for data common to all Dreyfus funds)

Portfolio manager: Karen M. Hand (1991)
Investment objective and policies: High current income exempt from federal and Ohio income taxes, consistent with preservation of capital and liquidity. Invests in municipal money market instruments, principally of the State of Ohio and its subdivisions.
Year organized: 1991
Ticker symbol: DOHXX
Deadline for same day wire purchase: 12 NN
Qualified for sale in: DC, FL, HI, NJ, NY, OH, WY
Check redemptions: $500 minimum
Confirmations mailed: After each purchase and each check, mail or wire redemption
Checks returned: Monthly
Periodic account statements mailed: Quarterly
Dividends paid: Income - declared daily, paid monthly
Management fee: 0.50%
Expense ratio: 0.28% (year ending 11/30/94) (0.76% without waiver)

DREYFUS 100% U.S. TREASURY INTERMEDIATE TERM FUND ◆
(See first Dreyfus listing for data common to all Dreyfus funds)

Newspaper listing: UST Int
Portfolio manager: Gerald E. Thunelius (1994)
Investment objective and policies: High current

income exempt from state and local income taxes. Invests in securities issued and guaranteed by the U.S. Government and its agencies with weighted average maturity of 3 to 7 years.
Year organized: 1987 (name changed from Dreyfus U.S. Government Intermediate Securities, L.P. on 11/1/91)
Ticker symbol: DRGIX
Check redemptions: $500 minimum
Dividends paid: Income - declared daily, paid monthly; Capital gains - annually
Portfolio turnover (3 yrs): 334%, 116%, 22%
Management fee: 0.60%
Expense ratio: 0.73% (year ending 12/31/93) (0.86% without waiver)

DREYFUS 100% U.S. TREASURY LONG TERM FUND ◆
(See first Dreyfus listing for data common to all Dreyfus funds)

Newspaper listing: UST Lng
Portfolio manager: Gerald E. Thunelius (1994)
Investment objective and policies: High current income exempt from state and local income taxes. Invests in obligations of the U.S. Government and its agencies and instrumentalities with weighted average maturity greater than 10 years.
Year organized: 1987 (named changed from Dreyfus U.S. Government Bond Fund, L.P. on 11/1/91)
Ticker symbol: DRGBX
Discount broker availability: *White, Fidelity, Siebert
Check redemptions: $500 minimum
Dividends paid: Income - declared daily, paid monthly; Capital gains - annually
Portfolio turnover (3 yrs): 412%, 97%, 21%
Management fee: 0.60%
Expense ratio: 0.78% (year ending 12/31/93) (0.87% without waivers)

DREYFUS 100% U.S. TREASURY MONEY MARKET FUND ◆
(See first Dreyfus listing for data common to all Dreyfus funds)

Portfolio manager: Patricia A. Larkin (1994)
Investment objective and policies: High current income exempt from state and local income taxes consistent with preservation of capital and maintenance of liquidity. Invests in U.S. Government money market obligations.
Year organized: 1987 (formerly U.S. Guaranteed Money Market Account, LP)
Ticker symbol: DUSXX
Wire orders accepted: Subsequent only
Check redemptions: $500 minimum
Confirmations mailed: After each purchase and each check, mail or wire redemption
Checks returned: Monthly
Periodic account statements mailed: Quarterly
Dividends paid: Income - declared daily, paid monthly
Management fee: 0.5%
Expense ratio: 0.65% (year ending 12/31/93) (0.67% without waiver)

DREYFUS 100% U.S. TREASURY SHORT TERM FUND ◆
(See first Dreyfus listing for data common to all Dreyfus funds)

Newspaper listing: UST Sh
Portfolio manager: Gerald E. Thunelius (1994)
Investment objective and policies: High current income exempt from state and local income taxes consistent with preservation of capital. Invests only in U.S. Treasury securities with weighted average maturity of 2 to 3 years.
Year organized: 1987 (objectives and name changed from Dreyfus Foreign Investors U.S. Government Bond Fund, L.P. on 10/2/91)
Ticker symbol: DRTSX

Discount broker availability: *White, Fidelity, Siebert
Check redemptions: $500 minimum
Dividends paid: Income - declared daily, paid monthly; Capital gains - annually
Portfolio turnover (3 yrs): 323%, 138%, 60%
Management fee: 0.6%
Expense ratio: 0.11% (year ending 12/31/93) (0.96% without waiver)

DREYFUS PENNSYLVANIA INTERMEDIATE MUNICIPAL BOND FUND ◆
(See first Dreyfus listing for data common to all Dreyfus funds)

Portfolio manager: Monica S. Wieboldt (1993)
Investment objective and policies: High current income exempt from federal and Pennsylvania income taxes consistent with preservation of capital. Invests in debt securities of the state of Pennsylvania, its political subdivisions, authorities and corporations, with at least 80% rated BBB or better and a weighted average maturity of 3 to 10 years. May invest in AMT securities without limit and have up to 15% of assets in illiquid securities. May use futures and options and sell short against the box.
Year organized: 1993
Ticker symbol: DPABX
Qualified for sale in: DC, FL, HI, NJ, NY, OH, PA, WY
Check redemptions: $500 minimum
Dividends paid: Income - declared daily, paid monthly; Capital gains - annually
Portfolio turnover (1 yr): 20%
Management fee: 0.60%
Expense ratio: 0.00% (11 months ending 11/30/94) (1.39% without waiver)

DREYFUS PENNSYLVANIA MUNICIPAL MONEY MARKET FUND ◆
(See first Dreyfus listing for data common to all Dreyfus funds)

Portfolio manager: Jill C. Shaffro (1991)
Investment objective and policies: High current income exempt from federal and Pennsylvania income taxes consistent with preservation of capital and liquidity. Invests in municipal money market instruments, principally of the State of Pennsylvania and its subdivisions.
Year organized: 1990
Ticker symbol: DPAXX
Deadline for same day wire purchase: 12 NN
Qualified for sale in: DC, FL, HI, NJ, NY, PA, WY
Check redemptions: $500 minimum
Confirmations mailed: After each purchase and each check, mail or wire redemption
Checks returned: Monthly
Periodic account statements mailed: Quarterly
Dividends paid: Income - declared daily, paid monthly
Management fee: 0.50%
Expense ratio: 0.20% (year ending 9/30/94) (0.67% without waiver)

DREYFUS PEOPLES INDEX FUND ◆
(See first Dreyfus listing for data common to all Dreyfus funds)

Portfolio manager: Wells Fargo Nikko Investment Advisors
Custodian: Wells Fargo Institutional Trust Co., N.A.
Investment objective and policies: Investment results that correspond to the price and yield performance of the common stocks that comprise the S&P 500. Invests in a representative mix of S&P 500 stocks to achieve income and capital gains on a par with the S&P 500 composite average. Fund may use stock index futures.
Year organized: 1990
Ticker symbol: PEOPX

Discount broker availability: *Schwab, *White, Waterhouse
Redemption fee: 1% for shares held less than 6 months, payable to the fund
Dividends paid: Income - annually; Capital gains - annually
Portfolio turnover (3 yrs): 19%, 4%, 3%
Largest holding: General Electric Co. (2.4%)
Index management fee: 0.10%
Administration fee: 0.20%
Transfer agency fee: $10 per year, paid quarterly
Expense ratio: 0.61% (year ending 10/31/94) (0.64% without waiver)

DREYFUS PEOPLES S&P MIDCAP INDEX FUND ◆
(See first Dreyfus listing for data common to all Dreyfus funds)

Adviser: Woodbridge Capital Management, Inc.
Custodian: Comerica Bank of Detroit, N.A.
Investment objective and policies: Provide investment results that correspond to the price and yield performance of common stocks of medium-size domestic companies that comprise the S&P MidCap 400 Index. Invests in a representative mix of S&P MidCap 400 stocks to achieve income and capital gains on a par with the average. Fund may use stock index futures. Reclassified from a growth and income fund to simply growth.
Year organized: 1991
Ticker symbol: PESPX
Discount broker availability: *Schwab, *White
Redemption fee: 1% for shares held less than 6 months, payable to the fund
Dividends paid: Income - annually; Capital gains - annually
Portfolio turnover (3 yrs): 20%, 17%, 16%
Largest holding: General Motors Class E (1.9%)
Index management fee: 0.10%
Administration fee: 0.30%
Transfer agency fee: $10 per year, paid quarterly
Expense ratio: 0.40% (year ending 10/31/94) (0.83% without waiver)

DREYFUS SHORT-INTERMEDIATE GOVERNMENT FUND ◆
(See first Dreyfus listing for data common to all Dreyfus funds)

Portfolio manager: Gerald E. Thunelius (1994)
Investment objective and policies: High current income consistent with preservation of capital. Invests in securities issued or guaranteed by the U.S. Government or its agencies or instrumentalities with maximum remaining individual maturities of three and one-half years.
Year organized: 1987
Ticker symbol: DSIGX
Discount broker availability: *Schwab, *White, Waterhouse, *Fidelity, *Siebert
Check redemptions: $500 minimum
Dividends paid: Income - declared daily, paid monthly; Capital gains - annually
Portfolio turnover (3 yrs): 696%, 317%, 226%
Management fee: 0.5%
Expense ratio: 0.47% (year ending 11/30/94) (0.77% without waiver)

DREYFUS SHORT-INTERMEDIATE MUNICIPAL BOND FUND ◆
(See first Dreyfus listing for data common to all Dreyfus funds)

Portfolio manager: Samuel Weinstock (1987)
Investment objective and policies: High current income exempt from federal income tax. Invests primarily in municipal obligations with a weighted average maturity of 2 to 3 years. May invest in AMT securities without limit and have up to 15% of assets in illiquid securities. Fund may buy options up to 5% of assets, write options on up to 20% of portfolio assets and use municipal bond index futures and options thereon.
Year organized: 1987 (name changed from Short-Intermediate Tax Exempt Bond Fund in 1993)

Ticker symbol: DSIBX
Discount broker availability: *Schwab, *White, Waterhouse, *Fidelity, *Siebert
Check redemptions: $500 minimum
Dividends paid: Income - declared daily, paid monthly; Capital gains - annually
Portfolio turnover (3 yrs): 35%, 32%, 64%
Management fee: 0.50%
12b-1 distribution fee: 0.10%
Expense ratio: 0.74% (year ending 3/31/94)

DREYFUS SHORT-TERM
INCOME FUND
(See first Dreyfus listing for data common to all Dreyfus funds)

Portfolio manager: Gerald E. Thunelius (1994)
Investment objective and policies: High current income consistent with preservation of capital. Invests primarily in investment-grade debt securities of domestic and foreign issuers with weighted average maturity of 3 years or less. May invest in bonds, debentures, notes, mortgage-related securities, asset-backed securities and municipal obligations. Up to 35% of assets may be in junk bonds, 30% in securities of foreign issuers and 15% in illiquid securities. May leverage.
Year organized: 1992
Ticker symbol: DSTIX
Discount broker availability: *Schwab, *White, *Fidelity, *Siebert
Check redemptions: $500 minimum
Dividends paid: Income - declared daily, paid monthly; Capital gains - annually
Portfolio turnover (2 yrs): 75%, 55%
Management fee: 0.5%
12b-1 distribution fee: 0.24%
Expense ratio: 0.24% (year ending 7/31/94) (0.95% without waiver)

DREYFUS STRATEGIC GROWTH, L.P.
(See first Dreyfus listing for data common to all Dreyfus funds)

Portfolio manager: Robert Jermain (1994)
Investment objective and policies: Maximum capital growth. Invests primarily in common stocks. May invest up to 30% of assets in foreign securities and use foreign currency exchange contracts, futures and options thereon. Fund may use debt securities rated as low as Caa and zero coupon U.S. Treasuries, and invest up to 15% of assets in illiquid securities. May sell short up to 25% of total assets, leverage up to 1/3 of net assets, and use futures and options transactions on indices, securities and interest rates.
Year organized: 1987 (name changed from Dreyfus Strategic Aggressive Investing on 6/26/92)
Ticker symbol: DSAIX
Minimum purchase: Subsequent: $500
Retirement accounts: Not offered
Sales charges: 3%, reduced for volume purchases
Number of switches permitted: 2 outbound per year
Dividends paid: Income - December; Capital gains - December
Portfolio turnover (3 yrs): 301%, 209%, 95%
Largest holding: Granite Capital, L.P. (2.5%)
Management fee: 0.75%
12b-1 distribution fee: 0.32%
Expense ratio: 1.62% (year ending 12/31/93) (1.68% without waiver)

DREYFUS THIRD
CENTURY FUND ◆
(See first Dreyfus listing for data common to all Dreyfus funds)

Newspaper listing: Thrd C
Sub-adviser: NCM Capital Management, Inc.
Portfolio managers: Maceo K. Sloan (1994), Diane M. Coffey (1990)
Investment objective and policies: Capital growth with current income secondary. Invests in equity securities of companies which not only meet tradi-

tional investment standards but also contribute to the enhancement of the quality of life in America. Companies are considered for their protection and improvement of the environment and natural resources, occupational health and safety, consumer protection and product purity, and equal employment opportunity. Up to 15% of assets may be in illiquid securities. May use options on up to 20% of net assets.
Year organized: 1972
Ticker symbol: DRTHX
Discount broker availability: *Schwab, *White, Waterhouse, *Fidelity, *Siebert
Dividends paid: Income - annually; Capital gains - annually
Portfolio turnover (3 yrs): 72%, 67%, 48%
Largest holding: AFLAC (2.8%)
Management fee: 0.75%
Expense ratio: 1.17% (year ending 5/31/94)

DREYFUS-WILSHIRE TARGET
FUNDS - LARGE COMPANY
GROWTH PORTFOLIO
(See first Dreyfus listing for data common to all Dreyfus funds)

Portfolio manager: Wilshire Associates, Inc. (1992)
Custodian: Comerica Bank of Detroit, MI
Investment objective and policies: Investment results comparable to the performance of the companies from the Wilshire 5000 Index classified by Wilshire as large capitalization growth companies. Invests in a representative mix of Wilshire 5000 companies with capitalizations of $960M or more and above average earnings or sales growth and relatively high P/E ratios.
Year organized: 1992
Discount broker availability: *Schwab, *White
Redemption fee: 1.0% for shares held less than 6 months
Telephone switching: With other Dreyfus-Wilshire Target Funds, Inc. portfolios
Dividends paid: Income - annually; Capital gains - annually
Portfolio turnover (2 yrs): 22%, 12%
Largest holding: General Electric Company (6.0%)
Management fee: 0.10%
Administration fee: 0.20%
Expense ratio: 0.68% (year ending 8/31/94) (1.39% without waiver)

DREYFUS-WILSHIRE TARGET
FUNDS - LARGE COMPANY
VALUE PORTFOLIO
(See first Dreyfus listing for data common to all Dreyfus funds)

Portfolio manager: Wilshire Associates, Inc. (1992)
Custodian: Comerica Bank of Detroit, MI
Investment objective and policies: Investment results comparable to the performance of the companies from the Wilshire 5000 Index classified by Wilshire as large capitalization value companies. Invests in a representative mix of Wilshire 5000 companies with capitalizations of $960M or more and above average dividends in relation to price and relatively low P/E ratios.
Year organized: 1992
Discount broker availability: *Schwab, *White
Redemption fee: 1.0% for shares held less than 6 months
Telephone switching: With other Dreyfus-Wilshire Target Funds, Inc. portfolios
Dividends paid: Income - annually; Capital gains - annually
Portfolio turnover (2 yrs): 47%, 22%
Largest holding: Exxon Corp. (10.2%)
Management fee: 0.10%
Administration fee: 0.20%
Expense ratio: 0.58% (year ending 8/31/94) (1.18% without waiver)

DREYFUS-WILSHIRE TARGET
FUNDS - SMALL COMPANY
GROWTH PORTFOLIO
(See first Dreyfus listing for data common to all Dreyfus funds)

Portfolio manager: Wilshire Associates, Inc. (1992)
Custodian: Comerica Bank of Detroit, MI
Investment objective and policies: Investment results comparable to the performance of the companies from the Wilshire 5000 Index classified by Wilshire as small capitalization growth companies. Invests in a representative mix of Wilshire 5000 companies with capitalizations less than $960M and above average earnings or sales growth and relatively high P/E ratios.
Year organized: 1992
Ticker symbol: DTSGX
Discount broker availability: *Schwab, *White
Redemption fee: 1.0% for shares held less than 6 months
Telephone switching: With other Dreyfus-Wilshire Target Funds, Inc. portfolios
Dividends paid: Income - annually; Capital gains - annually
Portfolio turnover (2 yrs): 46%, 55%
Largest holding: Dell Computer (1.0%)
Management fee: 0.10%
Administration fee: 0.20%
Expense ratio: 0.74% (year ending 8/31/94) (1.47% without waiver)

DREYFUS-WILSHIRE TARGET
FUNDS - SMALL COMPANY
VALUE PORTFOLIO
(See first Dreyfus listing for data common to all Dreyfus funds)

Portfolio manager: Wilshire Associates, Inc. (1992)
Custodian: Comerica Bank of Detroit, MI
Investment objective and policies: Investment results comparable to the performance of the companies from the Wilshire 5000 Index classified by Wilshire as small capitalization value companies. Invests in a representative mix of Wilshire 5000 companies with capitalizations of less than $960M and above average dividends in relation to price and relatively low P/E ratios.
Year organized: 1992
Ticker symbol: DSTVX
Discount broker availability: *Schwab, *White
Redemption fee: 1.0% for shares held less than 6 months
Telephone switching: With other Dreyfus-Wilshire Target Funds, Inc. portfolios
Dividends paid: Income - annually; Capital gains - annually
Portfolio turnover (2 yrs): 49%, 27%
Largest holding: Fleetwood Enterprises (1.6%)
Management fee: 0.10%
Administration fee: 0.20%
Expense ratio: 0.50% (year ending 8/31/94) (1.16% without waiver)
Management fee: 0.30%

DREYFUS WORLDWIDE DOLLAR
MONEY MARKET FUND ◆
(See first Dreyfus listing for data common to all Dreyfus funds)

Portfolio manager: Patricia A. Larkin (1995)
Investment objective and policies: High current income consistent with preservation of capital and maintenance of liquidity. Invests in dollar-denominated money market obligations issued around the world.
Year organized: 1989
Ticker symbol: DWDXX
Check redemptions: $500 minimum
Confirmations mailed: After each purchase and each check, mail or wire redemption
Checks returned: Monthly
Periodic account statements mailed: Quarterly

Dividends paid: Income - declared daily, paid monthly
Management fee: 0.5%
Expense ratio: 0.84% (year ending 10/31/94)

DREYFUS/LAUREL FUNDS

(Data common to all Dreyfus/Laurel funds are shown below. See subsequent listing for data specific to individual Dreyfus/Laurel funds.)

The Dreyfus Family of Funds
P.O. Box 9692
Providence, RI 02940
800-548-2868

Shareholder service hours: Full service: M-F 9 A.M.-5 P.M. EST; After hours service: prices, yields
Adviser: The Dreyfus Corporation (a wholly-owned subsidiary of Mellon Bank, N.A.)
Custodian: Mellon Bank, N.A., Pittsburgh
Transfer agent: The Shareholder Services Group
Minimum purchase: Initial: $1,000, Subsequent: $100; IRA/Keogh: Initial $500
Telephone orders: No
Wire orders accepted: Yes
Deadline for same day wire purchase: 4 P.M. (12 NN for money market funds)
Qualified for sale in: All states
Telephone redemptions: Yes
Wire redemptions: Yes, $1,000 minimum
Letter redemptions: Signature guarantee required over $25,000
Telephone switching: With other Dreyfus/Laurel funds and Dreyfus funds
Number of switches permitted: Unlimited
Deadline for same day switch: 4 P.M. (12 NN for money market funds)
Shareholders services: Keogh, IRA, 401(k), corporate retirement plans, automatic investment plan (waives initial minimum), withdrawal plan min. req. $10,000, electronic funds transfer
IRA/Keogh fees: None
Note: Dreyfus/Laurel funds were, prior to October 1994, Laurel funds. They are not listed with the Dreyfus funds because, as former Laurel funds, they were, at press time, administered separately from the Dreyfus funds. They have a different custodial bank, different minimum purchase requirements, fee structures and shareholder services. It is anticipated that by the end of 1995 they will be completely integrated into the regular Dreyfus family.

DREYFUS BOND MARKET INDEX FUND

(See first Dreyfus/Laurel listing for data common to all Dreyfus/Laurel funds)

Portfolio manager: Laurie Carroll (1993)
Investment objective and policies: Replicate the total return of the Lehman Brothers Government/Corporate Bond Index. Invests in a representative sample of the securities contained in the Index, selecting one or two issues to represent an entire "class" or type of securities in the Index.
Year organized: 1993 (name changed from Laurel Bond Market Index Fund on 10/17/94)
Discount broker availability: *White, *Fidelity, *Siebert
Dividends paid: Income - declared and paid monthly; Capital gains - December
Management fee: 0.40%
12b-1 distribution fee: Maximum of 0.25%
Expense ratio: 0.40% (11 months ending 10/31/94) (1.41% without waiver)

DREYFUS CORE VALUE FUND

(See first Dreyfus/Laurel listing for data common to all Dreyfus/Laurel funds)

Portfolio managers: Guy R. Scott (1991), Mark E. Donovan (1994)
Investment objective and policies: Long-term growth of capital with current income secondary. Invests in common stocks and securities convertible into common stocks of companies believed to have particular possibilities for long-term growth. Up to

20% of assets may be in foreign securities. May use futures and options.
Year organized: 1947 (formerly Johnston Capital Appreciation Fund. Name changed from Boston Company Capital Appreciation Fund on 4/1/94 and from Laurel Capital Appreciation Fund on 10/17/94)
Ticker symbol: DCVIX
Discount broker availability: Schwab, *White, Waterhouse, *Fidelity, *Siebert
Dividends paid: Income - April, July, October, December; Capital gains - December
Portfolio turnover (3 yrs): 75%, 66%, 157%
Management fee: 0.90%
12b-1 distribution fee: Maximum of 0.25%
Expense ratio: 1.15% (year ending 12/31/93) (1.16% without waiver)

DREYFUS DISCIPLINED MIDCAP STOCK FUND

(See first Dreyfus/Laurel listing for data common to all Dreyfus/Laurel funds)

Portfolio manager: John O'Toole (1993)
Investment objective and policies: Total return exceeding that of the S&P 400 MidCap Index. Invests in common stocks with market capitalizations of $200M to $5B chosen by the application of quantitative security selection and risk control techniques to provide aggregate characteristics similar to the S&P MidCap but with a higher total return. Fund may hedge.
Year organized: 1993 (name changed from Laurel Midcap Stock Fund on 10/17/94)
Discount broker availability: *White, *Fidelity, *Siebert
Dividends paid: Income - May, August, November, December; Capital gains - December
Portfolio turnover (1 yr) 83%
Largest holding: Baltimore Gas & Electric Co. (1.7%)
Management fee: 1.10%
12b-1 distribution fee: Maximum of 0.25%
Expense ratio: 1.40% (7 months ending 10/31/94)

DREYFUS DISCIPLINED STOCK FUND

(See first Dreyfus/Laurel listing for data common to all Dreyfus/Laurel funds)

Portfolio manager: Bert Mullins (1987)
Investment objective and policies: Total return exceeding that of the S&P 500 Index. Invests in equity securities chosen by the application of quantitative security selection and risk control techniques. Up to 20% of assets may be in money market instruments and 15% in illiquid securities.
Year organized: 1987 (name changed from Laurel Stock Fund on 10/17/94)
Discount broker availability: *White, *Fidelity, *Siebert
Dividends paid: Income - February, May, August, November; Capital gains - December
Portfolio turnover (3 yrs): 106%, 64%, 84%
Largest holding: Exxon Corp. (2.8%)
Management fee: 0.90%
12b-1 distribution fee: Maximum of 0.25%
Expense ratio: 1.15% (year ending 10/31/94)

DREYFUS EQUITY INCOME FUND

(See first Dreyfus/Laurel listing for data common to all Dreyfus/Laurel funds)

Portfolio manager: Bert Mullins (1994)
Investment objective and policies: Above average income with moderate long-term capital growth. Invests primarily in dividend-paying common stocks including securities of foreign issuers. May have up to 15% of assets in illiquid securities and use futures and options.
Year organized: 1994 (name changed from Laurel Equity Income Fund on 10/17/94)
Discount broker availability: *White, *Fidelity, *Siebert
Dividends paid: Income - May, August, November,

December; Capital gains - December
Management fee: 0.90%
12b-1 distribution fee: Maximum of 0.25%

DREYFUS EUROPEAN FUND

(See first Dreyfus/Laurel listing for data common to all Dreyfus/Laurel funds)

Sub-adviser: CCF S.A.M. Finance, S.A.
Portfolio manager: Catherine Adibi (1989)
Investment objective and policies: Total return exceeding that of the Morgan Stanley Capital International Europe Index. Invests in common stocks chosen from among the Western European countries and industry sectors represented in the Index. Fund may use futures and options and hedge up to 25% of total assets. Up to 15% of assets may be in illiquid securities.
Year organized: 1987 (name changed from Capstone European Fund on 11/1/93 and from Laurel European Fund on 10/17/94)
Discount broker availability: *White, *Fidelity, *Siebert
Dividends paid: Income - December; Capital gains - December
Portfolio turnover (3 yrs): 44%, 12%, 7%
Largest holding: Air Liquide (L') (3.2%)
Management fee: 1.75%
12b-1 distribution fee: Maximum of 0.25%
Expense ratio: 2.00% (year ending 10/31/94) (2.27% without waiver)

DREYFUS INTERNATIONAL EQUITY ALLOCATION FUND

(See first Dreyfus/Laurel listing for data common to all Dreyfus/Laurel funds)

Sub-adviser: CCF S.A.M. Finance, S.A.
Portfolio manager: Patrice Conxicoeur (1994)
Investment objective and policies: Total return exceeding that of the Morgan Stanley Capital International—Europe Australia Far East (EAFE) Index. Invests in common stocks chosen from among the countries and industry sectors represented in the Index and may invest up to 20% of assets in emerging markets countries. Fund may use futures and options and hedge up to 25% of total assets. Up to 15% of assets may be in illiquid securities.
Year organized: 1994 (name changed from Laurel International Equity Allocation Fund on 10/17/94)
Discount broker availability: *White
Dividends paid: Income - December; Capital gains - December
Management fee: 1.50%
12b-1 distribution fee: Maximum of 0.25%

DREYFUS S&P 500 STOCK INDEX FUND

(See first Dreyfus/Laurel listing for data common to all Dreyfus/Laurel funds)

Portfolio manager: John O'Toole (1993)
Investment objective and policies: Replicate the total return of the S&P 500 Index. Invests in a representative sample of the stocks from each sector in the S&P 500 Index in proportion to their weighting in the Index.
Year organized: 1993 (name changed from Laurel S&P 500 Stock Index Fund on 10/17/94)
Discount broker availability: *White, *Fidelity, *Siebert
Dividends paid: Income - February, May, August, November; Capital gains - December
Portfolio turnover (2 yrs): 13%, 22%
Management fee: 0.40%
12b-1 distribution fee: Maximum of 0.25%
Expense ratio: 0.65% (7 months ending 10/31/94)

DREYFUS SPECIAL GROWTH FUND

(See first Dreyfus/Laurel listing for data common to all Dreyfus/Laurel funds)

Portfolio manager: Guy R. Scott (1990)
Investment objective and policies: Above-average growth of capital through common stock invest-

ments selected solely on the basis of appreciation potential. Dividend income, if any, is incidental. Emphasis is on smaller companies in high technology, consumer services and energy development and in special situations. May invest up to 20% of assets in foreign securities and use futures and options.
Year organized: 1982 (Name changed from Boston Company Special Growth Fund on 4/1/94 and from Laurel Special Growth Fund on 10/17/94)
Ticker symbol: DSGRX
Discount broker availability: *Schwab, *White, Waterhouse, *Fidelity, *Siebert
Dividends paid: Income - December; Capital gains - December
Portfolio turnover (3 yrs): 94%, 112%, 141%
Largest holding: Global Marine, Inc. (4.1%)
Management fee: 1.15%
12b-1 distribution fee: Maximum of 0.25%
Expense ratio: 1.73% (year ending 12/31/93) (1.79% without waiver)

DREYFUS/LAUREL CALIFORNIA TAX-FREE MONEY FUND
(See first Dreyfus/Laurel listing for data common to all Dreyfus/Laurel funds)

Portfolio manager: Andrew S. Windmueller (1988)
Investment objective and policies: Maximum current income exempt from federal and California state personal income taxes consistent with preservation of capital and liquidity. Invests at least 80% of assets in high quality California municipal money market obligations.
Year organized: 1988 (Name changed from Boston Company California Tax-Free Money Fund on 4/1/94 and from Laurel California Tax-Free Money Fund on 10/17/94)
Ticker symbol: DCLXX
Check redemptions: $250 minimum
Confirmations mailed: Not mailed
Checks returned: Monthly
Periodic account statements mailed: Monthly
Dividends paid: Income - declared daily, paid monthly
Management fee: 0.35%
12b-1 distribution fee: Maximum of 0.25%
Expense ratio: 0.47% (7 months ending 6/30/94) (0.85% without waiver)

DREYFUS/LAUREL CONTRARIAN FUND
(See first Dreyfus/Laurel listing for data common to all Dreyfus/Laurel funds)

Portfolio manager: Guy R. Scott (1994)
Investment objective and policies: Long term growth. Invests primarily in common stocks believed undervalued. May invest up to 20% of assets in bonds believed undervalued. May use futures and options.
Year organized: 1988 (Name changed from Boston Company Contrarian Fund on 4/1/94 and from Laurel Contrarian Fund on 10/17/94)
Ticker symbol: DCNTX
Discount broker availability: *White, *Fidelity, *Siebert
Dividends paid: Income - December; Capital gains - December
Portfolio turnover (3 yrs): 65%, 39%, 76%
Largest holding: Pentair, Inc. (3.9%)
Management fee: 1.25%
12b-1 distribution fee: Maximum of 0.25%
Expense ratio: 1.83% (year ending 8/31/94) (3.69% without waiver)

DREYFUS/LAUREL INTERNATIONAL FUND
(See first Dreyfus/Laurel listing for data common to all Dreyfus/Laurel funds)

Portfolio managers: Sandor Cseh (1994), D. Kirk Henry (1994)
Investment objective and policies: Long-term capi-

tal growth with current income secondary. Invests primarily in common stocks and securities convertible into common stocks of companies located outside the U.S. Maximum 35% of assets in any one country. May use futures and options.
Year organized: 1988 (Name changed from Boston Company International Fund on 4/1/94 and from Laurel International Fund on 10/17/94)
Ticker symbol: DINTX
Discount broker availability: *White, *Fidelity, *Siebert
Dividends paid: Income - June, December; Capital gains - December
Portfolio turnover (3 yrs): 114%, 202%, 110%
Largest holding: Deutsche Bank AG (4.0%)
Management fee: 1.50%
12b-1 distribution fee: 0.07%
Expense ratio: 1.84% (year ending 8/31/94) (4.21% without waiver)

DREYFUS/LAUREL MASSACHUSETTS TAX-FREE MONEY FUND
(See first Dreyfus/Laurel listing for data common to all Dreyfus/Laurel funds)

Portfolio manager: Andrew S. Windmueller (1986)
Investment objective and policies: Current income exempt from federal and Massachusetts personal income taxes consistent with preservation of capital and liquidity. Invests at least 80% of assets in high quality, short-term Massachusetts municipal money market obligations.
Year organized: 1983 (Name changed from Boston Company Massachusetts Tax-Free Money Fund on 4/1/94 and from Laurel Massachusetts Tax-Free Money Fund on 10/17/94)
Ticker symbol: DLMXX
Qualified for sale in: MA, FL, IL
Check redemptions: $250 minimum
Confirmations mailed: Not mailed
Checks returned: Monthly
Periodic account statements mailed: Monthly
Dividends paid: Income - declared daily, paid monthly
Management fee: 0.35%
12b-1 distribution fee: Maximum of 0.25%
Expense ratio: 0.70% (year ending 6/30/94) (0.78% without waiver)

DREYFUS/LAUREL NEW YORK TAX-FREE MONEY FUND
(See first Dreyfus/Laurel listing for data common to all Dreyfus/Laurel funds)

Portfolio manager: Andrew S. Windmueller (1988)
Investment objective and policies: Maximum current income exempt from federal and New York State and New York City personal income taxes consistent with preservation of capital and liquidity. Invests at least 80% of assets in high quality New York municipal money market obligations.
Year organized: 1988 (name changed from Boston Company New York Tax-Free Money Fund on 4/1/94 and from Laurel New York Tax-Free Money Fund on 10/17/94)
Telephone redemptions: Yes
Check redemptions: $250 minimum
Confirmations mailed: Not mailed
Checks returned: Monthly
Periodic account statements mailed: Monthly
Dividends paid: Income - declared daily, paid monthly
Management fee: 0.35%
12b-1 distribution fee: Maximum of 0.25%
Expense ratio: 0.56% (year ending 6/30/94) (0.97% without waiver)

DREYFUS/LAUREL PRIME MONEY MARKET FUND
(See first Dreyfus/Laurel listing for data common to all Dreyfus/Laurel funds)

Portfolio manager: Laurie Carroll (1987)
Investment objective and policies: High current income consistent with stability of principal. Invests

in high quality money market instruments.
Year organized: 1987 (name changed from Laurel Prime Money Market Fund on 10/17/94)
Check redemptions: $500 minimum
Confirmations mailed: After each purchase and each check, mail or wire redemption
Checks returned: On request
Periodic account statements mailed: Monthly
Dividends paid: Income: declared daily, paid monthly
Management fee: 0.50%
12b-1 distribution fee: Maximum of 0.25%
Expense ratio: 0.71% (7 months ending 10/31/94)

DREYFUS/LAUREL SHORT-TERM BOND FUND
(See first Dreyfus/Laurel listing for data common to all Dreyfus/Laurel funds)

Portfolio manager: Roberta A. Shea (1989)
Investment objective and policies: High current income consistent with preservation of capital. Invests primarily in a broad range of investment-grade fixed-income securities with a weighted average maturity of 3 years or less. Up to 20% of assets may be in junk bonds and 15% in illiquid securities. May use futures and options.
Year organized: 1988 (Name changed from Boston Company Cash Management Plus in 1991, from Boston Company Short-Term Bond Fund on 4/1/94 and from Laurel Short-Term Bond Fund on 10/17/94)
Discount broker availability: *White, *Fidelity, *Siebert
Dividends paid: Income - declared daily, paid monthly; Capital gains - December
Portfolio turnover (3 yrs): 53%, 6%, 30%
Management fee: 0.55%
12b-1 distribution fee: Maximum of 0.25%
Expense ratio: 0.95% (year ending 8/31/94) (4.21% without waiver)

DREYFUS/LAUREL SHORT-TERM GOVERNMENT SECURITIES FUND
(See first Dreyfus/Laurel listing for data common to all Dreyfus/Laurel funds)

Portfolio manager: Laurie Carroll (1994)
Investment objective and policies: High current income consistent with preservation of capital. Invests in debt obligations of the U.S. government, its agencies or instrumentalities with a weighted average maturity of 18 months to 3 years. Up to 15% of assets may be in illiquid securities.
Year organized: 1994
Discount broker availability: *White, *Fidelity, *Siebert
Dividends paid: Income - declared daily, paid monthly; Capital gains - December
Management fee: 0.55%
12b-1 distribution fee: Maximum of 0.25%
Expense ratio: 0.80% (7 months ending 10/31/94)

DREYFUS/LAUREL TAX-EXEMPT MONEY MARKET FUND
(See first Dreyfus/Laurel listing for data common to all Dreyfus/Laurel funds)

Portfolio manager: Emily Heuer (1993)
Investment objective and policies: High current income exempt from federal income tax consistent with stability of principal. Invests in tax-exempt municipal money market instruments maturing in one year or less.
Year organized: 1987 (name changed from Laurel Tax-Exempt Money Market Fund on 10/17/94)
Check redemptions: $500 minimum
Confirmations mailed: After each purchase and each check, mail or wire redemption
Checks returned: On request
Periodic account statements mailed: Monthly
Dividends paid: Income: declared daily, paid monthly
Management fee: 0.50%
12b-1 distribution fee: Maximum of 0.25%
Expense ratio: 0.70% (6 months ending 10/31/94)

DREYFUS/LAUREL U.S. TREASURY MONEY MARKET FUND
(See first Dreyfus/Laurel listing for data common to all Dreyfus/Laurel funds)

Portfolio manager: Laurie Carroll (1991)
Investment objective and policies: High current income consistent with stability of principal. Invests in direct money market obligations of the U.S. Treasury and repurchase agreements secured by such obligations.
Year organized: 1991 (name changed from Laurel U.S. Treasury Money Market Fund on 10/17/94)
Check redemptions: $500 minimum
Confirmations mailed: After each purchase and each check, mail or wire redemption
Checks returned: On request
Periodic account statements mailed: Monthly
Dividends paid: Income: declared daily, paid monthly
Management fee: 0.50%
12b-1 distribution fee: Maximum of 0.25%
Expense ratio: 0.70% (6 months ending 10/31/94)

DUPREE FUNDS ◆
(Data common to all Dupree series are shown below. See subsequent listing for data specific to individual Dupree series.)

P.O. Box 1149
Lexington, KY 40589
606-254-7741, 800-866-0614
fax 606-254-1399

Adviser: Dupree Investment Advisers, Inc.
Portfolio manager: William T. Griggs II
Custodian: Trust Company of Kentucky
Transfer agent: Dupree Investment Advisers, Inc.
Minimum purchase: Initial: $100, Subsequent: $100
Telephone orders accepted: No
Wire orders accepted: Yes
Deadline for same day wire purchase: 3 P.M.
Telephone redemptions: Yes
Wire redemptions: Yes, $500 minimum
Letter redemptions: Signature guarantee required
Telephone switching: With other Dupree funds
Number of switches permitted: Unlimited
Shareholder services: IRA (Intermediate Government Bond Series only), automatic investment plan, withdrawal plan min. req. $10,000
Management fee: 0.5% first $100M to 0.4% over $150M (except Intermediate Government Bond Series)
IRA fees: None

DUPREE INTERMEDIATE GOVERNMENT BOND SERIES ◆
(See first Dupree listing for data common to all Dupree series)

Investment objective and policies: High current income and preservation of capital. Invests in securities issued by the U.S. Government and its agencies or instrumentalities, collateralized repurchase agreements and bank accounts. Portfolio has a weighted average maturity of 3 to 10 years.
Year organized: 1992
Ticker symbol: DPIGX
Qualified for sale in: FL, IN, KY, TN, TX
Check redemptions: $500 minimum
Dividends paid: Income - declared daily, paid monthly; Capital gains - December
Portfolio turnover (2 yrs): 23%, 0%
Management fee: 0.2%
Expense ratio: 0.40% (year ending 6/30/94) (0.65% without waiver)

DUPREE KENTUCKY TAX-FREE INCOME SERIES ◆
(See first Dupree listing for data common to all Dupree series)

Investment objective and policies: High current income exempt from federal and Kentucky income taxes, and Kentucky ad valorem tax. Invests primarily in investment-grade Kentucky municipal securities with a weighted average maturity of 10 years or more. Up to 20% of assets may be in unrated securities believed of investment-grade quality.
Year organized: 1979 (name changed from Kentucky Tax-Free Income Fund in 1987)
Ticker symbol: KYTFX
Qualified for sale in: FL, IN, KY, TX
Dividends paid: Income - March, June, September, December; Capital gains - December
Portfolio turnover (3 yrs): 31%, 32%, 12%
Expense ratio: 0.69% (year ending 6/30/94)

DUPREE KENTUCKY TAX-FREE SHORT-TO-MEDIUM SERIES ◆
(See first Dupree listing for data common to all Dupree series)

Investment objective and policies: High current income exempt from federal and Kentucky income taxes, and Kentucky ad valorem tax. Invests primarily in investment-grade Kentucky municipal securities with a weighted average maturity of 3 to 5 years. Up to 20% of assets may be in unrated securities believed of investment-grade quality.
Year organized: 1987
Ticker symbol: KYSMX
Qualified for sale in: FL, IN, KY, TX
Check redemptions: $500 minimum
Dividends paid: Income - declared daily, paid monthly; Capital gains - December
Portfolio turnover (3 yrs): 18%, 23%, 29%
Expense ratio: 0.72% (year ending 6/30/94)

DUPREE TENNESSEE TAX-FREE INCOME SERIES ◆
(See first Dupree listing for data common to all Dupree series)

Investment objective and policies: High current income exempt from federal income tax and the Tennessee Hall tax. Invests primarily in investment-grade Tennessee municipal securities with a weighted average maturity of 10 years or more. Up to 20% of assets may be in unrated securities believed of investment-grade quality.
Year organized: 1993
Qualified for sale in: IN, KY, TN
Dividends paid: Income - March, June, September, December; Capital gains - December
Portfolio turnover (1 yr): 16%
Expense ratio: 0.12% (6 months ending 6/30/94) (4.01% without waiver)

DUPREE TENNESSEE TAX-FREE SHORT-TO-MEDIUM SERIES ◆
(See first Dupree listing for data common to all Dupree series)

Investment objective and policies: High current income exempt from federal income tax and the Tennessee Hall tax. Invests primarily in investment-grade Tennessee municipal securities with a weighted average maturity of 2 to 5 years. Up to 20% of assets may be in unrated securities believed of investment-grade quality.
Year organized: 1994
Qualified for sale in: IN, KY, TN
Check redemptions: $500 minimum
Dividends paid: Income - March, June, September, December

EASTCLIFF TOTAL RETURN FUND

900 Second Avenue South
300 International Centre
Minneapolis, MN 55402
612-338-7881, 800-338-1579

Adviser: Resource Capital Advisers, Inc.
Administrator: Fiduciary Management, Inc.
Portfolio manager: Donald S. Wilson (1986)
Custodian and transfer agent: Firstar Trust Co.

Investment objective and policies: Maximum total return - capital growth and income - consistent with reasonable risk. Invests in common stocks, preferred stocks, convertible stocks, and corporate and governmental debt securities. Mix of equity and debt securities will be adjusted to reflect changes in market and economic conditions. May invest up to 25% of assets in securities of foreign issuers.
Year organized: 1986 (originally ValSearch Total Return Fund. Name changed from Fiduciary Total Return Fund, Inc. on 12/30/94)
Minimum purchase: Initial: $1,000, Subsequent: $100
Telephone orders accepted: No
Wire orders accepted: Yes
Deadline for same day wire purchase: 4 P.M.
Qualified for sale in: AZ, CA, CO, DC, HI, IL, IN, KS, MI, MN, MO, NY, PA, SD, TX, WI
Wire redemptions: Yes, $7.50 fee
Letter redemptions: Signature guarantee not required
Dividends paid: Income - October, December; Capital gains - October, December
Portfolio turnover (3 yrs): 13%, 28%, 35%
Largest holding: U.S. Treasury Notes 8.500% due 5/15/97 (6.3%)
Shareholder services: Keogh, IRA, SEP-IRA, 401(k), corporate retirement plans, automatic investment plan—minimum $50/month, withdrawal plan min. req. $10,000, electronic funds transfer
Management fee: 1.0% first $30M, 0.75% over $30M
Administration fee: 0.2% first $30M, 0.1$ over $30M
12b-1 distribution fee: Maximum of 1.0%
Expense ratio: 2.0% (year ending 9/30/94) (3.0% without waiver)
IRA/Keogh fees: Annual $12.50, Closing $15

EATON VANCE SHORT-TERM TREASURY FUND
24 Federal Street
Boston, MA 02110
617-482-8260, 800-225-6265
800-262-1122

Newspaper listing: STTsy
Adviser: Eaton Vance Management
Portfolio manager: Michael B. Terry (1991)
Custodian: Investors Bank & Trust Co.
Transfer agent: The Shareholder Services Group, Inc.
Investment objective and policies: High current income and liquidity. Invests exclusively in U.S. Treasury obligations with remaining maturities of less than one year and a weighted average maturity of less than 90 days. Unlike most money market funds, portfolio does not declare dividends daily. This policy allows the NAV to rise, in effect converting dividends to capital gains.
Year organized: 1991
Ticker symbol: EVTYX
Minimum purchase: Initial: $5,000, Subsequent: $50
Wire orders accepted: Yes
Deadline for same day wire purchase: 12 NN
Qualified for sale in: All states
Wire redemptions: Yes, $1,000 minimum
Letter redemptions: Signature guarantee required over $25,000
Check redemptions: $500 minimum
Telephone switching: With Eaton Vance Cash Management Fund
Number of switches permitted: Unlimited
Dividends paid: Income - December; Capital gains - December
Shareholder services: Keogh, IRA, 403(b), corporate retirement plans
Management fee: 0.25% first $500M to 0.17% over $3B plus 1.5% of daily income first $500M to 1.7% over $3B
12b-1 distribution fee: 0.25%
Expense ratio: 0.60% (year ending 12/31/93) (0.70% without waiver)
IRA/Keogh fees: Annual $10, Closing $10

ECLIPSE FUNDS ◆
(Data common to all Eclipse funds are shown below. See subsequent listings for data specific to individual Eclipse funds.)

P.O. Box 2196
Peachtree City, GA 30269
404-631-0414, 800-872-2710
fax 404-487-0676

Adviser: Towneley Capital Management, Inc.
Custodian and transfer agent: Investors Fiduciary Trust Co.
Minimum purchase: Initial: $1,000, Subsequent: None
Telephone orders accepted: No
Wire orders accepted: Yes
Deadline for same day wire purchase: 3 P.M.
Qualified for sale in: All states
Letter redemptions: Signature guarantee required
Telephone switching: With other Eclipse funds and Vista money market funds
Number of switches permitted: Unlimited
Shareholder services: IRA, automatic investment plan—minimum $50/month (waives initial minimum), withdrawal plan min. req. $10,000
IRA fees: None

ECLIPSE BALANCED FUND ◆
(See fist Eclipse listing for data common to all Eclipse funds)

Portfolio manager: Wesley G. McCain (1989)
Investment objective and policies: High total return - dividend and interest income and capital gains. Invests in equity and fixed-income securities with at least 25% of assets in fixed-income securities. May invest in securities of foreign issuers with up to 20% of assets in securities of foreign governments and supranational entities.
Year organized: 1989
Ticker symbol: EBALX
Discount broker availability: Schwab, *White
Dividends paid: Income - March, June, September, December; Capital gains - December
Portfolio turnover (3 yrs): 65%, 96%, 102%
Largest holding: Tandem Computers, Inc. (1.6%)
Management fee: 0.8%
Expense ratio: 0.69% (year ending 12/31/93) (1.19% without waiver)

ECLIPSE EQUITY FUND ◆
(See fist Eclipse listing for data common to all Eclipse funds)

Portfolio manager: Wesley G. McCain (1987)
Investment objective and policies: High total return - dividend income and realized and unrealized capital gains. Normally invests at least 65% of assets in equity securities of below S&P average market capitalization companies, using intrinsic value, projected earnings growth and expected dividends as investment criteria. Up to 20% of assets may be in securities of foreign issuers.
Year organized: 1987
Ticker symbol: EEQFX
Discount broker availability: Schwab, *White
Dividends paid: Income - December; Capital gains - December
Portfolio turnover (3 yrs): 101%, 111%, 119%
Largest holding: Terra Industries, Inc. (1.3%)
Management fee: 1.0%
Expense ratio: 1.12% (year ending 12/31/93)

ECLIPSE GROWTH AND INCOME FUND ◆
(See fist Eclipse listing for data common to all Eclipse funds)

Portfolio manager: Wesley G. McCain (1995)
Investment objective and policies: High total return - dividend and interest income and capital gains. Invests primarily in dividend-paying equity securities of North American companies listed on major

exchanges or the OTC market. May have up to 20% of assets in securities of foreign issuers.
Year organized: 1995
Dividends paid: Income - December; Capital gains - December
Management fee: 0.9%

ECLIPSE ULTRA SHORT TERM INCOME FUND ◆
(See fist Eclipse listing for data common to all Eclipse funds)

Portfolio manager: Wesley G. McCain (1995)
Investment objective and policies: High current income consistent with preservation of capital and relatively stable NAV. Invests primarily in high quality short-term fixed-income securities with a weighted average maturity of one year or less. May invest in domestic government and corporate debt securities and have up to 10% of assets in debt securities of stable foreign governments.
Year organized: 1995
Dividends paid: Income - March, June, September, December; Capital gains - December
Management fee: 0.4%

ELFUN FUNDS ◆
(Data common to all Elfun funds are shown below. See subsequent listings for data specific to individual Elfun funds.)

3003 Summer Street
P.O. Box 120074
Stamford, CT 06912-0074
203-326-4040, 800-242-0134
prices/yields 800-843-3359

Adviser: General Electric Investment Corp.
Servicing agent: Elfun Mutual Funds
Custodian and transfer agent: State Street Bank & Trust Co.
Special sales restrictions: Available to members of the Elfun Society and immediate families, General Electric board members, and GE and its subsidiaries. (Members are selected from active employees of the General Electric Co.)
Telephone orders accepted: No
Wire orders accepted: Yes
Deadline for same day wire purchase: 4 P.M.
Qualified for sale in: All states
Telephone redemptions: Yes, $15 fee
Wire redemptions: Yes, $1,000 minimum, $15 fee
Letter redemptions: Signature guarantee required over $10,000
Telephone switch privilege: With other Elfun Funds
Number of switches permitted: Unlimited
Shareholder services: IRA, automatic investment plan, directed dividends, withdrawal plan min. req. $10,000, payroll deduction ($25 per month minimum)
IRA fees: None

ELFUN DIVERSIFIED FUND ◆
(See first Elfun listing for data common to all Elfun funds)

Newspaper listing: Under GE Invst Elfun/S&S
Portfolio managers: David B. Carlson (1988), Robert A. MacDougall (1988)
Investment objective and policies: High total return consistent with prudent investment management and preservation of capital. Invests in common stocks, convertible securities, preferred stocks, investment-grade taxable and non-taxable bonds, other registered investment companies, and restricted non-public securities with allocation adjusted to reflect changes in market and economic conditions. Up to 20% of assets may be in foreign securities not listed on U.S. exchanges. Fund may use forward contracts, futures and options and hedge.
Year organized: 1987
Ticker symbol: ELDFX
Minimum purchase: Initial: $100, Subsequent: $25

Dividends paid: Income - December; Capital gains - December
Portfolio turnover (3 yrs): 25%, 31%, 67%
Largest holding: SPDR Trust (2.6%)
Management fee: 0.10%
Expense ratio: 0.39% (year ending 12/31/93)

ELFUN GLOBAL FUND ◆
(See first Elfun listing for data common to all Elfun funds)

Newspaper listing: Under GE Invst Elfun/S&S
Portfolio manager: Ralph R. Layman (1991)
Investment objective and policies: Long term growth of capital and future income. Invests primarily in foreign securities with at least 65% of assets in securities listed on domestic and foreign exchanges - primarily stocks, convertible securities, and foreign-denominated bonds - of at least 3 countries, including the U.S. Fund may use forward contracts, futures and options and hedge.
Year organized: 1987
Ticker symbol: EGLBX
Minimum purchase: Initial: $100, Subsequent: $25
Dividends paid: Income - December Capital gains - December
Portfolio turnover (3 yrs): 43%, 63%, 100%
Largest holding: Grupo Financiero Bancomer ADR (2.5%)
Management fee: 0.11%
Expense ratio: 0.31% (year ending 12/31/93)

ELFUN INCOME FUND ◆
(See first Elfun listing for data common to all Elfun funds)

Newspaper listing: Under GE Invst Elfun/S&S
Portfolio manager: Robert A. MacDougall (1982)
Investment objective and policies: High current income consistent with prudent investment management and preservation of capital. Invests in both domestic and foreign issued bonds and debentures, government obligations and preferred and common stock. Up to 25% of assets may be in junk bonds. May use forward contracts, futures and options and hedge.
Year organized: 1982
Ticker symbol: EINFX
Minimum purchase: Initial: None, Subsequent: None
Dividends paid: Income - declared daily, paid monthly; Capital gains - January
Portfolio turnover (3 yrs): 131%, 62%, 133%
Management fee: 0.05%
Expense ratio: 0.17% (year ending 12/31/93)

ELFUN MONEY MARKET FUND ◆
(See first Elfun listing for data common to all Elfun funds)

Portfolio manager: Don Torey (1992)
Investment objective and policies: High current income consistent with prudent investment management and preservation of capital. Invests in short-term money market instruments.
Year organized: 1990
Ticker symbol: EINXX
Minimum purchase: Initial: $100, Subsequent: $25
Check redemptions: $500 minimum, $20 fee to establish
Checks returned: As clear
Dividends paid: Income - declared daily, paid monthly
Management fee: 0.00%
Expense ratio: 0.00% (year ending 12/31/93) (includes waiver)

ELFUN TAX-EXEMPT INCOME FUND ◆
(See first Elfun listing for data common to all Elfun funds)

Newspaper listing: Under GE Invst Elfun/S&S
Portfolio manager: Robert R. Kaelin
Investment objective and policies: Current income exempt from federal income tax. Invests in high-

grade municipal bonds. Fund may use zero coupon bonds, and lower-grade issues (as low as B) up to 10% of assets. Fund may use futures and options and hedge.
Year organized: 1977
Ticker symbol: ELFTX
Minimum purchase: Initial: None, Subsequent: None
Dividends paid: Income - declared daily, paid monthly; Capital gains - December
Portfolio turnover (3 yrs): 29%, 29%, 36%
Management fee: 0.06%
Expense ratio: 0.10% (year ending 12/31/93)

ELFUN TRUSTS ◆
(See first Elfun listing for data common to all Elfun funds)

Newspaper listing: Under GE Invst Elfun/S&S
Portfolio manager: David B. Carlson (1988)
Investment objective and policies: Long-term growth of capital, and future income rather than current income. Fund may invest in any securities and in any proportions it deems proper or suitable. Normally will invest in equities and convertibles. May use futures and options and hedge.
Year organized: 1935
Ticker symbol: ELFNX
Minimum purchase: Initial: None, Subsequent: None
Dividends paid: Income - December, Capital gains - December
Portfolio turnover (3 yrs): 18%, 11%, 14%
Management fee: 0.06%
Expense ratio: 0.11% (year ending 12/31/93)

THE EVERGREEN FUNDS
(Data common to all Evergreen funds are shown below. See subsequent listings for data specific to individual Evergreen funds.)

2500 Westchester Ave.
Purchase, NY 10577
914-694-2020, 800-235-0064
fax 914-641-2310

Shareholder service hours: Full service: M-F 9 A.M.-6 P.M. EST; After hours service: prices, yields, prospectuses, distributions
Adviser: Evergreen Asset Management Corp. (a wholly owned subsidiary of First Union National Bank of North Carolina)
Custodian and transfer agent: State Street Bank & Trust Co.
Qualified for sale in: All states (exceptions noted)
Sales charge: 4.75% effective 1/1/95 (except money market funds. Does not apply to shareholders of record prior to 1/1/95 who may purchase shares in any Evergreen fund no-load.

THE EVERGREEN AMERICAN RETIREMENT FUND
(See first Evergreen listing for data common to all Evergreen funds)

Portfolio manager: Irene D. O'Neill (1988)
Investment objective and policies: Conservation of capital, reasonable income, and capital growth for retired or close to retirement investors. Invests in equities and fixed-income securities, emphasizing income-producing securities with capital growth potential. Equities account for no more than 75% of total fund assets. Fund may sell short and write options on up to 15% of equity positions.
Year organized: 1988
Ticker symbol: EAMRX
Discount broker availability: *Schwab, *White, Waterhouse, Fidelity, Siebert

THE EVERGREEN FUND
(See first Evergreen listing for data common to all Evergreen funds)

Portfolio manager: Stephen A. Lieber (1971)
Investment objective and policies: Capital appreciation. Invests in securities of little-known or rela-

tively small companies undergoing changes believed favorable.
Year organized: 1971 (4 for 1 split 1985)
Ticker symbol: EVGRX
Discount broker availability: *Schwab, *White, Waterhouse, Fidelity, Siebert

THE EVERGREEN FOUNDATION FUND
(See first Evergreen listing for data common to all Evergreen funds)

Portfolio manager: Stephen A. Lieber (1990)
Investment objective and policies: Reasonable income, conservation of capital and capital appreciation. Invests maximum of 75% of assets in above average dividend paying common stocks and convertible bonds.
Year organized: 1990
Ticker symbol: EFONX
Special sales restrictions: Designed for private charitable foundations but open to all investors. Will generate an annual income stream equal to at least 5% of net assets to help shareholders meet current federal tax laws regarding distribution of assets for foundations. Foundations may exchange eligible securities for fund shares.
Discount broker availability: *Schwab, *White, Waterhouse, Fidelity, Siebert

THE EVERGREEN GLOBAL REAL ESTATE EQUITY FUND
(See first Evergreen listing for data common to all Evergreen funds)

Portfolio manager: Samuel A. Lieber (1989)
Investment objective and policies: Long term capital growth with current income secondary. Invests primarily in securities of domestic and foreign companies engaged in the real estate industry or which own significant real estate assets but will not purchase direct interests in real estate. May use currency options and futures and write covered calls to hedge up to 15% of assets.
Year organized: 1989
Ticker symbol: EGLRX
Discount broker availability: *Schwab, *White, Waterhouse, Fidelity, Siebert

THE EVERGREEN GROWTH AND INCOME FUND
(See first Evergreen listing for data common to all Evergreen funds)

Portfolio manager: Edmund H. Nicklin, Jr. (1986)
Investment objective and policies: Capital appreciation and current income. Invests in securities of companies which are undervalued relative to those companies' assets, breakup value, earnings, or potential earnings. This approach will also include the purchase of convertible and non-convertible preferred stocks and debt securities. May write covered call options to hedge up to 25% of total assets.
Year organized: 1986 (Opened to public July, 1987. Name changed from Value Timing Fund in 1994)
Ticker symbol: EVVTX
Discount broker availability: *Schwab, *White, Waterhouse, Fidelity, Siebert

THE EVERGREEN LIMITED MARKET FUND
(See first Evergreen listing for data common to all Evergreen funds)

Portfolio manager: Derrick Wenger (1993)
Investment objective and policies: Long-term capital growth. Invests in stocks of small companies for which there is a relatively limited trading market, those with market capitalizations under $150M and/or out of favor with the securities industry in general. Up to 15% of assets may be in illiquid securities.
Year organized: 1983

Ticker symbol: EVLMX
Discount broker availability: *Schwab, *White, Waterhouse, Fidelity, Siebert

THE EVERGREEN MONEY MARKET TRUST ◆
(See first Evergreen listing for data common to all Evergreen funds)

Portfolio manager: Ethel B. Sutton (1987)
Investment objective and policies: High level of current income consistent with preservation of capital and liquidity. Invests in money market instruments.
Year organized: 1988
Ticker symbol: EGMXX

THE EVERGREEN NATIONAL TAX-FREE FUND
(See first Evergreen listing for data common to all Evergreen funds)

Portfolio manager: James Colby III (1992)
Investment objective and policies: High level of current income exempt from federal income tax. Invests at least 80% of assets in long-term debt obligations issued by states, territories and possessions of the U.S. and their political subdivisions and authorities, insured as to payment of principal and interest, with a weighted average maturity of 15 years or longer.
Year organized: 1992 (name changed from Evergreen National Tax-Free Fund to Insured National Tax-Free Fund in 1993 and back to original name in 1994)
Ticker symbol: EINSX
Discount broker availability: *Schwab, *White, Fidelity, Siebert

THE EVERGREEN SHORT-INTERMEDIATE MUNICIPAL FUND
(See first Evergreen listing for data common to all Evergreen funds)

Portfolio manager: Steven C. Shachat (1991)
Investment objective and policies: High current income exempt from federal income tax consistent with preservation of capital and liquidity. Invests in municipal securities with a weighted average maturity of 2-5 years. Up to 50% of assets may be in AMT securities.
Year organized: 1991
Ticker symbol: EMUNX
Discount broker availability: *Schwab, *White. Waterhouse, Fidelity, Siebert

THE EVERGREEN SHORT-INTERMEDIATE MUNICIPAL FUND - CALIFORNIA
(See first Evergreen listing for data common to all Evergreen funds)

Portfolio manager: Steven C. Shachat (1988)
Investment objective and policies: High current income exempt from federal and California income taxes consistent with preservation of capital and liquidity. Invests in municipal securities exempt from federal and California income taxes with a weighted average maturity of 2 to 5 years. Up to 20% of assets may be in AMT securities.
Year organized: 1988 (formerly Evergreen Tax Exempt Money Market Fund - California. Name and objective changed on 7/7/92).
Ticker symbol: EMUCX
Discount broker availability: *Schwab, *White. Waterhouse, Fidelity, Siebert

THE EVERGREEN SMALL CAP EQUITY INCOME FUND
(See first Evergreen listing for data common to all Evergreen funds)

Portfolio manager: Nola Maddox Falcone (1993)
Investment objective and policies: Maximum total return - current income and capital growth. Invests in common and preferred stocks, securities convert-

ible into common stock and fixed-income securities, primarily of companies with market capitalizations of less than $500M. May use futures and options to hedge.
Year organized: 1993
Discount broker availability: *Schwab, *White, Fidelity, Siebert

THE EVERGREEN TAX EXEMPT MONEY MARKET FUND ◆
(See first Evergreen listing for data common to all Evergreen funds)

Portfolio manager: Steven C. Shachat (1988)
Investment objective and policies: High current income exempt from federal income tax consistent with preservation of capital and liquidity. Invests in short-term municipal money market instruments.
Year organized: 1988
Ticker symbol: EVTXX

THE EVERGREEN TAX STRATEGIC FOUNDATION FUND
(See first Evergreen listing for data common to all Evergreen funds)

Portfolio managers: Stephen A. Lieber (1993), James T. Colby III (1993)
Investment objective and policies: Maximum after-tax total return - current income and capital growth. Invests in common and preferred stocks, securities convertible into common stock and municipal debt securities exempt from federal income tax. Fund anticipates having at least 50% of total assets in municipal securities at the end of each quarter of its taxable year.
Year organized: 1993
Discount broker availability: *Schwab, *White, Fidelity, Siebert

THE EVERGREEN TOTAL RETURN FUND
(See first Evergreen listing for data common to all Evergreen funds)

Portfolio manager: Nola Maddox Falcone (1978)
Investment objective and policies: Current income and capital appreciation. Invests in common and preferred stocks, convertible securities, and fixed-income securities. Up to 20% of of assets may be in ADRs and EDRs of foreign issuers and 15% in illiquid securities. May write covered call options.
Year organized: 1978
Ticker symbol: EVTRX
Discount broker availability: *Schwab, *White, Waterhouse, Fidelity, Siebert

THE EVERGREEN U.S. GOVERNMENT SECURITIES FUND
(See first Evergreen listing for data common to all Evergreen funds)

Portfolio manager: James T. Colby III
Investment objective and policies: High total return from a combination of current income and capital appreciation, consistent with prudent investment risk and safety of principal. Invests at least 65% of assets in obligations issued or guaranteed by the US Government or its agencies and instrumentalities and in certificates representing undivided interests in the interest or principal of US Treasury securities with a weighted average maturity of 10-30 years.
Year organized: 1993
Discount broker availability: *Schwab, *White, Waterhouse, Fidelity, Siebert

THE EVERGREEN U.S. REAL ESTATE EQUITY FUND
(See first Evergreen listing for data common to all Evergreen funds)

Portfolio manager: Samuel A. Lieber (1993)
Investment objective and policies: Long term capital growth with current income secondary. Invests primarily in securities of U.S. companies engaged in

the real estate industry or which own significant real estate assets, but will not purchase direct interests in real estate. May use currency options and futures and write covered calls to hedge up to 30% of assets.
Year organized: 1993
Discount broker availability: *Schwab, *White, Waterhouse, Fidelity, Siebert

THE EVERGREEN VALUE TIMING FUND ◆
(See Evergreen Growth & Income Fund)

FAIRMONT FUND ◆
1346 S. Third Street
Louisville, KY 40208
502-636-5633, 800-262-9936
fax 502-634-6025

Adviser: The Sachs Co.
Portfolio manager: Morton H. Sachs (1981)
Custodian: National City Bank of Cleveland
Transfer agent: The Fairmont Fund Trust
Investment objective and policies: Capital appreciation. Invests in equity securities of established companies with appreciation potential. Up to 25% of assets may be in ADRs of foreign issuers.
Year organized: 1981 (3 for 1 split on 2/15/90, 4 for 1 split 11/30/86)
Ticker symbol: FAIMX
Minimum purchase: Initial: $1,000, Subsequent: None
Telephone orders accepted: No
Wire orders accepted: Yes, with advance notification
Deadline for same day wire purchase: 4 P.M.
Discount broker availability: *White
Qualified for sale in: All states except AK, AZ, AR, CO, DE, ID, IA, KS, LA, ME, MT, NE, NH, ND, OK, RI, SC, UT, VT, WV
Letter redemptions: Signature guarantee not required
Telephone switching: Subsequent exchanges only with Kentucky Tax-Free Income or Short to Medium Series of Dupree Mutual Funds (KY residents only)
Number of switches permitted: Unlimited
Dividends paid: Income - December; Capital gains - December
Portfolio turnover (3 yrs): 155%, 132%, 115%
Largest holding: Brite Voice Systems, Inc. (5.1%)
Shareholder services: IRA
Management fee: 2.0% first $10M to 1.0% over $30M
Expense ratio: 1.78% (year ending 12/31/93)
IRA fees: Annual $30, Initial $30

FAM VALUE FUND ◆
P.O. Box 399
Cobleskill, NY 12043
518-234-7400, 800-932-3271
fax 518-234-7793

Adviser: Fenimore Asset Management, Inc.
Portfolio managers: Thomas O. Putnam (1987), Diane C. Van Buren (1987)
Custodian: U.S. Trust Company of New York
Transfer agent: Fenimore Asset Management Trust
Investment objective and policies: Maximum total return - capital appreciation and dividend income. Invests primarily in common stocks, but may also acquire convertible bonds and convertible preferred stocks. Selects stocks of companies believed undervalued with a favorable price to value relationship.
Year organized: 1987
Ticker symbol: FAMVX
Minimum purchase: Initial: $2,000, Subsequent: $100; IRA/Keogh: Initial: $100, Subsequent: $50
Telephone orders accepted: No
Wire orders accepted: Yes, subsequent only
Deadline for same day wire purchase: 4 P.M.
Discount broker availability: Schwab, White, Fidelity, Siebert
Qualified for sale in: All states except NE, RI

Letter redemptions: Signature guarantee required over $10,000
Dividends paid: Income - December; Capital gains - December
Portfolio turnover (3 yrs): 5%, 10%, 14%
Largest holding: Fourth Financial (3.8%)
Shareholder services: IRA
Management fee: 1.0%
Expense ratio: 1.39% (year ending 12/31/93)
IRA fees: Annual $15

FASCIANO FUND ◆
190 South LaSalle Street, Suite 2800
Chicago, IL 60603
312-444-6050, 800-848-6050
fax 312-444-6011

Adviser: Fasciano Company, Inc.
Portfolio manager: Michael F. Fasciano (1987)
Custodian and transfer agent: Firstar Trust Co.
Investment objective and policies: Long-term capital growth with income secondary. Invests in common stocks of companies with market capitalizations under $1B believed undervalued in relation to expected sales and earnings increases, on a 3- to 5-year horizon basis. May invest in ADRs of foreign issuers and sell short.
Year organized: 1987
Ticker symbol: FASCX
Minimum purchase: Initial: $1,000, Subsequent: $100
Telephone orders accepted: No
Wire orders accepted: Yes
Deadline for same day wire purchase: 4 P.M.
Discount broker availability: White
Qualified for sale in: All states except AZ, AR, IA, NH, NM, ND, OK, VT
Letter redemptions: Signature guarantee required over $20,000
Dividends paid: Income - December; Capital gains - December
Portfolio turnover (3 yrs): 99%, 43%, 29%
Largest holdings: VIVRA (4.3%), International Speedway Corp. (4.3%)
Shareholder services: IRA, SEP-IRA, automatic investment plan—min. $50/month (waives initial minimum)
Management fee: 1.0%
Expense ratio: 1.7% (year ending 6/30/94)
IRA fees: Annual $12.50

FBP CONTRARIAN BALANCED FUND ◆
P.O. Box 5354
Cincinnati, OH 45201
804-845-4900, 800-327-9375
prices 800-443-4249

Adviser: Flippin, Bruce, & Porter, Inc.
Administrator: MGF Service Corp.
Portfolio manager: John T. Bruce (1990)
Custodian: Wachovia Bank of North Carolina
Transfer agent: MGF Service Corp.
Investment objective and policies: Long-term capital appreciation and current income. Invests in a balanced portfolio of equity and fixed-income securities with at least 65% of assets in securities of companies believed undervalued according to contrarian investment approach. Under normal circumstances 40-70% of assets are in equity securities, 25-50% in fixed-income securities and 0-35% in money market instruments. Equity assets are normally apportioned 25% to freshly identified contrarian companies, 50% to recovering companies and 25% to recovered companies.
Year organized: 1990 (name changed from FBP Contrarian Fund in 1993)
Ticker symbol: FBPBX
Minimum purchase: Initial: $25,000, Subsequent: $1,000; IRA/Keogh: Initial: $1,000, Subsequent: $100
Telephone orders accepted: No
Wire orders accepted: Yes
Deadline for same day wire purchase: 2 P.M.
Discount broker availability: Schwab
Qualified for sale in: CA, CO, DC, FL, GA, MI, NY, NC, OH, OR, PA, SC, TN, TX, VA, WA, WV
Letter redemptions: Signature guarantee not required

Dividends paid: Income - March, June, September, December; Capital gains - November
Portfolio turnover (3 yrs): 28%, 27%, 14%
Largest holding: International Business Machines Corp. (3.2%)
Shareholder services: IRA, automatic investment plan—minimum $100/month, withdrawal plan min. req. $25,000
Management fee: 0.75% first $250M to 0.5% over $500M
Administration fee: 0.20%
Expense ratio: 1.25% (year ending 3/31/94) (1.36% without waiver)
IRA fees: None

FBP CONTRARIAN EQUITY FUND ◆
P.O. Box 5354
Cincinnati, OH 45201
804-845-4900, 800-327-9375
prices 800-443-4249

Adviser: Flippin, Bruce, & Porter, Inc.
Administrator: MGF Serivce Corp.
Portfolio manager: John T. Bruce
Custodian: Wachovia Bank of North Carolina
Transfer agent: MGF Service Corp.
Investment objective and policies: Long-term capital appreciation. Invests primarily in equity securities with at least 70% of assets in securities of companies believed undervalued according to contrarian investment approach. Under normal circumstances 70-100% of assets are in equity securities and 0-30% in money market instruments. Equity assets are normally apportioned 25% to freshly identified contrarian companies, 50% to recovering companies and 25% to recovered companies.
Year organized: 1993
Minimum purchase: Initial: $25,000, Subsequent: $1,000; IRA/Keogh: Initial: $1,000, Subsequent: $100
Telephone orders accepted: No
Wire orders accepted: Yes
Deadline for same day wire purchase: 2 P.M.
Qualified for sale in: CA, CO, FL, GA, NC, OH, OR, PA, SC, TN, VA, WV
Letter redemptions: Signature guarantee not required
Dividends paid: Income - March, June, September, December; Capital gains - November
Portfolio turnover (1 yr): 7%
Largest holding: International Business Machines Corp. (4.1%)
Shareholder services: IRA, automatic investment plan—minimum $100/month, withdrawal plan min. req. $25,000
Management fee: 0.75% first $250M to 0.5% over $500M
Administration fee: 0.20%
Expense ratio: 1.25% (year ending 3/31/94) (3.10% without waiver)
IRA fees: None

FEDERATED FUNDS ◆
(Data common to all Federated funds are shown below. See subsequent listings for data specific to individual Federated funds.)

Federated Investors Tower
Pittsburgh, PA 15222-3779
412-288-1900, 800-245-0242
fax 412-288-1982

Shareholder service hours: Full service: M-F 9 A.M.-5 P.M. EST
Adviser: Federated Management
Custodian: State Street Bank & Trust Co.
Transfer agent: Federated Services Company
Special sales restrictions: Designed for corporate investors, banks in a fiduciary, advisory, agency or custodial capacity, but open to individuals.
Classes of shares: Some Federated funds offer Institutional Shares (sold directly without 12b-1 distribution fees) and Institutional Service Shares (sold to banks and other financial institutions with 12b-1 distribution fees). Where such multiple classes exist data shown in listings are for Institutional shares.

Minimum purchase: Initial: $25,000 (90 days to achieve minimum level); Subsequent: None
Telephone orders accepted: No
Wire orders accepted: Yes
Deadline for same day wire purchase: 4 P.M.
Qualified for sale in: All states
Wire redemptions: Yes
Letter redemptions: Signature guarantee required over $50,000

FEDERATED ARMS FUND ◆
(See first Federated listing for data common to all Federated funds)

Portfolio managers: Gary J. Madich (1992), Susan M. Nason (1993)
Investment objective and policies: Current income with minimal volatility of principal. Invests at least 65% of assets in adjustable and floating rate mortgage securities issued or guaranteed as to payment of principal and interest by the U.S. Government, its agencies or instrumentalities. May invest in other government obligations and mortgage-related securities issued by private entities such as banks and companies related to the construction industry.
Year organized: 1985 (objective changed on 1/31/92 and name changed from U.S. Government Fund on 4/23/92. Prior performance may be misleading)
Ticker symbols: FEUGX (Institutional), FASSX (Institutional Service)
Discount broker availability: *Schwab, *White, *Waterhouse, *Fidelity, *Siebert
Dividends paid: Income - declared daily, paid monthly; Capital Gains - August, December
Portfolio turnover (3 yrs): 65%, 36%, 38%
Management fee: 0.60
Expense ratio: 0.55% (year ending 8/31/94) (0.69% without waiver)

FEDERATED GNMA TRUST ◆
(See first Federated listing for data common to all Federated funds)

Portfolio manager: Gary J. Madich (1987)
Investment objective and policies: Current income. Invests in U.S. Government obligations, with at least 65% of assets in instruments issued or guaranteed by the Government National Mortgage Association.
Year organized: 1981 (formerly Federated Government Trust)
Ticker symbols: FGMAX (Institutional), FGSSX (Institutional Service)
Discount broker availability: *Schwab, *White, *Waterhouse, *Fidelity, *Siebert
Dividends paid: Income - declared daily, paid monthly: Capital gains - December
Portfolio turnover (3 yrs): 117%, 33%, 57%
Management fee: 0.4%
Expense ratio: 0.51% (year ending 1/31/94)

FEDERATED GROWTH TRUST ◆
(See first Federated listing for data common to all Federated funds)

Portfolio manager: Gregory M. Melvin (1987)
Investment objective and policies: Appreciation of capital. Invests in equity securities of companies with prospects for above-average growth in earnings and dividends or companies with market capitalizations over $100M where significant fundamental changes are taking place. May invest in ADRs of foreign issuers. Fund hedges
Year organized: 1984
Ticker symbol: FGTRX
Discount broker availability: *Schwab, *White, *Waterhouse, Fidelity, Siebert
Dividends paid: Income - March, June, September, December; Capital gains - December
Portfolio turnover (3 yrs): 59%, 57%, 46%
Largest holding: Dr. Pepper/7-Up Holding Co. (6.8%)
Management fee: 0.75%
Expense ratio: 0.99% (year ending 10/31/94)

FEDERATED HIGH YIELD TRUST ◆
(See first Federated listing for data common to all Federated funds)

Portfolio manager: Mark E. Durbiano (1984)
Investment objective and policies: High current income. Invests primarily in lower-rated (BBB or lower) fixed rate corporate debt obligations. Up to 15% of assets may be in illiquid securities and 10% in foreign securities not publicly traded in the U.S. May use options to increase return and hedge.
Year organized: 1984
Ticker symbol: FHYTX
Discount broker availability: *Schwab, *White, *Waterhouse, *Fidelity, *Siebert
Dividends paid: Income - declared daily, paid monthly; Capital gains - December
Portfolio turnover (3 yrs): 112%, 93%, 61%
Management fee: 0.75%
Expense ratio: 0.83% (year ending 2/28/94) (0.96% without waiver)

FEDERATED INCOME TRUST ◆
(See first Federated listing for data common to all Federated funds)

Newspaper listing: FIT
Portfolio managers: Gary Madich (1987), Kathleen M. Foody-Malus (1990)
Investment objective and policies: Current income. Invests exclusively in U.S. Government and agency securities and certain collateralized mortgage obligations (CMOs).
Year organized: 1981
Ticker symbol: FICMX (Institutional)
Discount broker availability: *Schwab, *White, *Waterhouse, *Fidelity, *Siebert
Dividends paid: Income - Declared daily, paid monthly; Capital gains - December
Portfolio turnover (3 yrs): 178%, 52%, 51%
Management fee: 0.4%
Expense ratio: 0.51% (year ending 1/31/94)

FEDERATED INTERMEDIATE GOVERNMENT TRUST ◆
(See first Federated listing for data common to all Federated funds)

Newspaper listing: Figt
Portfolio manager: Susan M. Nason (1991)
Investment objective and policies: Current income. Invests in U.S. Government and agency securities with remaining maturities of 5 years or less and a weighted average maturity of 2 to 5 years.
Year organized: 1982
Ticker symbol: FIGTX (Institutional)
Discount broker availability: *Schwab, *White, *Waterhouse, *Fidelity, *Siebert
Dividends paid: Income - declared daily, paid monthly; Capital gains - December
Portfolio turnover (3 yrs): 131%, 85%, 108%
Management fee: 0.4%
Expense ratio: 0.52% (year ending 1/31/94)

FEDERATED INTERMEDIATE MUNICIPAL TRUST ◆
(See first Federated listing for data common to all Federated funds)

Newspaper listing: FIMT
Portfolio manager: Jonathan C. Conley (1985)
Investment objective and policies: Current income exempt from federal income tax. Invests at least 80% of assets in municipal securities with a weighted average maturity of 3 to 10 years. Up to 15% of assets may be in illiquid securities.
Year organized: 1985
Ticker symbol: FIMTX (Institutional)
Discount broker availability: *Schwab, *White, Waterhouse, *Fidelity, *Siebert
Dividends paid: Income - declared daily, paid monthly; Capital gains - December
Portfolio turnover (3 yrs): 7%, 3%, 9%
Management fee: 0.40%
Expense ratio: 0.61% (year ending 5/31/94) (0.62% without waiver)

FEDERATED MANAGED AGGRESSIVE GROWTH FUND ◆
(See first Federated listing for data common to all Federated funds)

Investment objective and policies: Capital growth. Allocates investments among asset categories within predetermined ranges to maximize return as market conditions change. Invests 60-100% of assets in stocks using large companies (0-100%), small companies (0-40%), and foreign companies (0-40%). Invests 0-40% in bonds using U.S. Treasury securities (0-32%), mortgage-backed securities (0-12%), investment-grade corporate bonds (0-12%), high-yield corporate bonds (0-16%) and foreign bonds (0-16%). Remaining 0-20% of assets will be in cash equivalents.
Year organized: 1994
Discount broker availability: *White, *Fidelity, *Siebert
Dividends paid: Income - March, June, September, December; Capital gains - December
Management fee: 0.75%

FEDERATED MANAGED GROWTH FUND ◆
(See first Federated listing for data common to all Federated funds)

Investment objective and policies: Capital growth with current income secondary. Allocates investments among asset categories within predetermined ranges to maximize return as market conditions change. Invests 50-70% of assets in stocks using large companies (0-70%), utilities (0-7%), small companies (0-21%), and foreign companies (0-21%). Invests 30-50% in bonds using U.S. Treasury securities (0-45%), mortgage-backed securities (0-15%), investment-grade corporate bonds (0-15%), high-yield corporate bonds (0-15%) and foreign bonds (0-15%). Remaining 0-14% of assets will be in cash equivalents.
Year organized: 1994
Discount broker availability: *White, *Fidelity, *Siebert
Dividends paid: Income - March, June, September, December; Capital gains - December
Management fee: 0.75%

FEDERATED MANAGED GROWTH AND INCOME FUND ◆
(See first Federated listing for data common to all Federated funds)

Investment objective and policies: Current income and capital growth. Allocates investments among asset categories within predetermined ranges to maximize return as market conditions change. Invests 30-50% of assets in stocks using large companies (0-50%), utilities (0-20%), small companies (0-7.5%), and foreign companies (0-7.5%). Invests 50-70% in bonds using U.S. Treasury securities (0-70%), mortgage-backed securities (0-35%), investment-grade corporate bonds (0-35%), high-yield corporate bonds (0-7%) and foreign bonds (0-7%). Remaining 0-15% of assets will be in cash equivalents.
Year organized: 1994
Discount broker availability: *White, *Fidelity, *Siebert
Dividends paid: Income - March, June, September, December; Capital gains - December
Management fee: 0.75%

FEDERATED MANAGED INCOME FUND ◆
(See first Federated listing for data common to all Federated funds)

Investment objective and policies: Current income. Allocates investments among asset categories within predetermined ranges to maximize return as market conditions change. Invests 10-30% of assets in stocks using large companies (0-30%), utilities (0-15%), small companies (0-3%), and foreign companies (0-3%). Invests 70-90% in bonds using

U.S. Treasury securities (0-90%), mortgage-backed securities (0-45%), investment-grade corporate bonds (0-45%), high-yield corporate bonds (0-9%) and foreign bonds (0-9%). Remaining 0-12% of assets will be in cash equivalents.
Year organized: 1994
Discount broker availability: *White, *Fidelity, *Siebert
Dividends paid: Income - declared and paid monthly; Capital gains - December
Management fee: 0.75%

FEDERATED MAX-CAP FUND ◆
(See first Federated listing for data common to all Federated funds)

Sub-adviser: ANB Investment Management and Trust Co.
Portfolio manager: Frederick L. Plautz (1994)
Investment objective and policies: Total return - income and capital appreciation that correspond to the price and dividend performance of the S&P 500 Composite Stock Price Index. Normally invests at least 80% of assets in the stocks that comprise the S&P 500 Index with goal of achieving a total return correlation of between 0.95 and 1.00 with the performance of the Index.
Year organized: 1990 (name changed from S&P 500 Fund on 8/23/91)
Ticker symbol: FISPX (Institutional)
Discount broker availability: Schwab, *White, Waterhouse
Dividends paid: Income - March, June, September, December; Capital gains - December
Portfolio turnover (3 yrs): 2%, 13%, 46%
Largest holding: American Telephone & Telegraph (2.0%)
Management fee: 0.3%
Expense ratio: 0.32% (year ending 10/31/94) (0.39% without waiver)

FEDERATED MID-CAP FUND ◆
(See first Federated listing for data common to all Federated funds)

Sub-adviser: ANB Investment Management and Trust Co.
Portfolio manager: Frederick L. Plautz (1994)
Investment objective and policies: Total return - income and capital appreciation that corresponds to the price and dividend performance of the S&P 400 Mid-Cap Index of companies with market capitalization of $200M-$5B. Normally invests at least 80% of assets in the stocks that comprise the S&P 400 Mid-Cap Index with goal of achieving a total return correlation of between 0.95 and 1.00 with the performance of the Index.
Year organized: 1992
Ticker symbol: FMDCX
Discount broker availability: Schwab
Dividends paid: Income - March, June, September, December; Capital gains - December
Portfolio turnover (2 yrs): 30%, 59%
Largest holding: General Motors Corp. Class E (1.8%)
Management fee: 0.4%
Expense ratio: 0.54% (year ending 10/31/94) (1.13% without waiver)

FEDERATED MINI-CAP FUND ◆
(See first Federated listing for data common to all Federated funds)

Sub-adviser: ANB Investment Management and Trust Co.
Portfolio manager: Frederick L. Plautz (1994)
Investment objective and policies: Total return - income and capital appreciation that corresponds to the price and dividend performance of the Russell 2000 Index of small capitalization stocks. Normally invests at least 80% of assets in the stocks that comprise the Russell 2000 Index with goal of achieving a total return correlation of between 0.95 and 1.00 with the performance of the Index.
Year organized: 1992
Ticker symbol: FMCPX

Discount broker availability: Schwab, *White
Dividends paid: Income - March, June, September, December; Capital gains - December
Portfolio turnover (2 yrs): 32%, 48%
Largest holding: Home Finance Corp., Del Hollywood (0.4%)
Management fee: 0.5%
Expense ratio: 0.73% (year ending 10/31/94) (0.84% without waiver)

FEDERATED SHORT-INTERMEDIATE GOVERNMENT TRUST ◆
(See first Federated listing for data common to all Federated funds)

Newspaper listing: Fsigt
Portfolio manager: Susan M. Nason (1991)
Investment objective and policies: Current income. Invests in securities issued or guaranteed by the U.S. Government, its agencies or instrumentalities with remaining maturities of 3 1/2 years or less. Up to 15% of assets may be in illiquid securities.
Year organized: 1984
Ticker symbol: FSGVX (Institutional), FSGIX (Institutional Service)
Discount broker availability: *Schwab, *White, *Waterhouse, *Fidelity, *Siebert
Dividends paid: Income - declared daily, paid monthly; Capital gains - December
Portfolio turnover (3 yrs): 150%, 132%, 114%
Management fee: 0.4%
Expense ratio: 0.51% (year ending 2/28/94)

FEDERATED SHORT-TERM INCOME FUND ◆
(See first Federated listing for data common to all Federated funds)

Portfolio manager: Deborah A. Cunningham (1991)
Investment objective and policies: Current income. Invests primarily in short and medium-term high grade debt securities with a weighted average maturity of 3 years or less. May invest in corporate debt obligations, asset-backed securities, commercial paper, bank instruments, U.S. dollar denominated foreign debt securities, obligations of the U.S. Government and its agencies and instrumentalities, and money market instruments. Up to 15% of assets may be in illiquid securities.
Year organized: 1986 (name changed from Federated Floating Rate Trust on 12/31/91)
Ticker symbol: FSTIX (Institutional), FSISX (Institutional Service)
Discount broker availability: *Schwab, *White, *Waterhouse, *Fidelity, *Siebert
Portfolio turnover (3 yrs): 44%, 62%, 114%
Dividends paid: Income - declared daily, paid monthly; Capital gains - December
Management fee: 0.40%
Expense ratio: 0.56% (year ending 4/30/94) (0.64% without waiver)

FEDERATED SHORT-TERM MUNICIPAL TRUST ◆
(See first Federated listing for data common to all Federated funds)

Newspaper listing: STMT
Portfolio manager: Jonathan C. Conley (1984)
Investment objective and policies: Dividend income exempt from federal regular income taxes by investing in municipal securities with a weighted average maturity of less than 3 years. Up to 15% of assets may be in illiquid securities.
Year organized: 1981 (name changed from Federated Short-Intermediate Municipal Trust in 1993)
Ticker symbol: FSHIX (Institutional)
Discount broker availability: *Schwab, *White, Waterhouse, *Fidelity, *Siebert
Dividends paid: Income - declared daily, paid monthly; Capital gains - June, December
Portfolio turnover (3 yrs): 36%, 15%, 42%
Management fee: 0.4%
Expense ratio: 0.47% (year ending 6/30/94) (0.60% without waiver)

FEDERATED STOCK AND BOND FUND ◆

(See first Federated listing for data common to all Federated funds)

Portfolio managers: Frederick L. Plautz (1994), Joseph M. Balestrino (1994)
Investment objective and policies: Safety of capital with the possibility of long-term growth of capital and income. Invests in common and preferred stocks, bonds, notes and short-term obligations. May invest in ADRs of foreign issuers.
Year organized: 1934 (formerly Boston Foundation Fund)
Ticker symbol: FSTBX
Discount broker availability: *Schwab, *White, Waterhouse, Fidelity, Siebert
Dividends paid: Income - February, May, August, November; Capital gains - November
Portfolio turnover (3 yrs): 45%, 51%, 43%
Largest holding: General Motors Corp. (1.5%)
Management fee: 0.55% plus 4.5% gross income
Expense ratio: 1.06% (year ending 10/31/94) (1.13% without waiver)

FEDERATED STOCK TRUST ◆

(See first Federated listing for data common to all Federated funds)

Portfolio manager: Peter R. Anderson (1982)
Investment objective and policies: Growth of income and capital. Invests primarily (at least 80% of assets) in common stocks of high-quality companies. May also invest in other corporate securities, U.S. Government securities, repurchase agreements, and money market instruments.
Year organized: 1982
Ticker symbol: FSTKX
Discount broker availability: *Schwab, *White, *Waterhouse, Fidelity, Siebert
Dividends paid: Income - March, June, September, December; Capital gains - December
Portfolio turnover (3 yrs): 28%, 26%, 54%
Largest holding: Phelps Dodge Corp. (3.1%)
Management fee: 0.75% first 500M to 0.4% over $2B
Expense ratio: 0.97% (year ending 10/31/94)

FEDERATED U.S. GOVERNMENT BOND FUND ◆

(See first Federated listing for data common to all Federated funds)

Newspaper listing: FUSGB
Portfolio manager: Susan M. Nason (1994)
Investment objective and policies: Total return - current income with some capital growth. Invests at least 65% of assets in U.S. Government bonds. May invest up to 10% of assets in restricted securities and use options and hedge up to 25% of total assets.
Year organized: 1985 (formerly Federated Bond Fund. Name and objective changed on 8/30/93)
Ticker symbol: FEDBX
Discount broker availability: *Schwab, *White, Fidelity, Siebert
Dividends paid: Income - declared daily, paid monthly; Capital gains - August
Portfolio turnover (3 yrs): 22%, 53%, 98%
Management fee: 0.60%
Expense ratio: 0.83% (year ending 8/31/94) (1.00% without waiver)

FFB LEXICON FUNDS ◆

(Data common to all FFB Lexicon funds are shown below. See subsequent listings for data specific to individual FFB Lexicon funds.)

680 East Swedesford Road
Wayne, PA 19087-1658
610-254-1000, 800-833-8974

Adviser: First Fidelity Bank, N.A., New Jersey
Administrator: SEI Financial Management Co.

Custodian: First Fidelity Bank, N.A., New Jersey
Transfer agent: SEI Financial Services Co.
Special sales restrictions: Offered primarily to institutional investors, including First Fidelity Bank, N.A., New Jersey, its affiliates and correspondents for the investment of funds or funds for which they act in a fiduciary, agency or custodial capacity.
Minimum purchase: None
Telephone orders accepted: No
Wire orders accepted: Yes
Deadline for same day wire purchase: 4 P.M. (3 P.M. for Cash Management fund)
Qualified for sale in: CT, FL, ME, PA
Telephone redemptions: Yes
Wire redemptions: Yes

FFB LEXICON CAPITAL APPRECIATION EQUITY FUND ◆

(See first FFB Lexicon listing for data common to all FFB Lexicon funds)

Portfolio manager: Art Fitilis (1994)
Investment objective and policies: Long-term capital appreciation. Invests primarily in common stocks believed undervalued. Emphasizes companies with market capitalization in excess of $500M. May also invest in preferred stocks, convertible securities and dollar denominated securities of foreign issuers. May write covered call options.
Year organized: 1991
Ticker symbol: FFCAX
Dividends paid: Income - monthly; Capital gains - August
Portfolio turnover (3 yrs): 41%, 54%, 78%
Largest holding: Lincare Holdings (3.3%)
Management fee: 0.75%
Administration fee: 0.17%
Expense ratio: 0.55% (year ending 8/31/94) (0.98% without waiver)

FFB LEXICON CASH MANAGEMENT FUND ◆

(See first FFB Lexicon listing for data common to all FFB Lexicon funds)

Portfolio manager: Robert Corner (1991)
Investment objective and policies: Current income consistent with liquidity and preservation of capital. Invests in money market instruments.
Year organized: 1991
Ticker symbol: FFCXX
Dividends paid: Income - declared daily, paid monthly
Management fee: 0.40%
Administration fee: 0.17%
Expense ratio: 0.55% (year ending 8/31/94) (0.66% without waiver)

FFB LEXICON FIXED INCOME FUND ◆

(See first FFB Lexicon listing for data common to all FFB Lexicon funds)

Portfolio managers: Lynn Mander (1991), Bruce Besecker (1991)
Investment objective and policies: Current income consistent with preservation of capital. Invests in U.S. Treasury obligations, obligations issued or guaranteed as to principal and interest by agencies and instrumentalities of the U.S. Government,, corporate bonds and debentures, commercial paper, short-term bank obligations, foreign government securities, mortgage- and asset-backed securities and repurchase agreements. Fund maintains a weighted average maturity of 5 to 15 years.
Year organized: 1991
Ticker symbol: FFFIX
Dividends paid: Income - declared and paid monthly; Capital gains - August
Portfolio turnover (3 yrs): 69%, 49%, 65%

Management fee: 0.60%
Administration fee: 0.17%
Expense ratio: 0.55% (year ending 8/31/94) (0.83% without waiver)

FFB LEXICON INTERMEDIATE-TERM GOVERNMENT SECURITIES FUND ◆

(See first FFB Lexicon listing for data common to all FFB Lexicon funds)

Portfolio manager: Robert Cheshire (1991)
Investment objective and policies: Current income consistent with preservation of principal and liquidity. Invests exclusively in U.S. Treasury obligations, obligations issued or guaranteed as to principal and interest by agencies and instrumentalities of the U.S. Government, obligations of supranational entities (maximum 35% of assets) and repurchase agreements. Fund maintains a weighted average maturity of 3 to 6 years.
Year organized: 1991
Ticker symbol: FFIGX
Dividends paid: Income - declared and paid monthly; Capital gains - August
Portfolio turnover (3 yrs): 45%, 31%, 47%
Management fee: 0.60%
Administration fee: 0.17%
Expense ratio: 0.55% (year ending 8/31/94) (0.82% without waiver)

FFB LEXICON SELECT VALUE FUND ◆

(See first FFB Lexicon listing for data common to all FFB Lexicon funds)

Portfolio manager: Timothy O'Grady (1993)
Investment objective and policies: Long term capital appreciation. Invests at least 75% of assets in quality common stocks believed undervalued, with lower than average debt to equity and price to book ratios. Remainder of assets may be in preferred stocks, convertible securities, covered call options and U.S. dollar-denominated securities of foreign issuers.
Year organized: 1992
Ticker symbol: FFSVX
Dividends paid: Income - monthly; Capital gains - August
Portfolio turnover (2 yrs): 80%, 32%
Largest holding: YPF S.A. (4.3%)
Management fee: 0.75%
Administration fee: 0.17%
Expense ratio: 0.44% (year ending 8/31/94) (1.02% without waiver)

FFB LEXICON SMALL COMPANY GROWTH FUND ◆

(See first FFB Lexicon listing for data common to all FFB Lexicon funds)

Portfolio manager: Mark Sipe (1994)
Investment objective and policies: Long-term capital appreciation. Invests at least 75% of assets in common stocks of growth oriented companies with market capitalization under $500M. A majority of the funds common stocks will normally pay a dividend. Remainder of assets may be in preferred stocks, convertible securities, covered call options and U.S. dollar-denominated securities of foreign issuers.
Year organized: 1992
Ticker symbol: FLSGX
Dividends paid: Income - monthly; Capital gains - August
Portfolio turnover (2 yrs): 72%, 35%
Largest holding: Bantec (2.6%)
Management fee: 0.75%
Administration fee: 0.17%
Expense ratio: 0.45% (year ending 8/31/94) (1.02% without waiver)

FIDELITY FUNDS
(Data common to all Fidelity funds are shown below. See subsequent listing for data specific to individual Fidelity funds.)

82 Devonshire Street
Boston, MA 02109
617-523-1919, 800-544-8888
800-544-6666 (shareholder services)
800-544-7777 (exchange/redemptions)
800-544-7544 (account balances)
800-544-8544 (fund quotes)
800-544-0118 (TDD)

Shareholder service hours: Full service: Sun-Sat 24 hours
Adviser: Fidelity Management & Research Co.
Transfer agent: Fidelity Service Co. (exceptions noted)
Minimum purchase: Initial: $2,500, Subsequent: $250; IRA/Keogh: Initial: $500, Subsequent: $250 (exceptions noted)
Telephone orders accepted: No
Wire orders accepted: Yes
Deadline for same day wire purchase: 4 P.M. (exceptions noted)
Qualified for sale in: All states (exceptions noted)
Breakpoint pricing: Fidelity load funds (except Select Money Market and Foreign Currency Portfolios) will have load reduced from 3% to 2% for purchases from $250,000-$499,999; from 2% to 1% for purchases from $500,000-$999,999; and eliminated for purchases over $1M.
Telephone redemptions: Yes, fee may apply
Wire redemptions: Yes, $5,000 minimum, fee may apply
Letter redemptions: Signature guarantee required
Telephone switching: With all open Fidelity retail funds except Fidelity Destiny, Congress St., and Exchange Fund, unless otherwise noted; fee may apply.
Number of switches permitted: Reserves right to limit switches to 4 per year (exceptions noted); on 10/18/90, Fidelity instituted a policy of reserving the right to refuse, without prior notice, any exchange which a fund would not be able to invest effectively, applicable to a number of funds normally used by market timers (exceptions noted)
Shareholder services: Keogh, IRA, SEP-IRA, 401(k), 403(b), corporate retirement plans, automatic investment plan, directed dividends, withdrawal plan min. req. $10,000, electronic funds transfer
IRA/Keogh fees: Annual $10 (waived for IRA accounts with balances of $5,000 or more), Closing $10
Low balance fee: $12 for individual fund holdings under $2,500, maximum of $60 (waived for shareholders with Total Fidelity holdings in excess of $50,000)

FIDELITY AGGRESSIVE TAX-FREE PORTFOLIO ◆
(See first Fidelity listing for data common to all Fidelity funds)

Portfolio manager: Anne Punzak (1986)
Custodian: United Missouri Bank, N.A.
Investment objective and policies: High current income exempt from federal income taxes. Invests primarily in medium and lower quality municipal bonds rated BB or lower with maturities of 20 years or more. Fund may invest up to 20% of assets in AMT securities and 10% in obligations in default. May use futures and options and hedge up to 25% of total assets.
Year organized: 1985
Ticker symbol: FATFX
Group fund code: 012
Discount broker availability: White, Waterhouse, *Fidelity, *Siebert
Redemption fee: 1% for shares held less than 180 days
Dividends paid: Income - declared daily, paid monthly; Capital gains - February, December
Portfolio turnover (3 yrs): 40%, 54%, 43%
Management fee: 0.30% plus group fee of 0.12% to 0.37%
12b-1 distribution fee: Yes (not currently imposed)
Expense ratio: 0.63% (year ending 12/31/94)

FIDELITY ASSET MANAGER ◆
(See first Fidelity listing for data common to all Fidelity funds)

Portfolio manager: Bob Beckwitt (1988)
Custodian: Chase Manhattan Bank, N.A.
Investment objective and policies: High total return with reduced risk over the long term by allocating its assets among equities, bonds, and money market instruments. May vary holdings in equities from 10-60%, in bonds 20-70%, and in money market instruments 0-70%. Fund's neutral asset allocation is 40% stocks, 40% bonds, and 20% money market instruments. May own foreign equities (up to 20% of assets); use forward, futures and options on futures in currencies; use options, futures and options on futures on stock, stock indexes and interest rates; sell short against the box; and hold zero coupon bonds.
Year organized: 1988
Ticker symbol: FASMX
Group fund code: 314
Discount broker availability: Schwab, White, Waterhouse, *Fidelity, *Siebert
Dividends paid: Income - March, June, September, December; Capital gains - December
Portfolio turnover (3 yrs): 109%, 98%, 134%
Management fee: 0.40% plus group fee of 0.285% to 0.52%
Largest holding: U.S. Treasury Bill 6 1/4% due 2/15/03 (10.5%)
Expense ratio: 1.04% (year ending 9/30/94)

FIDELITY ASSET MANAGER: GROWTH ◆
(See first Fidelity listing for data common to all Fidelity funds)

Portfolio manager: Bob Beckwitt (1991)
Custodian: Chase Manhattan Bank, N.A.
Investment objective and policies: High total return with reduced risk over the long term by allocating its assets among equities, bonds, and money market instruments. Unlike Fidelity Asset Manager, there is no upper limit on the percent of assets invested in equities although normal distribution is 65% stocks, 30% bonds, and 5% money market instruments. Fund may use foreign equities, options, futures and options on futures on stock, stock indexes and interest rates; sell short against the box; and hold zero coupon bonds. Shifts among classes are made gradually over time, with a single reallocation decision generally involving less than 20% of total assets.
Year organized: 1991
Ticker symbol: FASGX
Group fund code: 321
Discount broker availability: Schwab, White, Waterhouse, *Fidelity, *Siebert
Dividends paid: Income - December; Capital gains - December
Portfolio turnover (3 yrs): 104%, 97%, 693%
Largest holding: Mexican Government Brady 6 1/4% Par B due 12/31/19 (1.5%)
Management fee: 0.40% plus group fee of 0.27% to 0.52%
Expense ratio: 1.15% (year ending 9/30/94)

FIDELITY ASSET MANAGER: INCOME ◆
(See first Fidelity listing for data common to all Fidelity funds)

Portfolio manager: Bob Beckwitt (1992)
Custodian: Chase Manhattan Bank, N.A.
Investment objective and policies: High current income by allocating its assets among stocks, bonds, and money market instruments. May vary holdings in stocks from 10-30%, in bonds 20-40%, and in money market instruments 30-80%. Fund's neutral asset allocation is 20% stocks, 30% bonds, and 50% money market instruments. May own debt securities of foreign governments (up to 35% of assets); use forward, futures and options on futures in currencies; use options, futures and options on futures on stock, stock indexes and interest rates; sell short against the box; and hold zero coupon bonds.

Year organized: 1992
Ticker symbol: FASIX
Group fund code: 328
Discount broker availability: White, *Fidelity, *Siebert
Dividends paid: Income - Monthly; Capital gains - December
Portfolio turnover (2 yrs): 83%, 47%
Management fee: 0.35% plus group fee of 0.12% to 0.37%
Expense ratio: 0.71% (year ending 9/30/94) (1.00% without waiver)

FIDELITY BALANCED FUND ◆
(See first Fidelity listing for data common to all Fidelity funds)

Portfolio managers: Robert Haber (1988)
Custodian: Brown Brother Harriman & Co.
Investment objective and policies: High current income consistent with preservation of capital with moderate long-term capital growth secondary. Invests primarily in high-yielding securities, including common stocks, preferred stocks and bonds. Debt will be the equivalent of Baa or better and be at least 25% of assets. Fund may use foreign securities without limit and use currency exchange contracts, stock index futures and options.
Year organized: 1986
Ticker symbol: FBALX
Group fund code: 304
Discount broker availability: Schwab, White, Waterhouse, *Fidelity, *Siebert
Dividends paid: Income - March, June, September, December; Capital Gains - September, December
Portfolio turnover (3 yrs): 157%, 162%, 242%
Largest holding: French Government OAT 8 1/2% due 4/25/23 (8.4%)
Management fee: 0.20% plus group fee of 0.27% to 0.52%
Expense ratio: 1.01% (year ending 7/31/94) (1.02% without waiver)

FIDELITY BLUE CHIP GROWTH FUND
(See first Fidelity listing for data common to all Fidelity funds)

Portfolio manager: Michael Gordon (1993)
Custodian: Brown Brothers Harriman & Co.
Investment objective and policies: Long-term growth of capital. Invests at least 65% of assets in companies with market capitalization of at least $200M and included in the S&P 500 or DJIA, or have capitalization of $1B or more. Stocks chosen on expectations for greater than average long term earnings growth. Fund may invest in foreign securities, use currency exchange contracts, stock index futures and options on stocks and indexes, and leverage.
Year organized: 1988
Ticker symbol: FBGRX
Group fund code: 312
Sales charge: 3% (waived for retirement accounts using Fidelity prototype plans)
Discount broker availability: Schwab, White, Waterhouse, Fidelity, Siebert
Dividends paid: Income - September, December; Capital Gains - September, December
Portfolio turnover (3 yrs): 271%, 319%, 71%
Largest holding: Oracle Systems Corp. (3.3%)
Management fee: 0.30% plus group fee of 0.27% to 0.52% plus performance fee of +/- 0.20% (relative to S&P 500 over 36 months)
Expense ratio: 1.22% (year ending 7/31/94) (1.27% without waiver)

FIDELITY CALIFORNIA TAX-FREE HIGH YIELD PORTFOLIO ◆
(See first Fidelity listing for data common to all Fidelity funds)

Newspaper listing: CA TF
Portfolio manager: John F. Haley (1985)
Custodian: United Missouri Bank, N.A.
Investment objective and policies: High current

income exempt from federal and California state income taxes. Invests primarily in California municipal bonds judged investment grade with a weighted average maturity of 15 years or more. May invest 1/3 assets in bonds rated lower than BBB but not lower than B or equivalent. Fund may use options and futures (up to 25% of assets hedged) and zero coupon bonds.
Year organized: 1984 (name and objective changed 2/2/86)
Ticker symbol: FCTFX
Group fund code: 091
Discount broker availability: Schwab, White, Waterhouse, *Fidelity, *Siebert
Qualified for sale in: CA
Check redemptions: $500 minimum
Dividends paid: Income - declared daily, paid monthly; Capital gains - April, December
Portfolio turnover (3 yrs): 44%, 32%, 23%
Management fee: 0.25% plus group fee of 0.12% to 0.37%
12b-1 distribution fee: Yes (not currently imposed)
Expense ratio: 0.57% (year ending 2/28/94)

FIDELITY CALIFORNIA TAX-FREE INSURED PORTFOLIO ◆
(See first Fidelity listing for data common to all Fidelity funds)

Newspaper listing: CA In
Portfolio manager: John F. Haley (1986)
Custodian: United Missouri Bank, N.A.
Investment objective and policies: Current income exempt from federal and California state income taxes. Insurance will cover the timely payment of interest and principal on municipal obligations. Fund may invest up to 35% in uninsured obligations rated Baa or better. Fund may use options and futures (up to 25% of assets hedged) and zero coupon bonds. Weighted average maturity will be at least 15 years.
Year organized: 1986
Ticker symbol: FCXIX
Group fund code: 403
Discount broker availability: Schwab, White, Waterhouse, *Fidelity, *Siebert
Qualified for sale in: CA
Check redemptions: $500 minimum
Dividends paid: Income - declared daily, paid monthly; Capital gains - April, December
Portfolio turnover (3 yrs): 60%, 27%, 19%
Management fee: 0.25% plus group fee of 0.12% to 0.37%
12b-1 distribution fee: Yes (not currently imposed)
Expense ratio: 0.48% (year ending 2/28/94) (0.60% without waiver)

FIDELITY CALIFORNIA TAX-FREE MONEY MARKET PORTFOLIO ◆
(See first Fidelity listing for data common to all Fidelity funds)

Portfolio manager: Deborah Watson (1988)
Custodian: United Missouri Bank, N.A.
Investment objective and policies: Current income exempt from federal and California state income taxes. Invests in high quality short-term California municipal money market obligations with remaining maturities of one year or less.
Year organized: 1984 (name and objective change 2/2/86. Formerly Short-term portfolio)
Ticker symbol: FCFXX
Group fund code: 097
Minimum purchase: Initial: $5,000, Subsequent: $250
Deadline for same day wire purchase: 12 NN
Qualified for sale in: CA
Number of switches permitted: Unlimited
Check redemptions: $500 minimum
Confirmations mailed: After each purchase and each check, mail or wire redemption
Checks returned: Quarterly
Periodic account statements mailed: Quarterly
Dividends paid: Income - declared daily, paid monthly
Management fee: 0.25% plus group fee of 0.12% to 0.37%

12b-1 distribution fee: Yes (not currently imposed)
Expense ratio: 0.64% (year ending 2/28/94)

FIDELITY CANADA FUND
(See first Fidelity listing for data common to all Fidelity funds)

Portfolio manager: George Domolky (1987)
Custodian: Brown Brothers Harriman & Co.
Investment objective and policies: Long-term growth of capital. Invests at least 65% of assets in equity and debt securities of Canadian issuers, primarily companies listed on the Toronto Stock Exchange. Fund may use currency exchange contracts, futures contracts and options and hedge up to 25% of total assets.
Year organized: 1987
Ticker symbol: FICDX
Group fund code: 309
Sales charge: 3% (waived for all accounts through 5/31/94 and for retirement accounts using Fidelity prototype plans)
Redemption fee: 1% on shares purchased prior to 10/12/90
Discount broker availability: Schwab, White, Waterhouse, *Fidelity, *Siebert
Dividends paid: Income - December; Capital gains - December
Portfolio turnover (3 yrs): 59%, 131%, 55%
Largest holding: American Barrick Resources Corp. (4.6%)
Management fee: 0.45% plus group fee of 0.27% to 0.52% plus performance fee of +/- 0.20%, relative to Toronto Stock Exchange 300 Composite Index over 36 months
Expense ratio: 1.57% (year ending 10/31/94)

FIDELITY CAPITAL & INCOME FUND ◆
(See first Fidelity listing for data common to all Fidelity funds)

Newspaper listing: CpInc
Portfolio manager: David Breazzano (1990)
Custodian: Bank of New York
Investment objective and policies: Income and capital growth. Invests in debt securities and common and preferred stocks, with majority of assets in debt instruments. Fund focuses on lower quality debt in troubled or uncertain companies (or in default). Will exploit opportunities in bankruptcies, mergers, consolidations, liquidations, reorganizations and restructurings. Up to 10% of assets may be in illiquid securities. Fund may use foreign securities.
Year organized: 1977 (formerly Fidelity High Income Fund (name and objective change as of 1/1/91)
Ticker symbol: FAGIX
Group fund code: 038
Discount broker availability: Schwab, Waterhouse, *Fidelity, *Siebert
Redemption fee: 1.5% to fund on shares held less than 1 year, payable to the fund.
Dividends paid: Income - declared daily, paid monthly; Capital gains - June, December
Portfolio turnover (3 yrs): 100%, 102%, 132%
Largest holding: Thermodyne Holdings Corp. bonds (5.2%)
Management fee: 0.55% plus group fee of 0.12% to 0.37%
12b-1 distribution fee: Yes (not currently imposed)
Expense ratio: 0.97% (year ending 4/30/94)

FIDELITY CAPITAL APPRECIATION FUND
(See first Fidelity listing for data common to all Fidelity funds)

Newspaper listing: CapAp
Portfolio manager: Thomas Sweeney (1986)
Custodian: Brown Brother Harriman & Co.
Investment objective and policies: Capital appreciation. Invests primarily in common stocks. Seeks opportunities in prospective acquisitions, reorgani-

zations, spinoffs, consolidations, and liquidations. Fund may use both domestic and foreign issues without limit. Fund may use stock index futures and options (up to 15% of assets) and currency exchange contracts. Fund may use junk bonds up to 5% of assets.
Year organized: 1986
Ticker symbol: FDCAX
Group fund code: 307
Sales charge: 3% (waived for retirement accounts using Fidelity prototype plans)
Discount broker availability: Schwab, White, Waterhouse, Fidelity, Siebert
Dividends paid: Income - February, December; Capital Gains - February, December
Portfolio turnover (3 yrs): 124%, 120%, 99%
Management fee: 0.30% plus group fee of 0.27% to 0.52% plus performance fee of +/- 0.20%, relative to S&P 500 Index over 36 months
Expense ratio: 1.17% (year ending 10/31/94) (1.19% without waiver)

FIDELITY CASH RESERVES ◆
(See first Fidelity listing for data common to all Fidelity funds)

Portfolio manager: Robert Litterst (1992)
Sub-adviser: FMR Texas
Custodian: Bank of New York
Investment objective and policies: High current income consistent with preservation of capital and liquidity. Invests in high-grade domestic and international money market instruments.
Year organized: 1979
Ticker symbol: FDRXX
Group fund code: 055
Deadline for same day wire purchase: 12 NN
Number of switches permitted: Unlimited
Check redemptions: $500 minimum
Confirmations mailed: After each purchase and each check, mail or wire redemption
Checks returned: Quarterly
Periodic account statements mailed: Quarterly
Dividends paid: Income - declared daily, paid monthly
Management fee: 0.03% plus group fee of 0.12% to 0.37% plus 6.0% of gross income for portion of fund's gross income that represents a gross yield of more than 5.0% per year.
Expense ratio: 0.52% (year ending 11/30/94)

FIDELITY CONNECTICUT MUNICIPAL MONEY MARKET PORTFOLIO ◆
(See first Fidelity listing for data common to all Fidelity funds)

Sub-adviser: FMR Texas, Inc.
Portfolio manager: Scott Orr (1993)
Custodian: United Missouri Bank, N.A.
Investment objective and policies: High current income exempt from federal and Connecticut income taxes. Invests in money market instruments issued by the State of Connecticut.
Year organized: 1989
Ticker symbol: FCMXX
Group fund code: 418
Minimum purchase: Initial: $5,000, Subsequent: $500
Deadline for same day wire purchase: 12 NN
Qualified for sale in: CT, NJ, NY
Number of switches permitted: Unlimited
Check redemptions: $500 minimum
Confirmations mailed: After each purchase and each check, mail or wire redemption
Checks returned: Quarterly
Periodic account statements mailed: Quarterly
Dividends paid: Income - declared daily, paid monthly
Management fee: 0.25% plus group fee of 0.12% to 0.37%
12b-1 distribution fee: Yes (not currently imposed)
Expense ratio: 0.60% (year ending 11/30/94)

FIDELITY CONTRAFUND

(See first Fidelity listing for data common to all Fidelity funds)

Portfolio manager: Will Danoff (1990)
Custodian: Brown Brothers Harriman & Co.
Investment objective and policies: Capital appreciation. Invests primarily in common stocks and securities convertible into common stock of companies believed to be undervalued due to an overly pessimistic appraisal by the public. Fund may use foreign securities without limit and use currency exchange contracts, stock index futures and options and hedge up to 25% of total assets.
Year organized: 1967
Ticker symbol: FCNTX
Group fund code: 022
Sales charge: 3% (waived for retirement accounts using Fidelity prototype plans)
Discount broker availability: Schwab, White, Waterhouse, Fidelity, Siebert
Dividends paid: Income - February, December; Capital gains - February, December
Portfolio turnover (3 yrs): 235%, 255%, 297%
Largest holding: Intel Corp. (1.7%)
Management fee: 0.30% plus group fee of 0.27% to 0.52% plus performance fee, relative to S&P 500 over 36 months, of +/- 0.20%
Expense ratio: 1.00% (year ending 12/31/94) (1.03% without waiver)

FIDELITY CONVERTIBLE SECURITIES FUND ◆

(See first Fidelity listing for data common to all Fidelity funds)

Portfolio manager: Charles Mangum (1995)
Custodian: Brown Brother Harriman & Co.
Investment objective and policies: High total return - current income and capital appreciation. Invests at least 65% of assets in securities convertible into common stock. Fund may also invest in common stocks, non-convertible securities, junk bonds, zero coupon bonds, restricted securities and pay-in-kind bonds. May use puts and short sales to hedge (limited to 15% of assets). Fund may use foreign securities without limit and foreign currency exchange contracts.
Year organized: 1987
Ticker symbol: FCVSX
Group fund code: 308
Discount broker availability: Schwab, White, Waterhouse, *Fidelity, *Siebert
Dividends paid: Income - March, June, September, December; Capital Gains - January, December
Portfolio turnover (3 yrs): 318%, 312%, 258%
Largest holding: RJR Nabisco Holdings Corp. (6.1%)
Management fee: 0.20% plus group fee of 0.27% to 0.52% plus performance fee, relative to the Merrill Lynch Convertible Securities Index over 36 months, of +/- 0.15%
12b-1 distribution fee: Yes (not currently imposed)
Expense ratio: 0.85% (year ending 11/30/94) (0.86% without waiver)

FIDELITY DAILY INCOME TRUST ◆

(See first Fidelity listing for data common to all Fidelity funds)

Portfolio manager: Burnell Stehman (1985)
Sub-adviser: FMR Texas, Inc.
Custodian: Bank of New York
Investment objective and policies: Current income consistent with preservation of capital and liquidity. Invests in high-grade money market instruments.
Year organized: 1974
Ticker symbol: FDTXX
Group fund code: 031
Minimum purchase: Initial: $5,000, Subsequent: $500; IRA/Keogh: Initial: $500, Subsequent: $250
Deadline for same day wire purchase: 12 NN
Number of switches permitted: Unlimited
Check redemptions: Yes, $1 fee to fund on non-USA shareholder checks less than $500
Confirmations mailed: After each purchase and each check, mail or wire redemption

Checks returned: Quarterly
Periodic account statements mailed: Quarterly
Service fee: $5 per month per account
Dividends paid: Income - declared daily, paid monthly
Management fee: 0.10% first $2B to 0.05% over $6B plus 4% of fund's monthly income (bounded by 0.20% and 0.40% of total assets)
Expense ratio: 0.56% (year ending 8/31/94)

FIDELITY DISCIPLINED EQUITY FUND ◆

(See first Fidelity listing for data common to all Fidelity funds)

Portfolio manager: Bradford Lewis (1989)
Custodian: Brown Brothers Harriman & Co.
Investment objective and policies: Capital growth. Invests primarily in common stocks, at least 65% domestic issuers, believed undervalued relative to their industries as determined by a proprietary computer model supported by conventional fundamental research. Maintains S&P sector weightings but targets stocks with greatest growth potential. Up to 35% of assets may be in foreign stocks. Fund uses foreign currency exchange contracts, and futures and options and may hedge up to 25% of total assets.
Year organized: 1989
Ticker symbol: FDEQX
Group fund code: 315
Discount broker availability: Schwab, White, Waterhouse, *Fidelity, *Siebert
Dividends paid: Income - December; Capital gains - December
Portfolio turnover (3 yrs): 139%, 279%, 255%
Largest holding: Amoco Corp. (2.8%)
Management fee: 0.30% plus group fee of 0.27% to 0.52% plus performance fee, relative to S&P 500 over 36 months, of +/- 0.20%
Expense ratio: 1.05% (year ending 10/31/94) (1.07% without waiver)

FIDELITY DIVERSIFIED INTERNATIONAL FUND

(See first Fidelity listing for data common to all Fidelity funds)

Sub-advisers: FMR U.K., FMR Far East
Portfolio manager: Greg Fraser (1991)
Custodian: Chase Manhattan Bank, N.A.
Investment objective and policies: Growth of capital. Invests in equity securities of companies located anywhere outside the U.S., primarily with market capitalizations of $100M or more, but may invest in smaller companies. Equity selection based on computer-aided quantitative analysis supported by fundamental research. Invests in the major markets of the Morgan Stanley Capital International Europe, Australia, Far East (EAFE) Index. May use currency exchange contracts, futures contracts and options and hedge up to 25% of total assets.
Year organized: 1991
Ticker symbol: FDIVX
Group fund code: 325
Sales charge: 3% (waived for all accounts through 6/30/95 and retirement accounts using Fidelity prototype plans)
Discount broker availability: Schwab, White, Waterhouse, *Fidelity, *Siebert
Dividends paid: Income - December; Capital gains - December
Portfolio turnover (3 yrs): 89%, 56%, 56%
Largest holding: Veba AG Ord., Germany (1.9%)
Management fee: 0.45% plus group fee of 0.27% to 0.52% plus performance fee of +/- 0.20% relative to the EAFE Index
Expense ratio: 1.25% (year ending 10/31/94)

FIDELITY DIVIDEND GROWTH FUND ◆

(See first Fidelity listing for data common to all Fidelity funds)

Portfolio manager: Abigail Johnson (1993)
Custodian: Brown Brothers Harriman & Co.
Investment objective and policies: Capital growth. Normally invests at least 65% in equity

securities of companies with potential for dividend growth. Fund may invest in all types of equity securities, including common and preferred stock and securities convertible into common and preferred stock. May invest up to 35% of assets in junk bonds, other debt securities of all types and warrants. Fund may use foreign stocks, foreign currency exchange contracts, and stock index futures and options on up to 25% of assets).
Year organized: 1993
Ticker symbol: FDGFX
Group fund code: 330
Discount broker availability: White, Waterhouse, *Fidelity, *Siebert
Dividends paid: Income - March, December; Capital gains - March, December
Portfolio turnover (1 yr): 291%
Largest holding: Ericson (L.M.) Telephone Co. Class B ADR (3.8%)
Management fee: 0.30% plus group fee of 0.27% to 0.52%
Expense ratio: 1.40% (year ending 7/31/94) (1.43% without waiver)

FIDELITY EMERGING GROWTH FUND

(See first Fidelity listing for data common to all Fidelity funds)

Portfolio manager: Lawrence Greenberg (1993)
Custodian: Brown Brothers Harriman & Co.
Investment objective and policies: Capital appreciation. Invests at least 65% of assets in equity securities of emerging growth companies of small to medium size (less than $1B market capitalization) with potential for accelerated earnings and revenue growth due to new products or technologies, new channels of distribution, revitalized management and/or industry conditions. May use convertibles, warrants and rights, foreign securities and closed-end investment companies. May hold restricted securities, use currency exchange contracts, futures contracts and options thereon (up to 15% of assets), and sell short against the box (up to 15% of assets).
Year organized: 1991
Ticker symbol: FDEGX
Group fund code: 324
Sales charge: 3% (waived for retirement accounts using Fidelity prototype plans)
Discount broker availability: Waterhouse, Fidelity, Siebert
Redemption fee: 0.75% on shares held less than 90 days
Dividends paid: Income - January, December; Capital gains - January, December
Portfolio turnover (3 yrs): 180%, 332%, 531%
Largest holding: Oracle Systems Corp. (4.6%)
Management fee: 0.35% plus group fee of 0.27% to 0.52% plus performance fee of +/- 0.20% relative to Russell 2000 Index over 36 months
Expense ratio: 1.02% (year ending 11/30/94) (1.04% without waiver)

FIDELITY EMERGING MARKETS FUND

(See first Fidelity listing for data common to all Fidelity funds)

Portfolio manager: Richard Hazelwood (1993)
Custodian: Chase Manhattan Bank, N.A.
Investment objective: Capital appreciation. Invests in common stocks and other equity securities of foreign issuers in the emerging economies and developing markets of Europe (such as Greece and Turkey), Asia (such as Thailand and Malaysia) and Latin America (particularly Mexico). May use forward currency contracts, currency swap agreements and options and hedge up to 25% of total assets.
Year organized: 1990 (name changed from Fidelity International Opportunities Fund in February 1993)
Ticker symbol: FEMKX
Group fund code: 322
Sales charge: 3% (waived for retirement accounts using Fidelity prototype plans)
Discount broker availability: Schwab, Waterhouse, Fidelity, Siebert
Redemption fee: 1.5% on shares held less than 90 days

Dividends paid: Income - December; Capital gains - December
Portfolio turnover (3 yrs): 107%, 57%, 159%
Largest holding: Grupo Carso SA de CV Class A-1, Mexico (1.9%)
Management fee: 0.45% plus group fee of 0.27% to 0.52%
Expense ratio: 1.52% (year ending 10/31/94)

FIDELITY EQUITY-INCOME FUND ◆
(See first Fidelity listing for data common to all Fidelity funds)

Portfolio manager: Stephen R. Peterson (1993)
Custodian: Chase Manhattan Bank, N.A.
Investment objective and policies: Income exceeding the yield on the securities comprising the S&P 500 and some capital appreciation. Invests at least 80% of assets in income-producing common or preferred stocks. Debt obligations will normally be convertible. May use junk bonds (up to 20% of assets), foreign securities and foreign currency exchange contracts and stock index futures and options (up to 15% of assets). Fund may hedge up to 25% of total assets.
Year organized: 1966
Ticker symbol: FEQIX
Group fund code: 023
Discount broker availability: Schwab, White, Waterhouse, *Fidelity, *Siebert
Sales charge: 2% (waived though 12/31/95)
Dividends paid: Income - March, June, September, December; Capital gains - March, December
Portfolio turnover (3 yrs): 70%, 84%, 111%
Largest holding: General Electric Company (2.7%)
Management fee: 0.12% plus group fee of 0.27% to 0.52%
Expense ratio: 0.66% (year ending 1/31/94)

FIDELITY EQUITY-INCOME II FUND ◆
(See first Fidelity listing for data common to all Fidelity funds)

Portfolio manager: Brian Posner (1992)
Custodian: Chase Manhattan Bank, N.A.
Investment objective and policies: Reasonable income with potential for capital growth. Invests at least 65% of assets in income-producing equity securities with goal of exceeding total return of the S&P 500. May use junk bonds (up to 20% of assets), foreign securities and foreign currency exchange contracts and stock index futures and options (up to 15% of assets). Fund may hedge up to 25% of total assets.
Year organized: 1990
Ticker symbol: FEQTX
Group fund code: 319
Discount broker availability: Schwab, White, Waterhouse, *Fidelity, *Siebert
Dividends paid: Income - March, June, September, December; Capital gains - January, December
Portfolio turnover (3 yrs): 75%, 55%, 89%
Largest holding: American Express Co. (3.6%)
Management fee: 0.20% plus group fee of 0.27% to 0.52%
Expense ratio: 0.81% (year ending 11/30/94) (0.83% without waiver)

FIDELITY EUROPE FUND
(See first Fidelity listing for data common to all Fidelity funds)

Sub-adviser: FMR (U.K.)
Portfolio manager: Sally Walden (1992)
Custodian: Chase Manhattan Bank, N.A.
Investment objective and policies: Long-term growth of capital. Invests at least 65% of assets in securities of companies which have their principal business activities in Western Europe. Fund will be invested in at least 3 countries. May use currency exchange contracts, futures contracts and options and hedge up to 25% of total assets.

Year organized: 1986 (Fidelity United Kingdom Fund merged into fund 4/28/89)
Ticker symbol: FIEUX
Group fund code: 301
Sales charge: 3% (waived for retirement accounts using Fidelity prototype plans)
Discount broker availability: Schwab, White, Waterhouse, Fidelity, Siebert
Redemption fee: 1% on shares purchased before 10/12/90
Portfolio turnover (3 yrs): 49%, 76%, 95%
Largest holding: Nakia AB Free shares, Finland (3.5%)
Dividends paid: Income - December; Capital gains - December
Management fee: 0.45% plus group fee of 0.27% to 0.52% plus performance fee of +/- 0.20% relative to Morgan Stanley Capital International Europe Index over 36 months
Expense ratio: 1.35% (year ending 10/31/94)

FIDELITY EUROPE CAPITAL APPRECIATION FUND
(See first Fidelity listing for data common to all Fidelity funds)

Sub-advisers: FMR (U.K.), FMR (Far East), FIIA
Portfolio manager: Kevin McCarey (1993)
Custodian: Chase Manhattan Bank, N.A.
Investment objective and policies: Long-term growth of capital. Invests at least 65% of assets in securities of companies which have their principal business activities in Eastern and Western Europe. Fund will be invested in at least 3 countries. May use currency exchange contracts, futures contracts and options and hedge up to 25% of total assets. Up to 15% of assets may be in illiquid securities. Fund will invest more aggressively than Fidelity Europe Fund.
Year organized: 1993
Ticker symbol: FECAX
Group fund code: 341
Sales charge: 3% (waived for all accounts through 6/30/95 and retirement accounts using Fidelity prototype plans)
Discount broker availability: Schwab, White, Waterhouse, *Fidelity, *Siebert
Dividends paid: Income - December; Capital gains - December
Portfolio turnover (1 yr): 317%
Largest holding: Schering AG, Germany (2.8%)
Management fee: 0.45% plus group fee of 0.27% to 0.52% plus performance fee of +/- 0.20% relative to Morgan Stanley Capital International Europe Index over 36 months
Expense ratio: 1.54% (10 months ending 10/31/94)

FIDELITY EXPORT FUND
(See first Fidelity listing for data common to all Fidelity funds)

Sub-advisers: FMR (U.K.), FMR (Far East)
Portfolio manager: Arieh Coll (1994)
Custodian: Brown Brothers Harriman & Co.
Investment objective: Long-term capital growth. Invests primarily in common stocks and other equity securities of North American companies with 10% or more of annual revenues from sale of exported goods or services or engaged in export-related businesses. May use futures and options and hedge up to 25% of total assets. Fund is non-diversified.
Year organized: 1994
Group fund code: 332
Sales charge: 3% (waived for retirement accounts using Fidelity prototype plans and for all shareholders through 12/31/95)
Discount broker availability: Waterhouse, *Fidelity, *Siebert
Dividends paid: Income - October, December; Capital gains - October, December
Management fee: 0.30% plus group fee of 0.27% to 0.52%

FIDELITY FIFTY FUND
(See first Fidelity listing for data common to all Fidelity funds)

Sub-advisers: FMR (U.K.), FMR (Far East)
Portfolio manager: Scott Stewart (1993)
Custodian: Brown Brothers Harriman & Co.
Investment objective: Capital appreciation. Invests in common stocks and other equity securities of domestic and foreign companies believed to have the greatest growth potential. Fund will normally be invested in 50-60 stocks and is non-diversified. May use forward currency contracts, currency swap agreements and options for hedging purposes (up to 25% of assets). Fund is non-diversified.
Year organized: 1993
Ticker symbol: FFTYX
Group fund code: 500
Sales charge: 3% (waived for retirement accounts using Fidelity prototype plans and for all shareholders through 12/31/96)
Discount broker availability: Schwab, White, Fidelity, Siebert
Dividends paid: Income - December; Capital gains - December
Portfolio turnover (1 yr): 320%
Largest holding: Olin Corp. (2.5%)
Management fee: 0.30% plus group fee of 0.27% to 0.52% plus performance fee of +/- 0.20% relative to S&P 500 Index
Expense ratio: 1.58% (9 months ending 6/30/94)

FIDELITY FOREIGN CURRENCY PORTFOLIOS
(See first Fidelity listing for data common to all Fidelity funds)

Portfolio manager: Scott Kuldell (1994)
Custodian: Chase Manhattan Bank, N.A.
Investment objective and policies: Stability of principal with reasonable current income. Each portfolio's performance will approximate the performance of its reference currency relative to the U.S. dollar, while earning income at money market rates prevailing in its reference currency. Each portfolio invests in dollar-denominated money market instruments along with forward currency exchange contracts or money market instruments denominated in its reference currency. Funds are organized as limited partnerships.
Portfolios: Deutsche Mark (Germany), Pound Sterling (United Kingdom), Yen (Japan)
Year organized: 1989
Group fund code: Deutsche Mark 497, Pound Sterling 498, Yen 499
Sales charge: 0.4% less than $25,000, 0.3% $25,000-$100,000, 0.2% over $100,000
Minimum purchase: Initial: $5,000, Subsequent: $1,000
Discount broker availability: White
Exchange privileges: None; sales charge offset if funds transferred to another Fidelity load fund
Dividends paid: None
Management fee: 0.50%
Expense ratio: Deutsche Mark - 1.50% (2.10% without waiver); Sterling - 1.50% (2.60% without waiver); Yen - 1.50% (2.60% without waiver) (year ending 12/31/94)
Reports: K-1 issued annually, semi-annual fund reports

FIDELITY FUND ◆
(See first Fidelity listing for data common to all Fidelity funds)

Newspaper listing: Fidel
Portfolio manager: Beth Terrana (1993)
Custodian: Chase Manhattan Bank, N.A.
Investment objective and policies: Long-term capital growth with reasonable current income. Invests primarily in common stocks and convertible securities of established companies. Fund may use foreign securities and currency exchange contracts, stock index futures, options, and options on futures. Fund may hedge up to 25% of total assets.
Year organized: 1930
Ticker symbol: FFIDX

Group fund code: 003
Discount broker availability: Schwab, White, Waterhouse, *Fidelity, *Siebert
Dividends paid: Income - March, June, September, December; Capital gains - August, December
Portfolio turnover (3 yrs): 207%, 261%, 151%
Largest holding: British Petroleum PLC ADR (2.4%)
Management fee: 0.09% plus group fee of 0.27% to 0.52%
12b-1 distribution fee: Yes (not currently imposed)
Expense ratio: 0.65% (year ending 6/30/94) (0.68% without waiver)

FIDELITY GINNIE MAE PORTFOLIO ◆
(See first Fidelity listing for data common to all Fidelity funds)

Portfolio manager: Kevin Grant (1995)
Custodian: Bank of New York
Investment objective and policies: High current income consistent with prudent investment risk. Invests at least 65% of assets in Government National Mortgage Association pass-through certificates. Remainder will be in any type of U.S. or foreign debt or other income-producing investments, including other types of mortgage securities, government or government agency securities, asset-backed securities, and corporate debt instruments. All non-government debt securities will be rated within the three highest grades by Moody's or S&P.
Year organized: 1985
Ticker symbol: FGMNX
Group fund code: 015
Discount broker availability: Schwab, White, Waterhouse, *Fidelity, *Siebert
Check redemptions: $500 minimum
Dividends paid: Income - declared daily, paid monthly; Capital gains - September, December
Portfolio turnover (3 yrs): 303%, 259%, 114%
Management fee: 0.30% plus group fee of 0.12% to 0.37%
12b-1 distribution fee: Yes (not currently imposed)
Expense ratio: 0.82% (year ending 7/31/94)

FIDELITY GLOBAL BALANCED FUND ◆
(See first Fidelity listing for data common to all Fidelity funds)

Portfolio managers: Robert Haber (1993), Rick Mace (1995)
Custodian: Brown Brother Harriman & Co.
Investment objective and policies: High current income consistent with preservation of capital with moderate capital growth secondary. Invests in common stocks and fixed-income securities (preferred stocks, bonds and money market instruments) issued anywhere in the world. Fund adjusts distribution of assets to changing market and economic conditions with at least 25% of assets in fixed-income senior securities. Fund may use foreign securities without limit and use currency exchange contracts, stock index futures and options and hedge up to 25% of total assets.
Year organized: 1993
Ticker symbol: FGBLX
Group fund code: 334
Discount broker availability: Schwab, White, Waterhouse, *Fidelity, *Siebert
Dividends paid: Income - March, June, September, December; Capital Gains - September, December
Portfolio turnover (2 yrs): 226%, 172%
Largest holding: Argentina Republic Brady euro 4 1/4% due 3/31/23 (8.3%)
Management fee: 0.45% plus group fee of 0.27% to 0.52%
Expense ration: 1.67% (year ending 7/31/94) (1.68% without waiver)

FIDELITY GLOBAL BOND FUND ◆
(See first Fidelity listing for data common to all Fidelity funds)

Sub-advisers: FMR (U.K.), FMR (Far East)
Portfolio manager: Jonathan Kelly (1993)
Custodian: Chase Manhattan Bank, N.A.
Investment objective and policies: High total return. Invests at least 65% of assets in debt securities issued anywhere in the world, primarily in Australia, Canada, Japan, the Netherlands, New Zealand, U.S., and Western Europe with a weighted average maturity of 15 years or less. Up to 35% of assets may be in junk bonds and 15% in illiquid securities. May use currency exchange and futures contracts and options, as well as securities indexed to foreign currencies. May use options and futures on indexes.
Year organized: 1987
Ticker symbol: FGBDX
Group fund code: 451
Discount broker availability: Schwab, White, Waterhouse, *Fidelity, *Siebert
Dividends paid: Income - declared daily, paid monthly; Capital gains - February, December
Portfolio turnover (3 yrs): 367%, 198%, 81%
Management fee: 0.55% plus group fee of 0.12% to 0.37%
12b-1 distribution fee: Yes (not currently imposed)
Expense ratio: 1.14% (year ending 12/31/94)

FIDELITY GOVERNMENT SECURITIES FUND ◆
(See first Fidelity listing for data common to all Fidelity funds)

Portfolio manager: Robert Ives (1995)
Custodian: Bank of New York
Investment objective and policies: High current income consistent with preservation of principal. Invests at least 65% of assets in obligations issued by U.S. Government, its agencies or instrumentalities whose income is exempt from state and local taxes. Fund may use futures and options to hedge up to 25% of total assets.
Year organized: 1979
Ticker symbol: FGOVX
Group fund code: 054
Discount broker availability: Schwab, White, Waterhouse, *Fidelity, *Siebert
Check redemptions: $500 minimum
Dividends paid: Income - declared daily, paid monthly; Capital gains - December
Portfolio turnover (3 yrs): 402%, 323%, 219%
Management fee: 0.30% plus group fee of 0.12% to 0.37%
12b-1 distribution fee: Yes (not currently imposed)
Expense ratio: 0.69% (year ending 9/30/94)

FIDELITY GROWTH AND INCOME PORTFOLIO
(See first Fidelity listing for data common to all Fidelity funds)

Portfolio manager: Steven Kaye (1993)
Custodian: Chase Manhattan Bank, N.A.
Investment objective and policies: Long term capital growth, current income and growth of income, consistent with reasonable investment risk. Invests in securities of companies which offer growth of earnings potential while paying current dividends. May invest in any combination of common stock, convertibles, preferred stock and fixed-income securities. May use foreign securities, currency exchange contracts, stock index futures and options (up to 15% of assets) and junk bonds (up to 35% of assets). May hedge up to 25% of total assets.
Year organized: 1986
Ticker symbol: FGRIX
Group fund code: 027
Sales charge: 3% (waived for retirement accounts using Fidelity prototype plans)
Discount broker availability: Schwab, White, Waterhouse, Fidelity, Siebert
Dividends paid: Income - March, June, September, December; Capital gains - September, December
Portfolio turnover (3 yrs): 92%, 87%, 221%
Largest holding: General Electric Company (2.8%)
Management fee: 0.20% plus group fee of 0.27% to 0.52%
Expense ratio: 0.82% (year ending 7/31/94) (0.83% without waiver)

FIDELITY GROWTH COMPANY FUND
(See first Fidelity listing for data common to all Fidelity funds)

Portfolio manager: Robert Stansky (1987)
Custodian: Brown Brothers Harriman & Co.
Investment objective and policies: Capital appreciation. Invests primarily in common stocks and securities convertible into common stocks of companies with above average growth characteristics relative to the S&P 500. May be in emerging or mature industries. May use foreign securities and currency exchange contracts and stock index options, futures and options thereon. May hedge up to 25% of total assets.
Year organized: 1983 (formerly Fidelity Mercury Fund)
Ticker symbol: FDGRX
Group fund code: 025
Sales charge: 3% (waived for retirement accounts using Fidelity prototype plans and for all shareholders through 12/31/96)
Discount broker availability: Schwab, White, Fidelity, Siebert
Dividends paid: Income - January, December; Capital gains - January, December
Portfolio turnover (3 yrs): 135%, 159%, 250%
Largest holding: General Electric Co. (2.0%)
Management fee: 0.30% plus group fee of 0.27% to 0.52% plus performance fee of +/- 0.20% relative to S&P 500 over 36 months
Expense ratio: 1.05% (year ending 11/30/94) (1.06% without waiver)

FIDELITY HIGH YIELD TAX-FREE PORTFOLIO ◆
(See first Fidelity listing for data common to all Fidelity funds)

Newspaper listing: HiYld
Portfolio manager: Anne Punzak (1993)
Custodian: United Missouri Bank, N.A.
Investment objective and policies: High current income exempt from federal income taxes. Invests in long-term medium quality municipal bonds (A or Baa-Moody's), generally with maturities of 20 years or more. Up to 25% can be in bonds below BBB or unrated equivalent but no more than 10% may be in B or lower obligations. Up to 20% of assets may be in AMT securities. May use futures and options and hedge up to 25% of total assets.
Year organized: 1977 (formerly Fidelity High Yield Municipals, merged in Fidelity Texas Tax-Free Portfolio on 6/29/90)
Ticker symbol: FHIGX
Group fund code: 037
Discount broker availability: Schwab, White, Waterhouse, *Fidelity, *Siebert
Check redemptions: $500 minimum
Dividends paid: Income - declared daily, paid monthly; Capital gains - December
Portfolio turnover (3 yrs): 48%, 53%, 47%
Management fee: 0.25% plus group fee of 0.12% to 0.37%
12b-1 distribution fee: Yes (not currently imposed)
Expense ratio: 0.56% (year ending 11/30/94)

FIDELITY INSURED TAX-FREE PORTFOLIO ◆
(See first Fidelity listing for data common to all Fidelity funds)

Newspaper listing: InsMu
Portfolio manager: Guy E. Wickwire (1993)
Custodian: United Missouri Bank, N.A.
Investment objective and policies: High income exempt from federal income taxes consistent with preservation of capital. Invests primarily in municipal bonds covered by insurance guaranteeing the timely payment of principal and interest. Up to 35% of assets may be invested in uninsured obligations with not more than 5% below investment grade. May use futures and options and hedge up to 25% of total assets.
Year organized: 1985

Ticker symbol: FMUIX
Group fund code: 013
Discount broker availability: White, Waterhouse, *Fidelity, *Siebert
Check redemptions: $500 minimum
Dividends paid: Income - declared daily, paid monthly; Capital gains - February, December
Portfolio turnover (3 yrs): 56%, 78%, 69%
Management fee: 0.25% plus group fee of 0.12% to 0.37%
Portfolio insurance: estimated at 0.10% to 0.35%
12b-1 distribution fee: Yes (not currently imposed)
Expense ratio: 0.58% (year ending 12/31/94)

FIDELITY INTERMEDIATE BOND FUND ◆
(See first Fidelity listing on page 253 for data common to all Fidelity funds)

Newspaper listing: IntBd
Portfolio manager: Michael Gray (1987)
Custodian: Bank of New York
Investment objective and policies: High current income. Invests primarily in high and upper medium grade fixed-income obligations (BBB or better) with a weighted average maturity of 3 to 10 years. Fund may use options, futures and options thereon, and currency exchange contracts. May hedge up to 25% of total assets.
Year organized: 1975 (name changed from Fidelity Thrift Trust on 9/1/87)
Ticker symbol: FTHRX
Group fund code: 032
Discount broker availability: Schwab, White, Waterhouse, *Fidelity, *Siebert
Check redemptions: $500 minimum
Dividends paid: Income - declared daily, paid monthly; Capital gains - June, December
Portfolio turnover (3 yrs): 81%, 51%, 80%
Management fee: 0.30% plus group fee of 0.12% to 0.37%
12b-1 distribution fee: Yes (not currently imposed)
Expense ratio: 0.64% (year ending 4/30/94)

FIDELITY INTERNATIONAL GROWTH AND INCOME FUND ◆
(See first Fidelity listing on page 253 for data common to all Fidelity funds)

Newspaper listing: IntGr
Sub-advisers: FMR (U.K.), FMR (Far East)
Portfolio manager: Rick Mace (1994)
Custodian: Chase Manhattan Bank, N.A.
Investment objective and policies: Capital growth and current income. Normally invests at least 65% of assets in equity securities and bonds from at least 6 different countries, primarily in developed markets in Europe, the Far East, and the Pacific Basin. At least 25% of assets in debt securities rated Baa or better with up to 20% in securities of U.S. issuers. May use currency exchange contracts, futures contracts and options and hedge up to 25% of total assets.
Year organized: 1986
Ticker symbol: FIGRX
Group fund code: 305
Discount broker availability: Schwab, White, Waterhouse, *Fidelity, *Siebert
Redemption fee: 1% on shares purchased before 10/12/90
Dividends paid: Income - December; Capital gains - December
Portfolio turnover (3 yrs): 173%, 24%, 76%
Largest holding: Koninklijke PPT Nederland (2.3%)
Management fee: 0.45% plus group fee of 0.27% to 0.52%
Expense ratio: 1.21% (year ending 10/31/94)

FIDELITY INTERNATIONAL VALUE FUND
(See first Fidelity listing on page 253 for data common to all Fidelity funds)

Newspaper listing: IntGr
Sub-advisers: FMR (U.K.), FMR (Far East)
Portfolio manager: Rick Mace (1994)

Custodian: Chase Manhattan Bank, N.A.
Investment objective and policies: Long-term capital growth. Invests primarily in equity securities of foreign companies believed undervalued from at least 3 different countries, primarily in developed markets in Europe, the Far East, and the Pacific Basin. Up to 35% of assets may be in junk bonds and 15% in illiquid securities. May use currency exchange contracts, futures contracts and options and hedge up to 25% of total assets.
Year organized: 1994
Group fund code: 335
Sales charge: 3% (waived for all accounts through 6/30/95 and retirement accounts using Fidelity prototype plans)
Discount broker availability: *Fidelity, *Siebert
Dividends paid: Income - December; Capital gains - December
Management fee: 0.45% plus group fee of 0.27% to 0.52% plus performance fee of +/- 0.20% relative to EAFE Index over 36 months

FIDELITY INVESTMENT GRADE BOND FUND ◆
(See first Fidelity listing on page 253 for data common to all Fidelity funds)

Newspaper listing: InvGB
Portfolio manager: Michael Gray (1987)
Custodian: Bank of New York
Investment objective and policies: High current income consistent with reasonable risk. Invests primarily in investment-grade debt securities with maturities of 10-15 years. May use bonds, notes, convertible bonds, mortgage-related securities, domestic and foreign government and government agency securities, zero coupon bonds and preferred stocks. May invest up to 35% of assets in junk bonds and 20% in warrants. May use options and futures and hedge up to 25% of total assets.
Year organized: 1971 (formerly Fidelity Flexible Bond Fund, name changed 4/15/92. Previously Fidelity Corporate Bond Fund)
Ticker symbol: FBNDX
Group fund code: 026
Discount broker availability: Schwab, White, Waterhouse, *Fidelity, *Siebert
Check redemptions: $500 minimum
Dividends paid: Income - declared daily, paid monthly; Capital gains - June, December
Portfolio turnover (3 yrs): 61%, 74%, 77%
Management fee: 0.30% plus group fee of 0.12% to 0.37%
12b-1 distribution fee: Yes (not currently imposed)
Expense ratio: 0.74% (year ending 4/30/94)

FIDELITY JAPAN FUND
(See first Fidelity listing on page 253 for data common to all Fidelity funds)

Sub-adviser: FMR (Far East)
Portfolio manager: Shigeki Makino (1994)
Custodian: Chase Manhattan Bank, N.A.
Investment objective and policies: Long-term growth of capital. Invests at least 65% of assets in securities of issuers that have their principal activities in Japan or are organized under Japanese law. May invest in common and preferred stocks, securities convertible into stocks, equity securities of closed-end investment companies, and depository receipts of equity securities. May invest in Japanese debt securities and U.S. and foreign money market instruments for defensive purposes. May buy and sell options and futures contracts to hedge up to 25% of assets.
Year organized: 1992
Ticker symbol: FJAPX
Group fund code: 350
Sales charge: 3% (waived for all accounts through 6/30/95 and retirement accounts using Fidelity prototype plans)
Discount broker availability: Schwab, White, Waterhouse, *Fidelity, *Siebert
Dividends paid: Income - December; Capital gains - December
Portfolio turnover (2 yrs): 153%, 257%

Largest holding: Matsushita Electric Industrial Co., Ltd. (2.0%)
Management fee: 0.45% plus group fee of 0.27% to 0.52% plus performance fee of +/- 0.20% relative to the TOPIX, an index of stocks in the first section of the Tokyo Stock Exchange over 36 months
Expense ratio: 1.42% (year ending 10/31/94)

FIDELITY LATIN AMERICA FUND
(See first Fidelity listing on page 253 for data common to all Fidelity funds)

Sub-adviser: FMR (U.K.)
Portfolio manager: Patricia A. Satterthwaite (1993)
Custodian: Brown Brothers Harriman & Co.
Investment objective and policies: Long-term growth of capital. Invests at least 65% of assets in securities of Latin American (Mexico and all countries in Central America and South America) issuers. May invest in common and preferred stocks, securities convertible into stocks, equity securities of closed-end investment companies, depository receipts of equity securities, debt securities and U.S. and foreign money market instruments for defensive purposes. May buy and sell options and futures contracts to hedge up to 25% of assets. May invest up to 15% of assets in illiquid securities
Year organized: 1993
Ticker symbol: FLATX
Group fund code: 349
Sales charge: 3% (waived for retirement accounts using Fidelity prototype plans)
Discount broker availability: Schwab, Waterhouse, *Fidelity, *Siebert
Redemption fee: 1.5% on shares held less than 90 days
Portfolio turnover (2 yrs): 77%, 72%
Largest holding: Grupo Carso SA de CV Class A-1 (4.0%)
Dividends paid: Income - December; Capital gains - December
Management fee: 0.45% plus group fee of 0.27% to 0.52%
Expense ratio: 1.48% (year ending 10/31/94)

FIDELITY LIMITED TERM MUNICIPALS ◆
(See first Fidelity listing on page 253 for data common to all Fidelity funds)

Newspaper listing: LtdMun
Portfolio manager: David Murphy (1989)
Custodian: United Missouri Bank, N.A.
Investment objective and policies: High current income exempt from federal income taxes. Invests at least 80% of assets in high-quality municipal obligations (Baa or higher) having individual maturities of 15 years or less with weighted average maturity of 12 years or less. May use futures and options and hedge up to 25% of total assets.
Year organized: 1977
Ticker symbol: FLTMX
Group fund code: 036
Discount broker availability: Schwab, White, Waterhouse, *Fidelity, *Siebert
Check redemptions: $500 minimum
Dividends paid: Income - declared daily, paid monthly; Capital gains - February, December
Portfolio turnover (3 yrs): 30%, 111%, 50%
Management fee: 0.10% plus 5% of gross income
12b-1 distribution fee: Yes (not currently imposed)
Expense ratio: 0.56% (year ending 12/31/94)

FIDELITY LOW-PRICED STOCK FUND
(See first Fidelity listing on page 253 for data common to all Fidelity funds)

Portfolio manager: Joel Tillinghast (1990)
Custodian: Brown Brothers Harriman & Co.
Investment objective and policies: Capital appreciation. Invests at least 65% of assets in equity securities priced at or below $25 per share at time of purchase. Remainder of assets may be in higher priced equity securities, convertible securities and debt

instruments. Fund may use foreign securities and currency exchange contracts, junk bonds, stock index futures and options, and short sales against the box. May hedge up to 25% of total assets.
Year organized: 1990
Ticker symbol: FLPSX
Group fund code: 316
Sales Charge: 3% (waived for retirement accounts using Fidelity prototype plans)
Discount broker availability: Schwab, Waterhouse, Fidelity, Siebert
Redemption fee: 1.5% for shares held less than 90 days
Dividends paid: Income - September, December; Capital gains - September, December
Portfolio turnover (3 yrs): 54%, 47%, 82%
Largest holding: Universal Health Services, Inc. Class B (1.4%)
Management fee: 0.35% plus group fee of 0.27% to 0.52% plus performance fee of +/- 0.20% relative to Russell 2000 Index over 36 months
Expense ratio: 1.13% (year ending 7/31/94) (1.14% without waiver)

FIDELITY MAGELLAN FUND
(See first Fidelity listing on page 253 for data common to all Fidelity funds)

Portfolio manager: Jeff Vinik (1992)
Custodian: Brown Brothers Harriman & Co.
Investment objective and policies: Long term capital growth. Invests primarily in common stocks and securities convertible into common stocks of both domestic and foreign companies. Fund may invest up to 20% of assets in debt securities, use currency exchange contracts, and stock index futures and options thereon. May hedge up to 25% of total assets.
Year organized: 1963 (opened for general public sale June 24, 1981)
Ticker symbol: FMAGX
Group fund code: 021
Sales charge: 3%
Discount broker availability: Schwab, White, Waterhouse, Fidelity, Siebert
Dividends paid: Income - May, December; Capital gains - May, December
Portfolio turnover (3 yrs): 132%, 155%, 172%
Largest holding: Motorola, Inc. (2.4%)
Management fee: 0.30% plus group fee of 0.27% to 0.52% plus performance fee of +/- 0.20% relative to S&P 500 over 36 months
Expense ratio: 0.99% (year ending 3/31/94) (1.00% without waiver)

FIDELITY MARKET INDEX FUND ◆
(See first Fidelity listing on page 253 for data common to all Fidelity funds)

Portfolio manager: Jennifer Farrelly (1994)
Custodian: Brown Brothers Harriman & Co.
Investment objective and policies: Investment results that correspond to the total return of the S&P 500 Index. Long-term correlation target is 0.98. Invests in equity securities of companies which compose the S&P 500 Index, allocated in approximately the same weightings as the Index. Fund may use index futures and options to maintain fully invested position.
Year organized: 1990 (name changed from Fidelity Spartan Market Index Fund on 11/1/91)
Ticker symbol: FSMKX
Group fund code: 317
Redemption fee: 0.5% to fund for shares held less than 180 days
Index account fee: $10 per year, applied quarterly against dividends
Dividends paid: Income - March, June, September, December; Capital gains - June, December
Portfolio turnover (3 yrs): 3%, 0%, 1%
Largest holding: AT & T Corp. (2.4%)
Management fee: 0.45%
12b-1 distribution fee: Yes (not currently imposed)
Expense ratio: 0.44% (year ending 4/30/93) (0.45% without waiver)

FIDELITY MASSACHUSETTS TAX-FREE HIGH YIELD PORTFOLIO ◆
(See first Fidelity listing on page 253 for data common to all Fidelity funds)

Portfolio manager: Guy E. Wickwire (1983)
Sub-adviser: FMR Texas
Custodian: United Missouri Bank, N.A.
Investment objective and policies: Current income exempt from federal and Massachusetts personal income taxes. Invests at least 80% of assets in municipal obligations exempt from federal and Massachusetts income taxes, rated Baa or better, with a weighted average maturity of 15 years or more. Fund may use zero-coupon obligations and futures contracts and options thereon. May hedge up to 25% of total assets.
Year organized: 1983
Ticker symbol: FDMMX
Group fund code: 070
Discount broker availability: Schwab, White, Waterhouse, *Fidelity, *Siebert
Qualified for sale in: MA
Check redemptions: $500 minimum
Dividends paid: Income - declared daily, paid monthly; Capital gains - March, December
Management fee: 0.25% plus group fee of 0.12% to 0.37%
12b-1 distribution fee: Yes (not currently imposed)
Expense ratio: 0.54% (year ending 1/31/94)

FIDELITY MASSACHUSETTS TAX-FREE MONEY MARKET PORTFOLIO ◆
(See first Fidelity listing on page 253 for data common to all Fidelity funds)

Portfolio manager: Janice Bradburn (1992)
Custodian: United Missouri Bank, N.A.
Investment objective and policies: Current income exempt from federal and Massachusetts personal income taxes consistent with preservation of capital. Invests primarily in high quality, short-term Massachusetts municipal money market obligations.
Year organized: 1983
Ticker symbol: FDMXX
Group fund code: 074
Minimum purchase: Initial: $5,000, Subsequent: $250
Deadline for same day wire purchase: 12 NN
Qualified for sale in: MA
Number of switches permitted: Unlimited
Check redemptions: $500 minimum
Confirmations mailed: After each purchase and each check, mail or wire redemption
Checks returned: Quarterly
Periodic account statements mailed: Quarterly
Dividends paid: Income - declared daily, paid monthly
Management fee: 0.25% plus group fee of 0.12% to 0.37%
12b-1 distribution fee: Yes (not currently imposed)
Expense ratio: 0.66% (year ending 1/31/94)

FIDELITY MICHIGAN MUNICIPAL MONEY MARKET PORTFOLIO ◆
(See first Fidelity listing on page 253 for data common to all Fidelity funds)

Portfolio manager: Scott Orr (1992)
Sub-adviser: FMR Texas
Custodian: United Missouri Bank, N.A.
Investment objective and policies: High current income exempt from federal and Michigan state income taxes. Invests in money market instruments issued by the State of Michigan.
Year organized: 1990 (name changed from Michigan Tax-Free Money Market Portfolio on 8/10/90)
Ticker symbol: FMIXX
Group fund code: 420
Minimum purchase: Initial: $5,000, Subsequent: $500
Deadline for same day wire purchase: 12 NN
Qualified for sale in: MI
Number of switches permitted: Unlimited

Check redemptions: $500 minimum
Confirmations mailed: After each purchase and each check, mail or wire redemption
Checks returned: Quarterly
Periodic account statements mailed: Quarterly
Dividends paid: Income - declared daily, paid monthly
Management fee: 0.25% plus group fee of 0.12% to 0.37%
12b-1 distribution fee: Yes (not currently imposed)
Expense ratio: 0.61% (year ending 12/31/94)

FIDELITY MICHIGAN TAX-FREE HIGH YIELD PORTFOLIO ◆
(See first Fidelity listing on page 253 for data common to all Fidelity funds)

Portfolio manager: Maureen Newman (1994)
Custodian: United Missouri Bank, N.A.
Investment objective and policies: High current income exempt from federal and Michigan state personal income taxes. Invests primarily in investment-grade Michigan municipal bonds with a weighted average maturity of 15 years or more. Fund may use zero-coupon obligations and futures contracts and options thereon. May hedge up to 25% of total assets.
Year organized: 1985
Ticker symbol: FMHTX
Group fund code: 081
Discount broker availability: Schwab, Waterhouse, *Fidelity, *Siebert
Qualified for sale in: MI
Check redemptions: $500 minimum
Dividends paid: Income - declared daily, paid monthly; Capital gains - February, December
Portfolio turnover (3 yrs): 18%, 33%, 15%
Management fee: 0.25% plus group fee of 0.12% to 0.37%
12b-1 distribution fee: Yes (not currently imposed)
Expense ratio: 0.57% (year ending 12/31/94)

FIDELITY MID-CAP STOCK FUND
(See first Fidelity listing on page 253 for data common to all Fidelity funds)

Portfolio manager: Jennifer Uhrig (1994)
Custodian: Brown Brothers Harriman & Co.
Investment objective and policies: Long-term Capital appreciation. Invests primarily in common stocks and securities convertible into common stocks of companies with medium-sized market capitalizations ($100M to $7B). May use foreign securities and currency exchange contracts and stock index options, futures and options thereon. May hedge up to 25% of total assets.
Year organized: 1994
Ticker symbol: FDCSX
Group fund code: 337
Discount broker availability: White, *Fidelity, *Siebert
Dividends paid: Income - March, December; Capital gains - December
Largest holding: IBP, Inc. (3.0%)
Management fee: 0.30% plus group fee of 0.27% to 0.52% plus performance fee of +/- 0.20% relative to S&P MidCap 400 over 36 months

FIDELITY MINNESOTA TAX-FREE FUND ◆
(See first Fidelity listing on page 253 for data common to all Fidelity funds)

Portfolio manager: Steven Harvey (1993)
Custodian: United Missouri Bank, N.A.
Investment objective and policies: High current income exempt from federal and Minnesota state personal income taxes. Invests primarily in municipal obligations of the state of Minnesota or its political subdivisions exempt from federal and Minnesota taxes with a weighted average maturity of 15 years or more. Fund may use zero-coupon obligations and futures contracts and options thereon. May hedge up to 25% of total assets.
Year organized: 1985
Ticker symbol: FIMIX

Group fund code: 082
Discount broker availability: Schwab, Waterhouse, *Fidelity, *Siebert
Qualified for sale in: MN
Check redemptions: $500 minimum
Dividends paid: Income - declared daily, paid monthly; Capital gains - February, December
Portfolio turnover (3 yrs): 26%, 37%, 12%
Management fee: 0.25% plus group fee of 0.12% to 0.37%
12b-1 distribution fee: Yes (not currently imposed)
Expense ratio: 0.59% (year ending 12/31/94)

FIDELITY MORTGAGE SECURITIES PORTFOLIO ◆
(See first Fidelity listing on page 253 for data common to all Fidelity funds)

Portfolio manager: Kevin Grant (1993)
Custodian: Bank of New York
Investment objective and policies: High current income consistent with prudent investment risk. Invests at least 65% of assets in investment-grade mortgage-related securities. Potential for capital gain may also be considered. Invests in GNMA, FNMA, FHLMC, CMO's and debt obligations secured by mortgages on real estate. Remainder may be in any type of U.S. or foreign debt or other income-producing investments, including government or government agency securities, asset-backed securities, and corporate debt instruments. All non-government debt securities will be rated within the three highest grades by Moody's or S&P.
Year organized: 1984
Ticker symbol: FMSFX
Group fund code: 040
Discount broker availability: Schwab, White, Waterhouse, *Fidelity, *Siebert
Check redemptions: $500 minimum
Dividends paid: Income - declared daily, paid monthly; Capital gains - September, December
Portfolio turnover (3 yrs): 563%, 278%, 146%
Management fee: 0.30% plus group fee of 0.12% to 0.37%
12b-1 distribution fee: Yes (not currently imposed)
Expense ratio: 0.79% (year ending 7/31/94)

FIDELITY MUNICIPAL BOND PORTFOLIO ◆
(See first Fidelity listing on page 253 for data common to all Fidelity funds)

Newspaper listing: MunBd
Portfolio manager: Gary Swayze (1985)
Custodian: United Missouri Bank, N.A.
Investment objective and policies: High current income exempt from federal income taxes consistent with preservation of capital. Invests in upper medium (maximum 33% of assets) and high grade municipal bonds with a weighted average maturity of 20 years or more. May use futures and options and hedge up to 25% of total assets.
Year organized: 1976
Ticker symbol: FMBDX
Group fund code: 035
Discount broker availability: Schwab, White, Waterhouse, *Fidelity, *Siebert
Dividends paid: Income - declared daily, paid monthly; Capital gains - February, December
Check redemptions: $500 minimum
Portfolio turnover (3 yrs): 95%, 74%, 53%
Management fee: 0.25% plus group fee of 0.12% to 0.37%
12b-1 distribution fee: Yes (not currently imposed)
Expense ratio: 0.53% (year ending 12/31/94)

FIDELITY NEW JERSEY TAX-FREE MONEY MARKET PORTFOLIO ◆
(See first Fidelity listing on page 253 for data common to all Fidelity funds)

Portfolio manager: Scott Orr (1992)
Custodian: United Missouri Bank, N.A.
Investment objective and policies: High current income exempt from federal and New Jersey gross income tax. Invests primarily in money market

instruments issued by the State of New Jersey and its subdivisions.
Year organized: 1988
Ticker symbol: FNJXX
Group fund code: 417
Minimum purchase: Initial: $5,000, Subsequent: $250
Deadline for same day wire purchase: 12 NN
Qualified for sale in: NJ, NY, PA
Number of switches permitted: Unlimited
Check redemptions: $500 minimum
Confirmations mailed: After each purchase and each check, mail or wire redemption
Checks returned: Quarterly
Periodic account statements mailed: Quarterly
Dividends paid: Income - declared daily, paid monthly
Management fee: 0.25% plus group fee of 0.12% to 0.37%
12b-1 distribution fee: Yes (not currently imposed)
Expense ratio: 0.62% (year ending 11/30/94)

FIDELITY NEW MARKETS INCOME FUND ◆
(See first Fidelity listing on page 253 for data common to all Fidelity funds)

Portfolio manager: Jonathan Kelly (1995)
Custodian: Chase Manhattan Bank, N.A.
Investment objective and policies: High current income with capital appreciation secondary. Invests at least 65% of assets in debt securities of issuers whose principal activities are in emerging markets countries. May invest in corporate debt securities, sovereign debt instruments issued by governments or governmental entities, and all types of domestic and foreign money market instruments. At any one time substantially all assets may be in securities of poor quality or in default. May use currency forward contracts, futures and options and hedge up to 25% of total assets.
Year organized: 1993
Ticker symbol: FNMIX
Group fund code: 331
Discount broker availability: Schwab, White, Waterhouse, *Fidelity, *Siebert
Redemption fee: 1% for shares held less than 180 days, payable to the fund
Dividends paid: Income - declared daily, paid monthly; Capital gains - February, December
Portfolio turnover (1 yr): 409%
Management fee: 0.55% plus group fee of 0.12% to 0.37%
12b-1 distribution fee: Yes (not currently imposed)
Expense ratio: 1.28% (year ending 12/31/94) (1.50% without waiver)

FIDELITY NEW MILLENNIUM FUND
(See first Fidelity listing on page 253 for data common to all Fidelity funds)

Portfolio manager: Neal Miller (1992)
Custodian: Chase Manhattan Bank, N.A.
Investment objective and policies: Capital growth. Invests in equity securities, including common and preferred stock and securities convertible into common and preferred stock. Seeks securities of companies likely to benefit from social and economic change - in social attitudes, legislative actions, economic plans, demographics, and new product innovation. Although there is no restriction on company size, emphasis will be placed on small to medium capitalization companies. Fund may use foreign stocks, foreign currency exchange contracts, and stock index futures and options (limited to 15% of assets).
Year organized: 1992
Ticker symbol: FMILX
Group fund code: 300
Special sales restriction: Fund will close when assets reach $500M
Sales charge: 3%
Discount broker availability: Schwab, White, Waterhouse, Fidelity, Siebert
Dividends paid: Income - December; Capital gains - December
Portfolio turnover (2 yrs): 199%, 204%

Largest holding: Herman Miller, Inc. (3.7%)
Management fee: 0.35% plus group fee of 0.27% to 0.52% plus performance fee of +/- 0.20% relative to S&P 500 over 36 months
Expense ratio: 1.29% (year ending 11/30/94) (1.32% without waiver)

FIDELITY NEW YORK TAX-FREE HIGH YIELD PORTFOLIO ◆
(See first Fidelity listing on page 253 for data common to all Fidelity funds)

Newspaper listing: NY HY
Portfolio manager: Norman Lind (1993)
Custodian: United Missouri Bank, N.A.
Investment objective and policies: Current income exempt from federal, New York State and City income taxes. Invests primarily in long-term New York municipal bonds, up to 1/3 of which may be junk bonds, with a weighted average maturity of 15 years or more. Fund may use zero coupon bonds, and futures contracts and options thereon to hedge up to 25% of total assets.
Year organized: 1984 (name changed from New York Muni Bond Portfolio in October 1985)
Ticker symbol: FTFMX
Group fund code: 071
Discount broker availability: Schwab, White, Waterhouse, *Fidelity, *Siebert
Qualified for sale in: CT, NJ, NY
Check redemptions: $500 minimum
Portfolio turnover (3 yrs): 70%, 45%, 30%
Dividends paid: Income - declared daily, paid monthly; Capital gains - March, December
Management fee: 0.25% plus group fee of 0.12% to 0.37%
12b-1 distribution fee: Yes (not currently imposed)
Expense ratio: 0.58% (year ending 1/31/94)

FIDELITY NEW YORK TAX-FREE INSURED PORTFOLIO ◆
(See first Fidelity listing on page 253 for data common to all Fidelity funds)

Newspaper listing: NY Ins
Portfolio manager: Norman Lind (1994)
Custodian: United Missouri Bank, N.A.
Investment objective and policies: Current income exempt from federal, New York State and City income taxes. Invests primarily in New York municipal securities with a weighted average maturity of at least 20 years covered by insurance guaranteeing timely payment of principal and interest. Fund may use zero coupon bonds, and futures contracts and options thereon to hedge up to 25% of the portfolio's assets.
Year organized: 1985
Ticker symbol: FNTIX
Group fund code: 095
Discount broker availability: White, Waterhouse, *Fidelity, *Siebert
Qualified for sale in: CT, NJ, NY
Check redemptions: $500 minimum
Dividends paid: Income - declared daily, paid monthly; Capital gains - March, December
Portfolio turnover (3 yrs): 48%, 39%, 17%
Management fee: 0.25% plus group fee of 0.12% to 0.37%
12b-1 distribution fee: Yes (not currently imposed)
Expense ratio: 0.58% (year ending 1/31/94)

FIDELITY NEW YORK TAX-FREE MONEY MARKET PORTFOLIO ◆
(See first Fidelity listing on page 253 for data common to all Fidelity funds)

Portfolio manager: Janice Bradburn (1989)
Sub-adviser: FMR Texas
Custodian: United Missouri Bank, N.A.
Investment objective and policies: Income exempt from federal, New York State and City income taxes. Invests primarily in investment-grade New York municipal money market obligations.
Year organized: 1984 (formerly New York Short-term Portfolio)
Ticker symbol: FNYXX

Group fund code: 092
Minimum purchase: Initial: $5,000, Subsequent: $250
Deadline for same day wire purchase: 12 NN
Qualified for sale in: CT, NJ, NY
Number of switches permitted: Unlimited
Check redemptions: $500 minimum
Confirmations mailed: After each purchase and each check, mail or wire redemption
Checks returned: Quarterly
Periodic account statements mailed: Quarterly
Dividends paid: Income - declared daily, paid monthly
Management fee: 0.25% plus group fee of 0.12% to 0.37%
12b-1 distribution fee: Yes (not currently imposed)
Expense ratio: 0.62% (year ending 1/31/94)

FIDELITY OHIO MUNICIPAL MONEY MARKET PORTFOLIO ◆
(See first Fidelity listing on page 253 for data common to all Fidelity funds)

Portfolio manager: Janice Bradburn (1993)
Sub-adviser: FMR Texas
Custodian: United Missouri Bank, N.A.
Investment objective and policies: High current income exempt from federal and Ohio state income taxes. Invests in money market instruments issued by the state of Ohio.
Year organized: 1989 (name changed from Ohio Tax-Free Money Market Portfolio on 8/10/90)
Ticker symbol: FOMXX
Group fund code: 419
Minimum purchase: Initial: $5,000, Subsequent: $500
Deadline for same day wire purchase: 12 NN
Qualified for sale in: OH
Number of switches permitted: Unlimited
Check redemptions: $500 minimum
Confirmations mailed: After each purchase and each check, mail or wire redemption
Checks returned: Quarterly
Periodic account statements mailed: Quarterly
Dividends paid: Income - declared daily, paid monthly
Management fee: 0.25% plus group fee of 0.12% to 0.37%
12b-1 distribution fee: Yes (not currently imposed)
Expense ratio: 0.57% (year ending 12/31/94)

FIDELITY OHIO TAX-FREE HIGH YIELD PORTFOLIO ◆
(See first Fidelity listing on page 253 for data common to all Fidelity funds)

Portfolio manager: Steven Harvey (1994)
Custodian: United Missouri Bank, N.A.
Investment objective and policies: High current income exempt from federal and Ohio state income taxes. Invests primarily in investment-grade Ohio municipal bonds with a weighted average maturity of 15 years or more. At least 80% of its income distributions will be exempt from federal and Ohio income taxes.
Year organized: 1985
Ticker symbol: FOHFX
Group fund code: 088
Discount broker availability: Schwab, White, Waterhouse, *Fidelity, *Siebert
Qualified for sale in: OH
Check redemptions: $500 minimum
Dividends paid: Income - declared daily, paid monthly; Capital gains - February, December
Portfolio turnover (3 yrs): 22%, 41%, 20%
Management fee: 0.25% plus group fee of 10.12% to 0.37%
12b-1 distribution plan: Yes (not currently imposed)
Expense ratio: 0.57% (year ending 12/31/94)

FIDELITY OTC PORTFOLIO
(See first Fidelity listing on page 253 for data common to all Fidelity funds)

Portfolio manager: Abigail Johnson (1994)
Custodian: Brown Brother Harriman & Co.

Investment objective and policies: Capital appreciation. Invests at least 65% of assets in securities traded on the OTC securities market. Investments will be primarily in common stocks. No emphasis will be placed on dividend or interest income. May use foreign securities (up to 30% of assets), currency exchange contracts, and stock index futures and options thereon. May hedge up to 25% of total assets.
Year organized: 1984
Ticker symbol: FOCPX
Group fund code: 093
Sales charge: 3% (waived for retirement accounts using Fidelity prototype plans)
Discount broker availability: Schwab, White, Waterhouse, Fidelity, Siebert
Dividends paid: Income - September, December; Capital gains - September, December
Portfolio turnover (3 yrs): 222%, 213%, 245%
Largest holding: Intel Corp. (3.9%)
Management fee: 0.35% plus group fee of 0.27% to 0.52% plus performance fee of +/- 0.20% relative to NASDAQ Composite Index over 36 months.
Expense ratio: 0.88% (year ending 7/31/94) (0.89% without waiver)

FIDELITY OVERSEAS FUND
(See first Fidelity listing on page 253 for data common to all Fidelity funds)

Portfolio manager: John R. Hickling (1993)
Sub-advisers: FMR (U.K.), FMR (Far East)
Custodian: Chase Manhattan Bank, N.A.
Investment objective and policies: Long-term growth of capital. Invests primarily in foreign securities. Normally, at least 65% of assets will be in securities from at least three different countries located in the Americas (outside the U.S), the Far East and Pacific Basin, and Western Europe. Fund may use currency exchange contracts, futures contracts and options and hedge up to 25% of total assets.
Year organized: 1984
Ticker symbol: FOSFX
Group fund code: 094
Sales charge: 3% (waived for all accounts through 6/30/95 and retirement accounts using Fidelity prototype plans)
Discount broker availability: Schwab, White, Waterhouse, Fidelity, Siebert
Dividends paid: Income - December; Capital gains - December
Portfolio turnover (3 yrs): 49%, 64%, 122%
Largest holding: Deutsche Bank AG, Germany (1.9%)
Management fee: 0.45% plus group fee of 0.27% to 0.52% plus performance fee of +/- 0.20% relative to Morgan Stanley Capital International Europe, Australia, Far East Index over 36 months.
Expense ratio: 1.24% (year ending 10/31/94)

FIDELITY PACIFIC BASIN FUND
(See first Fidelity listing on page 253 for data common to all Fidelity funds)

Sub-adviser: FMR (Far East)
Portfolio manager: Simon Fraser (1993)
Custodian: Chase Manhattan Bank, N.A.
Investment objective and policies: Long-term capital growth. Invests at least 65% of assets in securities of companies that have their principal business activities in the Pacific Basin. Fund will generally be invested in at least 3 countries. Fund may use currency exchange contracts, futures contracts and options and hedge up to 25% of total assets.
Year organized: 1986
Ticker symbol: FPBFX
Group fund code: 302
Sales Charge: 3% (waived for all accounts through 6/30/95 and retirement accounts using Fidelity prototype plans)
Discount broker availability: Schwab, White, Waterhouse, *Fidelity, *Siebert
Redemption fee: 1% on shares bought before 10/12/90 or bought after 4/15/95 and held less than 90 days.
Dividends paid: Income - December; Capital gains - December

Portfolio turnover (3 yrs): 88%, 77%, 105%
Largest holding: Sumitomo Medical Industries, Ltd., Japan (1.7%)
Management fee: 0.45% plus group fee of 0.27% to 0.52% plus performance fee of +/- 0.20% relative to Morgan Stanley Capital International Pacific Index.
Expense ratio: 1.54% (year ending 10/31/94)

FIDELITY PURITAN FUND ◆
(See first Fidelity listing on page 253 for data common to all Fidelity funds)

Portfolio manager: Richard Fentin (1987)
Custodian: Chase Manhattan Bank, N.A.
Investment objective and policies: Maximum income consistent with preservation of capital. Invests primarily in high yielding securities, including common stocks, preferred stocks and bonds. May invest up to 35% of assets in junk bonds, use foreign stocks, currency exchange contracts and stock index futures and options thereon. May hedge up to 25% of total assets.
Year organized: 1947
Ticker symbol: FPURX
Group fund code: 004
Sales charge: 2% (waived for all accounts through 12/31/95 and for retirement accounts using Fidelity prototype plans)
Discount broker availability: Schwab, White, Waterhouse, *Fidelity, *Siebert
Dividends paid: Income - March, June, September, December; Capital gains - September, December
Portfolio turnover (3 yrs): 74%, 76%, 102%
Largest holding: U.S. Treasury 8 1/8% Bond due 8/15/19 (2.4%)
Management fee: 0.20% plus group fee of 0.27% to 0.52%
Expense ratio: 0.79% (year ending 7/31/94) (0.80% without waiver)

FIDELITY REAL ESTATE INVESTMENT PORTFOLIO ◆
(See first Fidelity listing on page 253 for data common to all Fidelity funds)

Portfolio manager: Barry A. Greenfield (1986)
Custodian: Brown Brothers Harriman & Co.
Investment objective and policies: Above average income and long-term capital growth consistent with reasonable investment risk. Invests at least 65% of assets in equity securities of companies principally engaged in the real estate industry. Equity securities include common stock, preferred stock and securities convertible into common stock. Remainder will generally be in companies with real estate-related themes or in debt securities with up to 20% of assets in junk bonds. Fund may use foreign securities and currency exchange contracts. May hedge up to 25% of total assets.
Year organized: 1986 (a portfolio of Fidelity Devonshire Trust)
Ticker symbol: FRESX
Group fund code: 303
Discount broker availability: Schwab, White, Waterhouse, *Fidelity, *Siebert
Dividends paid: Income - March, June, September, December; Capital gains - March, December
Portfolio turnover (3 yrs): 110%, 82%, 84%
Largest holding: Equity Residential Property Trust (6.2%)
Management fee: 0.30% plus group fee of 0.27% to 0.52%
Expense ratio: 1.13% (year ending 1/31/94) (1.17% without waiver)

FIDELITY RETIREMENT GROWTH FUND ◆
(See first Fidelity listing on page 253 for data common to all Fidelity funds)

Portfolio manager: Harris Leviton (1992)
Custodian: Brown Brothers Harriman & Co.
Investment objective and policies: Capital appreciation. Capital gains will be realized without regard to shareholder tax liability. Invests primarily in

common stocks, both domestic and foreign. May also invest in bonds, preferred stocks, warrants, real estate investment trusts and closed-end investment companies. May use currency exchange contracts, options and futures contracts. May hedge up to 25% of total assets.
Year organized: 1983 (name changed from Fidelity Freedom Fund on 1/29/91)
Ticker symbol: FDFFX
Group fund code: 073
Special sales restrictions: Limited to tax-qualified retirement plans and to tax-exempt organizations
Discount broker availability: Schwab, White, Waterhouse, *Fidelity, *Siebert
Dividends paid: Income - January, December; Capital gains - January, December
Portfolio turnover (3 yrs): 72%, 101%, 138%
Largest holding: International Business Machines Corp. (1.9%)
Management fee: 0.30% plus group fee of 0.27% to 0.52% plus performance fee of +/- 0.20% relative to S&P 500 over 36 months.
12b-1 distribution fee: Yes (not currently imposed)
Expense ratio: 1.07% (year ending 11/30/94) (1.13% without waiver)

FIDELITY SELECT PORTFOLIOS
(Data common to all Select portfolios are shown below. See subsequent listings for data specific to individual Select portfolios.)

Newspaper listing: Under Fidelity Inv Selects
Adviser: Fidelity Management & Research Co.
Sub-advisers: FMR (U.K.), FMR (Far East)
Custodians: Bank of New York, Brown Brothers Harriman & Co.
Transfer agent: Fidelity Service Co.
Investment policies: May invest in foreign securities without limit, use currency forward contracts, buy and sell options and futures contracts, hedge up to 25% of total assets, sell short against the box and invest in up to 10% of assets in illiquid securities and 5% in junk bonds. (except Money Market Portfolio)
Sales charge: 3% (except for certain employee benefit plans)
Wire orders accepted: Yes
Deadline for same day wire purchase: 4 P.M.
Discount broker availability: Schwab, White, Waterhouse, Fidelity, Siebert (except Select Money Market)
Qualified for sale in: All states
Wire redemptions: Yes, $2,500 minimum
Letter redemptions: Signature guarantee required
Redemption fee: 1.0% on shares purchased prior to 10/12/90. 0.75% of the amount redeemed (maximum of $7.50 for shares held 30 days or longer).
Fund pricing: Hourly from 10 A.M. to 4 P.M. when the New York Stock Exchange is open
Telephone switching: With All open Fidelity retail funds except Fidelity Destiny, Congress St., and Exchange Fund
Number switches permitted: Unlimited trades among Select portfolios, $250 minimum; 4 round trips per year to other Fidelity funds.
Charge for switching: Among Select equity portfolios: $15 per switch ($7.50 to Fidelity and $7.50 to the portfolio) for shares held 30 days or longer, $7.50 + 0.75% of the amount redeemed ($7.50 to Fidelity and remainder to the portfolio) for shares held less than 30 days - no charge for switches out of Select Money Market Portfolio.
Dividends paid: Income - June, December; Capital gains - June, December
Shareholder services: Keogh, IRA, 403(b), 401(k), qualified pension and profit-sharing plans, automatic investment plan, directed dividends, withdrawal plan, electronic funds transfer
Management fee: 0.30% plus group fee of 0.27% to 0.52%
IRA/Keogh fees: Annual $10, Closing $10

FIDELITY SELECT - AIR TRANSPORTATION PORTFOLIO
(See first Select listing for data common to all Select portfolios)

Portfolio manager: Jason Weiner (1994)

Investment objective and policies: Capital appreciation. Invests in companies engaged in the regional, national, and international movement of passengers, mail and freight via aircraft. Companies include airlines, air cargo and express delivery operators, freight forwarders, aviation service firms and manufacturers of aeronautical equipment.
Year organized: 1985
Ticker symbol: FSAIX
Group fund code: 034
Portfolio turnover (3 yrs): 171%, 96%, 261%
Largest holding: KLM Royal Dutch Airlines (8.4%)
Expense ratio: 2.31% (year ending 2/28/94) (2.33% without waiver)

FIDELITY SELECT - AMERICAN GOLD PORTFOLIO
(See first Select listing for data common to all Select portfolios)

Portfolio manager: Malcolm MacNaught (1985)
Investment objective and policies: Capital appreciation. Invests in companies engaged in exploration, mining, processing, or dealing in gold, or, to a lesser degree, in silver, platinum, diamonds, or other precious metals and minerals. Normally at least 80% of assets will be invested in gold bullion or coins (up to 50%) and in securities of North, Central and South American companies engaged in gold related activities.
Year organized: 1985
Ticker symbol: FSAGX
Group fund code: 041
Portfolio turnover (3 yrs): 39%, 30%, 40%
Largest holding: American Barrick Resources Corp. (10.6%)
Expense ratio: 1.49% (year ending 2/28/94) (1.50% without waiver)

FIDELITY SELECT - AUTOMOTIVE PORTFOLIO
(See first Select listing for data common to all Select portfolios)

Portfolio manager: Brenda Reed (1994)
Investment objective and policies: Capital appreciation. Invests in companies engaged in the manufacturing, marketing, and selling of automobiles, trucks, specialty vehicles, parts, tires, and related services.
Year organized: 1986
Ticker symbol: FSAVX
Group fund code: 502
Portfolio turnover (3 yrs): 64%, 140%, 29%
Largest holding: Magna International, Inc. Class A (8.6%)
Expense ratio: 1.68% (year ending 2/28/94) (1.69% without waiver)

FIDELITY SELECT - BIOTECHNOLOGY PORTFOLIO
(See first Select listing for data common to all Select portfolios)

Portfolio manager: Karen Firestone (1992)
Investment objective and policies: Capital appreciation. Invests in companies engaged in the research, development, scale up and manufacture of various biotechnological products, services, and processes, including such technologies as genetic engineering, hybridoma and recombinant DNA techniques and monoclonal antibodies.
Year organized: 1985
Ticker symbol: FBIOX
Group fund code: 042
Portfolio turnover (3 yrs): 51%, 79%, 160%
Largest holding: Genentech, Inc. (8.2%)
Expense ratio: 1.61% (year ending 2/28/94) (1.62% without waiver)

FIDELITY SELECT - BROADCAST AND MEDIA PORTFOLIO
(See Fidelity Select Multimedia Portfolio)

FIDELITY SELECT - BROKERAGE AND INVESTMENT MANAGEMENT PORTFOLIO
(See first Select listing for data common to all Select portfolios)

Portfolio manager: Jeffrey Feinberg (1995)
Investment objective and policies: Capital appreciation. Invests in companies engaged in stock brokerage, commodity brokerage, investment banking, tax-advantaged investment and investment sales, investment management or related investment advisory services.
Year organized: 1985
Ticker symbol: FSLBX
Group fund code: 068
Portfolio turnover (3 yrs): 295%, 111%, 254%
Largest holding: Invesco Mim PLC (8.8%)
Expense ratio: 1.77% (year ending 2/28/94) (1.79% without waiver)

FIDELITY SELECT - CHEMICALS PORTFOLIO
(See first Select listing for data common to all Select portfolios)

Portfolio manager: David Felman (1995)
Investment objective and policies: Capital appreciation. Invests in companies engaged in the research, development, manufacture, or marketing of products, processes, or services related to the chemical process industries.
Year organized: 1985
Ticker symbol: FSCHX
Group fund code: 069
Portfolio turnover (3 yrs): 81%, 214%, 87%
Largest holding: Union Carbide Corp. (7.5%)
Expense ratio: 1.93% (year ending 2/28/94)

FIDELITY SELECT - COMPUTERS PORTFOLIO
(See first Select listing for data common to all Select portfolios)

Portfolio manager: Harry Lange (1992)
Investment objective and policies: Capital appreciation. Invests in companies engaged in the research, design, development, manufacture, or distribution of products, processes, or services which relate to currently available or experimental hardware technology within the computer industry.
Year organized: 1985
Ticker symbol: FDCPX
Group fund code: 007
Portfolio turnover (3 yrs): 145%, 254%, 568%
Largest holding: Advanced Micro Devices, Inc. (7.6%)
Expense ratio: 1.89% (year ending 2/28/94) (1.90% without waiver)

FIDELITY SELECT - CONSTRUCTION AND HOUSING PORTFOLIO
(See first Select listing for data common to all Select portfolios)

Portfolio manager: Bill Bower (1994)
Investment objective and policies: Capital appreciation. Invests in companies engaged in the design and construction of residential, commercial, industrial and public works facilities, as well as companies engaged in the manufacture, supply, distribution or sale of products or services to these construction industries.
Year organized: 1986 (formerly Housing Portfolio)
Ticker symbol: FSHOX
Group fund code: 511
Portfolio turnover (3 yrs): 35%, 60%, 183%
Largest holding: Medusa Corp. (8.2%)
Expense ratio: 1.66% (year ending 2/28/94) (1.67% without waiver)

FIDELITY SELECT - CONSUMER PRODUCTS PORTFOLIO
(See first Select listing for data common to all Select portfolios)

Portfolio manager: Mary English (1994)
Investment objective and policies: Capital appreciation. Invests in companies engaged in the manufacture and distribution of goods, both durable and non-durable, to consumers both domestically and internationally.
Year organized: 1990
Ticker symbol: FSCPX
Group fund code: 517
Portfolio turnover (3 yrs): 169%, 215%, 140%
Largest holding: The Dial Corp. (6.0%)
Expense ratio: 2.48% (year ending 2/28/94) (2.62% without waiver)

FIDELITY SELECT - DEFENSE AND AEROSPACE PORTFOLIO
(See first Select listing for data common to all Select portfolios)

Portfolio manager: Bill Rubin (1994)
Investment objective and policies: Capital appreciation. Invests in companies involved in the defense and aerospace industries. May include air transport, computer related services, communications systems and general aviation companies.
Year organized: 1984
Ticker symbol: FSDAX
Group fund code: 067
Portfolio turnover (3 yrs): 324%, 87%, 32%
Largest holding: McDonnell Douglas Corp. (9.1%)
Expense ratio: 2.53% (year ending 2/28/94) (3.58% without waiver)

FIDELITY SELECT - DEVELOPING COMMUNICATIONS PORTFOLIO
(See first Select listing for data common to all Select portfolios)

Portfolio manager: Paul Antico (1993)
Investment objective and policies: Capital appreciation. Invests in companies engaged in the development, manufacture or sale of emerging communications services or equipment, such as cellular, paging, personal communications networks, facsimile, fiber optic transmission, voice mail, video conferencing, microwave, satellite, and others.
Year organized: 1990
Ticker symbol: FSDCX
Group fund code: 518
Portfolio turnover (3 yrs): 280%, 77%, 25%
Largest holding: DSC Communications Corp. (8.7%)
Expense ratio: 1.56% (year ending 2/28/94)

FIDELITY SELECT - ELECTRONICS PORTFOLIO
(See first Select listing for data common to all Select portfolios)

Portfolio manager: Harry Lange (1994)
Investment objective and policies: Capital appreciation. Invests in companies engaged in the design, manufacture, or sale of electronic components (semiconductors, connectors, printed circuit boards and other components); equipment vendors to electronic component manufacturers; electronic component distributors; and electronic instruments and electronic systems vendors.
Year organized: 1985
Ticker symbol: FSELX
Group fund code: 008
Portfolio turnover (3 yrs): 163%, 293%, 299%
Largest holding: Intel Corp. (9.8%)
Expense ratio: 1.67% (year ending 2/28/94)

FIDELITY SELECT - ENERGY PORTFOLIO
(See first Select listing for data common to all Select portfolios)

Portfolio manager: Albert Ruback (1994)
Investment objective and policies: Capital appreci-

---

ation. Invests in companies in the energy field, including the conventional areas of oil, gas, electricity and coal, and newer sources of energy such as nuclear, geothermal, oil shale and solar power.
Year organized: 1981
Ticker symbol: FSENX
Group fund code: 060
Portfolio turnover (3 yrs): 157%, 72%, 81%
Largest holding: British Petroleum PLC ADR (9.0%)
Expense ratio: 1.66% (year ending 2/28/94) (1.67% without waiver)

FIDELITY SELECT - ENERGY SERVICE PORTFOLIO
(See first Select listing for data common to all Select portfolios)

Portfolio manager: Dan Pickering (1994)
Investment objective and policies: Capital appreciation. Invests in companies in the energy service field, including those that provide services and equipment to the conventional areas of oil, gas, electricity and coal, and newer sources of energy such as nuclear, geothermal, oil shale and solar power. May include companies involved in providing services and equipment in the drilling process, drill bits, drilling rig equipment, etc.
Year organized: 1985
Ticker symbol: FSESX
Group fund code: 043
Portfolio turnover (3 yrs): 137%, 236%, 89%
Largest holding: Schlumberger Ltd. (9.9%)
Expense ratio: 1.65% (year ending 2/28/94) (1.66% without waiver)

FIDELITY SELECT - ENVIRONMENTAL SERVICES PORTFOLIO
(See first Select listing for data common to all Select portfolios)

Portfolio manager: Philip Barton (1993)
Investment objective and policies: Capital appreciation. Invests companies engaged in the research, development, manufacture or distribution of products, processes or services related to waste management or pollution control.
Year organized: 1989
Ticker symbol: FSLEX
Group fund code: 516
Portfolio turnover (3 yrs): 191%, 176%, 130%
Largest holding: Thermedics, Inc. (7.6%)
Expense ratio: 2.03% (year ending 2/28/94) (2.07% without waiver)

FIDELITY SELECT - FINANCIAL SERVICES PORTFOLIO
(See first Select listing for data common to all Select portfolios)

Portfolio manager: Louis Salemy (1994)
Investment objective and policies: Capital appreciation. Invests in companies providing financial services to consumers and industry. Companies in the field include commercial banks, S & L's, consumer and industrial finance companies, securities brokerage, real estate, leasing and insurance companies.
Year organized: 1981
Ticker symbol: FIDSX
Group fund code: 066
Portfolio turnover (3 yrs): 93%, 100%, 164%
Largest holding: Bank of New York Company, Inc. (6.8%)
Expense ratio: 1.63% (year ending 2/28/94) (1.64% without waiver)

FIDELITY SELECT - FOOD AND AGRICULTURE PORTFOLIO
(See first Select listing for data common to all Select portfolios)

Portfolio manager: Bill Mankivsky (1993)
Investment objective and policies: Capital appreciation. Invests in companies engaged in the manufacture, sale or distribution of food and beverage

---

products, agricultural products, and products related to the development of new food technologies.
Year organized: 1985
Ticker symbol: FDFAX
Group fund code: 009
Portfolio turnover (3 yrs): 96%, 515%, 63%
Largest holding: Philip Morris Companies, Inc. (9.6%)
Expense ratio: 1.64% (year ending 2/28/94) (1.65% without waiver)

FIDELITY SELECT - HEALTH CARE PORTFOLIO
(See first Select listing for data common to all Select portfolios)

Portfolio manager: Karen Firestone (1995)
Investment objective and policies: Capital appreciation. Includes securities of pharmaceuticals, firms designing manufacturing or selling medical, dental and optical products, etc.
Year organized: 1981
Ticker symbol: FSPHX
Group fund code: 063
Portfolio turnover (3 yrs): 213%, 112%, 154%
Largest holding: Pfizer, Inc. (9.2%)
Expense ratio: 1.55% (year ending 2/28/94) (1.59% without waiver)

FIDELITY SELECT - HOME FINANCE PORTFOLIO
(See first Select listing for data common to all Select portfolios)

Portfolio manager: David Ellison (1985)
Investment objective and policies: Capital appreciation. Invests in companies engaged in accepting public deposits and investing in real estate, usually through mortgages and other consumer, commercial, and construction loans.
Year organized: 1985 (name changed from Savings and Loan Portfolio on 2/17/93)
Ticker symbol: FSVLX
Group fund code: 098
Portfolio turnover (3 yrs): 95%, 61%, 134%
Largest holding: Standard Federal Bank (3.7%)
Expense ratio: 1.58% (year ending 2/28/94)

FIDELITY SELECT - INDUSTRIAL EQUIPMENT PORTFOLIO
(See first Select listing for data common to all Select portfolios)

Portfolio manager: Bob Bertelson (1994)
Investment objective and policies: Capital appreciation. Invests in companies engaged in the manufacture, distribution or service of products and equipment for the industrial sector, including integrated producers of capital equipment (such as general industry machinery, farm equipment and computers), parts suppliers and subcontractors.
Year organized: 1986 (formerly Capital Goods Portfolio and Automation and Machinery Portfolios. Renamed Industrial Technology Portfolio on 10/26/90. Renamed Industrial Equipment Portfolio on 6/29/92.)
Ticker symbol: FSCGX
Group fund code: 510
Portfolio turnover (3 yrs): 95%, 407%, 167%
Largest holding: Caterpiller, Inc. (10.3%)
Expense ratio: 1.68% (year ending 2/28/94) (1.69% without waiver)

FIDELITY SELECT - INDUSTRIAL MATERIALS PORTFOLIO
(See first Select listing for data common to all Select portfolios)

Portfolio manager: Doug Chase (1994)
Investment objective and policies: Capital appreciation. Invests in companies engaged in the manufacture, mining, processing, or distribution of raw materials and intermediate goods used in the industrial sector.
Year organized: 1986

Ticker symbol: FSDPX
Group fund code: 509
Portfolio turnover (3 yrs): 185%, 273%, 222%
Largest holding: Union Carbide Corp. (10.3%)
Expense ratio: 2.08% (year ending 2/28/94)
(2.10% without waiver)

FIDELITY SELECT - INSURANCE PORTFOLIO
(See first Select listing for data common to all Select portfolios)

Portfolio manager: Mike Tempero (1995)
Investment objective and policies: Capital appreciation. Invests in companies engaged in underwriting, reinsuring, selling, distributing or placing of property and casualty, life or health insurance. May invest in insurance brokers, reciprocals and claims processors, multi-line companies that provide health and life coverages.
Year organized: 1986 (formerly Life Insurance and Property & Casualty Insurance Portfolios)
Ticker symbol: FSPCX
Group fund code: 045
Portfolio turnover (3 yrs): 101%, 81%, 112%
Largest holding: Allied Group, Inc. (11.2%)
Expense ratio: 1.93% (year ending 2/28/94)

FIDELITY SELECT - LEISURE PORTFOLIO
(See first Select listing for data common to all Select portfolios)

Portfolio manager: Deborah Wheeler (1992)
Investment objective and policies: Capital appreciation. Invests in companies engaged in the design, production or distribution of goods or services in the leisure industries. This includes television and radio broadcast or manufacture, motion pictures, photography, musical instruments, publishing, sporting goods and camping, and sports arenas, among others.
Year organized: 1984
Ticker symbol: FDLSX
Group fund code: 062
Portfolio turnover (3 yrs): 170%, 109%, 45%
Largest holding: Capital Cities/ABC, Inc. (5.9%)
Expense ratio: 1.53% (year ending 2/28/94)
(1.55% without waiver)

FIDELITY SELECT - MEDICAL DELIVERY PORTFOLIO
(See first Select listing for data common to all Select portfolios)

Portfolio manager: Steve Binder (1994)
Investment objective and policies: Capital appreciation. Invests in companies engaged in the ownership or management of hospitals, nursing homes, health maintenance organizations, and other companies specializing in the delivery of health care services.
Year organized: 1986 (formerly Health Care Delivery Portfolio)
Ticker symbol: FSHCX
Group fund code: 505
Portfolio turnover (3 yrs): 164%, 155%, 181%
Largest holding: U.S. Healthcare, Inc. (11.1%)
Expense ratio: 1.79% (year ending 2/28/94)
(1.82% without waiver)

FIDELITY SELECT - MONEY MARKET PORTFOLIO
(See first Select listing for data common to all Select portfolios)

Portfolio manager: John Todd (1991)
Sub-adviser: FMR Texas
Investment objective and policies: High current income consistent with the preservation of capital and providing liquidity. Invests primarily in short-term money market obligations rated Aa or better.
Year organized: 1985
Group fund code: 085

Discount broker availability: Schwab (exchanges only), Waterhouse (exchanges only)
Management fee: 0.03% plus group fee of 0.12% to 0.37% plus 6.0% of the portion of the fund's gross income that represents a gross yield of more than 5.0% per year (up to a maximum of 0.24% of average net assets)
Expense ratio: 0.72% (year ending 2/28/94)

FIDELITY SELECT - MULTIMEDIA PORTFOLIO
(See first Select listing for data common to all Select portfolios)

Portfolio manager: Stephen Dufour (1993)
Investment objective and policies: Capital appreciation. Invests in companies engaged in the development, production, sale, and distribution of goods or services used in the broadcasting and media industries.
Year organized: 1986 (name changed from Broadcast and Media Portfolio on 4/30/94)
Ticker symbol: FBMPX
Group fund code: 503
Portfolio turnover (3 yrs): 340%, 70%, 111%
Largest holding: Scientific-Atlanta, Inc. (7.6%)
Expense ratio: 1.63% (year ending 2/28/94)
(1.66% without waiver)

FIDELITY SELECT - NATURAL GAS PORTFOLIO
(See first Select listing for data common to all Select portfolios)

Portfolio manager: Dan Ackering (1995)
Investment objective and policies: Capital appreciation. Invests in companies engaged in the production, transmission, and distribution of natural gas, and involved in the exploration of potential natural gas sources, as well as those companies that provide services and equipment to natural gas producers, refineries, cogeneration facilities, converters, and distributors. Companies participating in new activities working toward technological advances in the natural gas field may also be considered.
Year organized: 1993
Ticker symbol: FSNGX
Group fund code: 513
Portfolio turnover (1 yr): 44%
Largest holding: Burlington Resources, Inc. (5.2%)
Expense ratio: 1.93% (year ending 2/28/94)
(1.94% without waiver)

FIDELITY SELECT - PAPER AND FOREST PRODUCTS PORTFOLIO
(See first Select listing for data common to all Select portfolios)

Portfolio manager: Scott Offen (1993)
Investment objective and policies: Capital appreciation. Invests in companies engaged in the manufacture, research, sale, or distribution of paper products, packaging products, building materials such as lumber and paneling products, and other products related to the paper and forest products industry.
Year organized: 1986
Ticker symbol: FSPFX
Group fund code: 506
Portfolio turnover (3 yrs): 176%, 222%, 421%
Largest holding: Stone Container Corp. (12.8%)
Expense ratio: 2.07% (year ending 2/28/94)
(2.08% without waiver)

FIDELITY SELECT - PRECIOUS METALS AND MINERALS PORTFOLIO
(See first Select listing for data common to all Select portfolios)

Portfolio manager: Malcolm MacNaught (1981)
Investment objective and policies: Growth of capital via non-diversified common stock investments. Includes securities of companies engaged in exploration, mining, processing or dealing in gold, silver,

platinum, diamonds, etc. May invest up to 10% in gold bullion or coins.
Year organized: 1981
Ticker symbol: FDPMX
Group fund code: 061
Portfolio turnover (3 yrs): 73%, 36%, 44%
Largest holding: American Barrick Resources Corp. (7.8%)
Expense ratio: 1.55% (year ending 2/28/94)

FIDELITY SELECT - REGIONAL BANKS PORTFOLIO
(See first Select listing for data common to all Select portfolios)

Portfolio manager: Louis Salemy (1994)
Investment objective and policies: Capital appreciation. Invests in companies engaged in accepting deposits and making commercial and principally non-mortgage consumer loans.
Year organized: 1986
Ticker symbol: FSRBX
Group fund code: 507
Portfolio turnover (3 yrs): 74%, 63%, 89%
Largest holding: NationsBank Corp. (6.8%)
Expense ratio: 1.60% (year ending 2/28/94)
(1.62% without waiver)

FIDELITY SELECT - RETAILING PORTFOLIO
(See first Select listing for data common to all Select portfolios)

Portfolio manager: Erin Sullivan (1995)
Investment objective and policies: Capital appreciation. Invests in companies engaged in merchandising finished goods and services primarily to individual consumers. May include general merchandise retailers, department stores, food, drug stores and speciality retailers.
Year organized: 1985
Ticker symbol: FSRPX
Group fund code: 046
Portfolio turnover (3 yrs): 154%, 171%, 205%
Expense ratio: 1.83% (year ending 2/28/94)
(1.86% without waiver)

FIDELITY SELECT - SOFTWARE AND COMPUTER SERVICES PORTFOLIO
(See first Select listing for data common to all Select portfolios)

Portfolio manager: John Hurley (1994)
Investment objective and policies: Capital appreciation. Invests in companies engaged in research, design, production, or distribution of products or processes that relate to software or information based services.
Year organized: 1985
Ticker symbol: FSCSX
Group fund code: 028
Portfolio turnover (3 yrs): 376%, 402%, 348%
Largest holding: Cabletron Systems, Inc. (8.0%)
Expense ratio: 1.57% (year ending 2/28/94)

FIDELITY SELECT - TECHNOLOGY PORTFOLIO
(See first Select listing for data common to all Select portfolios)

Portfolio manager: Harry Lange (1993)
Investment objective and policies: Capital appreciation. Portfolio is comprised of securities believed to have or be developing products, processes or services which will provide or benefit significantly from technological advances and improvements including computers, communications, etc.
Year organized: 1981
Ticker symbol: FSPTX
Group fund code: 064
Portfolio turnover (3 yrs): 213%, 259%, 353%
Largest holding: Intel Corp. (6.4%)
Expense ratio: 1.54% (year ending 2/28/94)
(1.55% without waiver)

FIDELITY SELECT - TELECOMMUNICATIONS PORTFOLIO
(See first Select listing for data common to all Select portfolios)

Portfolio manager: David Felman (1994)
Investment objective and policies: Capital appreciation. Invests in companies engaged in the development, manufacture or sale of communications services or communications equipment including telephone operating companies, long distance telephone services, telegraph, satellite, microwave, cellular radio, paging, electronic mail and cable TV services companies.
Year organized: 1985
Ticker symbol: FSTCX
Group fund code: 096
Portfolio turnover (3 yrs): 241%, 115%, 20%
Largest holding: Ameritech Corp. (8.5%)
Expense ratio: 1.53% (year ending 2/28/94) (1.54% without waiver)

FIDELITY SELECT - TRANSPORTATION PORTFOLIO
(See first Select listing for data common to all Select portfolios)

Portfolio manager: Steve DuFour (1994)
Investment objective and policies: Capital appreciation. Invests in companies engaged in providing transportation services and/or companies engaged in the design, manufacture, distribution or sale of transportation equipment.
Year organized: 1986
Ticker symbol: FSRFX
Group fund code: 512
Portfolio turnover (3 yrs): 115%, 116%, 423%
Largest holding: Landstar System, Inc. (5.0%)
Expense ratio: 2.39% (year ending 2/28/94) (2.40% without waiver)

FIDELITY SELECT - UTILITIES GROWTH PORTFOLIO
(See first Select listing for data common to all Select portfolios)

Portfolio manager: John Muresianu (1992)
Investment objective and policies: Capital appreciation. Public utilities investments include companies engaged in the manufacture, production, generation, transmission and sale of gas and electric energy; and communications companies with telephone, telegraph, satellite and microwave facilities.
Year organized: 1981 (name changed from Utilities Portfolio on 8/3/94)
Ticker symbol: FSUTX
Group fund code: 065
Portfolio turnover (3 yrs): 61%, 34%, 45%
Expense ratio: 1.35% (year ending 2/28/94) (1.36% without waiver)

FIDELITY SHORT-INTERMEDIATE GOVERNMENT FUND ◆
(See first Fidelity listing on page 253 for data common to all Fidelity funds)

Portfolio manager: Curt Hollingsworth (1991)
Custodian: Bank of New York
Investment objective and policies: High current income consistent with preservation of capital. Invests at least 65% of assets in U.S. Government securities guaranteed as to principal and interest by the U.S. Government - including mortgage securities, as well as repurchase agreements secured by these obligations. May use futures and options related to government securities, and other high-quality securities. Fund maintains a weighted average maturity of 2 to 5 years.
Year organized: 1991 (Name changed from Limited Maturity Government on 10/16/92)
Ticker symbol: FLMGX
Group fund code: 464
Discount broker availability: White, *Fidelity, *Siebert
Check redemptions: $500 minimum

Dividends paid: Income - declared daily, paid monthly; Capital gains - December
Portfolio turnover (3 yrs): 184%, 348%, 419%
Management fee: 0.30% plus group fee of 0.12% to 0.37%
12b-1 distribution fee: Yes (not currently imposed)
Expense ratio: 0.95% (year ending 9/30/94)

FIDELITY SHORT-TERM BOND PORTFOLIO ◆
(See first Fidelity listing on page 253 for data common to all Fidelity funds)

Newspaper listing: ShtBd
Portfolio manager: Charles Morrison (1995)
Custodian: Bank of New York
Investment objective and policies: High current income consistent with preservation of capital. Invests in investment-grade fixed-income securities with a weighted average maturity of 3 years or less. May use foreign securities, currency forward contracts, options and futures contracts. May hedge up to 25% of total assets
Year organized: 1986
Ticker symbol: FSHBX
Group fund code: 450
Discount broker availability: Schwab, White, Waterhouse, *Fidelity, *Siebert
Check redemptions $500 minimum
Dividends paid: Income - declared daily, paid monthly; Capital gains - June, December
Portfolio turnover (3 yrs): 73%, 63%, 87%
Management fee: 0.30% plus group fee of 0.12% to 0.37%
12b-1 distribution fee: Yes (not currently imposed)
Expense ratio: 0.80% (year ending 4/30/94)

FIDELITY SHORT-TERM WORLD INCOME FUND ◆
(See first Fidelity listing on page 253 for data common to all Fidelity funds)

Sub-advisers: FMR (U.K.), F.M.R. (Far East)
Portfolio manager: Scott Kuldell (1994)
Custodian: Brown Brothers Harriman & Co.
Investment objective and policies: High current income consistent with preservation of capital. Invests primarily in foreign debt securities, including corporate, government and supranational securities, rated A or better with a weighted average maturity of 3 years or less. May use futures and options related to currency hedging. At least 25% of assets are in the financial services industry. May invest up to 15% of assets in illiquid securities.
Year organized: 1991
Ticker symbol: FSHWX
Group fund code: 465
Discount broker availability: Schwab, White, Waterhouse, *Fidelity, *Siebert
Check redemptions $500 minimum
Dividends paid: Income - declared daily, paid monthly; Capital gains - December
Portfolio turnover (3 yrs): 124%, 160%, 154%
Management fee: 0.45% plus group fee of 0.12% to 0.37%
12b-1 distribution fee: Yes (not currently imposed)
Expense ratio: 1.01% (year ending 12/31/94)

FIDELITY SMALL CAP STOCK FUND
(See first Fidelity listing on page 253 for data common to all Fidelity funds)

Portfolio manager: Bradford Lewis (1993)
Custodian: Brown Brothers Harriman & Co.
Investment objective and policies: Long-term growth of capital. Normally invests at least 65% of assets in stock of companies with market capitalizations of $750M or less chosen on expectations of above average long term earnings growth. May invest in preferred stocks, securities convertible into common or preferred stock and debt securities. May use securities of foreign issuers, currency exchange contracts, stock index futures and options on stocks and indexes, and leverage up to 25% of total assets.
Year organized: 1993

Ticker symbol: FDSCX
Group fund code: 336
Sales charge: 3% (waived for retirement accounts using Fidelity prototype plans)
Discount broker availability: Schwab, White, Waterhouse, Fidelity
Dividends paid: Income - June, December; Capital Gains - June, December
Portfolio turnover (1 yr): 210%
Largest holding: Novellus Systems, Inc. (3.2%)
Management fee: 0.35% plus group fee of 0.27% to 0.52% plus performance fee of +/- 0.20% relative to Russell 200 Index over 36 months
Expense ratio: 1.18% (10 months ending 4/30/94) (1.20% without waiver)

FIDELITY SOUTHEAST ASIA FUND
(See first Fidelity listing on page 253 for data common to all Fidelity funds)

Sub-adviser: FMR (Far East)
Portfolio manager: Allan Liu (1993)
Custodian: Chase Manhattan Bank, N.A.
Investment objective and policies: Long-term growth of capital. Invests at least 65% of assets in securities of Southeast Asian issuers. Southeast Asia is defined as all countries is Southeast Asia with the exceptions of Japan, Australia and New Zealand. Fund invests in common and preferred stocks, securities convertible into stocks, equity securities of closed-end investment companies, depository receipts of equity securities, debt securities and U.S. and foreign money market instruments for defensive purposes. May buy and sell options and futures contracts to hedge up to 25% of assets. May invest up to 15% of assets in illiquid securities
Year organized: 1993
Ticker symbol: FSEAX
Group fund code: 351
Sales charge: 3% (waived for retirement accounts using Fidelity prototype plans)
Discount broker availability: Schwab, Waterhouse, Fidelity, Siebert
Redemption fee: 1.5% on shares held less than 90 days
Dividends paid: Income - December; Capital gains - December
Portfolio turnover (2 yrs): 157%, 14%
Largest holding: Sun Hung Kai Properties, Ltd., Hong Kong (3.5%)
Management fee: 0.45% plus group fee of 0.27% to 0.52%
Expense ratio: 1.47% (year ending 10/31/94)

FIDELITY SPARTAN AGGRESSIVE MUNICIPAL FUND ◆
(See first Fidelity listing on page 253 for data common to all Fidelity funds)

Portfolio manager: Maureen Newman (1994)
Custodian: United Missouri Bank, N.A.
Investment objective and policies: High current income exempt from federal income taxes. Invests primarily in medium and lower-quality municipal securities with weighted average maturity of 20 years or more. Fund may invest in AMT securities. Designed to deliver extra high yields for long-term buy and hold investors by maintaining a lower than average expense ratio.
Year organized: 1993
Ticker symbol: SPAMX
Group fund code: 442
Minimum purchase: Initial: $10,000, Subsequent: $1,000
Wire orders accepted: Yes, $5 fee
Discount broker availability: *Fidelity, *Siebert
Telephone redemptions: Yes, $5 fee including exchanges
Wire redemptions: Yes, $5 fee
Redemption fee: 1.0% on shares held less than 180 days
Account closeout fee: $5
Dividends paid: Income - declared daily, paid monthly; Capital gains - October, December
Fee waivers: All wire purchase/redemption, redemption, check writing and account closeout

fees waived for Spartan accounts with balance of $50,000 or more at time of transaction.
Portfolio turnover (2 yrs): 64%, 53%
Management fee: 0.6%
12b-1 distribution fee: Yes (not currently imposed)
Expense ratio: 0.60% (year ending 8/31/94)

FIDELITY SPARTAN ARIZONA MUNICIPAL INCOME PORTFOLIO ◆
(See first Fidelity listing on page 253 for data common to all Fidelity funds)

Portfolio manager: Maureen Newman (1994)
Custodian: United Missouri Bank, N.A.
Investment objective and policies: High current income exempt from federal and Arizona state personal income taxes. Invests primarily in investment-grade Arizona municipal bonds with a weighted average maturity of 15 years or more. Up to 1/3 of assets may be in obligations rated below Baa, but not lower than Caa. Fund may use futures contracts and options thereon and zero coupon bonds. Designed to deliver extra high yields for long-term buy and hold investors by maintaining a lower than average expense ratio.
Year organized: 1994
Group fund code: 434
Minimum purchase: Initial: $10,000, Subsequent: $1,000
Wire orders accepted: Yes, $5 fee
Discount broker availability: *Fidelity, *Siebert
Qualified for sale in: AZ, CA, CO, NV, NM, NY, UT
Telephone redemptions: Yes, $5 fee including exchanges
Wire redemptions: Yes, $5 fee
Redemption fee: 0.5% to fund on shares held less than 180 days
Account closeout fee: $5
Dividends paid: Income - declared daily, paid monthly (not paid in cash); Capital gains - April, December
Fee waivers: All wire purchase/redemption, redemption, check writing and account closeout fees waived for Spartan accounts with balance of $50,000 or more at time of transaction.
Management fee: 0.55%
12b-1 distribution fee: Yes (not currently imposed)

FIDELITY SPARTAN ARIZONA MUNICIPAL MONEY MARKET PORTFOLIO ◆
(See first Fidelity listing on page 253 for data common to all Fidelity funds)

Sub-adviser: FMR (Texas)
Portfolio manager: Scott Orr (1994)
Custodian: United Missouri Bank, N.A.
Investment objective and policies: High current income exempt from federal and Arizona personal income taxes consistent with preservation of capital. Invests in Arizona municipal money market securities of two highest grades. Designed to deliver extra high yields for long-term buy and hold investors by maintaining a lower than average expense ratio.
Year organized: 1994
Group fund code: 433
Minimum purchase: Initial: $25,000, Subsequent: $1,000
Wire orders accepted: Yes, $5 fee
Qualified for sale in: AZ, CA, CO, NV, NM, NY, UT
Telephone redemptions: Yes, $5 fee including exchanges
Wire redemptions: Yes, $5 fee
Check redemption: $1,000 minimum, $2 fee per check
Confirmations mailed: After each purchase and each check, mail or wire redemption
Checks returned: Quarterly
Periodic account statements mailed: Quarterly
Dividends paid: Income - declared daily, paid monthly
Account closeout fee: $5
Fee waivers: All wire purchase/redemption,

redemption, check writing and account closeout fees waived for Spartan accounts with balance of $50,000 or more at time of transaction.
Management fee: 0.50%

FIDELITY SPARTAN BOND STRATEGIST FUND ◆
(See first Fidelity listing on page 253 for data common to all Fidelity funds)

Portfolio manager: George Fischer (1993)
Custodian: Bank of New York
Investment objective and policies: Maximum after-tax total investment return. Invests primarily in taxable and tax-exempt debt instruments allocating its portfolio between taxable and tax-exempt securities depending on which have higher returns after federal income taxes. Intends to have at least 50% of assets in municipal securities at the close of each quarter of its taxable year. May also invest in corporate debt securities, convertible bonds, U.S. and foreign government agency securities and junk bonds (up to 35% of assets). May use futures contracts and options thereon and hedge up to 50% of total assets. Designed to deliver extra high yields for long-term buy and hold investors by maintaining a lower than average expense ratio.
Year organized: 1993
Group fund code: 447
Minimum purchase: Initial: $10,000, Subsequent: $1,000
Wire orders accepted: Yes, $5 fee
Discount broker availability: *Fidelity, *Siebert
Telephone redemptions: Yes, $5 fee including exchanges
Wire redemptions: Yes, $5,000 minimum, $5 fee
Redemption fee: 0.5% on shares held less than 180 days, payable to the fund
Account closeout fee: $5
Number switches permitted: Reserves right to limit switches to 4 per year, $5 fee
Dividends paid: Income - declared daily, paid monthly; Capital gains - February, December
Portfolio turnover (2 yrs): 168%, 275%
Fee waivers: All wire purchase/redemption, redemption, check writing and account closeout fees waived for Spartan accounts with balance of $50,000 or more at time of transaction.
Management fee: 0.70%
12b-1 distribution fee: Yes (not currently imposed)
Expense ratio: 0.70% (year ending 12/31/94)

FIDELITY SPARTAN CALIFORNIA INTERMEDIATE MUNICIPAL FUND ◆
(See first Fidelity listing on page 253 for data common to all Fidelity funds)

Portfolio manager: David Murphy (1993)
Custodian: United Missouri Bank, N.A.
Investment objective and policies: High current income exempt from federal and California personal income taxes. Invests primarily in California municipal securities rated A or better by Moody's or S&P with a weighted average maturity of 3 to 10 years. Up to 40% of assets may be in lower quality bonds. Fund may use futures contracts and options thereon and hedge up to 25% of total assets. Designed to deliver extra high yields for long-term buy and hold investors by maintaining a lower than average expense ratio.
Year organized: 1993
Ticker symbol: FSCMX
Group fund code: 432
Minimum purchase: Initial: $10,000, Subsequent: $1,000
Wire orders accepted: Yes, $5 fee
Qualified for sale in: CA
Discount broker availability: *Fidelity, *Siebert
Telephone redemptions: Yes, $5 fee including exchanges
Wire redemptions: Yes, $5 fee
Account closeout fee: $5
Dividends paid: Income - declared daily, paid monthly; Capital gains - October, December
Fee waivers: All wire purchase/redemption,

redemption, check writing and account closeout fees waived for Spartan accounts with balance of $50,000 or more at time of transaction.
Management fee: 0.55%
12b-1 distribution fee: Yes (not currently imposed)

FIDELITY SPARTAN CALIFORNIA MUNICIPAL HIGH YIELD PORTFOLIO ◆
(See first Fidelity listing on page 253 for data common to all Fidelity funds)

Portfolio manager: John F. Haley (1989)
Custodian: United Missouri Bank, N.A.
Investment objective and policies: High current income exempt from federal and California state personal income taxes. Invests primarily in investment-grade California municipal bonds with a weighted average maturity of 15 years or more. Up to 1/3 of assets may be in obligations rated below Baa, but not lower than Caa. May use futures contracts and options thereon and zero coupon bonds. Designed to deliver extra high yields for long-term buy and hold investors by maintaining a lower than average expense ratio.
Year organized: 1989
Ticker symbol: FSCAX
Group fund code: 456
Minimum purchase: Initial: $10,000, Subsequent: $1,000
Wire orders accepted: Yes, $5 fee
Discount broker availability: *Fidelity, *Siebert
Qualified for sale in: CA
Telephone redemptions: $5 fee including exchanges
Wire redemptions: Yes, $5 fee
Redemption fee: 0.5% to fund on shares held less than 180 days
Account closeout fee: $5
Dividends paid: Income - declared daily, paid monthly (not paid in cash); Capital gains - April, December
Portfolio turnover (3 yrs): 54%, 26%, 13%
Fee waivers: All wire purchase/redemption, redemption, check writing and account closeout fees waived for Spartan accounts with balance of $50,000 or more at time of transaction.
Management fee: 0.55%
12b-1 distribution fee: Yes (not currently imposed)
Expense ratio: 0.52% (year ending 2/28/94) (0.55% without waiver)

FIDELITY SPARTAN CALIFORNIA MUNICIPAL MONEY MARKET PORTFOLIO ◆
(See first Fidelity listing on page 253 for data common to all Fidelity funds)

Sub-adviser: FMR (Texas)
Portfolio manager: Deborah Watson (1989)
Custodian: United Missouri Bank, N.A.
Investment objective and policies: High current income exempt from federal and California state personal income taxes consistent with preservation of capital. Invests in California municipal money market securities of two highest grades. Designed to deliver extra high yields for long-term buy and hold investors by maintaining a lower than average expense ratio.
Year organized: 1989
Ticker symbol: FSPXX
Group fund code: 457
Minimum purchase: Initial: $25,000, Subsequent: $1,000
Wire orders accepted: Yes, $5 fee
Qualified for sale in: CA
Telephone redemptions: Yes, $5 Fee including exchanges
Wire redemptions: Yes, $5 fee
Check redemption: $1,000 minimum, $2 fee per check
Confirmations mailed: After each purchase and each check, mail or wire redemption
Checks returned: Quarterly
Periodic account statements mailed: Quarterly
Dividends paid: Income - declared daily, paid monthly

Account closeout fee: $5
Fee waivers: All wire purchase/redemption, redemption, check writing and account closeout fees waived for Spartan accounts with balance of $50,000 or more at time of transaction.
Management fee: 0.50%
Expense ratio: 0.21% (year ending 2/28/94) (0.50% without waiver)

FIDELITY SPARTAN CONNECTICUT MUNICIPAL HIGH YIELD PORTFOLIO ◆
(See first Fidelity listing on page 253 for data common to all Fidelity funds)

Portfolio manager: Maureen Newman (1994)
Custodian: United Missouri Bank, N.A.
Investment objective and policies: High current income exempt from federal and Connecticut state income taxes. Invests primarily in investment-grade Connecticut municipal bonds with a weighted average maturity of 15 years or more. Up to 1/3 of assets may be in obligations rated below Baa, but not lower than Caa. Fund may use futures contracts and options thereon and zero coupon bonds. Designed to deliver extra high yields for long-term buy and hold investors by maintaining a lower than average expense ratio.
Year organized: 1987 (name changed from Fidelity Connecticut Tax-Free High Yield Portfolio on 3/1/91)
Ticker symbol: FICNX
Group fund code: 407
Minimum purchase: Initial: $10,000, Subsequent: $1,000
Discount broker availability: Waterhouse, *Fidelity, *Siebert
Qualified for sale in: CT, NJ, NY
Telephone redemptions: $5 fee including exchanges
Wire redemptions: Yes, $5 fee
Redemption fee: 0.5% to fund on shares held less than 180 days
Account closeout fee: $5
Discount broker availability: Schwab (redemptions only, Waterhouse
Qualified for sale in: CT, NJ, NY
Dividends paid: Income - declared daily, paid monthly; Capital gains - January, December
Portfolio turnover (3 yrs): 11%, 45%, 11%
Fee waivers: All wire purchase/redemption, redemption, check writing and account closeout fees waived for Spartan accounts with balance of $50,000 or more at time of transaction.
Management fee: 0.55%
12b-1 distribution fee: Yes (not currently imposed)
Expense ratio: 0.55% (year ending 11/30/94)

FIDELITY SPARTAN CONNECTICUT MUNICIPAL MONEY MARKET PORTFOLIO ◆
(See first Fidelity listing on page 253 for data common to all Fidelity funds)

Sub-adviser: FMR (Texas)
Portfolio manager: Scott Orr (1993)
Custodian: United Missouri Bank, N.A.
Investment objective and policies: High current income exempt from federal and Connecticut state income taxes, consistent with preservation of capital. Invests in Connecticut municipal money market securities of two highest grades. Designed to deliver extra high yields for long-term buy and hold investors by maintaining a lower than average expense ratio.
Year organized: 1991
Ticker symbol: SPCXX
Group fund code: 425
Minimum purchase: Initial: $25,000, Subsequent: $1,000
Wire orders accepted: Yes, $5 fee
Qualified for sale in: CT, NJ, NY
Telephone redemptions: Yes, $5 fee including exchanges
Wire redemptions: Yes, $5 fee
Account closeout fee: $5

Check redemption: $1,000 minimum, $2 fee per check
Confirmations mailed: After each purchase and each check, mail or wire redemption
Checks returned: Quarterly
Periodic account statements mailed: Quarterly
Dividends paid: Income - declared daily, paid monthly
Fee waivers: All wire purchase/redemption, redemption, check writing and account closeout fees waived for Spartan accounts with balance of $50,000 or more at time of transaction.
Management fee: 0.50%
Expense ratio: 0.50% (year ending 11/30/94)

FIDELITY SPARTAN FLORIDA MUNICIPAL INCOME PORTFOLIO ◆
(See first Fidelity listing on page 253 for data common to all Fidelity funds)

Portfolio manager: Anne Punzak (1992)
Custodian: United Missouri Bank, N.A.
Investment objective and policies: High current income exempt from federal income tax and Florida intangible personal property tax. Invests primarily in investment-grade Florida municipal bonds with a weighted average maturity of 15 years or more. Up to 1/3 of assets may be in obligations rated below Baa, but not lower than Caa. Fund may use futures contracts and options thereon and zero coupon bonds. Designed to deliver extra high yields for long-term buy and hold investors by maintaining a lower than average expense ratio.
Year organized: 1992
Ticker symbol: FFLIX
Group fund code: 427
Minimum purchase: Initial: $10,000, Subsequent: $1,000
Discount broker availability: *Fidelity, *Siebert
Qualified for sale in: CT, FL, MA, NJ, NY, PA
Telephone redemptions: $5 fee including exchanges
Wire redemptions: Yes, $5 fee
Redemption fee: 0.5% to fund on shares held less than 180 days
Account closeout fee: $5
Dividends paid: Income - declared daily, paid monthly; Capital gains - January, December
Fee waivers: All wire purchase/redemption, redemption, check writing and account closeout fees waived for Spartan accounts with balance of $50,000 or more at time of transaction.
Portfolio turnover (3 yrs): 49%, 50%, 38%
Management fee: 0.55%
12b-1 distribution fee: Yes (not currently imposed)
Expense ratio: 0.54% (year ending 11/30/94) (0.55% without waiver)

FIDELITY SPARTAN FLORIDA MUNICIPAL MONEY MARKET PORTFOLIO ◆
(See first Fidelity listing on page 253 for data common to all Fidelity funds)

Sub-adviser: FMR (Texas)
Portfolio manager: Deborah Watson (1992)
Custodian: United Missouri Bank, N.A.
Investment objective and policies: High level of current income exempt from federal income tax and Florida intangible personal property tax, consistent with preservation of capital. Invests in Florida municipal money market securities of two highest grades. Designed to deliver extra high yields for long-term buy and hold investors by maintaining a lower than average expense ratio.
Year organized: 1992
Ticker symbol: FSFXX
Group fund code: 428
Minimum purchase: Initial: $25,000, Subsequent: $1,000
Wire orders accepted: Yes, $5 fee
Qualified for sale in: CT, FL, MA, NJ, NY, PA
Telephone redemptions: Yes, $5 fee including exchanges
Wire redemptions: Yes, $5 fee
Account closeout fee: $5

Check redemption: $1,000 minimum, $2 fee per check
Confirmations mailed: After each purchase and each check, mail or wire redemption
Checks returned: Quarterly
Periodic account statements mailed: Quarterly
Dividends paid: Income - declared daily, paid monthly
Fee waivers: All wire purchase/redemption, redemption, check writing and account closeout fees waived for Spartan accounts with balance of $50,000 or more at time of transaction.
Management fee: 0.50%
Expense ratio: 0.46% (year ending 11/30/94) (0.50% without waiver)

FIDELITY SPARTAN GINNIE MAE FUND ◆
(See first Fidelity listing on page 253 for data common to all Fidelity funds)

Portfolio manager: Kevin Grant (1995)
Custodian: Bank of New York
Investment objective and policies: High current income consistent with prudent investment risk. Invests at least 65% of assets in GNMA pass-through certificates. Remainder will be in obligations guaranteed as to principal and interest by the U.S. Government. Designed to deliver extra high yields for long-term buy and hold investors by maintaining a lower than average expense ratio.
Year organized: 1990
Ticker symbol: SGNMX
Group fund code: 461
Minimum purchase: Initial: $10,000, Subsequent: $1,000
Wire orders accepted: Yes, $5 fee
Discount broker availability: Waterhouse, *Fidelity, *Siebert
Telephone redemptions: Yes, $5 fee including exchanges
Wire redemptions: Yes, $5 fee
Account closeout fee: $5
Check redemptions: $1,000 minimum, $2 fee per check
Dividends paid: Income - declared daily, paid monthly; Capital gains - October, December
Portfolio turnover (3 yrs): 285%, 241%, 168%
Fee waivers: All wire purchase/redemption, redemption, check writing and account closeout fees waived for Spartan accounts with balance of $50,000 or more at time of transaction.
Management fee: 0.65%
12b-1 distribution fee: Yes (not currently imposed)
Expense ratio: 0.65% (year ending 8/31/94)

FIDELITY SPARTAN GOVERNMENT INCOME FUND ◆
(See first Fidelity listing on page 253 for data common to all Fidelity funds)

Portfolio manager: Robert Ives (1993)
Custodian: Bank of New York
Investment objective and policies: High current income. Invests exclusively in U.S. Government securities and repurchase agreements thereon. Fund may use futures contracts and options thereon. Designed to deliver extra high yields for long-term buy and hold investors by maintaining a lower than average expense ratio.
Year organized: 1989 (name changed from Spartan Government Fund on 12/17/90)
Ticker symbol: SPGVX
Group fund code: 453
Minimum purchase: Initial: $10,000, Subsequent: $1,000
Wire orders accepted: Yes, $5 fee
Discount broker availability: Waterhouse, *Fidelity, *Siebert
Telephone redemptions: Yes, $5 fee including exchanges
Wire redemptions: Yes, $5 fee
Account closeout fee: $5
Check redemptions: $1,000 minimum, $2 fee per check
Dividends paid: Income - declared daily, paid monthly; Capital gains - June, December

Portfolio turnover (3 yrs): 354%, 170%, 59%
Fee waivers: All wire purchase/redemption, redemption, check writing and account closeout fees waived for Spartan accounts with balance of $50,000 or more at time of transaction.
Management fee: 0.65%
12b-1 distribution fee: Yes (not currently imposed)
Expense ratio: 0.65% (year ending 4/30/94)

FIDELITY SPARTAN HIGH INCOME FUND ◆

(See first Fidelity listing on page 253 for data common to all Fidelity funds)

Portfolio manager: David Glancy (1993)
Custodian: Bank of New York
Investment objective and policies: High current income. Normally invests at least 65% of assets high-yielding junk bonds. May use futures contracts and options thereon, invest up to 10% of assets in securities in default or restricted securities and up to 20% in equity securities. May hedge up to 25% of total assets and sell short against the box. Designed to deliver extra high yields for long-term buy and hold investors by maintaining a lower than average expense ratio.
Year organized: 1990
Ticker symbol: SPHIX
Group fund code: 455
Minimum purchase: Initial: $10,000, Subsequent: $1,000
Wire orders accepted: Yes, $5 fee
Discount broker availability: Waterhouse, *Fidelity, *Siebert
Telephone redemptions: Yes, $5 fee including exchanges
Wire redemptions: Yes, $5 fee
Redemption fee: 1.0% on shares held less than 270 days, payable to the fund
Account closeout fee: $5
Dividends paid: Income - declared daily, paid monthly; Capital gains - June, December
Portfolio turnover (3 yrs): 213%, 136%, 99%
Fee waivers: All wire purchase/redemption, redemption, check writing and account closeout fees waived for Spartan accounts with balance of $50,000 or more at time of transaction.
Management fee: 0.80%
12b-1 distribution fee: Yes (not currently imposed)
Expense ratio: 0.75% (year ending 4/30/94)

FIDELITY SPARTAN INTERMEDIATE MUNICIPAL FUND ◆

(See first Fidelity listing on page 253 for data common to all Fidelity funds)

Portfolio manager: David Murphy (1993)
Custodian: United Missouri Bank, N.A.
Investment objective and policies: High current income exempt from federal income tax. Normally invests at least 80% of assets in municipal securities whose interest is exempt from federal income tax, primarily securities rated A or better by Moody's or S&P with a weighted average maturity of 3 to 10 years. Up to 40% of assets may be in lower quality bonds. Fund may use futures contracts and options thereon and hedge up to 25% of total assets. Designed to deliver extra high yields for long-term buy and hold investors by maintaining a lower than average expense ratio.
Year organized: 1993
Ticker symbol: FSIMX
Group fund code: 443
Minimum purchase: Initial: $10,000, Subsequent: $1,000
Wire orders accepted: Yes, $5 fee
Discount broker availability: *Fidelity, *Siebert
Telephone redemptions: Yes, $5 fee including exchanges
Wire redemptions: Yes, $5 fee
Account closeout fee: $5
Dividends paid: Income - declared daily, paid monthly; Capital gains - October, December
Portfolio turnover (2 yrs): 69%, 95%
Fee waivers: All wire purchase/redemption, redemption, check writing and account closeout

fees waived for Spartan accounts with balance of $50,000 or more at time of transaction.
Management fee: 0.55%
12b-1 distribution fee: Yes (not currently imposed)
Expense ratio: 0.20% (year ending 4/30/94) (0.55% without waiver)

FIDELITY SPARTAN INVESTMENT GRADE BOND FUND ◆

(See first Fidelity listing on page 253 for data common to all Fidelity funds)

Portfolio manager: Michael Gray (1992)
Custodian: Bank of New York
Investment objective and policies: High current income. Invests primarily in investment-grade corporate debt securities issued by U.S. or foreign corporations, banks, or other business organizations. Fund generally focuses on longer-term bonds. Designed to deliver extra high yields for long-term buy and hold investors by maintaining a lower than average expense ratio.
Year organized: 1992
Ticker symbol: FSIBX
Group fund code: 448
Minimum purchase: Initial: $10,000, Subsequent: $1,000
Wire orders accepted: Yes, $5 fee
Discount broker availability: *Fidelity, *Siebert
Telephone redemptions: Yes, $5 fee including exchanges
Wire redemptions: Yes, $5 fee
Account closeout fee: $5
Check redemptions: $1,000 minimum, $2 fee per check
Dividends paid: Income - declared daily, paid monthly; Capital gains - June, December
Portfolio turnover (2 yrs): 44%, 55%
Fee waivers: All wire purchase/redemption, redemption, check writing and account closeout fees waived for Spartan accounts with balance of $50,000 or more at time of transaction.
Management fee: 0.65%
12b-1 distribution fee: Yes (not currently imposed)
Expense ratio: 0.65% (year ending 9/30/94)

FIDELITY SPARTAN LIMITED MATURITY GOVERNMENT FUND ◆

(See first Fidelity listing on page 253 for data common to all Fidelity funds)

Portfolio manager: Curt Hollingsworth (1988)
Custodian: Bank of New York
Investment objective and policies: High current income consistent with preservation of capital. Invests at least 65% of assets in obligations of the U.S. Government and its agencies. Fund normally maintains a weighted average maturity of 1 to 4 years but may reach a maximum of 10 years. Fund may use securities of foreign issuers, zero coupon bonds and pay in kind obligations and futures contracts and options thereon. May hedge up to 50% of total assets. Designed to deliver extra high yields for long-term buy and hold investors by maintaining a lower than average expense ratio.
Year organized: 1988 (formerly Short Term Government Portfolio. Name and objective changed in 1990)
Ticker symbol: FSTGX
Group fund code: 452
Minimum purchase: Initial: $10,000, Subsequent: $1,000
Wire purchases: $5 fee
Discount broker availability: White, Waterhouse, *Fidelity, *Siebert
Telephone redemptions: Yes, $5 fee including exchanges
Wire redemptions: Yes, $5 fee
Account closeout fee: $5
Check redemptions: $1,000 minimum, $2 fee per check
Dividends paid: Income - declared daily, paid monthly (not paid in cash); Capital gains - September, December
Portfolio turnover (3 yrs): 391%, 324%, 330%
Fee waivers: All wire purchase/redemption,

redemption, check writing and account closeout fees waived for Spartan accounts with balance of $50,000 or more at time of transaction.
Management fee: 0.65%
12b-1 distribution fee: Yes (not currently imposed)
Expense ratio: 0.65% (year ending 7/31/94)

FIDELITY SPARTAN LONG-TERM GOVERNMENT BOND FUND ◆

(See first Fidelity listing on page 253 for data common to all Fidelity funds)

Portfolio manager: Curt Hollingsworth (1993)
Custodian: Bank of New York
Investment objective and policies: Income and capital growth. Invests at least 65% of assets in U.S. Government and government agency securities with a weighted average maturity of at least ten years. Fund may use zero coupons, mortgage securities, CMOs, and futures contracts and options thereon. Designed to deliver extra high yields for long-term buy and hold investors by maintaining a lower than average expense ratio.
Year organized: 1990
Ticker symbol: SLTGX
Group fund code: 459
Minimum purchase: Initial: $10,000, Subsequent: $1,000
Wire purchases: $5 fee
Discount broker availability: Waterhouse, *Fidelity, *Siebert
Telephone redemptions: Yes, $5 fee including exchanges
Wire redemptions: Yes, $5 fee
Account closeout fee: $5
Check redemptions: $1,000 minimum, $2 fee per check
Dividends paid: Income - March, June, September, December; Capital gains - March, December
Portfolio turnover (3 yrs): 153%, 135%, 335%
Fee waivers: All wire purchase/redemption, redemption, check writing and account closeout fees waived for Spartan accounts with balance of $50,000 or more at time of transaction.
Management fee: 0.65%
12b-1 distribution fee: Yes (not currently imposed)
Expense ratio: 0.65% (year ending 1/31/94)

FIDELITY SPARTAN MARYLAND MUNICIPAL INCOME PORTFOLIO ◆

(See first Fidelity listing on page 253 for data common to all Fidelity funds)

Portfolio manager: Steven Harvey (1993)
Custodian: United Missouri Bank, N.A.
Investment objective and policies: Current income exempt from federal and Maryland state and county income taxes. Invests primarily in investment-grade municipal bonds issued by the State of Maryland with weighted average maturity of 15 years or more. Up to 33% of assets may be in junk bonds. Fund may use futures contracts and options thereon and hedge up to 25% of total assets. Designed to deliver extra high yields for long-term buy and hold investors by maintaining a lower than average expense ratio.
Year organized: 1993
Ticker symbol: SMDMX
Group fund code: 429
Minimum purchase: Initial: $10,000, Subsequent: $1,000
Wire orders accepted: Yes, $5 fee
Discount broker availability: *Fidelity, *Siebert
Qualified for sale in: DE, DC, HI, MD, NJ, VA, WY
Telephone redemptions: Yes, $5 fee including exchanges
Wire redemptions: Yes, $5 fee
Qualified for sale in: MD
Redemption fee: 0.50% on shares held less than 180 days
Account closeout fee: $5
Dividends paid: Income - declared daily, paid monthly; Capital gains - January, December
Portfolio turnover (2 yrs): 64%, 29%
Fee waivers: All wire purchase/redemption, redemption, check writing and account closeout

fees waived for Spartan accounts with balance of $50,000 or more at time of transaction.
Management fee: 0.55%
12b-1 distribution fee: Yes (not currently imposed)
Expense ratio: 0.03% (year ending 8/31/94) (0.55% without waiver)

FIDELITY SPARTAN MASSACHUSETTS MUNICIPAL MONEY MARKET PORTFOLIO ◆
(See first Fidelity listing on page 253 for data common to all Fidelity funds)

Sub-adviser: FMR (Texas)
Portfolio manager: Janice Bradburn (1992)
Custodian: United Missouri Bank, N.A.
Investment objective and policies: High current income exempt from federal and Massachusetts personal income taxes consistent with preservation of capital. Invests at least 65% of assets in Massachusetts municipal money market securities. Designed to deliver extra high yields for long-term buy and hold investors by maintaining a lower than average expense ratio.
Year organized: 1991
Ticker symbol: FMSXX
Group fund code: 426
Minimum purchase: Initial: $25,000, Subsequent: $1,000
Wire orders accepted: Yes, $5 fee
Qualified for sale in: MA
Telephone redemptions: Yes, $5 fee including exchanges
Wire redemptions: Yes, $5 fee
Account closeout fee: $5
Check redemption: $1,000 minimum, $2 fee
Confirmations mailed: After each purchase and each check, mail or wire redemption
Checks returned: Quarterly
Periodic account statements mailed: Quarterly
Dividends paid: Income - declared daily, paid monthly (not paid in cash)
Fee waivers: All wire purchase/redemption, redemption, check writing and account closeout fees waived for Spartan accounts with balance of $50,000 or more at time of transaction.
Management fee: 0.50%
Expense ratio: 0.40% (year ending 1/31/94) (0.50% without waiver)

FIDELITY SPARTAN MONEY MARKET FUND ◆
(See first Fidelity listing on page 253 for data common to all Fidelity funds)

Sub-adviser: FMR (Texas)
Portfolio manager: John Todd (1989)
Custodian: Bank of New York
Investment objective and policies: High current income. Invests in high quality U.S. dollar denominated money market instruments of domestic and foreign issuers. Designed to deliver extra high yields for long-term buy and hold investors by maintaining a lower than average expense ratio.
Year organized: 1989
Ticker symbol: SPRXX
Group fund code: 454
Minimum purchase: Initial: $20,000, Subsequent: $1,000: IRA: Initial: $10,000
Wire orders accepted: Yes, $5 fee
Telephone redemptions: Yes, $5 fee including exchanges
Wire redemptions: Yes, $5 fee
Account closeout fee: $5
Check redemptions: $1,000 minimum, $2 fee per check
Confirmations mailed: After each purchase and each check, mail or wire redemption
Checks returned: Quarterly
Periodic account statements mailed: Quarterly
Dividends paid: Income - declared daily, paid monthly
Fee waivers: All wire purchase/redemption, redemption, check writing and account closeout fees waived for Spartan accounts with balance of $50,000 or more at time of transaction.
Management fee: 0.45%

12b-1 distribution fee: Yes (not currently imposed)
Expense ratio: 0.31% (year ending 4/30/94) (0.32% without waiver)

FIDELITY SPARTAN MUNICIPAL INCOME PORTFOLIO ◆
(See first Fidelity listing on page 253 for data common to all Fidelity funds)

Portfolio manager: Norman Lind (1990)
Custodian: United Missouri Bank, N.A.
Investment objective and policies: High current income exempt from federal income taxes. Invests primarily in investment-grade municipal securities with a weighted average maturity of 15 years or more. Up to 1/3 of assets may be in lower quality bonds but not below B. Fund may use futures contracts and options thereon and hedge up to 25% of total assets. Designed to deliver extra high yields for long-term buy and hold investors by maintaining a lower than average expense ratio.
Year organized: 1990
Ticker symbol: FSMIX
Group fund code: 424
Minimum purchase: Initial: $10,000, Subsequent: $1,000
Wire orders accepted: Yes, $5 fee
Discount broker availability: *Fidelity, *Siebert
Telephone redemptions: Yes, $5 fee including exchanges
Wire redemptions: Yes, $5 fee
Redemption fee: 0.50% on shares held less than 180 days
Account closeout fee: $5
Dividends paid: Income - declared daily, paid monthly; Capital gains - October, December
Fee waivers: All wire purchase/redemption, redemption, check writing and account closeout fees waived for Spartan accounts with balance of $50,000 or more at time of transaction.
Portfolio turnover (3 yrs): 48%, 50%, 62%
Management fee: 0.55%
12b-1 distribution fee: Yes (not currently imposed)
Expense ratio: 0.55% (year ending 8/31/94)

FIDELITY SPARTAN MUNICIPAL MONEY FUND ◆
(See first Fidelity listing on page 253 for data common to all Fidelity funds)

Sub-adviser: FMR (Texas)
Portfolio manager: Sarah Zenoble (1992)
Custodian: United Missouri Bank, N.A.
Investment objective and policies: High current income exempt from federal income taxes consistent with preservation of capital and liquidity. Invests in high quality short-term municipal money market obligations of all types. Designed to deliver extra high yields for long-term buy and hold investors by maintaining a lower than average expense ratio.
Year organized: 1991
Ticker symbol: FIMXX
Group fund code: 460
Minimum purchase: Initial: $25,000, Subsequent: $1,000
Wire orders accepted: Yes, $5 fee
Telephone redemptions: Yes, $5 fee including exchanges
Wire redemptions: Yes, $5 fee
Account closeout fee: $5
Check redemptions: $1,000 minimum, $2 fee per check
Confirmations mailed: After each purchase and each check, mail or wire redemption
Checks returned: Quarterly
Periodic account statements mailed: Quarterly
Dividends paid: Income - declared daily, paid monthly
Fee waivers: All wire purchase/redemption, redemption, check writing and account closeout fees waived for Spartan accounts with balance of $50,000 or more at time of transaction.
Management fee: 0.50%
12b-1 distribution fee: Yes (not currently imposed)
Expense ratio: 0.33% (year ending 8/31/94) (0.50% without waiver)

FIDELITY SPARTAN NEW JERSEY MUNICIPAL HIGH YIELD PORTFOLIO ◆
(See first Fidelity listing on page 253 for data common to all Fidelity funds)

Portfolio manager: David Murphy (1991)
Custodian: United Missouri Bank, N.A.
Investment objective and policies: Current income exempt from federal and New Jersey state income taxes. Invests primarily in investment-grade municipal bonds issued by the State of New Jersey with weighted average maturity of 15 years or more. Fund may use futures contracts and options thereon and hedge up to 25% of total assets. Designed to deliver extra high yields for long-term buy and hold investors by maintaining a lower than average expense ratio.
Year organized: 1988 (name changed from Fidelity New Jersey Tax-Free High Yield Portfolio on 3/1/91)
Ticker symbol: FNJHX
Group fund code: 416
Minimum purchase: Initial: $10,000, Subsequent: $1,000
Wire orders accepted: Yes, $5 fee
Discount broker availability: Waterhouse, *Fidelity, *Siebert
Telephone redemptions: Yes, $5 fee including exchanges
Wire redemptions: Yes, $5 fee
Qualified for sale in: NJ, NY, PA
Redemption fee: 0.50% on shares held less than 180 days
Account closeout fee: $5
Dividends paid: Income - declared daily, paid monthly; Capital gains - January, December
Portfolio turnover (3 yrs): 8%, 25%, 33%
Fee waivers: All wire purchase/redemption, redemption, check writing and account closeout fees waived for Spartan accounts with balance of $50,000 or more at time of transaction.
Management fee: 0.55%
12b-1 distribution fee: Yes (not currently imposed)
Expense ratio: 0.55% (year ending 11/30/94)

FIDELITY SPARTAN NEW JERSEY MUNICIPAL MONEY MARKET PORTFOLIO ◆
(See first Fidelity listing on page 253 for data common to all Fidelity funds)

Sub-adviser: FMR (Texas)
Portfolio manager: Scott Orr (1992)
Custodian: United Missouri Bank, N.A.
Investment objective and policies: High current income exempt from federal and New Jersey state income taxes consistent with preservation of capital. Invests at least 65% of assets in New Jersey municipal money market securities. Designed to deliver extra high yields for long-term buy and hold investors by maintaining a lower than average expense ratio.
Year organized: 1990 (formerly Fidelity Tax-Exempt Money Market Trust)
Ticker symbol: FSJXX
Group fund code: 423
Minimum purchase: Initial: $25,000, Subsequent: $1,000
Wire orders accepted: Yes, $5 fee
Qualified for sale in: NJ, NY, PA
Telephone redemptions: Yes, $5 fee including exchanges
Wire redemptions: Yes, $5 fee
Account closeout fee: $5
Check redemption: $1,000 minimum, $2 fee per check
Confirmations mailed: After each purchase and each check, mail or wire redemption
Checks returned: Quarterly
Periodic account statements mailed: Quarterly
Dividends paid: Income - declared daily, paid monthly (not paid in cash)
Fee waivers: All wire purchase/redemption, redemption, check writing and account closeout fees waived for Spartan accounts with balance of $50,000 or more at time of transaction.

Management fee: 0.50%
Expense ratio: 0.28% (year ending 10/31/94) (0.50% before waiver)

FIDELITY SPARTAN NEW YORK INTERMEDIATE MUNICIPAL FUND ◆
(See first Fidelity listing on page 253 for data common to all Fidelity funds)

Portfolio manager: David Murphy (1993)
Custodian: United Missouri Bank, N.A.
Investment objective and policies: High current income exempt from federal and New York state and New York City personal income taxes. Invests primarily in New York municipal securities rated A or better by Moody's or S&P with a weighted average maturity of 3 to 10 years. Up to 40% of assets may be in lower quality bonds. Fund may use futures contracts and options thereon and hedge up to 25% of total assets. Designed to deliver extra high yields for long-term buy and hold investors by maintaining a lower than average expense ratio.
Year organized: 1993
Ticker symbol: FSNMX
Group fund code: 431
Minimum purchase: Initial: $10,000, Subsequent: $1,000
Wire orders accepted: Yes, $5 fee
Discount broker availability: *Fidelity, *Siebert
Qualified for sale in: CT, NJ, NY
Telephone redemptions: Yes, $5 fee including exchanges
Wire redemptions: Yes, $5 fee
Check redemptions: $1,000 minimum, $2 fee per check
Account closeout fee: $5
Dividends paid: Income - declared daily, paid monthly; Capital gains - October, December
Fee waivers: All wire purchase/redemption, redemption, check writing and account closeout fees waived for Spartan accounts with balance of $50,000 or more at time of transaction.
Management fee: 0.55%
12b-1 distribution fee: Yes (not currently imposed)

FIDELITY SPARTAN NEW YORK MUNICIPAL HIGH YIELD PORTFOLIO ◆
(See first Fidelity listing on page 253 for data common to all Fidelity funds)

Portfolio manager: Norman Lind (1993)
Custodian: United Missouri Bank, N.A.
Investment objective and policies: High current income exempt from federal and New York state and New York City personal income taxes. Invests primarily in investment-grade New York municipal bonds with a weighted average maturity of 15 years or more. Up to 1/3 of assets may be in securities rated less than Baa but not below Caa. Fund may use zero coupon securities and futures contracts and options thereon and hedge up to 25% of total assets. Designed to deliver extra high yields for long-term buy and hold investors by maintaining a lower than average expense ratio.
Year organized: 1990
Ticker symbol: FSNYX
Group fund code: 421
Minimum purchase: Initial: $10,000, Subsequent: $1,000
Wire orders accepted: Yes, $5 fee
Discount broker availability: Waterhouse, *Fidelity, *Siebert
Qualified for sale in: NJ, NY, PA
Telephone redemptions: Yes, $5 fee including exchanges
Wire redemptions: Yes, $5 fee
Redemption fee: 0.50% to fund on shares held less than 180 days
Account closeout fee: $5
Dividends paid: Income - declared daily, paid monthly; Capital gains - June, December
Portfolio turnover (3 yrs): 50%, 35%, 21%
Fee waivers: All wire purchase/redemption, redemption, check writing and account closeout

fees waived for Spartan accounts with balance of $50,000 or more at time of transaction.
Management fee: 0.55%
Expense ratio: 0.55% (year ending 1/31/94)

FIDELITY SPARTAN NEW YORK MUNICIPAL MONEY MARKET PORTFOLIO ◆
(See first Fidelity listing on page 253 for data common to all Fidelity funds)

Sub-adviser: FMR (Texas)
Portfolio manager: Janice Bradburn (1990)
Custodian: United Missouri Bank, N.A.
Investment objective and policies: High current income exempt from federal and New York state and New York City personal income taxes consistent with preservation of capital. Invests in New York municipal money market securities of 2 highest grades. Designed to deliver extra high yields for long-term buy and hold investors, by maintaining a lower than average expense ratio.
Year organized: 1990
Ticker symbol: FSNXX
Group fund code: 422
Minimum purchase: Initial: $25,000, Subsequent: $1,000
Wire orders accepted: Yes, $5 fee
Qualified for sale in: CT, NJ, NY
Telephone redemptions: Yes, $5 fee including exchanges
Wire redemptions: Yes, $5 fee
Account closeout fee: $5
Check redemption: $1,000 minimum, $2 fee per check
Confirmations mailed: After each purchase and each check, mail or wire redemption
Checks returned: Quarterly
Periodic account statements mailed: Quarterly
Dividends paid: Income - declared daily, paid monthly (not paid in cash)
Fee waivers: All wire purchase/redemption, redemption, check writing and account closeout fees waived for Spartan accounts with balance of $50,000 or more at time of transaction.
Management fee: 0.50%
Expense ratio: 0.50% (year ending 1/30/94)

FIDELITY SPARTAN PENNSYLVANIA MUNICIPAL HIGH YIELD PORTFOLIO ◆
(See first Fidelity listing on page 253 for data common to all Fidelity funds)

Portfolio manager: Steven Harvey (1993)
Custodian: United Missouri Bank, N.A.
Investment objective and policies: High current income exempt from federal and Pennsylvania income taxes. Invests primarily in investment-grade municipal securities issued by the Commonwealth of Pennsylvania with a weighted average maturity of 15 years or more. Up to 1/3 of assets may be in securities rated less than Baa but not below Caa. Fund may use zero coupon securities and futures contracts and options thereon. Designed to deliver extra high yields for long-term buy and hold investors by maintaining a lower than average expense ratio.
Year organized: 1986 (converted to Spartan 1990; formerly Fidelity Pennsylvania Tax-Free High Yield Portfolio)
Ticker symbol: FPXTX
Group fund code: 402
Minimum purchase: Initial: $10,000, Subsequent: $1,000
Wire orders accepted: Yes, $5 fee
Discount broker availability: Waterhouse, *Fidelity, *Siebert
Qualified for sale in: PA
Telephone redemptions: Yes, $5 fee including exchanges
Wire redemptions: Yes, $5 fee
Account closeout fee: $5
Dividends paid: Income - declared daily, paid monthly; Capital gains - February, December
Portfolio turnover (3 yrs): 26%, 38%, 8%
Fee waivers: All wire purchase/redemption,

redemption, check writing and account closeout fees waived for Spartan accounts with balance of $50,000 or more at time of transaction.
Management fee: 0.55%
12b-1 distribution fee: Yes (not currently imposed)
Expense ratio: 0.55% (year ending 12/31/94)

FIDELITY SPARTAN PENNSYLVANIA MUNICIPAL MONEY MARKET PORTFOLIO ◆
(See first Fidelity listing on page 253 for data common to all Fidelity funds)

Sub-adviser: FMR (Texas)
Portfolio manager: Deborah Watson (1989)
Custodian: United Missouri Bank, N.A.
Investment objective and policies: High current income exempt from federal and Pennsylvania income taxes consistent with preservation of capital. Invests primarily in Pennsylvania municipal money market instruments. Designed to deliver extra high yields for long-term buy and hold investors by maintaining a lower than average expense ratio.
Year organized: 1986 (formerly Fidelity Pennsylvania Tax-Free Money Market Portfolio)
Ticker symbol: FPTXX
Group fund code: 401
Minimum purchase: Initial: $25,000, Subsequent: $1,000
Wire orders accepted: Yes, $5 fee
Qualified for sale in: PA
Telephone redemptions: Yes, $5 fee including exchanges
Wire redemptions: Yes, $5 fee
Account closeout fee: $5
Check redemptions: $1,000 minimum, $2 fee per check
Confirmations mailed: After each purchase and each check, mail or wire redemption
Checks returned: Quarterly
Periodic account statements mailed: Quarterly
Dividends paid: Income - declared daily, paid monthly
Fee waivers: All wire purchase/redemption, redemption, check writing and account closeout fees waived for Spartan accounts with balance of $50,000 or more at time of transaction.
Management fee: 0.50%
12b-1 distribution fee: Yes (not currently imposed)
Expense ratio: 0.50% (year ending 12/31/94)

FIDELITY SPARTAN SHORT-INTERMEDIATE GOVERNMENT FUND ◆
(See first Fidelity listing on page 253 for data common to all Fidelity funds)

Portfolio manager: Curt Hollingsworth (1992)
Custodian: Bank of New York
Investment objective and policies: High current income consistent with preservation of capital. Invests exclusively in securities backed by the full faith and credit of the U.S. government with a weighted average maturity of 2 to 5 years. Designed to deliver extra high yields for long-term buy and hold investors by maintaining a lower than average expense ratio.
Year organized: 1992
Ticker symbol: SPSIX
Group fund code: 474
Minimum purchase: Initial: $10,000, Subsequent: $1.000
Wire orders accepted: Yes, $5 fee
Discount broker availability: *Fidelity, *Siebert
Telephone redemptions: Yes, $5 fee including exchanges
Wire redemptions: Yes, $5 fee
Check redemptions: $1,000 minimum, $2 fee per check
Account closeout fee: $5
Dividends paid: Income - declared daily, paid monthly; Capital gains - June, December
Portfolio turnover (2 yrs): 271%, 587%
Fee waivers: All wire purchase/redemption,

redemption, check writing and account closeout fees waived for Spartan accounts with balance of $50,000 or more at time of transaction.
Management fee: 0.65%
12b-1 distribution fee: Yes (not currently imposed)
Expense ratio: 0.10% (year ending 4/30/94) (0.65% without waver)

FIDELITY SPARTAN SHORT-INTERMEDIATE MUNICIPAL FUND ◆
(See first Fidelity listing on page 253 for data common to all Fidelity funds)

Portfolio manager: David Murphy (1989)
Custodian: United Missouri Bank, N.A.
Investment objective and policies: High price stability with income exempt from federal income taxes. Invests in municipal securities rated "A" or better with a weighted average maturity of 2 to 4 years. Fund may use zero coupon securities and futures contracts and options thereon and hedge up to 25% of total assets. Designed to deliver extra high yields for long-term buy and hold investors by maintaining a lower than average expense ratio.
Year organized: 1986 (name changed from Short-Term Tax-Free Portfolio on 12/1/90)
Ticker symbol: FSTFX
Group fund code: 404
Minimum purchase: Initial: $10,000, Subsequent: $1,000.
Wire orders accepted: Yes, $5 fee
Discount broker availability: White, Waterhouse, *Fidelity, *Siebert
Telephone redemptions: Yes, $5 fee including exchanges
Wire redemptions: Yes, $5 fee
Check redemptions: $1,000 minimum, $2 fee per check
Account closeout fee: $5
Dividends paid: Income - declared daily, paid monthly; Capital gains - February, December
Portfolio turnover (3 yrs): 44%, 56%, 28%
Fee waivers: All wire purchase/redemption, redemption, check writing and account closeout fees waived for Spartan accounts with balance of $50,000 or more at time of transaction.
Management fee: 0.55%
12b-1 distribution fee: Yes (not currently imposed)
Expense ratio: 0.47% (year ending 8/31/94) (0.55% without waiver)

FIDELITY SPARTAN SHORT-TERM INCOME FUND ◆
(See first Fidelity listing on page 253 for data common to all Fidelity funds)

Portfolio manager: Charles Morrison (1995)
Custodian: Bank of New York
Investment objective and policies: High current income consistent with preservation of capital. Invests primarily in shorter-term investment-grade debt securities including bonds, notes, and money market instruments with a weighted average maturity of 3 years or less. Securities may be issued by any type of U.S. or foreign issuer, and may be denominated in U.S. dollars or foreign currencies. Designed to deliver extra high yields for long-term buy and hold investors, by maintaining a lower than average expense ratio.
Year organized: 1992 (name changed from Spartan Short-Term Bond Fund on 11/19/93)
Ticker symbol: FASTX
Group fund code: 449
Minimum purchase: Initial: $10,000, Subsequent: $1,000
Wire orders accepted: Yes, $5 fee
Discount broker availability: White, Waterhouse, *Fidelity, *Siebert
Telephone redemptions: Yes, $5 fee including exchanges
Wire redemptions: Yes, $5 fee
Check redemptions: $1,000 minimum, $2 fee per check
Account closeout fee: $5
Dividends paid: Income - declared daily, paid monthly; Capital gains - June, December

Portfolio turnover (2 yrs): 97%, 112%
Fee waivers: All wire purchase/redemption, redemption, check writing and account closeout fees waived for Spartan accounts with balance of $50,000 or more at time of transaction.
Management fee: 0.65%
12b-1 distribution fee: Yes (not currently imposed)
Expense ratio: 0.54% (year ending 9/30/94) (0.65% without waiver)

FIDELITY SPARTAN U.S. GOVERNMENT MONEY MARKET FUND ◆
(See first Fidelity listing on page 253 for data common to all Fidelity funds)

Sub-adviser: FMR (Texas)
Portfolio manager: Leland Barron (1991)
Custodian: Morgan Guaranty Trust Co. of New York
Investment objective and policies: High current income consistent with preservation of capital and liquidity. Invests exclusively in money market instruments issued by the U.S. Government and agencies and repurchase agreements thereon. Designed to deliver extra high yields for long-term buy and hold investors by maintaining a lower than average expense ratio.
Year organized: 1990
Ticker symbol: SPAXX
Group fund code: 458
Minimum purchase: Initial: $20,000, Subsequent: $1,000; IRA/Keogh: Initial: $10,000
Wire orders accepted: Yes, $5 fee
Telephone redemptions: Yes, $5 fee including exchanges
Wire redemptions: Yes, $5 fee
Check redemptions: $1,000 minimum, $2 fee per check
Account closeout fee: $5
Confirmations mailed: After each purchase and each check, mail or wire redemption
Checks returned: Quarterly
Periodic account statements mailed: Quarterly
Dividends paid: Income - declared daily, paid monthly
Fee waivers: All wire purchase/redemption, redemption, check writing and account closeout fees waived for Spartan accounts with balance of $50,000 or more at time of transaction.
Management fee: 0.45%
12b-1 distribution fee: Yes (not currently imposed)
Expense ratio: 0.45% (year ending 4/30/94) (0.54% without waiver)

FIDELITY SPARTAN U.S. TREASURY MONEY MARKET FUND ◆
(See first Fidelity listing on page 253 for data common to all Fidelity funds)

Portfolio manager: Leland Baron (1991)
Sub-adviser: FMR (Texas)
Custodian: Morgan Guaranty Trust Co. of New York
Investment objective and policies: High current income consistent with security of principal and liquidity. Invests only in U.S. Treasury and agency money market obligations backed by the full faith and credit of the U.S. Government. Designed to deliver extra high yields for long-term buy and hold investors by maintaining a lower than average expense ratio.
Year organized: 1988 (formerly Fidelity U.S. Treasury Money Market)
Ticker symbol: FDLXX
Group fund code: 415
Minimum purchase: Initial: $20,000, Subsequent: $1,000; IRA/Keogh: Initial: $10,000
Wire orders accepted: Yes, $5 fee
Telephone redemptions: Yes, $5 fee including exchanges
Wire redemptions: Yes, $5 fee
Check redemptions: $1,000 minimum, $2 fee per check
Account closeout fee: $5
Confirmations mailed: After each purchase and each check, mail or wire redemption

Checks returned: Quarterly
Periodic account statements mailed: Quarterly
Dividends paid: Income - declared daily, paid monthly
Fee waivers: All wire purchase/redemption, redemption, check writing and account closeout fees waived for Spartan accounts with balance of $50,000 or more at time of transaction.
Management fee: 0.55%
12b-1 distribution fee: Yes (not currently imposed)
Expense ratio: 0.45% (year ending 7/31/94) (0.55% without waiver)

FIDELITY STOCK SELECTOR FUND ◆
(See first Fidelity listing on page 253 for data common to all Fidelity funds)

Portfolio manager: Bradford Lewis (1990)
Custodian: Brown Brothers Harriman & Co.
Investment objective and policies: Capital growth. Invests at least 65% of assets in domestic and foreign stocks of companies with market capitalizations of $100M or more believed undervalued relative to their industry norms by computer-aided quantitative analysis supported by fundamental research. Fund may use currency exchange contracts and futures contracts and options thereon and hedge up to 25% of total assets.
Year organized: 1990
Ticker symbol: FDSSX
Group fund code: 320
Discount broker availability: Schwab, White, Waterhouse, *Fidelity, *Siebert
Dividends paid: Income - December; Capital gains - December
Portfolio turnover (3 yrs): 187%, 192%, 268%
Management fee: 0.30% plus group fee of 0.27% to 0.52% plus performance fee of +/- 0.20% relative to the S&P 500 over 36 months
Expense ratio: 1.09% (year ending 10/31/94) (1.12% without waiver)

FIDELITY TAX-EXEMPT MONEY MARKET TRUST ◆
(See first Fidelity listing on page 253 for data common to all Fidelity funds)

Sub-adviser: FMR Texas, Inc.
Portfolio manager: Sarah Zenoble (1988)
Custodian: United Missouri Bank, N.A.
Investment objective and policies: Current income exempt from federal income taxes. Invests in high quality short-term municipal money market obligations.
Year organized: 1980
Ticker symbol: FTEXX
Group fund code: 010
Minimum purchase: Initial: $5,000, Subsequent: $500
Deadline for same day wire purchase: 12 NN
Number switches permitted: Unlimited
Check redemptions: No minimum
Confirmations mailed: After each purchase and each check, mail or wire redemption
Checks returned: Quarterly
Periodic account statements mailed: Quarterly
Dividends paid: Income - declared daily, paid monthly
Management fee: 0.15% plus group fee of 0.12% to 0.37%
Expense ratio: 0.52% (year ending 10/31/94)

FIDELITY TREND FUND ◆
(See first Fidelity listing on page 253 for data common to all Fidelity funds)

Portfolio manager: Alan Leifer (1987)
Custodian: Chase Manhattan Bank, N.A.
Investment objective and policies: Long-term growth of capital. Invests in securities of both established and smaller companies that will benefit from industry and/or market trends. May invest in common stock, investment-grade fixed-income securities or cash in any proportion, depending on market and economic conditions. May invest in foreign securities and have up to 35% of assets in junk

bonds. May use futures and options and hedge up to 25% of total assets.
Year organized: 1958
Ticker symbol: FTRNX
Group fund code: 005
Discount broker availability: Schwab, White, Waterhouse, *Fidelity, *Siebert
Dividends paid: Income - February, December; Capital gains - February, December
Portfolio turnover (3 yrs): 29%, 50%, 47%
Largest holding: Golden West Financial Corp. (4.4%)
Management fee: 0.30% plus group fee of 0.27% to 0.52% plus performance fee of +/- 0.20% relative to S&P 500 Index over 36 months
Expense ratio: 1.04% (year ending 12/31/94)

FIDELITY U.S. GOVERNMENT RESERVES ◆
(See first Fidelity listing on page 253 for data common to all Fidelity funds)

Portfolio manager: Leland Barron (1991)
Custodian: Morgan Guaranty Trust Co. of New York
Investment objective and policies: Current income, security of principal and liquidity. Invests exclusively in money market instruments issued or guaranteed by the U.S. Government, its agencies or instrumentalities.
Year organized: 1981
Ticker symbol: FGRXX
Group fund code: 050
Deadline for same day wire purchase: 12 NN
Number switches permitted: Unlimited
Check redemptions: $500 minimum
Confirmations mailed: After each purchase and each check, mail or wire redemption
Checks returned: Quarterly
Periodic account statements mailed: Quarterly
Dividends paid: Income - declared daily, paid monthly
Management fee: 0.03% plus group fee of 0.12% to 0.37% plus 6% of gross income in excess of 5% yield
Expense ratio: 0.51% (year ending 9/30/94)

FIDELITY UTILITIES FUND ◆
(See first Fidelity listing on page 253 for data common to all Fidelity funds)

Portfolio manager: John Muresianu (1992)
Custodian: Brown Brothers Harriman & Co.
Investment objective and policies: High current income with growth of income and capital appreciation secondary. Invests at least 65% of assets in equity securities of public utilities. Debt will be rated A or better. Fund may use foreign securities and stock index futures and options thereon and hedge up to 25% of total assets.
Year organized: 1987 (name changed from Utilities Income Fund on 8/4/94)
Ticker symbol: FIUIX
Group fund code: 311
Discount broker availability: Schwab, White, Waterhouse, *Fidelity, *Siebert
Dividends paid: Income - March, June, September, December; Capital gains - March, December
Portfolio turnover (3 yr): 47%, 73%, 39%
Management fee: 0.20% plus group fee of 0.27% to 0.52% plus performance fee of +/- 0.20% relative to S&P Utilities Index over 36 months
Expense ratio: 0.86% (year ending 1/31/94) (0.87% without waiver)

FIDELITY VALUE FUND ◆
(See first Fidelity listing on page 000 for data common to all Fidelity funds)

Portfolio manager: Jeffrey Ubben (1992)
Custodian: Brown Brothers Harriman & Co.
Investment objective and policies: Capital appreciation. Invests primarily in stocks and convertible securities of companies that possess valuable fixed

assets or are believed to be undervalued. May invest in foreign securities and have up to 35% of assets in junk bonds. May use futures and options and hedge up to 25% of total assets.
Year organized: 1978 (formerly Fidelity Discoverer Fund)
Ticker symbol: FDVLX
Group fund code: 039
Discount broker availability: Schwab, White, Waterhouse, *Fidelity, *Siebert
Dividends paid: Income - December; Capital gains - December
Portfolio turnover (3 yrs): 112%, 117%, 81%
Management fee: 0.30% plus group fee of 0.27% to 0.52% plus performance fee of +/- 0.20% relative to S&P 500 Index over 36 months
Expense ratio: 0.77% (year ending 10/31/94) (0.79% without waiver)

FIDELITY WORLDWIDE FUND
(See first Fidelity listing on page 253 for data common to all Fidelity funds)

Portfolio manager: Penelope Dobkin (1990)
Sub-adviser: FMR (U.K.), FMR (Far East)
Custodian: Chase Manhattan Bank, N.A.
Investment objective and policies: Capital growth. Invests primarily in equities, both domestic and foreign, including closed-end investment companies. Fund will focus on developed countries in North America, Europe and the Pacific Basin, spread among at least 3 countries, one of which will be the U.S. May invest in both established and smaller companies. Up to 35% of assets may be in junk bonds. Fund may use currency exchange contracts, futures and options and hedge up to 25% of total assets.
Year organized: 1990
Ticker symbol: FWWFX
Group fund code: 318
Sales charge: 3% (waived for all accounts through 6/30/95 and retirement accounts using Fidelity prototype plans)
Discount broker availability: Schwab, White, Waterhouse, *Fidelity, *Siebert
Dividends paid: Income - December; Capital gains - December
Portfolio turnover (3 yrs): 69%, 57%, 130%
Largest holding: Volker Stevin NV, Netherlands (1.1%)
Management fee: 0.45% plus group fee of 0.27% to 0.52%
Expense ratio: 1.32% (year ending 10/31/94)

FIDUCIARY CAPITAL GROWTH FUND ◆

225 East Mason Street
Milwaukee, WI 53202
414-226-4555, 800-338-1579

Adviser: Fiduciary Management, Inc.
Portfolio managers: Ted D. Kellner (1981), Donald S. Wilson (1981)
Custodian and transfer agent: Firstar Trust Co.
Investment objective and policies: Long-term capital appreciation with current income secondary. Invests in common stocks with growth potential and stocks priced significantly below estimated market value of a corporation's assets less its liabilities. Up to 10% of assets may be in securities of foreign issuers.
Year organized: 1981
Ticker symbol: FCGFX
Minimum purchase: Initial: $1,000, Subsequent: $100
Telephone orders accepted: No
Wire orders accepted: Yes
Deadline for same day wire purchase: 4 P.M.
Wire redemptions: Yes, $7.50 fee
Letter redemptions: Signature guarantee not required
Qualified for sale in: All states except AK, AR, ID, ME, MD, MA, MS, MT, NH, NC, ND, SD, VT, WV
Dividends paid: Income - October, December; Capital gains - October, December
Portfolio turnover (3 yrs): 21%, 33%, 59%

Largest holding: Policy Management Systems Corp. (3.6%)
Shareholder services: Keogh, IRA, 401(k), corporate retirement plans, automatic investment plan—minimum $50/month, withdrawal plan min. req. $10,000, electronic funds transfer
Management fee: 1.0% first $30M, 0.75% over $30M
Expense ratio: 1.2% (year ending 9/30/94)
IRA/Keogh fees: Annual $12.50, Closing $15

FIDUCIARY TOTAL RETURN FUND
(See Eastcliff Total Return Fund)

59 WALL STREAT FUNDS ◆
(Data common to all 59 Wall Street funds are shown below. See subsequent listings for data specific to individual 59 Wall Street funds.)

6 St. James Avenue
Boston, MA 02116
212-493-8100

Adviser & Administrator: Brown Brothers Harriman & Co.
Sub-administrator: 59 Wall Street Administrators, Inc.
Custodian: State Street Bank & Trust Co.
Transfer agent: Brown Brothers Harriman & Co.
Telephone orders accepted: No
Wire orders accepted: Yes
Deadline for same day wire purchase: 4 P.M. (11 A.M. for money market funds)
Letter redemptions: Signature guarantee required

59 WALL STREET EUROPEAN EQUITY FUND ◆
(See first 59 Wall Street listing for data common to all 59 Wall Street funds.)

Portfolio managers: John A. Nielsen (1990), Henry A. Frantzen (1992)
Investment objective and policies: Capital appreciation with income secondary. Invests primarily in common stocks of companies based in the European Economic Community. May also invest in convertible securities, trust or limited partnership interests, rights and warrants. May invest directly or in ADRs and EDRs and use futures and options to hedge.
Year organized: 1990
Ticker symbol: FNEEX
Minimum purchase: Initial: $25,000, Subsequent: $25,000; IRA/Keogh: Initial: $1,000, Subsequent: $1,000
Qualified for sale in: All states
Dividends paid: Income - December; Capital gains - December
Portfolio turnover (3 yrs): 124%, 37%, 50%
Largest holding: Television Francaise 1 (3.0%)
Management fee: 0.80%
Expense ratio: 1.37% (year ending 10/31/94)

59 WALL STREET MONEY MARKET FUND ◆
(See first 59 Wall Street listing for data common to all 59 Wall Street funds.)

Portfolio managers: Eugene Rainis (1983), John P. Nelson (1987)
Investment objective and policies: High current income consistent with preservation of capital and liquidity. Invests in high quality short-term money market instruments.
Year organized: 1983
Ticker symbol: FNMXX
Minimum purchase: Initial: $10,000, Subsequent: $5,000; IRA/Keogh: Initial: $1,000, Subsequent: $1,000
Qualified for sale in: All states
Confirmations mailed: After each purchase and each check, mail or wire redemption
Checks returned: As clear
Periodic account statements mailed: Monthly

Dividends paid: Income - declared daily, paid monthly
Management fee: 0.25%
Expense ratio: 0.55% (year ending 6/30/94)

59 WALL STREET PACIFIC BASIN FUND ◆
(See first 59 Wall Street listing for data common to all 59 Wall Street funds.)

Portfolio managers: John A. Nielsen (1990), Henry A. Frantzen (1992)
Investment objective and policies: Capital appreciation with income secondary. Invests primarily in common stocks of companies based in Pacific Basin countries. May also invest in convertible securities, trust or limited partnership interests, rights and warrants. May invest directly or in ADRs and EDRs and use futures and options to hedge.
Year organized: 1990
Ticker symbol: FNPEX
Minimum purchase: Initial: $25,000, Subsequent: $25,000; IRA/Keogh: Initial: $1,000, Subsequent: $1,000
Qualified for sale in: All states
Dividends paid: Income - December; Capital gains - December
Portfolio turnover (3 yrs): 86%, 79%, 84%
Largest holding: Cheung Kong Holdings, Hong Kong (4.9%)
Management fee: 0.80%
Expense ratio: 1.29% (year ending 10/31/94)

59 WALL STREET SHORT/INTERMEDIATE FIXED INCOME FUND ◆
(See first 59 Wall Street listing for data common to all 59 Wall Street funds.)

Portfolio managers: Vasken H. Setrakian (1992), John A. Lovito (1992)
Investment objective and policies: High income consistent with preservation of capital and liquidity. Invests primarily in investment-grade debt securities with a weighted average maturity of 2 to 4 years. May invest in municipal securities and foreign government securities. Fund may hedge.
Year organized: 1992
Ticker symbol: FNSIX
Minimum purchase: Initial: $25,000, Subsequent: $25,000; IRA/Keogh: Initial: $1,000, Subsequent: $1,000
Qualified for sale in: All states
Dividends paid: Income - declared daily, paid monthly; Capital gains - December
Portfolio turnover (2 yrs): 129%, 149%
Management fee: 0.65%
Expense ratio: 0.85% (year ending 10/31/94) (includes waiver)

59 WALL STREET SMALL COMPANY FUND ◆
(See first 59 Wall Street listing for data common to all 59 Wall Street funds.)

Portfolio managers: George J. Balco (1991), Catharine L. Mellon (1991)
Investment objective and policies: Capital appreciation with income secondary. Invests primarily in common stocks of small domestic companies with market capitalizations of $90M to $750M chosen through use of a proprietary selection model. May also invest in convertible securities, trust or limited partnership interests, rights and warrants.
Year organized: 1991
Ticker symbol: FNSMX
Minimum purchase: Initial: $25,000, Subsequent: $25,000; IRA/Keogh: Initial: $1,000, Subsequent: $1,000
Qualified for sale in: All states
Dividends paid: Income - December; Capital gains - December
Portfolio turnover (3 yrs): 140%, 116%, 67%
Largest holding: Nautica Enterprises (1.1%)
Management fee: 0.80%
Expense ratio: 1.10% (year ending 10/31/94) (includes waiver)

59 WALL STREET TAX FREE SHORT/INTERMEDIATE FIXED INCOME FUND ◆
(See first 59 Wall Street listing for data common to all 59 Wall Street funds.)

Portfolio managers: Eugene C. Rainis (1992), Barbara A. Brinkley (1992), Todd C. Jacobson (1993)
Investment objective and policies: High income exempt from federal income tax consistent with preservation of capital and liquidity. Invests primarily in investment-grade municipal securities with a weighted average maturity of 3 years or less.
Year organized: 1992
Ticker symbol: FNSIX
Minimum purchase: Initial: $10,000, Subsequent: $1,000
Special sales restriction: Available only to customers of Brown Brothers Harriman & Company
Qualified for sale in: All states
Dividends paid: Income - declared daily, paid monthly; Capital gains - December
Portfolio turnover (2 yrs): 27%, 13%
Management fee: 0.50%
Expense ratio: 0.70% (year ending 6/30/94)

59 WALL STREET U.S. EQUITY FUND ◆
(See first 59 Wall Street listing for data common to all 59 Wall Street funds.)

Portfolio managers: William M. Weiss (1992), Harry J. Martin (1992)
Investment objective and policies: Superior long-term capital growth with some current income. Invests primarily in common stocks of companies traded on major U.S. stock exchanges. May also purchase convertible securities, rights, warrants and ADRs of foreign issuers. May use futures and options to hedge.
Year organized: 1992
Minimum purchase: Initial: $25,000, Subsequent: $25,000; IRA/Keogh: Initial: $1,000, Subsequent: $1,000
Qualified for sale in: All states
Dividends paid: Income - June, December; Capital gains - December
Portfolio turnover (3 yrs): 61%, 52%, 2%
Largest holding: Scott Paper Co. (2.5%)
Management fee: 0.80%
Expense ratio: 1.20% (year ending 10/31/94)

59 WALL STREET U.S. TREASURY MONEY FUND ◆
(See first 59 Wall Street listing for data common to all 59 Wall Street funds.)

Portfolio manager: John P. Nelson (1991)
Investment objective and policies: High current income consistent with preservation of capital and liquidity. Invests exclusively in money market securities guaranteed as to principal and interest payments by the full faith and credit of the U.S.
Year organized: 1991
Ticker symbol: FNVXX
Minimum purchase: Initial: $10,000, Subsequent: $5,000
Qualified for sale in: All states
Confirmations mailed: After each purchase and each check, mail or wire redemption
Checks returned: As clear
Periodic account statements mailed: Monthly
Dividends paid: Income - declared daily, paid monthly
Management fee: 0.25%
Expense ratio: 0.55% (year ending 10/31/93)

FIRST EAGLE FUND OF AMERICA ◆
45 Broadway
New York, NY 10006
212-943-9200, 800-451-3623
fax 212-248-8861

Newspaper listing: FstEag
Adviser: Arnhold and S. Bleichroeder, Inc.
Portfolio managers: Harold J. Levy (1987), David L. Cohen (1989)
Custodian: Bank of New York

Transfer agent: Supervised Service Co., Inc.
Investment objective and policies: Capital appreciation. Invests in domestic and, to a lesser extent, foreign equity and debt securities deemed undervalued on an "intrinsic value" basis. Fund is non-diversified and will normally limit foreign holdings to 10% of total assets. May buy and sell options on stocks and indices and sell short.
Year organized: 1986
Ticker symbol: FEAFX
Minimum purchase: Initial: $5,000, Subsequent: $1,000; IRA: Initial: $2,000
Telephone orders accepted: No
Wire orders accepted: Yes
Deadline for same day wire purchase: 4 P.M.
Qualified for sale in: AL, CA, CO, CT, DE, DC, FL, GA, HI, IL, IA, MA, MD, MI, MN, MO, MT, NE, NH, NJ, NY, NC, OH, OR, PA, RI, SC, TX, WA
Letter redemptions: Signature guarantee required
Dividends paid: Income - November; Capital gains - November
Portfolio turnover (3 yrs): 110%, 141%, 145%
Largest holding: Tejas Gas Corp. (5.2%)
Shareholder services: IRA
Management fee: 1.6% +/- up to 0.9% based on performance
Expense ratio: 1.9% (year ending 10/31/94)
IRA fees: Annual $10, Initial $10, Closing $10

FIRST EAGLE INTERNATIONAL FUND ◆
45 Broadway
New York, NY 10006
212-943-9200, 800-451-3623
fax 212-248-8861

Adviser: Arnhold and S. Bleichroeder, Inc.
Portfolio managers: Allan Raphael (1994), Arthur F. Lerner (1994)
Custodian: Bank of New York
Transfer agent: Supervised Service Co., Inc.
Investment objective and policies: Capital appreciation. Normally invests at least 65% of assets in foreign equity and debt securities deemed undervalued on an "intrinsic value" basis. May also invest in domestic equity and debt securities, use futures and options on stocks and indices, hedge and leverage. Up to 15% of assets may be in illiquid securities. Fund is non-diversified
Year organized: 1994
Minimum purchase: Initial: $5,000, Subsequent: $1,000; IRA: Initial: $2,000
Telephone orders accepted: No
Wire orders accepted: Yes
Deadline for same day wire purchase: 4 P.M.
Qualified for sale in: AL, CA, CO, CT, DC, DE, FL, GA, HI, IL, MA, MD, MI, MN, MO, MT, NE, NH, NJ, NY, NC, OH, OR, PA, RI, SC, TX
Letter redemptions: Signature guarantee required
Dividends paid: Income - November; Capital gains - November
Largest holding: Tele-Denmark ADS (6.7%)
Shareholder services: IRA
Management fee: 1.6% +/- up to 0.9% based on performance
IRA fees: Annual $10, Initial $10, Closing $10
Expense ratio: 2.0% (9 months ending 12/31/94)

FIRST MUTUAL FUND
845 Third Avenue, Sixth Floor
New York, NY 10022
800-257-4414, fax 610-834-3539

Adviser: Trainer Wortham & Co., Inc.
Portfolio manager: David P. Como (1982)
Custodian: National Westminster Bank, NJ
Transfer agent: Fund/Plan Services, Inc.
Investment objective and policies: Capital appreciation with income secondary. Invests primarily in common stock and securities convertible into common stock such as convertible bonds and preferred stock. Fund is non-diversified
Year organized: 1959
Ticker symbol: FMFDX
Minimum purchase: Initial: $1,000, Subsequent: $50; IRA: Initial: None, Subsequent: None

Telephone orders accepted: No
Wire orders accepted: Yes, $1,000 minimum
Deadline for same day wire purchase: 4 P.M.
Qualified for sale in: AL, CA, CO, CT, DE, DC, FL, GA, HI, IL, MI, MO, NJ, NY, NC, OH, PA, RI, SC, VT, VA, WA, WV, WI, WY
Letter redemptions: Signature guarantee required over $5,000
Dividends paid: Income - December; Capital gains - December
Portfolio turnover (3 yrs): 178%, 172%, 175%
Largest holding: Cummins Engines (4.5%)
Shareholder services: IRA, automatic investment plan, withdrawal plan
Management fee: 0.75% first $40M, 0.50% over $40M
12b-1 distribution fee: 0.19%
Expense ratio: 1.97% (year ending 6/31/94)
IRA fees: Annual $12

FIRST OMAHA FUNDS ◆
(Data common to all First Omaha funds are shown below. See subsequent listings for data specific to individual First Omaha funds.)

1900 East Dublin-Granville Road
Columbus, OH 43229
800-662-4203, fax 614-899-1257

Adviser: First National Bank of Omaha
Administrator: The Winsbury Company
Custodian and transfer agent: First National Bank of Omaha
Minimum purchase: Initial: $500, Subsequent: $50
Telephone orders accepted: No
Wire orders accepted: Yes
Deadline for same day wire purchase: 4 P.M.
Telephone redemptions: Yes
Wire redemptions: Yes
Letter redemptions: Signature guarantee not required
Telephone switching: With other First Omaha funds
Number of switches permitted: Unlimited
Deadline for same day switch: 12:30 P.M.
Shareholder services: IRA, automatic investment plan (initial minimum $100), electronic funds transfer, withdrawal plan
Administration fee: 0.20%
IRA fees: Annual $12

FIRST OMAHA EQUITY FUND ◆
(See first First Omaha listing for data common to all First Omaha funds)

Portfolio manager: Vicki Hohenstein (1992)
Investment objective and policies: Long-term capital growth. Invests primarily in common stocks and securities convertible into common stocks of large capitalization companies with good earnings and dividend growth. May also invest in investment-grade debt securities and in securities of foreign issuers. Up to 15% of assets may be in illiquid securities.
Year organized: 1992
Ticker symbol: FOEQX
Qualified for sale in: AZ, CA, CO, DC, FL, GA, HI, IL, IA, KS, MI, MN, MO, MT, NE, NC, ND, OH, SD, TX, VA, WA, WI, WY
Dividends paid: Income - monthly; Capital gains - December
Portfolio turnover (2 yrs): 16%, 5%
Largest holding: IBM Corp. (4.2%)
Management fee: 0.75%
12b-1 distribution fee: 0.25% (not currently imposed)
Expense ratio: 1.04% (year ending 6/30/94) (1.54% without waiver)

FIRST OMAHA FIXED INCOME FUND ◆
(See first First Omaha listing for data common to all First Omaha funds)

Portfolio manager: Dick Chapman (1992)
Investment objective and policies: Current income consistent with preservation of capital. Invests at least 65% of assets in investment-grade bonds,

debentures, notes, mortgage-related securities, state, municipal or industrial revenue bonds, U.S. government & government agency obligations, and convertible securities. Up to 35% of assets may be in preferred stocks. May also invest in securities of foreign issuers. Up to 15% of assets may be in illiquid securities.
Year organized: 1992
Ticker symbol: FOFIX
Qualified for sale in: AZ, CA, CO, DC, FL, GA, HI, IL, IA, KS, MI, MN, MO, MT, NE, NC, ND, OH, SD, TX, VA, WA, WI, WY
Dividends paid: Income - monthly; Capital gains - December
Portfolio turnover (2 yrs): 13%, 3%
Management fee: 0.60%
12b-1 distribution fee: 0.25% (not currently imposed)
Expense ratio: 0.86% (year ending 6/30/94) (1.41% without waiver)

FIRST OMAHA SHORT/INTERMEDIATE FIXED INCOME FUND ◆
(See first First Omaha listing for data common to all First Omaha funds)

Portfolio manager: Dick Chapman (1992)
Investment objective and policies: Current income consistent with preservation of capital. Invests at least 65% of assets in investment-grade bonds, debentures, notes, mortgage-related securities, state, municipal or industrial revenue bonds, U.S. government & government agency obligations, and convertible securities with a weighted average maturity of 2 to 5 years. Up to 35% of assets may be in preferred stocks. May also invest in securities of foreign issuers. Up to 15% of assets may be in illiquid securities.
Year organized: 1992
Ticker symbol: FOSIX
Qualified for sale in: AZ, CA, CO, DC, FL, GA, HI, IL, IA, KS, MI, MN, MO, MT, NE, NC, ND, OH, SD, TX, VA, WA, WI, WY
Dividends paid: Income - monthly; Capital gains - December
Portfolio turnover (2 yrs): 21%, 16%
Management fee: 0.50%
12b-1 distribution fee: 0.25% (not currently imposed)
Expense ratio: 0.83% (year ending 6/30/94) (1.38% without waiver)

FIRST OMAHA U.S. GOVERNMENT OBLIGATIONS FUND ◆
(See first First Omaha listing for data common to all First Omaha funds)

Investment objective and policies: Maximum current income consistent with preservation of capital and liquidity. Invests exclusively in high quality money market instruments issued by the U.S. Government, its agencies and its instrumentalities.
Year organized: 1991
Ticker symbol: FOGXX
Qualified for sale in: AZ, CA, CO, DC, FL, GA, HI, ID, IL, IA, KS, LA, MI, MN, MO, MT, NE, NY, NC, ND, OH, OR, SD, TX, VA, WA, WI, WY
Dividends paid: Income - declared daily, paid monthly
Management fee: 0.35%
12b-1 distribution fee: 0.25% (not currently imposed)
Expense ratio: 0.60% (year ending 6/30/94) (1.13% without waiver)

THE FLEX-FUNDS
(Data common to all Flex-Funds funds are shown below. See subsequent listings for data specific to individual Flex-Funds funds.)

6000 Memorial Drive
P.O. Box 7177
Dublin, OH 43017
614-766-7000, 800-325-3539
fax 614-766-6669

Shareholder service hours: Full service: M-F 8:30 A.M.-5 P.M. EST; After hours service: prices, yields, messages, prospectuses

Adviser: R. Meeder & Assoc., Inc.
Custodian: Star Bank, N.A., Cincinnati
Transfer agent: Mutual Funds Service Co.
Minimum purchase: Initial: $2,500, Subsequent: $100; IRA: Initial: $500
Telephone orders accepted: Only for Growth Fund
Wire orders accepted: Yes, with prior notice
Deadline for same day wire purchase: 4 P.M. (12 NN for Money Market fund)
Telephone redemptions: Yes
Wire redemptions: Yes, $1,000 minimum
Letter redemptions: Signature guarantee required
Telephone switching: With other Flex-Fund funds
Number of switches permitted: Unlimited
Deadline for same day switch: 4 P.M. (12 NN for Money Market fund)
Shareholder services: Keogh, IRA, SEP-IRA, 401(k), corporate retirement plans, automatic investment plan, withdrawal plan min. req. $10,000, electronic funds transfer (purchase only)
IRA fees: Annual $5, Closing $12
Keogh fees: None

THE FLEX-FUND - BOND FUND
(See first Flex-Fund listing for data common to all Flex-Fund funds)

Portfolio manager: G. Robert Kincheloe (1994)
Investment objective and policies: Maximum current income. Invests in high quality fixed-income securities with, under stable market conditions, a weighted average maturity of roughly 10 years. Fund may hedge.
Year organized: 1985
Ticker symbol: FLXBX
Discount broker availability: *Schwab (only through financial advisers), *White, Fidelity, Siebert
Qualified for sale in: AL, AZ, CA, CO, DE, FL, GA, HI, IL, IN, KS, KY, MD, MI, MN, MO, NY, NC, OH, OR, PA, TX, VA, WA, WI, WY
Dividends paid: Income - declared daily, paid monthly; Capital gains - December
Portfolio turnover (3 yrs): 236%, 214%, 214%
Management fee: 0.4% first $100M, 0.2% over $100M
12b-1 distribution fee: 0.16%
Expense ratio: 0.99% (year ending 12/31/93) (1.09% without waiver)

THE FLEX-FUND - GROWTH FUND
(See first Flex-Fund listing for data common to all Flex-Fund funds)

Portfolio manager: Robert S. Meeder, Jr. (1992)
Investment objective and policies: Long-term growth of capital. Invests primarily in common stocks of both large capitalization and small capitalization companies. Fund may hedge.
Year organized: 1985 (formerly Capital Gains portfolio)
Ticker symbol: FLCGX
Qualified for sale in: AL, AZ, CA, CO, CT, DE, DC, FL, GA, HI, IL, IN, KS, KY, MD, MA, MI, MN, MO, NJ, NY, NC, OH, OR, PA, SC, TN, TX, VA, WA, WI, WY
Discount broker availability: *Schwab (only through financial advisers), *White, Fidelity, Siebert
Dividends paid: Income - March, June, September, December; Capital gains - December
Portfolio turnover (3 yrs): 100%, 39%, 265%
Largest holding: Cash equivalents (100.0%)
Management fee: 1.00% first $50M to 0.60% over $100M
12b-1 distribution fee: 0.12%
Expense ratio: 1.54% (year ending 12/31/93)

THE FLEX-FUND - MONEY MARKET FUND
(See first Flex-Fund listing for data common to all Flex-Fund funds)

Portfolio manager: Philip A. Voelker (1985)
Investment objective and policies: Income and stable asset values through investment in money market instruments which mature in less than a year.
Year organized: 1985

Ticker symbol: FFMXX
Qualified for sale in: AL, AZ, CA, CO, CT, DE, DC, FL, GA, HI, IL, IN, KS, KY, MD, MA, MI, MN, MO, NJ, NY, NC, OH, OR, PA, SC, TN, TX, VA, WA, WI, WY
Check redemptions: $100 minimum
Confirmations mailed: Not mailed
Checks returned: Monthly
Periodic account statements mailed: Monthly
Dividends paid: Income - declared daily, paid monthly
Management fee: 0.40% first $100M, 0.25% over $100M
12b-1 distribution fee: 0.07%
Expense ratio: 0.37% (year ending 12/31/93) (0.57% without waiver)

THE FLEX-FUND - MUIRFIELD FUND

(See first Flex-Fund listing for data common to all Flex-Fund funds)

Portfolio manager: Robert S. Meeder, Jr. (1988)
Investment objective and policies: Long-term growth of capital with current income secondary. Invests in shares of other equity mutual funds which seek long term growth, primarily no-loads. Fund may use index funds, sector funds and low load (maximum of 2%) funds. Fund will not use other Flex funds.
Year organized: 1988
Ticker symbol: FLMFX
Discount broker availability: *Schwab (only through financial advisers), *White, Fidelity, Siebert
Qualified for sale in: AL, AZ, CA, CO, CT, DE, DC, FL, GA, HI, IL, IN, KS, KY, MD, MA, MI, MN, MO, NJ, NY, NC, OH, OR, PA, SC, TN, TX, VA, WA, WY
Dividends paid: Income - March, June, September, December; Capital gains - December
Portfolio turnover (3 yrs): 280%, 324%, 107%
Management fee: 1.0% first $50M to 0.60% over $100M
12b-1 distribution fee: 0.13%
Expense ratio: 1.26% (year ending 12/31/93)

THE FLEX-FUND - SHORT-TERM GLOBAL INCOME FUND

(See first Flex-Fund listing for data common to all Flex-Fund funds)

Portfolio manager: Joseph A. Zarr (1992)
Investment objective and policies: Maximum current income. Invests roughly 50% of assets in short to intermediate maturity bills and notes of the U.S. Government with remainder in short-term debt instruments denominated in certain foreign currencies with remaining maturities of 3 years or less. Principal foreign currencies utilized are those of Canada, UK, Germany, France, Japan, Switzerland and other major economic powers which conduct significant foreign trade with the U.S. Fund may hedge.
Year organized: 1992
Ticker symbol: FLGIX
Discount broker availability: *Schwab (only through financial advisers), *White, Fidelity, Siebert
Qualified for sale in: AL, AZ, CA, CO, CT, DC, DE, FL, GA, HI, IL, IN, KS, KY, MD, MI, MN, MO, NJ, NY, NC, OH, OR, PA, SC, TN, TX, VA, WA, WI, WY
Dividends paid: Income - declared daily, paid monthly; Capital gains - December
Portfolio turnover (1 yr): 781%
Management fee: 0.4% first $100M, 0.2% over $100M
12b-1 distribution fee: 0.07%
Expense ratio: 0.82% (year ending 12/31/93)

FLORIDA DAILY MUNICIPAL INCOME FUND ◆

600 Fifth Avenue - 8th Floor
New York, NY 10020
212-830-5200, 800-676-6779
prices/yields 212-830-5225
fax 212-830-5476

Adviser: Reich & Tang Asset Management L.P.
Portfolio manager: Molly Flewharty (1994)

Custodian and transfer agent: Investors Fiduciary Trust Co.
Investment objective and policies: High current interest income exempt from federal income taxes and, to the extent possible, from Florida intangible personal property tax, consistent with preservation of capital and liquidity. Invests primarily in Florida municipal money market instruments.
Year organized: 1994
Minimum purchase: Initial: $5,000, Subsequent: $100
Wire orders accepted: Yes
Deadline for same day wire purchase: 12 NN
Qualified for sale in: FL
Telephone redemptions: Yes
Wire redemptions: Yes, $1,000 minimum
Letter redemptions: Signature guarantee required
Telephone switching: With other Reich & Tang Money Markets, R & T Equity, and R & T Government Securities Trust
Number of switches permitted: Unlimited, $1,000 minimum
Check redemptions: $250 minimum
Confirmations mailed: After each purchase and each check, mail or wire redemption
Checks returned: As clear
Periodic account statements mailed: Monthly
Dividends paid: Income - declared daily, paid monthly
Shareholder services: Withdrawal plan
Management fee: 0.40%
Administration fee: 0.30%

FONTAINE FUNDS ◆

(Data common to all Fontaine funds are shown below. See subsequent listings for data specific to individual Fontaine funds.)

210 West Pennsylvania Avenue - Suite 240
Towson, MD 21204
410-825-7890, 800-247-1550
fax 410-825-7945

Shareholder service hours: Full service: M-F 8:30 A.M.-5 P.M.; After hours service: prices, messages, account balances, last transaction, prospectuses
Adviser: Richard Fontaine Associates, Inc.
Custodian: Bank One Ohio Trust Co., N.A.
Transfer agent: Richard Fontaine & Co., Inc.
Minimum purchase: Initial: $1,000, Subsequent: $100
Telephone orders accepted: No
Wire orders accepted: Yes
Deadline for same day wire purchase: 4 P.M.
Letter redemptions: Signature guarantee required over $10,000
Shareholder services: IRA, written exchanges with other Fontaine funds
IRA/Keogh fees: Annual $8

FONTAINE CAPITAL APPRECIATION FUND ◆

(See first Fontaine listing for data common to all Fontaine funds)

Newspaper listing: Fontaine
Portfolio manager: Richard H. Fontaine (1989)
Investment objective and policies: Long-term capital appreciation with current income secondary. Invests primarily in common stocks believed undervalued or out of favor with investors, focusing on price/book value relative to 10-15 year range. Up to 20% of assets may be in securities of foreign issuers from developed countries.
Year organized: 1989
Ticker symbol: FAPPX
Qualified for sale in: CA, DE, DC, FL, MD, MA, NH, NJ, NY, OH, OR, PA, TN, TX
Dividends paid: Income - December; Capital gains - December
Portfolio turnover (3 yrs): 132%, 129%, 79%
Largest holding: IBM Corp. (6.9%)
Management fee: 0.95%
Expense ratio: 1.50% (year ending 12/31/93) (1.81% without waiver)

FONTAINE GLOBAL GROWTH FUND ◆

(See first Fontaine listing for data common to all Fontaine funds)

Portfolio manager: Richard H. Fontaine (1992)
Investment objective and policies: Long-term capital growth. Invests primarily in equity and equity-related securities of established medium and large capitalization domestic and foreign issuers. Will normally have at least 65% of assets invested in at least 3 different developed countries in North America, Europe and the Pacific Basin, one of which may be the U.S.
Year organized: 1992
Qualified for sale in: CA, DC, FL, MD, NH, NJ, NY, OH, OR, PA, TX
Dividends paid: Income - December; Capital gains - December
Portfolio turnover (2 yrs): 264%, 349%
Largest holding: Amax Gold, Inc. (6.1%)
Management fee: 0.85%
Expense ratio: 1.50% (year ending 12/31/93) (3.62% without waiver)

FONTAINE GLOBAL INCOME FUND ◆

(See first Fontaine listing for data common to all Fontaine funds)

Portfolio manager: Richard H. Fontaine (1992)
Investment objective and policies: High current income with capital appreciation secondary. Invests primarily in fixed-income securities of domestic and foreign issuers - high and medium quality bonds, debentures, and notes. Investments outside the U.S. will be principally in government and quasi-governmental issuers to maintain liquidity and reduce credit risk. May also use currency exchange transactions to reduce risk.
Year organized: 1992
Qualified for sale in: CA, DC, FL, MD, NH, NJ, NY, OH, OR, PA, TX
Dividends paid: Income - March, June, September, December; Capital gains - December
Portfolio turnover (2 yrs): 171%, 190%
Management fee: 0.75%
Expense ratio: 1.25% (year ending 12/31/93) (2.32% without waiver)

FORTIS MONEY FUND

P.O. Box 64284
St. Paul, MN 55164
612-738-4000, 800-800-2638
fax 612-738-5534

Adviser: Fortis Advisers, Inc.
Portfolio manager: Diane Gotham (1994)
Custodian: First Bank National Association, Minneapolis
Transfer agent: Fortis Advisers, Inc.
Investment objective and policies: Maximum current income consistent with stability of principal. Invests in money market instruments. Fund will have at least 25% of assets collectively in obligations of foreign branches of domestic banks and domestic branches of foreign banks.
Year organized: 1979 (formerly St. Paul Money Fund; name changed from AMEV Money Fund in January 1992)
Ticker symbol: FORXX
Minimum purchase: Initial: $500, Subsequent: $50
Wire orders accepted: Yes
Deadline for same day wire purchase: 4 P.M.
Qualified for sale in: All states
Telephone redemptions: Yes, $1,000 minimum
Wire redemptions: Yes, $1,000 minimum
Letter redemptions: Signature guarantee not required
Telephone switching: With other Fortis Funds, some of which are load
Number of switches permitted: 4 round trips per year
Check redemptions: $100 minimum
Confirmations mailed: Not mailed
Checks returned: Quarterly
Periodic account statements mailed: Quarterly

Dividends paid: Income: declared daily, paid monthly
Shareholder services: Keogh, IRA, SEP-IRA, 401(k), corporate retirement plans, automatic investment plan—minimum $25/month (waives initial minimum), electronic funds transfer (purchase only), withdrawal plan min. req. $4,000.
Management fee: 0.60% first $500M, 0.55% over $500M (includes 0.20% 12b-1 distribution fee)
12b-1 distribution fee: 0.20%
Expense ratio: 0.88% (year ending 9/30/94)
IRA fees: Annual $10, Closing $7, Distribution $1 to $7
Keogh fees: Annual $25, Initial $15, Closing $10, Distribution $1 to $10

THE 44 WALL STREET EQUITY FUND ◆
26 Broadway - Suite 205
New York, NY 10004
212-248-8080, 800-543-2620
prices 800-543-2875, fax 212-248-8578

Adviser: MDB Asset Management Corp.
Portfolio manager: Mark D. Beckerman (1988)
Custodian: Bank of New York
Transfer agent: Supervised Service Co.
Investment objective and policies: Long-term capital appreciation. Invests in a relatively few companies selected for potential long-term performance. There will be little or no income from dividends or interest. Fund is non-diversified and employs leverage. May invest 10% of assets in securities of foreign issuers and use options to enhance return and hedge.
Year organized: 1980, present management 1988
Ticker symbol: FWLEX
Minimum purchase: Initial: $1,000, Subsequent: $100
Telephone orders accepted: Yes, $2,500 initial minimum, $10,000 subsequent maximum
Wire orders accepted: Yes
Deadline for same day wire purchase: 4 P.M.
Discount broker availability: White
Qualified for sale in: CT, DC, FL, HI, IL, MD, MA, NJ, NY, PA, TX, VA, WA
Telephone redemptions: Yes
Wire redemption: Yes, $1,000 minimum
Letter redemptions: Signature guarantee required
Dividends paid: Income - annually, Capital gains - annually
Portfolio turnover (3 yrs): 160%, 167%, 136%
Largest holding: Americana Hotel and Realty Corp. (8.5%)
Shareholder services: Keogh, IRA, SEP-IRA, 403(b), automatic investment plan, withdrawal plan
Management fee: 1.0%
Expense ratio: 4.87% (year ending 6/30/94)
IRA fees: Annual $10, Initial $10, Closing $10

FORUM DAILY ASSETS TREASURY FUND ◆
P.O. Box 446
Portland, ME 04112
207-879-0001, fax 207-879-6050

Adviser: Forum Advisors, Inc.
Portfolio manager: Les Berthy (1992)
Custodian: First National Bank of Boston
Transfer agent: Forum Financial Corp.
Investment objective and policies: High current income consistent with liquidity and preservation of capital. Invests primarily in money market obligations issued or guaranteed by the U.S. Treasury or its agencies and instrumentalities.
Year organized: 1992
Minimum purchase: Initial: $10,000, Subsequent: $500; IRA: Initial: $2,000
Wire orders accepted: Yes
Deadline for same day wire purchase: 12 NN
Qualified for sale in: CA, CO, CT, DC, FL, GA, HI, IL, IN, ME, MA, NH, NJ, NY, NC, ND, PA
Telephone redemptions: Yes
Wire redemptions: Yes, $5,000 minimum
Letter redemptions: Signature guarantee required
Telephone switching: With Oak Hall Fund, Payson

funds, Sound Shore Fund, and other Forum (load) funds
Number of switches permitted: Unlimited
Deadline for same day switch: 12 NN
Confirmations mailed: After each purchase and each mail or wire redemption
Periodic account statements mailed: Monthly
Dividends paid: Income - declared daily, paid monthly
Shareholder services: IRA, withdrawal plan, electronic funds transfer
Management fee: 0.20%
IRA fees: Annual $10, Initial $10
Expense ratio: 0.33% (year ending 3/31/94) (1.17% without waiver)

FOUNDERS FUNDS
(Data common to all Founders funds are shown below. See subsequent listings for data specific to individual Founders funds.)

2930 East Third Ave.
Denver, CO 80206
303-394-4404, 800-525-2440
prices/yields 800-232-8088
fax 303-326-3848

Shareholder service hours: Full service: M-F 7 A.M.-6:30 P.M. MST, Sat 9:00 A.M.-2 P.M.; After hours service: prices, yields, balances, last transactions, messages, prospectuses, DJIA, order statements
Adviser: Founders Asset Management Inc.
Custodian and transfer agent: Investors Fiduciary Trust Co.
Minimum purchase: Initial: $1,000, Subsequent: $100; IRA: Initial: $500, Subsequent: $100
Telephone orders accepted: Yes
Wire orders accepted: Yes, $6 fee
Deadline for same day wire purchase: 4 P.M.
Qualified for sale in: All states
Telephone redemptions: Yes
Wire redemptions: Yes, $1,000 minimum, $6 fee
Letter redemptions: Signature guarantee required over $50,000
Telephone switching: With other Founders Funds
Number of switches permitted: 4 round trips per year
Shareholder services: Keogh, IRA, SEP-IRA, 403(b), 401(k), corporate retirement plans, automatic investment plan—minimum $50/month (waives initial minimum), withdrawal plan min. req. $5,000, electronic funds transfer
IRA fees: Annual $10 per social security number (waived for accounts with at least $5,000 in assets)
Keogh fees: Annual $10

FOUNDERS BALANCED FUND
(See first Founders listing for data common to all Founders funds)

Portfolio manager: Patrick S. Adams (1993)
Investment objective and policies: Current income and capital appreciation. Invests in dividend-paying common stocks, U.S. and foreign government obligations and corporate fixed-income securities. Minimum of 25% of assets in investment-grade bonds. Writes covered call options to increase income and hedge. May have up to 30% of assets in foreign securities, 15% in illiquid securities, and use futures and options to hedge.
Year organized: 1962
Ticker symbol: FRINX
Discount broker availability: *Schwab, White, *Waterhouse, *Fidelity, *Siebert
Dividends paid: Income - March, June, September, December; Capital gains - December
Portfolio turnover (3 yrs): 251%, 96%, 133%
Largest holding: Compaq Computer Corp. Note (3.9%)
Management fee: 0.65% first $250M to 0.50% over $750M
12b-1 distribution fee: 0.24%
Expense ratio: 1.34% (year ending 12/31/93)

FOUNDERS BLUE CHIP FUND
(See first Founders listing for data common to all Founders funds)

Portfolio manager: Patrick S. Adams (1993)
Investment objective and policies: Long-term growth of capital and income. Invests in common stocks of large companies with proven earnings and dividends records in sound financial condition. At least 65% of assets will be in "Blue Chips" in the DJIA, S&P 500, or NYSE with capitalizations over $1B. May have up to 30% of assets in foreign securities, 15% in illiquid securities, and use futures and options to hedge.
Year organized: 1938 (Name change 12/1/87, formerly Founders Mutual. Changed from a quasi-index fund in November 1983)
Ticker symbol: FRMUX
Discount broker availability: *Schwab, White, *Waterhouse, *Fidelity, *Siebert
Dividends paid: Income - December; Capital gains - December
Portfolio turnover (3 yrs): 212%, 103%, 95%
Largest holding: Federal National Mortgage Association (3.9%)
Management fee: 0.65% first 250M to 0.50% over $750M
12b-1 distribution fee: 0.22%
Expense ratio: 1.22% (year ending 12/31/93)

FOUNDERS DISCOVERY FUND
(See first Founders listing for data common to all Founders funds)

Portfolio manager: Michael Haines (1989)
Investment objective and policies: Capital appreciation. Invests primarily in common stocks of small, rapidly growing U.S. companies with market capitalizations between $10M and $250M. May have up to 30% of assets in foreign securities, 15% in illiquid securities, and use futures and options to hedge.
Year organized: 1989
Ticker symbol: FDISX
Discount broker availability: *Schwab, White, *Waterhouse, *Fidelity, *Siebert
Dividends paid: Income - December; Capital gains - December
Portfolio turnover (3 yrs): 99%, 111%, 165%
Largest holding: IDB Communications Group, Inc. (2.1%)
Management fee: 1.0% first $250M to 0.7% over $500M
12b-1 distribution fee: 0.24%
Expense ratio: 1.65% (year ending 12/31/93)

FOUNDERS FRONTIER FUND
(See first Founders listing for data common to all Founders funds)

Portfolio manager: Michael K. Haines (1990)
Investment objective and policies: Capital appreciation. Normally invests in domestic and foreign equities with at least 50% of assets in U.S. companies and no more than 25% in any one foreign country, but fund may be 100% invested in U.S. or foreign securities depending on opportunities. Buys common stocks of small and medium size companies with capitalizations from $200M to $750M, but will not be restricted from owning large companies if they represent better prospects for capital appreciation. May have up to 30% of assets in foreign securities, 15% in illiquid securities, and use futures and options to hedge.
Year organized: 1987
Ticker symbol: FOUNX
Discount broker availability: *Schwab, White, *Waterhouse, *Fidelity, *Siebert
Dividends paid: Income - December; Capital gains - December
Portfolio turnover (3 yrs): 109%, 155%, 158%
Largest holding: IDB Communications Group, Inc. (2.6%)
Management fee: 1.00% first $250M to 0.70% over $500M
12b-1 distribution fee: 0.23%
Expense ratio: 1.66% (year ending 12/31/93)

FOUNDERS GOVERNMENT SECURITIES FUND
(See first Founders listing for data common to all Founders funds)

Portfolio manager: Montgomery C. Cleworth (1993)
Investment objective and policies: Current income. Invests at least 65% of assets in obligations of the U.S. Government - Treasury bills, notes and bonds and Government National Mortgage Association pass-through securities. May also invest in U.S. Government agency & instrumentality obligations. Up to 25% of assets may be in securities of foreign governments and/or their agencies.
Year organized: 1988
Ticker symbol: FGVSX
Discount broker availability: *Schwab, White, *Waterhouse, *Fidelity, *Siebert
Check redemptions: $500 minimum
Dividends paid: Income - declared daily, paid monthly; Capital gains - December
Portfolio turnover (3 yrs): 429%, 204%, 261%
Management fee: 0.65% first $250M, 0.50% over $250M
12b-1 distribution fee: 0.06%
Expense ratio: 1.18% (year ending 12/31/93)

FOUNDERS GROWTH FUND
(See first Founders listing for data common to all Founders funds)

Portfolio manager: Edward F. Keely (1993)
Investment objective and policies: Long-term growth of capital. Invests primarily in common stocks of established companies with above average growth prospects and capitalizations of more than $500M. May have up to 30% of assets in foreign securities, 15% in illiquid securities, and use futures and options to hedge.
Year organized: 1962
Ticker symbol: FRGRX
Discount broker availability: *Schwab, White, *Waterhouse, *Fidelity, *Siebert
Dividends paid: Income - December; Capital gains - December
Portfolio turnover (3 yrs): 131%, 216%, 161%
Largest holding: Newbridge Networks Corp. (3.1%)
Management fee: 1.00% first $30M to 0.65% over $500M
12b-1 distribution fee: 0.24%
Expense ratio: 1.32% (year ending 12/31/93)

FOUNDERS MONEY MARKET FUND ◆
(See first Founders listing for data common to all Founders funds)

Portfolio manager: Montgomery C. Cleworth (1993)
Investment objective and policies: Maximum current income consistent with preservation of capital and liquidity. Invests in high-quality money market instruments with maturities of less than one year. May also invest in dollar denominated foreign securities.
Year organized: 1981
Ticker symbol: FMMXX
Check redemptions: $500 minimum
Confirmations mailed: After each purchase and each check, mail or wire redemption
Checks returned: Monthly
Periodic account statements mailed: Quarterly
Dividends paid: Income - declared daily, paid monthly
Management fee: 0.5% first $250M to 0.35% over $750M
Expense ratio: 0.95% (year ending 12/31/93)

FOUNDERS OPPORTUNITY BOND FUND ◆
(See first Founders listing for data common to all Founders funds)

Portfolio manager: Montgomery C. Cleworth (1993)
Investment objective and policies: Current income

with capital appreciation secondary. Invests at least 65% of assets in investment-grade corporate bonds of both domestic and foreign issuers. Up to 35% of assets may be in junk bonds and 30% in securities of foreign issuers.
Year organized: 1993
Discount broker availability: *Schwab, *Fidelity, *Siebert
Check redemptions: $500 minimum
Dividends paid: Income - declared daily, paid monthly; Capital gains - December
Management fee: 0.65% first $250M to 0.50% over $750M
12b-1 distribution fee: Maximum of 0.25% (not currently imposed)

FOUNDERS PASSPORT FUND
(See first Founders listing for data common to all Founders funds)

Portfolio manager: Michael W. Gerding (1993)
Investment objective and policies: Capital appreciation. Invests primarily in securities issued by foreign companies with market capitalizations under $1B. Normally invests at least 65% of assets in securities from at least 3 countries. May invest in established and emerging economies around the world. May have up to 15% of assets in illiquid securities and use futures and options to hedge.
Year organized: 1993
Ticker symbol: FPSSX
Discount broker availability: *Schwab, White, *Fidelity, *Siebert
Dividends paid: Income - December; Capital gains - December
Management fee: 1% first $250M to $0.7% over $500M
Largest holding: Human Genome Sciences, Inc. (2.4%)
12b-1 distribution fee: 0.18%

FOUNDERS SPECIAL FUND
(See first Founders listing for data common to all Founders funds)

Portfolio manager: Charles Hooper (1991)
Investment objective and policies: Capital appreciation. Invests in common stocks of medium-sized companies with market capitalizations generally higher than those selected for the Frontier Fund. Fund may purchase put and call options on stock indices for the purpose of hedging. Up to 30% of assets may be in foreign securities and 15% in illiquid securities.
Year organized: 1960 (5 for 1 split 8/31/87)
Ticker symbol: FRSPX
Discount broker availability: *Schwab, White, *Waterhouse, *Fidelity, *Siebert
Portfolio turnover (3 yrs): 285%, 223%, 102%
Largest holding: Cisco Systems, Inc. (3.0%)
Dividends paid: Income - December; Capital gains - December
Management fee: 1.00% first $30M to $0.65% over $500M
12b-1 distribution fee: 0.22%
Expense ratio: 1.33% (year ending 12/31/93)

FOUNDERS WORLDWIDE GROWTH FUND
(See first Founders listing for data common to all Founders funds)

Portfolio manager: Michael W. Gerding (1990)
Investment objective and policies: Long-term capital growth. Invests in securities of established growth companies around the world, including the U.S. Emphasizes common stocks of both emerging and established growth companies. At least 65% of assets will be invested in three or more countries with no more than 25% in any country other than the U.S. May have up to 15% of assets in illiquid securities and use futures and options to hedge.
Year organized: 1989
Ticker symbol: FWWGX
Discount broker availability: *Schwab, White, *Waterhouse, *Fidelity, *Siebert

Portfolio turnover (3 yrs): 117%, 152%, 84%
Largest holding: Grupo Embotellador de Mexico S.A. (1.7%)
Dividends paid: Income - December; Capital gains - December
Management fee: 1.0% first $250M to $0.7% over $500M
12b-1 distribution fee: 0.24%
Expense ratio: 1.80% (year ending 12/31/93)

FREMONT MUTUAL FUNDS ◆
(Data common to all Fremont funds are shown below. See subsequent listings for data specific to individual Fremont funds.)

50 Beale Street, Suite 100
San Francisco, CA 94105
415-284-8900, 800-548-4539
fax 415-284-8177

Adviser: Fremont Investment Advisors, Inc.
Custodian: Bankers Trust Company
Transfer agent: MGF Service Corp.
Minimum purchase: Initial: $2,000, Subsequent: $200; IRA/Keogh: Initial: $1,000, Subsequent: None
Telephone orders accepted: No
Wire orders accepted: Yes
Deadline for same day wire purchase: 4 P.M.
Qualified for sale in: All states (except California Intermediate Tax-Free Fund)
Telephone redemptions: Yes
Wire redemptions: Yes, $8 fee
Letter redemptions: Signature guarantee required over $5,000
Telephone switching: With other Fremont funds
Number of switches permitted: Unlimited
Shareholder services: Keogh, IRA, SEP-IRA, 401(k), 403(b), corporate retirement plans, automatic investment plan—minimum $50/month (waives initial minimum), electronic funds transfer, directed dividends, withdrawal plan
IRA/Keogh fees: None

FREMONT BOND FUND ◆
(See first Fremont listing for data common to all Fremont funds)

Sub-adviser: Pacific Investment Management Company
Portfolio manager: William H. Gross (1994)
Investment objective and policies: High total return consistent with preservation of capital and prudent investment management. Invests primarily in high-quality intermediate-term bonds issued by the U.S. government and U.S. corporations, as well as foreign governments and corporations. May leverage and use options on securities and futures contracts, swap agreements and forward foreign currency exchange contracts to hedge.
Year organized: 1993 (name changed from Income Fund in 1994)
Ticker symbol: FBDFX
Discount broker availability: *White
Check redemption: $250 minimum
Dividends paid: Income - monthly; Capital gains - October, December
Portfolio turnover (2 yrs): 205%, 13%
Management fee: 0.55%
Expense ratio: 0.66% (year ending 10/31/94) (1.04% without waiver)

FREMONT CALIFORNIA INTERMEDIATE TAX-FREE FUND ◆
(See first Fremont listing for data common to all Fremont funds)

Portfolio manager: William M. Feeney (1990)
Investment objective and policies: High current income exempt from federal and California state income taxes consistent with prudent investment management. Invests in tax-exempt securities of the State of California and its municipalities with a weighted average maturity of 3 to 10 years. Fund may also invest up to 5% of assets in mutual funds which invest in securities whose income is exempt

from federal and California income taxes. May hedge up to 25% of total assets.
Year organized: 1990
Ticker symbol: FCATX
Discount broker availability: Schwab, *White
Qualified for sale in: CA
Check redemption: $250 minimum
Dividends paid: Income - declared daily, paid monthly; Capital gains - October, December
Portfolio turnover (3 yrs): 21%, 26%, 18%
Management fee: 0.55% first $25M to 0.35% over $150M
Expense ratio: 0.51% (year ending 10/31/94) (0.71% without waiver)

FREMONT GLOBAL FUND ◆
(See first Fremont listing for data common to all Fremont funds)

Portfolio managers: James E. Rhodes (1988), David Redo (1988), Peter F. Landini (1988)
Investment objective and policies: Maximum total return - income and capital gains - with reduced risk. Fund allocates assets among seven classes - U.S. stocks, U.S. dollar denominated debt securities, foreign stocks, foreign bonds, real estate securities, precious metals, and cash equivalents - and adjusts allocation to changing market conditions. May use forward currency contracts, currency futures contracts and options.
Year organized: 1988 (name changed From Fremont Multi Asset Fund in 1993)
Ticker symbol: FMAFX
Discount broker availability: Schwab, *White
Dividends paid: Income - April, July, October, December; Capital gains - October, December
Portfolio turnover (3 yrs): 52%, 40%, 50%
Largest holding: U.S. Treasury Bonds 7.125% due 02/25/99 (0.8%)
Management fee: 0.75%
Expense ratio: 0.95% (year ending 10/31/94)

FREMONT GROWTH FUND ◆
(See first Fremont listing for data common to all Fremont funds)

Sub-adviser: Sit Investment Associates, Inc.
Portfolio managers: Andrew L. Pang (1992), Eugene C. Sit (1992)
Investment objective and policies: Long-term growth of income. Invests at least 65% of assets in U.S. common stocks. May also invest in securities convertible into common and preferred stocks, futures contracts, options on index futures and stock indices, ADRs of foreign companies and restricted securities. Fund may hedge up to 25% of total assets.
Year organized: 1992 (name changed from Fremont Equity Fund in 1993)
Ticker symbol: FEQFX
Discount broker availability: *White
Dividends paid: Income - April, July, October, December; Capital gains - October, December
Portfolio turnover (2 yrs): 55%, 44%
Largest holding: Royce Value Trust, Inc. (3.0%)
Management fee: 0.65%
Expense ratio: 0.94% (year ending 10/31/94) (1.08% without waiver)

FREMONT INTERNATIONAL GROWTH FUND ◆
(See first Fremont listing for data common to all Fremont funds)

Sub-adviser: Sit/Kim International Investment Associates, Inc.
Portfolio manager: Andrew B. Kim (1994)
Investment objective and policies: Long-term growth of capital. Invests primarily in equity securities of foreign companies believed undervalued. Up to 50% of total assets may be invested in the securities of small- to medium-sized companies in developed and emerging markets. May invest more than 25% in securities issued by companies in Japan, the United Kingdom and/or Germany and use ADRs

and EDRs and have up to 15% of assets in illiquid securities. May use forward currency futures and options to hedge.
Year organized: 1994
Ticker symbol: FIGFX
Discount broker availability: Schwab
Dividends paid: Income - October; Capital gains - October, December
Portfolio turnover (1 yr): 44%
Largest holding: Powergen PLC (2.2%)
Management fee: 1.50%
Expense ratio: 1.50% (8 months ending 10/31/94)

FREMONT INTERNATIONAL SMALL CAP FUND ◆
(See first Fremont listing for data common to all Fremont fund)

Sub-adviser: Acadian Asset Management, Inc.
Portfolio manager: Gary L. Bergstrom (1994)
Investment objective and policies: Long-term capital appreciation. Invests primarily in equities of foreign companies with market capitalizations under $1 billion in developed and emerging markets. May invest more than 25% in securities issued by companies in Japan, the United Kingdom and/or Germany. May use ADRs and EDRs, forward currency futures and options to hedge, and have up to 15% of assets in illiquid securities.
Year organized: 1994
Discount broker availability: *White
Dividends paid: Income - October; Capital gains - October, December
Portfolio turnover (1 yr): 0%
Largest holding: Aoki International Co. (1.6%)
Management fee: 2.5% first $30M to 1.5% over $70M
Expense ratio: 2.50% (4 months ending 10/31/94)

FREMONT MONEY MARKET FUND ◆
(See first Fremont listing for data common to all Fremont funds)

Portfolio manager: Norman Gee (1988)
Investment objective and policies: Maximum current income consistent with preservation of capital and liquidity. Invests in money market instruments including Eurodollar certificates of deposit and U.S. dollar denominated money market instruments of foreign financial institutions, corporations and governments.
Year organized: 1988
Ticker symbol: FRMXX
Check redemption: $250 minimum
Confirmations mailed: After each purchase and each check, mail or wire redemption
Checks returned: Monthly
Periodic account statements mailed: Monthly
Dividends paid: Income - declared daily, paid monthly
Management fee: 0.45% first $50M, 0.35% over $50M
Expense ratio: 0.46% (year ending 10/31/94) (0.61% without waiver)

FREMONT U.S. MICRO-CAP FUND ◆
(See first Fremont listing for data common to all Fremont funds)

Sub-adviser: Morgan Grenfell Capital Management, Inc.
Portfolio manager: Robert E. Kern (1994)
Investment objective and policies: Long-term capital appreciation. Invests primarily in securities of emerging growth companies in the bottom 10% of the Wilshire 5000 Index with market capitalizations currently under $425M. Up to 25% of assets may be in securities and ADRs of small foreign companies. May use futures and options to hedge up to 25% of total assets.
Year organized: 1994
Discount broker availability: Schwab, *White
Dividends paid: Income - October; Capital gains - October, December
Portfolio turnover (1 yr): 129%

Largest holding: CEM Corp. (7.3%)
Management fee: 2.5% first $30M to 1.5% over $100M
Expense ratio: 2.50% (4 months ending 10/31/94)

FUNDAMENTAL FUNDS
(Data common to all Fundamental funds are shown below. See subsequent listings for data specific to individual Fundamental funds.)

90 Washington Street - 19th Floor
New York, NY 10006
212-635-3005, 800-225-6864
fax 212-635-5009

Shareholder service hours: Full service: M-F 9 A.M.-5 P.M. EST; After hours service: prices, yields, messages, prospectuses
Adviser: Fundamental Portfolio Advisors Inc.
Custodian: U.S. Trust Co. of New York
Transfer agent: Fundamental Shareholder Services, Inc.
Minimum purchase: Initial: $1,000, Subsequent: $100 (except U.S. Government Strategic Income)
Telephone orders accepted: No
Wire orders accepted: Yes
Deadline for same day wire purchase: 4 P.M.
Telephone redemptions: Yes
Wire redemptions: Yes, $5,000 minimum
Letter redemptions: Signature guarantee required over $5,000
Telephone switching: With other Fundamental funds
Number of switches permitted: Unlimited
Check redemptions: $100 minimum
Shareholder services: Automatic investment plan (waives initial minimum), electronic funds transfer (purchase only)
12b-1 distribution fee: 0.5%

FUNDAMENTAL CALIFORNIA MUNI FUND
(See first Fundamental listing for data common to all Fundamental funds.)

Portfolio manager: Lance N. Brofman (1984)
Investment objective and policies: High current income exempt from federal and California state income taxes consistent with preservation of capital. Invests at least 80% of assets in California municipal bonds of the 4 highest grades or notes in the 3 highest categories. Fund may leverage up to 20% of assets.
Year organized: 1984
Ticker symbol: CAMFX
Discount broker availability: *White
Qualified for sale in: CA, DC, HI, NJ, WY
Dividends paid: Income - declared daily, paid monthly; Capital gains - December
Portfolio turnover (3 yrs): 51%, 19%, 47%
Management fee: 0.5% first $100M to 0.4% over $500M
Expense ratio: 1.77% (year ending 12/31/93) (2.27% without waiver)

FUNDAMENTAL FIXED-INCOME FUND: HIGH-YIELD MUNICIPAL BOND SERIES
(See first Fundamental listing for data common to all Fundamental funds.)

Portfolio manager: David P. Wieder (1987)
Investment objective and policies: High current income exempt from federal income taxes. Invests at least 65% of assets in lower quality high-yielding municipal bonds rated BB or lower by S&P or Ba or lower by Moody's or unrated equivalents, with maturities of 20 years or more. Fund may not purchase obligations rated lower than C or not paying income. May use futures and options and leverage up to 1/3 of assets.
Year organized: 1987
Discount broker availability: *White
Qualified for sale in: CA, CO, CT, DC, FL, GA, HI, IL, IN, NJ, NY, NC, PA, VA, WY

Dividends paid: Income - declared daily, paid monthly; Capital Gains - December
Portfolio turnover (3 yrs): 85%, 101%, 16%
Management fee: 0.8% first $100M, to 0.7% over $500M
Expense ratio: 2.50% (year ending 12/31/93) (8.26% without waiver)

FUNDAMENTAL FIXED-INCOME FUND: TAX-FREE MONEY MARKET SERIES
(See first Fundamental listing for data common to all Fundamental funds.)

Portfolio manager: Jane Tubis (1990)
Investment objective and policies: High current income exempt from federal income tax, consistent with liquidity and preservation of capital. Invests at least 80% of assets in municipal money market securities rated Aa or better.
Year organized: 1987
Ticker symbol: FUNXX
Qualified for sale in: CA, CO, CT, DC, FL, GA, HI, IL, IN, NJ, NY, NC, PA, VA, WY
Confirmations mailed: After each purchase and each check, mail or wire redemption.
Checks returned: As clear
Periodic account statements mailed: Monthly
Dividends paid: income - declared daily, paid monthly
Management fee: 0.50% of first $100M to 0.40% over $500M
Expense ratio: 0.95% (year ending 12/31/93) (1.62% without waiver)

FUNDAMENTAL NEW YORK MUNI FUND
(See first Fundamental listing for data common to all Fundamental funds.)

Portfolio manager: Lance N. Brofman (1981)
Investment objective and policies: High current income exempt from federal, New York State and New York City income taxes consistent with preservation of capital. Invests primarily in New York municipal bonds of the 4 highest grades or notes in the 3 highest categories. May invest up to 35% in obligations rated lower than Baa and as low as Caa, including zero coupon and pay-in-kind securities. May leverage, use financial futures and options thereon and use options on debt securities.
Year organized: 1981 (formerly New York Muni)
Ticker symbol: NYMFX
Discount broker availability: *White
Qualified for sale in: CA, CT, DC, FL, HI, NJ, NY, PA, WY
Dividends paid: Income - declared daily, paid monthly; Capital Gains - December
Portfolio turnover (3 yrs): 404%, 461%, 365%
Management fee: 0.5% first $100M to 0.4% over $500M
Expense ratio: 1.44% (year ending 12/31/93)

FUNDAMENTAL U.S. GOVERNMENT STRATEGIC INCOME SERIES
(See first Fundamental listing for data common to all Fundamental funds.)

Investment objective and policies: High current income with minimum risk of principal and stability of NAV. Invests primarily in obligations issued or guaranteed by the U.S. Government, its agencies or instrumentalities with a weighted average maturity of 3 years or less. Fund may use futures and options and leverage up to 1/3 of assets.
Year organized: 1992
Ticker symbol: FUSIX
Minimum purchase: Initial: $2,500, Subsequent: $100; IRA: Initial: $2,000
Discount broker availability: *White
Qualified for sale in: AZ, CA, CO, CT, DE, DC, FL, GA, HI, IL, IN, IA, ME, MD, MA, MI, MS, NV, NJ, NM, NY, NC, OH, OR, PA, UT, VA, WI, WY
Dividends paid: Income - declared daily, paid monthly; Capital Gains - December
Portfolio turnover (2 yrs): 91%, 115%

Shareholder services: Keogh, IRA, SEP-IRA, 403(b), corporate retirement plans, automatic investment plan (waives initial minimum), electronic funds transfer (purchase only)
Management fee: 0.75% first $500M, to 0.7% over $1B
Expense ratio: 1.39% (year ending 12/31/93) (1.52% without waiver)
IRA fees: Annual $10

FUNDTRUST FUNDS
(Data common to all FundTrust funds are shown below. See subsequent listings for data specific to individual FundTrust funds.)

6 St. James Avenue
Boston, MA 02116
617-422-6418, 800-344-9033
prices/yields 800-638-1896
fax 617-422-0361

Administrator and distributor: Signature Broker-Dealer Services, Inc.
Adviser: Republic Asset Management Corp., M.D. Hirsch Division
Portfolio manager: Michael D. Hirsch (1984)
Custodian & transfer agent: Investors Bank & Trust Co.
Minimum purchase: Initial: $1,000, Subsequent: $100; IRA/Keogh: Initial: $250
Sales charge: 1.5% (none for money market fund)
Telephone orders accepted: No
Wire orders accepted: Yes
Deadline for same day wire purchase: 4 P.M. (12 NN for money market fund)
Qualified for sale in: All states
Telephone redemptions: Yes
Wire redemptions: Yes
Letter redemptions: Signature guarantee required
Telephone switching: With other FundTrust Funds
Number of switches permitted: Unlimited
Shareholder services: IRA, Keogh, 401(k), 403(b), automatic investment plan—minimum $25/month, withdrawal plan min. req. $10,000
IRA/Keogh fees: None

FUNDTRUST AGGRESSIVE GROWTH FUND
(See first FundTrust listing for data common to all FundTrust funds)

Investment objective and policies: Capital appreciation. Invests in a portfolio of approximately 10 to 15 mutual funds with this objective, although it may invest up to 25% of assets in any one underlying fund. For defensive purposes investments may be made in money market funds or directly in money market instruments. Investments in closed-end funds are prohibited.
Year organized: 1984
Ticker symbol: FTAGX
Discount broker availability: Schwab
Dividends paid: Income - December; Capital gains: December
Portfolio turnover (3 yrs): 43%, 35%, 24%
Largest holding: FPA Paramount Fund (12.1%)
Management fee: 0.5% first $500M, 0.4% over $500M
Sponsor fee: 0.25%
12b-1 distribution fee: 0.36%
Expense ratio: 1.70% (year ending 9/30/94)

FUNDTRUST GROWTH FUND
(See first FundTrust listing for data common to all FundTrust funds)

Investment objective and policies: Long term capital appreciation with current income secondary. Invests in a portfolio of approximately 10 to 15 mutual funds with these objectives, although it may invest up to 25% of assets in any one underlying fund. For defensive purposes investments may be made in money market funds or directly in money market instruments. Investments in closed-end funds are prohibited.
Year organized: 1984

Ticker symbol: FTGFX
Discount broker availability: Schwab
Dividends paid: Income - June, December; Capital gains: December
Portfolio turnover (3 yrs): 44%, 40%, 44%
Largest holding: Oakmark Fund (10.1%)
Management fee: 0.5% first $500M, 0.4% over $500M
Sponsor fee: 0.25%
12b-1 distribution fee: 0.36%
Expense ratio: 1.71% (year ending 9/30/94)

FUNDTRUST GROWTH & INCOME FUND
(See first FundTrust listing for data common to all FundTrust funds)

Investment objective and policies: A combination of capital appreciation and current income. Invests in a portfolio of approximately 10 to 15 mutual funds with these objectives, although it may invest up to 25% of assets in any one underlying fund. For defensive purposes investments may be made in money market funds or directly in money market instruments. Investments in closed-end funds are prohibited.
Year organized: 1984
Ticker symbol: FTGIX
Discount broker availability: Schwab
Dividends paid: Income - March, June, September, December; Capital gains: December
Portfolio turnover (3 yrs): 35%, 24%, 26%
Largest holding: Washington Investors Mutual Fund (13.9%)
Management fee: 0.5% first $500M, 0.4% over $500M
Sponsor fee: 0.25%
12b-1 distribution fee: 0.36%
Expense ratio: 1.55% (year ending 9/30/94)

FUNDTRUST INCOME FUND
(See first FundTrust listing for data common to all FundTrust funds)

Investment objective and policies: High current income. Invests in a portfolio of approximately 10 to 15 mutual funds with this objective, although it may invest up to 25% of assets in any one underlying fund. For defensive purposes investments may be made in money market funds or directly in money market instruments. Investments in closed-end funds are prohibited.
Year organized: 1984
Ticker symbol: FTINX
Discount broker availability: Schwab
Dividends paid: Income - monthly; Capital gains: December
Portfolio turnover (3 yrs): 41%, 53%, 21%
Management fee: 0.5% first $500M, 0.4% over $500M
Sponsor fee: 0.25%
12b-1 distribution fee: 0.38%
Expense ratio: 1.43% (year ending 9/30/94)

FUNDTRUST MANAGED TOTAL RETURN FUND
(See first FundTrust listing for data common to all FundTrust funds)

Investment objective and policies: High total return (capital appreciation and dividend income). Invests in a portfolio of approximately 10 to 15 mutual funds, although it may invest up to 25% of assets in any one underlying fund. Assets are allocated among aggressive growth, growth, growth-income and fixed-income funds. For defensive purposes investments may be made in money market funds or directly in money market instruments. Investments in closed-end funds are prohibited.
Year organized: 1988
Ticker symbol: FMTRX
Discount broker availability: Schwab
Dividends paid: Income - March, June, September, December; Capital gains: December
Portfolio turnover (3 yrs): 50%, 40%, 37%
Largest holding: PIMCO Total Return Fund

Management fee: 0.5% first $500M, 0.4% over $500M
Sponsor fee: 0.25%
12b-1 distribution fee: 0.40%
Expense ratio: 1.94% (year ending 9/30/94)

FUNDTRUST - REPUBLIC U.S. GOVERNMENT MONEY MARKET FUND
(See first FundTrust listing for data common to all FundTrust funds)

Investment objective and policies: High current income consistent with liquidity and preservation of capital. Invests primarily in money market obligations issued or guaranteed by the U.S. Government, its agencies or instrumentalities.
Year organized: 1990 (name and objective changed from Fundtrust Moneytrust on 10/14/94)
Check redemptions: $250 minimum
Confirmations mailed: after each purchase and each check, mail or wire redemption.
Checks returned: Not returned
Periodic account statements mailed: Quarterly
Dividends paid: income - declared daily, paid monthly
Management fee: 0.20%
12b-1 distribution fee: 0.20%
Expense ratio: 0.24% (year ending 9/30/94) (0.67% without waiver)

GABELLI FUNDS
(Data common to all Gabelli funds are shown below. See subsequent listing for data specific to individual Gabelli funds.)

One Corporate Center
Rye, NY 10580
914-921-5100, 800-422-3554
fax 914-921-5118

Shareholder service hours: Full service: M-F 9 A.M.-8 P.M. EST; After hours service: prices, yields, balances, orders, last transaction, news and views, messages
Adviser: Gabelli Funds, Inc.
Custodian and transfer agent: State Street Bank & Trust Co.
Minimum purchase: Initial: $1,000, Subsequent: None (exceptions noted)
Telephone orders accepted: No
Wire orders accepted: Yes
Deadline for same day wire purchase: 12 NN
Qualified for sale in: All states (except ABC fund)
Telephone redemptions: Yes, $25,000 maximum
Wire redemptions: Yes, $1,000 minimum & $25,000 maximum
Letter redemptions: Signature guarantee required over $25,000
Telephone switching: With other Gabelli funds, some of which have loads, and Westwood funds
Number of switches permitted: Unlimited
Shareholder services: IRA, automatic investment plan—minimum $100/month (waives initial minimum), electronic funds transfer
Management fee: 1.00% (except U.S. Treasury Money Market Fund)
IRA fees: Annual $10, Initial $5

THE GABELLI ABC FUND
(See first Gabelli listing for data common to all Gabelli funds)

Portfolio manager: Mario J. Gabelli (1993)
Investment objective and policies: Total returns attractive to investors in various market conditions without excessive risk of capital loss. Invests in a mix of equity and debt securities of domestic and foreign issuers chosen for their attractive opportunities for appreciation or investment income. Fund guarantees a 5% return during 1995 for each shareholder's first $5,000 invested (limited to an aggregate total of $50M).
Year organized: 1993
Ticker symbol: GABCX
Sales charge: 2% over first $5,000

Special sales restrictions: Fund closed to new shareholders on 1/3/94, Reopened 11/21/94 to 1/3/95 with a new guarantee. Now closed.
Qualified for sale in: All states except IN, MO, TX
Dividends paid: Income: December; Capital gains: December
Portfolio turnover (1 yr): 232%
Largest holding: Syntex Corp. (15.1%)
12b-1 distribution fee: 0.25%
Expense ratio: 2.78% (8 months ending 12/31/93) (3.60% without waiver)

THE GABELLI ASSET FUND
(See first Gabelli listing for data common to all Gabelli funds)

Portfolio manager: Mario J. Gabelli (1986)
Investment objective and policies: Growth of capital with current income secondary. Invests in equity securities believed to have good growth potential or to be undervalued. May invest up to 35% of assets in companies undergoing corporate reorganizations, 10% in other closed-end mutual funds, and 25% in securities of foreign issuers.
Year organized: 1986
Ticker symbol: GABAX
Discount broker availability: Schwab, White, Waterhouse, Fidelity, Siebert
Dividends paid: Income - December; Capital gains - December
Portfolio turnover (3 yrs): 19%, 16%, 14%
Largest holding: American Cyanamid Co. (4.4%)
12b-1 distribution fee: 0.14%
Expense ratio: 1.28% (year ending 12/31/94)

THE GABELLI GLOBAL CONVERTIBLE SECURITIES FUND
(See first Gabelli listing for data common to all Gabelli funds)

Portfolio manager: A. Hartswell Woodson III (1994)
Investment objective and policies: Maximum total return - capital growth and current income. Invests primarily in securities convertible into common stock or other equity securities of domestic and foreign companies. May invest up to 25% of assets in junk bonds and 15% in illiquid securities and use futures and options and sell short.
Year organized: 1994
Ticker symbol: GAGCX
Sales charge: 4.5% on or after 7/1/95
Discount broker availability: Schwab, White, *Fidelity, *Siebert
Dividends paid: Income - December; Capital gains - December
Largest holding: Parker & Parsley Petroleum Company 6.25% convertible preferred (3.1%)
12b-1 distribution fee: Maximum of 0.25%

THE GABELLI GLOBAL INTERACTIVE COUCH POTATO FUND
(See first Gabelli listing for data common to all Gabelli funds)

Portfolio manager: Mario J. Gabelli (1994)
Investment objective and policies: Capital growth with current income secondary. Invests primarily in securities of companies involved with communications, creativity and copyright throughout the world. Such companies, which are participating in emerging technological advances in interactive services and products accessible through telephones, TVs, radios and personal computers, are typically in the communications, entertainment, media and publishing industries. May invest up to 25% of assets in junk bonds and 15% in illiquid securities and use futures and options and sell short.
Year organized: 1994
Ticker symbol: GICPX
Sales charge: 4.5% on or after 7/1/95
Discount broker availability: Schwab, White, *Fidelity, *Siebert
Dividends paid: Income - December; Capital gains - December
Largest holding: Lin Broadcasting Corp. (2.0%)
12b-1 distribution fee: Maximum of 0.25%

THE GABELLI GLOBAL TELECOMMUNICATIONS FUND
(See first Gabelli listing for data common to all Gabelli funds)

Portfolio manager: Salvatore Muoio (1993)
Investment objective and policies: Capital growth with current income secondary. Invests primarily in securities of companies involved with telecommunications throughout the world. May invest up to 25% of assets in junk bonds and 15% in illiquid securities and use futures and options and sell short.
Year organized: 1993
Ticker symbol: GABTX
Minimum purchase: Initial: $25,000, Subsequent: None; IRA: Initial: $1,000
Sales charge: 4.5% on or after 7/1/95
Discount broker availability: Schwab, White, Waterhouse, *Fidelity, *Siebert
Dividends paid: Income - December; Capital gains - December
Largest holding: McCaw Cellular Communications, Inc. Class A (4.2%)
12b-1 distribution fee: Maximum of 0.25%

THE GABELLI GOLD FUND
(See first Gabelli listing for data common to all Gabelli funds)

Portfolio manager: Caesar M.P. Bryan (1994)
Investment objective and policies: Long-term capital growth. Invests primarily in equity securities of foreign and domestic issuers principally engaged in the exploration, mining, fabrication, processing, distribution or trading of gold or other precious metals. May have up to 15% of assets in illiquid securities and use futures and options and sell short.
Year organized: 1994
Ticker symbol: GOLDX
Discount broker availability: Schwab, White, *Fidelity, *Siebert
Dividends paid: Income - December; Capital gains - December
12b-1 distribution fee: Maximum of 0.25%

THE GABELLI GROWTH FUND
(See first Gabelli listing for data common to all Gabelli funds)

Portfolio manager: Howard Frank Ward (1995)
Investment objective and policies: Capital growth with current income secondary. Invests in a diversified portfolio of common stocks and securities convertible into common stocks with favorable earnings growth prospects that are undervalued at prevailing market multiples. Up to 25% of assets may be in securities of foreign issuers.
Year organized: 1987
Ticker symbol: GABGX
Discount broker availability: Schwab, White, Waterhouse, Fidelity, Siebert
Dividends paid: Income - December; Capital gains - December
Portfolio turnover (3 yrs): 81%, 46%, 50%
Largest holding: Genentech, Inc. (3.5%)
12b-1 distribution fee: Maximum of 0.25%
Expense ratio: 1.41% (year ending 12/31/93)

THE GABELLI U.S. TREASURY MONEY MARKET FUND ◆
(See first Gabelli listing for data common to all Gabelli funds)

Portfolio manager: Ronald S. Eaker (1992)
Investment objective and policies: High current income consistent with preservation of principal and liquidity. Invests exclusively in U.S. Treasury money market obligations and repurchase agreements collateralized by U.S. Treasury obligations.
Year organized: 1992
Ticker symbol: GABXX
Minimum purchase: Initial: $10,000 ($3,000 for shareholders of other Gabelli funds), Subsequent: None; IRA: Initial: $1,000
Check redemptions: $500 minimum

Confirmations mailed: After each purchase and each check, mail or wire redemption
Checks returned: Monthly
Periodic account statements mailed: Quarterly
Dividends paid: Income - declared daily, paid quarterly
Management fee: 0.3%
Account closeout fee: $5
Expense ratio: 0.30% (year ending 9/30/94) (0.46% without waiver)

GALAXY FUNDS ◆
(Data common to all Galaxy funds are listed below. See subsequent listings for data specific to individual Galaxy funds.)

440 Lincoln Street
Worcester, MA 01605
800-628-0414, 800-628-0413

Shareholder service hours: Full service: M-F 9 A.M.-5 P.M. EST; After hours service: orders, prospectuses, total returns
Adviser: Fleet Investment Advisors Inc.
Administrator: 440 Financial Group of Worcester, Inc.
Custodian: Chase Manhattan Bank, N.A.
Transfer agent: 440 Financial Group of Worcester, Inc.
Minimum purchase: Initial: $2,500, Subsequent $100; IRA/Keogh: Initial: $500
Telephone purchase: No
Wire purchase: Yes
Deadline for same day wire purchase: 4 P.M. (11 A.M. for money market funds)
Qualified for sale in: All states
Telephone redemptions: Yes, $10,000 maximum
Wire redemptions: Yes, $1,000 minimum, $5 fee
Letter redemptions: Signature guarantee required over $50,000
Telephone switching: With other Galaxy funds
Number of switches permitted: Unlimited
Shareholder services: Keogh, IRA, SEP-IRA, 401(k), 403(b), automatic investment plan—minimum $50/month (waives initial minimum), electronic funds transfer
Administration fee: 0.09% first $2.5B to 0.08% over $5B (on combined assets of all Galaxy funds)
IRA/Keogh fees: Annual $15, Closing $10

GALAXY: ASSET ALLOCATION FUND ◆
(See first Galaxy listing for data common to all Galaxy funds)

Portfolio manager: Fred Thompson (1991)
Investment objective and policies: High total return - current income and long-term capital growth. Fund allocates its assets among short-term obligations, common stocks, preferred stocks and bonds with at least 25% of assets in fixed-income senior securities. May invest up to 20% of assets in foreign securities, either directly or through ADRs and EDRs, and use options to increase return and hedge.
Year organized: 1991
Ticker symbol: GAAAX
Dividends paid: Income - quarterly; Capital gains - annually
Portfolio turnover (3 yrs): 23%, 7%, 2%
Largest holding: Citicorp (3.4%)
Management fee: 0.75%
Expense ratio: 1.21% (year ending 10/31/94) (1.22% without waiver)

GALAXY: CONNECTICUT MUNICIPAL BOND FUND ◆
(See first Galaxy listing for data common to all Galaxy funds)

Portfolio manager: Steve Woodruff (1993)
Investment objective and policies: High current income exempt from federal income tax and, to the extent possible, from Connecticut personal income tax, consistent with relative stability of principal. Invests primarily in Connecticut municipal securi-

ties. May have up to 20% of assets in AMT securities and use futures to hedge.
Year organized: 1993
Ticker symbol: GACTX
Dividends paid: Income - declared daily, paid monthly; Capital gains - annually
Portfolio turnover (2 yrs): 4%, 7%
Management fee: 0.75%
Expense ratio: 0.25% (year ending 10/31/94) (1.42% without waiver)

GALAXY: CORPORATE BOND FUND ◆
(See first Galaxy listing for data common to all Galaxy funds)

Portfolio manager: David Lindsay (1994)
Investment objective and policies: High current income. Invests primarily in investment-grade corporate debt obligations of domestic and foreign issuers. May have up to 20% of assets in securities of foreign issuers and 15% in illiquid securities. May purchase municipal bonds and use interest rate futures and currency forward contracts to hedge.
Year organized: 1994
Dividends paid: Income - declared daily, paid monthly; Capital gains - annually
Management fee: 0.75%

GALAXY: EQUITY GROWTH FUND ◆
(See first Galaxy listing for data common to all Galaxy funds)

Portfolio manager: Bob Armknecht (1990)
Investment objective and policies: Long term capital appreciation. Invests at least 75% in equities and equivalents believed to have above average potential for earnings growth with remainder in investment-grade bonds. May invest up to 20% of assets in ADRs and EDRs of foreign issuers and use options to increase income and hedge.
Year organized: 1990
Ticker symbol: GAEGX
Dividends paid: Income - quarterly; Capital gains - annually
Portfolio turnover (3 yrs): 18%, 16%, 22%
Largest holding: Hewlett-Packard Co. (2.7%)
Management fee: 0.75%
Expense ratio: 0.98% (year ending 10/31/94) (0.99% without waiver)

GALAXY: EQUITY INCOME FUND ◆
(See first Galaxy listing for data common to all Galaxy funds)

Portfolio manager: Edward Klisiewicz (1990)
Investment objective and policies: Current income and capital appreciation. Invests at least 75% of assets in common stocks and equivalents with anticipated current yields at least 30% higher than the S&P 500 average with remainder in investment-grade bonds. Fund may invest up to 20% of assets in ADRs and EDRs of foreign issuers and use options to increase income and hedge.
Year organized: 1990
Ticker symbol: GAEIX
Dividends paid: Income - quarterly; Capital gains - annually
Portfolio turnover (3 yrs): 31%, 27%, 18%
Largest holding: Halliburton Co. (3.1%)
Management fee: 0.75%
Expense ratio: 1.11% (year ending 10/31/94) (1.12% without waiver)

GALAXY: EQUITY VALUE FUND ◆
(See first Galaxy listing for data common to all Galaxy funds)

Portfolio manager: G. Jay Evans (1992)
Investment objective and policies: Long-term capital appreciation with income secondary. Invests at least 75% of assets in common stocks and equivalents of companies with market capitalizations of $100M or more believed undervalued based on cash flow, return on equity, return on assets and other measures. Remainder of assets are in invest-

ment-grade bonds. May invest up to 20% of assets in ADRs and EDRs of foreign issuers and use options to increase income and hedge.
Year organized: 1988 (formerly the Galaxy Equity Fund)
Ticker symbol: GALEX
Dividends paid: Income - quarterly; Capital gains - annually
Portfolio turnover (3 yrs): 71%, 50%, 136%
Largest holding: Intel Corp. (2.3%)
Management fee: 0.75%
Expense ratio: 1.08% (year ending 10/31/94) (1.11% without waiver)

GALAXY: GOVERNMENT FUND ◆
(See first Galaxy listing for data common to all Galaxy funds)

Portfolio manager: Pat Galuska (1994)
Investment objective and policies: High current income consistent with liquidity and stability of principal. Invests in money market instruments guaranteed by the U.S. Government, its agencies and instrumentalities, and repurchase agreements.
Year organized: 1986
Dividends paid: Income - declared daily, paid monthly
Management fee: 0.40%
Expense ratio: 0.54% (year ending 10/31/94)

GALAXY: HIGH QUALITY BOND FUND ◆
(See first Galaxy listing for data common to all Galaxy funds)

Portfolio manager: Kenneth W. Thomae (1990)
Investment objective and policies: High current income consistent with prudent risk of capital. Invests substantially all assets in Aa or better corporate debt obligations and in U.S. Government and agency securities. Fund may use interest rate futures, municipal bonds and convertibles.
Year organized: 1990
Ticker symbol: GAHQX
Dividends paid: Income - declared daily, paid monthly; Capital gains - annually
Portfolio turnover (3 yrs): 108%, 128%, 121%
Management fee: 0.75%
Expense ratio: 0.81% (year ending 10/31/94) (1.02% without waiver)

GALAXY: INTERMEDIATE BOND FUND ◆
(See first Galaxy listing for data common to all Galaxy funds)

Portfolio manager: Bruce R. Barton (1992)
Investment objective and policies: High current income consistent with prudent risk of capital. Invests at least 75% of assets in investment-grade corporate debt obligations and in U.S. Government and agency securities. Fund maintains a weighted average maturity of 3 to 10 years. May use interest rate futures to enhance income and hedge.
Year organized: 1988 (formerly the Galaxy Bond Fund)
Ticker symbol: GALBX
Dividends paid: Income - declared daily, paid monthly; Capital gains - annually
Portfolio turnover (3 yrs): 124%, 153%, 103%
Management fee: 0.75%
Expense ratio: 0.78% (year ending 10/31/94) (1.00% without waiver)

GALAXY: INTERNATIONAL EQUITY FUND ◆
(See first Galaxy listing for data common to all Galaxy funds)

Sub-adviser: Wellington Management Company
Portfolio managers: Jerry Mitchell (1991), David von Hemert (1994)
Investment objective and policies: Long term capital appreciation. Invests at least 75% of assets in equity securities of foreign issuers located in at

least 3 different foreign countries. May also invest in ADRs and EDRs and use options on securities and foreign stock indexes to increase income and hedge.
Year organized: 1991
Ticker symbol: GAIEX
Dividends paid: Income - quarterly; Capital gains - annually
Portfolio turnover (3 yrs): 39%, 29%, 21%
Largest holding: HSBC Holdings, PLC (2.4%)
Management fee: 1.15% first $50M to 0.85% over $100M
Expense ratio: 1.49% (year ending 10/31/94) (1.79% without waiver)

GALAXY: LARGE COMPANY INDEX FUND ◆
(See first Galaxy listing for data common to all Galaxy funds)

Investment objective and policies: Investment results that match the price and yield performance of the stocks contained in the S&P 500 Composite Stock Price Index. Invests at least 80% of assets in a proportional representative mix of the S&P 500 stocks to achieve a total return approximately equal to the performance of the total Index.
Year organized: 1990 (name changed from IBM Large Company Index Fund in 1994)
Ticker symbol: ILCIX
Dividends paid: Income - March, June, September, December; Capital gains - December
Portfolio turnover (3 yrs): 4%, 0%, 0%
Management fee: 0.40%
Expense ratio: 0.40% (year ending 3/31/94) (manager waives all expenses other than management fees)

GALAXY: MASSACHUSETTS MUNICIPAL BOND FUND ◆
(See first Galaxy listing for data common to all Galaxy funds)

Portfolio manager: David Lindsay (1993)
Investment objective and policies: High current income exempt from federal and Massachusetts personal income taxes consistent with relative stability of principal. Invests primarily in Massachusetts municipal securities. May have up to 20% of assets in AMT securities and use futures to hedge.
Year organized: 1993
Ticker symbol: GMAMX
Dividends paid: Income - monthly; Capital gains - annually
Portfolio turnover (2 yrs): 11%, 0%
Management fee: 0.75%
Expense ratio: 0.33% (year ending 10/31/94) (1.43% without waiver)

GALAXY: MONEY MARKET FUND ◆
(See first Galaxy listing for data common to all Galaxy funds)

Portfolio manager: Pat Galuska (1994)
Investment objective and policies: High current income consistent with liquidity and stability of principal. Invests in high quality money market instruments.
Year organized: 1986
Dividends paid: Income - declared daily, paid monthly
Management fee: 0.40%
Expense ratio: 0.64% (year ending 10/31/94)

GALAXY: MUNICIPAL BOND FUND ◆
(See first Galaxy listing for data common to all Galaxy funds)

Portfolio manager: Mary McGoldrick (1994)
Investment objective and policies: High income exempt from regular federal income tax consistent with prudent investment management and preservation of capital. Invests at least 80% of assets in municipal securities rated A or high by Moody's or

S&P. and at least 65% in municipal securities issued as municipal bonds, with a weighted average maturity of 7 to 12 years. May have up to 20% of assets in AMT bonds and use futures and options to increase return and hedge.
Year organized: 1993 (name changed from IBM Municipal Bond Fund in 1994)
Ticker symbol: IMBDX
Dividends paid: Income - declared daily and paid monthly; Capital gains - December
Portfolio turnover (1 yr): 56%
Management fee: 0.60%
Expense ratio: 0.60% (year ending 3/31/94) (manager waives all expenses other than management fees)

GALAXY: NEW YORK MUNICIPAL BOND FUND ◆
(See first Galaxy listing for data common to all Galaxy funds)

Portfolio manager: Donald Jones (1994)
Investment objective and policies: High current income exempt from federal and New York State and New York City personal income taxes consistent with relative stability of principal. Invests primarily in New York municipal securities. May have up to 20% of assets in AMT securities and use futures to hedge.
Year organized: 1991
Ticker symbol: GANYX
Dividends paid: Income - declared daily, paid monthly; Capital gains - annually
Portfolio turnover (3 yrs): 18%, 3%, 19%
Management fee: 0.75%
Expense ratio: 0.87% (year ending 10/31/94) (1.10% without waiver)

GALAXY: SHORT-TERM BOND FUND ◆
(See first Galaxy listing for data common to all Galaxy funds)

Portfolio manager: Kenneth W. Thomae (1991)
Investment objective and policies: High current income consistent with preservation of capital. Invests in investment-grade debt obligations of domestic and foreign issuers rated within the three highest ratings of S&P or Moody's and in obligations issued or guaranteed by the U.S. Government, its agencies and instrumentalities and other money market instruments. Fund maintains a weighted average maturity of less than 3 years. Up to 35% of assets may be in debt securities of foreign issuers.
Year organized: 1991
Year organized: GASTX
Dividends paid: Income - declared daily, paid monthly; Capital gains - annually
Portfolio turnover (3 yrs): 223%, 100%, 114%
Management fee: 0.75%
Expense ratio: 0.93% (year ending 10/31/94) (1.14% without waiver)

GALAXY: SMALL COMPANY EQUITY FUND ◆
(See first Galaxy listing for data common to all Galaxy funds)

Portfolio manager: Steve Barbaro (1991)
Investment objective and policies: Long term capital appreciation. Invests at least 65% of assets in equity securities of companies with market capitalization of $500M or less. Fund may have up to 20% of assets securities of foreign issuers and invest in corporate debt securities for defensive purposes. and use options to increase income and hedge.
Year organized: 1991
Year organized: GASEX
Dividends paid: Income - quarterly; Capital gains - annually
Portfolio turnover (3 yrs): 35%, 57%, 87%
Largest holding: Sports & Recreation, Inc. (1.3%)
Management fee: 0.75%
Expense ratio: 1.31% (year ending 10/31/94) (1.34% without waiver)

GALAXY: SMALL COMPANY INDEX FUND ◆
(See first Galaxy listing for data common to all Galaxy funds)

Investment objective and policies: Investment results that match the price and yield performance of the stocks with smaller capitalizations as represented by the Russell Special Small Company Index. Invests at least 80% of assets in a proportional representative mix of the Russell Special Small Company Index stocks to achieve a total return approximately equal to the performance of the total Index.
Year organized: 1990 (name changed from IBM Small Company Index Fund in 1994)
Ticker symbol: ISCIX
Dividends paid: Income - December; Capital gains - December
Portfolio turnover (3 yrs): 17%, 5%, 6%
Management fee: 0.40%
Expense ratio: 0.40% (year ending 3/31/94) (manager waives all expenses other than management fees)

GALAXY: TAX-EXEMPT BOND FUND ◆
(See first Galaxy listing for data common to all Galaxy funds)

Portfolio manager: Mary McGoldrick (1991)
Investment objective and policies: High current income exempt from federal income tax. Invests at least 65% of assets in high-quality municipal securities. Up to 20% of assets may be in AMT securities.
Year organized: 1991
Year organized: GABDX
Dividends paid: Income - declared daily, paid monthly; Capital gains - annually
Portfolio turnover (3 yrs): 17%, 38%, 11%
Management fee: 0.75%
Expense ratio: 0.80% (year ending 10/31/94) (1.03% without waiver)

GALAXY: TAX-EXEMPT FUND ◆
(See first Galaxy listing for data common to all Galaxy funds)

Portfolio manager: Pat Galuska (1988)
Investment objective and policies: High current income exempt from federal taxes consistent with liquidity and stability of principal. Invests in municipal money market obligations.
Year organized: 1988
Dividends paid: Income - declared daily, paid monthly
Management fee: 0.40%
Expense ratio: 0.58% (year ending 10/31/94)

GALAXY: U.S. TREASURY FUND ◆
(See first Galaxy listing for data common to all Galaxy funds)

Portfolio manager: Pat Galuska (1994)
Investment objective and policies: High current income consistent with liquidity and stability of principal. Invests in money market securities issued or guaranteed as to principal and interest by the U.S. Government or its agencies or instrumentalities, the interest income from which is generally exempt from state income taxes. Fund invests at least 65% of assets in direct U.S. Government obligations.
Year organized: 1991
Dividends paid: Income - declared daily, paid monthly
Management fee: 0.40% first $750M, 0.35% over $750M
Expense ratio: 0.56% (year ending 10/31/94)

GALAXY: U.S. TREASURY INDEX FUND ◆
(See first Galaxy listing for data common to all Galaxy funds)

Investment objective and policies: Investment results that match the price and yield performance

of U.S. Treasury notes and bonds as represented by the U.S. Treasury component (U.S. Treasury Index) of the Salomon Brothers Broad Investment-Grade Bond Index. Invests at least 80% of assets in a proportional representative mix of U.S. Treasury obligations to achieve a total return approximately equal to the performance of the U.S. Treasury Index.
Year organized: 1991 (name changed from IBM U.S. Treasury Index Fund in 1994)
Ticker symbol: IMTIX
Dividends paid: Income - declared and paid monthly; Capital gains - December
Portfolio turnover (3 yrs): 75%, 35%, 57%
Management fee: 0.40%
Expense ratio: 0.40% (year ending 3/31/94) (manager waives all expenses other than management fees)

GALAXY: UTILITY INDEX FUND ◆
(See first Galaxy listing for data common to all Galaxy funds)

Investment objective and policies: Investment results that match the price and yield performance of the stocks included in the Russell 1000 Utility Index. Invests at least 80% of assets in a proportional representative mix of the Russell 1000 Utility Index stocks to achieve a total return approximately equal to the performance of the total Index.
Year organized: 1992 (name changed from IBM Utility Index Fund in 1994)
Ticker symbol: IUTLX
Dividends paid: Income - March, June, September, December; Capital gains - December
Portfolio turnover (2 yrs): 19%, 0%
Management fee: 0.40%
Expense ratio: 0.40% (year ending 3/31/94) (manager waives all expenses other than management fees)

GATEWAY FUNDS ◆
(Data common to all Gateway funds are listed below. See subsequent listings for data specific to individual Gateway funds.)

400 TechneCenter Drive, Suite 220
Milford, OH 45150
513-248-2700, 800-354-6339
fax 513-248-2699

Shareholder service hours: Full service: M-F 9 A.M.-5 P.M. EST; After hours service: prices, yields, total returns, balances, orders, last transaction, messages, prospectuses
Adviser: Gateway Investment Advisers, Inc.
Custodian: Star Bank, Cincinnati
Transfer agent: The Gateway Trust
Minimum purchase: Initial: $1,000, Subsequent: $100
Telephone orders accepted: No
Wire orders accepted: Yes
Deadline for same day wire purchase: 3 P.M.
Qualified for sale in: All states (except Cincinnati Fund)
Telephone redemptions: Yes
Wire redemption: Yes, $10 fee
Letter redemptions: Signature guarantee required over $10,000
Telephone switching: With other Gateway Funds and Kemper Cash Equivalent Fund (MM)
Number of switches permitted: Unlimited
Deadline for same day switch: 3 P.M.
Shareholder services: IRA, SEP-IRA, automatic investment plan, withdrawal plan min. req. $5,000, electronic funds transfer (purchase only)
IRA fees: None

GATEWAY CINCINNATI FUND ◆
(See first Gateway listing for data common to all Gateway funds)

Portfolio manager: J. Patrick Rogers (1994)
Investment objective and policies: Long-term capital growth. Invests in common stocks of companies with an important presence in the Greater Cincinnati Area - either headquartered in or rank-

ing among the 25 largest employers in the Cincinnati area. Fund uses a proprietary model to select stocks and allocate assets among chosen stocks.
Year organized: 1994
Qualified for sale in: FL, IN, KY, NJ, OH
Dividends paid: Income - December; Capital gains - December
Management fee: 0.5%

GATEWAY GOVERNMENT BOND PLUS FUND ◆
(Fund liquidated in May 1994)

GATEWAY INDEX PLUS FUND ◆
(See first Gateway listing for data common to all Gateway funds)

Portfolio manager: Peter W. Thayer (1977)
Investment objective and policies: High current return at a reduced level of risk. Invests in stocks included in the S&P 100 Index (OEX) and writes options on this portfolio (currently the index vs. individual issues). Prior to Mar. 22, 1985, fund's objective was to invest in a diversified portfolio of common stocks and sell covered call options on these stocks.
Year organized: 1977 (name changed from Gateway Option Index Fund in March 1990; originally Gateway Option Income Fund)
Ticker symbol: GATEX
Discount broker availability: Schwab, *White, Waterhouse
Dividends paid: Income - March, June, September, December; Capital gains - December
Portfolio turnover (3 yrs): 17%, 15%, 31%
Largest holding: General Electric (6.0%)
Management fee: 0.9% first $50M to 0.6% over $100M
Expense ratio: 1.11% (year ending 12/31/93)

GATEWAY MATRIX GROWTH FUND ◆
(See Matrix Growth Fund)

GATEWAY MID CAP INDEX FUND ◆
(See first Gateway listing for data common to all Gateway funds)

Portfolio manager: Peter W. Thayer (1992)
Investment objective and policies: Long-term capital growth with conservation of principal secondary. Invests in the 400 stocks in the S&P 400 Midcap Index (in the proportions that they are represented in that index) and occasionally writes options on this portfolio to maximize return in up or down markets.
Year organized: 1992 (Name and objective changed from Gateway Capital Fund on 12/20/93)
Ticker symbol: GATCX
Discount broker availability: *White
Dividends paid: Income - December; Capital gains - December
Portfolio turnover (2 yrs): 105%, 0%
Largest holding: General Motors Corp. Class E (1.7%)
Management fee: 0.9% first $50M to 0.6% over $100M
Expense ratio: 1.50% (year ending 12/31/93) (2.23% without waiver)

GATEWAY SMALL CAP INDEX FUND ◆
(See first Gateway listing for data common to all Gateway funds)

Portfolio manager: Peter W. Thayer (1993)
Investment objective and policies: Long-term capital growth. Invests in the 250 stocks in the Wilshire Small Cap Index in the same proportions that they are represented in that index. Fund may buy index put options to reduce the risk of principal loss and index call options to increase the potential for gain.
Year organized: 1993
Ticker symbol: GSCIX
Discount broker availability: *White

Dividends paid: Income - December; Capital gains - December
Portfolio turnover (1 yr): 3%
Largest holding: Pittston Services Group (0.9%)
Management fee: 0.9% first $50M to 0.6% over $100M
Expense ratio: 1.92% (6 months ending 12/31/93) (2.23% without waiver)

GE FUNDS
(Data common to all GE funds are shown below. See subsequent listings for data specific to individual GE funds.)

3003 Summer Street
Stamford, CT 06904
203-326-4040, 800-242-0134

Adviser: GE Investment Management Inc.,
Custodian & transfer agent: State Street Bank & Trust Co.
Special sales restrictions: Funds are offered in 4 share classes. Only Class C shares - available without load to employees, retirees, officers or directors of G.E. or an affiliate of G.E. and their relatives - are covered below. Class A and B shares have sales loads and Class D shares are only available to institutional investors.
Minimum purchase: Initial: $500, Subsequent: $100; IRA: Initial: $250
Telephone orders accepted: No
Wire orders accepted: Yes, $1,000 minimum
Deadline for same day wire purchase: 4 P.M.
Qualified for sale in: All states
Telephone redemptions: Yes, $500 minimum
Wire redemptions: Yes, $1,000 minimum, $15 fee
Letter redemptions: Signature guarantee required over $10,000
Telephone switching: With other GE funds
Number of switches permitted: Unlimited
Shareholder services: IRA, Keogh, 401(k), 403(b), automatic investment plan—minimum $25/month (waives initial minimum), withdrawal plan min. req. $10,000
IRA/Keogh fees: Annual $25 (maximum $50)

GE FIXED INCOME FUND
(See first GE listing for data common to all GE funds)

Newspaper listing: Income
Portfolio manager: Robert A. MacDougall (1993)
Investment objective and policies: Maximum income consistent with prudent investment management and preservation of capital. Invests in U.S. and foreign government debt securities, bonds, convertible bonds, debentures, notes and non-convertible preferred stocks, mortgage-backed and related securities, asset-backed and receivables-backed securities, and money market instruments with a weighted average maturity of 5 to 10 years. Up to 35% of assets may be in obligations of foreign issuers. May use futures and options.
Year organized: 1993
Ticker symbol: GEFIX
Dividends paid: Income - declared daily, paid monthly; Capital gains - December
Portfolio turnover (2 yrs): 298%, 68%
Management fee: 0.35%
12b-1 distribution fee: 0.25%
Expense ratio: 0.79% (year ending 9/30/94) (1.26% without waiver)

GE GLOBAL EQUITY FUND
(See first GE listing for data common to all GE funds)

Portfolio manager: Ralph R. Layman (1993)
Investment objective and policies: Long term growth of capital. Invests primarily in foreign equity securities issued by companies in developed and developing countries throughout the world. Normally invests at least 65% of assets in common and preferred stocks, convertible securities and warrants or rights of established companies from at least 3 different countries including the U.S. May use futures and options and sell short.

Year organized: 1993
Ticker symbol: GEGEX
Dividends paid: Income - December; Capital gains - December
Portfolio turnover (2 yrs): 26%, 28%
Largest holding: International Paper Co. (2.4%)
Management fee: 0.75%
12b-1 distribution fee: 0.25%
Expense ratio: 1.31% (year ending 9/30/94) (1.77% without waiver)

GE INTERNATIONAL EQUITY FUND

(See first GE listing for data common to all GE funds)

Portfolio manager: Ralph R. Layman (1994)
Investment objective and policies: Long term growth of capital. Invests primarily in foreign equity securities issued by companies in developed and developing countries throughout the world. Normally invests at least 65% of assets in common and preferred stocks, convertible securities and warrants or rights of established companies from at least 3 different countries outside the U.S. May use futures and options and sell short.
Year organized: 1994
Ticker symbol: GEIEX
Dividends paid: Income - December; Capital gains - December
Portfolio turnover (1 yr): 6%
Largest holding: Hutchison Whampoa Ltd. (3.0%)
Management fee: 0.80%
12b-1 distribution fee: 0.25%
Expense ratio: 1.35% (7 months ending 9/30/94) (1.68% without waiver)

GE MONEY MARKET FUND ◆

(See first GE listing for data common to all GE funds)

Portfolio manager: Don Torey (1993)
Investment objective and policies: High current income consistent with preservation of capital and liquidity. Invests in dollar-denominated money market instruments of U.S. and foreign issuers.
Year organized: 1993
Ticker symbol: GEMXX
Checks redemptions: $500 minimum
Confirmations mailed: After each purchase and each check, mail or wire redemption
Checks returned: Monthly
Periodic account statements mailed: Quarterly
Dividends paid: Income - declared daily, paid monthly
Management fee: 0.25%
Expense ratio: 0.45% (year ending 9/30/94) (1.04% without waiver)

GE SHORT-TERM GOVERNMENT FUND

(See first GE listing for data common to all GE funds)

Portfolio manager: Robert A. MacDougall (1994)
Investment objective and policies: Maximum income consistent with prudent investment management and preservation of capital. Invests primarily in securities issued or guaranteed by the U.S. Government, its agencies or instrumentalities with a weighted average maturity of approximately 3 years. May also invest in debt securities of U.S. and foreign companies and foreign governments. May use futures and options.
Year organized: 1994
Dividends paid: Income - declared daily, paid monthly; Capital gains - December
Portfolio turnover (1 yr): 146%
Management fee: 0.30%
12b-1 distribution fee: 0.25%
Expense ratio: 0.70% (7 months ending 9/30/94) (1.46% without waiver)

GE STRATEGIC INVESTMENT FUND

(See first GE listing for data common to all GE funds)

Portfolio managers: David B. Carlson (1993), Robert A. MacDougall (1993)
Investment objective and policies: Maximum total

return - capital appreciation and income. Invests in equity (common and preferred stocks, convertible securities and warrants), fixed-income (bonds, debentures and government obligations) and money market instruments. Fund adjusts allocation of assets among categories to changing market conditions. Up to 20% of assets may be in securities of foreign issuers and 10% in non-publicly traded securities. May use futures and options.
Year organized: 1993
Ticker symbol: GESIX
Dividends paid: Income - December; Capital gains - December
Portfolio turnover (2 yrs): 68%, 20%
Largest holding: U.S. Treasury Note 6.50% due 4/30/99 (3.2%)
Management fee: 0.35%
12b-1 distribution fee: 0.25%
Expense ratio: 0.85% (year ending 9/30/94) (1.33% without waiver)

GE TAX-EXEMPT FUND

(See first GE listing for data common to all GE funds)

Portfolio manager: Robert R. Kaelin (1993)
Investment objective and policies: High current income exempt from federal income tax consistent with prudent investment management and preservation of capital. Invests in municipal debt obligations issued by, or on behalf of, states, territories and possessions of the U.S. and their political subdivisions, agencies and instrumentalities, or multi-state agencies or authorities.
Year organized: 1993
Ticker symbol: GETEX
Dividends paid: Income - declared daily, paid monthly; Capital gains - December
Portfolio turnover (2 yrs): 23%, 29%
Management fee: 0.35%
12b-1 distribution fee: 0.25%
Expense ratio: 0.79% (year ending 9/30/94) (1.33% without waiver)

GE U.S. EQUITY FUND

(See first GE listing for data common to all GE funds)

Portfolio manager: Eugene Bolton (1993)
Investment objective and policies: Long term growth of capital. Invests primarily in equity securities of U.S. companies to selected to have similar characteristics to the S&P 500 Index. Normally invests at least 65% of assets in common and preferred stocks, convertible securities and warrants or rights of established companies. May invest in ADRs without limit and have up to 15% of assets in foreign securities not traded on U.S. exchanges. May use futures and options.
Year organized: 1993
Ticker symbol: GEEQX
Dividends paid: Income - December; Capital gains - December
Portfolio turnover (2 yrs): 51%, 15%
Largest holding: American Telephone & Telegraph Co. (2.2%)
Management fee: 0.40%
12b-1 distribution fee: 0.25%
Expense ratio: 0.62% (year ending 9/30/94) (1.21% without waiver)

GENERAL ELECTRIC S&S LONG TERM INTEREST FUND ◆

3003 Summer Street
P.O. Box 7900
Stamford, CT 06904
203-326-2300, 800-242-0134

Newspaper listing: S&S Lg
Adviser: General Electric Investment Corp.
Portfolio manager: Robert MacDougall (1987)
Custodian: The Bank of New York
Transfer agent: Elfun Mutual Funds
Investment objective and policies: High interest rate of return through investments in debt securities consisting of corporate bonds and debentures, real estate sale, U.S. Government obligations, etc.

Special sales restrictions: Available to employees of General Electric Co. who are participants in the GE Savings & Security Program
Year organized: 1980
Ticker symbol: GESLX
Minimum purchase: Initial: None, Subsequent: None
Telephone orders accepted: No
Qualified for sale in: All states
Letter redemptions: Signature guarantee not required
Dividends paid: Income - monthly
Portfolio turnover (3 yrs): 154%, 45%, 65%
Shareholder services: Keogh, IRA
Expense ratio: 0.07% (year ending 12/31/93)

GENERAL ELECTRIC S&S PROGRAM MUTUAL FUND ◆

3003 Summer Street
P.O. Box 7900
Stamford, CT 06904
203-356-2300, 800-242-0134

Newspaper listing: S&S
Adviser: General Electric Investment Corp.
Portfolio manager: David Beck (1991)
Custodian: The Bank of New York
Transfer agent: Elfun Mutual Funds
Investment objective and policies: Long-term growth of capital and income, invests principally in common stocks.
Special sales restrictions: Available to employees of General Electric Co. who are participants in the GE Savings & Security Program
Year organized: 1967
Ticker symbol: GESSX
Minimum purchase: Initial: None, Subsequent: None
Telephone orders accepted: No
Qualified for sale in: All states
Letter redemptions: Signature guarantee not required
Dividends paid: Income - January; Capital gains - January
Portfolio turnover (3 yrs): 37%, 40%, 29%
Largest holding: Royal Dutch Petroleum Co. (1.9%)
Shareholder services: Keogh, IRA
Expense ratio: 0.11% (year ending 12/31/93)

GENERAL SECURITIES ◆

701 Fourth Avenue South, Suite 1000
Minneapolis, MN 55415
612-332-1212, 800-939-9990
fax 816-435-3209

Adviser: Robinson Capital Management, Inc.
Portfolio manager: John P. Robinson (1951)
Custodian and transfer agent: Investors Fiduciary Trust Co.
Investment objective and policies: Long term capital growth and security of principal with reasonable risk. Invests primarily in common stocks but may also invest in preferred stocks and fixed-income securities. May use options to hedge up to 25% of assets.
Year organized: 1951
Ticker symbol: GSECX
Minimum purchase: Initial: $500, Subsequent: $100
Telephone orders accepted: No
Wire orders accepted: Yes
Deadline for same day wire purchase: 4 P.M.
Qualified for sale in: All states except AL, AR, DE, LA, ME, MA, MO, NH, OH, RI, SC, TN, TX, UT, VT, WA, WI
Telephone redemptions: Yes
Wire redemptions: Yes, $2,500 minimum, $20 fee
Letter redemptions: Signature guarantee required over $50,000
Dividends paid: Income - February, May, August, November; Capital gains - December
Portfolio turnover (3 yrs): 42%, 30%, 39%
Largest holding: GTE Corp. (5.1%)
Shareholder services: Keogh, IRA, SEP-IRA, automatic investment plan (waives initial minimum), withdrawal plan min. req. $10,000

Management fee: 0.60% first $100M to 0.10% over $250M
Expense ratio: 1.50% (year ending 11/30/94)
IRA/Keogh fees: Annual $12

GIBRALTER EQUITY GROWTH FUND ◆
1201 County Line Road
Rosemont, PA 19010
610-525-6102, fax 610-525-6243

Adviser: Barclay Funds Management, Inc.
Portfolio manager: Norman McAvoy (1990)
Custodian: Bank of New York
Transfer agent: Barclay Financial Services, Inc.
Investment objective and policies: Long-term capital appreciation with current income secondary. Invests at least 65% of assets in common stocks believed undervalued. May invest 10% of assets in other mutual funds.
Year organized: 1983
Minimum purchase: Initial: $1,000, Subsequent: $100
Telephone orders accepted: No
Wire orders accepted: Yes
Deadline for same day wire purchase: 4 P.M.
Qualified for sale in: PA
Letter redemptions: Signature guarantee required
Dividends paid: Income - annually; Capital gains - annually
Portfolio turnover (3 yrs): 3%, 75%, 76%
Largest holding: Schering-Plough Co. (7.0%)
Shareholder services: IRA
Management fee: 1.5% first $10M to 0.75% over $60M
12b-1 distribution fee: 0.2% (not currently imposed)
Expense ratio: 5.03% (year ending 11/30/94)
IRA fees: None

GINTEL ERISA FUND ◆
6 Greenwich Office Park
Greenwich, CT 06831
203-622-6400, 800-243-5808
800-344-3092, prices 800-759-4171

Portfolio manager: Robert M. Gintel (1982)
Adviser: Gintel Equity Management, Inc.
Custodian: U.S. Trust Co. of New York
Transfer agent: Mutual Funds Service Co.
Investment objective and policies: Maximum total return - long-term appreciation, investment income and short-term capital gains without regard to tax consequences. Invests in common stock, securities convertible into common stock, and fixed-income securities. Up to 25% of assets may be in OTC securities and 15% in illiquid securities. Fund is non-diversified.
Year organized: 1981
Ticker symbol: GINTX
Special sales restrictions: Offered exclusively to pension plans, trusts, IRA and Keogh plans, educational, religious, and charitable institutions, foundations exempt from Federal income taxation.
Minimum purchase: Initial: $10,000, Subsequent: None; IRA/Keogh: Initial: $2,000
Telephone orders accepted: No
Wire orders accepted: Yes
Deadline for same day wire purchase: 4 P.M.
Discount broker availability: Schwab, *White
Qualified for sale in: All states except AR, IL, IA, KY, ME, MI, MT, NE, NH, ND, OH, OK, WA, WV
Letter redemptions: Signature guarantee required
Telephone switching: With Gintel Fund and UST Master money market funds
Number of switches permitted: Unlimited
Dividends paid: Income - December; Capital gains - December
Portfolio turnover (3 yrs): 99%, 80%, 97%
Largest holding: Capstead Mortgage Corp. (13.4%)
Shareholder services: Keogh, IRA, SEP-IRA, 401(k), 403(b), corporate retirement plans, automatic investment plan, withdrawal plan min. req. $10,000
Management fee: 1.0%
Expense ratio: 2.2% (year ending 12/31/93)
IRA/Keogh fees: Annual $10, Initial $5

GINTEL FUND ◆
6 Greenwich Office Park
Greenwich, CT 06831
203-622-6400, 800-243-5808
800-344-3092, prices 800-724-4171

Portfolio managers: Robert M. Gintel (1981), Cecil A. Godman III
Adviser: Gintel Equity Management, Inc.
Custodian: U.S. Trust Co. of New York
Transfer agent: Mutual Funds Service Co.
Investment objective and policies: Capital appreciation. Invests in common stocks or securities convertible into common stock. Up to 25% of assets may be in OTC securities, 20% in securities of foreign issuers and 15% in illiquid securities. Fund leverages and sells short against the box and is non-diversified.
Year organized: 1981
Ticker symbol: GINLX
Minimum purchase: Initial: $5,000, Subsequent: None
Telephone orders accepted: No
Wire orders accepted: Yes
Deadline for same day wire purchase: 4 P.M.
Discount broker availability: Schwab, *White, Waterhouse, Fidelity, Siebert
Qualified for sale in: All states except AR, NE, OH
Telephone redemptions: Yes
Wire redemptions: Yes, $1,000 minimum, $8 fee
Letter redemptions: Signature guarantee required
Telephone switching: With Gintel Erisa and UST Master money market funds
Number of switches permitted: Unlimited
Dividends paid: Income - December; Capital gains - December
Portfolio turnover (3 yrs): 51%, 56%, 66%
Largest holding: Federal National Mortgage (11.3%)
Shareholder services: Keogh, IRA, SEP-IRA, 401(k), 403(b), corporate retirement plans, automatic investment plan—minimum $100/month, withdrawal plan min. req. $10,000
Management fee: 1.0%
Expense ratio: 2.2% (year ending 12/31/93)
IRA/Keogh fees: Annual $10, Initial $5

GIT TRUSTS ◆
(Data common to all GIT portfolios are shown below. See subsequent listings for data specific to individual GIT portfolios.)

1655 Fort Myer Drive, Suite 1000
Arlington, VA 22209
703-528-6500, 800-336-3063
prices/yields 800-448-4422
fax 703-528-9143

Shareholder service hours: Full service: M-F 9 A.M.-7 P.M. EST; After hours service: prices, yields, balances
Adviser: Bankers Finance Investment Management Corp.
Custodian: Star Bank N.A., Cincinnati
Transfer agent: GIT Investment Services, Inc.
Minimum purchase: Initial: $2,500 ($5,000 for Worldwide Growth Portfolio), Subsequent: $50; IRA/Keogh: Initial: $500, Subsequent: None
Telephone orders accepted: No
Wire orders accepted: Yes, with telephone notification
Deadline for same day wire purchase: 1 P.M.
Telephone redemptions: Yes
Wire redemptions: Yes, $10 fee under $10,000
Letter redemptions: Signature guarantee not required
Telephone switching: With other GIT Trust portfolios and Government Investors Trust money market
Number of switches permitted: Unlimited
Shareholder services: Keogh, IRA, SEP-IRA, 401(k), 403(b), corporate retirement plans, automatic investment plan, withdrawal plan no min. req., electronic funds transfer
Account fee: $3 per month if ending balance less than $700
IRA fees: Annual: $12
Keogh fees: Annual: $15

GIT ARIZONA TAX-FREE PORTFOLIO ◆
(See first GIT listing for data common to all GIT Trust portfolios)

Portfolio manager: Dan Gillespie (1994)
Investment objective and policies: Current income exempt from federal and Arizona state income taxes. Invests primarily in municipal securities issued by the state of Arizona. Up to 20% of assets may be invested in taxable securities including AMT securities.
Year organized: 1989 (a portfolio of GIT Tax-Free Trust)
Discount broker availability: Schwab
Qualified for sale in: AZ, DC
Check redemptions: $5 fee under $500
Dividends paid: Income - declared daily, paid monthly; Capital gains - November
Portfolio turnover (3 yrs): 67%, 63%, 23%
Management fee: 0.625%
Expense ratio: 1.29% (year ending 9/30/94)

GIT EQUITY INCOME PORTFOLIO ◆
(See first GIT listing for data common to all GIT Trust portfolios)

Portfolio manager: Charles J. Tennes (1993)
Investment objective and policies: Current income with capital appreciation secondary. Invests primarily in regular dividend paying stocks with some capital appreciation potential. Fund may write covered calls and invest in foreign securities.
Year organized: 1983 (a portfolio of GIT Equity Trust)
Discount broker availability: Schwab
Qualified for sale in: All states except AK, CT, IA, KS, ME, MS, MT, NV, NM, ND, RI, SD, VT, WA
Dividends paid: Income - March, June, September, December; Capital gains - March, December
Portfolio turnover (3 yrs): 34%, 55%, 32%
Largest holding: Williams Companies, Inc. (3.4%)
Management fee: 0.75%
Expense ratio: 2.17% (year ending 3/31/94)

GIT GOVERNMENT PORTFOLIO ◆
(See first GIT listing for data common to all GIT Trust portfolios)

Portfolio managers: Jonathan Edwards (1988), Charles J. Tennes (1993)
Investment objective and policies: Current income. Invests exclusively in U.S. Government securities, including those issued or guaranteed by the U.S. Treasury, federal government agencies and instrumentalities with a weighted average maturity of 20 years or longer. May invest 10% of assets in illiquid securities.
Year organized: 1983 (a portfolio of GIT Income Trust, formerly A-Rated Income)
Ticker symbol: GITGX
Discount broker availability: White
Qualified for sale in: All states except AK, AR, ME, MA, MS, MT, NE, NH, NM, ND, RI, SD, UT, VT
Check redemptions: $5 fee under $500
Dividends paid: Income - declared daily, paid monthly; Capital gains - November
Portfolio turnover (3 yrs): 287%, 357%, 123%
Management fee: 0.625%
Expense ratio: 1.54% (year ending 3/31/94)

GIT MARYLAND TAX-FREE PORTFOLIO ◆
(See first GIT listing for data common to all GIT Trust portfolios)

Portfolio manager: Dan Gillespie (1994)
Investment objective and policies: Current income exempt from federal and Maryland state income taxes. Invests primarily in municipal securities issued by the state of Maryland. Up to 20% of assets may be invested in taxable securities including AMT securities.
Year organized: 1993 (a portfolio of GIT Tax-Free Trust)

Qualified for sale in: DC, MD
Check redemptions: $5 fee under $500
Dividends paid: Income - declared daily, paid monthly; Capital gains - November
Portfolio turnover (2 yrs): 78%, 35%
Management fee: 0.625%
Expense ratio: 0.64% (year ending 9/30/94) (1.34% without waiver)

GIT MAXIMUM INCOME PORTFOLIO ◆
(See first GIT listing for data common to all GIT Trust portfolios)

Newspaper listing: HiYd
Portfolio managers: Jonathan Edwards (1988), Charles J. Tennes (1993)
Investment objective and policies: Current income. Invests in corporate bonds, notes and debentures (including convertibles), as well as U.S. Government securities with a weighted average maturity of 20 years or more. To obtain higher yields fund invests primarily in lower rated securities ("junk bonds"), including those rated as low as "Caa" or "CCC." May invest up to 10% of assets in illiquid securities.
Year organized: 1983 (a portfolio of GIT Income Trust)
Ticker symbol: GITMX
Discount broker availability: White
Qualified for sale in: All states except AK, AR, ME, MS, MT, NE, NH, ND, RI, SD, UT, VT
Check redemptions: $5 fee under $500
Dividends paid: Income - declared daily, paid monthly; Capital gains - November
Portfolio turnover (3 yrs): 251%, 73%, 124%
Management fee: 0.625%
Expense ratio: 1.54% (year ending 3/31/94)

GIT MISSOURI
TAX-FREE PORTFOLIO ◆
(See first GIT listing for data common to all GIT Trust portfolios)

Portfolio manager: Dan Gillespie (1994)
Investment objective and policies: Current income exempt from federal and Missouri state income taxes. Invests primarily in municipal securities issued by the state of Missouri. Up to 20% of assets may be invested in taxable securities including AMT securities.
Year organized: 1989 (a portfolio of GIT Tax-Free Trust)
Qualified for sale in: DC, MO
Check redemptions: $5 fee under $500
Dividends paid: Income - declared daily, paid monthly; Capital gains - November
Portfolio turnover (3 yrs): 52%, 65%, 8%
Management fee: 0.625%
Expense ratio: 1.29% (year ending 9/30/94)

GIT SELECT GROWTH PORTFOLIO ◆
(See first GIT listing for data common to all GIT Trust portfolios)

Portfolio managers: Charles J. Tennes (1993)
Investment objective and policies: Capital appreciation with current income secondary. Invests primarily in equity securities of established companies that may be undervalued or may have good management and significant growth potential. Fund may write covered calls and invest in foreign securities.
Year organized: 1983 (a portfolio of GIT Equity Trust)
Qualified for sale in: All states except AK, DE, KS, ME, MA, MS, MT, NE, NV, NM, ND, RI, SD, VT
Dividends paid: Income - March, December; Capital gains - March, December
Portfolio turnover (3 yrs): 48%, 125%, 60%
Largest holding: Louisiana-Pacific Corp. (3.1%)
Management fee: 0.75%
Expense ratio: 2.02% (year ending 3/31/94)

GIT SPECIAL GROWTH PORTFOLIO ◆
(See first GIT listing for data common to all GIT Trust portfolios)

Newspaper listing: EqSpc
Sub-adviser: Cramblit & Carney, Inc.
Portfolio manager: Richard C. Carney (1983)
Investment objective and policies: Maximum capital appreciation. Invests primarily in equity securities of smaller companies that may offer rapid growth potential. Fund may write covered calls and invest in foreign securities.
Year organized: 1983 (a portfolio of GIT Equity Trust)
Ticker symbol: GTSGX
Discount broker availability: White
Qualified for sale in: All states except AK, ME, MT, ND, SD, VT
Dividends paid: Income - March, December; Capital gains - March, December
Portfolio turnover (3 yrs): 7%, 13%, 24%
Largest holding: American List Corp. (3.6%)
Management fee: 0.75%
Expense ratio: 1.45% (year ending 3/31/94)

GIT TAX-FREE
MONEY MARKET PORTFOLIO ◆
(See first GIT listing for data common to all GIT Trust portfolios)

Portfolio manager: Dan Gillespie (1994)
Investment objective and policies: Current income exempt from federal income taxes, safety of principal and liquidity. Invests in short term municipal money market securities. Up to 20% of assets may be invested in taxable securities including AMT securities.
Year organized: 1982 (a portfolio of GIT Tax-Free Trust)
Wire fee: $6 if less than $2,500
Qualified for sale in: All states except AK, AR, CO, DE, IA, KS, KY, LA, MI, MN, MS, MT, NE, NH, NM, ND, OK, RI, SD, UT, VT
Check redemptions: $0.15 fee under $500
Confirmations mailed: After each purchase and each check, mail or wire redemption
Checks returned: Not returned
Periodic account statements mailed: Quarterly
Dividends paid: Income - declared daily, paid monthly
Management fee: 0.5%
Expense ratio: 0.81% (year ending 9/30/94) (1.02% without waiver)

GIT TAX-FREE
NATIONAL PORTFOLIO ◆
(See first GIT listing for data common to all GIT Trust portfolios)

Portfolio manager: Dan Gillespie (1994)
Investment objective and policies: Current income exempt from federal income taxes. Invests primarily in medium grade municipal securities with a weighted average maturity of 15 years or more. Up to 20% of assets may be invested in taxable securities including AMT securities.
Year organized: 1982 (a portfolio of GIT Tax-Free Trust) (name changed from Tax-Free High Yield Portfolio on 2/1/94)
Ticker symbol: GTFHX
Discount broker availability: White
Qualified for sale in: All states except AK, AR, CO, DE, IA, KS, KY, LA, MN, MS, MT, NE, NH, ND, OK, RI, SD, UT, VT
Check redemptions: $5 fee under $500
Dividends paid: Income - declared daily, paid monthly; Capital gains - November
Portfolio turnover (3 yrs): 175%, 212%, 114%
Management fee: 0.625%
Expense ratio: 1.23% (year ending 9/30/94)

GIT VIRGINIA
TAX-FREE PORTFOLIO ◆
(See first GIT listing for data common to all GIT Trust portfolios)

Newspaper listing: TFVA
Portfolio manager: Dan Gillepsie (1994)
Investment objective and policies: Current income

exempt from federal and Virginia state income taxes. Invests primarily in municipal securities issued by the Commonwealth of Virginia. Up to 20% of assets may be invested in taxable securities including AMT securities.
Year organized: 1987 (a portfolio of GIT Tax-Free Trust)
Ticker symbol: GTVAX
Qualified for sale in: VA
Check redemptions: $5 fee under $500
Dividends paid: Income - declared daily, paid monthly; Capital gains - November
Portfolio turnover (3 yrs): 104%, 80%, 74%
Management fee: 0.625%
Expense ratio: 1.18% (year ending 9/30/94)

GIT WORLDWIDE
GROWTH PORTFOLIO ◆
(See first GIT listing for data common to all GIT Trust portfolios)

Portfolio managers: A. Bruce Cleveland (1993), Charles J. Tennes (1993)
Investment objective and policies: Capital appreciation. Invests at least 65% of assets in equity securities of issuers whose principal activities are outside the US with emphasis on companies that are likely to benefit from the growth of the world's smaller and emerging capital markets. May invest in US and foreign debt securities that present an opportunity for capital growth. Fund may hedge, engage in foreign currency transactions and write covered call options.
Year organized: 1993
Discount broker availability: White
Qualified for sale in: All states except AK, AR, DE, IA, ME, MS, MT, NE, NM, ND, RI, SD, UT, VT, WI
Dividends paid: Income - March, December; Capital gains - March, December
Portfolio turnover (1 yr): 83%
Largest holding: Compania Peruana De Telefono (3.4%)
Management fee: 1.0%
Expense ratio: 1.81% (year ending 3/31/94) (includes waiver)

GOLDEN RAINBOW
A JAMES ADVISED MUTUAL FUND
Citizens Federal Trust Department
One First National Plaza
130 West 2nd St. , Suite 910
Dayton, OH 45402
513-461-0332, 800-227-4648
fax 513-461-6781

Adviser: James Investment Research, Inc.
Portfolio manager: Frank E. James (1991)
Custodian and transfer agent: Fifth Third Bank of Cincinnati
Investment objective and policies: Total return - capital growth and income and preservation of capital in declining markets. Invests primarily in equity securities traded on a national securities exchange or NASDAQ, debt securities rated "A" or better by Moody's or S&P, securities issued or guaranteed by the U.S. government or its agencies or instrumentalities, preferred stocks, and convertible securities. Up to 30% of assets may be in securities of foreign issuers. Fund may hedge.
Year organized: 1991
Ticker symbol: GLRBX
Special sales restrictions: Available to individuals or entities who have established a trust or agency account with Citizens Federal Bank, F.S.B.
Minimum purchase: Initial: $5,000; Subsequent: $100
Telephone orders accepted: No
Wire orders accepted: Yes
Deadline for same day wire purchase: 11 A.M.
Qualified for sale in: All states
Letter redemptions: Signature guarantee not required
Dividends paid: Income - March, June, September, December; Capital gains - December
Portfolio turnover (3 yrs): 31%, 38%, 10%
Largest holding: U.S. Treasury Notes 8.500% due 5/15/97 (7.0%)

Shareholder services: Keogh, IRA, corporate retirement plans
Management fee: 0.74%
12b-1 distribution fee: 0.20%
Expense ratio: 0.96% (year ending 6/30/94) (1.24% without waiver)
IRA/Keogh fees: Annual $100 + 0.55% of fair market value (paid quarterly)

GOLDMAN SACHS FUNDS

(Data common to all Goldman Sachs funds are shown below. See subsequent listings for date specific to individual Goldman Sachs fund.)

4900 Sears Tower
Chicago, IL 60606
312-655-4400, 800-621-2550

Adviser: GSAM (a division of Goldman Sachs)
Custodian: State Street Bank & Trust Co.
Transfer agent: Goldman Sachs
Year organized: 1981
Minimum purchase: Initial: $50,000 (among all Money Market Trust portfolio), Subsequent: None
Wire orders accepted: Yes
Deadline for same day wire purchase: 1 P.M.
Qualified for sale in: All states
Telephone redemptions: Yes
Wire redemptions: Yes
Letter redemptions: Signature guarantee not required
Check redemptions: $500 minimum
Telephone switching: With other Goldman Sachs Money Market Trust portfolios and Oakmark funds

GOLDMAN SACHS MONEY MARKET TRUST - GOVERNMENT PORTFOLIO ◆

(See first Goldman Sachs listing for data common to all Goldman Sachs funds)

Investment objective and policies: Current income consistent with preservation of capital and liquidity. Invests in short-term U.S. Government money market instruments
Year organized: 1981 (name changed from Goldman Sachs Institutional Liquid Assets Government Portfolio on 10/14/94)
Dividends paid: Income - declared daily, paid monthly
Management fee: 0.35%
Expense ratio: 0.40% (year ending 12/31/93)

GOLDMAN SACHS MONEY MARKET TRUST - TAX-EXEMPT DIVERSIFIED PORTFOLIO ◆

(See first Goldman Sachs listing for data common to all Goldman Sachs funds)

Investment objective and policies: Current income exempt from federal income taxes consistent with preservation of capital and liquidity. Invests in short-term municipal money market instruments
Year organized: 1984 (name changed from Goldman Sachs Institutional Liquid Assets Tax-Exempt Diversified Portfolio on 10/14/94)
Dividends paid: Income - declared daily, paid monthly
Management fee: 0.25%
Expense ratio: 0.30% (year ending 12/31/93)

GOVERNMENT CASH SERIES

Federated Investors Tower
Pittsburgh, PA 15222-3779
412-288-1900, 800-245-0242
fax 412-288-1982

Adviser: Federated Advisers
Portfolio manager: Susan M. Nason (1990)
Custodian: State Street Bank & Trust Co.
Transfer agent: Federated Services Co.
Investment objective and policies: Income consistent with stability of principal and liquidity. Invests

in short-term U.S. Government money market instruments
Year organized: 1989
Ticker symbol: CTGXX
Minimum purchase: Initial: $10,000, Subsequent: $500; IRA: Initial: $1,000
Wire orders accepted: Yes
Deadline for same day wire purchase: 12 NN
Qualified for sale in: All states
Telephone redemptions: Yes
Wire redemptions: Yes, $10,000 minimum
Letter redemptions: Signature guarantee required over $50,000
Check redemptions: $100 minimum
Management fee: 0.5%
12b-1 distribution fee: 0.10%
Expense ratio: 0.99% (year ending 5/31/94) (1.08% without waiver)

GOVERNMENT INVESTORS TRUST MONEY MARKET ◆

1655 Fort Myer Drive, Suite 1000
Arlington, VA 22209
703-528-6500, 800-336-3063
prices/yields 800-448-4422
fax 703-528-9143

Adviser: Bankers Finance Investment Management Corp.
Portfolio manager: Jonathan Edwards (1988)
Custodian: Star Bank N.A., Cincinnati
Transfer agent: GIT Investment Services, Inc.
Investment objective and policies: High current income consistent with liquidity and stability of principal. Invests solely in money market instruments issued or guaranteed by the U.S. Government, its agencies or its instrumentalities
Year organized: 1979
Ticker symbol: GITXX
Minimum purchase: Initial: $2,500, Subsequent: None; IRA/Keogh: Initial: $500
Wire orders accepted: Yes
Deadline for same day wire purchase: 1 P.M.
Wire fee: $6 if less than $2,500
Qualified for sale in: All states except AK, AR, MT, NE, ND, SD, VT
Telephone redemptions: Yes
Wire redemptions: Yes, $10 fee under $10,000
Letter redemptions: Signature guarantee not required
Check redemptions: Yes, $0.15 fee under $500
Confirmations mailed: After each purchase and each check, mail or wire redemption
Checks returned: Not returned
Periodic account statements mailed: Quarterly
Telephone switching: With all GIT Trust portfolios
Number of switches permitted: Unlimited
Dividends paid: Income - declared daily, paid monthly
Shareholder services: Keogh, IRA, SEP-IRA, 403(b), corporate retirement plans, automatic investment plan, withdrawal plan no min. req., electronic funds transfer
Account fee: $3 per month if ending balance less than $700
Management fee: 0.5%
Expense ratio: 1.11% (year ending 3/31/94)
IRA fees: Annual $12
Keogh fees: Annual $15

THE GOVERNMENT STREET FUNDS ◆

(Data common to all Government Street funds are shown below. See subsequent listings for data specific to individual Government Street funds.)

P.O. Box 5354
Cincinnati, OH 45201
800-443-4249
prices/yields 800-852-4052

Adviser: T. Leavell & Associates, Inc.
Custodian: Wachovia Bank of North Carolina N.A.
Administrator and transfer agent: MGF Service Corp.

Minimum purchase: Initial: $5,000, Subsequent: $500; IRA/Keogh: Initial: $1,000, Subsequent: $500
Telephone orders accepted: No
Wire orders accepted: Yes
Deadline for same day wire purchase: 5 P.M.
Wire redemptions: Yes, $5,000 minimum
Letter redemptions: Signature guarantee not required
Shareholder services: Keogh, IRA, automatic investment plan, withdrawal plan min. req. $10,000, electronic funds transfer
IRA/Keogh fees: None

THE GOVERNMENT STREET ALABAMA TAX FREE BOND FUND ◆

(See first Government Street listing for data common to all Government Street funds)

Portfolio manager: Timothy S. Healey (1993)
Investment objective and policies: Current income exempt from federal and Alabama personal income taxes consistent with preservation of capital and protection from inflation. Invests at least 80% of assets in Alabama municipal bonds and notes and other debt instruments. May invest up to 20% of assets in AMT securities.
Year organized: 1993
Discount broker availability: Schwab
Qualified for sale in: AL
Dividends paid: Income - monthly; Capital gains - December
Portfolio turnover (1 yr): 3%
Management fee: 0.35% first $100M, 0.25% over $100M
Administration fee: 0.15% first $200M, 0.10% over $200M
Expense ratio: 0.75% (7 months ending 3/31/94) (1.76% without waiver)

GOVERNMENT STREET BOND FUND ◆

(See first Government Street listing for data common to all Government Street funds)

Portfolio manager: Thomas W. Leavell (1991)
Investment objective and policies: Current income with capital appreciation secondary. Invests in fixed-income securities of the four highest grades. At least 40% of assets are in U.S. Government obligations. Fund maintains a weighted averaged maturity of 3 to 7 years.
Year organized: 1991
Ticker symbol: GVSBX
Discount broker availability: Schwab
Qualified for sale in: AL, CA, CO, FL, GA, ID, IL, KY, ME, MS, NC, PA, TN, VA, WV
Dividends paid: Income - monthly; Capital gains - December
Portfolio turnover (3 yrs): 10%, 17%, 15%
Management fee: 0.50% first $100M, 0.40% over $100M
Administration fee: 0.075% first $200M, 0.05% over $200M
Expense ratio: 0.86% (year ending 3/31/94) (1.03% without waiver)

GOVERNMENT STREET EQUITY FUND ◆

(See first Government Street listing for data common to all Government Street funds)

Portfolio manager: Thomas W. Leavell (1991)
Investment objective and policies: Capital appreciation through the compounding of dividends and capital gains. Invests primarily in common stocks of medium to large capitalization companies. May invest in ADRs of foreign issuers without limit.
Year organized: 1991
Ticker symbol: GVEQX
Discount broker availability: Schwab
Qualified for sale in: AL, CA, CO, FL, GA, ID, IL, KY, ME, MS, NC, PA, TN, VA, WV
Dividends paid: Income - March, June, September, December; Capital gains - December

Portfolio turnover (3 yrs): 63%, 59%, 20%
Largest holding: Becton Dickinson & Co. (3.3%)
Management fee: 0.60% first $100M, 0.50% over $100M
Administration fee: 0.20% first $25M to 0.15% over $50M
Expense ratio: 1.00% (year ending 3/31/94) (1.16% without waiver)

GRADISON-MCDONALD FUNDS
(Data common to all Gradison-McDonald funds are shown below. See subsequent listings for data specific to individual Gradison-McDonald funds.)

580 Walnut Street
Cincinnati, OH 45202
513-579-5000, 800-869-5999
fax 513-579-5847

Shareholder service hours: Full service: M-F 8:30 A.M.-5 P.M. EST; After hours service: prices, yields, balances, last transaction, DJIA
Adviser: Gradison Division of McDonald & Company Inc.
Custodian: Star Bank, Cincinnati
Transfer agent: Gradison-McDonald Mutual Funds
Minimum purchase: Initial: $1,000, Subsequent: $50
Telephone orders accepted: No
Wire orders accepted: Yes
Deadline for same day wire purchase: 4 P.M. (12 NN for U.S. Government Reserves)
Telephone redemptions: Yes
Wire redemptions: Yes, $1,000 minimum
Letter redemptions: Signature guarantee not required
Telephone switching: With other Gradison-McDonald funds, some of which have loads
Number of switches permitted: Unlimited
Shareholder services: IRA, automatic investment plan, withdrawal plan min. req. $10,000
IRA fees: Annual $10, Initial $10

GRADISON-MCDONALD ESTABLISHED VALUE FUND
(See first Gradison listing for data common to all Gradison funds)

Portfolio manager: William J. Leugers, Jr. (1983)
Investment objective and policies: Long term capital growth. Invests in the common stocks of established companies with market capitalizations of at least $500M, selected from the S&P 500 and other markets, considered undervalued, selected on the basis of a disciplined portfolio construction and comprehensive computer modeling.
Year organized: 1983 (name changed from Gradison Established Growth Fund on 8/1/92)
Ticker symbol: GETGX
Discount broker availability: Schwab, White
Qualified for sale in: All states except HI
Dividends paid: Income: February, May, August, November; Capital gains - November, December
Portfolio turnover (3 yrs): 38%, 28%, 68%
Largest holding: Andrew Corp. (3.1%)
Management fee: 0.9% first $100M to 0.7% over $200M
12b-1 distribution fee: 0.23%
Expense ratio: 1.22% (year ending 4/30/94)

GRADISON-MCDONALD OPPORTUNITY VALUE FUND
(See first Gradison listing for data common to all Gradison funds)

Portfolio manager: William J. Leugers, Jr. (1983)
Investment objective and policies: Long term capital growth. Invests in the common stocks of smaller companies, generally with market capitalizations under $500M with potential for high earnings growth but with prices not reflecting this potential, selected on the basis of a disciplined portfolio con-

struction and comprehensive computer modeling.
Year organized: 1983 (Formerly Gradison Emerging Growth Fund. Name changed from Gradison Opportunity Growth Fund on 8/1/92.)
Ticker symbol: GOGFX
Discount broker availability: Schwab, White
Qualified for sale in: All states except HI
Dividends paid: Income - February, May, August, November; Capital gains - November, December
Portfolio turnover (3 yrs): 40%, 39%, 64%
Largest holding: Michaels Stores, Inc. (3.0%)
Management fee: 0.9% first $100M to 0.7% over $200M
12b-1 distribution fee: 0.22%
Expense ratio: 1.38% (year ending 4/30/94)

GRADISON-MCDONALD U.S. GOVERNMENT RESERVES
(See first Gradison listing for data common to all Gradison funds)

Portfolio manager: C. Stephen Wesselkamper (1993)
Investment objective and policies: Maximum current income consistent with preservation of capital and maintenance of liquidity. Invests in money market securities issued or guaranteed as to principal and interest by the US Government or its agencies or instrumentalities and repurchase agreements in respect to these securities. Fund attempts to maximize the portion of its dividends not subject to state and local taxation.
Year organized: 1993
Ticker symbol: GMUXX
Qualified for sale in: All states
Check redemptions: No minimum ($0.30 fee under $100)
Confirmations mailed: After each wire redemption
Checks returned: Monthly
Periodic account statements mailed: Monthly
Dividends paid: Income: declared and paid daily
Management fee: 0.5% first $400M to 0.35% over $2B
12b-1 distribution fee: 0.1%
Expense ratio: 0.80% (year ending 9/30/94) (0.81% without waiver)

THE PETER GRANDICH CONTRARIAN FUND ◆
707 Skokie Boulevard, Suite 200
Northbrook, Ill 60062
708-564-5764, 800-957-4386
fax 708-564-2120

Adviser: Grandich Advisory Company, Inc.
Portfolio manager: Peter Grandich (1994)
Custodian and Transfer Agent: The Provident Bank, Cincinnati
Investment objective and policies: Maximum long-term growth. Invests primarily in equity securities of domestic, multinational and foreign companies with potential values generally overlooked by other investors. May invest up to 35% of assets in debt securities, including junk bonds, and have up to 15% of assets in illiquid securities. May sell short, leverage and buy and sell options and futures contracts on up to 25% of total assets.
Year organized: 1994
Minimum purchase: Initial: $5,000, Subsequent: $500; IRA: Initial: $1,000, Subsequent: $100; Keogh: Initial: $5,000, Subsequent: $500
Telephone orders accepted: No
Wire orders accepted: Yes
Deadline for same day wire purchase: 3 P.M.
Discount broker availability: *White
Qualified for sale in: All states
Telephone redemptions: Yes
Wire redemptions: Yes, $1,000 minimum
Letter redemptions: Signature guarantee required
Dividends paid: Income - June, December; Capital gains - December
Shareholder services: Keogh, IRA, 403(b), automatic investment plan—minimum $250/month, withdrawal plan min. req. $10,000
Management fee: 1.50%
12b-1 distribution fee: 0.75%
IRA/Keogh fees: Annual $10, Initial $10

GREEN CENTURY BALANCED FUND
29 Temple Place, Suite 200
Boston, MA 02111
617-482-0800, 800-934-7336

Adviser: Green Century Capital Management, Inc.
Sub-adviser: Scudder, Stevens & Clark
Portfolio manager: Julia Cox (1992)
Custodian: Bank of New York
Transfer agent: Fund/Plan Services, Inc.
Investment objective and policies: Capital growth and income. Invests in equity (maximum 75% of assets) and fixed-income securities compatible with the fund's commitment to environmental responsibility. At least 25% of assets are in fixed-income senior securities. Seeks protection of capital through by adjusting allocation of assets to changing economic and market conditions. Up to 25% of assets may be in securities of foreign issuers. May use futures and options to increase return and hedge.
Year organized: 1992
Ticker symbol: GCBLX
Minimum purchase: Initial: $2,000; Subsequent: $100; IRA: Initial: $500
Telephone orders accepted: No
Wire orders accepted: Yes
Deadline for same day wire purchase: 4 P.M.
Qualified for sale in: All states except AL, AR, KS, NV, ND, OK, SC, UT
Telephone redemptions: Yes
Wire redemptions: Yes, $10 fee
Letter redemptions: Signature guarantee required
Telephone switching: With Green Century Money Market Fund
Number of switches permitted: Unlimited
Deadline for same day switch: 12 NN
Dividends paid: Income - June, December; Capital gains - December
Portfolio turnover (2 yrs): 14%, 11%
Largest holding: U.S. Treasury Bond 7.250% due 8/15/22 (5.6%)
Shareholder services: IRA, SEP-IRA, automatic investment plan (waives initial minimum), electronic funds transfer (purchase only)
Management fee: 0.75%
12b-1 distribution fee: 0.25%
Expense ratio: 2.50% (year ending 6/30/94)
IRA fees: Annual $12

GREEN CENTURY MONEY MARKET FUND ◆
29 Temple Place, Suite 200
Boston, MA 02111
617-482-0800, 800-934-7336

Adviser: Green Century Capital Management, Inc.
Sub-adviser: Scudder, Stevens & Clark
Portfolio manager: Joan Aglione (1994)
Custodian: Bank of New York
Transfer agent: Fund/Plan Services, Inc.
Investment objective and policies: High current income consistent with liquidity and preservation of capital. Invests in money market instruments compatible with the fund's commitment to environmental responsibility.
Year organized: 1992
Minimum purchase: Initial: $2,000; Subsequent: $100; IRA: Initial: $500
Wire orders accepted: Yes
Deadline for same day wire purchase: 12 NN
Qualified for sale in: All states except AL, AR, KS, NV, OK, SC, UT
Telephone redemptions: Yes
Wire redemptions: Yes, $10 fee
Letter redemptions: Signature guarantee required
Check redemption: $500 minimum
Confirmations mailed: After each purchase and each check, mail or wire redemption
Checks returned: Not returned
Periodic account statements mailed: Quarterly
Telephone switching: With Green Century Balanced Fund
Number of switches permitted: Unlimited
Deadline for same day switch: 12 NN

Dividends paid: Income - declared daily, paid monthly
Shareholder services: IRA, SEP-IRA, automatic investment plan (waives initial minimum), electronic funds transfer (purchase only)
Management fee: 0.35%
12b-1 distribution fee: 0.25% (not currently imposed)
Expense ratio: 0.69% (year ending 6/30/94)
IRA fees: Annual $12

GREENSPRING FUND ◆
2330 West Joppa Road, Suite 110
Lutherville, MD 21093
410-823-5353, 800-366-3863
fax 410-823-0903

Adviser: Key Equity Management Corp.
Portfolio manager: Charles vK. Carlson (1987)
Custodian: Signet Trust Co. of Baltimore
Transfer agent: Greenspring Fund, Inc.
Investment objective and policies: Long term capital growth with income secondary. Invests primarily in common stocks believed undervalued but may also invest in preferred stocks and fixed-income securities. May use options and hedge.
Year organized: 1982
Ticker symbol: GRSPX
Minimum purchase: Initial: $1,000, Subsequent: $100
Telephone orders accepted: No
Wire orders accepted: Yes
Deadline for same day wire purchase: 4 P.M.
Discount broker availability: Schwab, Fidelity, White
Qualified for sale in: All states except ID, MT, SD, WY
Letter redemptions: Signature guarantee required over $10,000
Dividends paid: Income - July, December; Capital gains - December
Portfolio turnover (3 yrs): 122%, 100%, 70%
Largest holding: The Town and Country Trust (11.9%)
Shareholder services: IRA, SEP-IRA
Management fee: 0.75%
Expense ratio: 1.31% (year ending 12/31/93)
IRA fees: Annual $10

GS SHORT-TERM GOVERNMENT AGENCY FUND ◆
4900 Sears Tower
Chicago, IL 60606
312-655-4400, 800-621-2550

Adviser: Goldman Sachs Asset Management
Custodian: State Street Bank & Trust Co.
Transfer agent: Goldman, Sachs & Co.
Investment objective and policies: Current income with capital gains secondary. Invests exclusively in securities issued and guaranteed as to principal and interest by the U.S. Government, its agencies and instrumentalities with remaining maturities of 6 years or less and a weighted average maturity of 3 years or less. Up to 15% of assets may be in illiquid securities.
Year organized: 1988
Minimum purchase: Initial: $50,000, Subsequent: None
Telephone orders accepted: No
Wire orders accepted: Yes, $7.50 fee
Deadline for same day wire purchase: 4 P.M.
Qualified for sale in: All states
Telephone redemptions: Yes
Wire redemptions: Yes, $7.50 fee
Letter redemptions: Signature guarantee required
Dividends paid: Income - monthly, Capital gains - December
Portfolio turnover (3 yrs): 290%, 412%, 216%
Management fee: 0.50%
Expense ratio: 0.45% (year ending 10/31/94) (0.59% without waiver)

GUINNESS FLIGHT CHINA & HONG KONG FUND ◆
201 South Lake Avenue, Suite 510
Pasadena, CA 91101
800-915-6565
prices/yields 800-434-5623
fax 617-774-2796

Adviser: Guinness Flight Investment Management Ltd.
Administrator: Investment Company Administration Corp.
Portfolio manager: Lynda Johnstone (1994)
Custodian: Investors Bank & Trust Co.
Transfer agent: State Street Bank & Trust Co.
Investment objective and policies: Long term capital growth. Normally invests at least 85% of assets in equity securities primarily traded in China and Hong Kong. May invest in other mutual funds and restricted securities and use foreign currency contracts, futures and options to hedge. Up to 15% of assets may be in illiquid securities.
Year organized: 1994
Minimum purchase: Initial: $5,000, Subsequent: $250; IRA: Initial: $2,000
Telephone orders accepted: No
Wire orders accepted: Yes
Deadline for same day wire purchase: 4 P.M.
Discount broker availability: *Schwab, *White, Fidelity, Siebert
Qualified for sale in: All states
Telephone redemptions: Yes
Wire redemptions: Yes, $500 minimum, $10 fee
Letter redemptions: Signature guarantee required over $50,000
Telephone switching: With Guinness Flight Global Government Bond Fund and Seven Seas Money Market Fund
Number of switches permitted: 4 per year (currently not enforced)
Dividends paid: Income - June, December; Capital gains - December
Shareholder services: IRA, automatic investment plan—minimum $100/month (waives initial minimum), electronic funds transfer (purchase only), withdrawal plan min. req. $1,000
Management fee: 1.00%
Administration fee: 0.25%
12b-1 distribution fee: Yes (not currently imposed)
IRA fees: Annual $10, Initial $5, Closing $10

GUINNESS FLIGHT GLOBAL GOVERNMENT BOND FUND ◆
201 South Lake Avenue, Suite 510
Pasadena, CA 91101
800-915-6565
prices/yields 800-434-5623
fax 617-774-2796

Adviser: Guinness Flight Investment Management Ltd.
Administrator: Investment Company Administration Corp.
Portfolio manager: Philip Saunders (1994)
Custodian: Investors Bank & Trust Co.
Transfer agent: State Street Bank & Trust Co.
Investment objective and policies: Current income with some capital growth. Invests primarily in government bonds issued by at least 3 countries, including the U.S. and supranational entities throughout the world. Up to 15% of assets may be in fixed-income securities of issuers in emerging markets and 15% in illiquid securities. May use foreign currency contracts, futures and options to hedge.
Year organized: 1994
Minimum purchase: Initial: $5,000, Subsequent: $250; IRA: Initial: $2,000
Telephone orders accepted: No
Wire orders accepted: Yes
Deadline for same day wire purchase: 4 P.M.
Discount broker availability: *Schwab, *White, Fidelity, Siebert
Qualified for sale in: All states

Telephone redemptions: Yes
Wire redemptions: Yes, $500 minimum, $10 fee
Letter redemptions: Signature guarantee required over $50,000
Telephone switching: With Guinness Flight China & Hong Kong Fund and Seven Seas Money Market Fund
Number of switches permitted: 4 per year (currently not enforced)
Dividends paid: Income - declared and paid monthly; Capital gains - December
Shareholder services: IRA, automatic investment plan—minimum $100/month (waives initial minimum), electronic funds transfer (purchase only), withdrawal plan min. req. $1,000
Management fee: 0.75%
Administration fee: 0.25%
12b-1 distribution fee: Yes (not currently imposed)
IRA fees: Annual $10, Initial $5, Closing $10

HARBOR FUNDS ◆
(Data common to all Harbor funds are shown below. See subsequent listings for data specific to individual Harbor funds.)

One SeaGate, 15th Floor
Toledo, OH 43666
419-247-2477, 800-422-1050
prices/yields 800-422-1065
fax 419-247-3093

Shareholder service hours: Full service: M-F 9 A.M.-5 P.M. EST; After hours service: prices, yields, prospectuses
Adviser: Harbor Capital Advisors, Inc.
Custodian: State Street Bank & Trust Co.
Transfer agent: Harbor Transfer, Inc.
Minimum purchase: Initial: $2,000, Subsequent: $500; IRA: Initial: $500, Subsequent $100
Telephone orders accepted: No
Wire orders accepted: Yes, $25,000 initial minimum
Deadline for same day wire purchase: 4 P.M.
Qualified for sale in: All states
Telephone redemptions: Yes
Wire redemptions: Yes, $5 fee under $5,000
Letter redemptions: Signature guarantee required over $50,000
Telephone switching: With other open Harbor funds
Number of switches permitted: Unlimited, 15 day hold
Shareholder services: IRA, SEP-IRA, automatic investment plan—minimum $100/quarter (initial minimum $500), withdrawal plan min. req. $10,000
IRA fees: None

HARBOR BOND FUND ◆
(See first Harbor listing for data common to all Harbor funds)

Sub-adviser: Pacific Investment Management Co.
Portfolio manager: William H. Gross (1987)
Investment objective and policies: Maximum total return consistent with the preservation of capital and prudent investment management. Invests primarily in investment-grade fixed-income securities with a weighted average maturity of 8 to 15 years. May invest up to 40% of assets in debt securities of foreign issuers with maximum 20% of assets in debt securities denominated in currencies other than the U.S. dollar.
Year organized: 1987
Ticker symbol: HABDX
Discount broker availability: Schwab, White, Waterhouse
Dividends paid: Income - March, June, September, December; Capital gains - December
Portfolio turnover (3 yrs): 151%, 120%, 53%
Management fee: 0.7%
Expense ratio: 0.77% (year ending 10/31/94) (includes waiver)

HARBOR CAPITAL APPRECIATION FUND ◆
(See first Harbor listing for data common to all Harbor funds)

Sub-adviser: Jennison Associates Capital Corporation (an affiliate of Prudential Insurance Co.)
Portfolio manager: Spiros Segalas (1990)
Investment objective and policies: Long term growth of capital. Invests in equities, including convertibles, of establish companies with above average growth prospects and capitalizations exceeding $1B. Companies selected will have superior absolute and relative earnings growth, high returns on equity and assets, and strong balance sheets. Fund may use stock and index options and futures and options thereon. Fund may hedge.
Year organized: 1987 (name changed from Harbor U.S. Equities Fund on April 26, 1990)
Ticker symbol: HACAX
Discount broker availability: Schwab, White, Waterhouse
Dividends paid: Income - December; Capital gains - December
Portfolio turnover (3 yrs): 73%, 93%, 69%
Largest holding: Hewlett-Packard Co. (4.1%)
Management fee: 0.6%
Expense ratio: 0.81% (year ending 10/31/94)

HARBOR GROWTH FUND ◆
(See first Harbor listing for data common to all Harbor funds)

Sub-adviser: Nicholas-Applegate Capital Management
Portfolio managers: Arthur E. Nicholas (1993), Jack Marshall (1993)
Investment objective and policies: Long-term growth of capital. Invests primarily in common stocks of companies capable of achieving future earnings exceeding investor expectation as reflected in the current market value of such companies' securities. Proprietary software and models aid in stock selection. Fund may use stock and index options, futures and options on futures. Fund may hedge.
Year organized: 1986
Ticker symbol: HAGWX
Discount broker availability: Schwab, White, Waterhouse
Dividends paid: Income - December; Capital gains - December
Portfolio turnover (3 yrs): 116%, 171%, 84%
Largest holding: Vodafone Group PLC ADR (2.8%)
Management fee: 0.75%
Expense ratio: 0.93% (year ending 10/31/94)

HARBOR INTERNATIONAL FUND ◆
(See first Harbor listing for data common to all Harbor funds)

Newspaper listing: Intl
Sub-adviser: Northern Cross Investments Limited
Portfolio manager: Hakan Castegren (1987)
Investment objective and policies: Long-term growth of capital with current income secondary. Invests primarily in equity securities of non-U.S. issuers, principally domiciled in Europe, the Pacific Basin and other more highly developed emerging industrialized countries. Fund may use ADRs, EDRs, GDRs and IDRs; options and futures on currencies and options on futures; options and futures on stock indexes and options on futures; and stock options, both puts and calls.
Year organized: 1987
Ticker symbol: HAINX
Special sales restrictions: Fund closed to new shareholders on 9/10/93
Discount broker availability: Schwab, White, Waterhouse
Dividends paid: Income - December; Capital gains - December
Portfolio turnover (3 yrs): 29%, 16%, 25%

Largest holding: Gencor Ltd. ADR (3.1%)
Management fee: 0.85%
Expense ratio: 1.10% (year ending 10/31/94) (includes waiver)

HARBOR INTERNATIONAL GROWTH FUND ◆
(See first Harbor listing for data common to all Harbor funds)

Sub-adviser: Jennison Associates Capital Corporation (an affiliate of Prudential Insurance Co.)
Portfolio manager: Howard B. Moss (1993)
Investment objective and policies: Long-term growth of capital. Invests primarily in equity securities of a focused selection of non-U.S. issuers that demonstrate a tendency toward long-term secular growth. Normally invests at least 65% of assets in 30-40 selected stocks of issuers from at least 3 countries other than the U.S. May invest up to 40% of assets in companies in one of 3 designated industries - pharmaceuticals, banking, and telephone with more than 25% of assets in either of the other 2 designated industries. Fund may use ADRs, EDRs, GDRs and IDRs; options and futures on currencies and options on futures; options and futures on stock indexes and options on futures; and stock options, both puts and calls.
Year organized: 1993
Ticker symbol: HAIGX
Discount broker availability: White, Waterhouse
Dividends paid: Income - December; Capital gains - December
Portfolio turnover (1 yr): 42%
Largest holding: Astra A Fria (SW) (5.7%)
Management fee: 0.75%
Expense ratio: 1.32% (year ending 10/31/94) (includes waiver)

HARBOR MONEY MARKET FUND ◆
(See first Harbor listing for data common to all Harbor funds)

Sub-adviser: Fischer, Francis, Trees, & Watts, Inc.
Portfolio manager: John H. Watts (1987)
Investment objective and policies: High level of current income consistent with preservation of capital and liquidity. Invests in short-term money market debt securities.
Year organized: 1987
Ticker symbol: HARXX
Dividends paid: Income - declared daily, paid monthly
Check redemptions: $500 minimum
Confirmations mailed: After each purchase and each check, mail or wire redemption.
Checks returned: As clear
Periodic account statements mailed: Quarterly
Management fee: 0.3%
Expense ratio: 0.67% (year ending 10/31/94) (includes waiver)

HARBOR SHORT DURATION FUND ◆
(See first Harbor listing for data common to all Harbor funds)

Sub-adviser: Fischer, Francis, Trees, & Watts, Inc.
Portfolio manager: Adnan Akant (1992)
Investment objective and policies: Maximum total return consistent with prudent investment risk. Invests primarily in high-grade domestic and foreign debt securities with a weighted average maturity of less than three years. May invest up to 40% of assets in debt securities of foreign issuers with maximum 20% of assets in debt securities denominated in currencies other than the U.S. dollar.
Year organized: 1992
Ticker symbol: HASDX
Discount broker availability: White, Waterhouse
Dividends paid: Income - declared and paid monthly; Capital gains - December
Portfolio turnover (3 yrs): 896%, 1212%, 2760%
Management fee: 0.4%
Expense ratio: 0.38% (year ending 10/31/94) (includes waiver)

HARBOR VALUE FUND ◆
(See first Harbor listing for data common to all Harbor funds)

Sub-advisers: SunBank Capital Management, N.A. (75% of assets), Richards & Tierney, Inc. (25% of assets)
Portfolio managers: Gregory M. DePrince (1994), David E. Tierney (1993)
Investment objective and policies: Maximum long-term total return from capital growth and income. SunBank invests primarily in dividend-paying common stocks of undervalued companies with market capitalizations in excess of $300M. R&T selects stocks using quantitative analysis techniques. Up to 15% of assets may be in non-dividend paying stocks. Fund may use stock and index options, futures and options on futures. Fund may hedge.
Year organized: 1986
Ticker symbol: HAVLX
Discount broker availability: Schwab, White, Waterhouse
Dividends paid: Income - March, June, September, December; Capital gains - December
Portfolio turnover (3 yrs): 151%, 50%, 20%
Largest holding: General Electric Co. (2.4%)
Management fee: 0.6%
Expense ratio: 1.04% (year ending 10/31/94)

THE HAVEN FUND ◆
655 Third Avenue
New York, NY 10017
212-953-2322, 800-897-8789
fax 212-818-9044

Adviser: Haven Capital Management, Inc.
Portfolio manager: Colin C. Ferenbach (1994)
Custodian: PNC Bank, N.A.
Transfer agent: PFPC, Inc.
Investment objective and policies: Long-term capital growth. Invests at least 65% of assets in equity securities of domestic companies. May also invest in investment-grade fixed-income securities of domestic and foreign issuers. Up to 35% of assets may be in foreign securities (including ADRs), 15% in illiquid securities and 10% in closed end mutual funds. May use forward foreign currency contracts to hedge.
Year organized: 1994
Ticker symbol: HAVEX
Minimum purchase: Initial: $10,000, Subsequent: $5,000
Telephone orders accepted: No
Wire orders accepted: Yes
Deadline for same day wire purchase: 4 P.M.
Qualified for sale in: CA, CT, DE, FL, HI, IL, IN, MD, MA, MO, NJ, NY, OH, PA, TN, TX, VA
Telephone redemptions: Yes
Wire redemptions: Yes, $10,000 minimum
Letter redemptions: Signature guarantee required over $25,000
Dividends paid: Income - December; Capital gains - December
Largest holding: The Sports Authority (2.9%)
Shareholder services: None
Management fee: 0.60%
12b-1 distribution fee: Maximum of 0.25%
Expense ratio: 1.20% (4 months ending 10/31/94) (1.43% without waiver)

HEARTLAND FUNDS
(Data common to all Heartland funds are shown below. See subsequent listings for data specific to individual Heartland funds.)

790 North Milwaukee Street
Milwaukee, WI 53202
414-347-7777, 800-432-7856
800-478-3863
prices/yields 800-248-1162
fax 414-347-0661

Adviser: Heartland Advisors, Inc.
Custodian and transfer agent: Firstar Trust Company

Minimum purchase: Initial: $1,000, Subsequent: $100; IRA/Keogh: Initial: $500, Subsequent: $50 (except tax-free bond funds)
Telephone orders accepted: No
Wire orders accepted: Yes
Deadline for same day wire purchase: 4 P.M.
Qualified for sale in: All states (except tax-free bond funds)
Telephone redemptions: Yes
Wire redemptions: Yes, $500 minimum, $7.50 fee
Letter redemptions: Signature guarantee required over $25,000
Deferred sales charge: 3% for shares held less than 1 year declining to 0% for shares held longer than 3 years - for shares purchased prior to 6/1/94
Telephone switching: With other Heartland funds and Portico Money Market Fund
Number of switches permitted: 4 per year
Shareholder services: IRA, automatic investment plan—minimum $50/month (waives initial minimum), withdrawal plan min. req. $25,000
IRA fees: Annual $12.50, Closing $15

HEARTLAND NEBRASKA TAX FREE FUND ◆
(See first Heartland listing for data common to all Heartland funds

Portfolio managers: Patrick J. Retzer (1993), William J. Nasgovitz (1993)
Investment objective and policies: High current income exempt from federal and Nebraska personal income taxes. Invests primarily in Nebraska municipal securities and general obligation bonds issued by Puerto Rico, the Virgin Islands and Guam. Up to 25% of assets may be in junk bonds and 20% in AMT securities.
Year organized: 1993
Ticker symbol: HRNEX
Minimum purchase: Initial: $10,000, Subsequent: $1,000
Discount broker availability: *White
Qualified for sale in: NE
Dividends paid: Income - declared daily, paid monthly; Capital gains - December
Management fee: 0.65%

HEARTLAND U.S. GOVERNMENT SECURITIES FUND
(See first Heartland listing for data common to all Heartland funds

Portfolio managers: Patrick J. Retzer (1988), William J. Nasgovitz (1988)
Investment objective and policies: High current income consistent with liquidity and safety of principal. Invests primarily in obligations issued or guaranteed by the U.S. government or by its agencies or instrumentalities. Up to 35% of assets may be in corporate and convertible debt securities and 25% may be in junk bonds. May hedge up to 25% of total assets.
Year organized: 1987 (name changed from U.S. Government Fund in 1994)
Ticker symbol: HRUSX
Discount broker availability: *Schwab, *White, *Waterhouse, *Fidelity, *Siebert
Dividends paid: Income - declared daily, paid monthly; Capital gains - December
Portfolio turnover (3 yrs): 200%, 149%, 185%
Management fee: 0.50%
12b-1 distribution fee: 0.25%
Expense ratio: 1.06% (year ending 12/31/93)

HEARTLAND VALUE FUND
(See first Heartland listing for data common to all Heartland funds

Portfolio managers: William J. Nasgovitz (1984), Hugh F. Denison (1988)
Investment objective and policies: Long-term capital appreciation. Invests primarily in equity securities of small companies with market capitalizations of less than $300M selected on a value basis. May

invest in ADRs of foreign issuers and have up to 15% of assets directly in foreign securities. May hedge up to 25% of total assets and sell short.
Year organized: 1984
Ticker symbol: HRTVX
Discount broker availability: *Schwab, *White, *Waterhouse, *Fidelity, *Siebert
Dividends paid: Income - December; Capital gains - December
Portfolio turnover (3 yrs): 58%, 76%, 79%
Largest holding: CMAC Investment Corp. (3.0%)
Management fee: 0.75%
12b-1 distribution fee: 0.25%
Expense ratio: 1.51% (year ending 12/31/93)

HEARTLAND VALUE & INCOME FUND
(See first Heartland listing for data common to all Heartland funds

Portfolio manager: William J. Nasgovitz (1993)
Investment objective and policies: Capital growth and current income. Invests in equity and debt securities. Equity securities are primarily of companies with market capitalizations of $300M to $1B selected on a value basis. Up to 25% of assets may be in junk bonds. May invest in ADRs of foreign issuers and have up to 15% of assets directly in foreign securities. May hedge up to 25% of total assets and sell short.
Year organized: 1993
Ticker symbol: HRVIX
Discount broker availability: *Schwab, *White, *Waterhouse, *Fidelity, *Siebert
Dividends paid: Income - March, June, September, December; Capital gains - December
Largest holding: U.S. Treasury Strips due 8/15/2014 (21.9%)
Management fee: 0.70%
12b-1 distribution fee: 0.25%

HEARTLAND WISCONSIN TAX FREE FUND ◆
(See first Heartland listing for data common to all Heartland funds

Portfolio managers: Patrick J. Retzer (1992), William J. Nasgovitz (1992)
Investment objective and policies: High current income exempt from federal and Wisconsin personal income taxes. Invests primarily in Wisconsin municipal securities and general obligation bonds issued by Puerto Rico, the Virgin Islands and Guam. Up to 25% of assets may be in junk bonds and 20% in AMT securities.
Year organized: 1992
Ticker symbol: HRWIX
Minimum purchase: Initial: $10,000, Subsequent: $1,000
Discount broker availability: *White, Fidelity, Siebert
Qualified for sale in: WI
Dividends paid: Income - declared daily, paid monthly; Capital gains - December
Portfolio turnover (2 yrs): 6%, 7%
Management fee: 0.65%
Expense ratio: 0.84% (year ending 12/31/93)

THE HENLOPEN FUND ◆
400 West Ninth Street, Suite 100
Wilmington, DE 53202
302-654-3131, 800-338-1579
fax 302-654-3252, TDD 800-684-3416

Adviser: Landis Associates, Inc.
Portfolio manager: Michael L. Hershey (1992)
Custodian and transfer agent: Firstar Trust Co.
Investment objective and policies: Long-term capital appreciation with current income secondary. Invests primarily in common stocks expected to appreciate significantly over 1-2 year period. Up to 30% of assets may be in debt securities and 10% in securities of foreign issuers.

Year organized: 1992
Minimum purchase: Initial: $10,000, Subsequent: $1,000; IRA: Initial: $2,000, Subsequent: $500
Telephone orders accepted: No
Wire orders accepted: Yes
Deadline for same day wire purchase: 3 P.M.
Qualified for sale in: CA, CT, DE, DC, MD, NJ, NY, PA, VA, WA
Letter redemptions: Signature guarantee not required
Dividends paid: Income - July, December; Capital gains - July, December
Portfolio turnover (2 yrs): 63%, 54%
Largest holding: Farah, Inc. (3.7%)
Shareholder services: Keogh, IRA, SEP-IRA, 401(k), corporate retirement plans, automatic investment plan—minimum $500/month (waives initial minimum), withdrawal plan min. req. $5,000
Management fee: 1.00%
Expense ratio: 2.0% (year ending 6/30/94) (3.0% without waiver)
IRA/Keogh fees: Annual $12.50

HERCULES FUNDS
(Data common to all Hercules funds are shown below. See subsequent listings for data specific to individual Hercules funds.)

Piper Jaffray Tower
222 South Ninth Street
Minneapolis, MN 55402
612-342-1100, 800-584-1317

Adviser: Hercules International Management L.L.C.
Custodian and transfer agent: Investors Fiduciary Trust Co.
Minimum purchase: Initial: $250, Subsequent: $100
Telephone orders accepted: No
Wire orders accepted: Yes, subsequent only
Deadline for same day wire purchase: 4 P.M.
Qualified for sale in: All states
Telephone redemptions: Yes, $25,000 maximum
Wire redemptions: Yes, $25,000 minimum
Letter redemptions: Signature guarantee required over $25,000
Telephone switching: With other Hercules funds
Number of switches permitted: Unlimited, $50 fee after 12 per year
Shareholder services: Keogh, IRA, SEP-IRA, corporate retirement plans, automatic investment plan, withdrawal plan min. req. $5,000

HERCULES EUROPEAN VALUE FUND
(See first Hercules listing for data common to all Hercules funds)

Sub-adviser: Pictet International Management Ltd.
Portfolio manager: Christian Simond (1993)
Investment objective and policies: Long-term capital appreciation with current income secondary. Invests primarily in equity securities of issuers in at least 3 of the developed countries of Europe. As securities markets of other European countries develop, they may be added. Funds are allocated in accordance with sub-adviser's proprietary asset allocation system. Up to 15% of assets may be in illiquid securities. May use currency transactions, futures and options to enhance return and hedge.
Year organized: 1993
Ticker symbol: HEVFX
Dividends paid: Income - December; Capital gains - December
Portfolio turnover (1 yr): 60%
Largest holding: Great Universal Stores, U.K. (2.1%)
Management fee: 1.00%
12b-1 distribution fee: 0.50%
Expense ratio: 2.00% (8 months ending 6/30/94) (3.25% without waiver)

HERCULES GLOBAL
SHORT-TERM FUND
(See first Hercules listing for data common to all Hercules funds)

Sub-adviser: Salomon Brothers Asset Management Ltd.
Portfolio managers: Mark Spindel (1993), David Scott (1994)
Investment objective and policies: High total return - current income and capital appreciation. Invests primarily in short-term debt securities of issuers in at least 3 countries around the world, including the U.S., with a weighted average maturity of 3 years or less. Up to 15% of assets may be in illiquid securities. May use currency transactions, futures and options to enhance return and hedge.
Year organized: 1993
Ticker symbol: HGSTX
Dividends paid: Income - declared and paid monthly; Capital gains - December
Portfolio turnover (1 yr): 362%
Management fee: 0.50%
12b-1 distribution fee: 0.25%
Expense ratio: 1.25% (8 months ending 6/30/94) (6.25% without waiver)

HERCULES LATIN AMERICAN
VALUE FUND
(See first Hercules listing for data common to all Hercules funds)

Sub-adviser: Bankers Trust Co.
Portfolio manager: Maria-Elena Carrion (1993)
Investment objective and policies: Long-term capital appreciation with current income secondary. Invests primarily in equity and debt securities of issuers in at least 3 of the countries of Latin America - Mexico, Central America and South America. Funds are allocated in accordance with sub-adviser's proprietary asset allocation system. Up to 35% of assets may be in junk bonds and 15% in illiquid securities. May use currency transactions, futures and options to enhance return and hedge.
Year organized: 1993
Ticker symbol: HLAVX
Dividends paid: Income - December; Capital gains - December
Portfolio turnover (1 yr): 78%
Largest holding: Telefonos de Mexico Class L (3.7%)
Management fee: 1.00%
12b-1 distribution fee: 0.50%
Expense ratio: 2.00% (8 months ending 6/30/94) (3.10% without waiver)

HERCULES MONEY MARKET FUND
(See first Hercules listing for data common to all Hercules funds)

Sub-adviser: SBAM Inc.
Portfolio manager: Mary Beth Whyte (1995)
Investment objective and policies: High current income consistent with preservation of capital and liquidity. Invests in high-quality money market instruments.
Year organized: 1995
Dividends paid: Income - declared daily, paid monthly
Management fee: 0.50%
12b-1 distribution fee: 0.10%

HERCULES NORTH AMERICAN
GROWTH AND INCOME FUND
(See first Hercules listing for data common to all Hercules funds)

Sub-advisers: Piper Capital Management, Inc.; Acci Worldwide, S.A. de C.V.; AGF Investment Advisors, Inc.
Portfolio managers: Paul Dow (1993), Maru Eugenia Pichardo (1993), Stephen Uzielli (1993)
Investment objective and policies: Long-term capital appreciation and current income. Invests primarily in equity and debt securities of corporate

and government issuers in Canada, the U.S. and Mexico. Funds are allocated in accordance with sub-adviser's proprietary asset allocation system. Up to 35% of assets may be in securities of issuers located outside North America and 15% in illiquid securities. May use currency transactions, futures and options to enhance return and hedge.
Year organized: 1993
Ticker symbol: HNAGX
Dividends paid: Income - December; Capital gains - December
Portfolio turnover (1 yr): 23%
Largest holding: Telefonos de Mexico (2.0%)
Management fee: 1.00%
12b-1 distribution fee: 0.50%
Expense ratio: 2.00% (8 months ending 6/30/94) (3.41% without waiver)

HERCULES PACIFIC BASIN
VALUE FUND
(See first Hercules listing for data common to all Hercules funds)

Sub-adviser: Edinburgh Fund Managers plc
Portfolio manager: Jamie Sandison (1993)
Investment objective and policies: Long-term capital appreciation with current income secondary. Invests primarily in equity securities of issuers from at least 3 countries in the Pacific Basin - The Far East, Australia and New Zealand. May also invest in debt securities and have up to 15% of assets may be in illiquid securities. May use currency transactions, futures and options to enhance return and hedge.
Year organized: 1993
Ticker symbol: HPBVX
Dividends paid: Income - December; Capital gains - December
Portfolio turnover (1 yr): 39%
Largest holding: Mitsui Fudosan (4.0%)
Management fee: 1.00%
12b-1 distribution fee: 0.50%
Expense ratio: 2.00% (8 months ending 6/30/94) (2.36% without waiver)

HERCULES WORLD BOND FUND
(See first Hercules listing for data common to all Hercules funds)

Sub-adviser: Salomon Brothers Asset Management Ltd.
Portfolio managers: Mark Spindel (1993), David Scott (1994)
Investment objective and policies: High total return - current income and capital appreciation. Invests primarily in investment-grade debt securities of issuers from at least 3 countries around the world, including the U.S., with a weighted average maturity of 15 years or less. Up to 35% of assets may be in junk bonds and 15% in illiquid securities. May use currency transactions, futures and options to enhance return and hedge.
Year organized: 1993
Ticker symbol: HWBFX
Dividends paid: Income - March, June, September, December; Capital gains - December
Portfolio turnover (1 yr): 291%
Management fee: 1.00%
12b-1 distribution fee: 0.30%
Expense ratio: 1.80% (8 months ending 6/30/94) (2.03% without waiver)

HOMESTEAD FUNDS ◆
(Data common to all Homestead funds are shown below. See subsequent listings for data specific to individual Homestead funds.)

1800 Massachusetts Avenue, N.W.
Washington, DC 20036
800-258-3030, fax 202-857-4157

Adviser: RE Advisers Corp.
Custodian and transfer agent: Investors Bank & Trust Co.

Minimum purchase: Initial: $1,000, Subsequent: $100; IRA: Initial: $200
Telephone orders accepted: No
Wire orders accepted: Yes
Deadline for same day wire purchase: 10 A.M.
Qualified for sale in: All states
Telephone redemptions: Yes
Wire redemptions: Yes, $10 fee
Letter redemptions: Signature guarantee required over $25,000
Telephone switching: With other Homestead funds
Number of switches permitted: Unlimited
Shareholder services: IRA, SEP-IRA, automatic investment plan—minimum $50/month ($250 initial minimum), withdrawal plan, electronic funds transfer
IRA fees: Annual $10

HOMESTEAD DAILY
INCOME FUND ◆
(See first Homestead listing for data common to all Homestead funds)

Portfolio manager: John J. Szczur (1993)
Investment objective and policies: Maximum current income consistent with preservation of capital and liquidity. Invests in high quality money market securities.
Year organized: 1990
Ticker symbol: HDIXX
Check redemptions: Yes, $100 minimum
Confirmations mailed: After each purchase and each check, mail or wire redemption
Checks returned: Not returned
Periodic account statements mailed: Monthly
Dividends paid: Income - declared daily, paid monthly
Management fee: 0.5% first $100M to 0.25% over $500M
Expense ratio: 0.75% (year ending 12/31/94) (0.99% without waiver)

HOMESTEAD SHORT-TERM
BOND FUND ◆
(See first Homestead listing for data common to all Homestead funds)

Portfolio manager: Douglas G. Kern (1991)
Investment objective and policies: High current income consistent with stability of principal and liquidity. Invests primarily in short-term debt securities rated within the three highest categories assigned by Moody's or S&P with a weighted average maturity of 3 years or less. May use options to hedge up to 25% of total assets.
Year organized: 1991
Ticker symbol: HOSBX
Dividends paid: Income - declared daily, paid monthly; Capital gains - December
Portfolio turnover (3 yrs): 13%, 14%, 19%
Management fee: 0.50% first $50M to 0.30% over $100M
Expense ratio: 0.75% (year ending 12/31/94) (0.98% without waiver)

HOMESTEAD VALUE FUND ◆
(See first Homestead listing for data common to all Homestead funds)

Portfolio manager: Stuart E. Teach (1990)
Investment objective and policies: Long term growth of capital and income for the conservative investor with current income secondary. Invests at least 80% of assets in a carefully selected portfolio of common stocks of established companies believed undervalued. Up to 10% of assets may be invested in ADRs of foreign issuers. May use options to hedge up to 25% of total assets.
Year organized: 1990
Dow Jones ticker symbol: HOVLX
Dividends paid: Income - June, December; Capital gains - December
Portfolio turnover (3 yrs): 4%, 2%, 5%
Largest holding: BankAmerica Corp. (2.4%)

Management fee: 0.65% first $50M to 0.40% over $100M
Expense ratio: 1.15% (year ending 12/31/94)

HOTCHKIS AND WILEY FUNDS ◆
(Data common to all Hotchkis and Wiley funds are shown below. See subsequent listing for data specific to individual Hotchkis and Wiley funds.)

800 West Sixth St., Fifth Floor
Los Angeles, CA 90017
213-362-8900, 800-346-7301
fax 213-623-7880

Shareholder service hours: Full service: M-F 7:30 A.M.-4:30 P.M. PST; After hours service: prices, messages, prospectuses
Adviser: Hotchkis and Wiley
Custodian and transfer agent: Firstar Trust Company
Year organized: Group changed name from Olympic Trust to Hotchkis and Wiley in 10/94
Minimum purchase: Initial: $5,000, Subsequent: None; IRA: Initial: $1,000
Qualified for sale in: All states
Telephone orders accepted: No
Wire orders accepted: Yes
Deadline for same day wire purchase: 4 P.M.
Letter redemptions: Signature guarantee required over $50,000
Telephone switching: With other Hotchkis and Wiley funds
Number of switches permitted: Unlimited
Shareholder services: IRA
IRA fees: Annual $12.50

HOTCHKIS AND WILEY BALANCED INCOME FUND ◆
(See first Hotchkis and Wiley listing for data common to all Hotchkis and Wiley funds)

Portfolio managers: Roger DeBard (1985), Tad Rivelle (1992), Laird Landmann (1992)
Investment objective and policies: Preserve capital while producing a high total return. Assets will be allocated among equity securities (at least 20%), fixed-income securities (at least 25%), and money market obligations. May invest up to 20% of assets in foreign securities. Allocation of assets varies depending on market conditions.
Year organized: 1985 (formerly Olympic Total Return Series)
Ticker symbol: HWBAX
Discount broker availability: *Schwab, *White, *Waterhouse
Dividends paid: Income - March, June, September, December; Capital gains - December
Portfolio turnover (3 yrs): 97%, 155%, 36%
Largest holding: RYMS 1992-15, 8.3157%, due 11/25/2022 (CMO) (4.8%)
Management fee: 0.75%
Expense ratio: 1.00% (year ending 6/30/94) (1.20% without waiver)

HOTCHKIS AND WILEY EQUITY INCOME FUND ◆
(See first Hotchkis and Wiley listing for data common to all Hotchkis and Wiley funds)

Portfolio managers: George Wiley (1987), Gail Bardin (1994)
Investment objective and policies: Current income, long-term growth of income, and growth of capital. Normally invests at least 80% of assets in income-producing equity securities issued by companies with a record of earnings and dividends. Fund seeks a dividend yield which exceeds that of the S&P 500. May invest in foreign securities.
Year organized: 1987
Ticker symbol: HWEQX
Discount broker availability: *Schwab, *White, *Waterhouse
Dividends paid: Income - March, June, September, December; Capital gains - December

Portfolio turnover (3 yrs): 36%, 25%, 32%
Largest holding: Ford Motor Co. (4.97%)
Management fee: 0.75%
Expense ratio: 1.00% (year ending 6/30/94) (1.05% without waiver)

HOTCHKIS AND WILEY INTERNATIONAL FUND ◆
(See first Hotchkis and Wiley listing for data common to all Hotchkis and Wiley funds)

Portfolio managers: Dennis Bouwer (1990), Sarah Ketterer (1990), Harry Hartford (1994)
Investment objective and policies: Current income, long-term growth of income, and growth of capital. Fund is normally fully invested in equity securities of at least 3 non-U.S. countries. Companies are chosen from a universe of about 20 foreign markets on criteria relating to value, stability, and price/earnings ratio. May use currency options and forward foreign currency exchange contracts for hedging purposes.
Year organized: 1990 (53.3% of fund is owned by the Retirement Plan for Employees of Texas Utilities Company System)
Ticker symbol: HWINX
Discount broker availability: *Schwab, *White, *Waterhouse
Dividends paid: Income - June, December; Capital gains - December
Portfolio turnover (3 yrs): 23%, 24%, 88%
Largest holding: Daiwa House Industry Co., Ltd. (2.5%)
Management fee: 0.75%
Expense ratio: 1.00% (year ending 6/30/94) (1.61% without waiver)

HOTCHKIS AND WILEY LOW DURATION FUND ◆
(See first Hotchkis and Wiley listing for data common to all Hotchkis and Wiley funds)

Portfolio managers: Laird Landmann (1993), Tad Rivelle (1993)
Investment objective and policies: High total return consistent with preservation of capital. Invests at least 75% of assets in investment-grade fixed-income securities with a weighted average maturity of 1 to 5 years. Invests in government securities, corporate debt securities, commercial paper, mortgage and other asset-backed securities, variable and floating rate debt securities, bank CDs and repurchase agreements. May invest up to 15% of assets in non-U.S. dollar denominated securities of foreign issuers, 25% in securities of foreign issuers denominated in U.S. dollars and 25% in Eurodollar securities.
Year organized: 1993
Ticker symbol: HWLDX
Discount broker availability: *Schwab, *White, *Waterhouse
Dividends paid: Income - declared daily, paid monthly; Capital gains - December
Portfolio turnover (1 yr): 254%
Management fee: 0.40%
Expense ratio: 0.58% (year ending 6/30/94) (1.10% without waiver)

HOTCHKIS AND WILEY SHORT-TERM INVESTMENT FUND ◆
(See first Hotchkis and Wiley listing for data common to all Hotchkis and Wiley funds)

Portfolio managers: Laird Landmann (1993), Tad Rivelle (1993)
Investment objective and policies: High total return consistent with preservation of capital. Invests at least 75% of assets in investment-grade fixed-income securities with a weighted average maturity of 2 years or less. Invests in government securities, corporate debt securities, commercial paper, mortgage and other asset-backed securities, variable and floating rate debt securities, bank CDs and repur-

chase agreements. May invest up to 15% of assets in non-U.S. dollar denominated securities of foreign issuers, 25% in securities of foreign issuers denominated in U.S. dollars and 25% in Eurodollar securities.
Year organized: 1993 (64% of fund is owned by United Air Lines, Inc. Group Administration Trust)
Discount broker availability: Schwab, *White, *Waterhouse
Discount broker availability: Schwab
Dividends paid: Income - declared daily, paid monthly; Capital gains - December
Portfolio turnover (1 yr): 135%
Management fee: 0.40%
Expense ratio: 0.48% (year ending 6/30/94) (2.06% without waiver)

HOTCHKIS AND WILEY SMALL CAP FUND ◆
(See first Hotchkis and Wiley listing for data common to all Hotchkis and Wiley funds)

Portfolio managers: George Davis (1988), John Hitchman (1994)
Investment objective and policies: Capital appreciation. Invests primarily in undervalued common stocks with capitalizations of less than $500M, a projected high rate of growth in earnings per share over a 5 year horizon, and a return of equity higher than that of the S&P 500. Fund may invest up to 20% of assets in foreign securities.
Year organized: 1985 (formerly Olympic Series B) (25.7% of fund is owned by Pfizer Retirement Annuity Plan)
Discount broker availability: *Schwab, *White, *Waterhouse
Dividends paid: Income - December; Capital gains - December
Portfolio turnover (3 yrs): 44%, 20%, 26%
Largest holding: First Republic BanCorp Inc. (2.9%)
Management fee: 0.75%
Expense ratio: 1.00% (year ending 6/30/94) (1.65% without waiver)

HOTCHKIS AND WILEY TOTAL RETURN FUND ◆
(See first Hotchkis and Wiley listing for data common to all Hotchkis and Wiley funds)

Portfolio managers: Laird R. Landmann (1994), Tad Rivelle (1994)
Investment objective and policies: Maximum long-term total return. Invests at least 70% of assets in investment-grade fixed-income securities believed undervalued with a weighted average maturity of 2 to 15 years. Invests in government securities, corporate debt securities, commercial paper, mortgage and other asset-backed securities, variable and floating rate debt securities, bank CDs and repurchase agreements. May invest up to 15% of assets in junk bonds and 15% in emerging markets foreign securities.
Year organized: 1994
Discount broker availability: *Schwab, *White, *Waterhouse
Dividends paid: Income - declared daily, paid monthly; Capital gains - December
Management fee: 0.70%

THE HOUGH GROUP - FLORIDA TAXFREE MONEY MARKET FUND ◆
P.O. Box 11688
St. Petersburg, FL 33733
813-825-7730, 800-557-7555
fax 813-895-8895

Adviser: William R. Hough & Co.
Custodian and transfer agent: Bankers Trust Co.
Investment objective and policies: High current income exempt from federal income tax and Florida intangible personal property tax consistent with preservation of capital and liquidity. Invests in

high quality, short-term Florida municipal money market obligations.
Year organized: 1993
Ticker symbol: HFMXX
Minimum purchase: Initial: $1,000, Subsequent: $50
Wire orders accepted: Yes, $1,000 minimum
Deadline for same day wire purchase: 4 P.M.
Qualified for sale in: AL, CA, CO, CT, DE, DC, FL, GA, IN, KS, KY, ME, MD, MI, MS, NC, NJ, NY, NM, OH, OK, PA, SC, TN, TX, VA, WA, WI
Wire redemptions: Yes, $1,000 minimum, $10 fee
Letter redemptions: Signature guarantee required over $10,000
Check redemptions: No minimum
Telephone switching: With Hough Florida TaxFree ShortTerm fund, $1,000 minimum
Number of switches permitted: 15 day hold
Confirmations mailed: After each purchase and each mail or wire redemption
Checks returned: On request
Periodic account statements mailed: Monthly
Dividends paid: Income - declared daily, paid monthly
Shareholder services: Automatic investment plan—minimum $100/quarter, withdrawal plan min. req. $10,000, electronic funds transfer
Management fee: 0.50%
Expense ratio: 0.00% (5 months ending 4/30/94) (1.71% without waiver)

THE HOUGH GROUP - FLORIDA TAXFREE SHORTTERM FUND ◆
P.O. Box 11688
St. Petersburg, FL 33733
813-825-7730, 800-557-7555
fax 813-895-8895

Adviser: William R. Hough & Co.
Custodian and transfer agent: Bankers Trust Co.
Investment objective and policies: High current income exempt from federal income tax and Florida intangible personal property tax consistent with preservation of capital and liquidity. Invests primarily in Florida municipal bonds with a weighted average maturity of 3 years or less. May hedge (up to 25%) and invest in reverse repurchase agreements, and buy and sell options and futures contracts. Up to 20% of assets may be in AMT securities.
Year organized: 1993
Minimum purchase: Initial: $1,000, Subsequent: $50
Telephone orders accepted: No
Wire orders accepted: Yes, $1,000 minimum
Deadline for same day wire purchase: 4 P.M.
Qualified for sale in: AL, CA, CO, CT, DE, DC, FL, GA, IN, KS, KY, ME, MD, MI, MS, NC, NJ, NY, NM, OH, OK, PA, SC, TN, TX, VA, WA, WI
Wire redemptions: Yes, $1,000 minimum, $10 fee
Letter redemptions: Signature guarantee required over $10,000
Check redemptions: No minimum
Telephone switching: With Hough Florida TaxFree Money Market fund, $1,000 minimum
Number of switches permitted: 15 day hold
Dividends paid: Income - declared daily, paid monthly; Capital gains - December
Portfolio turnover (1 yr): 11%
Shareholder services: Automatic investment plan—minimum $100/quarter, withdrawal plan min. req. $10,000, electronic funds transfer
Management fee: 0.60%
Expense ratio: 0.05% (5 months ending 4/30/94) (2.52% without waiver)

HOUSEHOLD PERSONAL PORTFOLIOS
(All Household Personal Portfolios portfolios were liquidated on 2/28/95)

IAI FUNDS
(Data common to all IAI funds are shown below. See subsequent listings for data specific to individual IAI funds.)

3700 First Bank Place
P.O. Box 357
Minneapolis, MN 55440
612-376-2700, 800-945-3863
fax 612-376-2640

Shareholder service hours: Full service: M-F 7:30 A.M.-5:30 P.M. CST; After hours service: prices, messages, prospectuses, DJIA
Adviser: Investment Advisers, Inc.
Name change: Group was called North Star funds until 1987
Custodian: Norwest Bank Minnesota, N.A.
Transfer agent: Investment Advisers, Inc.
Minimum purchase: Initial: $5,000 group total, $1,000 individual fund, Subsequent: $100; IRA: Initial: $2000 group total, $1,000 individual fund
Telephone orders accepted: No
Wire orders accepted: No
Qualified for sale in: All states
Telephone redemptions: Yes
Wire redemptions: Yes
Letter redemptions: Signature guarantee required over $50,000
Telephone switching: With other IAI funds
Number of switches permitted: 4 per year
Shareholder services: IRA, automatic investment plan, withdrawal plan min. req. $10,000
IRA fees: None

IAI BALANCED FUND
(See first IAI listing for data common to all IAI funds)

Portfolio managers: James Diedrich (1993), Mark Simenstad (1993)
Investment objective and policies: Maximum total return - capital appreciation and current income. Invests in common stocks (25-75% of assets), bonds (25-75%) and short-term instruments (0-50%). Allocation among asset categories varies depending on market conditions. May invest up to 15% of assets in illiquid securities and use foreign securities, options, futures contracts and currency exchange contracts. Fund may sell short.
Year organized: 1992
Ticker symbol: IABLX
Discount broker availability: *Schwab, *White, *Waterhouse, *Fidelity, *Siebert
Dividends paid: Income - June, December; Capital gains - December
Portfolio turnover (2 yrs): 212%, 83%
Largest holding: Resolution Funding Corp. (4.8%)
Management fee: 0.75% first $200M to 0.65% over $500M
12b-1 distribution fee: 0.04%
Expense ratio: 1.25% (year ending 3/31/94) (includes waiver)

IAI BOND FUND INC.
(See first IAI listing for data common to all IAI funds)

Portfolio manager: Larry R. Hill (1984)
Investment objective and policies: High current income consistent with preservation of capital. Normally invests at least 65% of assets in investment-grade bonds and other high quality debt securities. Up to 25% of assets may be in non-dollar denominated securities of foreign issuers. May use options, futures contracts, currency exchange contracts and sell short.
Year organized: 1977
Ticker symbol: IAIBX
Discount broker availability: *Schwab, *White, Waterhouse, *Fidelity, *Siebert

Dividends paid: Income - monthly; Capital gains - December
Portfolio turnover (3 yrs): 333%, 161%, 126%
Management fee: 0.55%
12b-1 distribution fee: 0.19%
Expense ratio: 1.09% (year ending 3/31/94) (includes waiver)

IAI DEVELOPING COUNTRIES FUND
(See additional funds listings on page 406)

IAI EMERGING GROWTH FUND
(See first IAI listing for data common to all IAI funds)

Portfolio manager: Rick D. Leggott (1991)
Investment objective and policies: Long-term capital appreciation. Invests primarily in common stocks of small and medium sized companies (capitalization under $1B) in the early stages of their life cycles with proven or potential for above average growth. May invest in convertible securities, non-convertible preferred stocks and non-convertible debt securities. May invest in securities of foreign issuers with up to 10% of assets denominated in foreign currencies and 15% in illiquid securities. May use options, futures contracts, currency exchange contracts and sell short.
Year organized: 1991
Ticker symbol: IAEGX
Discount broker availability: *Schwab, *White, *Waterhouse, *Fidelity, *Siebert
Dividends paid: Income - June, December; Capital gains - December
Portfolio turnover (3 yrs): 76%, 96%, 127%
Largest holding: American Power Conversion (4.1%)
Management fee: 0.75% first $200M to 0.65% over $500M
12b-1 distribution fee: 0.19%
Expense ratio: 1.25% (year ending 3/31/94) (includes waiver)

IAI GOVERNMENT FUND INC.
(See first IAI listing for data common to all IAI funds)

Portfolio manager: Scott A. Bettin (1991)
Investment objective and policies: High current income consistent with preservation of capital. Invests primarily in debt securities issued, guaranteed or collateralized by the U.S. Government, its agencies or instrumentalities with a weighted average maturity of 5 years or less. May invest in debt securities of foreign issuers and use options, futures contracts and currency exchange contracts. Fund may sell short.
Year organized: 1991
Ticker symbol: IAGVX
Discount broker availability: *Schwab, *White, *Fidelity, *Siebert
Dividends paid: Income - March, June, September, December; Capital gains - December
Portfolio turnover (3 yrs): 641%, 236%, 170%
Management fee: 0.55%
12b-1 distribution fee: 0.04%
Expense ratio: 1.10% (year ending 3/31/94) (includes waiver)

IAI GROWTH FUND
(See first IAI listing for data common to all IAI funds)

Portfolio manager: Managed by committee
Investment objective and policies: Long-term capital appreciation. Invests primarily in equity securities of established companies expected to increase earnings at an above average rate. May also invest in government securities, investment-grade corporate bonds and debentures, commercial paper, preferred stocks, CDs or other securities. Fund may invest in ADRs of foreign issuers and have up to

15% of assets in securities denominated in foreign currencies and 15% in illiquid securities, and use futures, options and currency exchange contracts. Fund may sell short.
Year organized: 1993
Discount broker availability: *Schwab, *White, *Waterhouse, *Fidelity, *Siebert
Dividends paid: Income - June, December; Capital gains - December
Portfolio turnover (1 yr): 105%
Largest holding: Microsoft Corp. (3.1%)
Management fee: 0.75% first $200M to 0.65% over $500M
12b-1 distribution fee: Maximum of 0.25%
Expense ratio: 1.25% (year ending 7/31/94) (includes waiver)

IAI GROWTH AND INCOME FUND
(See first IAI listing for data common to all IAI funds)

Portfolio manager: Todd McCallister (1994)
Investment objective and policies: Capital appreciation with income secondary. Invests primarily in common stocks and may also invest in convertible securities, non-convertible preferred stocks and non-convertible debt securities. May invest in securities of foreign issuers with up to 10% of assets in securities denominated in foreign currencies and 15% in illiquid securities. May use futures, options and currency exchange contracts. Fund may sell short.
Year organized: 1971 (name changed from IAI Stock Fund in 1993)
Ticker symbol: IASKX
Discount broker availability: *Schwab, *White, *Waterhouse, *Fidelity, *Siebert
Dividends paid: Income - June, December; Capital gains - December
Portfolio turnover (3 yrs): 206%, 176%, 210%
Largest holding: General Electric (2.9%)
Management fee: 0.75% first $100M to 0.55% over $400M
12b-1 distribution fee: 0.12%
Expense ratio: 1.25% (year ending 3/31/94) (includes waiver)

IAI INTERNATIONAL FUND
(See first IAI listing for data common to all IAI funds)

Sub-adviser: IAI International Limited
Portfolio manager: Roy C. Gillson (1990)
Investment objective and policies: Capital appreciation with current income secondary. Invests at least 95% of assets in equity and equity-related securities of non-U.S. issuers. Fund may concentrate investments in Japan, the UK and Germany, but at least four economies will be represented at any one time. May use forward currency exchange contracts, futures, options and short sales.
Year organized: 1987
Ticker symbol: IAINX
Discount broker availability: *Schwab, *White, *Waterhouse, *Fidelity, *Siebert
Dividends paid: Income - June, December; Capital gains - December
Portfolio turnover (3 yrs): 51%, 29%, 35%
Largest holding: Matsushita Electric (3.3%)
Management fee: 1.0% first $100M to 0.7% over $600M
12b-1 distribution fee: 0.25%
Expense ratio: 1.74% (year ending 3/31/94)

IAI MIDCAP GROWTH FUND ◆
(See first IAI listing for data common to all IAI funds)

Portfolio manager: Suzanne Zak (1993)
Investment objective and policies: Long-term capital appreciation. Invests in equity securities of companies with market capitalization of $1B-$3B with

superior performance records, solid market positions, strong balance sheets and a management team capable of sustaining growth. May invest in securities of foreign issuers with up to 10% of assets in securities denominated in foreign currencies and 15% in illiquid securities. May use futures, options and currency exchange contracts and sell short.
Year organized: 1992
Ticker symbol: IAMCX
Discount broker availability: *Schwab, *White, *Waterhouse, *Fidelity, *Siebert
Dividends paid: Income - June, December; Capital gains - December
Portfolio turnover (2 yrs): 50%, 58%
Largest holding: Minerals Technologies (3.0%)
Management fee: 0.75% first $200M to 0.65% over $500M
12b-1 distribution fee: Maximum of 0.25% (not currently imposed)
Expense ratio: 1.25% (year ending 3/31/94) (includes waiver)

IAI MINNESOTA TAX FREE FUND ◆
(See first IAI listing for data common to all IAI funds)

Portfolio manager: Stephen C. Coleman (1992)
Investment objective and policies: High level of current income exempt from federal and Minnesota state income taxes consistent with preservation of capital. Invests primarily in Minnesota investment-grade municipal bonds. Up to 20% of assets may be in AMT securities. May use futures, options and currency exchange contracts. Fund may sell short.
Year organized: 1992 (name and objective changed from IAI Tax Free Fund on 12/15/94)
Discount broker availability: *Schwab, *White, *Fidelity, *Siebert
Dividends paid: Income - monthly; Capital gains - December
Portfolio turnover (2 yrs): 16%, 5%
Management fee: 0.55%
12b-1 distribution fee: Yes (not currently imposed)
Expense ratio: 0.25% (year ending 3/31/94)

IAI MONEY MARKET FUND ◆
(See first IAI listing for data common to all IAI funds)

Portfolio manager: Timothy A. Palmer (1993)
Investment objective and policies: High current income consistent with preservation of capital and liquidity. Invests in a diversified portfolio of short-term money market instruments both domestic and foreign.
Year organized: 1993
Ticker symbol: IAIXX
Check redemptions: $500 minimum
Confirmations mailed: After each purchase and each check, mail or wire redemption
Checks returned: Not returned
Periodic account statements mailed: Quarterly
Dividends paid: Income - declared daily, paid monthly
Management fee: 0.3%
Expense ratio: 0.45% (year ending 3/31/94) (includes waiver)

IAI REGIONAL FUND
(See first IAI listing for data common to all IAI funds)

Portfolio manager: Julian P. Carlin (1980)
Investment objective and policies: Capital appreciation. Invests at least 80% of assets in equity securities of companies headquartered in Minnesota, Wisconsin, Iowa, Illinois, Nebraska, Montana,

North Dakota or South Dakota. May invest in securities of foreign issuers with up to 10% of assets in securities denominated in foreign currencies and 15% in illiquid securities. May use futures, options and currency exchange contracts and sell short.
Year organized: 1980
Ticker symbol: IARGX
Discount broker availability: *Schwab, *White, *Waterhouse, *Fidelity, *Siebert
Dividends paid: Income - June, December; Capital gains - December
Portfolio turnover (3 yrs): 163%, 140%, 141%
Largest holding: Johnson Controls (2.3%)
Management fee: 0.75% first $200M to 0.65% over $500M
12b-1 distribution fee: 0.20%
Expense ratio: 1.25% (year ending 3/31/94) (includes waiver)

IAI RESERVE FUND ◆
(See first IAI listing for data common to all IAI funds)

Portfolio manager: Timothy A. Palmer (1991)
Investment objective and policies: High level of capital stability and liquidity and a high level of current income. Invests primarily in investment-grade bonds and other debt securities with maturities of 25 months or less. Up to 15% of assets may be in non-dollar denominated securities of foreign issuers. May use futures, options and currency exchange contracts and sell short.
Year organized: 1986
Ticker symbol: IARVX
Discount broker availability: *Schwab, *White, Waterhouse, *Fidelity, *Siebert
Check redemptions: $500 minimum
Dividends paid: Income - monthly; Capital gains - June, December
Portfolio turnover (3 yrs): 235%, 539%, 218%
Management fee: 0.5%
12b-1 distribution fee: Yes (not currently imposed)
Expense ratio: 0.85% (year ending 3/31/94) (includes waiver)

IAI VALUE FUND ◆
(See first IAI listing for data common to all IAI funds)

Portfolio manager: Douglas R. Platt (1991)
Investment objective and policies: Long term capital appreciation. Invests primarily in out-of-favor common stocks believed undervalued and having unusual opportunities for capital growth. May invest in securities of foreign issuers with up to 10% of assets in securities denominated in foreign currencies and 15% in illiquid securities. May use futures, options and currency exchange contracts and sell short.
Year organized: 1983 (name changed from IAI Apollo Fund in Aug. 1991)
Ticker symbol: IAAPX
Discount broker availability: *Schwab, *White, *Waterhouse, *Fidelity, *Siebert
Dividends paid: Income - June, December; Capital gains - December
Portfolio turnover (3 yrs): 192%, 118%, 125%
Largest holding: LifeUSA Holdings (3.4%)
Management fee: 0.75% first $200M to 0.65% over $500M
12b-1 distribution fee: Maximum of 0.25%, not currently imposed
Expense ratio: 1.25% (year ending 3/31/94) (includes waiver)

IBM MUTUAL FUNDS ◆
(See Galaxy funds)

INVESCO FUNDS

(Data common to all INVESCO funds are shown below. See subsequent listings for data specific to individual INVESCO funds.)

7800 E. Union Ave., Suite 800
Denver, CO 80237
303-930-6300, 800-525-8085
prices/yields 800-424-8085

Shareholder service hours: Full service: M-F 7 A.M.-6 P.M. MST; After hours service: prices, yields, balances, orders, last transaction, news and views
Adviser: INVESCO Funds Group, Inc. (name changed from Financial Programs, Inc. on 1/1/91. Fund names changed from Financial to INVESCO on 7/1/93.)
Custodian: State Street Bank & Trust Co.
Transfer agent: INVESCO Funds Group, Inc.
Minimum purchase: Initial: $1,000, Subsequent: $50; Ira/Keogh: Initial: $250 (exceptions noted)
Telephone orders accepted: Yes
Wire orders accepted: Yes
Deadline for same day wire purchase: 4 P.M.
Qualified for sale in: All states
Telephone redemptions: Yes, $25,000 maximum
Wire redemptions: Yes, $1,000 minimum
Letter redemptions: Signature guarantee not required
Telephone switching: With other INVESCO funds
Number of switches permitted: 4 per fund per year ($250 subsequent minimum)
Shareholder services: Keogh, IRA, SEP-IRA, 403(b), corporate retirement plans, automatic investment plan—minimum $50/month (waives initial minimum), electronic funds transfer, withdrawal plan min. req. $10,000
IRA fees: Annual $10, Initial $5
Keogh fees: Annual $10

INVESCO BALANCED FUND

(See first INVESCO listing for data common to all INVESCO funds)

Portfolio manager: Brian F. Kelly (1993), Donovan J. Paul (1994)
Investment objective and policies: High total return through capital appreciation and current income. Normally invests 50-70% of assets in equity securities (primarily common stocks with some preferred stocks and convertible securities). Remainder of assets are in fixed-income securities including cash reserves with at least 25% of total assets in fixed-income senior securities. Up to 25% of assets may be invested directly foreign securities and 15% in illiquid securities. Fund may use futures and options to hedge.
Year organized: 1993
Ticker symbol: IMABX
Discount broker availability: *Schwab, White
Dividends paid: Income - January, April, July, October; Capital gains - December
Portfolio turnover (1 yr): 61%
Largest holding: Student Loan Marketing Association Notes due 3/7/2001 (11.6%)
Management fee: 0.60% first $350M to 0.25% over $700M
12b-1 distribution fee: 0.25%
Expense ratio: 1.25% (8 months ending 7/31/94) (4.37% without waiver)

INVESCO CASH RESERVES ◆

(See first INVESCO listing for data common to all INVESCO funds)

Portfolio manager: Richard Hinderlie (1993)
Investment objective and policies: Current income consistent with liquidity and safety of capital. Invests in money market instruments.
Year organized: 1976 (name changed from Daily Income Shares on 7/1/93)
Ticker symbol: FDSXX
Check redemptions: $500 minimum
Confirmations mailed: After each purchase and each check, mail or wire redemption
Checks returned: Not returned
Periodic account statements mailed: Monthly

Dividends paid: Income - declared daily, paid monthly
Management fee: 0.5% first $300M to 0.3% over $500M
Expense ratio: 0.81% (year ending 5/31/94)

INVESCO DYNAMICS FUND

(See first INVESCO listing for data common to all INVESCO funds)

Portfolio manager: Timothy J. Miller (1993)
Investment objective and policies: Capital appreciation through aggressive investment policies. Invests primarily in common stocks, but may also invest in bonds, convertible debentures, and preferred stocks when deemed appropriate. May hold securities for relatively short periods, resulting in high turnover. Up to 25% of assets may be in non-dollar denominated foreign securities.
Year organized: 1967
Ticker symbol: FIDYX
Discount broker availability: *Schwab, White, Waterhouse, Fidelity, Siebert
Dividends paid: Income - April, December; Capital gains - December
Portfolio turnover (3 yrs): 169%, 144%, 174%
Largest holding: Deere & Co. (2.5%)
Management fee: 0.6% first $350M to 0.5% over $700M
12b-1 distribution fee: 0.25%
Expense ratio: 1.17% (year ending 4/30/94)

INVESCO EMERGING GROWTH FUND

(See first INVESCO listing for data common to all INVESCO funds)

Portfolio manager: Douglas N. Pratt (1993)
Investment objective and policies: Long-term capital growth. Invests primarily in equity securities of emerging growth companies with market capitalization of less than $500M at time of purchase. Up to 25% of assets may be in non-dollar denominated foreign securities with securities of Canadian issuers and ADRs of other foreign issuers not subject to this limitation. Stocks selected are believed undervalued and/or to have earnings that may be expected to grow faster than the U.S. economy in general.
Year organized: 1991
Ticker symbol: FIEGX
Discount broker availability: *Schwab, White, Waterhouse, Fidelity, Siebert
Dividends paid: Income - May, December; Capital gains - December
Portfolio turnover (3 yrs): 196%, 153%, 50%
Largest holding: Transnational Re Class A (3.3%)
Management fee: 0.75% first $350M to 0.55% over $700M
12b-1 distribution fee: 0.25%
Expense ratio: 1.37% (year ending 5/31/94)

INVESCO EUROPEAN FUND ◆

(See first INVESCO listing for data common to all INVESCO funds)

Portfolio managers: Steven Chamberlain (1990), Jerry W. Mill (1986)
Investment objective and policies: Capital appreciation. Invests at least 80% of assets in equity securities (common stocks and securities convertible into common stock) of companies domiciled in Western Europe. There are no limitations on size of company or percentage of assets invested in companies domiciled in any one country.
Year organized: 1986 (name changed from Strategic - European Portfolio on 7/1/93)
Ticker symbol: FEURX
Discount broker availability: *Schwab, White, Waterhouse, Fidelity, Siebert
Dividends paid: Income - October, December; Capital gains - December
Portfolio turnover (3 yrs): 70%, 44%, 87%
Largest holding: Repsol SA Sponsored ADR (1.7%)

Management fee: 0.75% first $350M to 0.55% over $700M
Expense ratio: 1.20% (year ending 10/31/94)

INVESCO EUROPEAN SMALL COMPANY FUND

(See additional fund listings on page 406)

INVESCO GROWTH FUND

(See first INVESCO listing for data common to all INVESCO funds)

Newspaper listing: Indust
Portfolio manager: R. Dalton Sim (1988)
Investment objective and policies: Long-term capital growth with income secondary. Invests primarily in common stocks of companies representing major fields of business and industrial activity. May also invest in bonds, convertible debentures, and preferred stocks when deemed appropriate. Up to 25% of assets may be in non-dollar denominated foreign securities with securities of Canadian issuers and ADRs of other foreign issuers not subject to this limitation.
Year organized: 1935 (name changed from Industrial Fund on 7/1/93)
Ticker symbol: FLRFX
Discount broker availability: *Schwab, White, Waterhouse, Fidelity, Siebert
Dividends paid: Income - February, May, August, November; Capital gains - December
Portfolio turnover (3 yrs): 63%, 77%, 77%
Largest holding: Telefonos de Mexico SA ADR (3.9%)
Management fee: 0.6% first $350M to 0.5% over $700M
12b-1 distribution fee: 0.25%
Expense ratio: 1.03% (year ending 8/31/94)

INVESCO HIGH YIELD FUND

(See first INVESCO listing for data common to all INVESCO funds)

Portfolio manager: Donovan J. Paul (1994)
Investment objective and policies: High current income. Invests primarily in bonds and other debt securities, including municipals, rated in the medium and lower categories (BB or lower, but not below CCC); may also invest in unrated and restricted (up to 10% of assets) securities.
Year organized: 1984 (name changed from Bond Shares - High Yield Portfolio on 7/1/93)
Ticker symbol: FHYPX
Discount broker availability: *Schwab, Waterhouse, Fidelity, Siebert
Dividends paid: Income - declared daily, paid monthly; Capital gains - December
Portfolio turnover (3 yrs): 195%, 45%, 120%
Management fee: 0.5% first $300M to 0.3% over $500M
12b-1 distribution fee: 0.25%
Expense ratio: 0.97% (year ending 8/31/94) (0.98% without waiver)

INVESCO INDUSTRIAL INCOME FUND

(See first INVESCO listing for data common to all INVESCO funds)

Newspaper listing: IndInc
Portfolio managers: Donovan J. Paul (1994), Charles P. Mayer (1993)
Investment objective and policies: Best possible current income with capital growth secondary. Normally invests 60-75% of assets in dividend-paying common stocks providing relatively high yield and stable return with potential for long-term capital appreciation. May also invest in convertible bonds, preferred stocks, and straight debt securities. Up to 25% of assets may be in foreign debt securities and 15% in junk bonds.
Year organized: 1960
Ticker symbol: FIIIX
Discount broker availability: *Schwab, White, Waterhouse, Fidelity, Siebert
Dividends paid: Income - March, June, September, December; Capital gains - December

Portfolio turnover (3 yrs): 56%, 121%, 119%
Largest holding: El Paso Natural Gas (1.9%)
Management fee: 0.60% first $350M to 0.50% over $700M
12b-1 distribution fee: 0.25%
Expense ratio: 0.92% (year ending 6/30/94)

INVESCO INTERMEDIATE GOVERNMENT BOND FUND ◆
(See first INVESCO listing for data common to all INVESCO funds)

Sub-adviser: INVESCO MIM, Inc.
Portfolio managers: James Baker (1993), Ralph Jenkins (1994)
Investment objective and policies: High total return without regard to federal income tax considerations. Invests primarily in obligations of the U.S. Government and agencies with maturities of 3 to 5 years. Fund may use interest rate futures and options thereon and covered options on portfolio securities.
Year organized: 1986 (prior to 1/1/91 fund was Institutional Income Fund, the successor to Shearwater Income, Inc.; 80 to 1 split 1/2/91.)
Ticker symbol: FIGBX
Minimum purchase: Fund became Institutional on 3/1/93 with an initial minimum investment of $1,000,000. Shareholders of other INVESCO funds prior to 3/1/93 may still open accounts in this fund for the retail $1,000 minimum.
Discount broker availability: *Schwab, White, Fidelity, Siebert
Dividends paid: Income - declared daily, paid monthly; Capital gains - December
Portfolio turnover (3 yrs): 49%, 34%, 93%
Management fee: 0.60% of first $500M to 0.40% over $1B
Expense ratio: 1.07% (year ending 8/31/94)

INVESCO INTERNATIONAL GROWTH FUND ◆
(See first INVESCO listing for data common to all INVESCO funds)

Sub-adviser: INVESCO MIM, Inc., then INVESCO MIM International, Inc.
Portfolio managers: Phillip Ehrman (1993), W. Lindsay Davidson (1987)
Investment objective and policies: High total return without regard to federal income tax considerations. Invests at least 65% of assets in foreign equities, generally in developed countries, of at least 3 different countries outside of the U.S. Up to 10% of assets can be in developing countries. Fund may use forward currency exchange contracts to manage exchange rate risk.
Year organized: 1987 (prior to 1/1/91 fund was Institutional International Fund; 80 to 1 split 1/2/91)
Ticker symbol: FSIGX
Discount broker availability: *Schwab, White, Waterhouse, Fidelity, Siebert
Dividends paid: Income - October; Capital gains - December
Portfolio turnover (3 yrs): 87%, 46%, 50%
Largest holding: Total Cie Francaise des Petroles B Shrs (1.5%)
Management fee: 1.00% of first $500M to 0.65% over $1B
Expense ratio: 1.50% (year ending 10/31/94)

INVESCO LATIN AMERICA GROWTH FUND
(See additional fund listings on page 406)

INVESCO MULTI-ASSET ALLOCATION FUND
(See first INVESCO listing for data common to all INVESCO funds)

Portfolio manager: Robert Slotpole (1994)
Investment objective and policies: High total return - capital growth and current income. Fund allocates assets among 6 classes. Numbers in parens indicate default weightings and range. Large cap stocks

(35%, 0-70%), fixed-income (25%, 0-50%), small cap stocks, real estate stocks, international stocks and cash (all 10%, 0-30% each). Allocations are adjusted to reflect changes in economic and market conditions.
Year organized: 1993
Ticker symbol: IMAAX
Discount broker availability: *Schwab, White
Dividends paid: Income - July; Capital gains - December
Portfolio turnover (1 yr): 42%
Largest holding: U.S. Treasury Notes due 4/30/99 (3.7%)
Management fee: 0.75% first $500M to 0.50% over $1B
12b-1 distribution fee: 0.25%
Expense ratio: 1.50% (8 months ending 7/31/94) (5.14% without waiver)

INVESCO PACIFIC BASIN FUND ◆
(See first INVESCO listing for data common to all INVESCO funds)

Portfolio managers: Julian Pickstone (1993), Douglas N. Pratt (1994)
Investment objective and policies: Capital appreciation. Invests at least 80% in equity securities (common stocks and securities convertible into common stock) of companies domiciled in the following Far Eastern or Western Pacific countries: Japan, Australia, Hong Kong, Malaysia, Singapore and the Philippines. There are no limitations on size of company or percentage of assets invested in companies domiciled in any one country.
Year organized: 1984 (name changed from Strategic - Pacific Basin Portfolio on 7/1/93)
Ticker symbol: FPBSX
Discount broker availability: *Schwab, White, Waterhouse, Fidelity, Siebert
Dividends paid: Income - October, December; Capital gains - December
Portfolio turnover (3 yrs): 70%, 30%, 123%
Largest holding: Hitachi Metals (1.9%)
Management fee: 0.75% first $350M to 0.55% over $700M
Expense ratio: 1.24% (year ending 10/31/94)

INVESCO SELECT INCOME FUND
(See first INVESCO listing for data common to all INVESCO funds)

Portfolio manager: Donovan J. Paul (1994)
Investment objective and policies: High current income. Normally invests at least 90% in marketable debt securities of established companies and government and municipal issues. At least 50% of assets will be in securities rated investment-grade. Up to 50% may be invested in lower grade (Ba or less by Moody's, BB or less by S&P) or unrated securities.
Year organized: 1976 (formerly Bond Shares - Bond Shares Portfolio. Name changed from Bond Shares - Select Income Portfolio on 7/1/93)
Ticker symbol: FBDSX
Discount broker availability: *Schwab, White, Waterhouse, Fidelity, Siebert
Dividends paid: Income - declared daily, paid monthly; Capital gains - December
Portfolio turnover (3 yrs): 135%, 105%, 178%
Management fee: 0.55% first $300M to 0.35% over $500M
12b-1 distribution fee: 0.25%
Expense ratio: 1.11% (year ending 8/31/94) (1.15% without waiver)

INVESCO SHORT-TERM BOND FUND
(See first INVESCO listing for data common to all INVESCO funds)

Portfolio manager: Richard R. Hinderlie (1993)
Investment objective and policies: High current income consistent with minimum fluctuation in principal value and liquidity. Invests at least 65% of assets in investment-grade debt securities. Up to 25% of assets may be invested in foreign debt secu-

rities; securities of Canadian issuers and ADRs of other foreign issuers are not subject to this limitation. Fund maintains a weighted average maturity of 3 years or less.
Year organized: 1993
Ticker symbol: INIBX
Discount broker availability: *Schwab
Dividends paid: Income - declared daily, paid monthly; Capital Gains - December
Portfolio turnover (1 yr): 169%
Management fee: 0.50% first $300M to 0.30% over $500M
12b-1 distribution fee: 0.25%
Expense ratio: 0.46% (11 months ending 8/31/94) (2.04% without waiver)

INVESCO SMALL COMPANY FUND ◆
(See first INVESCO listing for data common to all INVESCO funds)

Portfolio manager: Kevin M. Means (1993)
Investment objective and policies: Long-term capital growth. Invests primarily in equity securities of U.S. companies with market capitalizations below the 1,000 U.S. companies having the largest capitalizations - generally in the $10M to $600M range. Up to 25% of assets may be in foreign securities and 15% in illiquid securities. May use futures and options and hedge up to 25% of total assets.
Year organized: 1993
Minimum purchase: Initial: $10,000, Subsequent: $50
Discount broker availability: *Schwab, White
Dividends paid: Income - July; Capital gains - December
Portfolio turnover (1 yr): 55%
Largest holding: Allwaste, Inc. (2.1%)
Management fee: 0.75%
Expense ratio: 1.00% (8 months ending 7/31/94) (1.64% without waiver)

INVESCO STRATEGIC - ENERGY PORTFOLIO ◆
(See first INVESCO listing for data common to all INVESCO funds)

Portfolio manager: Daniel B. Leonard (1994)
Investment objective and policies: Capital appreciation. Invests at least 80% of assets in common stocks and securities convertible into common stock of companies in oil, natural gas, coal, uranium, etc., transportation, distribution or processing services, production services, and research and development of energy, including energy conversion, conservation and pollution control. Up to 25% of assets may be in non-dollar denominated foreign securities with securities of Canadian issuers and ADRs of other foreign issuers not subject to this limitation.
Year organized: 1984
Ticker symbol: FSTEX
Discount broker availability: *Schwab, White, Waterhouse, Fidelity, Siebert
Dividends paid: Income - October, December; Capital gains - December
Portfolio turnover (3 yrs): 123%, 190%, 370%
Largest holding: Barrett Resources (4.8%)
Management fee: 0.75% first $350M to 0.55% over $700M
Expense ratio: 1.35% (year ending 10/31/94)

INVESCO STRATEGIC - ENVIRONMENTAL SERVICES PORTFOLIO ◆
(See first INVESCO listing for data common to all INVESCO funds)

Portfolio manager: John Schroer (1993)
Investment objective and policies: Capital appreciation. Invests at least 80% of assets in common stocks and securities convertible into common stock of companies engaged in products and services concerning waste management, pollution control and other companies offering products and services related to environmental concerns in the

United States and foreign countries. May invest in securities of foreign issuers without limit.
Year organized: 1991
Ticker symbol: FSEVX
Discount broker availability: *Schwab, White, Waterhouse, Fidelity, Siebert
Dividends paid: Income - October, December; Capital gains - December
Portfolio turnover (3 yrs): 211%, 155%, 113%
Largest holding: American Cyanamid (6.7%)
Management fee: 0.75% first $350M to 0.55% over $700M
Expense ratio: 1.29% (year ending 10/31/94) (1.43% without waiver)

INVESCO STRATEGIC - FINANCIAL SERVICES PORTFOLIO ◆
(See first INVESCO listing for data common to all INVESCO funds)

Portfolio manager: Douglas N. Pratt (1992)
Investment objective and policies: Capital appreciation. Invests at least 80% of assets in common stocks and securities convertible into common stock of companies primarily engaged in businesses involving financial services, including banks, savings and loans, finance companies, leasing, securities brokerage and insurance. Up to 25% of assets may be in non-dollar denominated foreign securities with securities of Canadian issuers and ADRs of other foreign issuers not subject to this limitation.
Year organized: 1986
Ticker symbol: FSFSX
Discount broker availability: *Schwab, White, Waterhouse, Fidelity, Siebert
Dividends paid: Income - October, December; Capital gains - December
Portfolio turnover (3 yrs): 88%, 236%, 208%
Largest holding: CitiCorp (8.1%)
Management fee: 0.75% first $350M to 0.55% over $700M
Expense ratio: 1.18% (year ending 10/31/94)

INVESCO STRATEGIC - GOLD PORTFOLIO ◆
(See first INVESCO listing for data common to all INVESCO funds)

Portfolio manager: Daniel B. Leonard (1989)
Investment objective and policies: Capital appreciation. Invests at least 80% of assets in common stocks and securities convertible into common stock of companies in mining, exploration, processing, dealing or investing in gold. Up to 10% of assets may be in gold bullion. May invest in securities of foreign issuers without limit.
Year organized: 1984
Ticker symbol: FGLDX
Discount broker availability: *Schwab, White, Waterhouse, Fidelity, Siebert
Dividends paid: Income - October, December; Capital gains - December
Portfolio turnover (3 yrs): 97%, 142%, 101%
Largest holding: Golden Star Resources (5.8%)
Management fee: 0.75% first $350M to 0.55% over $700M
Expense ratio: 1.07% (year ending 10/31/94)

INVESCO STRATEGIC - HEALTH SCIENCES PORTFOLIO ◆
(See first INVESCO listing for data common to all INVESCO funds)

Portfolio managers: Barry Kurokawa (1992), John Schroer (1994)
Newspaper listing: HlthSc
Investment objective and policies: Capital appreciation. Invests at least 80% of assets in common stocks and securities convertible into common stock of companies in medical equipment, pharmaceuticals, health care facilities fields, and research and development in these fields. Up to 25% of assets may be in non-dollar denominated foreign securities with securities of Canadian issuers and

ADRs of other foreign issuers not subject to this limitation.
Year organized: 1984
Ticker symbol: FHLSX
Discount broker availability: *Schwab, White, Waterhouse, Fidelity, Siebert
Dividends paid: Income - October, December; Capital gains - December
Portfolio turnover (3 yrs): 80%, 87%, 91%
Largest holding: Nellcor, Inc. (3.8%)
Management fee: 0.75% first $350M to 0.55% over $700M
Expense ratio: 1.19% (year ending 10/31/94)

INVESCO STRATEGIC - LEISURE PORTFOLIO ◆
(See first INVESCO listing for data common to all INVESCO funds)

Portfolio manager: Timothy J. Miller (1992)
Investment objective and policies: Capital appreciation. Invests at least 80% of assets in common stocks and securities convertible into common stock of companies in sporting goods, recreational equipment, photography, music, broadcasting, movie, hotel, casinos and amusement parks. Up to 25% of assets may be in non-dollar denominated foreign securities with securities of Canadian issuers and ADRs of other foreign issuers not subject to this limitation.
Year organized: 1984
Ticker symbol: FLISX
Discount broker availability: *Schwab, White, Waterhouse, Fidelity, Siebert
Dividends paid: Income - October, December; Capital gains - December
Portfolio turnover (3 yrs): 116%, 116%, 148%
Largest holding: La Quinta Inns (2.6%)
Management fee: 0.75% first $350M to 0.55% over $700M
Expense ratio: 1.17% (year ending 10/31/94)

INVESCO STRATEGIC - TECHNOLOGY PORTFOLIO ◆
(See first INVESCO listing for data common to all INVESCO funds)

Portfolio manager: Daniel B. Leonard (1984)
Investment objective and policies: Capital appreciation. Invests at least 80% of assets in common stocks and securities convertible into common stock of companies principally engaged in the field of technology. Included are companies engaged in such fields as computers, communications, video, electronics, oceanography, office and factory automation, and robotics. Up to 25% of assets may be in non-dollar denominated foreign securities with securities of Canadian issuers and ADRs of other foreign issuers not subject to this limitation.
Year organized: 1984
Ticker symbol: FTCHX
Discount broker availability: *Schwab, White, Waterhouse, Fidelity, Siebert
Dividends paid: Income - October, December; Capital gains - December
Portfolio turnover (3 yrs): 145%, 184%, 169%
Largest holding: International Business Machines (4.6%)
Management fee: 0.75% first $350M to 0.55% over $700M
Expense ratio: 1.17% (year ending 10/31/94)

INVESCO STRATEGIC - UTILITIES PORTFOLIO ◆
(See first INVESCO listing for data common to all INVESCO funds)

Portfolio manager: Brian F. Kelly (1993)
Investment objective and policies: Capital appreciation. Invests at least 80% of assets in common stocks and securities convertible into common stock of companies principally engaged in the public utilities industry. These may include companies which manufacture, produce, generate, transmit, or sell gas or electric energy; and companies engaged

in various aspects of communications, such as telephone, telegraph, satellite, microwave, and the provision of other communication facilities, excluding broadcasting, for public use and benefit. Up to 25% of assets may be in non-dollar denominated foreign securities with securities of Canadian issuers and ADRs of other foreign issuers not subject to this limitation.
Year organized: 1986
Ticker symbol: FSTUX
Discount broker availability: *Schwab, White, Waterhouse, Fidelity, Siebert
Dividends paid: Income - January, April, July, October, December; Capital gains - December
Portfolio turnover (3 yrs): 180%, 202%, 226%
Largest holding: CINergy Corp. (3.7%)
Management fee: 0.75% first $350M to 0.55% over $700M
Expense ratio: 1.13% (year ending 10/31/94)

INVESCO TAX-FREE INTERMEDIATE BOND FUND
(See first INVESCO listing for data common to all INVESCO funds)

Portfolio manager: William W. Veronda (1993)
Investment objective and policies: High current income exempt from federal income taxes consistent with preservation of capital. Normally invests at least 80% of assets in municipal bonds within the four highest grades with a weighted average maturity of 5 to 10 years. Up to 20% of assets may be in AMT securities. May use futures and options to hedge.
Year organized: 1993
Discount broker availability: *Schwab
Dividends paid: Income - declared daily, paid monthly; Capital Gains - December
Portfolio turnover (1 yr): 55%
Management fee: 0.50% first $300M to 0.30% over $500M
12b-1 distribution fee: 0.25%
Expense ratio: 0.70% (7 months ending 6/30/94) (3.09% without waiver)

INVESCO TAX-FREE LONG-TERM BOND FUND
(See first INVESCO listing for data common to all INVESCO funds)

Newspaper listing: TxFre
Portfolio manager: William W. Veronda (1984)
Investment objective and policies: High current income exempt from federal income taxes consistent with preservation of capital. Normally invests at least 80% of assets in municipal bonds within the four highest grades with a weighted average maturity of 20 years or more. May use futures to hedge.
Year organized: 1981 (name changed from Tax-Free Income Shares on 7/1/93)
Ticker symbol: FTIFX
Discount broker availability: *Schwab, White, Waterhouse, Fidelity, Siebert
Dividends paid: Income - declared daily, paid monthly; Capital Gains - December
Portfolio turnover (3 yrs): 28%, 30%, 28%
Management fee: 0.55% first $300M to 0.35% over $500M
12b-1 distribution fee: 0.25%
Expense ratio: 1.00% (year ending 6/30/94)

INVESCO TAX-FREE MONEY FUND ◆
(See first INVESCO listing for data common to all INVESCO funds)

Portfolio manager: Ingeborg Cosby (1992)
Investment objective and policies: Current income exempt from federal income taxes consistent with liquidity and preservation of capital. Invests in municipal money market obligations issued by states and other municipalities.
Year organized: 1983
Ticker symbol: FFRXX
Check redemptions: $500 minimum

Confirmations mailed: After each purchase and each check, mail or wire redemption
Checks returned: Not returned
Periodic account statements mailed: Monthly
Dividends paid: Income - declared daily, paid monthly
Management fee: 0.5% first $300M to 0.3% over $500M
Expense ratio: 0.75% (year ending 5/31/94) (1.00% without waiver)

INVESCO TOTAL RETURN FUND ◆
(See first INVESCO listing for data common to all INVESCO funds)

Sub-adviser: INVESCO MIM, Inc.
Portfolio managers: Edward C. Mitchell (1987), David Griffin (1994)
Investment objective and policies: High total return without regard to federal income tax considerations. Maintains minimum of 30% in equities and 30% in fixed and variable debt obligations. The remaining 40% will vary in asset allocation according to business, economic and market conditions, determined systematically using current versus expected levels. Up to 25% of assets may be in securities of foreign issuers. May use futures and options to hedge.
Year organized: 1987 (prior to 1/1/91 fund was Institutional Flex Fund; 80 to 1 split 1/2/91. Name changed from Flex Fund on 7/1/93)
Ticker symbol: FSFLX
Minimum purchase: Fund became Institutional on 3/1/93 with an initial minimum investment of $1,000,000. Shareholders of other INVESCO funds prior to 3/1/93 may still open accounts in this fund for the retail $1,000 minimum.
Discount broker availability: *Schwab, White, Waterhouse, Fidelity, Siebert
Dividends paid: Income - February, May, August, November; Capital gains - December
Portfolio turnover (3 yrs): 12%, 19%, 13%
Largest holding: U.S. Treasury Note due 8/15/00 (1.9%)
Management fee: 0.75% of first $500M to 0.50% over $1B
Expense ratio: 0.96% (year ending 8/31/94)

INVESCO U.S. GOVERNMENT MONEY FUND ◆
(See first INVESCO listing for data common to all INVESCO funds)

Sub-adviser: INVESCO MIM, Inc.
Portfolio manager: Richard R. Hinderlie (1993)
Investment objective and policies: High current income consistent with liquidity and safety of capital. Invests only in money market obligations issued or guaranteed by the U.S. Government or its agencies or instrumentalities.
Year organized: 1991
Ticker symbol: FUGXX
Check redemptions: $500 minimum
Confirmations mailed: After each purchase and each check, mail or wire redemption
Checks returned: Not returned
Periodic account statements mailed: Monthly
Dividends paid: Income - declared daily, paid monthly
Management fee: 0.50% of first $300M to 0.30% over $500M
Expense ratio: 0.75% (year ending 5/31/94) (1.00% without waiver)

INVESCO U.S. GOVERNMENT SECURITIES FUND
(See first INVESCO listing for data common to all INVESCO funds)

Portfolio manager: Richard R. Hinderlie (1994)
Investment objective and policies: High current income. Invests at least 65% of assets in bonds and other debt securities issued or guaranteed by the U.S. Government or its agencies or instrumentali-

ties. May invest a substantial portion of its assets in GNMA certificates and use interest rate futures contracts to hedge.
Year organized: 1986 (name changed from Bond Shares - U.S. Government Securities Portfolio on 7/1/93)
Ticker symbol: FBDGX
Discount broker availability: *Schwab, White, Waterhouse, Fidelity, Siebert
Dividends paid: Income - declared daily, paid monthly; Capital gains - December
Portfolio turnover (3 yrs): 95%, 100%, 115%
Management fee: 0.55% first $300M to 0.35% over $500M
12b-1 distribution fee: 0.25%
Expense ratio: 1.32% (year ending 8/31/94) (1.42% without waiver)

INVESCO VALUE EQUITY FUND ◆
(See first INVESCO listing for data common to all INVESCO funds)

Sub-adviser: INVESCO MIM, Inc.
Portfolio managers: Michael Harhai (1993), Terrence Irrgang (1993)
Investment objective and policies: High total return without regard to federal income tax considerations. Invests primarily in common stocks and, to a lesser extent, in convertible securities. Most of the common stocks pay regular dividends. Up to 35% of assets may be in investment-grade debt securities and 25% in securities of foreign issuers.
Year organized: 1986 (name changed from Equity Fund on 7/1/93. Prior to 1/1/91 fund was Institutional Equity Fund, the successor to Shearwater Equity, Inc.; 80 to 1 split 1/2/91)
Ticker symbol: FSEQX
Minimum purchase: Fund became Institutional on 3/1/93 with an initial minimum investment of $1,000,000. Shareholders of other INVESCO funds prior to 3/1/93 may still open accounts in this fund for the retail $1,000 minimum.
Discount broker availability: *Schwab, White, Fidelity, Siebert
Dividends paid: Income - February, May, August, November; Capital gains - December
Portfolio turnover (3 yrs): 53%, 35%, 37%
Management fee: 0.75% of first $500M to 0.50% over $1B
Expense ratio: 1.01% (year ending 8/31/94)

INVESCO WORLDWIDE CAPITAL GOODS FUND
(See first INVESCO listing for data common to all INVESCO funds)

Portfolio manager: Jerry W. Mill (1994)
Investment objective and policies: Capital appreciation. Invests at least 65% of assets in equity securities of companies engaged in design, development, manufacture, distribution, sale or service of capital goods, or in the mining, processing, manufacture or distribution of raw materials and intermediate goods used by industry and agriculture. Invests in at least 3 countries, one of which may be the U.S. There are no limitations on percentage of assets invested in companies domiciled in any one country. Up to 15% of assets may be in illiquid securities. May use futures and options to hedge.
Year organized: 1994
Discount broker availability: *Schwab
Dividends paid: Income - July; Capital gains - December
Management fee: 0.65% first $500M to 0.45% over $1B
12b-1 distribution fee: 0.25%

INVESCO WORLDWIDE COMMUNICATIONS FUND
(See first INVESCO listing for data common to all INVESCO funds)

Portfolio manager: Brian F. Kelly (1994)
Investment objective and policies: Capital appreciation. Invests at least 65% of assets in equity securi-

ties of companies engaged in design, development, manufacture, distribution or sale of communications services and equipment. May invest in companies involved in telephone service, wireless communications, local and wide area networks, fiber optic transmission, satellite communication, microwave transmission, television and movie programming, broadcasting and cable television. Invests in at least 3 countries, one of which may be the U.S. There are no limitations on percentage of assets invested in companies domiciled in any one country. Up to 15% of assets may be in illiquid securities. May use futures and options to hedge.
Year organized: 1994
Discount broker availability: *Schwab
Dividends paid: Income - July; Capital gains - December
Management fee: 0.65% first $500M to 0.45% over $1B
12b-1 distribution fee: 0.25%

JANUS FUNDS ◆
(Data common to all Janus funds are shown below. See subsequent listings for data specific to individual Janus funds.)

100 Fillmore Street, Suite 300
Denver, CO 80206
303-333-3863, 800-525-3713
prices/yields 800-525-0024
800-525-6125 for account information
fax 303-782-3055, TDD 800-525-0056

Shareholder service hours: Full service: M-F 7 A.M.-10 P.M. EST, Sat-Sun 10 A.M.-7 P.M.; After hours service: prices, yields, balances, last transaction, exchanges
Adviser: Janus Capital Corp.
Custodians: Investors Fiduciary Trust Co. (U.S. assets), State Street Bank & Trust Co. (foreign assets)
Sub-custodian: United Missouri Bank of Kansas City, N.A. (U.S. assets)
Transfer agent: Investors Fiduciary Trust Co.
Transfer sub-agent: Janus Service Corp.
Minimum purchase: Initial: $1,000, Subsequent: $50; IRA/Keogh: Initial: $250
Telephone orders accepted: No
Wire orders accepted: Yes, subsequent only
Deadline for same day wire purchase: 4 P.M.
Qualified for sale in: All states
Telephone redemptions: Yes
Wire redemptions: Yes, $8 fee
Letter redemptions: Signature guarantee required over $50,000
Telephone switching: With other open Janus funds
Number of switches permitted: 4 per year out of each Janus Group fund, $1,000 minimum; unlimited money market
Shareholder services: Keogh, IRA, SEP-IRA, 403(b), corporate retirement plans, automatic investment plan—minimum $50/month (waives initial minimum), withdrawal plan min. req. $10,000, electronic funds transfer
IRA/Keogh fees: Annual $12 per fund, $24 maximum (or $100 lifetime for all IRA/Keogh account fund holdings)

JANUS BALANCED FUND ◆
(See first Janus listing for data common to all Janus funds)

Portfolio manager: James P. Craig III (1993)
Investment objective and policies: Long-term capital growth consistent with preservation of capital and balanced by current income. Invests 40-60% of assets in equity securities selected for growth and 40-60% in fixed-income securities. At least 25% of assets in fixed-income senior securities, including debt securities and preferred stocks. Up to 25% of assets may be in securities of foreign issuers but fund will not invest in foreign corporate debt securities. Fund may use futures and options to hedge.
Year organized: 1992
Ticker symbol: JABAX
Discount broker availability: *Schwab, White,

Waterhouse, *Fidelity, *Siebert
Dividends paid: Income - March, June, September, December; Capital gains - December
Portfolio turnover (2 yrs): 167%, 131%
Largest holding: U.S. Treasury Notes 6.50% due 4/30/99 (5.2%)
Management fee: 1.0% first $30M to 0.65% over $500M
Expense ratio: 1.42% (year ending 10/31/94)

JANUS ENTERPRISE FUND ◆
(See first Janus listing for data common to all Janus funds)

Portfolio manager: James P. Goff (1992)
Investment objective and policies: Long-term growth of capital consistent with preservation of capital. Invests primarily in medium-sized companies with market capitalizations of $1B to $5B but may also invest in smaller and/or larger companies. Fund is non-diversified. May invest up to 25% of assets in securities of foreign issuers and use futures and options to hedge.
Year organized: 1992
Ticker symbol: JAENX
Discount broker availability: *Schwab, White, Waterhouse, *Fidelity, *Siebert
Dividends paid: Income - December; Capital gains - December
Portfolio turnover (2 yrs): 193%, 201%
Largest holding: Exide Corp. (14.5%)
Management fee: 1.0% first $30M to 0.65% over $500M
Expense ratio: 1.25% (year ending 10/31/94)

JANUS FEDERAL TAX EXEMPT FUND ◆
(See first Janus listing for data common to all Janus funds)

Portfolio manager: Ronald V. Speaker (1993)
Investment objective and policies: High current income exempt from federal income tax consistent with preservation of capital. Invests at least 80% of assets in municipal obligations whose interest is exempt from federal income tax. Up to 35% of assets may be in junk bonds, 20% in AMT securities and 15% in illiquid securities.
Year organized: 1993
Ticker symbol: JATEX
Discount broker availability: *Schwab, White
Dividends paid: Income - declared daily, paid monthly; Capital gains - December
Portfolio turnover (2 yrs): 160%, 124%
Management fee: 0.6% first $300, 0.55% over $300M
Expense ratio: 0.65% (year ending 10/31/94) (1.41% without waiver)

JANUS FLEXIBLE INCOME FUND ◆
(See first Janus listing for data common to all Janus funds)

Portfolio manager: Ronald V. Speaker (1991)
Investment objective and policies: Maximum total return consistent with preservation of capital. Invests primarily in income-producing securities - debt securities, mortgage- or asset-backed securities, preferred stocks, income-producing common stocks and/or securities convertible into common stocks. Income will be the dominant component of total return. May invest in securities of foreign issuers and junk bonds without limit and use futures and options to hedge. Up to 15% of assets may be in illiquid securities.
Year organized: 1987
Ticker symbol: JAFIX
Discount broker availability: *Schwab, White, Waterhouse, *Fidelity, *Siebert
Dividends paid: Income - declared daily, paid monthly; Capital gains - December
Portfolio turnover (3 yrs): 137%, 201%, 210%
Management fee: 0.65% first $300, 0.55% over $300M
Expense ratio: 0.93% (year ending 10/31/94)

JANUS FUND ◆
(See first Janus listing for data common to all Janus funds)

Portfolio manager: James P. Craig III (1986)
Investment objective and policies: Growth of capital consistent with preservation of capital. Invests primarily in common stocks of companies with favorable demand for their products and services operating in favorable competitive environments and regulatory climates, regardless of their size. May invest in foreign securities without limit. Up to 15% of assets may be in illiquid securities. Fund may use futures and options to hedge.
Year organized: 1970
Ticker symbol: JANSX
Discount broker availability: *Schwab, White, Waterhouse, *Fidelity, *Siebert
Dividends paid: Income - December; Capital gains - December
Portfolio turnover (3 yrs): 139%, 127%, 153%
Largest holding: Citicorp (3.8%)
Management fee: 1.0% first $30M to 0.65% over $500M
Expense ratio: 0.91% (year ending 10/31/94)

JANUS GROWTH AND INCOME FUND ◆
(See first Janus listing for data common to all Janus funds)

Portfolio manager: Thomas F. Marsico (1991)
Investment objective and policies: Long-term growth of capital and current income. Invests in equity securities, convertible securities and fixed-income securities of domestic and foreign issuers. Normally invests up to 75% (at least 25%) of assets based on capital growth potential and at least 25% based on income paying properties. Up to 35% of assets may be in junk bonds and 15% in illiquid securities. Fund may use futures and options to hedge.
Year organized: 1991
Ticker symbol: JAGIX
Discount broker availability: *Schwab, White, Waterhouse, *Fidelity, *Siebert
Dividends paid: Income - March, June, September, December; Capital gains - December
Portfolio turnover (3 yrs): 123%, 138%, 120%
Largest holding: American Express Co., Exchange Notes, 6.25% (5.4%)
Management fee: 1.0% first $30M to 0.65% over $500M
Expense ratio: 1.22% (year ending 10/31/94)

JANUS INTERMEDIATE GOVERNMENT SECURITIES FUND ◆
(See first Janus listing for data common to all Janus funds)

Portfolio manager: Ronald V. Speaker (1992)
Investment objective and policies: High current income consistent with preservation of capital. Invests primarily in obligations of the U.S. Government and its agencies and instrumentalities with a weighted average maturity of less than 10 years. Up to 20% of assets may be in commercial paper of U.S. issuers rated in the highest category.
Year organized: 1991
Ticker symbol: JAIGX
Discount broker availability: *Schwab, White, Waterhouse, *Fidelity, *Siebert
Dividends paid: Income - declared daily, paid monthly; Capital gains - December
Portfolio turnover (3 yrs): 304%, 371%, 270%
Management fee: 0.5% first $300M, 0.4% over $300M
Expense ratio: 0.65% (year ending 10/31/94) (1.15% without waiver)

JANUS MERCURY FUND ◆
(See first Janus listing for data common to all Janus funds)

Portfolio manager: Warren B. Lammert (1993)
Investment objective and policies: Long-term growth of capital. Invests primarily in equity securities of companies believed to have strong earnings growth potential with emphasis on those whose potential has not been recognized by the market. May invest in securities of foreign issuers without limit. Up to 15% of assets may be in illiquid securities. Fund may use futures and options to hedge and is non-diversified.
Year organized: 1993
Ticker symbol: JAMRX
Discount broker availability: *Schwab, White, Waterhouse, *Fidelity, *Siebert
Dividends paid: Income - December; Capital gains - December
Portfolio turnover (2 yrs): 283%, 151%
Largest holding: Nokia A.B. Preferred (6.7%)
Management fee: 1.0% first $30M to 0.65% over $500M
Expense ratio: 1.33% (year ending 10/31/94)

JANUS MONEY MARKET FUNDS
(See additional fund listings on page 406)

JANUS OVERSEAS FUND ◆
(See first Janus listing for data common to all Janus funds)

Portfolio manager: Helen Young Hayes (1994)
Investment objective and policies: Long-term growth of capital. Invests primarily in common stocks of foreign issuers, regardless of size, country of organization or place of principal business activity. May invest in fixed-income securities of foreign corporations, governments, government agencies and other government entities. Normally invests in securities of issuers from at least five different countries, excluding the U.S. Up to 15% of assets may be in illiquid securities. Fund may use futures and options to hedge.
Year organized: 1994
Ticker symbol: JAOSX
Discount broker availability: *Schwab, White, Waterhouse, *Fidelity, *Siebert
Dividends paid: Income - December; Capital gains - December
Portfolio turnover (1 yr): 181%
Largest holding: Kinnevik A.B. B-Free (5.4%)
Management fee: 1.0% first $30M to 0.65% over $500M
Expense ratio: 2.16% (6 months ending 10/31/94)

JANUS SHORT-TERM BOND FUND ◆
(See first Janus listing for data common to all Janus funds)

Portfolio manager: Ronald V. Speaker (1992)
Investment objective and policies: High current income consistent with preservation of capital. Invests primarily in short- and intermediate-term investment-grade fixed-income securities with a weighted average maturity of less than 5 years. May invest in foreign debt securities without limit. Up to 35% of assets may be in junk bonds and 15% in illiquid securities.
Year organized: 1992
Ticker symbol: JASBX
Discount broker availability: *Schwab, White, Waterhouse, *Fidelity, *Siebert
Dividends paid: Income - declared daily, paid monthly; Capital gains - December
Portfolio turnover (2 yrs): 346%, 372%
Management fee: 0.65% first $300M, 0.55% over $300M
Expense ratio: 0.65% (year ending 10/31/94) (1.15% without waiver)

JANUS TWENTY FUND ◆
(See first Janus listing for data common to all Janus funds)

Portfolio manager: Thomas F. Marsico (1987)
Investment objective and policies: Capital growth consistent with preservation of capital. Normally remains fully invested in a limited number of common stocks of companies with rapid growth potential. May invest in ADRs of foreign companies and in non-dollar denominated foreign securities. Up to 35% of assets may be in junk bonds and 15% in

illiquid securities. Fund is non-diversified and may use futures and options to hedge.
Year organized: 1984 (name changed from Janus Value on 5/19/89)
Ticker symbol: JAVLX
Special sales restrictions: Fund closed to new shareholders on 2/12/93
Discount broker availability: *Schwab, White, Waterhouse, *Fidelity, *Siebert
Dividends paid: Income - December; Capital gains - December
Portfolio turnover (3 yrs): 102%, 99%, 83%
Largest holding: Lowe's Companies, Inc. (6.3%)
Management fee: 1.0% first $30M to 0.65% over $500M
Expense ratio: 1.02% (year ending 10/31/94)

JANUS VENTURE FUND ◆
(See first Janus listing for data common to all Janus funds)

Portfolio managers: Warren B. Lammert (1993), James P. Goff (1993)
Investment objective and policies: Capital appreciation consistent with preservation of capital. Invests in common stocks of companies with potential strong growth in revenues, earnings and assets, primarily with market capitalization less than $750M. Some will have limited operating histories (less than 5 years) and may depend on new products, services or processes. May invest in securities of foreign issuers without limit. Up to 35% of assets may be in junk bonds and 15% in illiquid securities. Fund is non-diversified and may use futures and options to hedge.
Year organized: 1984
Ticker symbol: JAVTX
Special sales restrictions: Fund closed to new shareholders 9/30/91
Discount broker availability: *Schwab, White, Waterhouse, *Fidelity, *Siebert
Dividends paid: Income - December; Capital gains - December
Portfolio turnover (3 yrs): 114%, 139%, 166%
Largest holding: Nokia A.B. Preferred (8.6%)
Management fee: 1.0% first $30M to 0.65% over $500M
Expense ratio: 0.96% (year ending 10/31/94)

JANUS WORLDWIDE FUND ◆
(See first Janus listing for data common to all Janus funds)

Portfolio manager: Helen Young Hayes (1992)
Investment objective and policies: Long-term growth of capital consistent with preservation of capital. Invests primarily in common stocks of foreign and domestic issuers, regardless of size, country of organization or place of principal business activity. May invest in fixed-income securities of corporations, domestic and foreign governments, government agencies and other government entities. Normally invests in securities of issuers from at least five different countries, including the U.S. Up to 35% of assets may be in junk bonds and 15% in illiquid securities. Fund may use futures and options to hedge.
Year organized: 1991
Ticker symbol: JAWWX
Discount broker availability: *Schwab, White, Waterhouse, *Fidelity, *Siebert
Dividends paid: Income - December; Capital gains - December
Portfolio turnover (3 yrs): 158%, 124%, 147%
Largest holding: Astra A.B. A-Free (5.7%)
Management fee: 1.0% first $30M to 0.65% over $500M
Expense ratio: 1.12% (year ending 10/31/94)

JAPAN FUND ◆
P.O. Box 2291
Boston, MA 02107-2291
617-295-1000, 800-535-2726
800-225-2470 prices 800-343-2890
TDD 800-543-7916, fax 617-261-4420

Adviser and manager: Asia Management Corp. (a wholly-owned subsidiary of Scudder, Stevens & Clark, Ltd.)

Investment research adviser: Nikko Int'l Capital Mngt. Co., Ltd.
Portfolio managers: Seung Kwak (1989), Elizabeth J. Allan (1990)
Custodian: Brown Brothers Harriman & Co.
Sub-custodian: Sumitomo Trust & Banking Co. Ltd. (Tokyo Office)
Transfer agent: Scudder Service Corp.
Investment objective and policies: Long-term capital appreciation. Invests primarily in equity securities, including ADRs, of Japanese companies - common stock, preferred stock, warrants, and convertible debentures. May invest 50% of assets in affiliates of Japanese companies listed on non-Japanese exchanges and issuers not organized under the laws of Japan but deriving 50% or more of their revenues from Japan. May use currency transactions, futures and options to hedge.
Year organized: 1961 (formerly a closed-end fund, open-ended 8/14/87)
Ticker symbol: SJPNX
Minimum purchase: Initial: $1,000, Subsequent: $100; IRA/Keogh: $500, Subsequent: $50
Telephone orders accepted: Yes, subsequent only, $2,500 minimum
Wire orders accepted: Yes
Deadline for same day wire purchase: 4 P.M.
Discount broker availability: Schwab, White, Waterhouse, Fidelity, Siebert
Qualified for sale in: All states
Telephone redemptions: Yes
Wire redemptions: Yes, $5 fee
Letter redemptions: Signature guarantee required over $50,000
Telephone switching: With all Scudder funds
Number of switches permitted: 4 round trips per year
Dividends paid: Income - December; Capital gains - December
Portfolio turnover (3 yrs): 82%, 47%, 46%
Largest holding: Nichiei Co., Ltd. (4.9%)
Shareholder services: Keogh, IRA, SEP-IRA, 401(k), 403(b), corporate retirement plans, automatic investment plan—minimum $50/month, withdrawal plan min. req. $10,000, electronic funds transfer
Management fee: 0.85% first $200M to 0.65% over $600M
Expense ratio: 1.25% (year ending 12/31/93)
IRA fees: None
Keogh fees: Annual $10, Initial $10

THE JENSEN PORTFOLIO ◆
430 Pioneer Tower
888 S.W. Fifth Avenue
Portland, OR 97204
503-274-2044, 800-221-4384

Adviser: Jensen Investment Management, Inc.
Portfolio manager: Val E. Jensen (1992)
Custodian and transfer agent: Firstar Trust Co.
Investment objective and policies: Long-term capital appreciation with income secondary. Invests in common stocks of 20 to 30 companies selected by the adviser based on criteria that evaluate a company's current financial strength and potential for increasing long-term returns. May invest in securities of foreign issuers. Fund is non-diversified.
Year organized: 1992
Minimum purchase: Initial: $10,000, Subsequent: None
Telephone orders accepted: No
Wire orders accepted: Yes
Deadline for same day wire purchase: 4 P.M.
Discount broker availability: Schwab
Qualified for sale in: CA, ID, OR, WA
Letter redemptions: Signature guarantee required over $10,000
Dividends paid: Income - March, June, September, December; Capital gains - December
Portfolio turnover (2 yrs): 5%, 4%
Largest holding: Equifax, Inc. (7.5%)
Shareholder services: IRA, 403(b)
Management fee: 0.5%
Expense ratio: 1.13% (year ending 5/31/94) (1.72% without waiver)
IRA fees: Annual $12.50

KAUFMANN FUND
140 East 45th Street, 43rd Floor
New York, NY 10017
610-834-3675, 610-834-3500
prices 212-661-4699

Adviser: Edgemont Asset Management Corp.
Portfolio managers: Hans P. Utsch (1986), Lawrence Auriana (1986)
Custodian: Citibank, N.A.
Transfer agent: Fund/Plan Services, Inc.
Investment objective and policies: Long-term capital appreciation. Invests primarily in common stocks of smaller companies with annual sales under $500M and, to a lesser extent, convertible preferred stocks and convertible bonds. Fund may sell short up to 25% of total assets, leverage up to 1/3 of assets, have up to 10% in restricted securities, 25% in foreign securities, 10% in other mutual funds, and write, purchase and/or sell puts and covered calls with aggregate premiums up to 10% of assets.
Year organized: 1967
Ticker symbol: KAUFX
Minimum purchase: Initial: $1,500, Subsequent: $100; IRA: Initial: $500, Subsequent: $50
Telephone orders accepted: Yes, subsequent only, $1,000 minimum, $10,000 maximum
Wire orders accepted: Yes, $1,000 subsequent minimum, $9 fee
Deadline for same day wire purchase: 4 P.M.
Discount broker availability: *Schwab, *White, *Waterhouse, *Fidelity, *Siebert
Qualified for sale in: All states
Telephone redemptions: Yes
Letter redemptions: Signature guarantee required
Redemption fee: 0.2% on shares purchased after 2/1/85
Telephone switching: With Reserve Fund, $1,000 minimum
Number of switches permitted: Unlimited
Dividends paid: Income - November; Capital gains - November
Portfolio turnover (3 yrs): 55%, 51%, 128%
Largest holding: Microchip Technology, Inc. (3.3%)
Shareholder services: IRA, automatic investment plan, withdrawal plan min. req. $5,000
Management fee: 1.5%
12b-1 distribution fee: Maximum of 0.75%
Expense ratio: 2.53% (year ending 12/31/93)
IRA fees: Annual $10

KEMPER MONEY MARKET FUND - MONEY MARKET PORTFOLIO ◆
120 S. LaSalle Street
Chicago, IL 60603
312-781-1121, 800-537-6001
yields 800-972-3060, TDD 800-972-3006

Adviser: Kemper Financial Services, Inc.
Portfolio manager: Frank J. Rachwalski (1974)
Custodian and transfer agent: Investors Fiduciary Trust Co.
Investment objective and policies: Maximum current income consistent with stability of principal. Invests primarily in short-term commercial paper and bank obligations.
Year organized: 1974
Ticker symbol: KMMXX
Minimum purchase: Initial: $1,000, Subsequent: $100; IRA/Keogh: Initial: $250, Subsequent: $50
Wire orders accepted: Yes
Deadline for same day wire purchase: 2 P.M.
Qualified for sale in: All states
Wire redemptions: Yes, $1,000 minimum
Letter redemptions: Signature guarantee required over $25,000
Telephone switching: With Kemper Funds
Check redemptions: $500 minimum
Confirmations mailed: After each purchase and each mail or wire redemption
Checks returned: Monthly
Periodic account statements mailed: Monthly
Dividends paid: Income - declared daily, paid monthly

Shareholder services: Keogh, IRA, 401(k), 403(b), withdrawal plan min. req. $5,000, electronic funds transfer
Management fee: 0.5% first $215M to 0.25% over $800M
Expense ratio: 0.52% (year ending 7/31/94)
IRA/Keogh fees: Annual $12

KIDDER PEABODY MONEY FUNDS
(Data common to all Kidder Peabody money funds are shown below. See subsequent listings for data specific to individual Kidder Peabody money funds.)

60 Broad Street
New York, NY 10004-2350
212-656-1737, Premium account customers only 800-543-3377

Adviser: Kidder Peabody Asset Management, Inc.
Custodian and transfer agent: Investors Fiduciary Trust Co.
Special sales restrictions: Kidder, Peabody customers only
Wire orders accepted: Yes
Deadline for same day wire purchase: 12 NN
Qualified for sale in: All states (CA for California Tax Exempt Money Fund)
Wire redemptions: Yes
Letter redemptions: Signature guarantee required
Telephone switching: With other Kidder funds, most of which have loads
Number of switches permitted: Unlimited
Deadline for same day switch: 12 NN
Dividends paid: Income - declared daily, paid monthly
Shareholder services: Keogh, IRA, automatic investment plan, fund may be used as part of a central assets account
IRA/Keogh fees: Annual $12
Periodic account statements mailed: Monthly

KIDDER PEABODY CALIFORNIA TAX EXEMPT MONEY FUND
(See first Kidder Peabody listing for data common to all Kidder Peabody funds)

Portfolio manager: David A. Hartman (1989)
Investment objective and policies: Current income exempt from federal and State of California income taxes, consistent with preservation of capital and liquidity. Invests in California municipal money market obligations.
Year organized: 1988
Ticker symbol: KPCXX
Minimum purchase: Initial: $1,000, Subsequent: None
Management fee: 0.5%
12b-1 distribution fee: 0.12%
Expense ratio: 0.70% (year ending 7/31/94)

KIDDER PEABODY CASH RESERVE FUND
(See first Kidder Peabody listing for data common to all Kidder Peabody funds)

Portfolio manager: O. Beirne Chisolm (1979)
Investment objective and policies: Current income consistent with preservation of capital and liquidity. Invests in short-term money market instruments.
Year organized: 1979 (name changed from Webster Cash Reserve in 1991)
Ticker symbol: WCRXX
Minimum purchase: Initial: $1,000, Subsequent: None; IRA/Keogh: Initial: $250, Subsequent: None
Management fee: 0.5%
12b-1 distribution fee: 0.12%
Expense ratio: 0.69% (year ending 7/31/93)

KIDDER PEABODY GOVERNMENT MONEY FUND
(See first Kidder Peabody listing for data common to all Kidder Peabody funds)

Portfolio manager: David A. Hartman
Investment objective and policies: Current income consistent with preservation of capital and liquidity. Invests in short-term money market instruments issued or guaranteed by the U.S. Government, its agencies or instrumentalities, and repurchase agreements.
Year organized: 1983
Ticker symbol: KPGXX
Minimum purchase: Initial: $1,000, Subsequent: None; IRA/Keogh: Initial: $500, Subsequent: None
Management fee: 0.5%
12b-1 distribution fee: 0.12%
Expense ratio: 0.71% (year ending 3/31/94)

KIDDER PEABODY PREMIUM ACCOUNT FUND
(See first Kidder Peabody listing for data common to all Kidder Peabody funds)

Portfolio manager: O. Beirne Chisolm (1982)
Investment objective and policies: Current income consistent with preservation of capital and liquidity. Invests in short-term money market instruments.
Year organized: 1982
Minimum purchase: None (fund is part of Kidder Peabody Premium Account asset management system. Clients must have $25,000 in cash and/or securities in system to open account)
Management fee: 0.5%
12b-1 distribution fee: 0.12%
Expense ratio: 0.69% (year ending 3/31/94)

KIDDER PEABODY TAX EXEMPT MONEY FUND
(See first Kidder Peabody listing for data common to all Kidder Peabody funds)

Portfolio manager: David A. Hartman (1983)
Investment objective and policies: Current income exempt from federal income taxes, consistent with preservation of capital and liquidity. Invests in municipal money market instruments.
Year organized: 1983
Ticker symbol: KPTXX
Minimum purchase: Initial: $1,500, Subsequent: None
Management fee: 0.5%
12b-1 distribution fee: 0.12%
Expense ratio: 0.69% (year ending 9/30/94)

KPM EQUITY PORTFOLIO
10250 Regency Circle
Omaha, NE 68114
402-392-7976, 800-776-5782
fax 402-392-8370

Adviser: KPM Investment Management, Inc.
Portfolio managers: Rodney D. Cerny (1994), Thomas J. Sudyka, Jr. (1994)
Custodian: First National Bank of Omaha
Transfer agent: Smith Hayes Portfolio Management, Inc.
Investment objective and policies: Capital appreciation. Invests primarily in common stocks and securities convertible into common stock. Concentrates on large ($1B+ capitalization) companies currently out of favor and smaller ($100M to $1B) companies not well received or followed by the financial research community. Up to 20% of assets may be in securities of foreign issuers. May use options to hedge.
Year organized: 1994
Minimum purchase: Initial: $25,000, Subsequent: None; IRA/Keogh: Initial: $2,000

Telephone orders accepted: No
Wire orders accepted: Yes
Deadline for same day wire purchase: 4 P.M.
Qualified for sale in: CO, IA, NE
Letter redemptions: Signature guarantee required
Telephone switching: With KPM Fixed Income Portfolio
Number of switches permitted: Unlimited
Dividends paid: Income - March, June, September, December; Capital gains - December
Shareholder services: None
Management fee: 0.8%
12b-1 distribution fee: 0.25%

KPM FIXED INCOME PORTFOLIO
10250 Regency Circle
Omaha, NE 68114
402-392-7976, 800-776-5782
fax 402-392-8370

Adviser: KPM Investment Management, Inc.
Portfolio manager: Patrick M. Miner (1994)
Custodian: First National Bank of Omaha
Transfer agent: Smith Hayes Portfolio Management, Inc.
Investment objective and policies: Current income with capital appreciation secondary. Invests only in investment-grade fixed-income securities with a weighted average maturity of 7 to 15 years. Up to 20% of assets may be in securities of foreign issuers.
Year organized: 1994
Minimum purchase: Initial: $25,000, Subsequent: None; IRA/Keogh: Initial: $2,000
Telephone orders accepted: No
Wire orders accepted: Yes
Deadline for same day wire purchase: 4 P.M.
Qualified for sale in: CO, IA, NE
Letter redemptions: Signature guarantee required
Telephone switching: With KPM Equity Portfolio
Number of switches permitted: Unlimited
Dividends paid: Income - March, June, September, December; Capital gains - December
Shareholder services: None
Management fee: 0.6%
12b-1 distribution fee: 0.25%

THE LAUREL FUNDS
(See Dreyfus/Laurel funds)

LEAHI TAX-FREE INCOME TRUST
Ward Plaza
210 Ward Avenue - Suite 129
Honolulu, HI 96814
808-522-7777

Adviser: Leahi Management Company, Inc.
Portfolio manager: Dianne J. Qualtrough (1987)
Custodian: First National Bank of Boston
Transfer agent: Fund/Plan Services, Inc.
Investment objective and policies: Maximum income exempt from federal and state of Hawaii personal income taxes. Invests primarily in investment-grade municipal securities of issuers in Hawaii, Guam, Puerto Rico and the Virgin Islands. Up to 20% of assets may be in AMT securities.
Year Organized: 1987
Minimum purchase: Initial: $1,000, Subsequent: $50
Telephone orders accepted: No
Wire orders accepted: No
Discount broker availability: Schwab
Qualified for sale in: HI
Telephone redemptions: Yes
Wire redemptions: Yes, $1,000 minimum
Letter redemptions: Signature guarantee required
Dividends paid: Income - declared daily, paid monthly; Capital gains - December
Shareholder services: Withdrawal plan min. req. $10,000
Portfolio turnover (3 yrs): 22%, 13%, 8%
Management fee: 0.5%
12b-1 distribution fee: Maximum of 0.25%
Expense ratio: 0.85% (year ending 9/30/94)

LEEB PERSONAL FINANCE FUND ◆
1101 King Street, Suite 400
Alexandria, VA 22314
703-548-2400, 800-224-5332
800-545-0103, prices 800-852-4052
fax 703-683-6974

Adviser: Leeb Investment Advisors
Portfolio manager: Stephen Leeb (1991)
Custodian: Fifth Third Bank of Cincinnati
Transfer agent: MGF Service Corp.
Investment objective and policies: Long-term capital appreciation with income secondary. Invests primarily in common stocks of established larger companies with market capitalizations of $300M or more believed undervalued. May move entirely into debt securities and/or money market instruments depending on market conditions.
Year Organized: 1991
Ticker symbol: LBPFX
Minimum purchase: Initial: $2,500, Subsequent: None; IRA/Keogh: Initial: $250
Telephone orders accepted: No
Wire orders accepted: Yes, $8 fee
Deadline for same day wire purchase: 4 P.M.
Discount broker availability: *White
Qualified for sale in: All states
Telephone redemptions: Yes
Wire redemptions: Yes, $8 fee
Letter redemptions: Signature guarantee required over $5,000
Dividends paid: Income - June, December; Capital gains - June, December
Shareholder services: Keogh, IRA, 401(k), 403(b), corporate retirement plans, automatic investment plan, withdrawal plan min. req. $5,000
Portfolio turnover (3 yrs): 143%, 83%, 75%
Largest holding: Salomon, Inc. (6.2%)
Management fee: 1.0%
Expense ratio: 1.50% (year ending 6/30/94) (1.81% without waiver)
IRA/Keogh fees: Annual $10

LEGG MASON FUNDS
(Data common to all Legg Mason funds are shown below. See subsequent listings for data specific to individual Legg Mason funds.)

111 So. Calvert Street
P.O. Box 1476
Baltimore, MD 21203
410-539-0000, 800-822-5544

Shareholder service hours: Full service: M-F 8 A.M.-8 P.M. EST; After hours service: prices, yields, DJIA
Custodian: State Street Bank & Trust Co.
Transfer agent: Boston Financial Data Services
Minimum purchase: Initial: $1,000, Subsequent: $100; IRA/Keogh: Initial: $250
Telephone orders: Yes
Wire orders accepted: Money market funds only
Deadline for same day wire purchase: 12 NN
Telephone redemptions: Yes
Wire redemptions: Money market funds only, $18 fee
Letter redemptions: Signature guarantee not required
Telephone switching: With other Legg Mason funds
Number of switches permitted: 4 per year
Shareholders services: Keogh, IRA, SEP-IRA, 401(k), corporate retirement plans, automatic investment plan, directed dividends, withdrawal plan min. req. $5,000, electronic funds transfer
IRA/Keogh fees: Annual $10, Closing $10

**LEGG MASON AMERICAN
LEADING COMPANIES TRUST**
(See first Legg Mason listing for data common to all Legg Mason funds)

Adviser: Legg Mason Fund Adviser, Inc.
Portfolio manager: J. Eric Leo (1993)
Investment objective and policies: Long-term capital appreciation and income consistent with prudent investment risk. Invests at least 75% of assets in dividend-paying common stocks of Leading

Companies with market capitalizations of at least $2B. Up to 25% of assets may be foreign securities and 25% in debt securities. Fund may sell covered call options to generate additional income.
Year organized: 1993
Ticker symbol: LMALX
Qualified for sale in: All states except AK, ID, SD
Dividends paid: Income - March, June, September, December; Capital gains - December
Portfolio turnover (1 yr): 21%
Largest holding: Emerson Electric Co. (3.0%)
Management fee: 0.75%
12b-1 distribution fee: 0.67%
Expense ratio: 1.95% (6 months ending 3/31/94) (2.28% without waiver)

**LEGG MASON
CASH RESERVE TRUST** ◆
(See first Legg Mason listing for data common to all Legg Mason funds)

Adviser: Western Asset Management Co.
Portfolio manager: Carl Eichstoedt (1994)
Investment objective and policies: Stability of principal and current income. Invests in high quality money market instruments.
Year organized: 1979
Ticker symbol: LMCXX
Qualified for sale in: All states
Check redemptions: $500 minimum
Confirmations mailed: Not mailed
Checks returned: Monthly
Periodic account statements mailed: Monthly
Dividends paid: Income: declared daily, paid monthly
Management fee: 0.5% first $500M to 0.4% over $2B
Expense ratio: 0.72% (year ending 8/31/94)

**LEGG MASON GLOBAL
GOVERNMENT TRUST**
(See first Legg Mason listing for data common to all Legg Mason funds)

Adviser: Legg Mason Fund Adviser, Inc.
Portfolio manager: Keith J. Gardner (1993)
Investment objective and policies: Total return - capital appreciation and current income - consistent with prudent investment risk. Invests at least 75% of assets in debt obligations issued or guaranteed by foreign governments, the U.S. Government, their agencies, instrumentalities and political subdivisions. Up to 25% of assets may be in junk bonds and 15% in illiquid securities. May use options, futures and forward contracts to hedge and increase income.
Year organized: 1993
Ticker symbol: LMGGX
Qualified for sale in: All states except AK, ID, SD
Dividends paid: Income - declared daily, paid monthly; Capital gains - December
Portfolio turnover (1 yr): 128%
Management fee: 0.75%
12b-1 distribution fee: 0.75%
Expense ratio: 0.27% (9 months ending 12/31/93) (includes waiver)

**LEGG MASON HIGH YIELD
PORTFOLIO**
(See first Legg Mason listing for data common to all Legg Mason funds)

Adviser: Western Asset Management Co.
Portfolio manager: Trudie D. Whitehead (1994)
Investment objective and policies: High current income with capital growth secondary. Invests primarily in high-yield lower-rated corporate debt securities, preferred stock, convertible securities and mortgage- and asset-backed securities. Up to 25% of assets may be in securities of foreign issuers and 15% in illiquid securities. May use futures and options to increase income and hedge.
Year organized: 1994
Ticker symbol: LMHYX
Qualified for sale in: All states except AK

Dividends paid: Income - declared daily, paid monthly; Capital gains - December
Management fee: 0.65%
12b-1 distribution fee: 0.5%

**LEGG MASON INVESTMENT GRADE
INCOME PORTFOLIO**
(See first Legg Mason listing for data common to all Legg Mason funds)

Adviser: Western Asset Management Co.
Portfolio manager: Kent S. Engel (1987)
Investment objective and policies: High current income. Invests primarily in investment-grade debt securities of domestic and foreign corporate and government issuers. Up to 50% of assets may be in mortgage-related securities and 25% in junk bonds. May use futures and options to increase income and hedge.
Year organized: 1987
Ticker symbol: LMIGX
Qualified for sale in: All states except AK
Dividends paid: Income - declared daily, paid monthly; Capital gains - December
Portfolio turnover (3 yrs): 348%, 317%, 213%
Management fee: 0.6%
12b-1 distribution fee: 0.5%
Expense ratio: 0.85% (year ending 12/31/93) (1.45% without waiver)

**LEGG MASON SPECIAL
INVESTMENT TRUST**
(See first Legg Mason listing for data common to all Legg Mason funds)

Adviser: Legg Mason Fund Adviser, Inc.
Portfolio manager: William H. Miller III (1985)
Investment objective and policies: Capital appreciation. Invests primarily in equity securities of companies with market capitalizations under $1B which are generally out of favor or undervalued on an earnings or asset basis; undergoing significant change; and in which actual/anticipated reorganizations or restructuring are taking place (limited to 20% of assets). Up to 35% of assets may be in junk bonds and 25% in foreign securities and use futures and options to enhance income and hedge.
Year organized: 1985
Ticker symbol: LMASX
Discount broker availability: White
Qualified for sale in: All states except AK, MO
Dividends paid: Income - July, December; Capital gains - July, December
Portfolio turnover (3 yrs): 17%, 33%, 57%
Largest holding: Caesar's World, Inc. (4.7%)
Management fee: 1.0% first $100M, 0.75% over $100M
12b-1 distribution fee: 0.97%
Expense ratio: 1.94% (year ending 3/31/94)

LEGG MASON TAX EXEMPT TRUST ◆
(See first Legg Mason listing for data common to all Legg Mason funds)

Adviser: Legg Mason Fund Adviser, Inc.
Portfolio manager: Victoria Schwatka (1988)
Investment objective and policies: High current income exempt from federal income taxes consistent with preservation of capital and liquidity. Invests in short-term, high-quality municipal money market instruments exempt from federal income tax.
Year organized: 1982
Ticker symbol: LGMXX
Qualified for sale in: All states except AK, ID, KS, MT, NE, OR, SD, UT, WI
Check redemptions: $250 minimum
Confirmations mailed: Not mailed
Checks returned: Monthly
Periodic account statements mailed: Monthly
Dividends paid: Income: declared daily, paid monthly
Management fee: 0.5%
12b-1 distribution fee: 0.2% (not currently imposed)
Expense ratio: 0.69% (year ending 12/31/93)

LEGG MASON TOTAL RETURN TRUST

(See first Legg Mason listing for data common to all Legg Mason funds)

Adviser: Legg Mason Fund Adviser, Inc.
Portfolio manager: William H. Miller III (1990)
Investment objective and policies: Capital appreciation and current income consistent with reasonable risk. Invests primarily in dividend-paying common stocks and securities convertible into common stock believed to have potential for long-term growth. Up to 50% of assets may be in intermediate- and long-term debt securities and 25% in foreign securities. Fund may use futures and options to enhance income and hedge.
Year organized: 1985
Ticker symbol: LMTRX
Discount broker availability: White
Qualified for sale in: All states except AK
Dividends paid: Income - March, June, September, December; Capital gains - December
Portfolio turnover (3 yrs): 41%, 38%, 62%
Largest holding: Grupo Financiero Serfin S.A. de C.V. ADR (3.7%)
Management fee: 0.75%
12b-1 distribution fee: 0.98%
Expense ratio: 1.94% (year ending 3/31/94)

LEGG MASON U.S. GOVERNMENT INTERMEDIATE-TERM PORTFOLIO

(See first Legg Mason listing for data common to all Legg Mason funds)

Adviser: Western Asset Management Co.
Portfolio manager: Carl L. Eichstaedt (1994)
Investment objective and policies: High current income consistent with prudent investment risk and liquidity. Invests at least 75% of assets in debt obligations issued or guaranteed by the U.S. Government, its agencies or instrumentalities with a weighted average maturity of 3 to 10 years. Up to 50% of assets may be in mortgage-backed securities and 25% in investment-grade corporate debt securities. May invest in dollar-denominated securities of foreign issuers and use futures and options to enhance income and hedge.
Year organized: 1987
Ticker symbol: LGINX
Qualified for sale in: All states except AK
Dividends paid: Income - declared daily, paid monthly; Capital gains - December
Portfolio turnover (3 yrs): 490%, 513%, 643%
Management fee: 0.55%
12b-1 distribution fee: 0.5%
Expense ratio: 0.90% (year ending 12/31/93) (1.17% without waiver)

LEGG MASON U.S. GOVERNMENT MONEY MARKET PORTFOLIO ◆

(See first Legg Mason listing for data common to all Legg Mason funds)

Adviser: Western Asset Management, Inc.
Portfolio manager: Carl L. Eichstaedt (1994)
Investment objective and policies: High current income consistent with liquidity and conservation of principal. Invests in money market debt obligations issued or guaranteed by the U.S. Government, its agencies or instrumentalities and in repurchase agreements secured by such instruments.
Year organized: 1989
Ticker symbol: LMGXX
Qualified for sale in: All states except AK
Check redemptions: $500 minimum
Confirmations mailed: Not mailed
Checks returned: Monthly
Periodic account statements mailed: Monthly
Dividends paid: Income: declared daily, paid monthly
Management fee: 0.5%
12b-1 distribution fee: 0.2% (not currently imposed)
Expense ratio: 0.71% (year ending 12/31/93)

LEGG MASON VALUE TRUST

(See first Legg Mason listing for data common to all Legg Mason funds)

Adviser: Legg Mason Adviser, Inc.
Portfolio manager: William L. Miller III (1982)
Investment objective and policies: Long-term growth of capital. Invests primarily in common stocks undervalued in relation to earnings power and/or asset value, with emphasis on companies with a record of earnings and dividends, reasonable return on equity and sound finances. Up to 25% of assets may be in foreign securities, 25% in long-term debt securities and 10% in junk bonds. Fund may use futures and options to enhance income and hedge.
Year organized: 1982 (split 2 for 1 on 8/6/91)
Ticker symbol: LMVTX
Discount broker availability: White
Qualified for sale in: All states except AK
Dividends paid: Income - May, July, October, December; Capital gains - May, December
Portfolio turnover (3 yrs): 26%, 22%, 39%
Largest holding: Federal National Mortgage Association (6.4%)
Management fee: 1.0% first $100M to 0.65% over $1B
12b-1 distribution fee: 0.92%
Expense ratio: 1.82% (year ending 3/31/94)

LEPERCQ-ISTEL TRUST - LEPERCQ-ISTEL FUND

1675 Broadway
New York, NY 10019
212-698-0749, 800-338-1579
fax 212-262-0155

Newspaper listing: Istel
Adviser: Lepercq, de Neuflize & Co. Inc.
Portfolio managers: Tsering Ngudu (1993), Andrew M. Hanson (1993)
Custodian: Investors Fiduciary Trust Co.
Transfer agent: Firstar Trust Co.
Investment objective and policies: Long-term growth of capital with income secondary. Invests primarily in equity securities of companies believed undervalued. Up to 25% of assets may be in junk bonds and 20% in securities of foreign issuers and use covered calls to hedge up to 25% of total assets.
Year organized: 1953 (formerly Istel Fund, name changed April 1986. Now a series fund)
Ticker symbol: ISTLX
Minimum purchase: Initial: $500, Subsequent: One share
Telephone orders accepted: No
Wire orders accepted: No
Qualified for sale in: All states
Letter redemptions: Signature guarantee required
Dividends paid: Income - July, December; Capital gains - December
Portfolio turnover (3 yrs): 20%, 20%, 22%
Largest holding: U.S. Treasury Bonds 9.875% due 11/15/15 (8.4%)
Shareholder services: Keogh, IRA, withdrawal plan min. req. $10,000
Management fee: 0.75%
12b-1 distribution fee: Maximum of 1.0%
Expense ratio: 1.51% (year ending 12/31/93)
IRA/Keogh fees: Annual $12.50

LEXICON FUNDS ◆

(See FFB Lexicon Funds)

LEXINGTON FUNDS

(Data common to all Lexington funds are shown below. See subsequent listings for data specific to individual Lexington funds.)

Park 80 West Plaza Two
Saddle Brook, NJ 07663
201-845-7300, 800-526-0056
prices/yields 800-526-0052
fax 201-845-3534

Shareholder service hours: Full service: M-F 9 A.M.-5 P.M. EST; After hours service: prices, yields, balances, orders, total returns, last transaction, prospectuses

Adviser: Lexington Management Corp.
Custodian and transfer agent: State Street Bank and Trust Co. (exceptions noted)
Minimum purchase: Initial: $1,000, Subsequent: $50; IRA/Keogh: Initial $250
Telephone orders accepted: No
Wire orders accepted: Yes
Deadline for same day wire purchase: 4 P.M.
Telephone redemptions: Yes (for money funds only)
Wire redemptions: Yes (for money funds only), $1,000 minimum, $5 fee
Letter redemptions: Signature guarantee required over $10,000
Telephone switching: With other Lexington funds, $500 subsequent minimum
Number of switches permitted: Unlimited, 7 day hold
Shareholder services: Keogh, IRA, SEP-IRA, 401(k), 403(b), corporate retirement plans, withdrawal plan min. req. $10,000, group sub-accounting, electronic funds transfer
IRA fees: Annual $12 (for all funds under single social security number)
Keogh fees: None

LEXINGTON CONVERTIBLE SECURITIES FUND

(See first Lexington listing for data common to all Lexington funds)

Sub-adviser: Ariston Capital Management Corp.
Portfolio manager: Richard Russell (1988)
Investment objective and policies: High total return - long-term capital growth and income. Invests primarily in convertible securities including those rated as low as B. May use options to increase income and hedge and sell short.
Year organized: 1988 (As Concord Income Trust a load fund. Current management since 5/15/92)
Ticker symbol: CNCVX
Discount broker availability: *Schwab, *White, *Waterhouse, *Fidelity, *Siebert
Qualified for sale in: All states except VT
Dividends paid: Income - March, June, September, December; Capital gains - December
Portfolio turnover (3 yrs): 38%, 7%, 13%,
Largest holding: Clayton Homes, Inc. (7.2%)
Management fee: 1.00%
12b-1 distribution fee: 0.25%
Expense ratio: 2.81% (year ending 12/31/94)

LEXINGTON CORPORATE LEADERS TRUST FUND ◆

(See first Lexington listing for data common to all Lexington funds)

Investment objective and policies: Long term capital growth and income. Invests in equal share amounts from a fixed list of blue chip corporations, currently 24, and therefore is not a managed portfolio.
Year organized: 1935 (as Corporate Leaders Trust Fund; name changed 10/31/88)
Ticker symbol: LEXCX
Discount broker availability: *Schwab, *White, *Waterhouse, *Fidelity, *Siebert
Qualified for sale in: All states
Dividends paid: Income - June, December; Capital gains - December
Largest holding: Mobil Corp. (9.3%)
Administration fee: 0.35%
Expense ratio: 0.62% (year ending 12/31/94)

LEXINGTON GLOBAL FUND ◆

(See first Lexington listing for data common to all Lexington funds)

Portfolio managers: Alan Wapnick (1994); Richard T. Saler (1994)
Custodian: Chase Manhattan Bank
Investment objective and policies: Capital appreciation. Invests at least 65% of assets in common stocks of companies in at least 3 countries from around the world - primarily Western Europe and the Pacific Basin - and the U.S. Fund may use for-

ward currency contracts to hedge and write covered calls.
Year organized: 1987
Ticker symbol: LXGLX
Discount broker availability: *Schwab, *White, *Waterhouse, *Fidelity, *Siebert
Qualified for sale in: All states
Dividends paid: Income - December; Capital gains - December
Portfolio turnover (3 yrs): 83%, 85%, 81%,
Largest holding: Telefonos de Mexico S.A. ADR (2.5%)
Management fee: 1.0%
Expense ratio: 1.61% (year ending 12/31/94)

LEXINGTON GNMA INCOME FUND ◆
(See first Lexington listing for data common to all Lexington funds)

Portfolio manager: Denis Jamison (1981)
Investment objective and policies: Current income consistent with liquidity and safety of principal. Invests at least 80% of assets in mortgage-backed, government guaranteed GNMA certificates.
Year organized: 1973 as Lexington Income Fund; present name and objective adopted 12/29/80
Ticker symbol: LEXNX
Discount broker availability: *Schwab, *White, *Waterhouse, *Fidelity, *Siebert
Qualified for sale in: All states
Dividends paid: Income - declared and paid monthly; Capital gains - December
Portfolio turnover (3 yrs): 37%, 52%, 180%,
Management fee: 0.6% first $150M to 0.4% over $800M
Expense ratio: 0.98% (year ending 12/31/94)

LEXINGTON GOLDFUND
(See first Lexington listing for data common to all Lexington funds)

Portfolio manager: Robert W. Radsch (1994)
Custodian: Wilmington Trust Co. (for gold bullion and gold coins)
Investment objective and policies: Capital appreciation and hedge against loss of buying power. Invests in gold and gold securities of companies engaged in mining or processing gold throughout the world. Securities of foreign issuers make up a substantial portion of the fund's assets. Up to 15% of assets may be in warrants.
Year organized: 1979 (formerly Goldfund)
Ticker symbol: LEXMX
Discount broker availability: *Schwab, *White, *Waterhouse, *Fidelity, *Siebert
Qualified for sale in: All states except WI
Dividends paid: Income - August, December; Capital gains - December
Portfolio turnover (3 yrs): 24%, 28%, 13%,
Largest holding: American Barrick Resources (5.5%)
Management fee: 1.00% first $50M, 0.75% over $50M
12b-1 distribution fee: 0.25%
Expense ratio: 1.54% (year ending 12/31/94)

LEXINGTON GOVERNMENT SECURITIES MONEY MARKET FUND ◆
(See Lexington Short-Intermediate Government Securities Fund, Inc.)

LEXINGTON GROWTH & INCOME FUND
(See first Lexington listing for data common to all Lexington funds)

Portfolio manager: Alan Wapnick (1994)
Investment objective and policies: Long term capital appreciation with income secondary. Invests in publicly traded common stocks and senior securities convertible into common stocks. Up to 20% of assets may be in securities of foreign issuers.
Year organized: 1939 (name changed from Lexington Research Fund in May 1991)
Ticker symbol: LEXRX
Discount broker availability: *Schwab, *White, *Waterhouse, *Fidelity, *Siebert

Qualified for sale in: All states
Dividends paid: Income - March, June, September, December; Capital gains - December
Portfolio turnover (3 yrs): 63%, 94%, 88%,
Largest holding: Ingersoll-Rand Company (2.3%)
Management fee: 0.75% first $100M to 0.4% over $250M
12b-1 distribution fee: 0.25%
Expense ratio: 1.15% (year ending 12/31/94)

LEXINGTON INTERNATIONAL FUND
(See first Lexington listing for data common to all Lexington funds)

Portfolio manager: Richard T. Saler (1994)
Custodian: Chase Manhattan Bank, N.A.
Investment objective and policies: Capital appreciation. Invests at least 65% of assets in common stocks of companies domiciled in foreign countries (primarily Western Europe and the Pacific Basin). At least 65% of assets will be invested in at least three countries, outside the U.S. Fund may use forward currency contracts to hedge and write covered calls.
Year organized: 1994
Ticker symbol: LEXIX
Discount broker availability: *Schwab, *White, *Waterhouse, *Fidelity, *Siebert
Qualified for sale in: All states except MO, VT, WI
Dividends paid: Income - December; Capital gains - December
Portfolio turnover: (1 yr.) 100%
Largest holding: Telefonos de Mexico S.A. ADR (3.3%)
Management fee: 1.0%
12b-1 distribution fee: 0.25%
Expense ratio: 2.39% (year ending 12/31/94)

LEXINGTON MONEY MARKET TRUST ◆
(See first Lexington listing for data common to all Lexington funds)

Portfolio manager: Denis P. Jamison (1981)
Investment objective and policies: High level of current income consistent with preservation of capital and liquidity. Invests in short term money market instruments.
Year organized: 1979
Ticker symbol: LMMXX
Qualified for sale in: All states
Check redemptions: $100 minimum
Confirmations mailed: After each purchase and each check, mail or wire redemption
Checks returned: Monthly
Periodic account statements mailed: Quarterly
Dividends paid: Income - declared daily, paid monthly
Management fee: 0.5% first $500M, 0.45% over $500M
Expense ratio: 1.00% (year ending 12/31/94)

LEXINGTON RAMIREZ GLOBAL INCOME FUND
(See first Lexington listing for data common to all Lexington funds)

Sub-adviser: MFR Advisors, Inc. (1995)
Portfolio managers: Denis P. Jamison (1986), Maria Fiorini Ramirez (1995)
Investment objective and policies: High current income with capital growth secondary. Invests primarily in lower rated and unrated debt securities ("junk bonds") issued by at least 3 countries, including the U.S. May invest in mature and emerging markets all over the world. May use forward foreign currency contracts, futures and options to increase return and hedge.
Year organized: 1986 (Formerly Lexington Tax-Exempt Bond Trust. Name and objectives changed on 1/3/95. Prior performance should be ignored.)
Discount broker availability: *Schwab, *White, *Waterhouse, *Fidelity, *Siebert
Qualified for sale in: All states
Dividends paid: Income - declared and paid monthly; Capital gains - December
Portfolio turnover (3 yrs): 31%, 31%, 29%

Management fee: 1.0%
12b-1 distribution fee: 0.25%
Expense ratio: 1.44% (year ending 12/31/93)

LEXINGTON SHORT-INTERMEDIATE GOVERNMENT SECURITIES FUND ◆
(See first Lexington listing for data common to all Lexington funds)

Portfolio manager: Denis P. Jamison (1981)
Investment objective and policies: High current income consistent with preservation of capital. Invests obligations of the U.S. Government and its agencies and instrumentalities with a weighted average maturity of 2 to 5 years.
Year organized: 1981 (formerly ASTA Government Securities Money Market Fund. Name and objective changed from Lexington Government Securities Money Market Fund in 1993)
Ticker symbol: LXSGX
Discount broker availability: *Schwab, *White, *Waterhouse, *Fidelity, *Siebert
Qualified for sale in: All states
Check redemptions: $100 minimum
Dividends paid: Income - declared daily, paid monthly; Capital gains - December
Portfolio turnover (1 yr): 76%
Management fee: 0.5% first $150M to 0.4% over $500M
Expense ratio: 1.00% (year ending 12/31/94) (2.35% without waiver)

LEXINGTON TAX EXEMPT BOND TRUST ◆
(See Lexington Ramirez Global Income Fund)

LEXINGTON TAX FREE MONEY FUND ◆
(See first Lexington listing for data common to all Lexington funds)

Portfolio manager: Denis P. Jamison (1981)
Investment objective and policies: Current income exempt from federal taxes, stability of principal, liquidity, and preservation of capital. Invests in high grade short-term municipal money market securities.
Year organized: 1977 (formerly Lexington Tax Free Daily Income Fund)
Ticker symbol: LTFXX
Qualified for sale in: All states
Check redemptions: $100 minimum
Confirmations mailed: After each purchase and each check, mail or wire redemption
Checks returned: Monthly
Periodic account statements mailed: Quarterly
Dividends paid: Income - declared daily, paid monthly
Management fee: 0.5% first $150M to 0.3% over $800M
Expense ratio: 1.00% (year ending 12/31/94)

LEXINGTON WORLDWIDE EMERGING MARKETS FUND ◆
(See first Lexington listing for data common to all Lexington funds)

Portfolio manager: Richard T. Saler (1941)
Investment objective and policies: Long-term growth of capital. Invests at least 65% of assets in equity securities of companies domiciled in, or doing business in, emerging countries and emerging markets. May use futures and options and hedge.
Year organized: 1969 (formerly Lexington Growth Fund, name and objectives changed in July 1991. Prior performance data are not reflective of fund's current makeup)
Ticker symbol: LEXGX
Discount broker availability: *Schwab, *White, *Waterhouse, *Fidelity, *Siebert
Qualified for sale in: All states
Dividends paid: Income - December; Capital gains - December
Portfolio turnover (3 yrs): 80%, 38%, 91%,

Largest holding: Telefonos de Mexico S.A. ADR (3.2%)
Management fee: 1.0%
Expense ratio: 1.65% (year ending 12/31/94)

LINDNER FUNDS ◆

(Data common to all Lindner funds are shown below. See subsequent listings for data specific to individual Lindner funds.)

7711 Carondelet, Suite 700
P.O. Box 11208
St. Louis, MO 63105
314-727-5305, 800-995-7777 (for shareholders)
fax 314-727-9306

Shareholder service hours: Full service: M-F 8 A.M.-5 P.M. CST; After hours service: prices, DJIA, prospectuses
Adviser: Ryback Management Corp.
Custodians: Chase Manhattan Bank NA and Magna Trust Co.
Transfer agent: Ryback Management Corporation
Telephone orders accepted: Yes, subsequent only
Wire orders accepted: Yes, subsequent only
Deadline for same day wire purchase: 4 P.M.
Telephone redemptions: Yes
Wire redemptions: Yes, $10 fee
Letter redemptions: Signature guarantee not required
Redemption fee: 2% for shares held less than 60 days, payable to the fund
Shareholder services: IRA, withdrawal plan min. req. $15,000
IRA fees: Annual $10

LINDNER BULWARK FUND ◆

(See first Lindner listing for data common to all Lindner funds)

Portfolio managers: Eric E. Ryback (1994), Lawrence G. Callahan (1994)
Investment objective and policies: Capital appreciation. Invests primarily in common stocks of domestic and foreign companies believed undervalued and selected with emphasis on capital preservation through periods of economic stress, including those engaged in the production of precious metals and other natural resources. Fund may purchase precious metals, use futures and options, and sell short. Up to 35% of assets may be in securities of foreign issuers, 35% in junk bonds and 15% in illiquid securities.
Year organized: 1994
Ticker symbol: LDNBX
Minimum purchase: Initial: $3,000, Subsequent: $100; IRA: Initial $250
Discount broker availability: Schwab, Waterhouse
Qualified for sale in: All states except AR, NE, OH
Dividends paid: Income - August, December; Capital gains - August, December
Portfolio turnover (1 yr): 1%
Largest holding: Gold Bullion (11.4%)
Management fee: 1.0%
Expense ratio: 0.66% (5 months ending 6/30/94)

LINDNER DIVIDEND FUND ◆

(See first Lindner listing for data common to all Lindner funds)

Portfolio manager: Eric E. Ryback (1982)
Investment objective and policies: Current income with capital appreciation secondary. Invests primarily in common stocks yielding substantial dividend income, preferred stocks and, to a lesser extent, corporate bonds and government debt securities. May invest up to 40% of assets in utility securities, 35% in junk bonds and 25% in real estate investment trusts (REITs).
Year organized: 1976 (Formerly Lindner Fund for Income)
Ticker symbol: LDDVX
Minimum purchase: Initial: $2,000, Subsequent: $100; IRA: Initial $250
Qualified for sale in: All states except NE

Discount broker availability: Schwab, White, Waterhouse
Dividends paid: Income - April, June, September, December; Capital gains - April, December
Portfolio turnover (3 yrs): 43%, 14%, 24%
Largest holding: Glendale Federal Bank F.S.B. Series E 8.75% convertible (1.9%)
Management fee: 0.7% first $50M to 0.5% over $200M
Expense ratio: 0.64% (year ending 2/28/94)

LINDNER FUND ◆

(See first Lindner listing for data common to all Lindner funds)

Portfolio managers: Robert A. Lange (1977), Eric E. Ryback (1984)
Investment objective and policies: Long-term capital appreciation with income secondary. Invests in common stocks and convertible securities. May invest in debt securities for defensive purposes. May invest up to 25% of assets in securities of foreign issuers, 25% in REITs, 15% in illiquid securities and 10% in junk bonds. Fund may leverage.
Year organized: 1973
Ticker symbol: LDNRX
Minimum purchase: Initial: $2,000, Subsequent: $100; IRA: Initial $250
Qualified for sale in: All states except NE
Discount broker availability: Schwab, White, Waterhouse
Dividends paid: Income - August, December; Capital gains - August, December
Portfolio turnover (3 yrs): 38%, 19%, 11%
Largest holding: Minorco - ADR (2.2%)
Management fee: 0.7% first $50M to 0.5% over $400M, subject to incentive adjustment depending on the fund's performance relative to the S&P 500
Expense ratio: 0.65% (year ending 6/30/94)

LINDNER INTERNATIONAL FUND ◆

(See first Lindner listing for data common to all Lindner funds)

Portfolio managers: Eric E. Ryback (1995), Robert A. Lange (1995)
Investment objective and policies: Capital appreciation with current income secondary. Invests primarily in common stocks and securities convertible into common stock of financially strong foreign companies in at least 3 countries. Fund may purchase precious metals, use futures and options, and sell short. Up to 25% of assets may be in restricted securities, 15% in REITs and 15% in illiquid securities.
Year organized: 1995
Minimum purchase: Initial: $3,000, Subsequent: $100; IRA: Initial $250
Qualified for sale in: N.A.
Dividends paid: Income - August, December; Capital gains - August, December
Management fee: 1.0%

LINDNER/RYBACK SMALL-CAP FUND ◆

(See first Lindner listing for data common to all Lindner funds)

Portfolio manager: Eric E. Ryback (1994)
Investment objective and policies: Capital appreciation with current income secondary. Invests primarily in common stocks or securities convertible into common stock of companies with market capitalizations under $750M. Fund may purchase precious metals, use futures and options, and sell short. Up to 25% of assets may be in securities of foreign issuers, 20% in junk bonds and 15% in REITs.
Year organized: 1994
Minimum purchase: Initial: $3,000, Subsequent: $100; IRA: Initial $250
Discount broker availability: Schwab
Qualified for sale in: All states except NE, OH
Dividends paid: Income - August, December; Capital gains - August, December
Portfolio turnover (1 yr): 5%

Largest holding: Mobile Telecommunications Technologies Corp. (2.4%)
Management fee: 0.7% first $50M to 0.5% over $200M
Expense ratio: 0.96% (5 months ending 6/30/94)

LINDNER UTILITY FUND ◆

(See first Lindner listing for data common to all Lindner funds)

Portfolio manager: Eric E. Ryback (1993)
Investment objective and policies: Current income with capital appreciation secondary. Invests primarily in common stocks of domestic and foreign public utilities (gas, electric, telecommunications, cable TV, water, energy, etc.), securities convertible into common stock issued by utilities and other preferred stocks or bonds issued by utilities. May invest up to 35% of assets in securities of foreign issuers and 35% in junk bonds.
Year organized: 1993
Ticker symbol: LDUTX
Minimum purchase: Initial: $3,000, Subsequent: $100; IRA: Initial $250
Discount broker availability: Schwab, Waterhouse
Qualified for sale in: All states except NE
Dividends paid: Income - April, June, September, December; Capital gains - April, December
Portfolio turnover (1 yr): 45%
Largest holding: Companhia Energetica De Minas Gerais - ADR (5.2%)
Management fee: 0.7% first $50M to 0.5% over $200M
Expense ratio: 1.30% (9 months ending 6/30/94)

LIQUID CAPITAL INCOME TRUST ◆

1228 Euclid Avenue - Suite 1100
Cleveland, OH 44115
216-781-4440, 800-321-2322
yields 800-321-2321

Adviser: Carnegie Capital Management Co.
Portfolio manager: Roy L. Wallace (1974)
Custodian: Boston Safe Deposit & Trust Co.
Transfer agent: The Shareholder Services Group, Inc.
Investment objective and policies: High current income consistent with preservation of capital and liquidity. Invests in U.S. Government, investment-grade corporate and other money market debt instruments.
Year organized: 1974
Ticker symbol: LCIXX
Minimum purchase: Initial: $1,000, Subsequent: $250; IRA/Keogh: Initial: $250, Subsequent: $50
Wire orders accepted: Yes
Deadline for same day wire purchase: 12 NN
Qualified for sale in: All states
Wire redemption: Yes
Letter redemptions: Signature guarantee required over $1,000
Telephone switching: With other Carnegie funds which have loads
Number of switches permitted: 4 per year
Check redemptions: $100 minimum
Confirmations mailed: After each check, mail or wire redemption
Checks returned: Monthly
Periodic account statements mailed: Monthly
Dividends paid: Income - declared and paid daily
Shareholder services: IRA, SEP-IRA, Keogh, corporate retirement plans, automatic investment plan, withdrawal plan, minimum $10,000
Management fee: 0.5% first $700M to 0.35% over $2B
Expense ratio: 0.88% (year ending 7/31/94)
IRA/Keogh fees: Annual $2.50, Initial $5

LKCM SMALL CAP EQUITY PORTFOLIO ◆

301 Commerce Street, Suite 1600
Fort Worth, TX 76102
817-332-3235

Adviser: Luther King Capital Management Corp.
Portfolio manager: Luther King (1994)
Custodian: U.S. Trust Company of New York

Transfer agent: Mutual Funds Service Co.
Investment objective and policies: Maximum capital appreciation. Invests primarily in equity securities of smaller companies with market capitalizations under $1B. May invest in foreign securities and engage in foreign currency transactions. May use futures and options to hedge.
Year Organized: 1994
Minimum purchase: Initial: $10,000, Subsequent: $1,000
Telephone orders accepted: No
Wire orders accepted: Yes
Deadline for same day wire purchase: 4 P.M.
Qualified for sale in: AR, AZ, CA, CO, CT, DC, FL, HI, KS, KY, LA, MD, MA, MS, MO, NV, NM, NY, NC, OK, OR, PA, TN, TX, VA, WY
Telephone redemptions: Yes
Wire redemptions: Yes, $8 fee
Letter redemptions: Signature guarantee not required
Dividends paid: Income - December; Capital gains - December
Shareholder services: IRA, SEP-IRA
Management fee: 0.75%
IRA fees: Annual $10

LMH FUND, LTD. ◆
560 Hudson Street
Hackensack, NJ 07601
201-641-4960, 800-847-6002
fax 203-226-7268

Adviser: Heine Management Group, Inc.
Portfolio managers: Leonard M. Heine, Jr. (1983), N. Russell Wayne (1991)
Custodian and transfer agent: Firstar Trust Co.
Investment objective and policies: Total return - capital appreciation and current income. Invests primarily in common stocks selected through Benjamin Graham valuation analysis or high yields relative to the S&P 400—typically stocks deemed undervalued. May also invest in preferred stocks and convertible securities and have up to 10% of assets in foreign securities. May use options to hedge.
Year Organized: 1983
Ticker symbol: LMHFX
Minimum purchase: Initial: $1,000, Subsequent: $100; IRA/Keogh: Initial $500
Telephone orders accepted: No
Wire orders accepted: Yes
Deadline for same day wire purchase: 4 P.M.
Discount broker availability: Schwab, *White
Qualified for sale in: All states except TX
Letter redemptions: Signature guarantee required over $5,000
Telephone switching: With Portico Money Market Fund, $1,000 minimum
Number of switches permitted: 4 per year, $5 fee
Dividends paid: Income - December; Capital gains - December
Portfolio turnover (3 yrs): 46%, 53%, 76%
Largest holding: Southwestern Bell (3.3%)
Shareholder services: IRA, automatic investment plan ($500 initial minimum)
Management fee: 1.0%
Expense ratio: 2.50% (year ending 6/30/94) (2.51% without waiver)
IRA fees: Annual $10

LONGLEAF PARTNERS FUND ◆
P.O. Box 419733
Kansas City, MO 64141
800-445-9469, prices/yields 800-378-3788
fax 816-435-6754

Shareholder service hours: Full service: M-F 9 A.M.-6 P.M. EST; After hours service: prices, balances, last transaction, prospectuses (Mon-Sun 8 A.M.-8 P.M.), messages
Adviser: Southeastern Asset Management, Inc.
Portfolio manager: O. Mason Hawkins (1987), G. Staley Cates (1994)
Custodian: State Street Bank & Trust Co.
Transfer agent: National Financial Data Services
Investment objective and policies: Long-term capital growth. Invests primarily in common stocks of a limited number of companies (with market capitalizations greater than $500M) believed undervalued.

Up to 15% of assets may be in securities of foreign issuers and 15% in illiquid and restricted securities.
Year organized: 1987 (name changed from Southeastern Asset Management Value Trust in 1994)
Ticker symbol: LLPFX
Minimum purchase: Initial: $10,000, Subsequent: None
Telephone orders accepted: No
Wire orders accepted: Yes
Deadline for same day wire purchase: 4 P.M.
Discount broker availability: Schwab, White, Waterhouse, Fidelity, Siebert
Qualified for sale in: All states except WI
Telephone redemptions: Yes
Wire redemptions: Yes
Letter redemptions: Signature guarantee required over $25,000
Dividends paid: Income - December; Capital gains - December
Portfolio turnover (3 yrs): 27%, 19%, 29%
Largest holding: Knight-Ridder, Inc. (5.7%)
Shareholder services: IRA, SEP-IRA, automatic investment plan—minimum $100/month, electronic funds transfer
Management fee: 1.1% first $400M, 0.85% over $400M
Expense ratio: 1.17% (year ending 12/31/94)
IRA fees: Annual $10, Initial $5

LONGLEAF PARTNERS SMALL-CAP FUND ◆
P.O. Box 419733
Kansas City, MO 64141
800-445-9469, prices/yields 800-378-3788
fax 816-435-6754

Adviser: Southeastern Asset Management, Inc.
Portfolio manager: O. Mason Hawkins (1991), G. Staley Cates (1991)
Custodian: State Street Bank & Trust Co.
Transfer agent: National Financial Data Services
Investment objective and policies: Long-term capital growth. Invests primarily in common stocks of a limited number of companies (with market capitalizations less than $500M) believed undervalued. Up to 15% of assets may be in securities of foreign issuers and 15% in illiquid and restricted securities.
Year organized: 1988 (name changed from Southeastern Asset Management Small-Cap fund in 1994)
Ticker symbol: LLSCX
Minimum purchase: Initial: $10,000, Subsequent: None
Telephone orders accepted: No
Wire orders accepted: Yes
Deadline for same day wire purchase: 4 P.M.
Discount broker availability: Schwab, White, Fidelity, Siebert
Qualified for sale in: All states except WI
Telephone redemptions: Yes
Wire redemptions: Yes
Letter redemptions: Signature guarantee required over $25,000
Dividends paid: Income - December; Capital gains - December
Portfolio turnover (3 yrs): 20%, 14%, 26%
Largest holding: Helene Curtis Industries, Inc. (7.0%)
Shareholder services: IRA, SEP-IRA, automatic investment plan—minimum $100/month, electronic funds transfer
Management fee: 1.1% first $400M, 0.85% over $400M
Expense ratio: 1.38% (year ending 12/31/94)
IRA fees: Annual $10, Initial $5

LOOMIS SAYLES FUNDS ◆
(Data common to all Loomis Sayles funds are shown below. See subsequent listings for data specific to individual Loomis Sayles funds.)

One Financial Center - 34th Floor
Boston, MA 02111
617-482-2450, 800-633-3330
800-626-9390, fax 617-338-0761

Shareholder service hours: Full service: M-F 8 A.M.-6 P.M. EST; After hours service: prices, yields, news

and views, messages, prospectuses
Adviser: Loomis, Sayles & Company, L.P.
Custodian and transfer agent: State Street Bank & Trust Co.
Minimum purchase: Initial: $2,500, Subsequent: $50; IRA: Initial $250
Telephone orders accepted: No
Wire orders accepted: Yes
Deadline for same day wire purchase: 4 P.M.
Qualified for sale in: All states
Wire redemptions: Yes, $5 fee
Letter redemptions: Signature guarantee required over $10,000
Telephone switching: With other Loomis Sayles funds and New England Cash Management Money Market Series
Number of switches permitted: 4 per year
Shareholder services: IRA, automatic investment plan—minimum $50/month ($1,000 initial minimum), withdrawal plan min. req. $10,000
IRA fees: Annual $10 (maximum $30)

LOOMIS SAYLES BOND FUND ◆
(See first Loomis Sayles listing for data common to all Loomis Sayles funds)

Portfolio manager: Daniel J. Fuss (1991)
Investment objective and policies: High total return - current income and capital appreciation. Invests primarily in investment-grade debt securities, including securities convertible into common stocks. May invest up to 35% of assets in junk bonds, 20% in preferred stocks and 20% in securities of foreign issuers other than Canada.
Year organized: 1991
Ticker symbol: LSBDX
Discount broker availability: Schwab, *White, *Waterhouse
Dividends paid: Income - April, July, October, December; Capital gains - December
Portfolio turnover (3 yrs): 170%, 101%, 126%
Management fee: 0.6%
Expense ratio: 0.94% (year ending 12/31/93)

LOOMIS SAYLES GLOBAL BOND FUND ◆
(See first Loomis Sayles listing for data common to all Loomis Sayles funds)

Portfolio manager: E. John deBeer (1991)
Investment objective and policies: High total return - current income and capital appreciation. Invests primarily in investment-grade fixed-income obligations, including securities convertible into common stocks, denominated in various currencies including U.S. dollars or in multicurrency units. Normally invests at least 65% of assets in bonds of issuers of at least three countries with maximum of 40% in one country. 100% of assets may be denominated in U.S. dollars. May invest up to 20% of assets in junk bonds. Fund may hedge.
Year organized: 1991
Ticker symbol: LSGBX
Discount broker availability: Schwab, *White, *Waterhouse
Dividends paid: Income - April, July, October, December; Capital gains - December
Portfolio turnover (3 yrs): 150%, 72%, 137%
Management fee: 0.75%
Expense ratio: 1.50% (year ending 12/31/93) (1.51 without waiver)

LOOMIS SAYLES GROWTH FUND ◆
(See first Loomis Sayles listing for data common to all Loomis Sayles funds)

Portfolio manager: Jerome A. Castellini (1991)
Investment objective and policies: Long-term growth of capital. Invests primarily in common stocks chosen for their growth potential. May invest in companies with small market capitalizations as well as larger companies. May invest up to 20% of assets in securities of foreign issuers.
Year organized: 1991
Ticker symbol: LSGRX
Discount broker availability: Schwab, *White, *Waterhouse

Dividends paid: Income - December; Capital gains - December
Portfolio turnover (3 yrs): 64%, 98%, 69%
Largest holding: Anadarko Petroleum Corp. (4.5%)
Management fee: 0.75%
Expense ratio: 1.20% (year ending 12/31/93)

LOOMIS SAYLES GROWTH & INCOME FUND ◆
(See first Loomis Sayles listing for data common to all Loomis Sayles funds)

Portfolio manager: Jeffrey W. Wardlow (1991)
Investment objective and policies: Long-term growth of capital and income. Invests primarily in common stocks believed undervalued in relation to their earnings, dividends, asset and growth prospects. May invest up to 20% of assets in securities of foreign issuers.
Year organized: 1991
Ticker symbol: LSGIX
Discount broker availability: Schwab, *White, *Waterhouse
Dividends paid: Income - December; Capital gains - December
Portfolio turnover (3 yrs): 53%, 67%, 27%
Largest holding: GFC Financial Corp. (2.7%)
Management fee: 0.75%
Expense ratio: 1.50% (year ending 12/31/93) (1.56 without waiver)

LOOMIS SAYLES INTERNATIONAL EQUITY FUND ◆
(See first Loomis Sayles listing for data common to all Loomis Sayles funds)

Portfolio manager: Frank E. Jedlicka (1991)
Investment objective and policies: High total return - capital appreciation and current income. Invests primarily in equity securities of companies organized or headquartered outside the U.S. Normally invests at least 65% of assets in at least 3 countries outside the U.S. with maximum of 40% in any one country. Fund may hedge.
Year organized: 1991
Ticker symbol: LSIEX
Discount broker availability: Schwab, *White, *Waterhouse
Dividends paid: Income - December; Capital gains - December
Portfolio turnover (3 yrs): 128%, 101%, 109%
Largest holding: Tessenderio Chemie, Belgium (1.1%)
Management fee: 1.00%
Expense ratio: 1.50% (year ending 12/31/93) (1.72% without waiver)

LOOMIS SAYLES MUNICIPAL BOND FUND ◆
(See first Loomis Sayles listing for data common to all Loomis Sayles funds)

Portfolio manager: Martha F. Hodgman (1993)
Investment objective and policies: High current income exempt from federal income tax consistent with preservation of capital. Invests in investment-grade municipal securities with at least 80% of assets in issues rated A or better and at least 65% of assets in bonds.
Year organized: 1991
Discount broker availability: Schwab, *White, *Waterhouse
Dividends paid: Income - declared and paid monthly; Capital gains - December
Portfolio turnover (3 yrs): 36%, 32%, 26%
Management fee: 0.6%
Expense ratio: 1.00% (year ending 12/31/93) (3.22% without waiver)

LOOMIS SAYLES SHORT-TERM BOND FUND ◆
(See first Loomis Sayles listing for data common to all Loomis Sayles funds)

Portfolio manager: John Hyll (1992)
Investment objective and policies: High total return - current income and capital appreciation - with relatively low fluctuation in NAV. Invests primarily in investment-grade debt securities, including securities convertible into common stocks, with a weighted average maturity of 1 to 3 years. May invest up to 20% of assets in junk bonds, 20% in non-convertible preferred stocks and 20% in securities of foreign issuers.
Year organized: 1992
Discount broker availability: Schwab, *White, *Waterhouse
Dividends paid: Income - declared daily, paid monthly; Capital gains - December
Portfolio turnover (2 yrs): 81%, 31%
Management fee: 0.5%
Expense ratio: 1.00% (year ending 12/31/93) (1.55% without waiver)

LOOMIS SAYLES SMALL CAP FUND ◆
(See first Loomis Sayles listing for data common to all Loomis Sayles funds)

Portfolio managers: Jeffrey Petherick (value) (1993), Barbara C. Friedman (growth) (1991)
Investment objective and policies: Long-term growth of capital. Invests in both undervalued securities and securities of companies with significant growth potential. Normally invests at least 65% of assets in companies with market capitalizations of less than $500M. May invest up to 20% of assets in securities of foreign issuers.
Year organized: 1991
Ticker symbol: LSSCX
Discount broker availability: Schwab, *White, *Waterhouse
Dividends paid: Income - December; Capital gains - December
Portfolio turnover (3 yrs): 106%, 109%, 56%
Largest holding: Crossman Communities, Inc. (1.6%)
Management fee: 1.00%
Expense ratio: 1.35% (year ending 12/31/93)

LOOMIS SAYLES U.S. GOVERNMENT SECURITIES FUND ◆
(See first Loomis Sayles listing for data common to all Loomis Sayles funds)

Portfolio manager: Kent P. Newmark (1991)
Investment objective and policies: High total return - current income and capital appreciation. Invests in securities issued or guaranteed by the U.S. Government or its authorities, agencies or instrumentalities and in certificates representing undivided interests in the interest or principal of U.S. Treasury Securities. Invests at least 65% of assets in U.S. Government Securities.
Year organized: 1991
Discount broker availability: Schwab, *White, *Waterhouse
Dividends paid: Income - April, July, October, December; Capital gains - December
Portfolio turnover (3 yrs): 277%, 344%, 273%
Management fee: 0.6%
Expense ratio: 1.00% (year ending 12/31/93) (1.29% without waiver)

MAIRS & POWER GROWTH FUND ◆
W-2062 First National Bank Bldg.
332 Minnesota Street
St. Paul, MN 55101
612-222-8478, fax 612-222-8470

Adviser: Mairs and Power, Inc.
Portfolio manager: George A. Mairs, III (1980)
Custodian: Norwest Bank Minnesota, N.A.
Transfer agent: Mairs and Power, Inc.
Investment objective and policies: Long-term capital appreciation. Normally invests in common stocks, usually held for a period of at least one year. Remains fully invested at all times.

Year organized: 1958
Minimum purchase: Initial: $1,000, Subsequent: $100
Telephone orders accepted: No
Wire orders accepted: No
Qualified for sale in: CO, MN, NY, WI
Letter redemptions: Signature guarantee required
Dividends paid: Income - June, December; Capital gains - December
Portfolio turnover (3 yrs): 4%, 4%, 5%
Largest holding: Meditronic, Inc. (7.8%)
Shareholder services: Keogh, IRA, withdrawal plan min. req. $10,000
Management fee: 0.6%
Expense ratio: 0.98% (year ending 12/31/93)
IRA/Keogh fees: Annual $12, Initial $6, Closing $12

MAIRS & POWER INCOME FUND ◆
W-2062 First National Bank Bldg.
332 Minnesota Street
St. Paul, MN 55101
612-222-8478, fax 612-222-8470

Adviser: Mairs and Power, Inc.
Portfolio manager: William B. Frels (1992)
Custodian: Norwest Bank Minnesota, N.A.
Transfer agent: Mairs and Powers, Inc.
Investment objective and policies: Current income with the possibility of modest long-term capital appreciation. Invests in equity, fixed-income and convertible securities. Up to 20% of assets may be in junk bonds.
Year organized: 1961
Minimum purchase: Initial: $1,000, Subsequent: $100
Telephone orders accepted: No
Wire orders accepted: No
Qualified for sale in: CO, MN, NY, PA
Letter redemptions: Signature guarantee required
Dividends paid: Income - March, June, September, December; Capital gains - December
Portfolio turnover (3 yrs): 24%, 16%, 24%
Largest holding: Norwest Corp. (3.7%)
Shareholder services: Keogh, IRA, withdrawal plan min. req. $10,000
Management fee: 0.6%
Expense ratio: 1.06% (year ending 12/31/93)
IRA/Keogh fees: Annual $12, Initial $6, Closing $12

THE MANAGERS FUNDS ◆
(Data common to all Managers funds are shown below. See subsequent listings for data specific to individual Managers funds.)

40 Richards Avenue
Norwalk, CT 06854
203-857-5321, 800-835-3879
fax 203-857-5316

Adviser: The Managers Funds, L.P.
Custodian: State Street Bank & Trust Co.
Transfer agent: Boston Financial Data Services, Inc.
Special sales restrictions: Designed for institutional investors and individuals investing through professional financial advisers.
Minimum purchase: Initial: $10,000 (total among all funds), Subsequent: None
Telephone orders accepted: No
Wire orders accepted: Yes
Deadline for same day wire purchase: 4 P.M. (11 A.M. for Money Market Fund)
Qualified for sale in: All states (except Global Opportunity Fund)
Telephone redemptions: Yes
Wire redemptions: Yes
Letter redemptions: Signature guarantee not required
Telephone switching: With other Managers funds
Number of switches permitted: Unlimited
Shareholder services: IRA, automatic investment plan, withdrawal plan min. req. $25,000
IRA fees: Annual $10

THE MANAGERS BALANCED FUND ◆
(See first Managers listing for data common to all Managers funds)

Asset manager: Munder Capital Management, Inc.
Portfolio manager: Otto G. Hinzman, Jr. (1993)
Investment objective and policies: Long-term capital growth and income. Normally invests up to 75% of assets in equity securities - common stocks, securities convertible into common stock, rights and warrants. At least 25% of assets will be in fixed-income senior securities and up to 15% in illiquid securities. May use futures and options to hedge.
Year organized: 1987 (name and policies changed from Core Equity Fund in 1993. Prior performance may be misleading.)
Ticker symbol: MIEQX
Discount broker availability: White
Dividends paid: Income - March, June, September, December; Capital gains - December
Portfolio turnover (3 yrs): 199%, 69%, 132%
Largest holding: Federal Home Loan Mortgage Corp. 7.000% due 2/15/15 (2.9%)
Management fee: 0.60%
Expense ratio: 1.31% (year ending 12/31/93)

THE MANAGERS BOND FUND ◆
(See first Managers listing for data common to all Managers funds)

Asset manager: Loomis, Sayles & Company, Inc.
Portfolio manager: Fuss, Daniel C. (1984)
Investment objective and policies: Income. Invests in obligations of the U.S. Government and its agencies and instrumentalities and corporate bonds, debentures, non-convertible preferred stocks, mortgage-related securities, asset-backed securities, Eurodollar certificates of deposit and Eurodollar bonds. Up to 20% of assets may be in variable rate interest securities and 10% in non-U.S. dollar denominated instruments. May have up to 15% of assets in illiquid securities and use futures and options to hedge.
Year organized: 1984 (name changed from Fixed Income Securities Fund in 1993)
Dow Jones ticker symbol: MGFIX
Discount broker availability: Schwab (only through financial advisers), *White
Dividends paid: Income - monthly; Capital gains - December
Portfolio turnover (3 yrs): 373%, 292%, 182%
Management fee: 0.625%
Expense ratio: 1.15% (year ending 12/31/93)

THE MANAGERS CAPITAL APPRECIATION FUND ◆
(See first Managers listing for data common to all Managers funds)

Asset managers: Hudson Capital Advisers; Dietche & Field Advisers, Inc.
Investment objective and policies: Long-term capital appreciation with income secondary. Invests primarily in common stock, securities convertible into common stocks, and securities having common stock characteristics such as rights and warrants. May have up to 15% of assets in illiquid securities and use futures and options to hedge.
Year organized: 1984
Ticker symbol: MGCAX
Discount broker availability: Schwab (only through financial advisers), *White
Dividends paid: Income - March, June, September, December; Capital gains - December
Portfolio turnover (3 yrs): 131%, 175%, 259%
Largest holding: Motorola, Inc. (2.2%)
Management fee: 0.80%
Expense ratio: 1.18% (year ending 12/31/93)

THE MANAGERS GLOBAL BOND FUND ◆
(See first Managers listing for data common to all Managers funds)

Asset manager: Rogge Global Partners
Portfolio manager: Olaf Rogge (1994)
Investment objective and policies: High total return

- income and capital appreciation. Invests in investment-grade domestic and foreign fixed-income securities issued by governments, corporations and supra-national organizations. Fund normally maintains a weighted average maturity of 10 years or less. May have up to 15% of assets in illiquid securities and use currency exchange contracts, options and futures to hedge.
Year organized: 1994
Discount broker availability: Schwab (only through financial advisers), *White
Dividends paid: Income - monthly; Capital gains - December
Management fee: 0.70%

THE MANAGERS GLOBAL OPPORTUNITY FUND ◆
(See first Managers listing for data common to all Managers funds)

Asset manager: Resource Capital Advisers, Inc.
Portfolio manager: Larry E. Jeddeloh (1994)
Investment objective and policies: Long-term capital appreciation and income. Invests in equity, fixed-income and cash equivalent securities of domestic and foreign issuers. Will normally invest in at least 3 different countries, one of which may be the U.S. Fixed-income securities are investment-grade with weighted average maturity of 3 years or lees. May have up to 15% of assets in illiquid securities and use futures and options to hedge and may sell short.
Year organized: 1994
Ticker symbol: MGGOX
Discount broker availability: Schwab (only through financial advisers)
Qualified for sale in: All states except AL, AK, AR, MD, MA, MI, MT, NE, NV, NM, NY, RI, SC, TN, TX, VT, WA, WV
Dividends paid: Income - December; Capital gains - December
Largest holding: Clark Automotive Products Group (4.5%)
Management fee: 0.90%

THE MANAGERS INCOME EQUITY FUND ◆
(See first Managers listing for data common to all Managers funds)

Asset managers: Scudder, Stevens & Clark, Inc.; Spare, Tengler, Kaplan & Bischel
Investment objective and policies: High current income. Invests at least 65% of assets in income producing equity securities - common stocks and securities convertible into common stocks such as bonds and preferred stocks. May invest in fixed-income debt securities with maximum remaining maturities of 15 years or less. May have up to 15% of assets in illiquid securities and use futures and options to hedge.
Year organized: 1984
Ticker symbol: MGIEX
Discount broker availability: Schwab (only through financial advisers), *White
Dividends paid: Income - monthly; Capital gains - December
Portfolio turnover (3 yrs): 41%, 41%, 64%
Largest holding: Baxter International, Inc. (2.3%)
Management fee: 0.75%
Expense ratio: 1.32% (year ending 12/31/93)

THE MANAGERS INTERMEDIATE MORTGAGE SECURITIES FUND ◆
(See first Managers listing for data common to all Managers funds)

Asset manager: Jennison Associates Capital Corp.
Portfolio managers: Michael Porreca (1994), John Feingold (1994)
Investment objective and policies: High current income. Invests at least 65% of assets in mortgage-related securities issued by governments, government-related and private organizations and at least 25% in the mortgage and mortgage finance industry. Fund maintains a weighted average maturity of

3 to 10 years. May have up to 15% of assets in illiquid securities and use futures and options to hedge.
Year organized: 1986
Ticker symbol: MGIGX
Discount broker availability: Schwab (only through financial advisers), *White
Dividends paid: Income - monthly; Capital gains - December
Portfolio turnover (3 yrs): 253%, 278%, 172%
Management fee: 0.45%
Expense ratio: 0.75% (year ending 12/31/93) (0.82% without waiver)

THE MANAGERS INTERNATIONAL EQUITY FUND ◆
(See first Managers listing for data common to all Managers funds)

Asset manager: Scudder, Stevens & Clark, Inc.
Portfolio manager: William E. Holzer (1989)
Investment objective and policies: Long-term capital appreciation with income secondary. Invests primarily in equity securities of companies domiciled outside the U.S. May invest up to 35% of assets in equity and fixed-income debt securities of domestic companies when domestic returns are expected to be greater than those of non-U.S. equity securities. May have up to 15% of assets in illiquid securities and use futures and options to hedge.
Year organized: 1986
Ticker symbol: MGITX
Discount broker availability: Schwab (only through financial advisers), *White
Dividends paid: Income - December; Capital gains - December
Portfolio turnover (3 yrs): 46%, 51%, 158%
Largest holding: Samsung Electronics Ltd. ADR (2.5%)
Management fee: 0.90%
Expense ratio: 1.47% (year ending 12/31/93)

THE MANAGERS MONEY MARKET FUND ◆
(See first Managers listing for data common to all Managers funds)

Asset manager: Advisers Capital Management, Inc.
Portfolio manager: Patricia deBlank Klink (1985)
Investment objective and policies: High current income consistent with preservation of capital and liquidity. Invests in money market instruments.
Year organized: 1984
Dividends paid: Income - declared daily, paid monthly
Check redemptions: $500 minimum
Confirmations mailed: After each purchase and each check, mail or wire redemption
Checks returned: Monthly
Periodic account statements mailed: Quarterly
Management fee: 0.35%
Expense ratio: 0.74% (year ending 12/31/93) (0.99% without waiver)

THE MANAGERS MUNICIPAL BOND FUND ◆
(See first Managers listing for data common to all Managers funds)

Asset manager: Massachusetts Financial Services Company
Portfolio manager: Robert A. Dennis (1984)
Investment objective and policies: High income exempt from federal income taxes. Invests at least 80% of assets in investment-grade municipal securities with widely varying maturities. May invest up to 20% of assets in cash equivalents. May have up to 15% of assets may be in illiquid securities and use futures and options to hedge.
Year organized: 1984
Discount broker availability: *White
Dividends paid: Income - monthly; Capital gains - December
Portfolio turnover (3 yrs): 125%, 84%, 52%
Management fee: 0.54%
Expense ratio: 1.00% (year ending 12/31/93)

THE MANAGERS SHORT AND INTERMEDIATE BOND FUND ◆
(See first Managers listing for data common to all Managers funds)

Asset managers: TCW Funds Management, Inc.; Standish, Ayer & Wood, Inc.
Investment objective and policies: High current income. Invests in obligations of the U.S. Government and its agencies and instrumentalities and corporate bonds, debentures, non-convertible fixed-income preferred stocks, mortgage-related securities, Eurodollar certificates of deposit and Eurodollar bonds with a weighted average maturity of 1 to 5 years. Up to 20% of assets may be in variable rate interest securities, 15% in illiquid securities and 10% in non-U.S. dollar denominated instruments. May use futures and options to hedge.
Year organized: 1984 (name changed from Short and Intermediate Fixed Income Securities Fund in 1993)
Ticker symbol: MGSIX
Discount broker availability: Schwab (only through financial advisers), *White
Dividends paid: Income - monthly; Capital gains - December
Portfolio turnover (3 yrs): 126%, 117%, 536%
Management fee: 0.50%
Expense ratio: 0.94% (year ending 12/31/93)

THE MANAGERS SHORT GOVERNMENT INCOME FUND ◆
(See first Managers listing for data common to all Managers funds)

Asset manager: Jennison Associates Capital Corp.
Portfolio manager: Thomas P. Doyle (1994)
Investment objective and policies: High current income consistent with preservation of capital. Invests at least 65% of assets in obligations of the U.S. Government and its agencies and instrumentalities with remainder in domestic and Eurodollar corporate bonds, commercial paper, bankers' acceptances, certificates of deposit, time deposits and repurchase agreements with a weighted average maturity of less than three years. May have up to 15% of assets in illiquid securities and use futures and options to hedge.
Year organized: 1987
Ticker symbol: MGSGX
Discount broker availability: Schwab (only through financial advisers), *White
Dividends paid: Income - declared daily, paid monthly; Capital gains - December
Portfolio turnover (3 yrs): 189%, 168%, 84%
Management fee: 0.45%
Expense ratio: 0.87% (year ending 12/31/93) (0.96% without waiver)

THE MANAGERS SHORT MUNICIPAL FUND ◆
(See first Managers listing for data common to all Managers funds)

Asset manager: T. Rowe Price Associates, Inc.
Portfolio manager: William T. Reynolds (1984)
Investment objective and policies: High level of current income exempt from federal income taxes. Invests at least 80% of assets in municipal securities with remaining maturities of three years or less. May invest up to 20% of assets in cash equivalents. May have up to 15% of assets may be in illiquid securities and use futures and options to hedge.
Year organized: 1984
Discount broker availability: Schwab (only through financial advisers), *White
Dividends paid: Income - monthly; Capital gains - December
Portfolio turnover (3 yrs): 272%, 237%, 50%
Management fee: 0.50%
Expense ratio: 0.77% (year ending 12/31/93) (1.31% without waiver)

THE MANAGERS SPECIAL EQUITY FUND ◆
(See first Managers listing for data common to all Managers funds)

Asset managers: Eagle Asset Management; Pilgrim Baxter & Associates; Westport Asset Management, Inc.
Investment objective and policies: Capital appreciation. Invests primarily in equity securities of companies expected to have superior earnings growth potential, generally small (under $500M) to medium ($500M to $1B) sized market capitalization companies. May invest up to 35% of assets in equities of larger companies believed to have prospects for accelerated earnings growth. May have up to 15% of assets may be in illiquid securities and use futures and options to hedge.
Year organized: 1984
Ticker symbol: MGSEX
Discount broker availability: Schwab (only through financial advisers), *White
Dividends paid: Income - December; Capital gains - December
Portfolio turnover (3 yrs): 45%, 54%, 70%
Largest holding: Airborne Freight Corp. (2.5%)
Management fee: 0.90%
Expense ratio: 1.26% (year ending 12/31/93)

MARSHALL FUNDS ◆
(Data common to all Marshall funds are shown below. See subsequent listings for data specific to individual Marshall funds.)

1000 North Water Street
P.O. Box 1348
Milwaukee, WI 53201-9482
414-287-8500, 800-236-8560
fax 414-287-8511

Shareholder service hours: Full service: M-F 8 A.M. - 5 P.M. CST; After hours service: prices, DJIA
Adviser: M&I Investment Management Corp.
Administrator: Federated Administrative Services
Custodian: Marsall & Illsley Trust Co., Milwaukee
Transfer agent: Federated Services Co.
Minimum purchase: Initial: $1,000, Subsequent: $50
Telephone orders accepted: No
Wire orders accepted: Yes
Deadline for same day wire purchase: 4 P.M. (1 P.M. for money market funds)
Qualified for sale in: All states
Telephone redemptions: Yes
Wire redemptions: Yes, $1,000 minimum, $10 fee
Letter redemptions: Signature guarantee required over $50,000
Telephone switching: With other Marshall funds
Number of switches permitted: Unlimited
Shareholder services: Keogh, IRA, SEP-IRA, 401(k), 403(b), corporate retirement plans, automatic investment plan, electronic funds transfer, withdrawal plan min. req. $10,000
Administrative fee: 0.150% first $250M to 0.075% over $750M
IRA/Keogh fees: Annual $10 per fund, $30 maximum

MARSHALL BALANCED FUND ◆
(See first Marshall listing for data common to all Marshall funds)

Portfolio managers: Lawrence J. Pavelec (1993), Charles L. Melhouse (1993)
Investment objective and policies: Long-term capital growth and current income. Invests primarily in common and preferred stocks and high grade debt securities. Normal mix is 40-60% stocks and 40-60% debt securities. At least 25% of assets are in fixed-income senior securities. May invest up to 20% of assets in ADRs of foreign issuers.
Year organized: 1993
Ticker symbol: MRBLX
Dividends paid: Income - March, June, September, December; Capital gains - December
Portfolio turnover (1 yr): 138%

Largest holding: U.S. Treasury Note due 6/30/99 (3.3%)
Management fee: 0.75%
Expense ratio: 0.86% (11 months ending 8/31/94) (1.34% without waiver)

MARSHALL EQUITY INCOME FUND ◆
(See first Marshall listing for data common to all Marshall funds)

Portfolio manager: Bruce P. Hutson (1993)
Investment objective and policies: Above average dividend income with capital growth. Normally invests at least 65% of assets in dividend-paying common and preferred stocks. Fund seeks to maintain a dividend level at least 1% higher than the composite of the stocks comprising the S&P 500. May also invest in convertible securities and government and corporate debt securities. Up to 20% of assets may be in ADRs of foreign issuers.
Year organized: 1993
Ticker symbol: MREIX
Dividends paid: Income - March, June, September, December; Capital gains - December
Portfolio turnover (1 yr): 44%
Largest holding: General Electric Co. (4.7%)
Management fee: 0.75%
Expense ratio: 1.01% (11 months ending 8/31/94) (1.17% without waiver)

MARSHALL GOVERNMENT INCOME FUND ◆
(See first Marshall listing for data common to all Marshall funds)

Portfolio manager: Lawrence J. Pavelec (1993)
Investment objective and policies: Current income. Normally invests at least 65% of assets in U.S. Government securities guaranteed at to payment of principal and interest by the U.S. government, its agencies or its instrumentalities. May also invest in mortgage-backed securities and use financial futures contracts, and options on financial futures contracts and its portfolio securities. Up to 15% of assets may be in illiquid securities.
Year organized: 1992 (includes asset exchange from Newton Income Fund at date of inception)
Ticker symbol: MRGIX
Discount broker availability: White
Dividends paid: Income - declared daily, paid monthly; Capital gains - December
Portfolio turnover (2 yrs): 175%, 218%
Management fee: 0.75%
Expense ratio: 0.86% (year ending 8/31/94) (1.26% without waiver)

MARSHALL INTERMEDIATE BOND FUND ◆
(See first Marshall listing for data common to all Marshall funds)

Portfolio manager: Lawrence J. Pavelec (1993)
Investment objective and policies: Maximum total return consistent with current income. Invests in high-grade bonds and notes with a weighted average maturity of 3 to 10 years with at least 65% of assets in bonds. May invest in debt securities of domestic issuers, obligations of the U.S., its agencies and its instrumentalities, commercial paper, certificates of deposit and other financial debt instruments. Up to 15% of assets may be in illiquid securities.
Year organized: 1992
Ticker symbol: MAIBX
Dividends paid: Income - declared daily, paid monthly; Capital gains - December
Portfolio turnover (2 yrs): 228%, 220%
Management fee: 0.60%
Expense ratio: 0.71% (year ending 8/31/94) (0.82% without waiver)

MARSHALL INTERMEDIATE TAX-FREE FUND ◆
(See first Marshall listing for data common to all Marshall funds)

Portfolio manager: John D. Baritzke (1994)
Investment objective and policies: Maximum total return exempt from federal income tax consistent with preservation of capital. Invests in high-grade municipal securities with a weighted average maturity of 3 to 10 years. May use options and futures to increase income and/or hedge. Up to 20% of assets may be in AMT securities and 15% in illiquid securities.
Year organized: 1994
Ticker symbol: MITFX
Dividends paid: Income - declared daily, paid monthly; Capital gains - December
Portfolio turnover (1 yr): 45%
Management fee: 0.60%
Expense ratio: 0.62% (7 months ending 8/31/94) (1.21% without waiver)

MARSHALL INTERNATIONAL STOCK FUND ◆
(See first Marshall listing for data common to all Marshall funds)

Sub-adviser: Templeton Investment Council, Inc.
Portfolio manager: James E. Chaney (1994)
Investment objective and policies: Capital growth. Normally invests at least 65% of assets in common and preferred stocks of companies domiciled in at least 3 countries outside the U.S. May invest directly and use ADRs, GDRs and EDRs. Up to 35% of assets may be in foreign debt and convertible securities and 15% in illiquid securities. May use foreign currency exchange contracts and options on foreign currencies to hedge.
Year organized: 1994
Ticker symbol: MRISX
Dividends paid: Income - March, June, September, December; Capital gains - December
Management fee: 1.00%
12b-1 distribution fee: Maximum of 0.25% (not currently imposed)

MARSHALL MID-CAP STOCK FUND ◆
(See first Marshall listing for data common to all Marshall funds)

Portfolio manager: Steven D. Hayward (1993)
Investment objective and policies: Capital growth. Normally invests at least 65% of assets in common and preferred stocks of companies with market capitalizations between $200M and $7.5B. Fund invests primarily in companies with above-average earnings growth prospects or likely to benefit from significant changes in their internal structure, products, or market environment. Up to 20% of assets may be in ADRs of foreign issuers and 15% in illiquid securities.
Year organized: 1993
Ticker symbol: MRMSX
Dividends paid: Income - March, June, September, December; Capital gains - December
Portfolio turnover (1 yr): 113%
Largest holding: Tellabs, Inc. (3.1%)
Management fee: 0.75%
Expense ratio: 1.01% (11 months ending 8/31/94) (1.29% without waiver)

MARSHALL MONEY MARKET FUND - INVESTMENT SHARES
(See first Marshall listing for data common to all Marshall funds)

Portfolio manager: Richard Rokus (1994)
Investment objective and policies: Current income consistent with stability of principal. Invests in high quality money market instruments. May invest in dollar-denominated Eurodollar commercial paper and other short-term debt instruments of foreign banks and other deposit institutions.
Year organized: 1992

Ticker symbol: MARXX
Check redemptions: $250 minimum
Confirmations mailed: Not mailed
Checks returned: Monthly
Periodic account statements: Monthly
Dividends paid: Income - declared daily, paid monthly
Management fee: 0.50%
12b-1 distribution fee: 0.30%
Expense ratio: 0.70% (year ending 8/31/94) (0.99% without waiver)

MARSHALL MONEY MARKET FUND - TRUST SHARES ◆
(See first Marshall listing for data common to all Marshall funds. All information for Trust Shares is identical to that for Investment shares except as listed below.)

Year organized: 1992 (includes asset exchange from Newton Money Market Fund at date of inception)
Special sales restrictions: Available only to former shareholders of the Newton funds, Marshall Life Members and institutional investors
12b-1 distribution fee: None
Expense ratio: 0.40% (year ending 8/31/94) (0.69% without waiver)

MARSHALL SHORT-TERM INCOME FUND ◆
(See first Marshall listing for data common to all Marshall funds)

Portfolio managers: Lawrence J. Pavelec (1992), Mark D. Pittman (1994)
Investment objective and policies: Maximum total return consistent with current income. Invests in high-grade bonds and notes with a weighted average maturity of 6 months to 3 years. May invest in debt securities of domestic issuers, obligations of the U.S. Government, its agencies and its instrumentalities, commercial paper, certificates of deposit and other financial debt instruments. Up to 15% of assets may be in illiquid securities.
Year organized: 1992
Ticker symbol: MSINX
Dividends paid: Income - declared daily, paid monthly; Capital gains - December
Portfolio turnover (2 yrs): 185%, 79%
Management fee: 0.60%
Expense ratio: 0.50% (year ending 8/31/94) (0.89% without waiver)

MARSHALL SHORT-TERM TAX-FREE FUND ◆
(See first Marshall listing for data common to all Marshall funds)

Portfolio manager: John D. Boritzke (1994)
Investment objective and policies: High current income exempt from federal income tax. Invests in high-grade municipal securities with a weighted average maturity of 3 years or less. Up to 20% of assets may be in AMT securities and 15% in illiquid securities.
Year organized: 1994
Ticker symbol: MOTFX
Dividends paid: Income - declared daily, paid monthly; Capital gains - December
Portfolio turnover (1 yr): 37%
Management fee: 0.50%
Expense ratio: 0.52% (7 months ending 8/31/94) (1.23% without waiver)

MARSHALL STOCK FUND ◆
(See first Marshall listing for data common to all Marshall funds)

Portfolio manager: Charles L. Melhouse (1993)
Investment objective and policies: Capital growth and income. Normally invests at least 65% of assets in common and preferred stocks of companies with established markets, primarily companies whose equity securities generate income. Up to 20% of

assets may be in ADRs of foreign issuers and 15% in illiquid securities.
Year organized: 1992 (includes asset exchange from Newton Growth Fund at date of inception)
Ticker symbol: MASTX
Discount broker availability: White
Dividends paid: Income - March, June, September, December; Capital gains - December
Portfolio turnover (2 yrs): 86%, 98%
Largest holding: Royal Dutch Petroleum Co. (3.2%)
Management fee: 0.75%
Expense ratio: 0.99% (year ending 8/31/94) (1.00% without waiver)

MARSHALL VALUE EQUITY FUND ◆
(See first Marshall listing for data common to all Marshall funds)

Portfolio manager: Gerry M. Sandel (1993)
Investment objective and policies: Long-term capital growth and income. Normally invests at least 65% of assets in common stocks, securities convertible into common stocks and preferred stocks of medium to large capitalization companies. Fund seeks companies with price/earnings ratios less than the S&P 500, above average dividend yields, below average price to book value and unrecognized or undervalued assets. Up to 20% of assets may be in ADRs of foreign issuers and 15% in illiquid securities.
Year organized: 1993
Ticker symbol: MRVEX
Dividends paid: Income - March, June, September, December; Capital gains - December
Portfolio turnover (1 yr): 39%
Largest holding: International Business Machines (2.7%)
Management fee: 0.75%
Expense ratio: 1.00% (11 months ending 8/31/94) (1.15% without waiver)

MATHERS FUND ◆
100 Corporate North, Suite 201
Bannockburn, IL 60015
708-295-7400, 800-962-3863
fax 708-295-7573

Adviser: Mathers and Company, Inc.
Portfolio manager: Henry G. Van der Eb, Jr. (1975)
Custodian: State Street Bank & Trust Co.
Transfer agent: DST Systems, Inc.
Investment objective and policies: Long-term capital appreciation with current income secondary. Invests primarily in common stocks believed to have favorable growth prospects. May invest in securities of foreign issuers traded on U.S. securities markets without limit and up to 10% in securities not publicly traded in the U.S. Fund may hedge.
Year organized: 1965
Ticker symbol: MATRX
Minimum purchase: Initial: $1,000, Subsequent: $200; IRA/Keogh: None
Telephone orders accepted: No
Wire orders accepted: Subsequent only
Deadline for same day wire purchase: 4 P.M.
Discount broker availability: Schwab, White, Waterhouse, Fidelity, Siebert
Qualified for sale in: All states
Letter redemptions: Signature guarantee required over $25,000
Dividends paid: Income - December; Capital gains - December
Portfolio turnover (3 yrs): 136%, 212%, 80%
Largest holding: U.S. Treasury Note due 2/15/04 (26.0%)
Shareholder services: Keogh, IRA, SEP-IRA, automatic investment plan—minimum $50/month, withdrawal plan
Management fee: 0.75% first $200M to 0.50% over $500M
Expense ratio: 0.89% (year ending 12/31/93)
IRA/Keogh fees: Annual $12

MATRIX EMERGING GROWTH FUND

300 Main Street
Cincinnati, OH 45202
513-621-2875, 800-877-3344
fax 513-241-9448

Adviser: Sena Weller Rohs Williams, Inc.
Portfolio managers: Fred W. Weller (1995),
Michael A. Coombe (1995)
Custodian and transfer agent: The Provident Bank
of Cincinnati
Investment objective and policies: Long-term capital growth. Invests primarily in common stocks of companies with long-term growth potential, particularly smaller companies in their emerging or developing growth phase. May have up to 15% of assets in illiquid securities.
Year organized: 1995
Minimum purchase: Initial: $1,000, Subsequent:
$100; IRA/Keogh: Initial: $500
Telephone orders accepted: Yes
Wire orders accepted: Yes
Deadline for same day wire purchase: 4 P.M.
Qualified for sale in: All states except AK, AR, HI,
ID, LA, MS, NE, NM, ND, OK, SD, UT, VT, WY
Telephone redemptions: Yes
Wire redemptions: Yes, $1,000 minimum
Telephone switching: With Matrix Growth Fund
and Riverfront Money Market Fund
Number of switches permitted: 12 per year
Dividends paid: Income - December; Capital gains
- December
Shareholder services: Keogh, IRA, 403(b), corporate retirement plans, automatic investment plan, redemption plan min. req. $10,000
Management fee: 0.9% first $50M to 0.6% over
$100M
12b-1 distribution fee: 0.25%
IRA/Keogh fees: None

MATRIX GROWTH FUND

300 Main Street
Cincinnati, OH 45202
513-621-2875, 800-877-3344
fax 513-241-9448

Adviser: Sena Weller Rohs Williams, Inc.
Portfolio managers: Peter H. Williams (1988),
David P. Osborn (1994)
Custodian and transfer agent: The Provident Bank
of Cincinnati
Investment objective and policies: Long-term capital growth with conservation of principal secondary. Invests primarily in common stocks of companies with potential for rising earnings and stable or rising share prices. May have up to 15% of assets in illiquid securities and use market index put options to hedge.
Year organized: 1986 (originally Gateway Growth
Plus Fund. Name changed from to SWRW Growth
Plus in 1992 and to current on 1/1/94)
Ticker symbol: GATGX
Minimum purchase: Initial: $1,000, Subsequent:
$100; IRA/Keogh: Initial: $500
Telephone orders accepted: Yes
Wire orders accepted: Yes
Deadline for same day wire purchase: 4 P.M.
Discount broker availability: Schwab, *White
Qualified for sale in: All states except AK, AR, HI,
ID, LA, MS, NE, NM, ND, OK, SD, UT, VT, WY
Telephone redemptions: Yes
Wire redemptions: Yes, $1,000 minimum
Telephone switching: With Matrix Emerging
Growth Fund and Riverfront Money Market Fund
Number of switches permitted: 12 per year
Dividends paid: Income - December; Capital gains
- December
Portfolio turnover (3 yrs): 30%, 51%, 70%
Largest holding: Enron Corp. (3.5%)
Shareholder services: Keogh, IRA, 403(b), corporate retirement plans, automatic investment plan, redemption plan min. req. $10,000
Management fee: 0.9% first $50M to 0.6% over
$100M
12b-1 distribution fee: 0.25%
Expense ratio: 1.67% (year ending 12/31/93)
IRA/Keogh fees: None

MATTHEWS ASIAN CONVERTIBLE SECURITIES FUND ◆

655 Montgomery Street, Suite 1438
San Francisco, CA 94111
415-788-6036, 800-789-2742
fax 415-788-6237

Adviser: Matthews International Capital
Management
Portfolio manager: G. Paul Matthews (1994)
Custodian: Citibank, N.A.
Transfer agent: Fund/Plan Services, Inc.
Investment objective and policies: Capital appreciation and current income. Invests primarily in convertible securities of issuers from at least 3 countries in the Asian markets of Hong Kong, Japan, Singapore, South Korea, Taiwan, Indonesia, Malaysia, the Philippines, Thailand, China and India. May invest in junk bonds without limit and in ADRs, GDRs and EDRs. May use options and futures and forward currency contracts to hedge. Up to 15% of assets may be in illiquid securities.
Year organized: 1994
Minimum purchase: Initial: $25,000, Subsequent:
$5,000; IRA: Subsequent: $2,000
Telephone orders accepted: Yes, only through
approved brokers
Wire orders accepted: Yes
Deadline for same day wire purchase: 4 P.M.
Qualified for sale in: AZ, CA, CO, CT, DC, FL,
HI, MD, MA, MS, NV, NJ, NY, OR, PA, TX, WA
Telephone redemptions: Yes
Wire redemptions: Yes, $9 fee
Letter redemptions: Signature guarantee required
over $100,000
Redemption fee: 1% for shares held less than 90
days including telephone switch
Telephone switching: With Matthews Pacific Tiger
Fund
Number of switches permitted: Unlimited
Dividends paid: Income - June, December; Capital
gains - December
Shareholder services: IRA, automatic investment
plan—minimum $500/month, electronic funds
transfer (redemption only)
Management fee: 1.0%
IRA fees: Annual $12

MATTHEWS PACIFIC TIGER FUND ◆

655 Montgomery Street, Suite 1438
San Francisco, CA 94111
415-788-6036, 800-789-2742
fax 415-788-6237

Adviser: Matthews International Capital
Management
Portfolio managers: G. Paul Matthews (1994),
Carol Chuang (1994)
Custodian: Citibank, N.A.
Transfer agent: Fund/Plan Services, Inc.
Investment objective and policies: Maximum capital appreciation. Invests primarily in equity securities of issuers from countries in the Pacific Tiger markets of Hong Kong, Japan, Singapore, South Korea, Taiwan, Indonesia, Malaysia, the Philippines, Thailand, and China. Up to 35% of assets may be in securities of issuers outside the Pacific Tiger region, including the U.S. and 25% in convertible securities of Pacific Tiger issuers. May invest in ADRs, GDRs and EDRs and use options and futures and forward currency contracts to hedge. Up to 15% of assets may be in illiquid securities.
Year organized: 1994
Minimum purchase: Initial: $5,000, Subsequent:
$1,000
Telephone orders accepted: Yes, only through
approved brokers
Wire orders accepted: Yes
Deadline for same day wire purchase: 4 P.M.
Qualified for sale in: AZ, CA, CO, CT, DC, FL,
HI, MD, MA, MS, NV, NJ, NY, OR, PA, TX, WA
Telephone redemptions: Yes
Wire redemptions: Yes, $9 fee
Letter redemptions: Signature guarantee required
over $100,000
Redemption fee: 1% for shares held less than 90
days including telephone switch

Telephone switching: With Matthews Asian
Convertible Securities Fund
Number of switches permitted: Unlimited
Dividends paid: Income - December; Capital gains
- December
Shareholder services: IRA, automatic investment
plan—minimum $500/month, electronic funds
transfer (redemption only)
Management fee: 1.0%
IRA fees: Annual $12

MAXUS FUNDS

(Data common to all Maxus funds are shown
below. See subsequent listings for data specific to
individual Maxus funds.)

28601 Chagrin Blvd
Cleveland, OH 44122
216-292-3434, 800-446-2987
fax 216-292-6084

Adviser: Maxus Asset Management, Inc.
Custodian: Bank One Trust Co., N.A.
Transfer agent: Mutual + Shareholder Services
Corp.
Minimum purchase: Initial: $1,000, Subsequent:
$100
Telephone orders accepted: Subsequent only (maximum 3 times share balance)
Wire orders accepted: Yes
Deadline for same day wire purchase: 12 NN
Telephone redemptions: Yes, $1,000 minimum
Wire redemptions: Yes, $1,000 minimum, $9 fee
Letter redemptions: Signature guarantee not
required
Telephone switching: With other Maxus funds
Number of switches permitted: Unlimited
Shareholder services: IRA, withdrawal plan min.
req. $15,000
Management fee: 1.0% first $150M, 0.75% over
$150M
IRA fees: Annual $8

MAXUS EQUITY FUND

(See first Maxus listing for data common to all
Maxus funds)

Portfolio manager: Richard A. Barone (1989)
Investment objective and policies: Total return -
income and capital appreciation. Invests in equity and debt securities. Normally at least 65% of assets will be in equity securities - common and preferred stock and securities convertible into common stock. Up to 35% of assets may be in debt securities, primarily of investment grade. May invest in closed-end mutual funds and use options to increase return.
Year organized: 1989
Ticker symbol: MXSEX
Discount broker availability: *White
Qualified for sale in: CA, CT, FL, MD, MI, NY,
OH, PA
Dividends paid: Income - December; Capital gains
- December
Portfolio turnover (3 yrs): 175%, 187%, 189%
Largest holding: Phillip Morris (3.4%)
12b-1 distribution fee: 0.50%
Expense ratio: 2.61% (year ending 12/31/93)

MAXUS INCOME FUND

(See first Maxus listing for data common to all
Maxus funds)

Portfolio manager: Richard A. Barone (1985)
Investment objective and policies: High total return
- income and capital appreciation - consistent with reasonable risk. Invests in debt securities and preferred and common stock. May invest in options and closed-end mutual funds. Fund will adjust mix of debt and equity securities to reflect changes in economic and market conditions.
Year organized: 1985 (formerly Maxus Fund)
Ticker symbol: MXSFX
Discount broker availability: *White
Qualified for sale in: CA, CT, FL, MD, MI, NY,
OH, PA

Dividends paid: Income - Monthly; Capital gains - December
Portfolio turnover (3 yrs): 88%, 91%, 108%
Largest holding: Global Yield Closed End Fund (4.9%)
12b-1 distribution fee: 0.50%
Expense ratio: 1.90% (year ending 12/31/93)

MAXUS LAUREATE FUND

(See first Maxus listing for data common to all Maxus funds)

Portfolio manager: Robert Beausoleil (1993)
Investment objective and policies: High total return - income and capital appreciation - consistent with reasonable risk. Invests exclusively in shares of other open-end mutual funds and allocates assets among equity and bond funds adjusting mix to reflect changes in economic and market conditions.
Year organized: 1993 (name changed from Maxux Prism Fund in 1994)
Ticker symbol: MXSPX
Qualified for sale in: FL, MI, NY, OH, PA
Dividends paid: Income - December; Capital gains - December
Portfolio turnover (1 yr): 152%
Largest holding: Gabelli Asset Fund (10.3%)
12b-1 distribution fee: 0.50%
Expense ratio: 2.42% (8 months ending 12/31/93)

MCM FUNDS ◆

(Data common to all McM funds are shown below. See subsequent listings for data specific to individual McM funds.)

One Bush Street, Suite 800
San Francisco, CA 94104
415-616-9320, 800-788-9485
prices/yields 800-788-9487
fax 415-616-9386

Adviser: McMorgan & Company
Custodian: Citibank, N.A.
Transfer agent: Fund/Plan Services, Inc.
Minimum purchase: Initial: $5,000, Subsequent: $250
Telephone orders accepted: No
Wire orders accepted: Yes
Deadline for same day wire purchase: 4 P.M. (1 P.M. for Principal Preservation Fund)
Qualified for sale in: AZ, CA, DC, HI, NV, OR, WA
Telephone redemptions: Yes
Wire redemptions: Yes, $9 fee
Letters redemptions: Signature guarantee required over $10,000
Telephone switching: With other McM funds
Number of switches permitted: Unlimited
Deadline for same day switch: 4 P.M. (1 P.M. for Principal Preservation fund)
Shareholder services: IRA, automatic investment plan—minimum $100/month, withdrawal plan min. req. $10,000, electronic funds transfer
IRA fees: Annual $12

MCM BALANCED FUND ◆

(See first McM listing for data common to all McM funds)

Investment objective and policies: Capital growth, income and preservation of capital over a market cycle of 3 to 5 years. Invests primarily in dividend-paying common stocks. May invest in ADRs and EDRs of foreign issuers and use futures and options to increase income and hedge. Normally invests 50-75% of assets in equity securities, with allocation adjusted to changes in market and economic conditions, and has at least 25% in fixed-income securities.
Year organized: 1994
Dividends paid: Income - March, June, September, December; Capital gains - December
Management fee: 0.45%

MCM EQUITY INVESTMENT FUND ◆

(See first McM listing for data common to all McM funds)

Investment objective and policies: Above average total return over a market cycle of 3 to 5 years consistent with reasonable risk. Invests primarily in common stocks of companies with earnings growth, dividend growth and capital appreciation potential. May have up to 15% of assets in ADRs and EDRs of foreign issuers and use futures and options to increase income and hedge.
Year organized: 1994
Dividends paid: Income - March, June, September, December; Capital gains - December
Management fee: 0.50%

MCM FIXED INCOME FUND ◆

(See first McM listing for data common to all McM funds)

Investment objective and policies: Above average total return consistent with low risk to principal over a market cycle of 3 to 5 years. Invests primarily in intermediate and long-term investment-grade debt securities with a weighted average maturity of 3 to 15 years. May invest in ADRs and EDRs of foreign issuers and use futures and options to increase income and hedge.
Year organized: 1994
Dividends paid: Income - declared daily, paid monthly; Capital gains - December
Management fee: 0.35%

MCM INTERMEDIATE
FIXED INCOME FUND ◆

(See first McM listing for data common to all McM funds)

Investment objective and policies: Above average total return consistent with low risk to principal and liquidity over a market cycle of 3 to 5 years. Invests primarily in short and intermediate-term investment-grade debt securities with a weighted average maturity of 3 to 10 years. May invest in ADRs and EDRs of foreign issuers and use futures and options to increase income and hedge.
Year organized: 1994
Dividends paid: Income - declared daily, paid monthly; Capital gains - December
Management fee: 0.35%

MCM PRINCIPAL
PRESERVATION FUND ◆

(See first McM listing for data common to all McM funds)

Investment objective and policies: Maximum income consistent with stability of principal and maintenance of liquidity. Invests high quality money market instruments.
Year organized: 1994
Check redemptions: No minimum
Confirmations mailed: After each purchase and each check, mail or wire redemption
Checks returned: Not returned
Periodic account statements mailed: Quarterly
Dividends paid: Income - declared daily, paid monthly
Management fee: 0.25%

THE MERGER FUND

100 Summit Lake Drive
Valhalla, NY 10595
914-741-5600, 800-343-8959
fax 914-741-5737

Adviser: Westchester Capital Management, Inc. (as of January 1989)
Portfolio managers: Frederick W. Green (1989), Bonnie L. Smith (1989)
Custodian and transfer agent: Firstar Trust Co.
Investment objective and policies: Maximum capital growth through risk arbitrage. Invests at least 65% of assets in companies which are acquisition

or reorganization targets. Positions hedged through short sales and the use of put (limited to 25% of assets) and covered call options (limited to 50% of assets). Fund may leverage its assets up to 50%.
Year organized: 1982 (formerly Ayco Risk Fund)
Ticker symbol: MERFX
Minimum purchase: Initial: $2,000, Subsequent: None; Keogh: Initial & Subsequent: None
Telephone orders accepted: No
Wire orders accepted: Yes
Deadline for same day wire purchase: 4 P.M.
Discount broker availability: *Schwab, *White, Waterhouse, Fidelity, Siebert
Qualified for sale in: All states
Letters redemptions: Signature guarantee required over $25,000
Dividends paid: Income - December; Capital gains - December
Portfolio turnover (3 yrs): 390%, 186%, 231%
Largest holding: Reliance Electric (4.9%)
Shareholder services: Keogh, IRA, withdrawal plan min. req. $10,000 ($15 annual fee)
Management fee: 1.0%
12b-1 distribution fee: 0.22%
Expense ratio: 1.58% (year ending 11/30/94) (3.30% without waiver)
IRA/Keogh fees: Annual $12.50, Closing $15

MERIDIAN FUND ◆

60 East Sir Francis Drake Blvd., Suite 306
Larkspur, CA 94939
415-461-6237, 800-446-6662

Adviser: Aster Capital Management, Inc.
Portfolio manager: Richard F. Aster, Jr. (1984)
Custodian: National Westminster Bank NJ
Transfer agent: Fund/Plan Services, Inc.
Investment objective and policies: Long-term growth of capital. Invests in equity and equity-related securities, primarily common stocks, of small and medium sized companies experiencing above average growth in revenues and earnings. May invest up to 10% of assets in ADRs of foreign companies.
Year organized: 1984
Ticker symbol: MERDX
Minimum purchase: Initial: $1,000, Subsequent: $50
Telephone orders accepted: No
Wire orders accepted: Yes
Deadline for same day wire purchase: 4 P.M.
Discount broker availability: Schwab, White
Qualified for sale in: All states except AR, MT, NE, ND, SD, VT, WV
Telephone redemptions: Yes
Wire redemptions: Yes, with signature guarantee on file, $5,000 minimum
Letter redemptions: Signature guarantee required over $5,000
Telephone switching: With Meridian Value Fund
Number of switches permitted: Unlimited
Dividends paid: Income - September; Capital gains - September
Portfolio turnover (3 yrs): 43%, 61%, 61%
Largest holding: Service Corporation International (3.1%)
Shareholder services: IRA
Management fee: 1.0% first $50M, 0.75% over $50M
Expense ratio: 1.22% (year ending 6/30/94)
IRA fees: Annual $12

MERIDIAN VALUE FUND ◆

60 East Sir Francis Drake Blvd., Suite 306
Larkspur, CA 94939
415-461-6237, 800-446-6662

Adviser: Aster Capital Management, Inc.
Portfolio manager: Richard F. Aster, Jr. (1994)
Custodian: National Westminster Bank NJ
Transfer agent: Fund/Plan Services, Inc.
Investment objective and policies: Long-term growth of capital. Invests in equity and equity-related securities, primarily common stocks, of companies believed undervalued in relation to their earning power or asset value. Up to 35% of assets may be in junk bonds. and 10% in ADRs of foreign companies.

Year organized: 1994
Minimum purchase: Initial: $1,000, Subsequent: $50
Telephone orders accepted: No
Wire orders accepted: Yes
Deadline for same day wire purchase: 4 P.M.
Qualified for sale in: CA, FL, GA, IL, PA
Telephone redemptions: Yes
Wire redemptions: Yes, with signature guarantee on file, $5,000 minimum
Letter redemptions: Signature guarantee required over $5,000
Telephone switching: With Meridian Fund
Number of switches permitted: Unlimited
Dividends paid: Income - September; Capital gains - September
Largest holding: Bancorp Hawaii, Inc. (5.3%)
Shareholder services: IRA
Management fee: 1.0%
IRA fees: Annual $12

MERRILL LYNCH MONEY FUNDS
(Data common to all Merrill Lynch money funds are shown below. See subsequent listings for data specific to individual Merrill Lynch money funds.)

P.O. Box 9011
Princeton, NJ 08543-9011
609-282-2800

Adviser: Merrill Lynch Asset Management, Inc.
Custodian: The Bank of New York
Transfer agent: Financial Data Services, Inc.
Wire orders accepted: Yes
Deadline for same day wire purchase: 4 P.M.
Qualified for sale in: All states
Telephone redemptions: Yes
Wire redemptions: Yes, $5,000 minimum
Letter redemptions: Signature guarantee required
Telephone switching: With other Merrill Lynch funds, $250 minimum
Number of switches permitted: Unlimited
Check redemptions: $500 minimum
Confirmations mailed: After each purchase and each check, mail or wire redemption
Checks returned: As clear
Periodic account statements mailed: Monthly
Dividends paid: Income - declared and paid daily
Shareholder services: IRA, Keogh, corporate retirement plans, withdrawal plan min. req. $5,000
IRA/Keogh fees: See Merrill Lynch broker

MERRILL LYNCH
READY ASSETS TRUST
(See first Merrill Lynch listing for data common to all Merrill Lynch money funds)

Portfolio manager: John Ng (1988)
Investment objective and policies: Preservation of capital, liquidity, and income. Invests in money market securities with a weighted average maturity of 90 days or less.
Year organized: 1975
Ticker symbol: MRAXX
Minimum purchase: Initial: $5,000, Subsequent: $1,000; IRA/Keogh: $250, Subsequent: None
Management fee: 0.5% first $500M to 0.25% over $20B
12b-1 distribution fee: 0.125%
Expense ratio: 0.65% (year ending 12/31/93)

MERRILL LYNCH RETIREMENT
RESERVES MONEY FUND ◆
(See first Merrill Lynch listing for data common to all Merrill Lynch money funds)

Portfolio manager: Chris Ayoub (1988)
Investment objective and policies: Preservation of capital, liquidity, and income. Invests primarily in U.S. Government and agency securities, bank CDs, commercial paper, repurchase agreements and purchase and sale contracts with a weighted average maturity of 90 days or less.
Year organized: 1982
Special sales restrictions: Available to participants

in self-directed retirement plans for which Merrill Lynch serves as passive custodian and certain independent pension, profit-sharing, annuity and other qualified plans.
Minimum purchase: None
Management fee: 0.5% first $1B to 0.4% over $2B
Expense ratio: 0.59 (year ending 10/31/94)

MERRILL LYNCH
U.S.A. GOVERNMENT RESERVES
(See first Merrill Lynch listing for data common to all Merrill Lynch money funds)

Portfolio manager: Linda Costanzo (1988)
Investment objective and policies: Preservation of capital, liquidity, and income. Invests in money market securities which are direct obligations of the U.S. Government with a weighted average maturity of 90 days or less.
Year organized: 1982
Minimum purchase: Initial: $5,000, Subsequent: $1,000; IRA/Keogh: $250, Subsequent: None
Management fee: 0.45%
12b-1 distribution fee: 0.125%
Expense ratio: 0.81 (year ending 8/31/94)

MERRIMAN FUNDS ◆
(Data common to all Merriman funds are shown below. See subsequent listings for data specific to individual Merriman funds.)

1200 Westlake Avenue North - Suite 700
Seattle, WA 98109
206-285-8877, 800-423-4893
prices 800-338-1579, fax 206-286-2079

Shareholder service hours: Full service: M-F 7 A.M.-5 P.M. PST
Adviser: Merriman Investment Management Co.
Custodian and transfer agent: Firstar Trust Co.
Minimum purchase: Initial: $1,000; Subsequent: $100; IRA: Initial: $250
Telephone orders accepted: No
Wire orders accepted: Yes
Deadline for same day wire purchase: 4 P.M.
Telephone redemptions: Yes
Wire redemptions: Yes, $1,000 minimum, $7.50 fee
Letter redemptions: Signature guarantee required
Telephone switching: With other Merriman funds and Portico money market funds, $1,000 minimum
Number of switches permitted: Unlimited, $5 fee
Dividends paid: Income - March, June, September, December; Capital gains - December
Shareholder services: Keogh, IRA, SEP-IRA, corporate retirement plans, automatic investment plan—minimum $50/month (waives initial minimum), electronic funds transfer (purchase only), withdrawal plan min. req. $10,000
IRA/Keogh fees: Annual $12.50

MERRIMAN ASSET
ALLOCATION FUND ◆
(See first Merriman listing for data common to all Merriman funds)

Portfolio managers: Paul A. Merriman (1989), William L. Notaro (1989)
Investment objective and policies: High total return consistent with reasonable risk. At least 25% and up to 100% of assets may be in other mutual funds, but can buy individual issues. Asset allocation: 50% equity, 20% fixed-income, 20% foreign, and 10% precious metals. May hedge substantially. Extensively utilizes independent market timing model for each sector.
Year organized: 1989
Ticker symbol: MTASX
Discount broker availability: Schwab, *White, *Waterhouse, Fidelity, Siebert
Qualified for sale in: All states except AR, DE, ME, NE, ND, RI, VT
Portfolio turnover (3 yrs): 450%, 226%, 133%
Largest holding: GT Global Emerging Markets Fund (5.7%)

Management fee: 1.25% first $250M to 1.00% over $500M
Expense ratio: 1.56% (year ending 9/30/94) (includes waiver)

MERRIMAN CAPITAL
APPRECIATION FUND ◆
(See first Merriman listing for data common to all Merriman funds)

Portfolio managers: Paul A. Merriman (1989), William L. Notaro (1989)
Investment objective and policies: Capital appreciation. Invests at least 25% and up to 100% of assets in other mutual funds, primarily aggressive growth and growth funds, but may use individual equities. Up to 35% may be in high quality money market instruments. May hedge substantially. Utilizes equity market timing model extensively.
Year organized: 1989
Ticker symbol: MNCAX
Discount broker availability: Schwab, *White, *Waterhouse, Fidelity, Siebert
Qualified for sale in: All states except AR, DE, MT, ND, RI, VT
Portfolio turnover (3 yrs): 344%, 242%, 122%
Largest holding: GT Global Emerging Markets Fund (6.0%)
Management fee: 1.25% first $250M to 1.00% over $500M
Expense ratio: 1.58% (year ending 9/30/94) (includes waiver)

MERRIMAN FLEXIBLE BOND FUND ◆
(See first Merriman listing for data common to all Merriman funds)

Portfolio managers: Paul A. Merriman (1988), William L. Notaro (1988)
Investment objective and policies: Income and preservation of capital with growth of capital secondary. Invests at least 25% and may invest up to 100% of assets in other mutual funds believed to be consistent with the fund's objectives. Those mutual funds will hold all types of debt securities. Fund may make direct investments in all types of debt securities other than convertible securities and preferred stocks.
Year organized: 1988 (formerly Government Fund. Name and objective changed in December 1992. Prior performance may be misleading)
Ticker symbol: MTGVX
Discount broker availability: Schwab, *White, *Waterhouse, Fidelity, Siebert
Qualified for sale in: All states except AL, AR, CT, DE, ME, MD, MA, MT, NE, NV, NH, ND, RI, SC, VT
Portfolio turnover (3 yrs): 472%, 273%, 3%
Management fee: 1.00% first $250M to 0.75% over $500M
Expense ratio: 1.50% (year ending 9/30/94) (includes waiver)

MERRIMAN GROWTH &
INCOME FUND ◆
(See first Merriman listing for data common to all Merriman funds)

Portfolio managers: Paul A. Merriman (1988), William L. Notaro (1988)
Investment objective and policies: Long-term capital appreciation, preservation of capital and income. Invests at least 25% and may invest up to 100% of assets in other mutual funds believed to be consistent with the fund's objectives. Those mutual funds will hold primarily common stocks, bonds and securities convertible into common stocks, both domestic and foreign. Up to 35% of assets may be invested directly in U.S. Government securities and high quality money market instruments. May use futures and options to enhance income and hedge.
Year organized: 1988 (formerly Merriman Blue Chip Fund. Name and objective changed on 1/12/94. Prior performance may be misleading.)
Ticker symbol: MTBCX
Discount broker availability: Schwab, *White, *Waterhouse, Fidelity, Siebert

Qualified for sale in: All states except AL, AR, CT, DE, ME, MD, MA, MT, NE, NV, NH, ND, RI, SC, VT
Portfolio turnover (3 yrs): 240%, 201%, 91%
Largest holding: Cash and money market instruments (100.0%)
Management fee: 1.25% first $250M to 1.00% over $500M
Expense ratio: 1.90% (year ending 9/30/94) (includes waiver)

MERRIMAN LEVERAGED GROWTH FUND ◆
(See first Merriman listing for data common to all Merriman funds)

Portfolio managers: Paul A. Merriman (1992), William L. Notaro (1992)
Investment objective and policies: Long-term capital growth. Invests at least 25% and up to 100% of assets in other mutual funds, primarily aggressive growth and growth funds, but may use individual equities including securities convertible into common stocks. Up to 35% may be in high quality money market instruments. May hedge substantially. Utilizes proprietary market timing model extensively. With exception of its use of leverage (borrowing), the policies of the Leveraged Growth Fund are the same as those of the Capital Appreciation Fund.
Year organized: 1992
Discount broker availability: Schwab, *White, *Waterhouse, Fidelity, Siebert
Qualified for sale in: All states except AR, DE, MT, NE, NH, ND, RI, VT
Portfolio turnover (2 yrs): 380%, 131%
Management fee: 1.25% first $250M to 1.00% over $500M
Expense ratio: 2.06% (year ending 9/30/94) (includes waiver)

MICHIGAN DAILY TAX FREE INCOME FUND ◆
600 Fifth Avenue - 8th Floor
New York, NY 10020
212-830-5200, 800-676-6779
prices/yields 212-830-5225
fax 212-830-5476

Adviser: Reich & Tang Asset Management, L.P.
Portfolio manager: Molly Flewharty (1987)
Custodian: Investors Fiduciary Trust Co.
Transfer agent: Fundtech Services L.P.
Investment objective and policies: High current interest income exempt from federal income taxes and, to the extent possible, from Michigan dividends and interest income taxes, consistent with preservation of capital and liquidity. Invests primarily in debt obligations issued by or on behalf of the State of Michigan and other municipal authorities. Up to 20% of assets may be in AMT securities.
Year organized: 1987
Ticker symbol: MIDXX
Minimum purchase: Initial: $5,000, Subsequent: $100
Wire orders accepted: Yes
Deadline for same day wire purchase: 12 NN
Qualified for sale in: CO, IL, MI, MS, NY
Telephone redemptions: Yes
Wire redemptions: Yes, $1,000 minimum
Letter redemptions: Signature guarantee required
Telephone switching: With other Reich & Tang funds, $1,000 minimum
Number of switches permitted: Unlimited
Check redemptions: $250 minimum
Confirmations mailed: After each purchase and each check, mail or wire redemption
Checks returned: As clear
Periodic account statements mailed: Monthly
Dividends paid: Income - declared daily, paid monthly
Shareholder services: Withdrawal plan
Management fee: 0.50%
12b-1 distribution fee: Yes (not currently imposed)
Expense ratio: 0.74% (year ending 2/28/94) (1.04% without waiver)

MIM FUNDS
(Data common to all MIM funds are shown below. See subsequent listings for data specific to individual MIM funds.)

4500 Rockside Road
Cleveland, OH 44131
216-642-3000, 800-233-1240
fax 216-642-1249

Shareholder service hours: Full service: M-F 8:30 A.M.-5 P.M. EST; After hours service: prices, prospectuses, messages, total returns
Adviser: Mathematical Investing Systems, Inc.
Custodian: Bank One Ohio Trust Co., N.A.
Transfer agent: Mathematical Dividend Transfer, Inc.
Minimum purchase: Initial: $250, Subsequent: $50; IRA/Keogh: None
Telephone orders accepted: No
Wire orders accepted: Yes, $12 fee
Deadline for same day Wire purchase: 4 P.M.
Qualified for sale in: All states
Telephone redemptions: Up to $10,000
Wire redemptions: $12 fee
Letter redemptions: Signature guarantee required over $25,000
Telephone switching: With other MIM funds
Number of switches permitted: Unlimited
Shareholder services: IRA, automatic investment plan—minimum $50, withdrawal plan min. req. $10,000
12b-1 distribution fee: 0.70% (None for Money Market Fund)
IRA fees: Annual $8

MIM AFA EQUITY INCOME FUND
(See first MIM listing for data common to all MIM funds)

Sub Adviser: AFA Financial, Inc.
Portfolio manager: James M. Mendell (1991)
Investment objective and policies: Income from dividends, preservation of capital and capital growth. Invests in common stocks with historically high current dividend yields and significant appreciation potential due to undervaluation. Also uses convertibles and warrants.
Year organized: 1991
Ticker symbol: MIEQX
Discount broker availability: *White
Dividends paid: Income - March, June, September, December; Capital gains - December
Portfolio turnover (3 yrs): 61%, 48%, 57%
Largest holding: Eli Lilly & Co. (8.2%)
Management fee: 1.3% first $10M to 0.7% over $30M
Expense ratio: 3.19% (year ending 9/30/94)

MIM BOND INCOME FUND
(See first MIM listing for data common to all MIM funds)

Portfolio manager: Harvey M. Salkin (1986)
Investment objective and policies: Current income with capital growth secondary. Invests in U.S. Government securities, U.S. corporate bonds, preferred and dividend paying common stock, and debt obligations of foreign issuers. At least 50% of assets will be in bonds rated A or better, but up to 50% may be in issues rated as low as Ca. Fund may sell short against the box and buy and write covered puts and calls.
Year organized: 1985
Ticker symbol: MIBIX
Discount broker availability: *White
Dividends paid: Income - March, June, September, December; Capital gains - December
Portfolio turnover (3 yrs): 38%, 95%, 64%
Management fee: 0.9% first $10M to 0.5% over $30M
Expense ratio: 3.02% (year ending 9/30/94)

MIM MONEY MARKET FUND ◆
(See first MIM listing for data common to all MIM funds)

Portfolio manager: Gregory B. Getts (1994)
Investment objective and policies: Maximum current income consistent with preservation of capital. Invests in money market instruments.
Year organized: 1985
Ticker symbol: MIMXX
Dividends paid: Income - declared daily, paid monthly
Management fee: 0.25% first $10M to 0.20% over $30M
Expense ratio: 1.00% (year ending 9/30/94)

MIM STOCK APPRECIATION FUND
(See first MIM listing for data common to all MIM funds)

Portfolio manager: Martin A. Weisberg (1994)
Investment objective and policies: Capital growth. Fund stays fully Invested in common stocks that meet adviser's criteria for growth potential. At least 65% of assets will always be in common stocks. Fund may use warrants.
Year organized: 1987
Ticker symbol: MISAX
Discount broker availability: Schwab, *White
Dividends paid: Income - March, June, September, December; Capital gains - December
Portfolio turnover (3 yrs): 254%, 216%, 288%
Largest holding: Microsoft Corp. (3.5%)
Management fee: 1.3% first $10M to 0.9% over $30M
Expense ratio: 2.44% (year ending 9/30/94)

MIM STOCK GROWTH FUND
(See first MIM listing for data common to all MIM funds)

Portfolio manager: Martin A. Weisberg (1993)
Investment objective and policies: Capital growth. Invests primarily in common stocks and convertible securities (including debentures) believed undervalued. In addition, fund writes and invests in secured put and covered call options, and index options as well as spreads. May sell stock and warrants short against the box.
Year organized: 1985 (name changed from MIM Stock, Convertible & Option Growth Fund on 7/29/91)
Ticker symbol: MISGX
Discount broker availability: *White
Dividends paid: Income - March, June, September, December; Capital gains - December
Portfolio turnover (3 yrs): 150%, 137%, 105%
Largest holding: Union Carbide Corp. (3.0%)
Management fee: 1.3% first $10M to 0.7% over $30M
Expense ratio: 2.80% (year ending 9/30/94)

MIM STOCK INCOME FUND
(See first MIM listing for data common to all MIM funds)

Portfolio manager: Harvey M. Salkin (1986)
Investment objective and policies: Current income and capital growth. Invests primarily in dividend paying common stocks and securities (including debentures) exchangeable for common stocks which have exchange traded options available on them. In addition, fund writes and invests in secured put and covered call options on stocks and indexes as well as spreads. May sell short against the box.
Year organized: 1985 (name changed from MIM Stock, Convertible & Option Income Fund on 7/29/91)
Ticker symbol: MICIX
Discount broker availability: *White
Dividends paid: Income - March, June, September, December; Capital gains - December
Portfolio turnover (3 yrs): 64%, 272%, 222%
Largest holding: Philip Morris Companies, Inc. (4.3%)

Management fee: 1.2% first $10M to 0.6% over $30M
Expense ratio: 2.75% (year ending 9/30/94)

MONETTA FUNDS ◆
(Data common to all Monetta funds are shown below. See subsequent listings for data specific to individual Monetta funds.)

1776-A South Naperville Road
Suite 207
Wheaton, IL 60187
708-462-9800, 800-666-3882
fax 708-462-9433

Shareholder service hours: Full service: M-F 8 A.M.-7 P.M. CST; After hours service: prices, yields, balances, last transaction, prospectuses
Adviser: Monetta Financial Services, Inc.
Custodian and transfer agent: Firstar Trust Co.
Telephone orders accepted: No
Wire orders accepted: Yes, subsequent only
Deadline for same day wire purchase: 4 P.M.
Qualified for sale in: All states except VT
Letter redemptions: Signature guarantee required over $25,000
Shareholder services: Keogh, IRA, SEP-IRA, 401(k), 403(b), corporate retirement plans, electronic funds transfer (purchase only), automatic investment plan—minimum $50
IRA fees: Annual $12.50 per fund (maximum $25), Closing $15

MONETTA FUND ◆
(See first Monetta listing for data common to all Monetta funds)

Portfolio manager: Robert S. Bacarella (1986)
Investment objective and policies: Capital appreciation with income secondary. Invests at least 70% of assets in equity securities of small to medium size companies (market capitalization from $50M-$1B) with growth potential and undervalued with respect to price/earnings ratio relative to estimated earnings growth rate. Remainder of assets are in dividend-paying equity securities and/or long-term debt securities.
Year organized: 1986
Ticker symbol: MONTX
Special sales restrictions: Closed to new shareholders on 3/31/93
Minimum purchase: Initial: $100, Subsequent: $50
Discount broker availability: Waterhouse
Dividends paid: Income - December; Capital gains - September, December
Portfolio turnover (3 yrs): 227%, 127%, 154%
Largest holding: Brinker International, Inc. (2.1%)
Management fee: 1.0%
Expense ratio: 1.38% (year ending 12/31/93)

MONETTA GOVERNMENT
MONEY MARKET FUND ◆
(See first Monetta listing for data common to all Monetta funds)

Portfolio manager: John A. Alogna (1994)
Investment objective and policies: Maximum current income, consistent with safety of capital and maintenance of liquidity. Invests in U.S. Government money market instruments.
Year organized: 1993 (a portfolio of Monetta Trust)
Minimum purchase: Initial: $1,000, Subsequent: $250
Telephone switching: With Monetta Mid-Cap Equity and Intermediate Bond funds
Number of switches permitted: Unlimited, $5 fee
Confirmations mailed: After each purchase and each mail or wire redemption
Checks returned: Not returned
Periodic account statements mailed: Quarterly
Dividends paid: Income - declared daily, paid monthly
Management fee: 0.35%
Expense ration: 0.03% (9 months ending 12/31/93) (1.66% without waiver)

MONETTA INTERMEDIATE
BOND FUND ◆
(See first Monetta listing for data common to all Monetta funds)

Portfolio manager: John M. Alogna (1994)
Investment objective and policies: High current income consistent with preservation of capital. Invests at least 70% of assets in investment-grade debt securities of U.S. issuers and foreign issuers payable in U.S. dollars, securities issued or guaranteed by the U.S. government or its agencies or instrumentalities, commercial paper, variable rate demand notes and bank obligations. Fund maintains a weighted average maturity of 3 to 10 years. May invest up to 20% of assets in junk bonds.
Year organized: 1993 (a portfolio of Monetta Trust)
Minimum purchase: Initial: $1,000, Subsequent: $250
Telephone switching: With Monetta Mid-Cap Equity and Government Money Market funds
Number of switches permitted: Unlimited, $5 fee
Dividends paid: Income - declared and paid monthly; Capital gains - December
Portfolio turnover (1 yr): 32%
Management fee: 0.60%
Expense ratio: 0.28% (9 months ending 12/31/93) (0.75% without waiver)

MONETTA MID-CAP EQUITY FUND ◆
(See first Monetta listing for data common to all Monetta funds)

Portfolio manager: John N. Alogna (1993)
Investment objective and policies: Long-term capital growth. Invests primarily in common stocks of medium sized companies with market capitalizations of $1B-$5B using a "bottom-up" stock selection process. Normally invests at least 90% of assets in equities and 65% of assets in common stocks of mid-cap companies.
Year organized: 1993 (a portfolio of Monetta Trust)
Ticker symbol: MMCEX
Minimum purchase: Initial: $1,000, Subsequent: $250
Telephone switching: With Monetta Intermediate Bond and Government Money Market funds
Number of switches permitted: Unlimited, $5 fee
Dividends paid: Income - December; Capital gains - December
Portfolio turnover (1 yr): 128%
Largest holding: Sara Lee Variable Demand Note (7.5%)
Management fee: 1.00%
Expense ratio: 1.12% (9 months ending 12/31/93)

MONTGOMERY FUNDS ◆
(Data common to all Montgomery funds are shown below. See subsequent listings for data specific to individual Montgomery funds.)

600 Montgomery Street
San Francisco, CA 94111
415-627-2485, 800-572-3863
fax 415-627-3195

Shareholder service hours: Full service: M-F 6 A.M.-4 P.M. PST; After hours service: prices, yields, prospectuses, messages, views
Adviser: Montgomery Asset Management, L.P.
Custodian: Morgan Stanley Trust Co.
Transfer agent: DST Systems, Inc.
Minimum purchase: Initial: $1,000 ($5,000 for Micro Cap) Subsequent: $100 ($500 for Micro Cap)
Telephone orders accepted: Yes, subsequent only, maximum 5 times value of account
Wire orders accepted: Yes
Deadline for same day wire purchase: 4 P.M. (12 NN for money market funds)
Telephone redemptions: Yes
Wire redemptions: Yes, $2,000 minimum, $10 fee
Letter redemptions: Signature guarantee required over $25,000
Telephone switching: With other open Montgomery funds

Number of switches permitted: Unlimited, reserves right to limit to 4 per year
Deadline for same day switch: 4 P.M. (12 NN for money market funds)
Shareholder services: IRA, automatic investment plan—minimum $100/month, withdrawal plan min. req. $1,000, electronic funds transfer (purchase only)
IRA fees: Annual $10

MONTGOMERY ASSET
ALLOCATION FUND ◆
(See first Montgomery listing for data common to all Montgomery funds.)

Portfolio managers: William C. Stevens (1994), Roger W. Honour (1993), Andrew Pratt (1994)
Investment objective and policies: High total return - current income and capital growth - with reduced risk. Invests in domestic stocks (20-80% of assets), investment-grade debt instruments (20-80%) and cash equivalents (0-50%) with allocation adjusted to reflect changes in market and economic conditions. May invest in ADRs and EDRs of foreign issuers, have up to 15% of assets in illiquid securities, leverage and use options and futures to hedge.
Year organized: 1994 (name changed from Strategic Allocation in 1994)
Discount broker availability: *Schwab, *White, *Waterhouse, *Fidelity, *Siebert
Qualified for sale in: All states
Dividends paid: Income - December; Capital gains - December
Largest holding: U.S. Treasury Note 8.875% due 11/15/97 (34.4%)
Management fee: 0.80% first $500M, 0.65% over $500M
Expense ratio: 1.43% (3 months ending 6/30/94) (8.86% without waiver)

MONTGOMERY CALIFORNIA
TAX-FREE MONEY FUND ◆
(See first Montgomery listing for data common to all Montgomery funds.)

Portfolio manager: William C. Stevens (1994)
Investment objective and policies: Maximum current income exempt from federal and California personal income taxes consistent with preservation of capital and liquidity. Invests primarily in California municipal money market instruments. May invest up to 35% of assets in other money market funds that invest in California municipal money market instruments.
Year organized: 1994
Qualified for sale in: CA, CO, DC, FL, GA, HI, IL, IN, KY, LA, MN, NJ, NC, OH, OK, OR, PA, UT, VA, WY
Dividends paid: Income - declared and paid daily
Management fee: 0.4% first $500M, 0.3% over $500M

MONTGOMERY CALIFORNIA
TAX-FREE SHORT/INTERMEDIATE
FUND ◆
(See first Montgomery listing for data common to all Montgomery funds.)

Portfolio manager: William C. Stevens (1993)
Investment objective and policies: Maximum current income exempt from federal and California personal income taxes consistent with preservation of capital and prudent investment management. Invests at least 80% of assets in California Municipal Securities that, at the time of purchase are rated within the four highest grades by Moody's or S&P with weighted average maturity of 3 years or less. Up to 20% of assets may be in AMT securities.
Year organized: 1993
Ticker symbol: MNCTX
Discount broker availability: *Schwab, *White, *Waterhouse, *Fidelity, *Siebert
Qualified for sale in: All states
Dividends paid: Income - declared and paid daily; Capital gains - June, December

Portfolio turnover (1 yr): 77%
Management fee: 0.50% first $500M, 0.40% over $500M
Expense ratio: 0.23% year ending 6/30/94) (1.63% without waiver)

MONTGOMERY EMERGING MARKETS FUND ◆
(See first Montgomery listing for data common to all Montgomery funds.)

Portfolio managers: Josephine S. Jimenez (1992), Bryan L. Sudweeks (1992)
Investment objective and policies: Capital appreciation. Invests at least 65% of assets in equity securities of companies in countries having emerging markets. Fund uses a proprietary quantitative asset allocation model in conjunction with fundamental industry analysis and stock selection methods in making investments. May invest up to 20% of assets in equity securities of companies comprising the EAFE Index, 10% in other investment companies and 15% in illiquid securities. May use options and futures to hedge.
Year organized: 1992
Ticker symbol: MNEMX
Discount broker availability: *Schwab, *White, *Waterhouse, *Fidelity, *Siebert
Qualified for sale in: All states
Dividends paid: Income - June, December; Capital gains - June, December
Portfolio turnover (2 yrs): 64%, 21%
Largest holding: Korea Electric Power Co. (1.4%)
Management fee: 1.25% first $250M, 1.00% over $250M
Expense ratio: 1.85% (year ending 6/30/94)

MONTGOMERY EQUITY INCOME FUND ◆
(See first Montgomery listing for data common to all Montgomery funds.)

Portfolio manager: John H. Brown (1995)
Investment objective and policies: Current income and capital appreciation. Invests primarily in equity securities of domestic companies, primarily those with market capitalization of $500M or more. Fund emphasizes investments in common stocks, but may also invest in other types of equity and equity derivative securities. Up to 20% of assets may be in equity or debt securities of foreign issuers and 15% in illiquid securities. May use options and futures to hedge.
Year organized: 1995
Discount broker availability: *Schwab, *White, *Fidelity, *Siebert
Qualified for sale in: All states
Dividends paid: Income - June, December; Capital gains - June, December
Management fee: 0.60% first $500M, 0.50% over $500M

MONTGOMERY GLOBAL COMMUNICATIONS FUND ◆
(See first Montgomery listing for data common to all Montgomery funds.)

Portfolio managers: Oscar A. Castro (1993), John D. Boich (1993)
Investment objective and policies: Capital appreciation. Invests at least 65% of assets in equity securities of communications companies, which may be of any size, throughout the world. A communications company is engaged in the development, manufacture or sale of communications equipment or services that derived at least 50% of either its revenues or earnings from these activities. Fund normally invests in at least three different countries with no country, other than the US, representing more than 40% of assets. May have up to 15% of assets in illiquid securities and use options and futures to hedge.
Year organized: 1993
Ticker symbol: MNGCX
Discount broker availability: *Schwab, *White, *Waterhouse, *Fidelity, *Siebert

Qualified for sale in: All states
Dividends paid: Income - June, December; Capital gains - June, December
Portfolio turnover (1 yr): 29%
Largest holding: Teledanmark A.S. ADR (2.6%)
Management fee: 1.25% first $250M, 1.00% over $250M
Expense ratio: 1.94% (year ending 6/30/94) (1.99% without waiver)

MONTGOMERY GLOBAL OPPORTUNITIES FUND ◆
(See first Montgomery listing for data common to all Montgomery funds.)

Portfolio managers: Oscar A. Castro (1993), John D. Boich (1993)
Investment objective and policies: Capital appreciation. Invests at least 65% of assets in equity securities of companies, which may be of any size, throughout the world. Fund emphasizes common stocks of companies with total market capitalization of more than $1B but may also invest in other types of equity and equity derivative securities. Fund normally invests in at least three different countries with no country, other than the US, representing more than 40% of assets. May have up to 15% of assets in illiquid securities and leverage and use options and futures to hedge.
Year organized: 1993
Ticker symbol: MNGOX
Discount broker availability: *Schwab, *White, *Waterhouse, *Fidelity, *Siebert
Qualified for sale in: All states
Dividends paid: Income - June, December; Capital gains - June, December
Portfolio turnover (1 yr): 67%
Largest holding:
Management fee: 1.25% first $500M to 1.00% over $1B
Expense ratio: 1.11% (9 months ending 6/30/94) (1.90% without waiver)

MONTGOMERY GOVERNMENT RESERVE FUND ◆
(See first Montgomery listing for data common to all Montgomery funds.)

Portfolio manager: William C. Stevens (1992)
Investment objective and policies: Current income consistent with liquidity and preservation of capital. Invests at least 65% of assets in U.S. Treasury money market obligations issued or guaranteed by the U.S. government, its agencies, or instrumentalities. May invest up to 35% of assets in other money market funds that invest exclusively in Government Securities.
Year organized: 1992
Ticker symbol: MNGXX
Qualified for sale in: All states
Dividends paid: Income - declared and paid daily
Management fee: 0.40% first $250M to 0.20% over $500M
Expense ratio: 0.60% (year ending 6/30/94) (0.71% without waiver)

MONTGOMERY GROWTH FUND ◆
(See first Montgomery listing for data common to all Montgomery funds.)

Portfolio managers: Roger W. Honour (1993), Andrew Pratt
Investment objective and policies: Capital appreciation. Invests at least 65% of assets in equity securities of domestic companies, primarily those with market capitalization of $500M or more. Fund emphasizes investments in common stocks, but may also invest in other types of equity and equity derivative securities. Up to 35% of assets may be in investment-grade debt securities and 15% in illiquid securities. May invest in ADRs and EDRs of foreign issuers, leverage and use options and futures to hedge.
Year organized: 1993
Ticker symbol: MNGFX
Discount broker availability: *Schwab, *White, *Waterhouse, *Fidelity, *Siebert

Qualified for sale in: All states
Dividends paid: Income - June, December; Capital gains - June, December
Portfolio turnover (1 yr): 111%
Largest holding: Xerox Corp. (4.3%)
Management fee: 1.0% first $500M to 0.8% over $1B
Expense ratio: 1.49% (9 months ending 6/30/94) (1.79% without waiver)

MONTGOMERY INTERMEDIATE DURATION GOVERNMENT FUND ◆
(Fund liquidated on 9/30/94)

MONTGOMERY INTERNATIONAL SMALL CAP FUND ◆
(See first Montgomery listing for data common to all Montgomery funds.)

Portfolio managers: Oscar A. Castro (1993), John D. Boich (1993)
Investment objective and policies: Capital appreciation. Invests at least 65% of assets in equity securities, primarily common stocks, of non-U.S. companies with market capitalizations under $1B with remainder invested similarly in larger capitalization non-US companies. Fund normally invests in at least three different countries with no single country representing more than 40% of assets. May have up to 15% of assets in illiquid securities. May leverage and use options and futures to hedge.
Year organized: 1993
Ticker symbol: MNISX
Discount broker availability: *Schwab, *White, *Waterhouse, *Fidelity, *Siebert
Qualified for sale in: All states
Dividends paid: Income - June, December; Capital gains - June, December
Portfolio turnover (1 yr): 124%
Largest holding: Angel Estrada (3.1%)
Management fee: 1.25% first $250M, 1.0% over $250M
Expense ratio: 1.99% (9 months ending 6/30/94) (2.32% without waiver)

MONTGOMERY MICRO CAP FUND ◆
(See first Montgomery listing for data common to all Montgomery funds.)

Custodian: Morgan Stanley
Portfolio managers: Roger W. Honour (1995), Andrew Pratt (1995)
Investment objective and policies: Capital appreciation. Invests at least 65% of assets in equity securities of domestic companies with market capitalizations under $425M and potential for rapid growth. May invest in ADRs and EDRs of foreign issuers and have up to 15% of assets in illiquid securities. May leverage and use options and futures to hedge.
Year organized: 1995
Special sales restrictions: Fund closed January 28, but will be periodically reopened at the discretion of the manager
Discount broker availability: *Schwab, *White, *Fidelity, *Siebert
Qualified for sale in: All states
Dividends paid: Income - June, December; Capital gains - June, December
Management fee: 1.40% first $200M, 1.25% over $200M

MONTGOMERY SHORT GOVERNMENT FUND ◆
(See first Montgomery listing for data common to all Montgomery funds.)

Portfolio manager: William C. Stevens (1992)
Investment objective and policies: Maximum total return consistent with preservation of capital and prudent investment risk. Invests at least 65% of assets in obligations issued or guaranteed by the U.S. government, its agencies, or instrumentalities with a weighted average maturity of less than 3 years. May invest up to 35% of assets in cash, commercial paper and investment-grade debt securities

and have up to 15% of assets in illiquid securities. May leverage and use options and futures to hedge.
Year organized: 1992
Ticker symbol: MNSGX
Discount broker availability: *Schwab, *White, *Waterhouse, *Fidelity, *Siebert
Qualified for sale in: All states
Dividends paid: Income - declared and paid daily; Capital gains - June, December
Portfolio turnover (2 yrs): 603%, 213%
Management fee: 0.5% first $500M, 0.4% over $500M
Expense ratio: 0.71% (year ending 6/30/94) (1.29% without waiver)

MONTGOMERY SMALL CAP FUND ◆
(See first Montgomery listing for data common to all Montgomery funds.)

Portfolio manager: Stuart O. Roberts (1990)
Investment objective and policies: Capital appreciation. Invests at least 65% of assets in common stocks of U.S. companies with market capitalization under $1B and above average growth prospects. May invest in ADRs and EDRs of foreign issuers and have up to 15% of assets in illiquid securities. May leverage and use options and futures to hedge.
Year organized: 1990
Ticker symbol: MNSCX
Special sales restriction: Fund closed to new accounts on 3/6/92
Qualified for sale in: All states
Discount broker availability: Schwab, Waterhouse
Dividends paid: Income - June, December; Capital gains - June, December
Portfolio turnover (3 yrs): 95%, 130%, 81%
Largest holding: Roberts Pharmaceuticals Corp. (3.0%)
Management fee: 1.0% first $250M, 0.8% over $250M
Expense ratio: 1.35% (year ending 6/30/94)

M.S.B. FUND INC. ◆
330 Madison Avenue
New York, NY 10017
212-551-1920

Adviser: Nationar (formerly Savings Bank Trust Co.)
Portfolio managers: Mark F. Trautman (1993), John J. McCabe (1993)
Custodian and transfer agent: Nationar
Investment objective and policies: Capital appreciation with income secondary. Invests in equity securities of companies with promising growth, earnings and dividend prospects. Normally invests at least 85% of assets in companies with market capitalization in excess of $500M.
Year organized: 1964
Ticker symbol: MSBFX
Minimum purchase: Initial: $50, Subsequent: $25
Telephone orders accepted: No
Wire orders accepted: No
Qualified for sale in: CT, DC, MA, NJ, NY, NC, PA
Letter redemptions: Signature guarantee required
Dividends paid: Income - March, June, October, December; Capital gains - December
Portfolio turnover (3 yrs): 26%, 13%, 17%
Largest holding: Iowa Beef, Inc. (4.0%)
Shareholder services: Withdrawal plan
Management fee: 0.75% first $75M to 0.25% over $150M
Expense ratio: 1.12% (year ending 12/31/93)

THE MUHLENKAMP FUND ◆
12300 Perry Highway
P.O. Box 598
Wexford, PA 15090
412-935-5520, 800-860-3863
fax 412-935-4720

Adviser: Muhlenkamp & Co. Inc.
Portfolio manager: Ronald H. Muhlenkamp (1988)
Custodian: PNC Bank, Pittsburgh
Transfer agent: Wexford Trust

Investment objective and policies: Maximum total return - current income and capital gains - consistent with reasonable risk. Invests primarily in common stocks but may hold fixed-income securities at appropriate times. Employs "value" approach, using low p/e, high return on equity and relative price to book criteria.
Year organized: 1988
Ticker symbol: MUHLX
Minimum purchase: Initial: $200, Subsequent: $100; IRA: Subsequent: None
Telephone orders accepted: No
Wire orders accepted: No
Qualified for sale in: All states except AK, AR, DC, HI, ME, MS, MT, NE, NV, NH, ND, OK, RI, SD, UT, VT, WY
Letter redemptions: Signature guarantee not required
Dividends paid: Income - December; Capital gains - December
Shareholder services: IRA, withdrawal plan min. req. $5,000
Portfolio turnover (3 yrs): 14%, 20%, 53%
Largest holding: Gemini II Capital Shares (3.1%)
Management fee: 1.0%
Expense ratio: 1.30% (year ending 12/31/93)
IRA fees: None

MUNICIPAL CASH SERIES
Federated Investors Tower
Pittsburgh, PA 15222-3779
412-288-1900, 800-245-0242
fax 412-288-1982

Adviser: Federated Advisers
Portfolio manager: Mary Jo Ochson (1989)
Custodian and transfer agent: State Street Bank & Trust Co.
Investment objective and policies: Current income exempt from federal income tax consistent with stability of principal. Invests in short-term municipal money market instruments.
Year organized: 1989
Ticker symbol: CMSXX
Minimum purchase: Initial: $10,000, Subsequent: $500; IRA: Initial: $1,000
Wire orders accepted: Yes
Deadline for same day wire purchase: 12 NN
Qualified for sale in: All states
Telephone redemptions: Yes
Wire redemptions: Yes, $10,000 minimum
Letter redemptions: Signature guarantee required over $50,000
Check redemptions: $100 minimum
Telephone switching: With Dremen Fund portfolios
Management fee: 0.5%
12b-1 distribution fee: 0.10%
Expense ratio: 0.99% (year ending 5/31/94) (1.05% without waiver)

MUTUAL SERIES FUNDS ◆
(Data common to all Mutual Series funds are shown below. See subsequent listing for data specific to individual Mutual Series funds.)

51 John F. Kennedy Parkway
Short Hills, NJ 07078
201-912-2100, 800-858-3013
800-448-3863 (shareholders)
800-553-3014 (information only)
fax 201-912-0148

Shareholder service hours: Full service: M-F 9 A.M.-5 P.M. EST; After hours service: prices
Adviser: Heine Securities Corp.
Custodian: State Street Bank & Trust Co.
Transfer agent: PFPC, Inc.
Investment objective and policies (except Discovery): Capital appreciation. Funds may invest up to 50% of assets in securities of companies involved in prospective mergers, consolidations, liquidations and reorganizations. Mutual Beacon, Mutual Shares, and Mutual Qualified all have growth-income objectives and similar portfolios. They differ in that Mutual Qualified is largely held by IRAs and pension plans. Thus Qualified is the same as Shares, except it doesn't hold

anything for tax reasons. Mutual Beacon is newer and smaller, so it has some securities whose capitalizations are too small to put into Mutual Shares. About 2-3% of Beacon is different; the balance is totally like Shares. All three portfolios are invested in three categories. First, 60% of the portfolio is made up of stocks trading at large discounts from asset values. Another portion is deal oriented, i.e. merges, liquidations, tender offers, spinoffs, sales of assets, and exchange offers. A third category is bankruptcy situations.
Telephone orders accepted: Subsequent only, $1,000 minimum
Wire orders accepted: Subsequent only, $1,000 minimum
Deadline for same day wire purchase: 4 P.M.
Qualified for sale in: All states
Letter redemptions: Signature guarantee required over $10,000
Dividends paid: Income - June, December; Capital gains - June, December
Shareholder services: Keogh, IRA, SEP-IRA, 403(b), automatic investment plan, withdrawal plan min. req. $10,000
IRA/Keogh fees: Annual $9

MUTUAL BEACON FUND ◆
(See first Mutual Series listing for data common to all Mutual Series funds)

Portfolio manager: Michael F. Price (1985)
Year organized: 1962 (Formerly Beacon Growth Fund; performance record before 1985 should be disregarded.)
Ticker symbol: BEGRX
Minimum purchase: Initial: $5,000, Subsequent: $1,000; IRA/Keogh: Initial: $2,000
Discount broker availability: Schwab, White, Waterhouse
Portfolio turnover (3 yrs): 53%, 58%, 57%
Largest holding: Sunbeam-Oster Equities L.P. (3.1%)
Management fee: 0.6%
Expense ratio: 0.73% (year ending 12/31/93)

MUTUAL DISCOVERY FUND ◆
(See first Mutual Series listing for data common to all Mutual Series funds)

Portfolio manager: Michael F. Price (1992)
Investment objective and policies: Long-term capital appreciation. Invests primarily in equities (common stock, preferred stock, convertibles securities, and debt securities) of small capitalization companies. Up to 50% of assets may be in securities of foreign issuers and 15% in illiquid debt securities. May invest in distressed first mortgage obligations and other debt secured by real property and sell short securities it does not own up to 5% of assets. May sell short against the box and hedge.
Year organized: 1992
Ticker symbol: MDISX
Special sales restrictions: Closed to new shareholders on 7/15/93. Fund still available to new subscribers through Charles Schwab.
Minimum purchase: Initial: $1,000, Subsequent: $50
Discount broker availability: Schwab, White, Waterhouse
Portfolio turnover (1 yr): 90%
Largest holding: Sears Roebuck & Co. (2.7%)
Management fee: 0.8%
Expense ratio: 1.07% (year ending 12/31/93)

MUTUAL QUALIFIED FUND ◆
(See first Mutual Series listing for data common to all Mutual Series funds)

Portfolio manager: Michael F. Price (1980)
Ticker symbol: MQIFX
Year organized: 1980 (Formerly Mutual Qualified Income Fund)
Minimum purchase: Initial: $1,000, Subsequent: $50
Discount broker availability: Schwab, White, Waterhouse
Portfolio turnover (3 yrs): 56%, 47%, 52%

Largest holding: Sunbeam-Oster Equities L.P. (6.8%)
Management fee: 0.6%
Expense ratio: 0.78% (year ending 12/31/93)

MUTUAL SHARES FUND ◆
(See first Mutual Series listing for data common to all Mutual Series funds)

Portfolio manager: Michael F. Price (1975)
Year organized: 1949 (Formerly Mutual Shares Corporation)
Ticker symbol: MUTHX
Minimum purchase: Initial: $5,000, Subsequent: $100; IRA/Keogh: Initial: $2,000
Discount broker availability: Schwab, White, Waterhouse
Portfolio turnover (3 yrs): 49%, 41%, 48%
Largest holding: Sunbeam-Oster Corp. (7.1%)
Management fee: 0.6%
Expense ratio: 0.74% (year ending 12/31/93)

NATIONAL INDUSTRIES FUND ◆
5990 Greenwood Plaza Blvd. - Suite 325
Englewood, CO 80111
303-220-8500, 800-367-7814
fax 303-220-8056

Adviser: Stonebridge Capital Management, Inc.
Portfolio manager: Richard C. Barrett (1984)
Custodian: Colorado National Bank
Transfer agent: NIF Management Co. Inc.
Investment objective and policies: Long-term capital appreciation and increased future income with current income secondary. Invests primarily in common stocks with potential growth rate greater than the overall economy. Up to 20% of assets may be in securities of foreign issuers. Fund may sell short against the box, write covered options, use futures contracts and hedge.
Year organized: 1958
Ticker symbol: NAIDX
Minimum purchase: Initial: $250, Subsequent: $25
Telephone orders accepted: No
Wire orders accepted: No
Qualified for sale in: All states except AK, MA, NH, UT, VT
Letter redemptions: Signature guarantee not required
Dividends paid: Income - December; Capital gains - December
Portfolio turnover (3 yrs): 36%, 56%, 45%
Largest holding: Gillette Company (2.6%)
Shareholder services: Withdrawal plan min. req. $10,000
Management fee: 0.75% first $10M to 0.625% over $25M
Expense ratio: 1.64% (year ending 11/30/94)

NEUBERGER & BERMAN FUNDS ◆
(Data common to all Neuberger & Berman funds are shown below. See subsequent listings for data specific to individual Neuberger & Berman funds.)

605 Third Avenue
New York, NY 10158
212-476-8800, 800-877-9700
fax 212-476-8942

Shareholder service hours: Full service: Mon-Sat 8 A.M.-6 P.M. EST; After hours service: prices, yields, total returns
Adviser: Neuberger & Berman Management Inc. (except International Fund)
Custodian and transfer agent: State Street Bank & Trust Co.
Telephone orders accepted: Yes, $1,000 subsequent minimum
Wire orders accepted: Yes, $1,000 subsequent minimum
Deadline for same day wire purchase: 4 P.M. (12 NN for money market funds)
Qualified for sale in: All states (except New York Insured Intermediate)
Telephone redemptions: Yes, $500 minimum
Wire redemptions: Yes, $1,000 minimum, $8 fee

Letter redemptions: Signature guarantee required over $50,000
Telephone switching: With other Neuberger & Berman funds. $1,000 minimum
Number of switches permitted: Monitored
Shareholder services: Keogh, IRA, SEP-IRA, 401(k), 403(b), corporate retirement plans, automatic investment plan, electronic funds transfers, withdrawal plan min. req. $5,000
IRA/Keogh fees: Annual $12 for all accounts

NEUBERGER & BERMAN
CASH RESERVES ◆
(See first Neuberger & Berman listing for data common to all Neuberger & Berman funds)

Portfolio manager: Theresa Havell (1988)
Investment objective and policies: Highest current income consistent with safety and liquidity. Invests in money market instruments.
Year organized: 1988
Ticker symbol: NBCXX
Minimum purchase: Initial: $2,000, Subsequent: $100; IRA/Keogh: Initial: $250
Check redemptions: $250 minimum
Confirmations mailed: After each purchase and each check, mail or wire redemption
Checks returned: Monthly
Periodic account statements mailed: Monthly
Dividends paid: Income - declared daily, paid monthly
Management fee: 0.5% first $500M to 0.40% over $2B
Expense ratio: 0.65% (year ending 10/31/94) (0.71% without waiver)

NEUBERGER & BERMAN
FOCUS FUND ◆
(See first Neuberger & Berman listing for data common to all Neuberger & Berman funds)

Portfolio managers: Lawrence Marx III (1988), Kent C. Simons (1988)
Investment objective and policies: Long-term capital appreciation. Invests in common stocks from 13 diversified economic sectors using a value oriented approach. Normally at least 90% of assets are in up to 6 sectors believed undervalued.
Year organized: 1952 (formerly Energy Fund, name changed to Selected Sectors Plus Energy and objective changed in 1988. Name and objective changed to Selected Sectors in October 1991 and to current name on 1/1/95.)
Ticker symbol: NBSSX
Minimum purchase: Initial: $1,000, Subsequent: $100; IRA/Keogh: Initial: $250
Discount broker availability: *Schwab, White, Waterhouse, *Fidelity, *Siebert
Dividends paid: Income - December; Capital gains - December
Portfolio turnover (3 yrs): 52%, 52%, 77%
Largest holding: Capital Cities/ABC (3.5%)
Management fee: 0.70% first $250M to 0.575% over $1.5B
Expense ratio: 0.85% (year ending 8/31/94)

NEUBERGER & BERMAN
GENESIS FUND ◆
(See first Neuberger & Berman listing for data common to all Neuberger & Berman funds)

Portfolio manager: Stephen Milman (1988)
Investment objective and policies: Long-term capital growth. Invests primarily in common stocks of small to mid-sized companies with market capitalization of $750M or less considered undervalued on a current earnings basis.
Year organized: 1988
Ticker symbol: NBGNX
Minimum purchase: Initial: $1,000, Subsequent: $100; IRA/Keogh: Initial: $250
Discount broker availability: *Schwab, White, Waterhouse, *Fidelity, *Siebert
Dividends paid: Income - December; Capital gains - December
Portfolio turnover (3 yrs): 63%, 54%, 23%

Largest holding: Offshore Logistics (2.9%)
Management fee: 1.0% first $250M to 0.80% over $1B
Expense ratio: 1.36% (year ending 8/31/94)

NEUBERGER & BERMAN
GOVERNMENT INCOME FUND ◆
(See first Neuberger & Berman listing for data common to all Neuberger & Berman funds)

Portfolio manager: Stephen A. White (1993)
Investment objective and policies: High current income and total return consistent with safety of principal. Invests at least 65% of assets in U.S. Government and Agency securities with at least 25% of assets in mortgage-backed securities. May also invest in investment-grade debt securities including foreign investments, securities issued by financial institutions and corporations. Fund may use covered options, interest rate and foreign currency futures contracts and options thereon. Fund may leverage.
Year organized: 1993
Minimum purchase: Initial: $2,000, Subsequent: $100; IRA/Keogh: Initial: $250
Discount broker availability: *Schwab, *Fidelity, *Siebert
Dividends paid: Income - declared daily, paid monthly; Capital gains - December
Portfolio turnover (1 yr): 263%
Management fee: 0.60% first $500M to 0.40% over $2B
Expense ratio: 0.75% (year ending 10/31/94) (2.07% without waiver)

NEUBERGER & BERMAN
GOVERNMENT MONEY FUND ◆
(See first Neuberger & Berman listing for data common to all Neuberger & Berman funds)

Portfolio manager: Theresa A. Havell (1983)
Investment objective and policies: Maximum safety and liquidity consistent with highest available current income. Invests in U.S. Treasury obligations and other money market instruments backed by the "full faith and credit" of the U.S. Government.
Year organized: 1983
Ticker symbol: NBGXX
Minimum purchase: Initial: $2,000, Subsequent: $100; IRA/Keogh: Initial: $250
Check redemptions: $250 minimum
Confirmations mailed: After each purchase and each check, mail or wire redemption
Checks returned: Monthly
Periodic account statements mailed: Monthly
Dividends paid: Income - declared daily, paid monthly
Management fee: 0.5% first $500M to 0.4% over $2B
Expense ratio: 0.72% (year ending 10/31/94)

NEUBERGER & BERMAN
GUARDIAN FUND ◆
(See first Neuberger & Berman listing for data common to all Neuberger & Berman funds)

Portfolio managers: Kent C. Simons (1981), Lawrence Marx III (1988)
Investment objective and policies: Capital appreciation with current income secondary. Invests in dividend-paying common stocks of long-established, well-managed companies selected on a value basis.
Year organized: 1950 (split 3 for 1 on 1/20/93)
Ticker symbol: NGUAX
Minimum purchase: Initial: $1,000, Subsequent: $100; IRA/Keogh: Initial: $250
Discount broker availability: *Schwab, White, Waterhouse, *Fidelity, *Siebert
Dividends paid: Income - March, June, September, December; Capital gains - December
Portfolio turnover (3 yrs): 24%, 27%, 41%
Largest holding: AT&T (2.0%)
Management fee: 0.70% first $250M to 0.575% over $1.5B
Expense ratio: 0.80% (year ending 8/31/94)

NEUBERGER & BERMAN INTERNATIONAL FUND ◆

(See first Neuberger & Berman listing for data common to all Neuberger & Berman funds)

Adviser: BNP-N&B Global Asset Management, L.P.
Portfolio manager: Felix Rovelli (1994)
Investment objective and policies: Long-term capital appreciation. Invests primarily in equity securities of medium to large capitalization companies traded on foreign exchanges. Will normally invest in at least 3 countries with up to 50% of assets in Japan. May use ADRs, EDRs, GDRs and IDRs, use options and futures to hedge and sell short. Up to 15% of assets may be in illiquid securities and 10% in other mutual funds.
Year organized: 1994
Minimum purchase: Initial: $1,000, Subsequent: $100; IRA/Keogh: Initial: $250
Discount broker availability: *Schwab
Dividends paid: Income - December; Capital gains - December
Largest holding: SM Prime Holdings (1.8%)
Management fee: 1.23% first $250M to 1.095% over $1.5B

NEUBERGER & BERMAN LIMITED MATURITY BOND FUND ◆

(See first Neuberger & Berman listing for data common to all Neuberger & Berman funds)

Portfolio managers: Theresa A. Havell (1986), Margaret Didi Weinblatt (1993)
Investment objective and policies: High current income consistent with low risk to principal and liquidity. Capital appreciation is secondary objective. Invests primarily in short- to intermediate-term investment-grade debt securities with a weighted average maturity of 5 years or less. May use options and futures to increase return and hedge.
Year organized: 1986
Ticker symbol: NLMBX
Minimum purchase: Initial: $2,000, Subsequent: $100; IRA/Keogh: Initial: $250
Discount broker availability: *Schwab, White, Waterhouse, *Fidelity, *Siebert
Dividends paid: Income - declared daily, paid monthly; Capital gains - December
Portfolio turnover (3 yrs): 102%, 114%, 113%
Management fee: 0.5% first $500M to 0.4% over $2B
Expense ratio: 0.69% (year ending 10/31/94) (0.71% without waiver)

NEUBERGER & BERMAN MANHATTAN FUND ◆

(See first Neuberger & Berman listing for data common to all Neuberger & Berman funds)

Portfolio manager: Mark Goldstein (1992)
Investment objective and policies: Long-term capital appreciation. Invests primarily in common stocks and securities convertible into common stocks of companies believed to have maximum potential for growth. May also invest in preferred stocks and debt securities with potential for capital growth.
Year organized: 1966 (Neuberger-Berman management since 3/1/79)
Ticker symbol: NMANX
Minimum purchase: Initial: $1,000, Subsequent: $100; IRA/Keogh: Initial: $250
Discount broker availability: *Schwab, White, Waterhouse, *Fidelity, *Siebert
Dividends paid: Income - December, Capital gains - December
Portfolio turnover (3 yrs): 50%, 76%, 83%
Largest holding: Wells Fargo Bank (3.9%)
Management fee: 0.70% first $250M to 0.575% over $1.5B
Expense ratio: 0.96% (year ending 8/31/94)

NEUBERGER & BERMAN MUNICIPAL MONEY FUND ◆

(See first Neuberger & Berman listing for data common to all Neuberger & Berman funds)

Portfolio manager: Theresa A. Havell (1984)
Investment objective and policies: Maximum current income exempt from federal income taxes consistent with safety and liquidity. Invests in short term, tax-exempt municipal money market securities.
Year organized: 1984 (formerly Neuberger & Berman Tax-Free Money Fund)
Ticker symbol: NBTXX
Minimum purchase: Initial: $2,000, Subsequent: $100
Check redemptions: $250 minimum
Confirmations mailed: After each purchase and each check, mail or wire redemption
Checks returned: Monthly
Periodic account statements mailed: Monthly
Dividends paid: Income - declared daily, paid monthly
Management fee: 0.5% first $500M to 0.4% over $2B
Expense ratio: 0.73% (year ending 10/31/94)

NEUBERGER & BERMAN MUNICIPAL SECURITIES TRUST

(See first Neuberger & Berman listing for data common to all Neuberger & Berman funds)

Portfolio manager: Theresa A. Havell (1987)
Investment objective and policies: High current tax-free income with low risk to principal, limited price fluctuation and liquidity. Invests in investment-grade municipal securities with a weighted average maturity of 12 years or less.
Year organized: 1987
Ticker symbol: NBMUX
Minimum purchase: Initial: $2,000, Subsequent: $100
Discount broker availability: *Schwab, White
Dividends paid: Income - declared daily, paid monthly; Capital gains - December
Portfolio turnover (3 yrs): 127%, 35%, 46%
Management fee: 0.5% first $500M to 0.4% over $2B
Expense ratio: 0.65% (year ending 10/31/94) (0.82% without waiver)

NEUBERGER & BERMAN NEW YORK INSURED INTERMEDIATE FUND ◆

(See first Neuberger & Berman listing for data common to all Neuberger & Berman funds)

Portfolio managers: Theresa A. Havell (1994), John F. Flahive (1994)
Investment objective and policies: High current income exempt from federal and New York State and New York City personal income taxes, consistent with preservation of capital. Invests primarily in investment-grade New York municipal securities, insured as to timely payment of principal and interest, with a weighted average maturity of 10 years or less.
Year organized: 1994
Minimum purchase: Initial: $2,000, Subsequent: $100
Discount broker availability: *Schwab
Qualified for sale in: FL, NY
Dividends paid: Income - declared daily, paid monthly; Capital gains - December
Portfolio turnover (1 yr): 96%
Management fee: 0.5% first $500M to 0.4% over $2B
Expense ratio: 0.65% (9 months ending 10/31/94) (1.53% without waiver)

NEUBERGER & BERMAN PARTNERS FUND ◆

(See first Neuberger & Berman listing for data common to all Neuberger & Berman funds)

Portfolio manager: Michael Kassen (1990)
Investment objective and policies: Capital growth with reasonable risk. Invests primarily in common

stocks and other equity securities of established companies. Seeks securities believed undervalued based on fundamentals.
Year organized: 1968
Ticker symbol: NPRTX
Minimum purchase: Initial: $1,000, Subsequent: $100; IRA/Keogh: Initial: $250
Discount broker availability: *Schwab, White, Waterhouse, *Fidelity, *Siebert
Dividends paid: Income - December; Capital gains - December
Portfolio turnover (3 yrs): 75%, 82%, 97%
Largest holding: EXEL Ltd. (2.9%)
Management fee: 0.70% first $200M to 0.575% over $1.5B
Expense ratio: 0.81% (year ending 6/30/94)

NEUBERGER & BERMAN PROFESSIONAL INVESTORS GROWTH FUND ◆

(Fund liquidated on 4/29/94)

NEUBERGER & BERMAN PROFESSIONAL INVESTORS MONEY FUND ◆

(Fund liquidated on 4/29/94)

NEUBERGER & BERMAN SOCIALLY RESPONSIVE FUND ◆

(See first Neuberger & Berman listing for data common to all Neuberger & Berman funds)

Portfolio managers: Janet Prindle (1994), Farha-Joyce Haboucha (1994)
Investment objective and policies: Long-term appreciation. Invests primarily in securities of companies whose policies, practices, products and services meet social criteria believed to be characteristic of a better society. Fund invests primarily in common stocks but may also invest in convertible securities, preferred stock and foreign securities and ADRs of foreign companies that meet the Social Policy. May use futures and options to enhance income and hedge and sell short against the box.
Year organized: 1994
Ticker symbol: NBDCX
Minimum purchase: Initial: $1,000, Subsequent: $100; IRA/Keogh: Initial: $250
Discount broker availability: *Schwab
Dividends paid: Income - December; Capital gains - December
Portfolio turnover (1 yr): 14%
Largest holding: Scott Paper (2.8%)
Management fee: 0.70% first $250M to 0.575% over $1.5B
Expense ratio: 1.50% (6 months ending 8/31/94) (2.50% without waiver)

NEUBERGER & BERMAN ULTRA SHORT BOND FUND ◆

(See first Neuberger & Berman listing for data common to all Neuberger & Berman funds)

Portfolio manager: Theresa A. Havell (1986)
Investment objective and policies: Higher total return than conventional money market funds, with minimal risk to principal and liquidity. Average maturity can vary from 30 days to one year. Unlike conventional money market funds, the NAV will vary because of the portfolio's occasional longer maturities.
Year organized: 1986 (name changed from Money Market Plus 3/1/91)
Ticker symbol: NBMMX
Minimum purchase: Initial: $2,000, Subsequent: $100; IRA/Keogh: Initial: $250
Discount broker availability: *Schwab, White, Waterhouse, *Fidelity, *Siebert
Check redemptions: $250 minimum
Confirmations mailed: Not mailed
Checks returned: Monthly
Periodic account statements mailed: Monthly
Dividends paid: Income - declared daily, paid monthly; Capital gains - December
Portfolio turnover (3 yrs): 94%, 115%, 66%

Management fee: 0.5% first $500M to 0.4% over $2B
Expense ratio: 0.65% (year ending 10/31/94) (0.86% without waiver)

NEW ENGLAND MONEY MARKET FUNDS ◆

(Data common to all New England money market funds are shown below. See subsequent listing for data specific to individual New England money market funds.)

399 Boylston Street
Boston, MA 02116
617-578-1400, 800-343-7104
800-225-5478, yields 800-346-5984
fax 617-578-1191

Shareholder service hours: Full service: M-F 8 A.M.-6 P.M. EST; After hours service: prices, yields, balances, orders, last transaction,news, messages, prospectuses, total return
Adviser: Back Bay Advisors, L.P.
Custodian and transfer agent: State Street Bank & Trust Co.
Minimum purchase: Initial: $1,000, Subsequent: $50; IRA/Keogh: Initial: $250
Wire orders accepted: Yes
Deadline for same day wire purchase: 4 P.M.
Qualified for sale in: All states
Telephone redemptions: Yes
Wire redemptions: Yes, $5 fee
Letter redemptions: Signature guarantee required over $100,000
Telephone switching: With other New England funds (which have loads) and CGM funds
Number of switches permitted: Unlimited, $0.50 fee
Check redemptions: $250 minimum
Dividends paid: Income - declared daily, paid monthly
Checks returned: Monthly
Periodic account statements mailed: Monthly
Shareholder services: Keogh, IRA, 401(k), 403(b), automatic investment plan, withdrawal plan min. req. $5,000, VISA redemptions, electronic funds transfer
IRA/Keogh fees: Annual $10 (per social security number)

NEW ENGLAND CASH MANAGEMENT TRUST - MONEY MARKET SERIES ◆

(See first New England listing for data common to all New England money market funds)

Portfolio manager: J. Scott Nicholson (1978)
Investment objective and policies: Current income consistent with preservation of capital and liquidity. Invests in high quality money market instruments.
Year organized: 1978
Ticker symbol: NELXX
Management fee: 0.425% first $500M to 0.25% over $2B
Expense ratio: 0.84% (year ending 6/30/94)

NEW ENGLAND CASH MANAGEMENT TRUST - U.S. GOVERNMENT SERIES ◆

(See first New England listing for data common to all New England money market funds)

Portfolio manager: J. Scott Nicholson (1982)
Investment objective and policies: Current income consistent with preservation of capital and liquidity. Invests only in obligations backed by the full faith and credit of the U.S. Government and in related repurchase agreements.
Year organized: 1982
Ticker symbol: NUSXX
Management fee: 0.425% first $500M, 0.25% over $2B
Expense ratio: 0.84% (year ending 6/30/94)

NEW ENGLAND TAX EXEMPT MONEY MARKET TRUST ◆

(See first New England listing for data common to all New England money market funds)

Portfolio manager: John E. Maloney (1992)
Investment objective and policies: Current income exempt from federal taxes consistent with preservation of capital and liquidity; invests in high quality short-term fixed, variable and floating rate municipal obligations.
Year organized: 1983
Ticker symbol: NTMXX
Management fee: 0.4% first $100M, 0.3% over $100M
Expense ratio: 0.56% (year ending 6/30/94) (0.89% without waiver)

NEW JERSEY DAILY MUNICIPAL INCOME FUND ◆

600 Fifth Avenue - 8th Floor
New York, NY 10020
212-830-5200, 800-676-6779
prices/yields 212-830-5225
fax 212-830-5476

Adviser: Reich & Tang Asset Management L.P.
Portfolio manager: Molly Flewharty (1990)
Custodian and transfer agent: Investors Fiduciary Trust Company
Investment objective and policies: Interest income exempt from federal and New Jersey income taxes and preservation of capital, liquidity and stability of principal. Invests in a non-diversified portfolio of high quality, short-term New Jersey municipal obligations.
Year organized: 1990
Minimum purchase: Initial: $5,000, Subsequent: $100
Wire orders accepted: Yes
Deadline for same day wire purchase: 12 NN
Qualified for sale in: CT, DE, KY, MD, NJ, NY, PA
Telephone redemptions: Yes
Wire redemptions: Yes, $1,000 minimum
Letter redemptions: Signature guarantee required
Telephone switching: With other Reich & Tang Funds
Number of switches permitted: Unlimited, $1,000 minimum
Deadline for same day switch: 12 NN
Check redemptions: $250 minimum
Confirmations mailed: After each purchase and each check, mail or wire redemption
Checks returned: As clear
Periodic account statements mailed: Monthly
Dividends paid: Income - declared daily, paid monthly
Shareholder services: Withdrawal plan
Management fee: 0.5%
12b-1 distribution fee: 0.20% (not currently imposed)
Expense ratio: 0.66% (year ending 10/31/94) (0.92% without waiver)

NEW YORK DAILY TAX-FREE INCOME FUND

600 Fifth Avenue - 8th Floor
New York, NY 10020
212-830-5220, 800-676-6779
prices/yields 212-830-5225
fax 212-830-5476

Adviser: Reich & Tang Asset Management L.P.
Portfolio manager: Molly Flewharty (1984)
Custodian and transfer agent: Investors Fiduciary Trust Company
Investment objective and policies: Interest income exempt from federal, New York State and New York City income taxes and preservation of capital, liquidity and stability of principal. Invests in a non-diversified portfolio of high quality, short-term New York municipal obligations.
Year organized: 1984 (formerly Empire Tax Free Money Market)

Ticker symbol: ETFXX
Minimum purchase: Initial: $5,000, Subsequent: $100
Wire orders accepted: Yes
Deadline for same day wire purchase: 12 NN
Qualified for sale in: AL, CA, CO, CT, FL, NJ, NM, NY, PA, VT
Telephone redemptions: Yes
Wire redemptions: Yes, $1,000 minimum
Letter redemptions: Signature guarantee required
Telephone switching: With other Reich & Tang Funds
Deadline for same day switch: 12 NN
Number of switches permitted: Unlimited, $1,000 minimum
Check redemptions: $250 minimum
Confirmations mailed: After each purchase and each check, mail or wire redemption
Checks returned: As clear
Periodic account statements mailed: Monthly
Dividends paid: Income - declared daily, paid monthly
Shareholder services: Withdrawal plan
Management fee: 0.5%
12b-1 distribution fee: 0.20%
Expense ratio: 0.89% (year ending 4/30/94)

NICHOLAS FUNDS ◆

(Data common to all Nicholas funds are shown below. See subsequent listings for data specific to individual funds.)

700 N. Water Street, Suite 1010
Milwaukee, WI 53202
414-272-6133

Shareholder service hours: Full service: M-F 8:15 A.M.-4:30 P.M. CST; After hours service: prices, yields, balances, dividends, last transactions, prospectuses
Adviser: Nicholas Company, Inc.
Custodian and transfer agent: Firstar Trust Co.
Telephone orders accepted: No
Wire orders accepted: Yes
Deadline for same day wire purchase: 4 P.M.
Qualified for sale in: All states
Letter redemptions: Signature guarantee required over $100,000
Shareholder services: Keogh, IRA, automatic investment plan—minimum $50/month, withdrawal plan min. req. $10,000 (Income Fund only), electronic funds transfer (purchase only)
IRA/Keogh fees: Annual $12.50, Closing $15

NICHOLAS EQUITY INCOME FUND ◆

(See first Nicholas listing for data common to all Nicholas funds)

Portfolio manager: Albert O. Nicholas (1993)
Investment objective and policies: Income greater than the composite dividend yield of the securities in the S&P 500 with moderate long-term growth secondary. Invests at least 65% of assets in income-producing equity securities - common stocks, preferred stocks and convertible securities. Up to 20% of assets may be in repurchase agreements for defensive purposes.
Year organized: 1993
Ticker symbol: NSEIX
Minimum purchase: Initial: $2,000, Subsequent: $100
Dividends paid: Income - April, July, October, December; Capital gains - December
Portfolio turnover (1 yr): 0%
Largest holding: Velcro Industries N.V. (4.6%)
Management fee: 0.70% first $50M, 0.60% over $50M
Expense ratio: 1.70% (4 months ending 3/31/94)

NICHOLAS FUND ◆

(See first Nicholas listing for data common to all Nicholas funds)

Portfolio manager: Albert O. Nicholas (1969)
Investment objective and policies: Capital appreciation with income secondary. Invests primarily in

common stocks of companies with favorable long-term growth potential.
Year organized: 1969
Ticker symbol: NICSX
Minimum purchase: Initial: $500, Subsequent: $100
Telephone switching: With Nicholas Money Market Fund, $1,000 minimum
Number of switches permitted: 2 per year, $5 fee
Discount broker availability: White, Waterhouse
Dividends paid: Income - May, December; Capital gains - May, December
Portfolio turnover (3 yrs): 33%, 10%, 15%
Largest holding: Federal Home Loan Mortgage Association (2.8%)
Management fee: 0.75% first $50M, 0.65% over $50M
Expense ratio: 0.78% (year ending 3/31/94)

NICHOLAS II ◆
(See first Nicholas listing for data common to all Nicholas funds)

Portfolio manager: David O. Nicholas (1993)
Investment objective and policies: Long term growth with income secondary. Invests primarily in common stocks with favorable long-term prospects. Emphasizes stocks of small and medium sized companies with market capitalizations under $1B.
Year organized: 1983
Ticker symbol: NCTWX
Minimum purchase: Initial: $1,000, Subsequent: $100
Discount broker availability: White, Waterhouse
Telephone switching: Nicholas Money Market Fund, $1,000 minimum
Number of switches permitted: 2 per year, $5 fee
Discount broker availability: White, Waterhouse
Dividends paid: Income - December; Capital gains - December
Portfolio turnover (3 yrs): 27%, 11%, 12%
Largest holding: Health Management Associates, Inc. (4.1%)
Management fee: 0.75% first $50M to 0.50% over $100M
Expense ratio: 0.67% (year ending 9/30/94)

NICHOLAS INCOME FUND ◆
(See first Nicholas listing for data common to all Nicholas funds)

Portfolio manager: Albert O. Nicholas (1977)
Investment objective and policies: High current income. Invests primarily in junk bonds but still attempts to preserve capital and provide some long-term growth of capital and income. Invests in bonds, debentures, preferred stocks, securities convertible into common stocks and common stocks. 10-50% of assets will be in securities of electric companies and systems, up to 25% in real estate-related securities.
Year organized: 1929 (formerly Wisconsin Income Fund)
Ticker symbol: NCINX
Minimum purchase: Initial: $500, Subsequent: $100
Discount broker availability: White, Waterhouse
Dividend paid: Income - April, July, October, December; Capital gains - December
Portfolio turnover (3 yrs): 39%, 56%, 28%
Largest holding: Omega Healthcare Investors, Inc. (3.0%)
Management fee: 0.5% first $50M to 0.3% over $100M
Expense ratio: 0.62% (year ending 12/31/93)

NICHOLAS LIMITED EDITION ◆
(See first Nicholas listing for data common to all Nicholas funds)

Portfolio manager: David O. Nicholas (1993)
Investment objective and policies: Long-term growth. Invests primarily in common stocks, and may invest in companies which carry greater risk because such stocks are not actively traded or the

companies are smaller, out of favor or have limited operating history upon which to base an evaluation of future performance. Fund name is derived from the fact that the fund is restricted in size to a maximum of 14 million shares, of which 10 million are available for purchase and 4 million reserved for reinvestment of capital gains and dividends.
Year organized: 1987
Ticker symbol: NCLEX
Minimum purchase: Subsequent: $100
Discount broker availability: Waterhouse
Dividends paid: Income - December; Capital gains - December
Portfolio turnover (3 yrs): 24%, 24%, 13%
Largest holding: Keane, Inc. (5.6%)
Management fee: 0.75%
Expense ratio: 0.88% (year ending 12/31/93)

NICHOLAS MONEY MARKET FUND ◆
(See first Nicholas listing for data common to all Nicholas funds)

Portfolio manager: Albert O. Nicholas (1988)
Investment objective and policies: Current income consistent with preservation of capital and liquidity. Invests in money market instruments.
Year organized: 1988
Ticker symbol: NICXX
Minimum purchase: Initial: $2,000, Subsequent: $100
Wire redemptions: Yes, $1,000 minimum, $7.50 fee
Telephone switching: With Nicholas Fund and Nicholas II, $1,000 minimum
Number of switches permitted: 4 per year, $1,000 minimum, $5 fee
Dividends paid: Income - declared daily, paid monthly
Confirmations mailed: After each purchase and each mail or wire redemption
Periodic account statements mailed: Quarterly
Management fee: 0.3%
Expense ratio: 0.54% (year ending 12/31/93)

NOMURA PACIFIC BASIN FUND ◆
180 Maiden Lane
New York, NY 10038
212-509-7893, 800-833-0018
fax 212-509-8835

Adviser: Nomura Investment Management Co., Ltd.
Portfolio manager: Takeo Nakamura (1985)
Custodian and transfer agent: State Street Bank & Trust Co.
Investment objective and policies: Long-term capital appreciation. Invests primarily in equity securities of companies domiciled in Japan and other Far Eastern and Western Pacific countries. Current income is not a consideration. Normally at least 70% of assets will consist of equity securities of Pacific Basin issuers - common stock and, to a lesser extent, securities convertible into common stock and rights to subscribe for common stock.
Year organized: 1985
Ticker symbol: NPBFX
Minimum purchase: Initial: $1,000, Subsequent: None
Telephone orders accepted: No
Wire orders accepted: No
Discount broker availability: White
Qualified for sale in: All states except AR, IA, ME, MT, NH, ND, RI, SD, VT
Letter redemptions: Signature guarantee required
Dividends paid: Income - May, December; Capital gains - December
Portfolio turnover (3 yrs): 76%, 55%, 41%
Largest holding: Canon, Inc. (2.6%)
Shareholder services: IRA
Management fee: 0.75%
12b-1 distribution fee: Defensive only
Expense ratio: 1.39% (year ending 3/30/94)
IRA fees: Initial $60

NORTH CAROLINA DAILY MUNICIPAL INCOME FUND
600 Fifth Avenue, 8th Floor
New York, NY 10020
212-830-5200, 800-676-6779
prices/yields 212-830-5225
fax 212-830-5476

Adviser: Reich & Tang Asset Management L.P.
Portfolio manager: Molly Flewharty (1991)
Custodian and transfer agent: Investors Fiduciary Trust Co.
Investment objective and policies: Interest income exempt from federal and North Carolina income taxes consistent with preservation of capital, liquidity and stability of principal. Invests primarily in a non-diversified portfolio of high quality, North Carolina municipal money market obligations.
Year organized: 1991
Minimum purchase: Initial: $5,000, Subsequent: $100
Wire orders accepted: Yes
Deadline for same day wire purchase: 12 NN
Qualified for sale in: NC
Telephone redemptions: Yes
Wire redemptions: Yes
Letter redemptions: Signature guarantee required
Telephone switching: With Reich & Tang Funds
Deadline for same day switch: 12 NN
Number of switches permitted: Unlimited, $1,000 minimum
Check redemptions: $250 minimum
Confirmations mailed: After each purchase and each check, mail or wire redemption
Checks returned: As clear
Periodic account statements mailed: Monthly
Dividends paid: Income - declared daily, paid monthly
Shareholder services: Withdrawal plan
Management fee: 0.6%
12b-1 distribution fee: 0.25%
Expense ratio: 0.75% (year ending 8/31/94) (1.04% without waiver)

THE NORTH CAROLINA TAX FREE BOND FUND ◆
105 North Washington Street
P.O. Box 69
Rocky Mount, NC 27802
919-972-9922, 800-525-3863
fax 919-442-4226

Adviser: Boys, Arnold & Company, Inc.
Administrator: The Nottingham Company
Custodian: Wachovia Bank of North Carolina, N.A.
Transfer agent: The Nottingham Company
Investment objective and policies: Current income exempt from federal and North Carolina personal income taxes consistent with preservation of capital and protection from inflation. Invests at least 80% of assets in North Carolina municipal bonds and notes and other debt instruments. May invest in AMT securities.
Year organized: 1993
Minimum purchase: Initial: $5,000, Subsequent: $500
Telephone orders accepted: No
Wire orders accepted: Yes
Deadline for same day wire purchase: 4 P.M.
Discount broker availability: Schwab
Qualified for sale in: NC
Telephone redemptions: Yes
Wire redemptions: Yes, $5,000 minimum
Letter redemptions: Signature guarantee required over $50,000
Dividends paid: Income - monthly; Capital gains - December
Portfolio turnover (2 yrs): 23%, 0%
Shareholder services: Automatic investment plan—minimum $100/month, withdrawal plan min. req. $10,000
Management fee: 0.35%
Administration fee: 0.25%
Expense ratio: 0.84% (year ending 8/31/94) (3.26% without waiver)

NORTHEAST INVESTORS GROWTH FUND ◆

50 Congress Street, Suite 1000
Boston, MA 02109
617-523-3588, 800-225-6704
fax 617-523-5412

Shareholder service hours: Full service: M-F 9 A.M.-5 P.M. EST; After hours service: prices, messages, prospectuses
Adviser: Northeast Mngt. & Research Co., Inc.
Portfolio manager: William A. Oates, Jr. (1980)
Custodian: Investors Bank & Trust Co.
Transfer agent: Northeast Investors Growth Fund
Investment objective and policies: Long-term growth of both capital and future income. Fund maintains flexible policy investing in common stocks, bonds and money market instruments. Fund may leverage.
Year organized: 1980
Ticker symbol: NTHFX
Minimum purchase: Initial: $1,000, Subsequent: None; IRA/Keogh: Initial: $500
Telephone orders accepted: Yes, subsequent only
Wire orders accepted: Yes, subsequent only
Deadline for same day wire purchase: 4 P.M.
Discount broker availability: Schwab, White, Waterhouse, Fidelity, Siebert
Qualified for sale in: All states
Letter redemptions: Signature guarantee required
Telephone switching: With Northeast Investors Trust
Number of switches permitted: Unlimited
Dividends paid: Income - December; Capital gains - December
Portfolio turnover (3 yrs): 35%, 29%, 16%
Largest holding: BayBanks, Inc. (7.4%)
Shareholder services: Keogh, IRA, 403(b), corporate retirement plans
Management fee: 1.0% first $10M to 0.5% over $30M
Expense ratio: 1.45% (year ending 12/31/93)
IRA/Keogh fees: Annual $10

NORTHEAST INVESTORS TRUST ◆

50 Congress Street, Suite 1000
Boston, MA 02109
617-523-3588, 800-225-6704
fax 617-523-5412

Shareholder service hours: Full service: M-F 9 A.M.-5 P.M. EST; After hours service: prices, messages, prospectuses
Adviser: Northeast Investors Trust
Portfolio manager: Ernest E. Monrad (1960)
Custodian: Investors Bank & Trust Co.
Transfer agent: Northeast Investors Trust
Investment objective and policies: Income with capital appreciation secondary. Invests primarily in bonds but may also hold preferred stocks, dividend paying common stocks, convertible securities & securities with warrants attached. Fund may leverage.
Year organized: 1950
Ticker symbol: NTHEX
Minimum purchase: Initial: $1,000, Subsequent: None; IRA/Keogh: Initial: $500
Telephone orders accepted: Yes, subsequent only
Wire orders accepted: Yes, subsequent only
Deadline for same day wire purchase: 4 P.M.
Discount broker availability: Schwab, White, Waterhouse, Fidelity, Siebert
Qualified for sale in: All states
Letter redemptions: Signature guarantee required
Telephone switching: With Northeast Investors Growth Fund
Number of switches permitted: Unlimited
Dividends paid: Income - February, May, August, November; Capital gains - February, May, August, November
Portfolio turnover (3 yrs): 73%, 76%, 59%
Largest holding: Mesa Capital Corp. Bond due 6/30/98 (4.0%)
Shareholder services: Keogh, IRA, 403(b), 401(k), corporate retirement plans
Management fee: 0.5%
Expense ratio: 0.70% (year ending 9/30/93)
IRA/Keogh fees: Annual $10

NORTHERN FUNDS ◆

(Data common to all Northern funds are shown below. See subsequent listings for data specific to individual Northern funds.)

207 E. Buffalo Street, Suite 400
Milwaukee, WI 53202
414-271-5885, 800-595-9111

Adviser: The Northern Trust Company
Administrator: Sunstone Financial Group, Inc.
Custodian and transfer agent: The Northern Trust Company
Minimum purchase: Initial: $2,500, Subsequent: $50; IRA/Keogh: Initial: $500
Telephone orders accepted: No
Wire orders accepted: Yes
Deadline for same day wire purchase: 4 P.M. (2 P.M. for money market funds)
Qualified for sale in: All states
Telephone redemptions: Yes
Wire redemptions: Yes, $250 minimum, $15 fee
Letter redemptions: Signature guarantee required
Telephone switching: With other Northern funds, $1,000 minimum
Number of switches permitted: 8 per year
Shareholder services: IRA, 401(k), corporate retirement plans, automatic investment plan ($250 initial minimum), directed dividends, electronic funds transfer (purchase only), withdrawal plan min. req. $10,000
Administration fee: 0.15%
12b-1 distribution fee: Maximum of 0.25% (not currently imposed)
IRA fees: None

NORTHERN CALIFORNIA MUNICIPAL MONEY MARKET FUND ◆

(See first Northern listing for data common to all Northern funds)

Portfolio manager: Brad Snyder (1994)
Investment objective and policies: High current income exempt from federal and California state income taxes consistent with preservation of capital. Invests primarily in high-quality California municipal money market instruments.
Year organized: 1994
Dividends paid: Income - declared daily, paid monthly
Management fee: 0.60%

NORTHERN FIXED INCOME FUND ◆

(See first Northern listing for data common to all Northern funds)

Portfolio managers: Michael J. Lannan (1994), James M. Snyder (1994)
Investment objective and policies: High current income. Invests primarily in investment-grade fixed-income securities with a weighted average maturity of 7 to 12 years. Up to 20% of assets may be in obligations of issuers within a single foreign country. May use options and futures and forward currency contracts to increase income and hedge.
Year organized: 1994
Ticker symbol: NOFIX
Dividends paid: Income - declared daily, paid monthly; Capital gains - December
Management fee: 0.75%

NORTHERN GROWTH EQUITY FUND ◆

(See first Northern listing for data common to all Northern funds)

Portfolio managers: David Burshtan (1994), Robert A. LaFleur (1994)
Investment objective and policies: Long-term capital growth. Invests primarily in common and preferred stocks and convertible securities of companies with above average growth prospects. Up to 25% of assets may be in ADRs of foreign issuers and 10% in EDRs and direct foreign investments. May use options and futures to increase income and hedge.
Year organized: 1994

Ticker symbol: NOGEX
Dividends paid: Income - March, June, September, December; Capital gains - December
Largest holding: FMC Corp. (3.1%)
Management fee: 1.00%

NORTHERN INCOME EQUITY FUND ◆

(See first Northern listing for data common to all Northern funds)

Portfolio managers: William E. Hyatt (1994), Robert A. LaFleur (1994)
Investment objective and policies: High current income with long-term capital growth secondary. Invests primarily in income-producing convertible and other equity securities. Up to 35% of assets may be in investment-grade bonds and 35% in junk bonds. Up to 25% of assets may be in ADRs of foreign issuers and 10% in EDRs and direct foreign investments. May use options and futures to increase income and hedge.
Year organized: 1994
Ticker symbol: NOIEX
Dividends paid: Income - declared and paid monthly; Capital gains - December
Largest holding: Olsten Corp. convertible bond due 5/15/03 (4.6%)
Management fee: 1.00%

NORTHERN INTERMEDIATE TAX-EXEMPT FUND ◆

(See first Northern listing for data common to all Northern funds)

Portfolio managers: Eric Boeckmann (1994), James M. Snyder (1994)
Investment objective and policies: High current income exempt from federal income taxes consistent with preservation of capital. Invests primarily in high-quality municipal debt obligations with a weighted average maturity of 3 to 10 years. Up to 20% of assets may be in AMT securities.
Year organized: 1994
Ticker symbol: NOITX
Dividends paid: Income - declared daily, paid monthly; Capital gains - December
Management fee: 0.75%

NORTHERN INTERNATIONAL FIXED INCOME FUND ◆

(See first Northern listing for data common to all Northern funds)

Portfolio managers: Michael J. Lannan (1994), James M. Snyder (1994)
Investment objective and policies: High total return consistent with reasonable current income. Invests primarily in investment-grade fixed-income securities of foreign issuers with a weighted average maturity of 3 to 11 years. May invest in ADRs and EDRs and use options and futures and forward currency contracts to increase income and hedge.
Year organized: 1994
Ticker symbol: NOIFX
Dividends paid: Income - declared daily, paid quarterly; Capital gains - December
Management fee: 0.90%

NORTHERN INTERNATIONAL GROWTH EQUITY FUND ◆

(See first Northern listing for data common to all Northern funds)

Portfolio managers: Gregory M. Jones (1994), Robert A. LaFleur (1994)
Investment objective and policies: Long-term capital growth. Invests primarily in common and preferred stocks and convertible securities of foreign issuers with above average growth prospects. May invest in ADRs and EDRs and use options and futures and forward currency contracts to increase income and hedge.
Year organized: 1994
Ticker symbol: NOIGX
Dividends paid: Income - December; Capital gains - December

Largest holding: American Barrick Resources Corp. ADR (1.3%)
Management fee: 1.20%

NORTHERN INTERNATIONAL SELECT EQUITY FUND ◆

(See first Northern listing for data common to all Northern funds)

Portfolio managers: Gregory M. Jones (1994), Robert A. LaFleur (1994)
Investment objective and policies: Long-term capital growth. Invests primarily in equity securities of foreign issuers believed growing faster than their markets and transact majority of their business in countries growing faster than the world average. May invest in ADRs and EDRs and use options and futures and forward currency contracts to increase income and hedge.
Year organized: 1994
Ticker symbol: NINEX
Dividends paid: Income - December; Capital gains - December
Largest holding: Jaya Real Property (3.2%)
Management fee: 1.20%

NORTHERN MONEY MARKET FUND ◆

(See first Northern listing for data common to all Northern funds)

Portfolio manager: Mary Ann Flynn (1994)
Investment objective and policies: Maximum current income consistent with preservation of capital and liquidity. Invests primarily in high-quality money market instruments.
Year organized: 1994
Ticker symbol: NORXX
Dividends paid: Income - declared daily, paid monthly
Management fee: 0.60%

NORTHERN MUNICIPAL MONEY MARKET FUND ◆

(See first Northern listing for data common to all Northern funds)

Portfolio manager: Brad Snyder (1994)
Investment objective and policies: Maximum current income exempt from federal income tax consistent with preservation of capital and liquidity. Invests primarily in high-quality municipal money market instruments.
Year organized: 1994
Ticker symbol: NOMXX
Dividends paid: Income - declared daily, paid monthly
Management fee: 0.60%

NORTHERN SELECT EQUITY FUND ◆

(See first Northern listing for data common to all Northern funds)

Portfolio managers: Robert N. Streed (1994), Lawrence P. Keblusek (1994)
Investment objective and policies: Long-term capital growth. Invests primarily in equity securities of companies with superior quality and growth characteristics and market capitalizations of more than $500M. Up to 10% of assets may be in foreign securities and EDRs, as well as 25% in ADRs. May use options and futures to increase income and hedge.
Year organized: 1994
Ticker symbol: NOEQX
Dividends paid: Income - December; Capital gains - December
Largest holding: Gillette Co. (3.8%)
Management fee: 1.20%

NORTHERN SMALL CAP GROWTH FUND ◆

(See first Northern listing for data common to all Northern funds)

Portfolio managers: Susan J. French (1994), John R. Goodwin (1994)
Investment objective and policies: Long-term capi-

tal growth. Invests primarily in equity securities of companies with market capitalizations lower than the median capitalization of stocks listed on the NYSE. Up to 25% of assets may be in ADRs of foreign issuers and 10% in EDRs and direct foreign investments. May use options and futures to increase income and hedge.
Year organized: 1994
Ticker symbol: NOSGX
Dividends paid: Income - December; Capital gains - December
Largest holding: KN Energy, Inc. (0.4%)
Management fee: 1.20%

NORTHERN TAX-EXEMPT FUND ◆

(See first Northern listing for data common to all Northern funds)

Portfolio managers: Peter J. Flood (1994), James M. Snyder (1994)
Investment objective and policies: High current income exempt from federal income taxes consistent with preservation of capital. Invests primarily in high-quality municipal debt obligations with a weighted average maturity of 10 to 30 years. Up to 20% of assets may be in AMT securities.
Year organized: 1994
Ticker symbol: NOTEX
Dividends paid: Income - declared daily, paid monthly; Capital gains - December
Management fee: 0.75%

NORTHERN U.S. GOVERNMENT FUND ◆

(See first Northern listing for data common to all Northern funds)

Portfolio managers: Monty M. Memler (1994), James M. Snyder (1994)
Investment objective and policies: High current income. Invests primarily in securities issued or guaranteed by the U.S. Government or its agencies or instrumentalities with a weighted average maturity of 1 to 10 years.
Year organized: 1994
Ticker symbol: NOUGX
Dividends paid: Income - declared daily, paid monthly; Capital gains - December
Management fee: 0.75%

NORTHERN U.S. GOVERNMENT MONEY MARKET FUND ◆

(See first Northern listing for data common to all Northern funds)

Portfolio manager: Ed Kyritz (1994)
Investment objective and policies: Maximum current income consistent with preservation of capital and liquidity. Invests in money market instruments guaranteed as to payment of principal and interest by the U.S. Government, its agencies or instrumentalities, repurchase agreements relating to the above instruments and custodial receipts for such money market securities.
Year organized: 1994
Ticker symbol: NOGXX
Dividends paid: Income - declared daily, paid monthly
Management fee: 0.60%

NORTHERN U.S. GOVERNMENT SELECT MONEY MARKET FUND ◆

(See first Northern listing for data common to all Northern funds)

Portfolio manager: Ed Kyritz (1995)
Investment objective and policies: Maximum current income consistent with preservation of capital and liquidity. Invests exclusively in money market instruments guaranteed as to payment of principal and interest by the U.S. Government, its agencies or instrumentalities.
Year organized: 1995
Dividends paid: Income - declared daily, paid monthly
Management fee: 0.60%

NORTHWEST INVESTORS TRUST FUNDS ◆

(Data common to all Northwest Investors Trust funds are shown below. See subsequent listings for data specific to individual Northwest Investors Trust funds.)

P.O. Box 2838
Bellingham, WA 98227
206-734-9900, 800-728-8762
fax 206-734-0755

Adviser: Saturna Capital Corp.
Custodian: National City Bank, Indianapolis
Transfer agent: Saturna Capital Corp.
Minimum purchase: Initial: $1000, Subsequent: $100; IRA/Keogh: Initial: $100
Telephone orders accepted: No
Wire orders accepted: Yes
Deadline for same day wire transfer: 4 P.M.
Telephone redemptions: Yes
Wire redemptions: Yes, $500 minimum, $15 fee
Letter redemptions: Signature guarantee not required
Check redemptions: $500 minimum
Telephone switching: With Amana funds and other Northwest Investors Trust funds
Number of switches permitted: Unlimited
Shareholder services: Keogh, IRA, corporate retirement plans, automatic investment plan, withdrawal plan, electronic funds transfer (minimums: $100 purchase, $500 redemption)

NORTHWEST INVESTORS TRUST: IDAHO TAX-EXEMPT FUND ◆

(See first Northwest Investors Trust listing for data common to all Northwest Investors Trust funds)

Portfolio manager: Vern M. Clemenson (1987)
Investment objective and policies: Income exempt from federal and Idaho income taxes with capital preservation secondary. Invests at least 65% of assets in Idaho tax-exempt securities rate A or better with a weighted average maturity of 6 to 15 years.
Year organized: 1987 (formerly Idaho Extended Maturity Tax-Exempt Fund)
Qualified for sale in: DC, HI, ID, OR, WA
Dividends paid: Income - declared daily, paid monthly; Capital gains - November
Portfolio turnover (3 yrs): 36%, 31%, 17%
Management fee: 0.50% first $250M to 0.30% over $1B
Expense ratio: 0.75% (year ending 11/30/94) (0.89% without waiver)

NORTHWEST INVESTORS TRUST: NORTHWEST GROWTH FUND ◆

(See first Northwest Investors Trust listing for data common to all Northwest Investors Trust funds)

Portfolio manager: Nicholas Kaiser (1990)
Investment objective and policies: Long-term capital growth. Invests primarily in equity securities of companies headquartered or primarily located in the Northwest (comprising northern California, Oregon, Washington, Idaho, western Montana, British Columbia and southeast Alaska). Up to 25% of assets may be in Canadian securities. Debt securities will be A rated or better.
Year organized: 1987 (formerly Idaho Limited Maturity Tax-Exempt Fund)
Qualified for sale in: AK, CA, DC, HI, ID
Dividends paid: Income - November; Capital gains - November
Portfolio turnover (3 yrs): 12%, 25%, 46%
Largest holding: Apple Computer Corp. (8.0%)
Management fee: 0.75%
Expense ratio: 1.50% (year ending 11/30/94)

NORTHWEST INVESTORS TRUST: WASHINGTON TAX-EXEMPT FUND ◆

(See first Northwest Investors Trust listing for data common to all Northwest Investors Trust funds)

Portfolio manager: Phelps S. McIlvaine (1994)
Investment objective and policies: Income exempt

from federal and Washington State income taxes with capital preservation secondary. Invests at least 65% of assets in Washington tax-exempt securities rate A or better with a weighted average maturity of 6 to 15 years.
Year organized: 1993
Qualified for sale in: DC, HI, WA
Dividends paid: Income - declared daily, paid monthly; Capital gains - November
Portfolio turnover (1 yr): 74%
Management fee: 0.50% first $250M to 0.30% above $1B
Expense ratio: 0.41% (year ending 11/30/94) (0.51% without waiver)

THE NOTTINGHAM INVESTMENT TRUST - FBP CONTRARIAN FUNDS ◆
(See FBP Contrarian funds)

THE NOTTINGHAM INVESTMENT TRUST - THE GOVERNMENT STREET FUNDS
(See The Government Street funds)

THE NOTTINGHAM INVESTMENT TRUST II - THE HATTERAS UTILITY INCOME FUND
(Fund liquidated on 11/8/94)

THE NOTTINGHAM INVESTMENT TRUST II - THE INVESTEK FIXED INCOME TRUST ◆
105 North Washington Street
P.O. Box 69
Rocky Mount, NC 27802
919-972-9922, 800-525-3863
fax 919-442-4226

Adviser: Investek Capital Management
Administrator: The Nottingham Company
Custodian: Wachovia Bank of North Carolina, N.A.
Transfer agent: The Nottingham Company
Investment objective and policies: Maximum total return - capital appreciation and income. Invests in U.S. Government securities, mortgage pass-through certificates, collateralized mortgage obligations, asset backed securities, zero-coupon bonds, corporate bonds and floating rate securities with a weighted average maturity of 3 to 12 years. At least 90% of bonds in portfolio will be rated A or better by Moody's or S&P.
Year organized: 1992
Special sales restrictions: Designed for institutional investors such as pension and profit-sharing plans, endowments, foundations, employee benefit trusts and high net worth individuals.
Minimum purchase: Initial: $50,000; Subsequent: $1,000; IRA/Keogh: Initial: $2,000
Telephone orders accepted: No
Wire orders accepted: Yes
Deadline for same day wire purchase: 4 P.M.
Qualified for sale in: All states
Telephone redemptions: Yes
Wire redemptions: Yes, $1,000 minimum, $10 fee
Letter redemptions: Signature guarantee required over $50,000
Dividends paid: Income - monthly; Capital gains - December
Portfolio turnover (2 yrs): 34%, 60%
Shareholder services: Keogh, IRA, automatic investment plan—minimum $100/month, electronic funds transfer (purchase only), withdrawal plan min. req. $50,000
Management fee: 0.45%
Administration fee: 0.15%
Expense ratio: 0.77% (year ending 3/31/94) (1.41% without waiver)
IRA/Keogh fees: Annual $15

NUVEEN TAX-FREE RESERVES ◆
333 West Wacker Drive
Chicago, IL 60606
312-917-7700, 800-858-4084
800-621-7227

Adviser: Nuveen Advisory Corp.
Custodian: U.S. Trust Co. of New York

Transfer agent: Shareholder Services, Inc.
Investment objective and policies: Current income exempt from federal income tax consistent with stability of principal and liquidity. Invests primarily in municipal money market instruments.
Year organized: 1982
Ticker symbol: NRFXX
Minimum purchase: Initial: $25,000, Subsequent: $500
Wire orders accepted: Yes
Deadline for same day wire purchase: 3 P.M.
Qualified for sale in: All states
Telephone redemptions: Yes, $1,000 minimum
Wire redemptions: Yes, $1,000 minimum, $5 fee under $5,000
Letter redemptions: Signature guarantee required over $25,000
Dividends paid: Income - declared daily, paid monthly
Management fee: 0.4% first $500M to 0.325% over $2B
Expense ratio: 0.42% (year ending 2/28/94)

OAK HALL EQUITY FUND
P.O. Box 446
Portland, ME 04112
207-879-0001, 800-625-4255
fax 207-879-6206

Adviser: Oak Hall Capital Advisors, Inc.
Portfolio manager: John C. Hathaway (1992)
Custodian: First National Bank of Boston
Transfer agent: Forum Financial Corp.
Investment objective and policies: Capital appreciation. Invests primarily in common stocks and securities convertible into common stocks with above average growth potential or attractive valuations. May invest up to 25% of assets in junk bonds and 30% of assets in foreign securities. May hedge up to 25% of assets.
Year organized: 1992
Ticker symbol: OHEFX
Minimum purchase: Initial: $10,000, Subsequent: $5,000; IRA: Initial: $2,000, Subsequent: $250
Telephone orders accepted: No
Wire orders accepted: Yes
Deadline for same day wire purchase: 4 P.M.
Discount broker availability: Schwab, White
Qualified for sale in: All states
Telephone redemptions: Yes
Wire redemptions: Yes, $10,000 minimum
Letter redemptions: Signature guarantee required
Dividends paid: Income - December; Capital gains - December
Portfolio turnover (2 yrs): 169%, 188%
Largest holding: Amax Gold, Inc. (3.4%)
Shareholder services: IRA
Management fee: 0.75%
12b-1 distribution fee: 0.20%
Expense ratio: 2.01% (year ending 6/30/94) (2.17% without waiver)
IRA fees: Annual $25

OAK VALUE FUND ◆
105 North Washington Street
P.O. Box 69
Rocky Mount, NC 27802
919-972-9922, 800-525-3863
fax 919-442-4226

Adviser: Oak Value Capital Management, Inc.
Administrator: The Nottingham Company
Portfolio manager: David R. Carr (1993)
Custodian: Wachovia Bank of North Carolina, N.A.
Transfer agent: The Nottingham Company
Investment objective and policies: Capital appreciation with income secondary. Invests primarily in common and preferred stocks and securities convertible into common stocks. May invest in securities of foreign issuers and use covered call options to hedge.
Year organized: 1993
Minimum purchase: Initial: $2,500, Subsequent: $100; IRA/Keogh: Initial: $1,000
Telephone orders accepted: No
Wire orders accepted: Yes

Deadline for same day wire purchase: 4 P.M.
Qualified for sale in: All states
Telephone redemptions: Yes
Wire redemptions: Yes, $5,000 minimum
Letter redemptions: Signature guarantee required over $50,000
Dividends paid: Income - March, June, September, December; Capital gains - December
Portfolio turnover: 91%, 43%
Largest holding: Oakwood Homes (5.1%)
Shareholder services: Keogh, IRA, automatic investment plan—minimum $100, withdrawal plan min. req. $10,000
Management fee: 0.90%
Administration fee: 0.25% first $10M to 0.15% over $25M
Expense ratio: 1.89% (year ending 8/31/94) (2.80% without waiver)
IRA/Keogh fees: Annual $15

OAKMARK FUND ◆
2 No. LaSalle St. - Suite 500
Chicago, IL 60602-3790
312-621-0600, 800-625-6275
prices 800-476-9625
fax 312-621-0582

Adviser: Harris Associates LP
Portfolio manager: Robert J. Sanborn (1991)
Custodian and transfer agent: State Street Bank & Trust Co.
Investment objective and policies: Long-term capital appreciation. Invests primarily in common stocks and securities convertible into common stocks. May invest up to 25% of assets in junk bonds and 25% in foreign securities and 10% in other mutual funds. May use forward currency transactions and sell short.
Year organized: 1991
Ticker symbol: OAKMX
Minimum purchase: Initial: $2,500, Subsequent: $100; IRA: Initial: $1,000
Telephone orders accepted: No
Wire orders accepted: Yes, subsequent only
Deadline for same day wire purchase: 3 P.M.
Discount broker availability: Schwab, White, Waterhouse
Qualified for sale in: All states
Telephone redemptions: Yes, $50,000 maximum
Wire redemptions: Yes, $500 minimum, $5 fee
Letter redemptions: Signature guarantee required over $50,000
Telephone switching: With Oakmark International Fund and Goldman Sachs Money Market Trust Government and Tax Exempt Diversified portfolios and Goldman Sachs Short Duration Tax Free Fund
Number of switches permitted: Unlimited, $5 fee to money market
Deadline for same day switch: 4 P.M.
Dividends paid: Income - December; Capital gains - December
Portfolio turnover (3 yrs): 29%, 18%, 34%
Largest holding: Philip Morris Companies, Inc. (5.9%)
Shareholder services: IRA, SEP-IRA, automatic investment plan, electronic funds transfer, withdrawal plan min. req. $25,000
Management fee: 1.0%
Expense ratio: 1.22% (year ending 10/31/94)
IRA fees: Annual $10, Initial $5, Closing $10

OAKMARK INTERNATIONAL FUND ◆
2 No. LaSalle St. - Suite 500
Chicago, IL 60602-3790
312-621-0600, 800-625-6275
prices 800-476-9625
fax 312-621-0582

Adviser: Harris Associates LP
Portfolio manager: David G. Herro (1992)
Custodian and transfer agent: State Street Bank & Trust Co.
Investment objective and policies: Long-term capital appreciation. Invests primarily in a diversified portfolio of international securities. Fund may

markets, less developed markets and in selected emerging markets. May invest 10% of assets in junk bonds and 10% in other investment companies holding foreign securities. May use forward currency transactions and sell short.
Year organized: 1992
Ticker symbol: OAKIX
Minimum purchase: Initial: $2,500, Subsequent: $100; IRA: Initial: $1,000
Telephone orders accepted: No
Wire orders accepted: Yes, subsequent only
Deadline for same day wire purchase: 3 P.M.
Discount broker availability: *Schwab, White, Waterhouse
Qualified for sale in: All states
Telephone redemptions: Yes, $50,000 maximum
Wire redemptions: Yes, $500 minimum, $5 fee
Letter redemptions: Signature guarantee required over $50,000
Telephone switching: With Oakmark Fund and Goldman Sachs Money Market Trust Government and Tax Exempt Diversified portfolios and Goldman Sachs Short Duration Tax Free Fund
Number of switches permitted: Unlimited, $5 fee to money market
Deadline for same day switch: 4 P.M.
Dividends paid: Income - December; Capital gains - December
Portfolio turnover (2 yrs): 55%, 21%
Largest holding: Banco Popular Espanol (4.5%)
Shareholder services: IRA, SEP-IRA, automatic investment plan, electronic funds transfer, withdrawal plan min. req. $25,000
Management fee: 1.0%
Expense ratio: 1.37% (year ending 10/31/94)
IRA fees: Annual $10, Initial $5, Closing $10

OBERWEIS EMERGING GROWTH FUND
One Constitution Drive
Aurora, IL 60506
708-897-7100, 800-323-6166
prices 800-245-7311
fax 708-896-5282

Adviser: Oberweis Asset Management, Inc.
Portfolio manager: James D. Oberweis (1987)
Custodian and transfer agent: Investors Fiduciary Trust Co.
Investment objective and policies: Long-term capital appreciation. Normally invests at least 80% of assets in equity securities of small capitalization companies (with market capitalizations under $400M) believed to have potential for above average long term growth. May buy common and preferred stocks, convertible securities and foreign securities. May use restricted securities (10% of assets) and hedge (up to 25% of assets).
Year organized: 1987
Ticker symbol: OBEGX
Minimum purchase: Initial: $1,000, Subsequent: $100
Telephone orders accepted: No
Wire orders accepted: Yes
Deadline for same day wire purchase: 4 P.M.
Discount broker availability: Schwab, White, *Fidelity, *Siebert
Qualified for sale in: All states
Telephone redemptions: Yes
Wire redemptions: Yes, $6 fee
Letter redemptions: Signature guarantee required
Dividends paid: Income - December; Capital gains - December
Shareholder services: IRA, automatic investment plan—minimum $100/quarter (waives initial minimum), withdrawal plan min. req. $10,000, electronic funds transfer
Portfolio turnover (3 yrs): 66%, 70%, 63%
Largest holding: U.S. Robotics, Inc. (3.0%)
Management fee: 0.85% first $50M, 0.80% over $50M
12b-1 distribution fee: 0.50%
Expense ratio: 1.78% (year ending 12/31/94) (1.82% without waiver)
IRA fees: Annual $12

OHIO MUNICIPAL CASH TRUST - CASH II SERIES
Federated Investors Tower
Pittsburgh, PA 15222
412-288-1900, 800-245-0242
fax 412-288-1982

Adviser: Federated Management
Portfolio manager: J. A. Kozemchak (1991)
Custodian and transfer agent: State Street Bank & Trust Co.
Investment objective and policies: Current income exempt from federal and Ohio state income taxes consistent with stability of principal. Invests primarily in short-term Ohio municipal money market instruments.
Year organized: 1991
Minimum purchase: Initial: $25,000, Subsequent: $500
Wire orders accepted: Yes
Qualified for sale in: OH
Telephone redemptions: Yes
Wire redemptions: Yes, $1,000 minimum, $5 fee
Letter redemptions: Signature guarantee required over $50,000
Check redemptions: $100 minimum
Dividends paid: Income - declared daily, paid monthly
Management fee: 0.4%
12b-1 distribution fee: 0.30%
Expense ratio: 0.85% (year ending 10/31/94) (1.09% without waiver)

OLYMPIC TRUST FUNDS ◆
(See Hotchkis and Wiley funds)

THE OMNI INVESTMENT FUND ◆
53 West Jackson, Suite 818
Chicago, IL 60604
312-922-0355, 800-223-9790
fax 312-922-0418

Adviser: Perkins, Wolf, McDonnell & Co.
Portfolio manager: Robert H. Perkins (1985)
Custodian and transfer agent: The Omni Investment Fund
Investment objective and policies: Capital appreciation. Invests in companies believed to have growth potential or to be undervalued relative to their assets. May invest in small unseasoned companies and special situations. Fund is non-diversified.
Year organized: 1984 (split 10 for 1 on 9/28/94)
Minimum purchase: Initial: $3,000, Subsequent: None; IRA/Keogh: Initial: $1,000
Telephone orders accepted: No
Wire orders accepted: No
Qualified for sale in: All states except ND
Letter redemptions: Signature guarantee required over $50,000
Dividends paid: Income - December; Capital gains - December
Portfolio turnover (3 yrs): 108%, 105%, 130%
Largest holding: Huntington Bankshares, Inc. (4.1%)
Shareholder services: IRA
Management fee: 1.0%
Expense ratio: 1.31% (year ending 12/31/93)
IRA fees: Annual $20

THE OREGON MUNICIPAL BOND FUND
(See The Crabbe Huson Oregon Municipal Bond Fund)

O.R.I. GROWTH FUND ◆
Oak Ridge Investments
233 N. Michigan Avenue, Suite 1807
Chicago, IL 60601
312-616-1040, 800-407-7298
fax 312-616-1069

Adviser: Oak Ridge Investments, Inc.
Administrator: Sunstone Financial Group, Inc.
Portfolio manager: David M. Klaskin (1994)
Custodian: United Missouri Bank, N.A.
Transfer agent: Supervised Service Company, Inc.

Investment objective and policies: Capital appreciation. Invests primarily in common stocks of domestic companies considered to be growing faster than the general market. May also invest in preferred stocks, convertible securities, warrants and ADRs of foreign issuers.
Year organized: 1994
Ticker symbol: ORIGX
Minimum purchase: Initial: $2,000, Subsequent: $100; IRA: Initial: $1,000; Keogh: Initial: None
Telephone orders accepted: No
Wire orders accepted: Yes, $1,000 subsequent minimum
Deadline for same day wire purchase: 4 P.M.
Discount broker availability: *White
Qualified for sale in: All states except AL, AK, AR, DE, ID, LA, ME, MN, MS, MT, NE, NV, NH, OK, RI, SC, SD, UT, WV, WY
Telephone redemptions: Yes
Wire redemptions: Yes, $9 fee
Letter redemptions: Signature guarantee required over $25,000
Dividends paid: Income - December; Capital gains - December
Portfolio turnover (1 yr): 80%
Largest holding: Methanex Corp. (4.7%)
Shareholder services: Keogh, IRA, 401(k), 403(b), corporate retirement plans, automatic investment plan—minimum $100/month (waives initial minimum)
Management fee: 1.0%
Administration fee: 0.20% first $50M to 0.075% over $100M
Expense ratio: 2.00% (11 months ending 11/30/94) (includes waiver)

PACIFIC HORIZON PRIME FUND ◆
555 California Street
San Francisco, CA 94104
800-332-3863, 800-346-2087
yields 800-227-1545

Adviser: Bank of America National Trust and Savings Association
Administrator: Concord Holding Corporation
Custodian: Bank of New York
Transfer agent: Supervised Service Company, Inc.
Investment objective and policies: High current income consistent with stability of principal. Invests in high-grade money market instruments.
Year organized: 1984
Minimum purchase: Initial: $1,000, Subsequent: $100; IRA: Initial: $750, Subsequent: None
Wire orders accepted: Yes
Deadline for same day wire purchase: 12 NN
Qualified for sale in: All states
Telephone redemptions: Yes
Wire redemptions: Yes, $1,000 minimum
Letter redemptions: Signature guarantee required over $50,000
Check redemptions: $500 minimum
Dividends paid: Income - declared daily, paid monthly
Shareholder services: IRA, SEP-IRA, automatic investment plan, withdrawal plan min req $5,000
Management fee: 0.20% first $3B to 0.16% over $10B
Expense ratio: 0.52% (year ending 2/28/94) (0.53% without waiver)
IRA fees: Annual $25, Initial $25, Closing $50

PACIFICA FUNDS
(Data common to all Pacifica funds are shown below. See subsequent listings for data specific to individual Pacifica funds.)

237 Park Avenue, Suite 910
New York, NY 10017
800-662-8417, fax 212-808-3983

Adviser: First Interstate Capital Management, Inc.
Custodian: First Interstat Bank of California
Transfer agent: Pacifica Funds Distributor, Inc.
Minimum purchase: Initial: $500, Subsequent: $50; IRA: Initial $250
Telephone orders accepted: No

Wire orders accepted: Yes
Deadline for same day wire purchase: 4 P.M. (12 NN for money market funds)
Telephone redemptions: Yes
Wire redemptions: Yes
Letter redemptions: Signature guarantee required over $25,000
Telephone switching: With other Pacifica funds (equity funds have loads)
Number of switches permitted: Unlimited
Shareholder services: IRA, automatic investment plan, withdrawal plan min. req. $10,000
IRA fees: Annual $12, Initial $5

PACIFICA ASSET PRESERVATION FUND
(See first Pacifica listing for data common to all Pacifica funds)

Newspaper listing: APrsn
Portfolio manager: Mark A. Romano (1990)
Investment objective and policies: High current income consistent with preservation of capital. Invests in short-term debt securities with a weighted average maturity of one year or less. May invest in U.S. Government & agency securities, bank obligations, commercial paper, corporate debt securities, mortgage-related securities, and asset-backed securities. Up to 10% of assets may be in securities of foreign issuers.
Year organized: 1990
Ticker symbol: PCASX
Discount broker availability: White
Qualified for sale in: All states except ME, MA, MN, NH, VT, WV
Dividends paid: Income - declared daily, paid monthly; Capital gains - December
Portfolio turnover (3 yrs): 32%, 49%, 21%
Management fee: 0.55%
12b-1 distribution fee: 0.11%
Expense ratio): 0.84% (year ending 9/30/94) (0.86% without waiver)

PACIFICA GOVERNMENT MONEY MARKET FUND
(See first Pacifica listing for data common to all Pacifica funds)

Portfolio manager: Ted J. Piorkowski (1988)
Investment objective and policies: High current income consistent with preservation of capital and liquidity. Invests exclusively in U.S. Government & agency money market instruments.
Year organized: 1988
Ticker symbol: FSGXX
Qualified for sale in: All states except ME, MA, MN, NH, VT, WV
Check redemptions: $500 minimum
Confirmations mailed: After each purchase and each check, mail or wire redemption
Checks returned: Monthly
Periodic account statements mailed: Monthly
Dividends paid: Income - declared daily, paid monthly
Management fee: 0.50%
12b-1 distribution fee: 0.10%
Expense ratio): 0.77% (year ending 9/30/94) (0.79% without waiver)

PACIFICA MONEY MARKET FUND
(See first Pacifica listing for data common to all Pacifica funds)

Portfolio manager: Ted J. Piorkowski (1987)
Investment objective and policies: High current income consistent with preservation of capital and liquidity. Invests in a diversified portfolio of government and corporate money market instruments.
Year organized: 1985
Ticker symbol: FVMXX
Qualified for sale in: All states except ME, NH, VT
Check redemptions: $500 minimum
Confirmations mailed: After each purchase and each check, mail or wire redemption
Checks returned: Monthly

Periodic account statements mailed: Monthly
Dividends paid: Income - declared daily, paid monthly
Management fee: 0.50%
12b-1 distribution fee: 0.03%
Expense ratio): 0.63% (year ending 9/30/94) (0.73% without waiver)

PACIFICA SHORT TERM CALIFORNIA TAX-FREE FUND
(See first Pacifica listing for data common to all Pacifica funds)

Portfolio manager: Keli Brereton Chaux (1993)
Investment objective and policies: High current income exempt from federal and California personal income taxes consistent with preservation of capital. Invests at least 65% of assets in short-term California municipal debt securities with a weighted average maturity of 3 years or less. Up to 20% of assets may be in AMT securities.
Year organized: 1993
Ticker symbol: PCATX
Qualified for sale in: CA, CO, DC, FL, GA, HI, IL, IN, IA, KS, LA, MT, NJ, NY, OH, OK, OR, PA, RI, UT, VA, WA, WY
Dividends paid: Income - declared daily, paid monthly; Capital gains - December
Portfolio turnover (2 yrs): 31%, 23%
Management fee: 0.55%
12b-1 distribution fee: 0.02%
Expense ratio): 0.56% (year ending 9/30/94) (1.09% without waiver)

PAINE WEBBER CASHFUND ◆
1285 Avenue of the Americas
New York, NY 10019
212-713-2000, 800-647-1568
local PaineWebber branch office

Adviser: PaineWebber
Sub-adviser: Mitchell Hutchins Asset Management, Inc.
Portfolio manager: Nichole Ridyard (1986)
Custodian: PNC Bank, N.A.
Transfer agent: Provident Financial Processing Corp.
Investment objective and policies: Current income, stability of principal and high liquidity. Invests in high-grade money market instruments.
Year organized: 1978
Ticker symbol: PWCXX
Minimum purchase: Initial: $5,000, Subsequent: $500; IRA: Initial: $1,000
Wire orders accepted: Yes
Deadline for same day wire purchase: 2 P.M.
Qualified for sale in: All states
Telephone redemptions: Yes
Wire redemptions: Yes, $5,000 minimum
Letter redemptions: Signature guarantee required
Check redemptions: $500 minimum
Checks returned: On request
Periodic account statements mailed: Monthly (quarterly if dividends are only transactions)
Dividends paid: Income - declared daily, paid monthly
Shareholder services: Keogh, IRA
Management fee: 0.50% first $500M to 0.28% over $5.5B
Expense ratio: 0.61% (year ending 3/31/94)
IRA/Keogh fees: Annual $25, Initial $25, Closing $50

PAPP AMERICA-ABROAD FUND ◆
4400 North 32nd Street - Suite 280
Phoenix, AZ 85018
602-956-1115, 800-421-4004
fax 602-956-7053

Shareholder service hours: Full service: 8:30 A.M.-5 P.M. MST; After hours service: messages, prospectuses
Adviser: L. Roy Papp & Associates
Portfolio manager: L. Roy Papp (1991)
Custodian: First Interstate Bank of Arizona
Transfer agent: L. Roy Papp & Associates

Investment objective and policies: Long-term capital growth. Invests in common stocks of U.S. companies that have substantial international activities, and common stocks of foreign companies traded publicly in U.S. securities markets.
Year organized: 1991
Minimum purchase: Initial: $10,000, Subsequent: $2,000; IRA/Keogh: Initial $2,000
Telephone orders accepted: No
Wire orders accepted: Yes
Deadline for same day wire purchase: 4 P.M.
Discount broker availability: Schwab, White
Qualified for sale in: AZ, CA, IL, NJ, TX
Letter redemptions: Signature guarantee required
Dividends paid: Income - June, December; Capital gains - December
Portfolio turnover (2 yrs): 8%, 16%
Largest holding: Motorola, Inc. (7.5%)
Management fee: 1.0%
Expense ratio: 1.25% (year ending 12/31/93) (includes waiver)

L. ROY PAPP STOCK FUND ◆
4400 North 32nd Street - Suite 280
Phoenix, AZ 85018
602-956-1115, 800-421-4004
fax 602-956-7053

Shareholder service hours: Full service: 8:30 A.M.-5 P.M. MST; After hours service: messages, prospectuses
Adviser: L. Roy Papp & Associates
Portfolio manager: L. Roy Papp (1989)
Custodian: First Interstate Bank of Arizona
Transfer agent: L. Roy Papp & Associates
Investment objective and policies: Long-term capital growth. Invests in common stocks believed undervalued, including those considered speculative. May invest 5% of assets in convertible securities. Fund is normally fully invested.
Year organized: 1989
Ticker symbol: LRPSX
Minimum purchase: Initial: $10,000, Subsequent: $2,000; IRA/Keogh: Initial $2,000
Telephone orders accepted: No
Wire orders accepted: Yes
Deadline for same day wire purchase: 4 P.M.
Discount broker availability: Schwab, White
Qualified for sale in: All states except AR, ND, VT
Letter redemptions: Signature guarantee required
Dividends paid: Income - June, December; Capital gains - December
Portfolio turnover (3 yrs): 20%, 15%, 11%
Largest holding: Marshall Industries, Inc. (8.9%)
Management fee: 1.0%
Expense ratio: 1.19% (year ending 12/31/94) (includes waiver)

PARNASSUS INCOME FUND PORTFOLIOS ◆
(Data common to all Parnassus Income Fund portfolios are shown below. See subsequent listings for data specific to individual Parnassus Income Fund portfolios.

244 California Street, suite 400
San Francisco, CA 94111
415-362-3505, 800-999-3505

Adviser: Parnassus Financial Management
Custodian: Bank of California
Transfer agent: Provident Financial Processing Corp.
Social policy: Adviser attempts to invest in companies which treat employees fairly, have sound environmental protection policies, support equal employment opportunity, provide quality products and services, are sensitive to the local communities in which they operate and engage in ethical business practices. Fund does not invest in companies that manufacture alcohol or tobacco products, are involved with gambling, are weapons contractors or generate electricity from nuclear power.
Year organized: 1992
Minimum purchase: Initial: $2,000, Subsequent: $50; IRA/Keogh: Initial: $1,000
Telephone orders accepted: No

Wire orders accepted: Yes
Deadline for same day wire purchase: 4 P.M.
Qualified for sale in: All states (CA for California Tax-Free Portfolio)
Letter redemptions: Signature guarantee not required
Telephone switching: With other Parnassus Income Fund portfolios and the Parnassus Fund which has a 3.5% load
Number of switches permitted: Unlimited
Shareholder services: Keogh, IRA, automatic investment plan
IRA/Keogh fees: Annual $15

PARNASSUS INCOME FUND - BALANCED PORTFOLIO ◆

(See first Parnassus listing for data common to all Parnassus Fund portfolios)

Portfolio manager: Jerome L. Dodson (1992)
Investment objective and policies: Current income and preservation of capital with capital growth secondary. Invests in a diversified portfolio of fixed-income and equity securities with the allocation dependent on the economic outlook and market conditions. At least 25% of assets are in fixed-income securities. Up to 10% of assets may be in community development loan funds.
Ticker symbol: PRBLX
Discount broker availability: Schwab
Dividends paid: Income - March, June, September, December; Capital gains - December
Portfolio turnover (2 yrs): 33%, 24%
Largest holding: Merck & Company (5.5%)
Management fee: 0.75% first $30M to 0.65% over $100M
Expense ratio: 0.81% (year ending 12/31/93) (2.05% without waiver)

PARNASSUS INCOME FUND - CALIFORNIA TAX-FREE PORTFOLIO ◆

(See first Parnassus listing for data common to all Parnassus Fund portfolios)

Portfolio manager: David Pogran (1992)
Investment objective and policies: High current income exempt from federal and California personal income taxes while choosing a portfolio that will have a positive social and environmental impact. Invests in a diversified portfolio of tax-exempt investment-grade securities issued by California state and local governments and by other public authorities. Up to 20% of assets may be in AMT securities.
Dividends paid: Income - declared daily, paid monthly; Capital gains - December
Portfolio turnover (2 yrs): 20%, 0%
Management fee: 0.50% first $200M to 0.40% over $400M
Expense ratio: 0.48% (year ending 12/31/93) (1.47% without waiver)

PARNASSUS INCOME FUND - FIXED INCOME PORTFOLIO ◆

(See first Parnassus listing for data common to all Parnassus Fund portfolios)

Portfolio manager: Jerome L. Dodson (1992)
Investment objective and policies: High current income consistent with safety and preservation of capital. Invests in a diversified portfolio of investment-grade securities - bonds and other fixed-income instruments - with weighted average maturity of 5 to 20 years depending on market conditions. Fund expects a substantial portion of its funds will be in FHLMC ("Freddie Mac"), FNMA ("Fannie Mae") and GNMA securities. Up to 10% of assets may be in community development loan funds.
Ticker symbol: PRFIX
Dividends paid: Income - declared daily, paid monthly; Capital gains - December
Portfolio turnover (2 yrs): 11%, 15%

Management fee: 0.50% first $200M to 0.40% over $400M
Expense ratio: 0.68% (year ending 12/31/93) (1.68% without waiver)

PAUZE SWANSON U.S. GOVERNMENT TOTAL RETURN BOND FUND
P.O. Box 781234
San Antonio, TX 78278
210-308-1234, 800-327-7170
TDD 800-677-1212, fax 210-308-1217

Adviser: Pauze, Swanson & Associates
Administrator: United Services Advisors, Inc.
Portfolio manager: Philip Pauze (1994)
Custodian: Bankers Trust Co.
Transfer agent: United Shareholder Services, Inc.
Investment objective and policies: Total return higher than the rate of other funds with similar objectives. Invests exclusively in fixed-income securities backed by the full faith and credit of the U.S. Government. Adjusts maturity to reflect changing conditions in the interest rate environment.
Year organized: 1994
Minimum purchase: Initial: $1,000, Subsequent: $50; IRA/Keogh: None
Telephone orders accepted: Subsequent only, up to 10 times account balance (except money market funds)
Wire orders accepted: Yes
Deadline for same day wire purchase: 4 P.M.
Qualified for sale in: CA, FL, NE, PA, TX
Wire redemptions: Yes, $10 fee
Letter redemptions: Signature guarantee required over $15,000
Redemption fee: 0.10% for shares held less than 14 days
Account closing fee: $10
Telephone switching: With United Services funds and Bonnel Growth Fund
Number of switches permitted: Unlimited, $5 fee
Dividends paid: Income - declared daily, paid monthly; Capital gains - December
Portfolio turnover (1 yr): 0%
Shareholder services: Keogh, IRA, SEP-IRA, 403(b), 401(k), corporate retirement plans, automatic investment plan—minimum $30/mo. ($100 initial minimum), withdrawal plan min. req. $5,000, electronic funds transfer (purchase only)
Management fee: 0.40%
Expense ratio: 1.50% (6 months ending 6/30/94) (3.30% without waiver)
IRA fees: Annual $10, Closing $10
Keogh fees: Closing $10

PAX WORLD FUND
224 State Street
Portsmouth, NH 03801
603-431-8022, 800-767-1729

Adviser: Pax World Management Corp.
Portfolio manager: Anthony S. Brown (1971)
Custodian: State Street Bank & Trust Co.
Transfer agent: Provident Financial Processing Corp.
Investment objective and policies: Income and conservation of principal, with long term capital growth secondary. Invests in common and preferred stock (up to 70% of assets) and bonds of companies that do not engage in manufacturing defense or weapons-related products, or are not in tobacco, liquor, or gambling industries. Invests in companies producing life-supportive goods and services.
Year organized: 1970
Ticker symbol: PAXWX
Minimum purchase: Initial: $250, Subsequent: $50
Telephone orders accepted: No
Wire orders accepted: Yes, subsequent only
Deadline for same day wire purchase: 4 P.M.
Discount broker availability: Schwab, White, Waterhouse
Qualified for sale in: All states
Letter redemptions: Signature guarantee required over $5,000
Dividends paid: Income - July, December; Capital gains - December
Portfolio turnover (3 yrs): 25%, 22%, 17%

Largest holding: Merck & Co., Inc. (5.3%)
Shareholder services: IRA, SEP-IRA, 403(b), automatic investment plan, electronic funds transfer (purchase only), withdrawal plan min. req. $10,000
Management fee: 0.75% first $25M, 0.5% over $25M
12b-1 distribution fee: 0.12%
Expense ratio: 0.98% (year ending 12/31/94)
IRA fees: Annual $10

PAYSON BALANCED FUND ◆
P.O. Box 446
Portland, ME 04112
207-879-0009, 800-456-6710
fax 207-879-6051

Adviser: H. M. Payson & Co.
Portfolio manager: Peter E. Robbins (1993)
Custodian: First National Bank of Boston
Transfer agent: Forum Financial Corp.
Investment objective and policies: High current income and capital appreciation. Invests primarily in common stock and securities convertible into common stock of companies believed undervalued, and in high grade debt securities. At least 25% of assets will be in fixed-income senior debt securities with percentage rising and falling dependent on market conditions. Up to 20% of assets may be in foreign securities and ADRs and 15% in illiquid securities. Fund may hedge.
Year organized: 1991
Ticker symbol: PBFDX
Minimum purchase: Initial: $5,000, Subsequent: $500; IRA: Initial: $2,000
Telephone orders accepted: No
Wire orders accepted: Yes
Deadline for same day wire purchase: 4 P.M.
Qualified for sale in: AK, AZ, CA, CO, CT, DC, FL, GA, HI, IL, IN, LA, ME, MD, MA, NH, NJ, NY, NC, OH, PA, RI, TN, TX, VT, WY
Telephone redemptions: Yes
Wire redemptions: Yes, $5,000 minimum
Letter redemptions: Signature guarantee required
Telephone switching: With Payson Value Fund, Forum Daily Assets Treasury Fund and other Forum (load) funds
Dividends paid: Income - March, June, September, December; Capital gains - December
Portfolio turnover (2 yrs): 80%, 31%
Largest holding: Boise Cascade Corporation bond (2.4%)
Shareholder services: IRA, automatic investment plan—minimum $250/quarter, electronic funds transfer, withdrawal plan
Management fee: 0.6%
Expense ratio: 1.15% (year ending 3/31/94) (1.95% without waiver)
IRA fees: Annual $10, Initial $10

PAYSON VALUE FUND ◆
P.O. Box 446
Portland, ME 04112
207-879-0009, 800-456-6710
fax 207-879-6051

Adviser: H. M. Payson & Co.
Portfolio manager: Mark D. Kaplan (1992)
Custodian: First National Bank of Boston
Transfer agent: Forum Financial Corp.
Investment objective and policies: High total return - current income and capital appreciation. Invests primarily in common stock and securities convertible into common stock of companies believed undervalued. Up to 20% of assets may be in foreign securities and ADRs and 15% in illiquid securities. Fund may hedge.
Year organized: 1992
Ticker symbol: PVFDX
Minimum purchase: Initial: $5,000, Subsequent: $500; IRA: Initial: $2,000
Telephone orders accepted: No
Wire orders accepted: Yes
Deadline for same day wire purchase: 4 P.M.
Qualified for sale in: CA, CO, CT, DC, FL, GA, HI, IL, IN, LA, ME, MA, NH, NJ, NY, NC, OH, PA, RI, VT, WY
Telephone redemptions: Yes

Wire redemptions: Yes, $5,000 minimum
Letter redemptions: Signature guarantee required
Telephone switching: With Payson Balanced Fund, Forum Daily Assets Treasury Fund and other Forum (load) funds
Dividends paid: Income - March, June, September, December; Capital gains - December
Portfolio turnover (2 yrs): 32%, 24%
Largest holding: Empresa National de Electricidad, S.A. (3.4%)
Shareholder services: IRA, automatic investment plan—minimum $250/quarter, electronic funds transfer, withdrawal plan
Management fee: 0.8%
Expense ratio: 1.45% (year ending 3/31/94) (3.04% without waiver)
IRA fees: Annual $10, Initial $10

PBHG FUNDS ◆
(Data common to all PBHG funds are shown below. See subsequent listings for data specific to individual PBHG funds.)

P.O. Box 419534
Kansas City, MO 64141
800-809-8008, 800-433-0051

Administrator: SEI Financial Management Corp.
Adviser: Pilgrim Baxter & Associates, Ltd.
Custodian: CoreStates Bank, N.A.
Transfer Agent: Supervised Service Company
Minimum purchase: Initial: $1,000, Subsequent: None; IRA/Keogh: Initial: $500
Telephone orders accepted: Yes, subsequent only, $1,000 minimum
Wire orders accepted: Yes
Deadline for same day wire purchase: 4 P.M.
Discount broker availability: White
Qualified for sale in: All states
Wire redemptions: Yes, $10 fee
Letter redemptions: Signature guarantee not required
Redemption fee: 2% for shares held less than six months (payable to the fund, waived indefinitely)
Telephone switching: With other PBHG funds
Number of switches permitted: Unlimited
Shareholder services: Keogh, IRA, SEP-IRA, automatic investment plan—minimum $25, electronic funds transfer, withdrawal plan min. req. $5,000
Administration fee: the higher of 0.20% or $75,000
IRA/Keogh fees: Annual $25

PBHG EMERGING GROWTH FUND ◆
(See first PBHG listing for data common to all PBHG funds)

Portfolio managers: Gary L. Pilgrim (1993), Christine Baxter (1993)
Investment objective and policies: Long-term capital growth. Invests primarily in common stocks of small (market capitalization $10-$250M) U.S. companies with records of exceptional growth and prospects for continued strong growth and ADRs of foreign companies. May invest up to 15% of assets in illiquid securities and may hedge.
Year organized: 1993
Ticker symbol: PBEGX
Discount broker availability: *Schwab, *White, Waterhouse, *Fidelity, *Siebert
Dividends paid: Income - May, December; Capital gains - December
Portfolio turnover (1 yr): 96%
Largest holding: IMRS (2.2%)
Management fee: 0.85%
Expense ratio: 1.45% (year ending 10/31/94)

PBHG GROWTH FUND ◆
(See first PBGH listing for data common to all PBHG funds)

Portfolio manager: Gary L. Pilgrim (1985)
Investment objective and policies: Capital growth. Invests primarily in common stocks of companies with prospects for strong earnings growth and significant capital appreciation. Fund will normally

have at least 50% of assets in OTC issues. May invest up to 15% of assets in securities of foreign issuers.
Year organized: 1985
Ticker symbol: PBHGX
Discount broker availability: *Schwab, *White, Waterhouse, *Fidelity, *Siebert
Dividends paid: Income - May, December; Capital gains - December
Portfolio turnover (3 yrs): 94%, 209%, 115%
Largest holding: Michaels Stores (1.4%)
Management fee: 0.85%
Expense ratio: 1.55% (year ending 3/31/94) (1.59% without waiver)

PBHG INTERNATIONAL FUND ◆
(See first PBGH listing for data common to all PBHG funds)

Portfolio manager: W. George Greig (1994)
Investment objective and policies: Capital growth. Invests at least 65% of assets in equity securities of non-U.S. issuers from at least three different countries. May use ADRs and GDRs and forward foreign currency contracts to hedge. Up to 25% of assets may be in securities of companies in emerging markets and 15% in illiquid securities.
Year organized: 1994
Discount broker availability: *Schwab, *White, *Fidelity, *Siebert
Dividends paid: Income - December; Capital gains - December
Management fee: 1.00%

PC&J PERFORMANCE FUND ◆
120 West Third St., Suite 300
Dayton, OH 45402
513-223-0600, fax 513-461-6691

Adviser: Parker, Carlson & Johnson, Inc.
Portfolio manager: James M. Johnson (1983)
Custodian: Star Bank, N.A. Cincinnati
Transfer Agent: PC&J Service Corp.
Investment objective and policies: Long-term capital growth with current income secondary. Invests in common stocks. Seeks to identify undervalued stocks based on comparison of current P/E ratios to 3-5 year earnings growth rate. Up to 15% of assets may be in illiquid securities.
Year organized: 1983 (name changed from PDC&J Performance Fund in 1994)
Minimum purchase: Initial: $1,000, Subsequent: None; IRA/Keogh: Initial: $2,000
Telephone orders accepted: No
Wire orders accepted: Yes
Deadline for same day wire purchase: 4 P.M.
Qualified for sale in: OH
Wire redemptions: Yes
Letter redemptions: Signature guarantee not required
Telephone switching: With PC&J Preservation Fund
Number of switches permitted: Unlimited
Dividends paid: Income - December; Capital gains - December
Portfolio turnover (3 yrs): 69%, 63%, 48%
Largest holding: Deere & Company (3.1%)
Shareholder services: Keogh, IRA
Management fee: 1%
12b-1 distribution fee: Yes (not currently imposed)
Expense ratio: 1.50% (year ending 12/31/94)
IRA/Keogh fees: Annual $20

PC&J PRESERVATION FUND ◆
120 West Third St., Suite 300
Dayton, OH 45402
513-223-0600, fax 513-461-6691

Adviser: Parker, Carlson & Johnson, Inc.
Portfolio manager: Kathleen A. Carlson (1985)
Custodian: Star Bank, N.A. Cincinnati
Transfer Agent: PC&J Service Corp.
Investment objective and policies: Preservation of capital by investing in fixed-income securities. Invests primarily in high grade corporate obligations, U.S. government obligations, CDs, prime

commercial paper and other securities believed of comparable quality with a weighted average maturity of less than 10 years.
Year organized: 1985 (name changed from PDC&J Preservation Fund in 1994)
Minimum purchase: Initial: $1,000, Subsequent: None; IRA/Keogh: Initial: $2,000
Telephone orders accepted: No
Wire orders accepted: Yes
Deadline for same day wire purchase: 4 P.M.
Qualified for sale in: OH
Wire redemptions: Yes
Letter redemptions: Signature guarantee not required
Telephone switching: With PC&J Performance Fund
Number of switches permitted: Unlimited
Dividends paid: Income - December; Capital gains - December
Portfolio turnover (3 yrs): 30%, 37%, 26%
Shareholder services: Keogh, IRA
Management fee: 0.5%
12b-1 distribution fee: Yes (not currently imposed)
Expense ratio: 1.00 (year ending 12/31/94) (includes waiver)
IRA/Keogh fees: Annual $20

PENN-ROYCE FUNDS
(See Royce funds)

PENNSYLVANIA DAILY MUNICIPAL INCOME FUND
600 Fifth Avenue - 8th Floor
New York, NY 10020
212-830-5200, 800-676-6779
prices/yields 212-830-5225
fax 212-830-5476

Adviser: Reich & Tang L.P.
Portfolio manager: Molly Flewharty (1992)
Custodian: Investors Fiduciary Trust Co.
Transfer agent: Fundtech Services L.P.
Investment objective and policies: Interest income exempt from federal and Pennsylvania income taxes consistent with preservation of capital, liquidity and stability of principal. Invests primarily in a non-diversified portfolio of high quality, Pennsylvania municipal money market obligations.
Year organized: 1992
Minimum purchase: Initial: $5,000, Subsequent: $100
Wire orders accepted: Yes
Deadline for same day wire purchase: 12 NN
Qualified for sale in: PA
Telephone redemptions: Yes
Wire redemptions: Yes
Letter redemptions: Signature guarantee required
Telephone switching: With Reich & Tang Funds
Deadline for same day switch: 12 NN
Number of switches permitted: Unlimited, $1,000 minimum
Check redemptions: $250 minimum
Confirmations mailed: After each purchase and each check, mail or wire redemption
Checks returned: As clear
Periodic account statements mailed: Monthly
Dividends paid: Income - declared daily, paid monthly
Shareholder services: Withdrawal plan
Management fee: 0.4%
12b-1 distribution fee: 0.25%
Expense ratio: 0.55% (year ending 11/30/94) (includes waiver)

PERMANENT PORTFOLIO FUNDS ◆
(Data common to all Permanent Portfolios are shown below. See subsequent listings for data specific to individual portfolios.)

625 Second Street, Suite 102
Petaluma, CA 94952
707-778-1000, 800-531-5142
fax 707-778-8804

Shareholder service hours: Full service: M-F 9 A.M.-5 P.M. PST; After hours service: orders, messages, prospectuses

Adviser: World Money Managers
Consultants to the funds: Harry Browne, Douglas Casey
Custodian: State Street Bank & Trust
Transfer agent: Mutual Funds Service Co.
Special accounting procedure: Funds apply special accounting with respect to redemptions and distributions to minimize taxable distributions and maximize capital gains versus ordinary income treatment under the tax laws.
Minimum purchase: Initial: $1,000, Subsequent: $100
Telephone orders accepted: Yes
Wire orders accepted: Yes
Deadline for same day wire purchase: 4 P.M.
Qualified for sale in: All states
Telephone redemptions: Yes
Wire redemptions: Yes, $8 fee
Letter redemptions: Signature guarantee not required
Telephone switching: With other Permanent Portfolio funds
Number of switches permitted: Unlimited, $5 fee
Dividends paid: Income - December; Capital gains - December
Shareholder services: IRA, electronic funds transfer, withdrawal plan min. req. $5,000
Management fee: 0.875% on first $200M to 0.688% over $600M (for total assets of all portfolios)
IRA fees: Annual $8
One-time account start up fee: $35 (covers multiple portfolio accounts)
Account maintenance fee: $1.50 per month (covers multiple portfolio accounts), payable annually from dividends and/or shares, or by check.

PERMANENT PORTFOLIO FUND - AGGRESSIVE GROWTH PORTFOLIO ◆
(See first Permanent Portfolio listing for data common to all Permanent Portfolio portfolios)

Portfolio manager: Terry Coxon (1990)
Investment objective and policies: Long-term capital appreciation in excess of the market as a whole. Remains fully invested at all times in stocks and warrants. At least 60% of its portfolio will be listed on the New York Stock Exchange. Selection will be based on appreciation potential versus current income, involving high technology, new products, price volatility, and/or above-average growth in income, profits or sales.
Year organized: 1990
Ticker symbol: PAGRX
Discount broker availability: Schwab, *White
Portfolio turnover (3 yrs): 30%, 26%, 53%
Largest holding: Syntex Corporation (3.9%)
Expense ratio: 1.20% (year ending 1/31/94)

PERMANENT PORTFOLIO FUND - PERMANENT PORTFOLIO ◆
(See first Permanent Portfolio listing for data common to all Permanent Portfolio portfolios)

Portfolio manager: Terry Coxon (1982)
Investment objective and policies: To preserve and increase the "purchasing power" value of Fund shares over the long term. Fund invests a fixed percentage, balanced continually, of its net assets in the following categories: Gold (20%), silver (5%), Swiss francs (10%), stocks of U.S. and foreign real estate and natural resource companies (15%), aggressive growth stocks (15%), and dollar assets (35%).
Year organized: 1982
Ticker symbol: PRPFX
Discount broker availability: Schwab, *White
Portfolio turnover (3 yrs): 50%, 71%, 8%
Largest holding: One ounce gold coins (12.1%)
Expense ratio: 1.21% (year ending 1/31/94)

PERMANENT PORTFOLIO FUND - TREASURY BILL PORTFOLIO ◆
(See first Permanent Portfolio listing for data common to all Permanent Portfolio portfolios)

Portfolio manager: Terry Coxon (1987)
Investment objective and policies: High current income consistent with safety of principal. Invests in U.S. Treasury bills, and U.S. Treasury bonds and notes having remaining maturities of 13 months or less. Unlike most money market funds, portfolio does not declare dividends daily. They are reinvested which allows the NAV to rise.
Year organized: 1987
Ticker symbol: PRTBX
Discount broker availability: Schwab, *White
Check redemptions: No minimum, $1 per check
Expense ratio: 0.72% (year ending 1/31/94) (1.21% without waiver)

PERMANENT PORTFOLIO FUND - VERSATILE BOND PORTFOLIO ◆
(See first Permanent Portfolio listing for data common to all Permanent Portfolio portfolios)

Portfolio manager: Terry Coxon (1991)
Investment objective and policies: High current income consistent with safety of principal. Invests in corporate bonds rated "A" or higher by S&P and having a remaining maturity of 24 months or less.
Year organized: 1991
Ticker symbol: PRVBX
Discount broker availability: Schwab, *White
Check redemptions: No minimum, $1 per check
Portfolio turnover (3 yrs): 75%, 225%, 602%
Expense ratio: 0.89% (year ending 1/31/94) (1.28% without waiver)

PERRITT CAPITAL GROWTH FUND ◆
680 N. Lake Shore Drive - Suite 2038
Chicago, IL 60611
312-649-6940, 800-338-1579
prices 800-326-6941, fax 312-649-5537

Shareholder service hours: Full service: M-F 8 A.M.-7 P.M. CST
Adviser: Perritt Investments, Inc.
Portfolio manager: Gerald W. Perritt (1988)
Custodian and transfer agent: Firstar Trust Co.
Investment objective and policies: Long-term capital growth. Invests primarily in common stocks of smaller (under $200M capitalization), rapidly growing companies. More than 20% of assets may be in money market instruments for defensive purposes. May use options to hedge up to 25% of total assets.
Year organized: 1988
Ticker symbol: PRCGX
Minimum purchase: Initial: $1,000, Subsequent: $250; IRA/Keogh: Initial: $250
Telephone orders accepted: No
Wire orders accepted: Yes
Deadline for same day wire purchase: 1 P.M.
Discount broker availability: Schwab, *White
Qualified for sale in: All states except AR, MT, NH, ND, SD, UT, VT
Letter redemptions: Signature guarantee required over $10,000
Dividends paid: Income - December; Capital gains - December
Portfolio turnover (3 yrs): 39%, 35%, 24%
Largest holding: Pomeroy Computer (4.3%)
Shareholder services: Keogh, IRA, SEP-IRA, 401(k), 403(b), automatic investment plan—minimum $50/month (waives initial minimum), electronic funds transfer (purchase only), withdrawal plan min. req. $10,000
Management fee: 0.7%
Expense ratio: 2.00% (year ending 10/31/94)
IRA/Keogh fees: Annual $12.50

PHILADELPHIA FUND
1200 North Federal Highway - Suite 424
Boca Raton, FL 33432
407-395-2155, 800-749-9933
fax 407-338-7590

Adviser: Baxter Financial Corp.
Portfolio manager: Donald H. Baxter (1987)
Custodian and transfer agent: State Street Bank & Trust Co.

Investment objective and policies: Long-term capital growth & income. Invests primarily in common stocks traded on major U.S. security exchanges but may acquire unlisted securities as well. May invest up to 20% of assets in foreign securities. Fund may buy & sell options and futures contracts.
Year organized: 1923
Ticker symbol: PHILX
Minimum purchase: Initial: $1,000, Subsequent: None
Telephone orders accepted: No
Wire orders accepted: No
Qualified for sale in: All states except AZ, AR, DE, ID, KS, LA, MN, MT, NE, NH, NM, ND, OK, OR, SD, UT, WA, WI
Letter redemptions: Signature guarantee required
Dividends paid: Income - March, June, September, December; Capital gains - December
Portfolio turnover (3 yrs): 28%, 24%, 39%
Largest holding: Treasury Note due 11/15/01 (12.3%)
Shareholder services: Keogh, IRA, corporate retirement plans, automatic investment plan
Management fee: 0.75% first $200M to 0.5% over $400M
12b-1 distribution fee: 0.25%
Expense ratio: 1.67% (year ending 11/30/94)
IRA/Keogh fees: Annual $10, Initial $10, Closing $10

THE PIERPONT FUNDS ◆
(Data common to all Pierpont funds are shown below. See subsequent listings for data specific to individual Pierpont funds.)

6 St. James Avenue
Boston, MA 02116
800-521-5411

Adviser: Morgan Guaranty Trust Co.
Distributor: Signature Broker-Dealer Services, Inc.
Custodian and transfer agent: State Street Bank & Trust Co.
Special sales restrictions: All transactions in fund accounts must be processed through a Morgan Guaranty account or a Morgan Stanley account. Prospective investors must apply to become customers of Morgan Stanley.
Minimum purchase: Initial: $25,000 ($10,000 for shareholders of another Pierpont fund), Subsequent: $5,000; IRA/Keogh: Initial: $10,000, Subsequent: $2,000
Telephone orders accepted: No
Wire orders accepted: No
Qualified for sale in: All states
Telephone redemptions: Yes
Telephone switching: With other Pierpont funds
Number of switches permitted: Unlimited
Shareholder services: IRA, Keogh, 403(b)

THE PIERPONT BOND FUND ◆
(See first Pierpont listing for data common to all Pierpont funds)

Portfolio managers: William G. Tennille (1994), Connie J. Plaehn (1994)
Investment objective and policies: High current income consistent with moderate risk of capital and maintenance of liquidity. Invests primarily in a mix of investment-grade corporate and government bonds. Up to 25% of assets may be invested in securities of foreign issuers. Fund maintains a weighted average maturity of +/- 1 year from the duration of the Salomon Brothers Broad Investment-grade Bond Index.
Year organized: 1988
Ticker symbol: PPBDX
Discount broker availability: White
Dividends paid: Income - declared daily, paid monthly, Capital gains - December
Portfolio turnover (3 yrs): 232%, 236%, 267%
Management fee: 0.30%
Expense ratio: 0.78% (year ending 10/31/94) (0.79% without waiver)

THE PIERPONT CAPITAL APPRECIATION FUND ◆

(See first Pierpont listing for data common to all Pierpont funds)

Portfolio managers: James B. Otness (1993), Fred W. Kittler (1994)
Investment objective and policies: Long-term capital appreciation and current income. Invests primarily in growth-oriented common stocks of small companies, primarily those listed in the Russell 2500 Index. May have up to 30% of assets in securities of foreign issuers and use futures and options to hedge.
Year organized: 1985
Ticker symbol: PPCAX
Discount broker availability: White
Dividends paid: Income - June, December, Capital gains - December
Portfolio turnover (3 yrs): 14%, 50%, 58%
Largest holding: Sbarro (1.8%)
Management fee: 0.60%
Expense ratio: 0.90% (year ending 5/31/94) (1.10% without waiver)

THE PIERPONT DIVERSIFIED FUND ◆

(See first Pierpont listing for data common to all Pierpont funds)

Portfolio managers: Gerald H. Osterberg (1993), Paul J. Stegmayer (1993)
Investment objective and policies: Long-term capital appreciation and current income. Normally invests 65% of assets in equity securities of companies with market capitalizations over $1.5B and 35% in fixed-income securities but will adjust mix to reflect changes in economic and market conditions. May invest up to 30% of assets in securities of foreign issuers and use futures and options to hedge.
Year organized: 1993
Dividends paid: Income - June, December; Capital gains - December
Portfolio turnover (1 yr): 115%
Largest holding: U.S. Treasury Notes 5.125% due 4/30/98 (3.7%)
Management fee: 0.55%
Expense ratio: 0.98% (7 months ending 6/30/94) (2.50% without waiver)

THE PIERPONT EMERGING MARKETS EQUITY FUND ◆

(See first Pierpont listing for data common to all Pierpont funds)

Portfolio managers: Douglas J. Dooley (1993), Mehta Satyen (1993)
Investment objective and policies: Long-term capital appreciation and current income. Normally invests at least 65% of assets in equity securities of established companies in at least 3 emerging markets countries the advisor has identified as attractive. May use forward foreign currency exchange contracts, futures and options to hedge.
Year organized: 1993
Ticker symbol: PPEEX
Discount broker availability: White
Dividends paid: Income - December; Capital gains - December
Portfolio turnover (1 yr): 27%
Largest holding: Compania Vale Do Rio Doce, Brazil (2.4%)
Management fee: 1.00%
Expense ratio: 1.84% (year ending 10/31/94) (1.96% without waiver)

THE PIERPONT EQUITY FUND ◆

(See first Pierpont listing for data common to all Pierpont funds)

Portfolio managers: William B. Petersen (1993), William M. Riegel (1993)
Investment objective and policies: Long-term capital appreciation and current income that exceeds return of the S&P 500 Index. Invests primarily in

common stock, preferred stock and convertible securities of domestic corporations with market capitalizations over $1.5B. May invest up to 30% of assets in securities of foreign issuers and use futures and options to hedge.
Year organized: 1985
Ticker symbol: PPEQX
Discount broker availability: White
Dividends paid: Income - March, June, October, December; Capital gains - December
Portfolio turnover (3 yrs): 10%, 60%, 99%
Largest holding: General Motors Corp. (2.4%)
Management fee: 0.40%
Expense ratio: 0.90% (year ending 5/31/94) (0.93% without waiver)

THE PIERPONT INTERNATIONAL EQUITY FUND ◆

(See first Pierpont listing for data common to all Pierpont funds)

Portfolio managers: Paul A. Quinsee (1993), Thomas P. Madsen (1993)
Investment objective and policies: Long-term capital appreciation and current income. Invests primarily in equity securities of foreign issuers from at least 3 countries outside the U.S. Issuers are normally established companies in developed countries but fund may also invest in securities of issuers based in emerging market countries. May use forward foreign currency contracts, futures and options to hedge.
Year organized: 1990
Ticker symbol: PPIEX
Discount broker availability: White
Dividends paid: Income - March, June, October, December; Capital gains - December
Portfolio turnover (1 yr): 56%, 34%, 30%
Largest holding: Tokai Bank of Japan (1.3%)
Management fee: 0.60%
Expense ratio: 1.36% (year ending 10/31/94) (1.43% without waiver)

THE PIERPONT MONEY MARKET FUND ◆

(See first Pierpont listing for data common to all Pierpont funds)

Portfolio managers: Robert K. Johnson (1988), Daniel B. Mulvey (1995)
Investment objective and policies: Maximum current income consistent with preservation of capital and maintenance of liquidity. Invests in money market instruments.
Year organized: 1982
Dividends paid: Income - declared daily, paid monthly
Management fee: 0.18% first $1.5B, 0.15% over $1.5B
Expense ratio: 0.43% (year ending 11/30/94)

THE PIERPONT SHORT TERM BOND FUND ◆

(See first Pierpont listing for data common to all Pierpont funds)

Investment objective and policies: High current income consistent with modest risk of capital and maintenance of liquidity. Invests primarily in a mix of investment-grade corporate and government bonds with a weighted average maturity of 1 to 3 years. May use futures and options to hedge.
Year organized: 1993
Dividends paid: Income - declared daily, paid monthly, Capital gains - December
Management fee: 0.25%
Expense ratio: 0.69% (year ending 10/31/94) (2.05% without waiver)

THE PIERPONT TAX EXEMPT BOND FUND ◆

(See first Pierpont listing for data common to all Pierpont funds)

Portfolio managers: Elbridge T. Gerry III (1992), Elizabeth A. Augustin (1992)
Investment objective and policies: High current

income exempt from federal income tax consistent with moderate risk of capital and maintenance of liquidity. Invests primarily in investment-grade municipal securities with a weighted average maturity of 4 to 7 years.
Year organized: 1984
Ticker symbol: PPTBX
Discount broker availability: White
Dividends paid: Income - declared daily, paid monthly, Capital gains - December
Portfolio turnover (3 yrs): 33%, 41%, 20%
Management fee: 0.30%
Expense ratio: 0.71% (year ending 8/31/94)

THE PIERPONT TAX EXEMPT MONEY MARKET FUND ◆

(See first Pierpont listing for data common to all Pierpont funds)

Portfolio managers: Elizabeth A. Augustin (1992), Elbridge T. Gerry III (1992)
Investment objective and policies: Maximum current income exempt from federal income tax consistent with preservation of capital and maintenance of liquidity. Invests in municipal money market instruments.
Year organized: 1983
Dividends paid: Income - declared daily, paid monthly
Management fee: 0.20% first $1B, 0.10% over $1B
Expense ratio: 0.52% (year ending 8/31/94) (0.53% without waiver)

THE PIERPONT TREASURY MONEY MARKET FUND ◆

(See first Pierpont listing for data common to all Pierpont funds)

Portfolio managers: James A. Hayes (1993), Robert R. Johnson (1993)
Investment objective and policies: Maximum current income consistent with preservation of capital and maintenance of liquidity. Invests exclusively in direct obligations of the U.S. Treasury with a weighted average maturity of 90 days or less.
Year organized: 1993
Dividends paid: Income - declared daily, paid monthly
Management fee: 0.20% first $1B, 0.10% over $1B
Expense ratio: 0.40% (year ending 10/31/94) (0.62% without waiver)

PILGRIM BAXTER EMERGING GROWTH FUND

(See PBHG Emerging Growth Fund)

PINNACLE FUND ◆

36 South Pennsylvania Street - Suite 610
Indianapolis, IN 46204
317-633-4080

Adviser: Heartland Capital Management, Inc.
Portfolio manager: Barry F. Ebert (1985)
Custodian and transfer agent: Firstar Trust Co.
Investment objective and policies: Long-term capital appreciation. Invests primarily in common stocks but may invest in fixed-income securities and money market instruments for defensive purposes.
Year organized: 1985 (2 for 1 split on 10/9/89)
Minimum purchase: Initial: $1,000, Subsequent: $100
Telephone orders accepted: No
Wire orders accepted: No
Qualified for sale in: IN, MI, OH
Letter redemptions: Signature guarantee required over $5,000
Dividends paid: Income - December; Capital gains - December
Portfolio turnover (3 yrs): 33%, 55%, 53%
Largest holding: General Motors Corp. Class H (3.0)
Shareholder services: IRA, automatic investment plan—minimum $50/month, electronic funds transfer (purchase only)

Management fee: 0.8%
Expense ratio: 1.17% (year ending 12/31/93)
IRA fees: Annual $12.50

PORTICO FUNDS ◆
(Data common to all Portico funds are shown below. See subsequent listings fro data specific to individual Portico funds.)

615 East Michigan Street
P.O. Box 3011
Milwaukee, WI 53201
414-287-3808, 800-982-8909
prices/yield 800-228-1024

Shareholder service hours: Full service: M-F 8 A.M.-7 P.M. CST; After hours service: prices, yields, balances, transactions, DJIA
Adviser: FIRMCO
Distributor/Administrator: Sunstone Financial Group, Inc.
Custodian and transfer agent: Firstar Trust Co.
Minimum purchase: Initial: $1,000, Subsequent: $100: IRA/Keogh: Initial: $100
Wire orders accepted: Yes, $7.50 fee
Deadline for same day wire purchase: 12:00 NN
Telephone redemptions: Yes, $500 minimum
Wire redemptions: Yes, $500 minimum, $7.50 fee
Letter redemptions: Signature guarantee required over $50,000
Telephone switching: With other Portico funds, $1,000 minimum (all Portico stock and bond funds have loads)
Number of switches permitted: 4 per year
Deadline for same day switch: 12:30 P.M.
Check redemptions: $250 minimum
Confirmations mailed: Not mailed
Checks returned: Not returned
Periodic account statements mailed: Monthly
Dividends paid: Income - declared daily, paid monthly
Shareholder services: Keogh, IRA, SEP-IRA, 401(k), automatic investment plan—minimum $50/month, directed dividends, withdrawal plan min. req. $15,000
Management fee: 0.5%
Administrative fee: 0.125% first $2B, 0.10% over $2B (for aggregate total of all Portico funds)
12b-1 distribution fee: Maximum of 0.25% (not currently imposed)
IRA/Keogh fees: Annual $12.50, Closing $15

PORTICO MONEY MARKET FUND ◆
(See first Portico listing for data common to all Portico funds)

Portfolio managers: Mary Ellen Stanek (1988), Jane Keelan (1988)
Investment objective and policies: Current income consistent with preservation of capital, liquidity and stable NAV. Invests in a broad range of government, bank and commercial money market instruments.
Year organized: 1988 (formerly Elan Money Market Fund)
Ticker symbol: POMXX
Qualified for sale in: All states
Expense ratio: 0.60% (year ending 10/31/94) (includes waiver)

PORTICO TAX-EXEMPT MONEY MARKET FUND ◆
(See first Portico listing for data common to all Portico funds)

Portfolio manager: Gary Elfe (1993)
Investment objective and policies: Current income exempt from federal income taxes consistent with preservation of capital, liquidity and stable NAV. Invests in municipal money market instruments.
Year organized: 1988 (formerly Elan Tax-Exempt Money Market Fund)
Ticker symbol: POTXX
Qualified for sale in: All states
Expense ratio: 0.60% (year ending 10/31/94) (includes waiver)

PORTICO U.S. FEDERAL MONEY MARKET FUND ◆
(See first Portico listing for data common to all Portico portfolios)

Portfolio managers: Mary Ellen Stanek (1991), Jane Keelan (1991)
Investment objective and policies: Current income exempt from state income taxes consistent with preservation of capital, liquidity and stable NAV. Invests in obligations issued or guaranteed by the U.S. Government, its agencies or instrumentalities, the interest income from which is generally exempt from state income taxation.
Year organized: 1991
Ticker symbol: PUJXX
Qualified for sale in: AZ, CA, CO, CT, DC, FL, GA, HI, ID, IL, IN, IA, KY, MI, MN, MT, NE, NV, NJ, NY, NC, OH, OK, OR, PA, SD, TX, UT, VA, WV, WI, WY
Expense ratio: 0.60% (year ending 10/31/94) (includes waiver)

PORTICO U.S. GOVERNMENT MONEY MARKET FUND ◆
(See first Portico listing for data common to all Portico portfolios)

Portfolio managers: Mary Ellen Stanek (1988), Jane Keelan (1988)
Investment objective and policies: Current income consistent with preservation of capital, liquidity and stable NAV. Invests in obligations issued or guaranteed by the U.S. Government, its agencies or instrumentalities, and in repurchase agreements relating to such obligations, irrespective of state income tax considerations.
Year organized: 1988 (formerly Elan U.S. Government Money Market Fund)
Ticker symbol: POGXX
Qualified for sale in: All states
Expense ratio: 0.60% (year ending 10/31/94) (includes waiver)

PRA REAL ESTATE SECURITIES FUND ◆
900 North Michigan Avenue, Suite 1000
Chicago, IL 60611
312-915-3600, 800-435-1405
fax 312-915-3604

Adviser: PRA Securities Advisors, L.P.
Portfolio managers: Michael T. Oliver (1989), Dean A. Sotter (1993)
Custodian: Wilmington Trust Co.
Transfer agent: Rodney Square Management Corp.
Investment objective and policies: High total return consistent with reasonable risk. Invests primarily in equity securities of public companies principally engaged in the real estate business - ownership, construction, management, financing or sale of, residential, commercial or industrial real estate. Fund normally invests 60% to 90% of assets in REITs.
Year organized: 1989
Ticker symbol: PRREX
Minimum purchase: Initial: $2,000, Subsequent: None
Telephone orders accepted: No
Wire orders accepted: Yes
Deadline for same day wire purchase: 4 P.M.
Discount broker availability: Schwab, White
Qualified for sale in: All states except CT, MA, MO, WI
Telephone redemptions: Yes
Wire redemptions: Yes, $10 fee
Letter redemptions: Signature guarantee not required
Dividends paid: Income - March, June, September, December; Capital gains - December
Portfolio turnover (3 yrs): 90%, 61%, 28%
Largest holding: Manufactured Home Communities, Inc. (5.7%)
Management fee: 0.75% first $100M, 0.65% over $100M
Expense ratio): 1.22% (year ending 9/30/94)
IRA fees: Annual $10

PREFERRED FUNDS INC. ◆
(Data common to all Preferred funds are shown below. See subsequent listings for data specific to individual Preferred funds.)

100 N.E. Adams Street
Peoria, IL 61629-5330
309-675-5123, 800-662-4769
fax 309-675-6991

Adviser: Caterpiller Investment Management Ltd.
Custodian: State Street Bank & Trust Co.
Transfer agent: Boston Financial Data Services, Inc.
Year organized: 1992
Minimum purchase: Initial: $1,000, Subsequent: $50; IRA: Initial $250
Telephone orders accepted: No
Wire orders accepted: Yes, $1,000 minimum
Deadline for same day wire purchase: 4 P.M.
Qualified for sale in: All states
Telephone redemptions: Yes
Wire redemptions: Yes, $100 minimum, $10 fee
Letter redemptions: Signature guarantee required over $50,000
Telephone switching: With other Preferred funds, 10 day hold
Number of switches permitted: Unlimited (fund reserves right to limit to 1 round trip every 120 days)
Shareholder services: IRA, SEP-IRA, automatic investment plan (waives initial minimum), electronic funds transfer, withdrawal plan
IRA/Keogh fees: Annual $10 per fund ($30 maximum, waived for accounts with assets of $5,000 or more)

PREFERRED ASSET ALLOCATION FUND ◆
(See first Preferred listing for data common to all Preferred funds)

Sub-advisers: Mellon Capital Management Corp. & PanAgora Asset Management, Inc.
Portfolio managers: Thomas B. Hazuka (1992), Edgar F. Peters (1992)
Investment objective and policies: Capital appreciation and current income. Invests in stocks, bonds and high quality money market instruments. Proportion in each asset class will vary depending on changes in interest rates and other economic factors. May invest without limit in securities of foreign issuers traded in domestic securities markets and invest up to 10% of assets directly in foreign securities. Up to 15% of assets may be in illiquid securities. May use futures and options and sell short.
Ticker symbol: PFAAX
Discount broker availability: White
Dividends paid: Income - June, December; Capital gains - December
Portfolio turnover (2 yrs): 25%, 34%
Largest holding: Treasury Bond due in 2016 (3.2%)
Management fee: 0.70%
Expense ratio: 1.25% (year ending 6/30/94)

PREFERRED FIXED INCOME FUND ◆
(See first Preferred listing for data common to all Preferred funds)

Sub-adviser: J.P. Morgan Investment Management, Inc.
Portfolio manager: Paul L. Zemsky (1994)
Investment objective and policies: High level of current income. Invests primarily in publicly traded investment-grade debt securities - U.S. Treasury and agency obligations, mortgage-backed securities and corporate debt securities - with a weighted average maturity of 3 to 7 years. May invest without limit in securities of foreign issuers traded in domestic securities markets and invest up to 10% of assets directly in foreign securities. Up to 15% of assets may be in illiquid securities. May sell short and use futures and options to increase current return and hedge.
Ticker symbol: PFIXX

Discount broker availability: White
Dividends paid: Income - declared daily, paid monthly; Capital gains - December
Portfolio turnover (2 yrs): 255%, 316%
Management fee: 0.65%
Expense ratio: 0.97% (year ending 6/30/94)

PREFERRED GROWTH FUND ◆
(See first Preferred listing for data common to all Preferred funds)

Sub-adviser: Jennison Associates Capital Corp.
Portfolio manager: Lulu C. Wang (1992)
Investment objective and policies: Long-term capital appreciation. Invests at least 65% of assets in equity securities believed to offer potential for capital appreciation, including stocks of companies experiencing above average earnings growth. May invest without limit in securities of foreign issuers traded in domestic securities markets and invest up to 10% of assets directly in foreign securities. Up to 15% of assets may be in illiquid securities. May use futures and options and sell short.
Ticker symbol: PFGRX
Discount broker availability: White
Dividends paid: Income - December; Capital gains - December
Portfolio turnover (2 yrs): 52%, 58%
Largest holding: United Healthcare Corp. (4.0%)
Management fee: 0.75%
Expense ratio: 0.91% (year ending 6/30/94)

PREFERRED INTERNATIONAL FUND ◆
(See first Preferred listing for data common to all Preferred funds)

Sub-adviser: Mercator Asset Management, Inc.
Portfolio manager: Peter F. Spano (1992)
Investment objective and policies: Long-term capital appreciation. Invests primarily in equity securities traded principally on markets outside the U.S. believed undervalued. Normally at least 65% of assets will be invested in at least 3 different countries not including the U.S. Up to 15% of assets may be in illiquid securities. May use futures and options and sell short.
Ticker symbol: PFIFX
Discount broker availability: White
Dividends paid: Income - December; Capital gains - December
Portfolio turnover (2 yrs): 28%, 16%
Management fee: 1.38%
Expense ratio: 1.38% (year ending 6/30/94)

PREFERRED MONEY MARKET FUND ◆
(See first Preferred listing for data common to all Preferred funds)

Sub-adviser: J.P. Morgan Investment Management, Inc.
Portfolio manager: Robert R. Johnson (1992)
Investment objective and policies: Maximum current income consistent with preservation of capital and liquidity. Invests in a broad range of government, bank and commercial money market instruments.
Check redemptions: $250 minimum
Confirmations mailed: After each purchase and each check, mail or wire redemption
Checks returned: Monthly
Periodic account statements mailed: Monthly
Dividends paid: Income - declared daily, paid monthly
Management fee: 0.3%
Expense ratio: 0.53% (year ending 6/30/94) (0.68% without waiver)

PREFERRED SHORT-TERM GOVERNMENT SECURITIES FUND ◆
(See first Preferred listing for data common to all Preferred funds)

Portfolio manager: Todd M. Sheridan (1993)
Investment objective and policies: High level of current income consistent with preservation of cap-

ital. Invests primarily in securities issued or guaranteed as to principal and interest by the U.S. Government, its agencies, authorities or instrumentalities with a weighted average maturity of 3 years or less. Up to 15% of assets may be in illiquid securities. May sell short and use futures and options to increase current return and hedge.
Ticker symbol: PFSGX
Discount broker availability: White
Check redemptions: $250 minimum
Dividends paid: Income - declared daily, paid monthly; Capital gains - December
Portfolio turnover (2 yrs): 134%, 268%
Management fee: 0.35%
Expense ratio: 0.74% (year ending 6/30/94)

PREFERRED VALUE FUND ◆
(See first Preferred listing for data common to all Preferred funds)

Sub-adviser: Oppenheimer Capital
Portfolio manager: John G. Lindenthal (1992)
Investment objective and policies: Capital appreciation and current income. Normally invests at least 65% of assets in equity securities - common stocks, preferred stocks and convertible securities - believed undervalued that offer above-average potential for capital appreciation. May invest without limit in securities of foreign issuers traded in domestic securities markets and invest up to 10% of assets directly in foreign securities. Up to 15% of assets may be in illiquid securities. May use futures and options and sell short.
Ticker symbol: PFVLX
Discount broker availability: White
Dividends paid: Income - December; Capital gains - December
Portfolio turnover (2 yrs): 12%, 18%
Largest holding: First Interstate Bancorp (3.8%)
Management fee: 0.75%
Expense ratio: 0.93% (year ending 6/30/94)

T. ROWE PRICE FUNDS ◆
(Data common to all T. Rowe Price funds are shown below. See subsequent listings for data specific to individual Price funds)

P.O. Box 89000
Baltimore, MD 21289-9999
410-547-2308, 410-625-6500
800-638-5660, 800-225-5132
prices/yields 800-638-2587
TDD 800-367-0763, fax 410-347-1572

Shareholder service hours: Full service: M-F 8 A.M.-10 P.M., Sat-Sun 8:30 A.M.-5 P.M. EST; After hours service: prices, yields, dividends, total returns, balances, orders, last transaction, prospectuses, DJIA
Adviser: T. Rowe Price Associates, Inc. (except International Trust)
Custodian and transfer agent: State Street Bank & Trust Co.
Minimum purchase: Initial: $2,500, Subsequent: $100; IRA/Keogh: Initial: $1,000, Subsequent: $50 (Summit funds)
Telephone orders accepted: Yes, $5,000 minimum
Wire orders accepted: Yes
Deadline for same day wire purchase: 4 P.M.
Qualified for sale in: All states (exceptions noted)
Telephone redemptions: Yes
Wire redemptions: Yes, $5 fee under $5,000
Letter redemptions: Signature guarantee required over $50,000
Telephone switching: With other T. Rowe Price Funds
Number of switches permitted: 2 per 120 days when switching more than 50% of assets except money funds
Shareholder services: Keogh, IRA, SEP-IRA, 401(k), 403(b), corporate retirement plans, automatic investment plan—minimum $50/month (waives initial minimum), directed dividends, withdrawal plan min. req. $10,000, electronic funds transfer
Management fee: Each fund pays a minimum amount plus a pro rata share, based on assets, of a

group fee levied on total assets of all funds under management, ranging from 0.48% of the first $1B down to 0.31% over $34B.
IRA fees: Annual $10 (waived for accounts with assets of $5,000 or more)
Keogh fees: Annual $10

T. ROWE PRICE ADJUSTABLE RATE U.S. GOVERNMENT FUND ◆
(See first T. Rowe Price listing for data common to all Price funds)

Portfolio manager: J. Peter Van Dyke (1991)
Investment objective and policies: High current income, consistent with minimum fluctuation in share price. Invests at least 65% of assets in adjustable rate mortgage securities (ARMs) and collateralized mortgage obligations (CMOs). May also invest in high-quality fixed and adjustable rate mortgage and debt securities rated within the two highest credit categories. Up to 10% of assets may be in derivatives.
Year organized: 1991
Ticker symbol: PRARX
Discount broker availability: Schwab, White, Waterhouse, Fidelity, Siebert
Check redemptions: $500 minimum
Dividends paid: Income - declared daily, paid monthly; Capital gains - March, December
Portfolio turnover (3 yrs): 70%, 111%, 98%
Management fee: 0.10% + pro-rata group fee
Expense ratio: 0.40% (year ending 2/28/94) (includes waiver)

T. ROWE PRICE BALANCED FUND ◆
(See first T. Rowe Price listing for data common to all Price funds)

Portfolio manager: Richard T. Whitney (1991)
Investment objective and policies: Long-term total return - capital growth and income - consistent with conservation of principal. Normally invests 60% of assets in stocks and 40% in bonds and money market securities. May invest up to 20% of assets in asset-backed securities and 15% in foreign securities and use futures and options on up to 25% of assets.
Year organized: 1991 (Axe-Houghton Fund B merged into T. Rowe Price Balanced Fund on 8/31/92)
Ticker symbol: RPBAX
Discount broker availability: Schwab, Fidelity, Siebert
Dividends paid: Income - March, June, September, December; Capital gains - December
Portfolio turnover (3 yrs): 33%, 9%, 208%
Largest holding: British Columbia Hydro & Power bond (1.0%)
Management fee: 0.15% + pro-rata group fee
Expense ratio: 1.00% (year ending 12/31/94) (includes waiver)

T. ROWE PRICE BLUE CHIP GROWTH FUND ◆
(See first T. Rowe Price listing for data common to all Price funds)

Portfolio manager: Thomas H. Broadus, Jr. (1993)
Investment objective and policies: Capital growth with current income secondary. Invests primarily in common stocks of well-established companies with potential for above-average growth in earnings. May invest in convertible securities, preferred stocks and fixed-income securities. Up to 20% of assets may be in foreign securities and 15% in illiquid securities. May use futures and options on up to 25% of assets.
Year organized: 1993
Ticker symbol: TRBCX
Discount broker availability: Schwab, Fidelity, Siebert
Dividends paid: Income - December; Capital gains - December
Portfolio turnover (2 yrs): 75%, 89%

Largest holding: NationsBank (1.9%)
Management fee: 0.30% + pro-rata group fee
Expense ratio: 1.25% (6 months ending 12/31/94)
(includes waiver)

T. ROWE PRICE CALIFORNIA
TAX-FREE BOND FUND ◆
(See first T. Rowe Price listing for data common to
all Price funds)

Portfolio manager: Mary J. Miller (1990)
Investment objective and policies: High current
income exempt from federal and California state
income taxes. Invests primarily in long-term municipal securities exempt from such taxes with a
weighted average maturity greater than 10 years.
Fund may use interest rate futures (initial margin
limited to 5% of assets, exposure limited to 30% of
portfolio) and private placements (limited to 10%
of assets). Up to 20% of assets may be in AMT
securities.
Year organized: 1986
Ticker symbol: PRXCX
Discount broker availability: White, Waterhouse
Qualified for sale in: AZ, CA, DC, HI, MD, NV,
OR, WY
Check redemptions: $500 minimum
Dividends paid: Income - declared daily, paid
monthly; Capital gains - December
Portfolio turnover (3 yrs): 73%, 58%, 80%
Management fee: 0.1% + pro-rata group fee
Expense ratio: 0.60% (year ending 2/28/94)
(0.67% without waiver)

T. ROWE PRICE CALIFORNIA
TAX-FREE MONEY FUND ◆
(See first T. Rowe Price listing for data common to
all Price funds)

Portfolio manager: Patrice L. Berchtenbreiter
(1990)
Investment objective and policies: Preservation of
capital, liquidity and high current income exempt
from federal and California state income taxes.
Invests primarily in California municipal money
market securities.
Year organized: 1986
Qualified for sale in: AZ, CA, DC, HI, MD, NV,
NJ, OR, WY
Check redemptions: $500 minimum
Confirmations mailed: After each purchase and
each check, mail or wire redemption
Checks returned: Monthly
Periodic account statements mailed: Monthly
Dividends paid: Income - declared daily, paid
monthly
Management fee: 0.1% + pro-rata group fee
Expense ratio: 0.55% (year ending 2/28/94)
(0.81% without waiver)

T. ROWE PRICE CAPITAL
APPRECIATION FUND ◆
(See first T. Rowe Price listing for data common to
all Price funds)

Portfolio manager: Richard P. Howard (1989)
Investment objective and policies: Capital appreci-
ation. Invests primarily in common stocks of under-
valued and out of favor companies and those
expected to increase in price in the short term. May
have up to 25% of assets in foreign securities, 15%
in junk bonds, 10% in derivatives and use futures
and options on up to 25% of assets.
Year organized: 1986
Ticker symbol: PRWCX
Discount broker availability: Schwab, White,
Waterhouse, Fidelity, Siebert
Dividends paid: Income - December; Capital gains
- December
Portfolio turnover (3 yrs): 44%, 39%, 30%
Largest holding: Automatic Data Processing Corp.
(3.8%)
Management fee: 0.30% + pro-rata group fee; fee
will be adjusted 0.02% per 1% the fund out/under-
performs the S&P 500 up to a 0.30% maximum per
year.
Expense ratio: 1.10% (year ending 12/31/94)

T. ROWE PRICE CAPITAL
OPPORTUNITY FUND ◆
(See first T. Rowe Price listing for data common to
all Price funds)

Portfolio manager: John F. Wakeman (1994)
Investment objective and policies: Capital appreciation. Invests primarily in common stocks believed
undervalued with no limits on capitalization. May
buy both growth and value stocks. Fund may have
more than 5% of assets in individual stocks and will
only invest in 30 to 50 different companies. May
have up to 20% of assets in foreign securities, 10%
in junk bonds, 10% in derivatives and use private
placements and futures and options on up to 25%
of assets.
Year organized: 1994
Dividends paid: Income - December; Capital gains
- December
Management fee: 0.45% + pro-rata group fee

T. ROWE PRICE DIVIDEND
GROWTH FUND ◆
(See first T. Rowe Price listing for data common to
all Price funds)

Portfolio managers: William J. Stromberg (1992)
Investment objective and policies: Increasing dividend income, long-term capital growth and reasonable current income. Invests primarily in common
stocks of dividend-paying companies with potential
for increasing dividends and capital growth. May
invest in convertible securities, preferred stocks and
fixed-income securities. Up to 25% of assets in for-
eign securities, 15% in illiquid securities and 10%
in derivatives. May use futures and options on up to
25% of assets.
Year organized: 1992
Ticker symbol: PRDGX
Discount broker availability: Schwab, White,
Fidelity, Siebert
Dividends paid: Income - March, June, September,
December; Capital gains - December
Portfolio turnover (2 yrs): 71%, 51%
Largest holding: Hubbell (3.0%
Management fee: 0.20% + pro-rata group fee
Expense ratio: 1.00% (year ending 12/31/94)
(includes waiver)

T. ROWE PRICE EMERGING
MARKETS BOND FUND ◆
(See first T. Rowe Price listing for data common to
all Price funds)

Adviser: Rowe Price-Fleming International, Inc.
Portfolio manager: Peter B. Askew (1995)
Investment objective and policies: High current
income with capital growth. Invests at least 65% of
assets in high-yield corporate and government
fixed-income securities of issuers in emerging foreign markets. Fund invests primarily in junk bonds
with a weighted average maturity of 5 to 10 years.
May hedge in currencies in spot/forward markets
(up to 50% of total assets) and use interest rate and
currency futures and options on up to 25% of
assets.
Year organized: 1995
Check redemptions: $500 minimum
Dividends paid: Income - declared daily, paid
monthly; Capital gains - December
Management fee: 0.45% + pro-rata group fee

T. ROWE PRICE EQUITY
INCOME FUND ◆
(See first T. Rowe Price listing for data common to
all Price funds)

Portfolio managers: Thomas H. Broadus, Jr.
(1985), Brian C. Rogers (1985)
Investment objective and policies: High current
income and capital growth. Invests primarily in dividend-paying common stocks of established companies having favorable prospects for increasing
dividend income with expected income higher than
that of the S&P 500. Up to 25% of assets may be in
foreign securities and 10% in derivatives. May use

options on up to 25% of net assets.
Year organized: 1985
Ticker symbol: PRFDX
Discount broker availability: Schwab, White,
Waterhouse, Fidelity, Siebert
Dividends paid: Income - March, June, September,
December; Capital gains - December
Portfolio turnover (3 yrs): 36%, 31%, 30%
Largest holding: Philip Morris (1.9%)
Management fee: 0.25% + pro-rata group fee
Expense ratio: 0.88% (year ending 12/31/94)

T. ROWE PRICE
EQUITY INDEX FUND ◆
(See first T. Rowe Price listing for data common to
all Price funds)

Portfolio manager: Richard T. Whitney (1990)
Investment objective and policies: Replicate the
performance of the S&P 500 Composite Price
Index. Fund attempts to own all 500 stocks in their
approximate index weightings, producing a correla-
tion of at least 0.95. May use stock index futures
(initial margin limited to 5% of assets) and options
to maintain a fully invested position and liquidity.
Year organized: 1990
Ticker symbol: PREIX
Dividends paid: Income - March, June, September,
December; Capital gains - December
Portfolio turnover (3 yrs): 1%, 1%, 0%
Largest holding: AT & T (2.1%)
Management fee: 0.20%
Expense ratio: 0.45% (year ending 12/31/94)
(includes waiver)
Maintenance fee: $2.50 per quarter

T. ROWE PRICE
EUROPEAN STOCK FUND ◆
(See first T. Rowe Price listing for data common to
all Price funds)

Adviser: Rowe Price-Fleming International, Inc.
Portfolio manager: Martin G. Wade (1990)
Investment objective and policies: Long-term
growth of capital with income secondary. Normally
invests in equity securities issued by companies
domiciled in at least 5 countries in Europe. May
also hold ADRs, EDRs, and ADSs. Up to 35% of
assets may be in high-grade non-dollar denominat-
ed debt securities, 15% in illiquid securities and
10% in derivatives. Fund may hedge via options
and currency exchange contracts on up to 25% of
total assets.
Year organized: 1990
Ticker symbol: PRESX
Discount broker availability: Schwab, White,
Waterhouse, Fidelity, Siebert
Dividends paid: Income - December; Capital gains
- December
Portfolio turnover (3 yrs): 25%, 21%, 52%
Largest holding: Wolters Kluwer, Netherlands
(3.4%)
Management fee: 0.50% + pro-rata group fee
Expense ratio: 1.25% (10 months ending
10/31/94)

T. ROWE PRICE FLORIDA INSURED
INTERMEDIATE TAX-FREE FUND ◆
(See first T. Rowe Price listing for data common to
all Price funds)

Portfolio manager: William T. Reynolds (1993)
Investment objective and policies: High current
income exempt from federal income tax and
Florida intangible personal property tax. Invests
primarily in investment-grade Florida municipal
bonds with a weighted average maturity of 5 to 10
years. Bonds are insured at to timely payment of
principal and interest.
Year organized: 1993
Ticker symbol: FLTFX
Qualified for sale in: AL, CT, DC, FL, GA, HI, IL,
MD, MI, NJ, NY, PA, WY
Check redemptions: $500 minimum
Dividends paid: Income - declared daily, paid
monthly; Capital gains - December

Portfolio turnover (1 yr): 71%
Management fee: 0.05% + pro-rata group fee
Expense ratio: 0.60% (11 months ending 2/28/94)
(1.27% without waiver)

T. ROWE PRICE GEORGIA TAX-FREE BOND FUND ◆
(See first T. Rowe Price listing for data common to all Price funds)

Portfolio manager: Mary J. Miller (1993)
Investment objective and policies: High current income exempt from federal and Georgia state income taxes. Invests primarily in long-term investment-grade Georgia municipal bonds with a weighted average maturity of more than 10 years.
Year organized: 1993
Ticker symbol: GTFBX
Qualified for sale in: AL, DC, FL, GA, HI, IL, MD, NJ, NC, SC, TN, VA, WY
Check redemptions: $500 minimum
Dividends paid: Income - declared daily, paid monthly; Capital gains - December
Portfolio turnover (1 yr) 155%
Management fee: 0.10% + pro-rata group fee
Expense ratio: 0.65% (11 months ending 2/28/94)
(1.59% without waiver)

T. ROWE PRICE GLOBAL GOVERNMENT BOND FUND ◆
(See first T. Rowe Price listing for data common to all Price funds)

Adviser: Rowe Price-Fleming International, Inc.
Portfolio manager: Peter B. Askew (1994)
Investment objective and policies: High current income with capital growth and principal protection secondary. Invests at least 65% of assets in U.S. and foreign high-quality (AA or better) government bonds, normally in at least 3 countries with weighted average maturity around 7 years. May also hold U.S. and foreign corporate debt, including convertibles. May write and/or buy options on debt securities, indexes and currencies (up to 25% of assets); use index, interest rate and currency futures transactions and use private placements (up to 10% of assets). Fund will normally hedge 50% of foreign holdings using currency transactions.
Year organized: 1990
Ticker symbol: RPPGX
Discount broker availability: Schwab, White, Waterhouse, Fidelity, Siebert
Dividends paid: Income - declared daily, paid monthly Capital gains - January
Check redemptions: $500 minimum
Portfolio turnover (3 yrs): 134%, 237%, 94%
Management fee: 0.35% + pro-rata group fee
Expense ratio: 1.20% (year ending 12/31/93)
(includes waiver)

T. ROWE PRICE GNMA FUND ◆
(See first T. Rowe Price listing for data common to all Price funds)

Portfolio manager: J. Peter Van Dyke (1987)
Investment objective and policies: Highest level of current income consistent with preservation of capital and maximum credit protection. Invests exclusively in securities backed by the full faith and credit of the U.S. Government, at least 65% of assets in GNMA mortgage backed securities. Fund may also use interest rate futures and options to hedge up to 25% of total assets.
Year organized: 1985
Ticker symbol: PRGMX
Check redemptions: $500 minimum
Discount broker availability: Schwab, White, Waterhouse, Fidelity, Siebert
Dividends paid: Income - declared daily, paid monthly; Capital gains - March, December
Portfolio turnover (3 yrs): 93%, 94%, 66%
Management fee: 0.15% + pro-rata group fee
Expense ratio: 0.77% (year ending 2/28/94)

T. ROWE PRICE GROWTH & INCOME FUND ◆
(See first T. Rowe Price listing for data common to all Price funds)

Portfolio manager: Stephen W. Boesel (1987)
Investment objective and policies: Long-term growth of capital, reasonable current income, and increasing future income. Invests primarily in income producing equity securities using a value-oriented approach. May invest in convertible and corporate debt securities and preferred stocks. Up to 25% of assets may be in securities of foreign issuers, 15% in illiquid securities and 10% in derivatives. May use options on up to 25% of total assets and index futures.
Year organized: 1982
Ticker symbol: PRGIX
Discount broker availability: Schwab, White, Waterhouse, Fidelity, Siebert
Dividends paid: Income - March, June, September, December; Capital gains - December
Portfolio turnover (3 yrs): 26%, 22%, 30%
Largest holding: California Federal Bank (4.0%)
Management fee: 0.15% + pro-rata group fee
Expense ratio: 0.81% (year ending 12/31/94)

T. ROWE PRICE GROWTH STOCK FUND ◆
(See first T. Rowe Price listing for data common to all Price funds)

Portfolio manager: John D. Gillespie (1994)
Investment objective and policies: Long-term growth of capital and increased dividend income. Invests primarily in common stocks of well-established growth companies. May invest up to 30% of assets in securities of foreign issuers, 15% in illiquid securities and 10% in derivatives May use futures and options and hedge up to 25% of total assets.
Year organized: 1950
Ticker symbol: PRGFX
Discount broker availability: Schwab, White, Waterhouse, Fidelity, Siebert
Dividends paid: Income - December; Capital gains - December
Portfolio turnover (3 yrs): 54%, 35%, 27%
Largest holding: Freddie Mac (4.0%)
Management fee: 0.25% + pro-rata group fee
Expense ratio: 0.81% (year ending 12/31/94)

T. ROWE PRICE HIGH YIELD FUND ◆
(See first T. Rowe Price listing for data common to all Price funds)

Portfolio manager: Catherine H. Bray (1994)
Investment objective and policies: High current income with capital growth secondary. Invests at least 80% of assets in junk bonds and preferred stocks with a weighted average maturity of 8-12 years. May invest up to 20% of assets in non-dollar denominated securities of foreign issuers and 10% in derivatives May use futures and options, sell short and hedge up to 25% of total assets.
Year organized: 1984 (name changed from High Yield Bond Fund in 1993)
Ticker symbol: PRHYX
Discount broker availability: White, Waterhouse
Check redemptions: $500 minimum
Redemption fee: 1.0% on shares held less than 1 year, payable to the fund
Dividends paid: Income - declared daily, paid monthly; Capital gains - March, December
Portfolio turnover (3 yrs): 107%, 104%, 59%
Management fee: 0.30% + pro-rata group fee
Expense ratio: 0.85% (year ending 2/28/94)

T. ROWE PRICE INTERNATIONAL BOND FUND ◆
(See first T. Rowe Price listing for data common to all Price funds)

Adviser: Rowe Price-Fleming International, Inc.

Portfolio manager: Peter B. Askew (1994)
Investment objective and policies: High current income with capital growth and protection of its principal value by actively managing its maturity structure and currency exposure. Invests at least 65% of assets in high-quality, non-dollar-denominated fixed-income securities rated the equivalent of A or better. Up to 10% of assets may be in derivatives. Fund may hedge in currencies in spot/forward markets (up to 50% of total assets) and use interest rate and currency futures and options on up to 25% of assets.
Year organized: 1986
Ticker symbol: RPIBX
Discount broker availability: Schwab, White, Waterhouse, Fidelity, Siebert
Check redemptions: $500 minimum
Dividends paid: Income - declared daily, paid monthly; Capital gains - December
Portfolio turnover (3 yrs): 345%, 396%, 358%
Management fee: 0.35% + pro-rata group fee
Expense ratio: 0.98% (year ending 12/31/94)

T. ROWE PRICE INTERNATIONAL DISCOVERY FUND ◆
(See first T. Rowe Price listing for data common to all Price funds)

Adviser: Rowe Price-Fleming International, Inc.
Portfolio manager: Martin G. Wade (1989)
Investment objective and policies: Long-term growth of capital. Invests primarily in common stocks of rapidly growing, small and medium sized foreign companies in developed and emerging markets. At least 65% of assets are in at least 3 countries and fund generally holds at least 100 issues in at least ten countries. Up to 15% of assets may be in illiquid securities and 10% in derivatives. May use ADRs, EDRs, and ADSs; spot/forward currency transactions; options on foreign currencies, securities and indices on up to 25% of total assets; and index and currency futures.
Year organized: 1988
Ticker symbol: PRIDX
Redemption fee: 2% for shares purchased after 2/27/94 and held less than 1 year, payable to the fund
Discount broker availability: Waterhouse
Dividends paid: Income - December; Capital gains - December
Portfolio turnover (3 yrs): 57%, 72%, 38%
Largest holding: Republic Hotels & Resorts, Singapore (1.0%)
Management fee: 0.75% + pro-rata group fee
Expense ratio: 1.50% (year ending 10/31/94)
(includes waiver)

T. ROWE PRICE INTERNATIONAL STOCK FUND ◆
(See first T. Rowe Price listing for data common to all Price funds)

Adviser: Rowe Price-Fleming International, Inc.
Portfolio manager: Martin G. Wade (1989)
Investment objective and policies: Long-term growth of capital. Invests primarily in common stocks of established non-U.S. issuers in developed, newly industrialized and emerging markets. Up to 15% of assets may be in illiquid securities and 10% in derivatives. Fund may use ADRs, EDRs and ADSs; spot/forward currency transactions; and options on foreign currencies, securities and indices on up to 25% of total assets.
Year organized: 1979 (2 for 1 stock split 8/31/87)
Ticker symbol: PRITX
Discount broker availability: Schwab, White, Waterhouse, Fidelity, Siebert
Dividends paid: Income - December; Capital gains - December
Portfolio turnover (3 yrs): 23%, 30%, 38%
Largest holding: Wolters Kluwer, Netherlands (1.8%)
Management fee: 0.35% + pro-rata group fee
Expense ratio: 0.96% (year ending 10/31/94)

T. ROWE PRICE JAPAN FUND ◆
(See first T. Rowe Price listing for data common to all Price funds)

Adviser: Rowe Price-Fleming International, Inc.
Portfolio manager: Martin G. Wade (1991)
Investment objective and policies: Long-term capital appreciation. Invests in equity securities of established Japanese companies with attractive growth potential. Includes securities of companies domiciled in Japan or with at least half their assets in Japan or deriving at least half their revenues from Japan. Up to 15% of assets may be in illiquid securities and 10% in derivatives. Fund may use ADRs, EDRs and ADSs; spot/forward currency transactions; and options on foreign currencies, securities and indices on up to 25% of total assets. Up to 25% of assets may be in Japanese debt securities for defensive purposes.
Year organized: 1991
Ticker symbol: PRJPX
Discount broker availability: Schwab, Waterhouse
Dividends paid: Income - December; Capital gains - December
Portfolio turnover (3 yrs): 62%, 61%, 42%
Largest holding: Komori (2.4%)
Management fee: 0.50% + pro-rata group fee
Expense ratio: 1.50% (year ending 10/31/94) (includes waiver)

T. ROWE PRICE LATIN AMERICA FUND ◆
(See first T. Rowe Price listing for data common to all Price funds)

Adviser: Rowe Price-Fleming International, Inc.
Portfolio manager: Martin G. Wade (1993)
Investment objective and policies: Long-term capital growth. Invests in equity securities of both large and small companies in Latin America - initially in Mexico, Brazil, Chile, Argentina, Venezuela and Columbia. Up to 15% of assets may be in illiquid securities and 10% in derivatives. Fund may use ADRs, ADSs and GDSs; spot/forward currency transactions; and options on foreign currencies, securities and indices on up to 25% of total assets.
Year organized: 1993
Ticker symbol: PRLAX
Redemption fee: 2% for shares held less than 1 year, payable to the fund
Dividends paid: Income - December; Capital gains - December
Portfolio turnover (1 yr): 12%
Largest holding: Telefonos de Mexico ADS (8.8%)
Management fee: 0.75% + pro-rata group fee
Expense ratio: 1.99% (10 months ending 10/31/94)

T. ROWE PRICE MARYLAND SHORT-TERM TAX-FREE BOND FUND ◆
(See first T. Rowe Price listing for data common to all Price funds)

Portfolio manager: Mary J. Miller (1993)
Investment objective and policies: High level of current income exempt from federal and Maryland state and local income taxes consistent with modest fluctuation of principal. Invests primarily in investment-grade Maryland municipal securities with a weighted average maturity of 1 to 3 years. Up to 20% of assets may be in AMT securities and 10% in derivatives.
Year organized: 1993
Ticker symbol: PRMDX
Qualified for sale in: DC, DE, FL, HI, MD, NJ, PA, VA, VT, WV, WY
Check redemptions: $500 minimum
Dividends paid: Income - declared daily, paid monthly; Capital gains - December
Portfolio turnover (1 yr): 21%
Management fee: 0.10% + pro-rata group fee
Expense ratio: 0.65% (year ending 2/28/94) (0.97% without waiver)

T. ROWE PRICE MARYLAND TAX-FREE BOND FUND ◆
(See first T. Rowe Price listing for data common to all Price funds)

Portfolio manager: Mary J. Miller (1990)
Investment objective and policies: High current income exempt from federal and Maryland state and local income taxes. Invests primarily in long-term investment-grade Maryland municipal bonds with a weighted average maturity of more than 10 years. Up to 20% of assets may be in AMT securities and 10% in derivatives.
Year organized: 1986
Ticker symbol: MDXBX
Discount broker availability: Schwab, Waterhouse
Qualified for sale in: DC, DE, FL, HI, MD, NJ, PA, VA, VT, WV, WY
Check redemptions: $500 minimum
Dividends paid: Income - declared daily, paid monthly; Capital gains - December
Portfolio turnover (3 yrs): 24%, 22%, 22%
Management fee: 0.10% + pro-rata group fee
Expense ratio: 0.57% (year ending 2/28/94)

T. ROWE PRICE MID-CAP GROWTH FUND ◆
(See first T. Rowe Price listing for data common to all Price funds)

Portfolio manager: Brian W.H. Berghuis (1992)
Investment objective and policies: Long-term growth of capital. Invests primarily in mid-cap common stocks (whose market capitalization falls within the range of the S&P 400 Mid-Cap Index) with above average growth potential. May invest up to 25% of assets in foreign securities, 15% in illiquid securities and 10% in derivatives and use stock index futures and options transactions on up to 25% of total assets.
Year organized: 1992
Ticker symbol: RPMGX
Discount broker availability: Schwab, White, Fidelity, Siebert
Dividends paid: Income - December; Capital gains - December
Portfolio turnover (3 yrs): 49%, 62%, 52%
Largest holding: CUC International (2.9%)
Management fee: 0.35% + pro-rata group fee
Expense ratio: 1.25% (year ending 12/31/94) (1.58% without waiver)

T. ROWE PRICE NEW AMERICA GROWTH FUND ◆
(See first T. Rowe Price listing for data common to all Price funds)

Portfolio manager: John H. Laporte (1985)
Investment objective and policies: Long-term growth of capital. Invests at least 75% of assets in common stocks of U.S. companies which operate in the service sector of the economy without regard to capitalization size. Fund may use companies closely allied to service sector. May invest up to 10% of assets in foreign securities, 15% in illiquid securities and 10% in derivatives and use stock index futures and options transactions on up to 25% of total assets.
Year organized: 1985
Ticker symbol: PRWAX
Discount broker availability: Schwab, White, Waterhouse, Fidelity, Siebert
Dividends paid: Income - December; Capital gains - December
Portfolio turnover (3 yrs): 31%, 44%, 26%
Largest holding: CUC International (4.4%)
Management fee: 0.35% + pro-rata group fee
Expense ratio: 1.14% (year ending 12/31/94)

T. ROWE PRICE NEW ASIA FUND ◆
(See first T. Rowe Price listing for data common to all Price funds)

Adviser: Rowe Price-Fleming International, Inc.
Portfolio manager: Martin G. Wade (1990)
Investment objective and policies: Long term growth of capital. Invests primarily in large and small capitalization companies domiciled or operating primarily in Asia (excluding Japan) and the Pacific Basin, including Australia and New Zealand. Fund will hold securities in at least 5 different countries. May purchase ADRs, EDRs, and ADSs and have up to 15% of assets in illiquid securities and 10% in derivatives. May use spot/forward currency transactions; options on foreign currencies, securities and indices on up to 25% of total assets; and index and currency futures.
Year organized: 1990
Ticker symbol: PRASX
Discount broker availability: Schwab, Waterhouse
Dividends paid: Income - December; Capital gains - December
Portfolio turnover (3 yrs): 63%, 40%, 36%
Largest holding: United Overseas Bank, Singapore (2.9%)
Management fee: 0.50% + pro-rata group fee
Expense ratio: 1.22% (year ending 10/31/94)

T. ROWE PRICE NEW ERA FUND ◆
(See first T. Rowe Price listing for data common to all Price funds)

Portfolio manager: George A. Roche (1979)
Investment objective and policies: Long-term growth of capital. Invests primarily in common stocks of companies which own or develop natural resources and other basic commodities, and other selected non-resource growth companies. May invest up to 10% of assets in foreign securities, 15% in illiquid securities and 10% in derivatives and use stock index futures and options transactions on up to 25% of total assets.
Year organized: 1968
Ticker symbol: PRNEX
Discount broker availability: Schwab, White, Waterhouse, Fidelity, Siebert
Dividends paid: Income - December; Capital gains - December
Portfolio turnover (3 yrs): 25%, 25%, 17%
Largest holding: Wal-Mart (4.9%)
Management fee: 0.25% + pro-rata group fee
Expense ratio: 0.80% (year ending 12/31/94)

T. ROWE PRICE NEW HORIZONS FUND ◆
(See first T. Rowe Price listing for data common to all Price funds)

Portfolio manager: John H. Laporte (1987)
Investment objective and policies: Long-term growth of capital. Invests primarily in common stocks of small, rapidly growing companies. May invest 10% of assets in foreign securities, 15% in illiquid securities and 10% in derivatives and use stock index futures and options transactions on up to 25% of total assets.
Year organized: 1960
Ticker symbol: PRNHX
Discount broker availability: Schwab, White, Waterhouse, Fidelity, Siebert
Dividends paid: Income - December; Capital gains - December
Portfolio turnover (3 yrs): 49%, 49%, 50%
Largest holding: CUC International (3.3%)
Management fee: 0.35% + pro-rata group fee
Expense ratio: 0.93% (year ending 12/31/94)

T. ROWE PRICE NEW INCOME FUND ◆
(See first T. Rowe Price listing for data common to all Price funds)

Newspaper listing: Incom
Portfolio manager: Charles P. Smith (1985)
Investment objective and policies: High long-term income consistent with preservation of capital. Invests at least 80% of assets in investment grade debt securities with a weighted average maturity of 4 to 15 years. Up to 25% of assets may be in preferred and common stocks or equivalents, 20% in non-dollar denominated foreign fixed-income securities, 15% in illiquid securities and 10% in deriva-

tives. May use foreign currency transactions and futures and options on up to 25% of total assets. May concentrate up to 50% of assets in any one of the following industries: gas, electric or telephone utility; gas transmission; or petroleum.
Year organized: 1973
Ticker symbol: PRCIX
Discount broker availability: Schwab, White, Waterhouse, Fidelity, Siebert
Check redemptions: $500 minimum
Dividends paid: Income - declared daily, paid monthly; Capital gains - March, December
Portfolio turnover (3 yrs): 58%, 86%, 50%
Management fee: 0.15% + pro-rata group fee
Expense ratio: 0.82% (year ending 2/28/94)

T. ROWE PRICE NEW JERSEY TAX-FREE BOND FUND ◆
(See first T. Rowe Price listing for data common to all Price funds)

Portfolio manager: William T. Reynolds (1991)
Investment objective and policies: High current income exempt from federal and New Jersey state and local income taxes. Invests principally in long-term investment-grade New Jersey municipal securities with a weighted average maturity of more than 10 years. Up to 20% of assets may be in AMT securities, 15% in illiquid securities and 10% in derivatives.
Year organized: 1991
Ticker symbol: PRNJX
Qualified for sale in: DC, HI, MD, NJ, WY
Check redemptions: $500 minimum
Dividends paid: Income - declared daily, paid monthly; Capital gains - December
Portfolio turnover (3 yrs): 69%, 103%, 152%
Management fee: 0.10% + pro-rata group fee
Expense ratio: 0.65% (year ending 2/28/94) (0.93% without waiver)

T. ROWE PRICE NEW YORK TAX-FREE BOND FUND ◆
(See first T. Rowe Price listing for data common to all Price funds)

Portfolio manager: William T. Reynolds (1986)
Investment objective and policies: High current income exempt from federal and New York State and City income taxes. Invests primarily in long-term investment-grade municipal securities exempt from such taxes, primarily New York but also Puerto Rico, Guam and the Virgin Islands, with a weighted average maturity of more than 10 years. Up to 20% of assets may be in AMT securities, 15% in illiquid securities and 10% in derivatives.
Year organized: 1986
Ticker symbol: PRNYX
Qualified for sale in: CT, DE, DC, FL, HI, MD, MA, NJ, NY, PA, RI, VA, VT, WV, WY
Discount broker availability: Waterhouse, Fidelity, Siebert
Check redemptions: $500 minimum
Dividends paid: Income - declared daily, paid monthly; Capital gains - December
Portfolio turnover (3 yrs): 85%, 42%, 49%
Management fee: 0.10% + pro-rata group fee
Expense ratio: 0.60% (year ending 2/28/94) (0.72% without waiver)

T. ROWE PRICE NEW YORK TAX-FREE MONEY FUND ◆
(See first T. Rowe Price listing for data common to all Price funds)

Portfolio manager: Patrice L. Berchtenbreiter (1991)
Investment objective and policies: High current income exempt from federal and New York State and City income taxes consistent with preservation of capital and liquidity. Invests primarily in New York municipal money market securities.
Year organized: 1986
Qualified for sale in: CT, DE, DC, FL, HI, MD, MA, NJ, NY, PA, RI, VA, VT, WV, WY

Check redemptions: $500 minimum
Confirmations mailed: After each purchase and each check, mail or wire redemption
Checks returned: Monthly
Periodic account statements mailed: Monthly
Dividends paid: Income - declared daily, paid monthly
Management fee: 0.1% + pro-rata group fee
Expense ratio: 0.55% (year ending 2/28/94) (0.86% without waiver)

T. ROWE PRICE OTC FUND ◆
(See first T. Rowe Price listing for data common to all Price funds)

Portfolio manager: Greg A. McCrickard (1992)
Investment objective and policies: Long-term growth of capital. Invests at least 80% of assets in equity and equity-related securities traded in the U.S. OTC market. Focuses on small rapidly growing companies believed undervalued. May invest 10% of assets in foreign securities, 15% in illiquid securities and 10% in derivatives and use futures and options on up to 25% of total assets.
Year organized: 1955 (As the OTC Fund. Name changed in 1988 to the USF&G OTC Fund. Management and name changed to T.Rowe Price OTC Fund on 8/31/92)
Ticker symbol: OTCFX
Discount broker availability: Schwab, White, Waterhouse, Fidelity, Siebert
Dividends paid: Income - December; Capital gains - December
Portfolio turnover (3 yrs): 42%, 41%, 31%
Largest holding: Selective Insurance Group (2.3%)
Management fee: 0.45% + pro-rata group fee
Expense ratio: 1.11% (year ending 12/31/94)

T. ROWE PRICE PERSONAL STRATEGY FUND - BALANCED ◆
(See first T. Rowe Price listing for data common to all Price funds)

Portfolio manager: J. Peter Van Dyke (1994)
Investment objective and policies: Highest total return consistent with primary emphasis on both capital growth and income. Allocation of assets is 50-70% stocks, 20-40% bonds and 0-20% money market instruments. Up to 35% of assets may be in securities of foreign issuers, 20% in junk bonds, 15% in illiquid securities, 10% in other mutual funds and 10% in derivatives. May use options on up to 25% of total assets and index futures.
Year organized: 1994
Dividends paid: Income - December; Capital gains - December
Management fee: 0.25% + pro-rata group fee

T. ROWE PRICE PERSONAL STRATEGY FUND - GROWTH ◆
(See first T. Rowe Price listing for data common to all Price funds)

Portfolio manager: J. Peter Van Dyke (1994)
Investment objective and policies: Highest total return consistent with primary emphasis on capital growth with income secondary. Allocation of assets is 70-90% stocks and 10-30% bonds and money market instruments. Up to 35% of assets may be in securities of foreign issuers, 15% in junk bonds, 15% in illiquid securities, 10% in other mutual funds and 10% in derivatives. May use options on up to 25% of total assets and index futures.
Year organized: 1994
Dividends paid: Income - December; Capital gains - December
Management fee: 0.30% + pro-rata group fee

T. ROWE PRICE PERSONAL STRATEGY FUND - INCOME ◆
(See first T. Rowe Price listing for data common to all Price funds)

Portfolio manager: J. Peter Van Dyke (1994)
Investment objective and policies: Highest total

return consistent with primary emphasis on both capital growth and income. Allocation of assets is 30-50% stocks, 30-50% bonds and 10-30% money market instruments. Up to 35% of assets may be in securities of foreign issuers, 20% in junk bonds, 25% in illiquid securities, 10% in other mutual funds and 10% in derivatives. May use options on up to 25% of total assets and index futures.
Year organized: 1994
Dividends paid: Income - December; Capital gains - December
Management fee: 0.15% + pro-rata group fee

T. ROWE PRICE PRIME RESERVE FUND ◆
(See first T. Rowe Price listing for data common to all Price funds)

Portfolio manager: Edward A. Wiese (1990)
Investment objective and policies: High current income consistent with preservation of capital and liquidity. Invests in domestic and foreign U.S. dollar-denominated money market securities in the two highest rating categories.
Year organized: 1975
Ticker symbol: PRRXX
Check redemptions: $500 minimum
Confirmations mailed: After each purchase and each check, mail or wire redemption
Checks returned: Monthly
Periodic account statements mailed: Monthly for regular, quarterly for retirement
Dividends paid: Income - declared daily, paid monthly
Management fee: 0.05% + pro-rata group fee
Expense ratio: 0.74% (year ending 2/28/94)

T. ROWE PRICE SCIENCE AND TECHNOLOGY FUND ◆
(See first T. Rowe Price listing for data common to all Price funds)

Portfolio manager: Charles A. Morris (1992)
Investment objective and policies: Long term growth of capital. Invests primarily in common stocks of companies expected to benefit from the development, advancement, and use of science & technology. May invest up to 30% of assets in foreign securities, 15% in illiquid securities and 10% in derivatives and use futures and options on up to 25% of total assets.
Year organized: 1987
Ticker symbol: PRSCX
Discount broker availability: Schwab, White, Waterhouse, Fidelity, Siebert
Dividends paid: Income - December; Capital gains - December
Portfolio turnover (3 yrs): 113%, 163%, 144%
Largest holding: First Financial Management (5.2%)
Management fee: 0.35% + pro-rata group fee
Expense ratio: 1.11% (year ending 12/31/94)

T. ROWE PRICE SHORT-TERM BOND FUND ◆
(See first T. Rowe Price listing for data common to all Price funds)

Portfolio manager: Veena A. Kutler (1991)
Investment objective and policies: High income consistent with minimum fluctuation in principal and liquidity. Invests in short and intermediate term (up to 7 years) securities in the three highest rating categories, with a weighted average maturity of less than 3 years. May concentrate up to 50% of assets in any one of the following industries: gas, electric or telephone utility; gas transmission; and petroleum. Fund may invest up to 10% of assets in non-dollar denominated foreign fixed-income securities, 15% in illiquid securities and 10% in derivatives. May use foreign currency transactions and U.S. interest rate futures to hedge, and use options on up to 25% of total assets.
Year organized: 1983
Ticker symbol: PRWBX

Check redemptions: $500 minimum
Discount broker availability: Schwab, White, Waterhouse, Fidelity, Siebert
Dividends paid: Income - declared daily, paid monthly; Capital gains - December
Portfolio turnover (3 yrs): 91%, 68%, 381%
Management fee: 0.10% + pro-rata group fee
Expense ratio: 0.74% (year ending 2/28/94)

T. ROWE PRICE SHORT-TERM GLOBAL INCOME FUND ◆
(See first T. Rowe Price listing for data common to all Price funds)

Adviser: Rowe Price-Fleming International, Inc.
Portfolio manager: Peter B. Askew (1994)
Investment objective and policies: High current income and preservation of principal. Invests primarily in high-quality short-term bonds and money market instruments issued throughout the world. At least 65% of assets in securities in the two highest rating categories, with a weighted average maturity of less than 3 years. May have up to 15% of assets in illiquid securities and 10% in derivatives. May use foreign currency transactions and U.S. interest rate futures to hedge, and use options on up to 25% of total assets.
Year organized: 1992
Ticker symbol: RPSGX
Discount broker availability: Schwab, White, Fidelity, Siebert
Check redemptions: $500 minimum
Dividends paid: Income - declared daily, paid monthly; Capital gains - December
Portfolio turnover (2 yrs): 93%, 334%
Management fee: 0.35% + pro-rata group fee
Expense ratio: 1.00% (year ending 12/31/93) (1.14% without waiver)

T. ROWE PRICE SMALL-CAP VALUE FUND ◆
(See first T. Rowe Price listing for data common to all Price funds)

Newspaper listing: SmCVl
Portfolio manager: Preston G. Athey (1988)
Investment objective and policies: Long-term capital growth. Invests primarily in common stocks of companies with market capitalizations under $500M believed undervalued and with good prospects for capital appreciation. Fund may invest up to 20% of assets in foreign securities, 15% in illiquid securities and 10% in derivatives and use futures and options on up to 25% of total assets.
Year organized: 1988, (previously PEMCO, a New York limited partnership)
Ticker symbol: PRSVX
Discount broker availability: Waterhouse
Redemption fee: 1% for shares purchased after 4/10/95 and held less than 1 year, payable to the fund
Dividends paid: Income - December; Capital gains - December
Portfolio turnover (3 yrs): 21%, 12%, 12%
Largest holding: La Quinta Inns (2.0%)
Management fee: 0.35% + pro-rata group fee
Expense ratio: 0.97% (year ending 12/31/94)

T. ROWE PRICE SPECTRUM GROWTH FUND ◆
(See first T. Rowe Price listing for data common to all Price funds)

Portfolio manager: J. Peter Van Dyke (1990)
Investment objective and policies: Long term growth of capital and growth of income by investing primarily in a diversified group of Rowe Price mutual funds which invest principally in equity securities (Prime Reserve 0-25%, Equity Income 5-20%, Growth & Income 5-20%, International Stock 5-20%, New Era 10-25%, New Horizons 10-25%, and Growth Stock 15-30%). Current income is secondary.
Year organized: 1990
Ticker symbol: PRSGX
Special sales restrictions: Designed for individuals

investing through tax-advantaged retirement accounts; annual limitation of $30,000, combined with Spectrum Income Fund investments
Discount broker availability: Schwab, White, Waterhouse, Fidelity, Siebert
Dividends paid: Income - December; Capital gains - December
Portfolio turnover (3 yrs): 21%, 7%, 8%
Management fee: No management fees except indirect fees allocated to shares of funds held.
Expense ratio: None (See expense ratios of underlying portfolio funds)

T. ROWE PRICE SPECTRUM INCOME FUND ◆
(See first T. Rowe Price listing for data common to all Price funds)

Portfolio manager: J. Peter Van Dyke (1990)
Investment objective and policies: High current income and preservation of capital by investing primarily in a diversified group of Rowe Price mutual funds which invest principally in fixed-income securities (Short-Term Bond 0-15%, GNMA 5-20%, International Bond 5-20%, Equity Income 10-25%, High Yield 10-25%, Prime Reserve 5-30%, and New Income 15-30%).
Year organized: 1990
Ticker symbol: RPSIX
Special sales restrictions: designed for individuals investing through tax-advantaged retirement accounts; annual limitation of $30,000, combined with Spectrum Growth Fund investments
Discount broker availability: Schwab, White, Waterhouse, Fidelity, Siebert
Dividends paid: Income - Monthly; Capital Gains - December
Check redemptions: $500 minimum
Portfolio turnover (3 yrs): 23%, 14%, 14%
Management fee: No management fees except indirect fees allocated to shares of funds held.
Expense ratio: None (See expense ratios of underlying portfolio funds)

T. ROWE PRICE SUMMIT CASH RESERVE FUND ◆
(See first T. Rowe Price listing for data common to all Price funds)

Portfolio manager: Edward A. Wiese (1993)
Investment objective and policies: High current income consistent with preservation of capital and liquidity. Invests in domestic and foreign U.S. dollar-denominated money market securities in the two highest rating categories. Designed to provide higher returns with low costs for long-term investors with substantial assets.
Year organized: 1993
Minimum purchase: Initial: $25,000, Subsequent: $1,000
Check redemptions: $500 minimum
Confirmations mailed: After each purchase and each check, mail or wire redemption
Checks returned: Monthly
Periodic account statements mailed: Monthly for regular, quarterly for retirement
Dividends paid: Income - declared daily, paid monthly
Management fee: 0.45% (covers all expenses)

T. ROWE PRICE SUMMIT GNMA FUND ◆
(See first T. Rowe Price listing for data common to all Price funds)

Portfolio manager: J. Peter Van Dyke (1993)
Investment objective and policies: High current income and maximum credit protection. Invests at least 65% of assets in GNMA certificates with remainder of assets in other government and corporate debt securities rated within the 2 highest rating categories with a weighted average maturity of 3 to 10 years. May have up to 15% of assets in illiquid securities and use options on up to 25% of total assets. Designed to provide higher returns with low costs for long-term investors with substantial assets.
Year organized: 1993

Minimum purchase: Initial: $25,000, Subsequent: $1,000
Check redemptions: $500 minimum
Dividends paid: Income - declared daily, paid monthly; Capital gains - November
Portfolio turnover (1 yr): 62%
Management fee: 0.60% (covers all expenses)

T. ROWE PRICE SUMMIT LIMITED TERM BOND FUND ◆
(See first T. Rowe Price listing for data common to all Price funds)

Portfolio manager: Veena A. Kutler (1993)
Investment objective and policies: High current income exempt from federal income taxes. Invests at least 65% of assets in short- and intermediate-term investment-grade bonds with a weighted average maturity of 1 to 5 years. May have up to 10% of assets in junk bonds, 15% in illiquid securities and use options on up to 25% of total assets. Designed to provide higher returns with low costs for long-term investors with substantial assets.
Year organized: 1993
Minimum purchase: Initial: $25,000, Subsequent: $1,000
Check redemptions: $500 minimum
Dividends paid: Income - declared daily, paid monthly; Capital gains - November
Portfolio turnover (1 yr): 296%
Management fee: 0.55% (covers all expenses)

T. ROWE PRICE SUMMIT MUNICIPAL INCOME FUND ◆
(See first T. Rowe Price listing for data common to all Price funds)

Portfolio manager: William T. Reynolds (1993)
Investment objective and policies: High income exempt from federal income taxes. Invests primarily in long-term investment-grade municipal securities with a weighted average maturity of 10 years or longer. May have up to 20% of assets in junk bonds and use AMT securities without limit. Designed to provide higher returns with low costs for long-term investors with substantial assets.
Year organized: 1993
Minimum purchase: Initial: $25,000, Subsequent: $1,000
Check redemptions: $500 minimum
Dividends paid: Income - declared daily, paid monthly; Capital gains - November
Portfolio turnover (1 yr): 161%
Management fee: 0.50% (covers all expenses)

T. ROWE PRICE SUMMIT MUNICIPAL INTERMEDIATE FUND ◆
(See first T. Rowe Price listing for data common to all Price funds)

Portfolio manager: Mary J. Miller (1993)
Investment objective and policies: High income exempt from federal income taxes consistent with moderate price fluctuation. Invests primarily in investment-grade municipal securities with a weighted average maturity of 5 to 10 years. May have up to 10% of assets in junk bonds and use AMT securities without limit. Designed to provide higher returns with low costs for long-term investors with substantial assets.
Year organized: 1993
Minimum purchase: Initial: $25,000, Subsequent: $1,000
Check redemptions: $500 minimum
Dividends paid: Income - declared daily, paid monthly; Capital gains - December
Portfolio turnover (1 yr): 158%
Management fee: 0.50% (covers all expenses)

T. ROWE PRICE SUMMIT MUNICIPAL MONEY MARKET FUND ◆
(See first T. Rowe Price listing for data common to all Price funds)

Portfolio manager: Patrice L. Berchtenbreiter (1993)
Investment objective and policies: High current

income exempt from federal income taxes consistent with preservation of capital and liquidity. Invests in municipal money market securities in the two highest rating categories. Designed to provide higher returns with low costs for long-term investors with substantial assets.
Year organized: 1993
Minimum purchase: Initial: $25,000, Subsequent: $1,000
Check redemptions: $500 minimum
Confirmations mailed: After each purchase and each check, mail or wire redemption
Checks returned: Monthly
Periodic account statements mailed: Monthly for regular, quarterly for retirement
Dividends paid: Income - declared daily, paid monthly
Management fee: 0.45% (covers all expenses)

T. ROWE PRICE TAX-EXEMPT MONEY FUND ◆
(See first T. Rowe Price listing for data common to all Price funds)

Portfolio manager: Patrice L. Berchtenbreiter (1991)
Investment objective and policies: High current income exempt from federal income taxes consistent with preservation of capital and liquidity. Invests in short-term municipal money market securities with remaining maturities of 1 year or less.
Year organized: 1980
Ticker symbol: PTEXX
Check redemptions: $500 minimum
Confirmations mailed: After each purchase and each mail or wire redemption
Checks returned: Monthly
Periodic account statements mailed: Monthly
Dividends paid: Income - declared daily, paid monthly
Management fee: 0.10% + pro-rata group fee
Expense ratio: 0.59% (year ending 2/28/94)

T. ROWE PRICE TAX-FREE HIGH YIELD FUND ◆
(See first T. Rowe Price listing for data common to all Price funds)

Portfolio managers: William T. Reynolds (1985), Stephan C. Wolfe II (1993)
Investment objective and policies: Maximum current income exempt from federal income taxes. Invests primarily in long-term, high-yielding, medium and lower quality municipal bonds, at least 80% with a weighted average maturity of more than 15 years. Up to 15% of assets may be in illiquid securities and 20% in AMT securities.
Year organized: 1985
Ticker symbol: PRFHX
Discount broker availability: Schwab, White, Waterhouse, Fidelity, Siebert
Check redemptions: $500 minimum
Dividends paid: Income - declared daily, paid monthly; Capital gains - December
Portfolio turnover (3 yrs): 59%, 35%, 51%
Management fee: 0.3% + pro-rata group fee
Expense ratio: 0.79% (year ending 2/28/94)

T. ROWE PRICE TAX-FREE INCOME FUND ◆
(See first T. Rowe Price listing for data common to all Price funds)

Portfolio manager: William T. Reynolds (1990)
Investment objective and policies: High income exempt from federal income taxes. Invests primarily in municipal securities in the 4 highest grades. Securities can be long, short, or intermediate term in management's response to market conditions, with a weighted average maturity of more than 15 years. Up to 20% of securities may be non-rated, but not below investment grade. Up to 15% of assets may be in illiquid securities and 20% in AMT securities.

Year organized: 1976
Ticker symbol: PRTAX
Discount broker availability: Schwab, White, Waterhouse, Fidelity, Siebert
Check redemptions: $500 minimum
Dividends paid: Income - declared daily, paid monthly; Capital gains - December
Portfolio turnover (3 yrs): 71%, 77%, 58%
Management fee: 0.15% + pro-rata group fee
Expense ratio: 0.59% (year ending 2/28/94)

T. ROWE PRICE TAX-FREE INSURED INTERMEDIATE BOND FUND ◆
(See first T. Rowe Price listing for data common to all Price funds)

Portfolio manager: William T. Reynolds (1992)
Investment objective and policies: High income exempt from federal income taxes with minimal credit risk and greater principal stability than a long-term bond fund. Invests primarily in investment-grade municipal bonds, insured as to timely payment of principal and interest, with a weighted average maturity of 5 to 10 years. Up to 15% of assets may be in illiquid securities and 20% in AMT securities.
Year organized: 1992
Ticker symbol: PRFSX
Discount broker availability: Fidelity, Siebert
Dividends paid: Income - declared daily, paid monthly; Capital gains - December
Portfolio turnover (1 yr): 75%
Management fee: 0.05% + pro-rata group fee
Expense ratio: 0.33% (year ending 2/28/94) (includes waiver)

T. ROWE PRICE TAX-FREE SHORT-INTERMEDIATE FUND ◆
(See first T. Rowe Price listing for data common to all Price funds)

Portfolio manager: Mary J. Miller (1989)
Investment objective and policies: High income exempt from federal income taxes. Invests primarily in short and intermediate term municipal bonds with a weighted average maturity of less than 5 years. None of the individual securities will have maturities greater than 7 years. Up to 15% of assets may be in illiquid securities and 20% in AMT securities.
Year organized: 1983
Ticker symbol: PRFSX
Discount broker availability: Schwab, White, Waterhouse, Fidelity, Siebert
Check redemptions: $500 minimum
Dividends paid: Income - declared daily, paid monthly; Capital gains - December
Portfolio turnover (3 yrs): 51%, 39%, 81%
Management fee: 0.15% + pro-rata group fee
Expense ratio: 0.60% (year ending 2/28/94)

T. ROWE PRICE U.S. TREASURY INTERMEDIATE FUND ◆
(See first T. Rowe Price listing for data common to all Price funds)

Portfolio manager: Charles P. Smith (1989)
Investment objective and policies: High current income. Invests at least 85% of assets in U.S. Treasury securities and repurchase agreements thereon with a weighted average maturity of 3 to 7 years. No individual security will have remaining maturity in excess of 7 1/2 years at time of purchase.
Year organized: 1989
Ticker symbol: PRTIX
Discount broker availability: White, Fidelity, Siebert
Check redemptions: $500 minimum
Dividends paid: Income - declared daily, paid monthly; Capital gains - December
Portfolio turnover (3 yrs): 20%, 23%, 91%
Management fee: 0.05% + pro-rata group fee
Expense ratio: 0.79% (year ending 2/28/94)

T. ROWE PRICE U.S. TREASURY LONG-TERM FUND ◆
(See first T. Rowe Price listing for data common to all Price funds)

Portfolio manager: J. Peter Van Dyke (1989)
Investment objective and policies: High current income. Invests at least 85% of assets in U.S. Treasury securities and repurchase agreements thereon with a weighted average maturity of 7 to 30 years, with expected average maturity of 15-20 years.
Year organized: 1989
Ticker symbol: PRULX
Discount broker availability: White, Waterhouse, Fidelity, Siebert
Check redemptions: $500 minimum
Dividends paid: Income - declared daily, paid monthly; Capital gains - December
Portfolio turnover (3 yrs): 59%, 165%, 162%
Management fee: 0.05% + pro-rata group fee
Expense ratio: 0.80% (year ending 2/28/94) (1.00% without waiver)

T. ROWE PRICE U.S. TREASURY MONEY FUND ◆
(See first T. Rowe Price listing for data common to all Price funds)

Portfolio manager: Edward A. Wiese (1990)
Investment objective and policies: Highest current income consistent with safety of capital and liquidity,. Invests in short-term U.S. Treasury securities, other money market securities carrying "full faith and credit" guarantee, and in repurchase agreements involving these securities.
Year organized: 1982
Ticker symbol: PRTXX
Check redemptions: $500 minimum
Confirmations mailed: After each purchase and each check, mail or wire redemption
Checks returned: Monthly
Periodic account statements mailed: Monthly (quarterly for retirement accounts)
Dividends paid: Income - declared daily, paid monthly
Management fee: 0.05% + pro-rata group fee
Expense ratio: 0.64% (year ending 2/28/94)

T. ROWE PRICE VALUE FUND ◆
(See first Rowe Price listing for data common to all Price funds)

Portfolio manager: Brian C. Rogers (1994)
Investment objective and policies: Long-term growth of capital with income secondary. Invests primarily in common stocks believed undervalued using a value-oriented approach. May invest in convertible and corporate debt securities and preferred stocks. Up to 30% of assets may be in securities of foreign issuers, 15% in illiquid securities, 10% in junk bonds and 10% in derivatives. May use options on up to 25% of total assets.
Year organized: 1994
Dividends paid: Income - March, June, September, December; Capital gains - December
Management fee: 0.35% + pro-rata group fee

T. ROWE PRICE VIRGINIA SHORT-TERM TAX-FREE BOND FUND ◆
(See first T. Rowe Price listing for data common to all Price funds)

Portfolio manager: Mary J. Miller (1995)
Investment objective and policies: High level of current income exempt from federal and Virginia state income taxes consistent with modest fluctuation of principal. Invests primarily in investment-grade Virginia municipal securities with a weighted average maturity of 1 to 3 years. Up to 20% of assets may be in AMT securities and 10% in derivatives.
Year organized: 1994
Qualified for sale in: DC, FL, GA, HI, IL, MD, NC, PA, VA, WY

339

Check redemptions: $500 minimum
Dividends paid: Income - declared daily, paid monthly; Capital gains - December
Management fee: 0.10% + pro-rata group fee

T. ROWE PRICE VIRGINIA TAX-FREE BOND FUND ◆
(See first T. Rowe Price listing for data common to all Price funds)

Portfolio manager: Mary J. Miller (1991)
Investment objective and policies: High current income exempt from federal and Virginia state and local income taxes. Invests primarily in long-term investment-grade Virginia municipal bonds with a weighted average maturity of 10 years or more. Up to 20% of assets may be in AMT securities, 15% in illiquid securities and 10% in derivatives.
Year organized: 1991
Ticker symbol: PRVAX
Discount broker availability: Fidelity, Siebert
Qualified for sale in: DC, HI, MD, NJ, VA, WY
Check redemptions: $500 minimum
Dividends paid: Income - declared daily, paid monthly; Capital gains - December
Portfolio turnover (3 yrs): 62%, 69%, 76%
Management fee: 0.10% + pro-rata group fee
Expense ratio: 0.65% (year ending 2/28/94) (0.73% without waiver)

PRIMARY FUNDS ◆
(Data common to all Primary funds are shown below. See subsequent listings for data specific to individual Primary funds.)

First Financial Centre
700 North Water Street
Milwaukee, WI 53202
800-443-6544, 800-338-1579
fax 414-271-2809

Shareholder service hours: Full service: M-F 8:30 A.M.-4:30 P.M. CST; After hours service: prices, orders, prospectuses
Adviser: Arnold Investment Counsel Inc.
Custodian and transfer agent: Firstar Trust Co.
Minimum purchase: Initial: $500, Subsequent: $50 (except Primary Trend Fund)
Telephone orders accepted: No
Wire orders accepted: Yes
Deadline for same day wire purchase: 4 P.M.
Wire redemptions: Yes, $7.50 fee
Letter redemptions: Signature guarantee required over $10,000
Telephone switching: With other Primary funds and Portico Money Market Fund, $1,000 minimum
Number of switches permitted: 5 per year or 3 per quarter, $5 fee
Shareholder services: IRA, SEP-IRA, Keogh, 401(k), 403(b), corporate retirement plans, automatic investment plan—minimum $50 (waives initial minimum), directed dividends, withdrawal plan min. required $25,000, electronic funds transfer (purchase only)
IRA fees: Annual $12.50
Keogh fees: None

PRIMARY INCOME FUND ◆
(See first Primary listing for data common to all Primary funds)

Portfolio manager: David R. Aushwitz (1989)
Investment objective and policies: High current income with capital appreciation secondary. Invests in fixed-income securities and/or dividend-paying common and preferred stocks of well-established companies with market capitalizations of $500M or more. Fund may invest 100% of assets in the utility industry.
Year organized: 1989
Ticker symbol: PINFX
Qualified for sale in: AL, AZ, CA,CT, DC, FL, GA, HI, IL, IN, LA, MI, MN, NJ, NY, OH, OR, PA, TX, UT, WA, WI
Dividends paid: Income - declared daily, paid monthly; Capital gains - August, December

Portfolio turnover (3 yrs): 39%, 44%, 24%
Largest Holding: Tenneco, Inc. (4.4%)
Management fee: 0.74%
Expense ratio: 0.84% (year ending 6/30/94) (1.19% without waiver)

PRIMARY TREND FUND ◆
(See first Primary listing for data common to all Primary funds)

Newspaper listing: PrimryT
Portfolio manager: David R. Aushwitz (1989)
Investment objective and policies: Maximum total return without exposing capital to undue risk. May hold varying amounts of cash, equities, or bonds in order to achieve this objective. Fund endeavors to provide returns in excess of the inflation rate, the 90 day U.S. Treasury Bill rate, and the returns produced by popular stock market indices.
Year organized: 1986
Ticker symbol: PTFDX
Minimum purchase: Initial: $2,500, Subsequent: $50; IRA/Keogh: Initial: $2,000
Discount broker availability: Schwab
Qualified for sale in: All states except AK, DE, ID, ME, MS, MT, NE, NV, NM, NC, RI, SD, VT, WV, WY
Dividends paid: Income - August, December; Capital gains - August, December
Portfolio turnover (3 yrs): 77%, 40%, 66%
Largest holding: Pennzoil Company (4.9%)
Management fee: 0.74%
Expense ratio: 1.27% (year ending 6/30/94)

PRIMARY U.S. GOVERNMENT FUND ◆
(See first Primary listing for data common to all Primary funds)

Portfolio manager: James T. Dean, Jr. (1989)
Investment objective and policies: High current income. Invests in diversified portfolio of securities issued or guaranteed as to principal and interest by the U.S. Government and its agencies or instrumentalities with a weighted average maturity of 2 to 30 years, depending on outlook for interest rates.
Year organized: 1989
Qualified for sale in: AL, AZ, CA, CT, DC, FL, GA, HI, IL, IN, LA, MT, MN, NJ, NY, OH, OR, PA, TX, UT, WA, WI
Dividends paid: Income - declared daily, paid monthly; Capital gains - August, December
Portfolio turnover (3 yrs): 94%, 65%, 109%
Management fee: 0.65%
Expense ratio: 0.75% (year ending 6/30/94) (2.44% without waiver)

PRIME CASH SERIES
Federated Investors Tower
Pittsburgh, PA 15222-3779
412-288-1900, 800-245-0242
fax 412-288-1982

Adviser: Federated Advisers
Portfolio manager: Deborah Cunningham (1991)
Custodian and transfer agent: State Street Bank & Trust Co.
Transfer agent: Federated Services Company
Investment objective and policies: Income consistent with stability of principal and liquidity. Invests in high quality money market instruments.
Year organized: 1989
Ticker symbol: CTPXX
Minimum purchase: Initial: $10,000, Subsequent: $500; IRA: Initial: $1,000
Wire orders accepted: Yes
Deadline for same day wire purchase: 12 NN
Qualified for sale in: All states
Telephone redemptions: Yes
Wire redemptions: Yes, $10,000 minimum
Letter redemptions: Signature guarantee required over $50,000
Check redemptions: $100 minimum
Telephone switching: With Dremen Fund portfolios
Management fee: 0.5%

12b-1 distribution fee: 0.10%
Expense ratio: 0.99% (year ending 5/31/94) (1.17% without waiver)

THE PRUDENT SPECULATOR FUND
P.O. Box 75231
Los Angeles, CA 90075
213-778-7732, 800-444-4778
fax 213-386-4050

Adviser: Prudent Speculator Group
Portfolio manager: Edwin R. Bernstein (1989)
Custodian: National Westminster Bank NJ
Transfer agent: Fund/Plan Services, Inc.
Investment objective and policies: Long-term capital growth. Invests substantially all of its assets in common stocks believed significantly undervalued, primarily of companies with market capitalizations under $500M. May write covered put and call options to hedge. Up to 20% of assets may be in ADRs of foreign issuers.
Year organized: 1987 (formerly Prudent Speculator Leveraged Fund. Name and objective changed in July 1993.)
Ticker symbol: PSLFX
Minimum purchase: Initial: $250; Subsequent: $25; IRA: Initial: $50
Telephone orders accepted: Yes, $1,000 minimum, maximum 5 times current asset value
Wire orders accepted: Yes
Deadline for same day wire purchase: 3 P.M.
Discount broker availability: White
Qualified for sale in: All states except AL, AR, KY, LA, ME, MT, NE, NH, ND, RI, SC, TN, VT
Telephone redemptions: Yes
Wire redemptions: Yes, $1,000 minimum
Letter redemptions: Signature guarantee required
Telephone switching: With Investors Cash Reserve money market fund
Dividends paid: Income - December; Capital gains - December
Portfolio turnover (3 yrs): 71%, 81%, 107%
Largest holding: Int'l Remote Imaging Systems (6.4%)
Shareholder services: IRA, SEP-IRA, automatic investment plan, withdrawal plan min. req. $10,000
Management fee: 0.875%
12b-1 distribution fee: 0.25%
Expense ratio: 4.41% (year ending 10/31/93) (4.42% without waiver)
IRA fees: Annual $10

PRUDENTIAL FUNDS
(Data common to all Prudential funds are shown below. See subsequent listings for data specific to individual Prudential funds.)

One Seaport Plaza
New York, NY 10292
800-225-1852

Adviser: Prudential Mutual Fund Management, Inc.
Custodian: State Street Bank & Trust Co.
Transfer agent: Prudential Mutual Fund Services, Inc.
Minimum purchase: Initial: $1,000, Subsequent: $100; IRA/Keogh: None
Telephone orders accepted: No
Wire orders accepted: Yes, $1,000 minimum
Deadline for same day wire purchase: 12 NN (4 P.M. for Government Securities Trust - Intermediate Term Series)
Qualified for sale in: All states
Wire redemptions: Yes
Letter redemptions: Signature guarantee required over $50,000
Telephone switching: With all Prudential funds (most of which have loads)
Number of switches permitted: Unlimited
Check redemptions: Money market funds only, $500 minimum (unless Prudential Securities account)
Confirmations mailed: After each purchase and each check, mail or wire redemption
Checks returned: Monthly
Periodic account statements mailed: Monthly

Dividends paid: Income - declared daily, paid monthly; Capital gains - December (Government Securities Trust - Intermediate Term Series only)
Shareholder services: Keogh, IRA, 401(k), 403(b), corporate retirement plans, automatic investment plan (waives initial minimum), withdrawal plan min. req. $10,000
IRA/Keogh fees: Annual $12, Initial $5, Closing $10

PRUDENTIAL GOVERNMENT SECURITIES TRUST - INTERMEDIATE TERM SERIES
(See first Prudential listing for data common to all Prudential funds)

Portfolio manager: David Graham (1994)
Investment objective and policies: High income consistent with reasonable safety. Invests at least 80% of assets in securities issued or guaranteed by the U.S. Government, its agencies or its instrumentalities with a weighted average maturity of 3 to 10 years.
Year organized: 1982 (name changed from Prudential-Bache Government Securities Trust in 1991)
Ticker symbol: PBGVX
Portfolio turnover (3 yrs): 431%, 44%, 60%
Management fee: 0.4%
12b-1 distribution fee: 0.21%
Expense ratio: 0.84% (year ending 11/30/94)

PRUDENTIAL GOVERNMENT SECURITIES TRUST - MONEY MARKET SERIES
(See first Prudential listing for data common to all Prudential funds)

Portfolio manager: Mary Dillon (1990)
Investment objective and policies: High current income, preservation of capital and liquidity. Invests in short-term money market instruments issued or guaranteed by the U.S. Government or its agencies or instrumentalities.
Year organized: 1982 (name changed from Prudential-Bache Government Securities Trust in 1991)
Ticker symbol: PBGXX
Management fee: 0.4%
12b-1 distribution fee: 0.125%
Expense ratio: 0.77% (year ending 11/30/94)

PRUDENTIAL MONEYMART ASSETS INC.
(See first Prudential listing for data common to all Prudential funds)

Portfolio manager: Bob Litterest (1990)
Investment objective and policies: Maximum current income consistent with stability of capital and liquidity. Invests in money market instruments.
Year organized: 1976 (name changed from Prudential-Bache MoneyMart Assets in 1991)
Ticker symbol: PBMXX
Dividends paid: Income - declared daily, paid monthly
Management fee: 0.50% first $50M, 0.30% over $50M
12b-1 distribution fee: 0.125%
Expense ratio: 0.71% (year ending 12/31/93)

PRUDENTIAL TAX-FREE MONEY FUND INC.
(See first Prudential listing for data common to all Prudential funds)

Portfolio manager: Rick Lynes (1987)
Investment objective and policies: High current income exempt from federal income taxes, preservation of capital and liquidity. Invests in municipal money market obligations issued by states, territories and possessions of the U.S. and their subdivisions.
Year organized: 1979 (name changed from Prudential-Bache Tax-Free Money Fund in 1991)

Ticker symbol: PBFXX
Management fee: 0.50%
12b-1 distribution fee: 0.125%
Expense ratio: 0.74 (year ending 12/31/93)

QUANTITATIVE FUNDS
(Data common to all Quantitative funds are shown below. See subsequent listings for data specific to individual Quantitative funds.)

Lincoln North
55 Old Bedford Road
Lincoln, MA 01773
617-259-1144, 800-331-1244
fax 617-259-1166

Shareholder service hours: Full service: M-F 8:30 A.M.-5 P.M. EST; After hours service: prices, messages, prospectuses
Manager: Quantitative Advisors, Inc. (formerly U.S. Boston Investment Management Corp.)
Custodian: State Street Bank & Trust Co.
Transfer agent: U.S. Boston Institutional Services, Inc.
Sales restrictions: Funds have 2 classes of shares - Ordinary and Institutional. Institutional shares have minimum initial investments of $0.5M to $1.0M but do not impose either 12b-1 distribution fees or redemption fees on their shareholders. All data listed are for Ordinary shares.
Minimum purchase: Initial: $5,000, Subsequent: None; IRA: Initial: None
Telephone orders accepted: No
Wire orders accepted: Yes
Deadline for same day wire purchase: 4 P.M.
Exchange privilege: Will accept approved securities in exchange for Fund shares
Telephone redemptions: Yes
Wire redemptions: Yes, $1,000 minimum
Letter redemptions: Signature guarantee required
Redemption fee: 1% deferred sales charge
Telephone switching: With other Quantitative funds
Number of switches permitted: Unlimited
Dividends paid: Income - December; Capital gains - December
Shareholder services: IRA, SEP-IRA, 403(b), automatic investment plan—minimum $100/month (waives initial minimum), electronic funds transfer (purchase only), withdrawal plan min. req. $10,000
12b-1 Distribution fee: 0.50%
IRA fees: Annual $10

QUANTITATIVE DISCIPLINED GROWTH FUND
(See first Quantitative listing for data common to all Quantitative funds)

Adviser: LBS Capital Management, Inc.
Portfolio managers: Dean S. Barr (1994), Ganesh Mani (1994)
Investment objective and policies: Long-term growth of capital. Invests at least 65% of assets in common stock and securities convertible into common stock of domestic companies primarily with capitalizations under $5B. May invest in equity securities of foreign issuers and sell short on up to 25% of total assets. May use covered call options to increase return and hedge up to 25% of total assets.
Year organized: 1994
Discount broker availability: *White
Qualified for sale in: AZ, CA, CO, CT, DC, FL, GA, HI, IL, IN, KY, MD, MA, MI, MN, MO, NJ, NY, NC, OH, OR, PA, RI, TN, TX, UT, VA, VT, WA
Management fee: 1.00%

QUANTITATIVE FOREIGN FRONTIER FUND
(See first Quantitative listing for data common to all Quantitative funds)

Adviser: Boston International Advisors, Inc.
Portfolio managers: Lyle H. Davis (1994), David A. Umstead (1994)
Investment objective and policies: Long-term

growth of capital. Invests at least 65% of assets in common stock and securities convertible into common stock of issuers located in emerging markets. Will normally be invested in at least 8 emerging markets. May use foreign currency futures to hedge against changes in exchange rates.
Year organized: 1994
Discount broker availability: *White
Qualified for sale in: AZ, CA, CO, CT, DC, FL, GA, HI, IL, IN, KY, MD, MA, MI, MN, MO, NJ, NY, NC, OH, OR, PA, RI, TN, TX, UT, VA, VT, WA
Management fee: 0.80%

QUANTITATIVE GROWTH AND INCOME FUND
(See first Quantitative listing for data common to all Quantitative funds)

Adviser: State Street Global Advisors (a unit of State Street Bank & Trust Co.)
Portfolio managers: Steven M. Esielonis (1992), Douglas T. Holmes (1994)
Investment objective and policies: Long-term growth of capital and income. Invests primarily in dividend-paying common stocks of large companies with substantial equity capital. May invest in ADRs of foreign issuers and use covered call options to increase return and hedge up to 25% of total assets.
Year organized: 1985
Ticker symbol: USBOX
Discount broker availability: Schwab (only through financial advisers), *White (only through financial advisers)
Qualified for sale in: AZ, CA, CO, CT, DC, FL, GA, HI, IL, IN, KY, LA, MD, MA, MI, MN, MO, NJ, NM, NY, NC, OH, OR, PA, RI, TN, TX, UT, VA, VT, WA
Portfolio turnover (3 yrs): 110%, 78%, 60%
Largest holding: General Electric Company (3.0%)
Management fee: 0.75%
Expense ratio: 1.72% (year ending 3/31/94)

QUANTITATIVE INTERNATIONAL EQUITY FUND
(See first Quantitative listing for data common to all Quantitative funds)

Adviser: Boston International Advisors, Inc.
Portfolio managers: Lyle H. Davis (1987), David A. Umsted (1987)
Investment objective and policies: Long-term growth of capital and income. Invests at least 65% of assets in equity securities and debt obligations of foreign companies and debt obligations of foreign governments. May use forward foreign currency contracts to hedge up to 25% of total assets.
Year organized: 1985 (name changed from Quantitative Boston Foreign Growth and Income Series in 1994)
Ticker symbol: USBFX
Discount broker availability: *White (only through financial advisers)
Qualified for sale in: AZ, CA, CO, CT, DC, FL, GA, HI, IL, IN, KY, LA, MD, MA, MI, MN, MO, NJ, NY, NC, OH, OR, PA, RI, SC, TN, TX, UT, VA, VT, WA
Portfolio turnover (3 yrs): 40%, 16%, 52%
Largest holding: BASF Ag (3.0%)
Management fee: 1.00%
Expense ratio: 2.20% (year ending 3/31/94)

QUANTITATIVE NUMERIC FUND
(See first Quantitative listing for data common to all Quantitative funds)

Adviser: Numeric Investors, L.P.
Portfolio manager: John C. Bogle, Jr. (1992)
Investment objective and policies: Long-term growth of capital with income secondary. Invests primarily in common stocks of smaller capitalization (under $800M) companies with above average growth potential. May also purchase convertible securities and other investment-grade fixed-income

securities. May use futures and options to increase return and hedge up to 25% of total assets.
Year organized: 1992
Ticker symbol: USBNX
Discount broker availability: Schwab (only through financial advisers), *White (only through financial advisers)
Qualified for sale in: AL, AZ, CA, CO, CT, DC, FL, GA, HI, IL, IN, KY, LA, MA, MD, MI, MN, MO, NJ, NM, NY, NC, OH, OR, PA, RI, SC, TN, TX, UT, VA, VT, WA, WI
Portfolio turnover (2 yrs): 389%, 139%
Largest holding: Gap, Inc. (2.3%)
Management fee: 1.00%
Expense ratio: 1.83% (year ending 3/31/94)

QUANTITATIVE NUMERIC II FUND
(See first Quantitative listing for data common to all Quantitative funds)

Adviser: Numeric Investors, L.P.
Portfolio manager: John C. Bogle, Jr. (1994)
Investment objective and policies: Long-term growth of capital. Invests primarily in common stocks of medium capitalization ($800M-$5B) companies with above average growth potential. May also purchase convertible securities and other investment-grade fixed-income securities. May sell short on up to 25% of total assets use futures and options to increase return and hedge up to 25% of total assets.
Year organized: 1994
Discount broker availability: *White
Qualified for sale in: AZ, CA, CO, CT, DC, FL, GA, HI, IL, IN, KY, MA, MD, MI, MN, MO, NJ, NY, NC, OH, OR, PA, RI, TN, TX, UT, VA, WA
Management fee: 1.00%

THE RAINBOW FUND ◆
225 Park Avenue, Suite 211
New York, NY 10169
212-983-2980

Adviser: Furman, Anderson & Co.
Portfolio manager: Robert M. Furman (1974)
Custodian: The Bank of California
Transfer agent: Investor Data Services
Investment objective and policies: Growth of capital. Invests primarily in common stocks with growth potential. Up to 25% of assets may be in foreign securities. Fund may purchase ADRs of foreign issuers without limit, use options on securities and stock indexes to increase return and hedge up to 25% of total assets, use warrants and sell short. Fund is non-diversified.
Year organized: 1967 (10 for 1 split on 6/30/89)
Ticker symbol: RBOWX
Minimum purchase: Initial: $300, Subsequent: $50
Telephone orders accepted: No
Wire orders accepted: No
Qualified for sale in: NJ, NY
Letter redemptions: Signature guarantee required
Dividends paid: Income - December; Capital gains - December
Portfolio turnover (3 yrs): 66%, 81%, 81%
Largest holding: Intel Corp. (7.4%)
Shareholder services: IRA
Management fee: 0.625% first $2M to 0.375% over $5M
Expense ratio: 3.36% (year ending 10/31/94)
IRA fees: None

REICH & TANG EQUITY FUND ◆
600 Fifth Avenue - 8th Floor
New York, NY 10020
212-676-5200, 800-676-6779
prices/yields 212-830-5225
fax 212-830-5476

Newspaper listing: RchTng
Adviser: Reich & Tang L. P.
Portfolio managers: Robert F. Hoerle (1985), Steven M. Wilson (1993)
Custodian and transfer agent: Investors Fiduciary Trust Co.
Investment objective and policies: Growth of capi-

tal with current income secondary. Invests at least 65% of assets in equity securities believed undervalued. May invest in debt securities and preferred stocks offering opportunity for price appreciation. Up to 15% of assets may be in foreign securities and 10% in restricted securities.
Year organized: 1985
Ticker symbol: RCHTX
Minimum purchase: Initial: $5,000, Subsequent: None, IRA: Initial: $250
Telephone orders accepted: No
Wire orders accepted: Yes
Deadline for same day wire purchases: 4 P.M.
Discount broker availability: Schwab, *White, *Waterhouse
Qualified for sale in: All states
Wire redemptions: Yes, $1,000 minimum
Letter redemptions: Signature guarantee required
Telephone switching: Other Reich & Tang funds, $1,000 minimum
Number of switches permitted: Unlimited
Dividends paid: Income - March, June, September, December; Capital gains - December
Portfolio turnover (3 yrs): 27%, 27%, 43%
Largest holding: Sonoco Products Co. (4.5%)
Shareholder services: IRA, withdrawal plan min. req. $10,000, electronic funds transfer
Management fee: 1.0%
12b-1 distribution fee: Yes (not currently imposed)
Expense ratio: 1.15% (year ending 12/31/93)
IRA fees: None

REICH & TANG GOVERNMENT
SECURITIES TRUST ◆
600 Fifth Avenue - 8th Floor
New York, NY 10020
212-676-5200, 800-676-6779
prices/yields 212-830-5225
fax 212-830-5476

Adviser: Reich & Tang, Inc.
Portfolio manager: Molly Flewharty (1988)
Custodian and transfer agent: Investors Fiduciary Trust Co.
Investment objective and policies: High current income consistent with prudent investment risk. Invests solely in securities issued or guaranteed by the U.S. Government or its agencies and instrumentalities and in repurchase agreements.
Year organized: 1986
Minimum purchase: Initial: $5,000, Subsequent: None, IRA: Initial: $250
Telephone orders accepted: No
Wire orders accepted: Yes
Deadline for same day wire purchases: 4 P.M.
Qualified for sale in: CO, CT, DE, MA, NY, NC, TX
Wire redemptions: Yes, $1,000 minimum
Letter redemptions: Signature guarantee required
Telephone switching: Other Reich & Tang funds, $1,000 minimum
Number of switches permitted: Unlimited
Dividends paid: Income - declared daily, paid monthly; Capital gains - annually
Portfolio turnover (3 yrs): 84%, 66%, 20%
Shareholder services: IRA, withdrawal plan min. req. $10,000, electronic funds transfer
Management fee: 0.55%
12b-1 distribution fee: 0.25% (not currently imposed)
Expense ratio: 0.55% (year ending 2/28/94) (0.80% without waiver)
IRA fees: None

RESERVE FUNDS
(Data common to all Reserve funds are shown below. See subsequent listing for data specific to individual Reserve funds.)

810 Seventh Avenue
New York, NY 10019
212-977-9982, 800-223-5547
yields 800-637-1700, fax 212-977-9897

Shareholder service hours: Full service: M-F 8 A.M.- 5 P.M. EST; After hours service: price, yields, balances, messages, prospectuses

Adviser: Reserve Management Co., Inc.
Custodian: Chemical Bank
Transfer agent: Reserve Partners, Inc.
Minimum purchase: Initial: $1,000, Subsequent: $250; IRA: Initial: $250
Small balance fee: $5 per month if under $1,000
Wire orders accepted: Yes
Deadline for same day wire purchase: 11 A.M. (exceptions noted)
Wire redemptions: Yes, $10 fee under $10,000
Letter redemptions: Signature guarantee required over $5,000
Telephone switching: With other Reserve Group funds
Number of switches permitted: Unlimited
Deadline for same day switch: 11 A.M. (exceptions noted)
Check redemptions: $500 minimum ($2 fee for processing checks for less than $500)
Dividends paid: Income - declared and paid daily
Transaction confirmations: Not sent
Checks returned: Quarterly
Periodic account statements mailed: Monthly if activity, quarterly if dividends only
Shareholder services: IRA, automatic investment plan, electronic fund transfer, withdrawal plan min. req. $5,000. Fund is also used as part of the Reserve Fund's CPA (central assets) accounts
IRA fees: Annual $10 (waived for accounts over $10,000), Initial $10, Closing $10

THE RESERVE FUND - PRIMARY FUND
(See first Reserve listing for data common to all Reserve funds)

Portfolio manager: Karen Quigley (1985)
Investment objective and policies: Current income consistent with preservation of capital and liquidity. Invests in short-term money market instruments.
Year organized: 1971
Ticker symbol: RFIXX
Deadline for same day wire purchase: 2 P.M.
Qualified for sale in: All states
Deadline for same day switch: 12 NN
Management fee: 0.5% first $500M to 0.4% over $2B
12b-1 distribution fee: 0.16%
Expense ratio: 0.97% (year ending 5/31/94)

THE RESERVE FUND -
U.S. GOVERNMENT FUND
(See first Reserve listing for data common to all Reserve funds)

Portfolio manager: Karen Quigley (1992)
Investment objective and policies: Current income consistent with preservation of capital and liquidity. Invests exclusively in marketable money market obligations issued or guaranteed by the U.S. Government or its agencies.
Year organized: 1981
Ticker symbol: RFGXX
Deadline for same day wire purchase: 2 P.M.
Qualified for sale in: All states
Deadline for same day switch: 12 NN
Management fee: 0.5% first $500M to 0.4% over $2B
12b-1 distribution fee: 0.18%
Expense ratio: 0.99% (year ending 5/31/94)

THE RESERVE FUND - U.S.
TREASURY FUND ◆
(See first Reserve listing for data common to all Reserve funds)

Portfolio manager: Karen Quigley (1992)
Investment objective and policies: Current income consistent with preservation of capital and liquidity. Invests exclusively in marketable money market obligations issued or guaranteed by the U.S. Government that provide income exempt from state and local income taxes.
Year organized: 1981
Qualified for sale in: All states
Management fee: 0.8% (comprehensive fee covering investment advisory and all ordinary operating expenses)

Expense ratio: 0.73% (year ending 5/31/94)
(0.80% without waiver)

RESERVE NEW YORK TAX-EXEMPT TRUST - NEW YORK FUND
(See first Reserve listing for data common to all Reserve funds)

Portfolio manager: Caren S. Elias (1992)
Investment objective and policies: High short-term interest income exempt from federal, New York State and New York City income taxes consistent with minimization of risk and maintenance of liquidity. Invests at least 80% of assets in money market obligations issued by the State of New York, its political subdivisions, authorities, and corporations.
Year organized: 1983
Ticker symbol: RTEXX
Qualified for sale in: NY
Management fee: 0.5% first $500M to 0.4% over $2B
12b-1 distribution fee: 0.17%
Expense ratio: 0.98% (year ending 5/31/94)

RESERVE TAX-EXEMPT TRUST - CALIFORNIA FUND
(See first Reserve listing for data common to all Reserve funds)

Portfolio manager: Caren S. Elias (1994)
Investment objective and policies: High level of current income exempt from federal and California income taxes consistent with preservation of capital and liquidity. Invests in municipal bonds and notes primarily issued by the State of California and its political subdivisions and authorities, at least 80% exempt from federal and California income taxes.
Year organized: 1994
Qualified for sale in: CA
Management fee: 0.5% first $500M to 0.4% over $2B
12b-1 distribution fee: 0.20%

RESERVE TAX-EXEMPT TRUST - CONNECTICUT FUND
(See first Reserve listing for data common to all Reserve funds)

Portfolio manager: Caren S. Elias (1992)
Investment objective and policies: High level of current income exempt from federal and Connecticut income taxes consistent with preservation of capital and liquidity. Invests in municipal bonds and notes primarily issued by the State of Connecticut, at least 80% exempt from federal and Connecticut income taxes.
Year organized: 1985
Ticker symbol: RCOXX
Qualified for sale in: CT
Management fee: 0.5% first $500M to 0.4% over $2B
12b-1 distribution fee: 0.17%
Expense ratio: 0.85% (year ending 5/31/94)
(0.95% without waiver)

RESERVE TAX-EXEMPT TRUST - INTERSTATE FUND
(See first Reserve listing for data common to all Reserve funds)

Portfolio manager: Caren S. Elias (1992)
Investment objective and policies: Current income consistent with preservation of capital and liquidity. Invests in short-term money market instruments issued by states, territories and possessions of the U.S. that are exempt from federal income taxes.
Year organized: 1983
Ticker symbol: RISXX
Qualified for sale in: All states
Management fee: 0.5% first $500M to 0.4% over $2B

12b-1 distribution fee: 0.19%
Expense ratio: 1.02% (year ending 5/31/94)

RESERVE TAX-EXEMPT TRUST - MASSACHUSETTS FUND
(See first Reserve listing for data common to all Reserve funds)

Portfolio manager: Caren S. Elias (1992)
Investment objective and policies: High level of current income exempt from federal and Massachusetts income taxes consistent with preservation of capital and liquidity. Invests in municipal bonds and notes primarily issued by the State of Massachusetts, at least 80% exempt from federal and Massachusetts income taxes.
Year organized: 1990
Qualified for sale in: MA
Management fee: 0.5% first $500M to 0.4% over $2B
12b-1 distribution fee: 0.02%
Expense ratio: 0.51% (year ending 5/31/94)
(1.01% without waiver)

RESERVE TAX-EXEMPT TRUST - NEW JERSEY FUND
(See first Reserve listing for data common to all Reserve funds)

Portfolio manager: Caren S. Elias (1994)
Investment objective and policies: High level of current income exempt from federal and New Jersey income taxes consistent with preservation of capital and liquidity. Invests in municipal bonds and notes primarily issued by the State of New Jersey and its political subdivisions and authorities, at least 80% exempt from federal and New Jersey income taxes.
Year organized: 1994
Qualified for sale in: NJ
Management fee: 0.5% first $500M to 0.4% over $2B
12b-1 distribution fee: 0.18%

RETIREMENT SYSTEM FUNDS
(Data common to all Retirement System funds are shown below. See subsequent listings for data specific to individual Retirement System funds.)

P.O. Box 2064
Grand Central Station
New York, NY 10163
212-503-2800, 800-722-3615
fax 212-503-0128

Shareholder service hours: Full service: M-F 9 A.M.- 5 P.M. EST
Adviser: Retirement System Investors, Inc.
Custodian: Custodial Trust Co.
Transfer agent: Retirement System Consultants, Inc.
Minimum purchase: Initial: $500, Subsequent: $250
Telephone orders accepted: No
Wire orders accepted: No
Qualified for sale in: CT, DE, DC, FL, ME, MD, MA, NH, NJ, NY, PA, RI
Letter redemptions: Signature guarantee required
12b-1 distribution fee: 0.20%

RETIREMENT SYSTEM FUND - CORE EQUITY FUND
(See first Retirement System listing for data common to all Retirement System funds)

Portfolio manager: James P. Coughlin (1991)
Investment objective and policies: Total return (income and capital appreciation) in excess of the Lipper Growth and Income Mutual Funds Average, measured over a period of 3 to 5 years. Invests at least 65% of assets in common stocks of companies

with market capitalization in excess of $750M. Up to 20% of assets may be in securities of foreign issuers. May use futures and options.
Year organized: 1991
Dividends paid: Income - December; Capital gains - December
Portfolio turnover (3 yrs): 10%, 22%, 61%
Largest holding: American Telephone & Telegraph Corp. (5.8%)
Management fee: 0.60% first $50M to 0.40% over $200M
Expense ratio: 0.90% (year ending 9/30/94)
(2.23% without waiver)

RETIREMENT SYSTEM FUND - EMERGING GROWTH EQUITY FUND
(See first Retirement System listing for data common to all Retirement System funds)

Investment manager: Putnam Advisory Company, Inc.
Portfolio managers: Richard Frucci (1994)
Investment objective and policies: Total return in excess of the Lipper Small Company Growth Mutual Fund Average, measured over a 3 to 5 year period. Invests at least 65% of assets in common stocks of rapidly growing companies, generally with market capitalizations from $50M to $750M. Up to 20% of assets may be in securities of foreign issuers. May use futures and options.
Year organized: 1991
Dividends paid: Income - December; Capital gains - December
Portfolio turnover (3 yrs): 73%, 144%, 138%
Largest holding: Maxim Integrated Products, Inc. (1.8%)
Management fee: 1.00% first $25M, 0.75% over $25M
Expense ratio: 1.85% (year ending 9/30/94)
(5.96% without waiver)

RETIREMENT SYSTEM FUND - INTERMEDIATE-TERM FIXED INCOME FUND
(See first Retirement System listing for data common to all Retirement System funds)

Portfolio manager: Herbert Kuhl, Jr. (1991)
Investment objective and policies: Total return (income and capital appreciation) in excess of the Lipper Intermediate (five to ten year) U.S. Government Mutual Funds Average measured over a period of 3 to 5 years. Invests in a diversified portfolio of debt securities with remaining maturities of 10 years or less and a weighted average maturity of 3 to 5 years.
Year organized: 1991
Dividends paid: Income - declared and paid monthly; Capital gains - December
Portfolio turnover (3 yrs): 9%, 28%, 9%
Management fee: 0.40% first $50M to 0.20% over $150M
Expense ratio: 0.90% (year ending 9/30/94)
(2.56% without waiver)

RETIREMENT SYSTEM FUND - MONEY MARKET FUND
(See first Retirement System listing for data common to all Retirement System funds)

Portfolio managers: John F. Meuser (1991), Deborah Dagiau (1994)
Investment objective and policies: Current income consistent with liquidity and stability of principal. Invests in high quality money market instruments. Up to 25% of assets may be in dollar-denominated securities of foreign issuers.
Year organized: 1991
Dividends paid: Income - declared daily, paid monthly
Management fee: 0.25% first $50M, 0.20% over $50M
Expense ratio: 0.42% (year ending 9/30/94)
(3.89% without waiver)

REYNOLDS FUNDS ◆
(Data common to all Reynolds funds are shown below. See subsequent listings for data specific to individual Reynolds funds.)

Wood Island, Third Floor
80 East Sir Francis Drake Blvd. - Suite 3A
Larkspur, CA 94939
415-461-7860, 800-338-1579

Shareholder service hours: Full service: M-F 9 A.M.- 5 P.M.; After hours service: prices, balances, last transactions
Adviser: Reynolds Capital Management
Administrator: Fiduciary Management, Inc.
Custodian and transfer agent: Firstar Trust Co.
Minimum purchase: Initial: $1,000, Subsequent: $100
Telephone orders accepted: No
Wire orders accepted: Yes, subsequent $500 minimum
Deadline for same day wire purchase: 4 P.M.
Letter redemptions: Signature guarantee required over $25,000
Telephone switching: With other Reynolds funds, $1,000 minimum
Number of switches permitted: Unlimited
Shareholder Services: Keogh, IRA, SEP-IRA, 401(k), 403(b), corporate retirement plans, automatic investment plan—minimum $50/month, electronic funds transfer, withdrawal plan min. req. $10,000
IRA/Keogh fees: Annual $12.50 ($25 maximum), Closing $15

REYNOLDS BLUE CHIP GROWTH FUND ◆
(See first Reynolds listing for data common to all Reynolds funds)

Newspaper listing: Rey BC
Portfolio manager: Frederick L. Reynolds (1988)
Investment objective and policies: Long-term capital growth with current income secondary. Invests at least 65% of assets in common stocks of well-established growth companies commonly known as "blue chip" companies, i.e. those with at least $300M in market capitalization and in either the Dow Jones or S&P 500 Indexes. Up to 15% of assets may be in ADRs of foreign issuers. Fund may use index put options to hedge.
Year organized: 1988
Ticker symbol: RBCGX
Discount broker availability: Schwab
Qualified for sale in: AL, CA, CO, CT, FL, HI, ID, IL, IA, KS, LA, MI, MN, MO, NV, NM, NY, OH, OR, PA, TX, WA, WI, WY
Dividends paid: Income - October, December; Capital gains - October, December
Portfolio turnover (3 yrs): 43%, 38%, 0%
Largest holding: Microsoft Corp. (2.9%)
Management fee: 1.0%
Administrative fee: 0.20% first $30M, 0.10% over $30M
Expense ratio: 1.5% (year ending 9/30/94)

REYNOLDS MONEY MARKET FUND ◆
(See first Reynolds listing for data common to all Reynolds funds)

Portfolio manager: Frederick L. Reynolds (1991)
Investment objective and policies: High current income consistent with liquidity and preservation of capital. Invests in money market instruments with remaining maturities of 13 months or less.
Year organized: 1991
Qualified for sale in: CA, CO, CT, FL, HI, ID, IL, LA, MI, MN, NM, NY, OH, OR, PA, TX, WA, WY
Telephone redemptions: Yes, $1,000 minimum
Wire redemptions: Yes, $1,000 minimum, $7.50 fee
Check redemptions: $500 minimum
Confirmations mailed: After each purchase and each check, mail or wire redemption
Checks returned: Not returned
Periodic statements mailed: Monthly

Dividends paid: Income - declared daily, paid monthly
Management fee: 0.5%
Administrative fee: 0.10%
Expense ratio: 0.63% (year ending 9/30/94) (1.47% without waiver)

REYNOLDS OPPORTUNITY FUND ◆
(See first Reynolds listing for data common to all Reynolds funds)

Portfolio manager: Frederick L. Reynolds (1992)
Investment objective and policies: Long-term capital growth. Invests primarily in securities of growth companies, believed undervalued, without regard to size. May invest up to 25% of assets in ADRs of foreign companies traded in the U.S. Fund hedges and engages in option trading.
Year organized: 1992
Qualified for sale in: CA, CO, CT, FL, HI, ID, IL, LA, MI, MN, NY, OH, OR, PA, WA, WY
Dividends paid: Income - October, December; Capital gains - October, December
Portfolio turnover (3 yrs): 17%, 68%, 30%
Largest holding: United Healthcare Corp. (2.9%)
Management fee: 1.0%
Administrative fee: 0.20% first $30M, 0.10% over $30M
Expense ratio: 2.0% (year ending 9/30/94) (2.1% without waiver)

REYNOLDS U.S. GOVERNMENT BOND FUND ◆
(See first Reynolds listing for data common to all Reynolds funds)

Portfolio manager: Frederick L. Reynolds (1992)
Investment objective and policies: High level of current income. Invests at least 65% of assets in securities issued or guaranteed by the U.S. Government, its agencies or instrumentalities with a weighted average maturity of 1 to 10 years. May invest in high quality corporate obligations.
Year organized: 1992
Qualified for sale in: CA, FL, HI, ID, IL, LA, MD, MI, MN, NY, OH, OR, PA, TX, WA
Dividends paid: Income - declared daily, paid monthly; capital gains - annually
Portfolio turnover (3 yrs): 20%, 6%, 0%
Management fee: 0.75%
Administrative fee: 0.10%
Expense ratio: 0.86% (year ending 9/30/94) (1.5% without waiver)

THE RIGHTIME FUND
The Forst Pavilion, Suite 1000
218 Glenside Avenue
Wyncote, PA 19095
610-887-8111, 800-242-1421

Newspaper listing: RT
Adviser: Rightime Econometrics, Inc.
Portfolio managers: David J. Rights (1985), Anthony W. Soslow (1985), Denis N. Houser (1988)
Custodian: CoreStates Bank N.A.
Transfer agent: Lincoln Investment Planning, Inc.
Investment objective and policies: High total return consistent with reasonable risk. Invests in other mutual funds. May invest in other funds with a sales load and has the right to engage in futures transactions for hedging purposes. Fund will adopt an aggressive portfolio strategy in rising markets and a conservative strategy in declining markets.
Year organized: 1985
Ticker symbol: RTFDX
Minimum purchase: Initial (regular and Keogh): $2,000, Subsequent: $100; IRA: None
Telephone orders accepted: No
Wire orders accepted: Yes
Deadline for same day wire purchase: 4 P.M.
Qualified for sale in: All states except NH
Wire redemptions: Yes

Letter redemptions: Signature guarantee required over $5,000
Telephone switching: With other Rightime funds, all of which are load funds
Number of switches permitted: Unlimited
Dividends paid: Income - December; Capital gains - December
Portfolio turnover (3 yrs): 11%, 2%, 73%
Largest holding: Columbia Special Fund (2.2%)
Shareholder services: Keogh, IRA, 403(b), withdrawal plan min. req. $10,000
Management fee: 0.5%
Administrative fee: 0.95%
12b-1 distribution fee: 0.75%
Expense ratio: 2.51% (year ending 10/31/94)
IRA/Keogh fees: Annual $10

RMA FUNDS
(Data common to all RMA portfolios are shown below. See subsequent listings for data specific to individual RMA portfolios.)

1285 Ave. of the Americas
New York, NY 10019
800-762-1000, local Paine Webber office

Adviser: Paine Webber
Sub-adviser: Mitchell Hutchins Asset Management, Inc.
Portfolio manager: Susan Messina (1990)
Custodian: State Street Bank & Trust Co.
Transfer agent: PFPC, Inc.
Special sales restrictions: Available only to Paine Webber Resource Management Account and Business Service Account clients
Minimum purchase: Initial: $15,000 equity, no minimum on individual fund purchases
Wire orders accepted: Yes, $5,000 minimum
Deadline for same day wire purchase: 12 NN
Qualified for sale in: All states
Wire redemptions: Yes, $5,000 minimum
Telephone switching: With other RMA funds
Number of switches permitted: Unlimited, $5 fee
Deadline for same day switch: Into RMA: 3:30 P.M.; out of RMA: 12 NN
Check redemptions: No minimum
Checks returned: Monthly
Periodic account statements mailed: Monthly
Service fee on account: $85 per year with gold Mastercard, $125 including Bank One line of credit
Dividends paid: Income - declared daily, paid monthly
Shareholder services: Keogh, IRA, Mastercard, fund is part of central assets account

RMA MONEY FUND - MONEY MARKET PORTFOLIO ◆
(See first RMA listing for data common to all RMA portfolios)

Investment objective and policies: Maximum current income consistent with liquidity and conservation of capital. Invests in short-term U.S. Government securities, bank CDs, banker's acceptances, commercial paper, repurchase agreements and other money market instruments.
Year organized: 1982
Ticker symbol: RMAXX
Management fee: 0.5%
Expense ratio: 0.59% (year ending 6/30/94)

RMA MONEY FUND - U.S. GOVERNMENT PORTFOLIO
(See first RMA listing for data common to all RMA portfolios)

Investment objective and policies: Maximum current income consistent with liquidity and conservation of capital. Invests exclusively in short-term U.S. Government securities.
Year organized: 1982
Ticker symbol: RUSXX
Management fee: 0.5% first $300M to 0.36% over $750M
12b-1 distribution fee: 0.08%
Expense ratio: 0.62% (year ending 6/30/94)

RMA TAX-FREE FUND
(See first RMA listing for data common to all RMA portfolios)

Investment objective and policies: Maximum current income, exempt from federal income tax, consistent with liquidity and conservation of capital. Invests in high-grade municipal money market instruments issued by states, municipalities, and public authorities. Up to 20% of assets may be in AMT securities.
Year organized: 1982
Ticker symbol: RTFXX
Management fee: 0.5% first $1B to 0.36% over $1.5B
12b-1 distribution fee: 0.08%
Expense ratio: 0.64% (year ending 6/30/94)

ROBERTSON STEPHENS FUNDS
(Data common to all Robertson Stephens funds are show below. See subsequent listings for data specific to individual Robertson Stephens funds.)

555 California Street - Suite 2600
San Francisco, CA 94104
415-781-9700, 800-766-3863
prices 800-624-8025, fax 415-433-7326

Shareholder service hours: Full service: M-F 6 A.M.-5 P.M. PST; After hours service: prices, yields, balances, last transaction, prospectuses
Adviser: Robertson Stephens Investment Management, Inc.
Custodian: State Street Bank & Trust Co.
Transfer agent: National Financial Data Services
Minimum purchase: Initial: $5,000, Subsequent: $100; IRA: Initial: $1,000, Subsequent: $1
Telephone orders accepted: Subsequent only, $1,000 minimum
Wire orders accepted: Yes
Deadline for same day wire purchase: 4 P.M.
Qualified for sale in: All states
Telephone redemption: Yes
Wire redemption: Yes, $9 fee
Letter redemptions: Signature guarantee not required
Dividends paid: Income - November; Capital gains - November
Telephone switching: With other Robertson Stevens funds
Number of switches permitted: 2 round trips per year
Shareholder services: IRA, automatic investment plan, electronic funds transfer
IRA fees: Annual $10

THE ROBERTSON STEPHENS CONTRARIAN FUND
(See first Robertson Stephens listing for data common to all Robertson Stephens funds)

Portfolio manager: Paul H. Stephens (1993)
Investment objective and policies: Long-term capital appreciation. Invests world-wide in equity securities of attractively priced growing companies. Fund seeks out companies, both domestic and foreign, that have not yet been discovered or become popular, have improved growth potential due to changed circumstances, companies that have declined in value and lost favor with investors and previously popular companies temporarily out of favor due to short-term factors. Up to 35% of assets may be in debt obligations, including junk bonds, and 15% in illiquid securities. May use options, futures, and options thereon. Fund may hedge up to 25% of assets.
Year organized: 1993
Ticker symbol: RSCOX
Discount broker availability: *Schwab, *White, Waterhouse, *Fidelity, *Siebert
Portfolio turnover (1 yr): 14%
Largest holding: Cambior, Inc. (4.9%)
Management fee: 1.50%
12b-1 distribution fee: 0.75%
Expense ratio: 2.22% (10 months ending 3/31/94) (includes waiver)

ROBERTSON STEPHENS EMERGING GROWTH FUND
(See first Robertson Stephens listing for data common to all Robertson Stephens funds)

Portfolio manager: Robert Charles Czepiel (1987)
Investment objective and policies: Long-term capital appreciation. Invests primarily in equity securities of emerging growth companies with above average growth prospects. Up to 35% of assets may be in securities of foreign issuers and 35% in debt obligations of the U.S. Government, its agencies and its instrumentalities.
Year organized: 1987 (formerly RCS Emerging Growth Fund)
Ticker symbol: RSEGX
Discount broker availability: *Schwab, *White, Waterhouse, *Fidelity, *Siebert
Portfolio turnover (3 yrs): 274%, 124%, 147%
Largest holding: Cabletron Systems, Inc. (2.4%)
Management fee: 1.0%
12b-1 distribution fee: 0.25%
Expense ratio: 1.61% (year ending 3/31/94)

ROBERTSON STEPHENS EMERGING MARKETS FUND
(See first Robertson Stephens listing for data common to all Robertson Stephens funds)

Portfolio manager: Michael Hoffman (1994)
Investment objective and policies: Long-term capital appreciation. Invests primarily in publicly traded equity securities of companies in emerging markets. Invests in ADRs, GDRs and directly in emerging markets. Up to 15% of assets may be in illiquid securities. May sell short up to 25% of assets and use options and futures to hedge up to 25%.
Year organized: 1994
Discount broker availability: *Schwab, *White, *Fidelity, *Siebert
Largest holding: Ashanti Goldfields - GDR (2.9%)
Management fee: 1.25%
12b-1 distribution fee: 0.50%

ROBERTSON STEPHENS VALUE + GROWTH FUND ◆
(See first Robertson Stephens listing for data common to all Robertson Stephens funds)

Portfolio manager: Ronald E. Elijah (1992)
Investment objective and policies: Long-term capital appreciation. Invests primarily in equity securities of small- and medium-sized companies (market capitalizations under $1B) with favorable growth prospects and modest valuations based on earnings and assets. May invest in securities of domestic, multinational and foreign companies without limit. Up to 35% of assets may be in debt obligations of the U.S. Government, its agencies and its instrumentalities. May sell short up to 25% of assets and use options and futures to hedge up to 25%.
Year organized: 1992 (name changed from Value Plus Fund in 1994)
Ticker symbol: RSVPX
Discount broker availability: *Schwab, *White, Waterhouse, *Fidelity, *Siebert
Portfolio turnover (2 yrs): 250%, 210%
Largest holding: 3COM Corporation (5.2%)
Management fee: 1.25%
Expense ratio: 1.55% (year ending 3/31/94) (2.35% without waiver)

ROYCE FUNDS
(Data common to all Royce funds are shown below. See subsequent listings for data specific to individual Royce funds.)

1414 Avenue of the Americas
New York, NY 10019
212-355-7311, 800-221-4268
800-841-1180 (for shareholders only)

Shareholder service hours: Full service: M-F 8:30 A.M.-5:30 P.M. EST; After hours service: prices, balances, transactions, messages, prospectuses, total returns
Adviser: Quest Advisory Corp. (Royce, Ebright &

Associates, Inc. for REvest Growth & Income Fund)
Custodian and transfer agent: State Street Bank & Trust Co. c/o N.F.D.S.
Minimum purchase: Initial: $2,000 ($10,000 for REvest Growth & Income Fund), Subsequent: $50; IRA: Initial: $500
Telephone orders accepted: Yes, subsequent minimum $500
Wire orders accepted: Yes, subsequent only, $1,000 minimum
Deadline for same day wire purchase: 4 P.M.
Qualified for sale in: All states
Telephone redemptions: Yes, $50,000 maximum
Wire redemptions: Yes
Letter redemptions: Signature guarantee required over $50,000
Redemption fee: 1% on purchases held less than 1 year, payable to the fund
Telephone switching: With other Royce funds
Number of switches permitted: Unlimited
Shareholder services: IRA, 403(b), automatic investment plan ($500 initial minimum), withdrawal plan min. req. $25,000, electronic funds transfer
IRA fees: Annual $15, Initial $5

ROYCE FUNDS - PENNSYLVANIA MUTUAL FUND ◆
(See first Royce listing for data common to all Royce funds)

Portfolio managers: Charles M. Royce (1973), Thomas R. Ebright (1987)
Investment objective and policies: Long-term capital growth. Invests primarily in common stocks and convertible securities of small and medium-sized companies (capitalizations under $750M) selected on a value basis. May use fixed-income securities and have up to 35% of assets in lowest investment-grade category bonds.
Year organized: 1962
Ticker symbol: PENNX
Discount broker availability: Schwab, White, Waterhouse, Fidelity, Siebert
Dividends paid: Income - December; Capital gains - December
Portfolio turnover (3 yrs): 24%, 22%, 29%
Largest holding: U.S. Treasury Note due 4/15/99 (3.5%)
Management fee: 1.0% first $50M to 0.75% over $100M
Expense ratio: 0.98% (year ending 12/31/93)

ROYCE FUNDS - ROYCE EQUITY INCOME FUND ◆
(See first Royce listing for data common to all Royce funds)

Portfolio managers: Charles M. Royce (1990), Thomas R. Ebright (1990)
Investment objective and policies: Reasonable income with potential for capital appreciation. Invests primarily in dividend-paying common stocks and securities convertible into common stocks of small and medium-sized companies (market capitalizations under $1B) selected on a value basis.
Year organized: 1990
Ticker symbol: RYEQX
Discount broker availability: Schwab, White, Fidelity, Siebert
Dividends paid: Income - March, June, September, December; Capital gains - December
Portfolio turnover (3 yrs): 100%, 59%, 72%
Largest holding: Wilmington Trust Corp. (1.4%)
Management fee: 1.0%
Expense ratio: 1.00% (year ending 12/31/93) (1.39% without waiver)
IRA fees: Annual $15, Initial $5, Closing $10

ROYCE FUNDS - ROYCE LOW-PRICED STOCK FUND ◆
(See first Royce listing for data common to all Royce funds)

Portfolio manager: Charles M. Royce (1993)
Investment objective and policies: Long-term capi-

tal growth. Invests primarily in common stocks and securities convertible into common stocks of small and medium-sized companies (capitalization under $1B), selected on a value basis, with common stock trading below $15 per share.
Year organized: 1993
Discount broker availability: *Fidelity, *Siebert
Dividends paid: Income - December; Capital gains - December
Largest holding: Allwaste, Inc. (6.6%)
Management fee: 1.50%
12b-1 distribution fee: Maximum of 0.25% (not currently imposed)

ROYCE FUNDS - ROYCE MICRO-CAP FUND ◆
(See first Royce listing for data common to all Royce funds)

Portfolio managers: Charles M. Royce (1991), Thomas R. Ebright (1992)
Investment objective and policies: Long-term capital growth. Invests primarily in common stocks and securities convertible into common stocks of small and medium-sized companies (market capitalizations under $500M) traded in the over-the-counter market, selected on a value basis.
Year organized: 1991 (name changed from Royce OTC Fund on 12/27/94)
Ticker symbol: RYOTX
Discount broker availability: Schwab, White, *Fidelity, *Siebert
Dividends paid: Income - December; Capital gains - December
Portfolio turnover (2 yrs): 116%, 171%
Largest holding: U.S. Treasury Note due 2/28/99 (12.4%)
Management fee: 1.50%
Expense ratio: 1.99% (year ending 12/31/93) (2.49% without waiver)

ROYCE FUNDS - ROYCE PREMIER FUND ◆
(See first Royce listing for data common to all Royce funds)

Portfolio managers: Charles M. Royce (1991), Thomas R. Ebright (1991)
Investment objective and policies: Long-term capital growth with current income secondary. Invests primarily in a limited portfolio of common stocks and securities convertible into common stocks of small and medium-sized companies (market capitalizations under $1B). Companies are picked for superior financial characteristics and/or unusually attractive business prospects.
Year organized: 1991
Ticker symbol: RYPRX
Discount broker availability: Schwab, White, Waterhouse, Fidelity, Siebert
Dividends paid: Income - December; Capital gains - December
Portfolio turnover (2 yrs): 85%, 116%
Largest holding: U.S. Treasury Note due 4/15/99 (9.2%)
Management fee: 1.0% on first $50M to 0.75% over $100M
Expense ratio: 1.50% (year ending 12/31/93) (1.68% without waiver)

ROYCE FUNDS - ROYCE REVEST GROWTH AND INCOME FUND ◆
(See first Royce listing for data common to all Royce funds)

Portfolio manager: Thomas R. Ebright (1994)
Investment objective and policies: Long-term capital growth with income secondary. Invests primarily in common stocks and securities convertible into common stocks of small and medium-sized companies (market capitalizations from $200M to $2B), selected on a value basis.
Year organized: 1994
Special sales restriction: Fund will close to new shareholders on March 1st of any year following a December 31st with total assets exceeding $350M

Discount broker availability: Schwab, White
Dividends paid: Income - March, June, September, December; Capital gains - December
Management fee: 1.00%

ROYCE FUNDS - ROYCE TOTAL RETURN FUND ◆
(See first Royce listing for data common to all Royce funds)

Portfolio manager: Charles M. Royce (1993)
Investment objective and policies: Long-term capital growth and current income. Invests primarily in dividend-paying common stocks and securities convertible into common stocks of small and medium-sized companies (capitalization under $1B), selected on a value basis.
Year organized: 1993
Dividends paid: Income - December; Capital gains - December
Largest holding: Pier 1 Imports 6.875% Convertible Debenture due 4/01/02 (11.6%)
Management fee: 1.00%
12b-1 distribution fee: Maximum of 0.25% (not currently imposed)

ROYCE FUNDS - ROYCE VALUE FUND
(See first Royce listing for data common to all Royce funds)

Portfolio manager: Charles M. Royce (1982), Thomas R. Ebright (1982)
Investment objective and policies: Long-term capital appreciation. Invests primarily in equity securities of companies with market capitalizations of under $750M selected on a value basis. Adviser puts primary emphasis on analysis of various internal returns indicative of profitability, balance sheets and cash flows and their relationships to the securities' prices.
Year organized: 1982
Ticker symbol: RYVFX
Discount broker availability: Schwab, *Fidelity, *Siebert
Dividends paid: Income - December; Capital gains - December
Portfolio turnover (3 yrs): 31%, 28%, 25%
Largest holding: U.S. Treasury Note due 4/15/99 (5.8%)
Management fee: 1.0% on first $50M to 0.75% over $100M
12b-1 distribution fee: 0.69%
Expense ratio: 1.84% (year ending 12/31/93) (2.15% without waiver)

RSI RETIREMENT TRUST FUNDS ◆
(Data common to all RSI Retirement Trust funds are shown below. See subsequent listings for data specific to individual RSI Retirement Trust funds.)

41 East 42nd Street
New York, NY 10017
212-503-0100, 800-722-3615
fax 212-503-0128

Shareholder service hours: Full service: M-F 9 A.M.- 5 P.M. EST
Adviser: Retirement System Investors Inc.
Transfer agent: Retirement System Consultants, Inc.
Special sales restrictions: Designed for corporate trusts exempt from taxation under Section 501(a) of the Internal Revenue Code of 1986 (tax-qualified retirement plans) and individual retirement trusts or custodial accounts exempt from taxation under Section 408(e) of the code (IRA Rollovers)
Minimum purchase: Initial: $500, Subsequent: $500
Telephone orders accepted: No
Wire orders accepted: No
Qualified for sale in: CT, DE, DC, FL, IL, ME, MD, NH, NJ, NY, PA, RI
Letter redemptions: Signature guarantee required over $25,000
Dividends paid: None
IRA Rollover fees: Annual $10 (waived for accounts with value of $5,000 or more)

RSI RETIREMENT TRUST - ACTIVELY MANAGED BOND FUND ◆
(See first RSI listing for data common to all RSI funds)

Portfolio manager: Herbert Kuhl, Jr. (1983)
Custodian: Chase Manhattan Bank, N.A.
Investment objective and policies: Total return (income and capital appreciation) in excess of the Lipper U.S. Government Bond Funds Average measured over a period of 3 to 5 years. Invests primarily in U.S. Government and agency securities, corporate debt securities rated A or better, foreign debt securities and zero coupon securities with no restrictions on maturity.
Year organized: 1983
Ticker symbol: RSIAX
Portfolio turnover (3 yrs): 170%, 133%, 125%
Management fee: 0.40% first $50M to 0.20% over $150M
Expense ratio: 0.82% (year ending 9/30/94)

RSI RETIREMENT TRUST - CORE EQUITY FUND ◆
(See first RSI listing for data common to all RSI funds)

Portfolio manager: James P. Coughlin (1983)
Custodian: Custodial Trust Co.
Investment objective and policies: Total return (income and capital appreciation) in excess of the Lipper Growth and Income Mutual Funds Average, measured over a period of 3 to 5 years. Invests at least 65% of assets in common stocks of companies with market capitalization in excess of $750M. Up to 20% of assets may be in securities of foreign issuers. May use futures and options.
Year organized: 1983
Ticker symbol: RSICX
Portfolio turnover (3 yrs): 6%, 13%, 19%
Largest holding: American Telephone & Telegraph Co. (7.1%)
Management fee: 0.60% first $50M to 0.40% over $200M
Expense ratio: 1.01% (year ending 9/30/94)

RSI RETIREMENT TRUST - EMERGING GROWTH EQUITY FUND ◆
(See first RSI listing for data common to all RSI funds)

Sub-advisers: Friess Associates, Inc., Putnam Advisory Company, Inc.
Portfolio managers: Foster S. Friess (1990), Richard Frucci (1994)
Custodian: Custodial Trust Co.
Investment objective and policies: Total return in excess of the Lipper Small Company Growth Mutual Fund Average, measured over a 3 to 5 year period. Invests at least 65% of assets in common stocks of rapidly growing companies, generally with market capitalizations from $50M to $750M. Up to 20% of assets may be in securities of foreign issuers. May use futures and options.
Year organized: 1983
Ticker symbol: RSIGX
Portfolio turnover (3 yrs): 114%, 146%, 135%
Largest holding: Ultratech Stepper, Inc. (2.2%)
Management fee: 1.0% (for assets managed by Friess), 1.0% first $25M and 0.75% over $25M (for assets managed by Putnam Advisory Co., Inc.)
Expense ratio: 2.08% (year ending 9/30/94)

RSI RETIREMENT TRUST - INTERMEDIATE-TERM BOND FUND ◆
(See first RSI listing for data common to all RSI funds)

Portfolio manager: Herbert Kuhl, Jr. (1983)
Custodian: Chase Manhattan Bank, N.A.
Investment objective and policies: Total return (income and capital appreciation) in excess of the Lipper Intermediate (five to ten year) U.S. Government Mutual Funds Average measured over

a period of 3 to 5 years. Invests in a diversified portfolio of debt securities with remaining maturities of 10 years or less and a weighted average maturity of 3 to 5 years.
Year organized: 1983
Ticker symbol: RSIBX
Portfolio turnover (3 yrs): 18%, 12%, 25%
Management fee: 0.40% first $50M to 0.20% over $150M
Expense ratio: 0.95% (year ending 9/30/94)

RSI RETIREMENT TRUST - INTERNATIONAL EQUITY FUND ◆
(See first RSI listing for data common to all RSI funds)

Sub-adviser: Morgan Grenfell Investment Services Ltd.
Portfolio manager: William G.M. Thomas (1984)
Custodian: Chase Manhattan Bank, N.A.
Investment objective and policies: Total return (income and capital appreciation) in excess of the Lipper International Mutual Funds Average measured over a period of 3 to 5 years. Invests primarily in equity securities of companies domiciled outside the U.S. with market capitalization in excess of $750M. May invest in securities of foreign governments and agencies and in U.S. companies which derive substantial income from operations outside the U.S.
Year organized: 1984
Ticker symbol: RSTEX
Portfolio turnover (3 yrs): 44%, 55%, 53%
Largest holding: Canon, Inc. (1.6%)
Management fee: 0.60% first $50M, 0.50% over $50M
Expense ratio: 1.96% (year ending 9/30/94)

RSI RETIREMENT TRUST - SHORT-TERM INVESTMENT FUND ◆
(See first RSI listing for data common to all RSI funds)

Portfolio managers: John F. Meuser (1987), Deborah Dagiau (1994)
Custodian: Chase Manhattan Bank, N.A.
Investment objective and policies: Current income and stability of principal. Invests in high quality short-term fixed-income securities with a weighted average maturity of one year or less.
Year organized: 1983
Ticker symbol: RSISX
Management fee: 0.25% first $50M, 0.20% over $50M
Expense ratio: 0.80% (year ending 9/30/94) (1.12% without waiver)

RSI RETIREMENT TRUST - VALUE EQUITY FUND ◆
(See first RSI listing for data common to all RSI funds)

Sub-adviser: NFJ Investment Group, Inc.
Portfolio manager: Ben J. Fischer (1992)
Custodian: Custodial Trust Co.
Investment objective and policies: Total return (income and capital appreciation) in excess of the Lipper Growth and Income Mutual Funds Average measured over a period of 3 to 5 years. Invests at least 65% of assets in common stocks of companies believed undervalued, generally with market capitalizations in excess of $750M. Up to 20% of assets may be in securities of foreign issuers. May use futures and options.
Year organized: 1983
Ticker symbol: RSIVX
Portfolio turnover (3 yrs): 40%, 54%, 14%
Largest holding: Melville Corp. (4.1%)
Management fee: 0.60% first $10M to 0.10% over $150M
Expense ratio: 1.41% (year ending 9/30/94)

RUSHMORE FUNDS ◆
(Data common to all Rushmore Fund portfolios are shown below. See subsequent listings for data specific to individual Rushmore portfolios.)

4922 Fairmont Avenue
Bethesda, MD 20814
301-657-1500, 800-343-3355
prices/yields 800-451-2234
fax 301-657-1520

Shareholder service hours: Full service: M-F 8:30 A.M.-4:30 P.M. EST; After hours service: prices, yields, DJIA
Adviser: Money Management Associates
Custodian and transfer agent: Rushmore Trust & Savings, FSB
Minimum purchase: Initial: $2,500, Subsequent: None; IRA/Keogh: Initial: $500
Telephone orders accepted: No
Wire orders accepted: Yes, $10 fee under $5,000
Telephone redemptions: Yes
Wire redemptions: Yes, $5,000 minimum
Letter redemptions: Signature guarantee not required
Telephone switching: With other Rushmore funds
Number of switches permitted: Unlimited (except American Gas Index Fund)
Shareholder services: Keogh, IRA, 401(k), corporate retirement plans, electronic funds transfer (purchase only)
IRA/Keogh fees: Annual $10

RUSHMORE AMERICAN GAS INDEX FUND ◆
(See first Rushmore listing for data common to all Rushmore funds)

Administrator: American Gas Association
Investment objective and policies: Total return that correlates to that of an index comprising the common stocks of approximately 110 natural gas distribution and transmission company members who belong to the American Gas Association.
Year organized: 1989
Ticker symbol: GASFX
Deadline for same day wire purchase: 3:30 P.M.
Discount broker availability: *Schwab, *White, *Waterhouse, *Fidelity, *Siebert
Qualified for sale in: All states
Number of switches permitted: 5 per year
Deadline for same day switch: 3:30 P.M.
Dividends paid: Income - March, June, September, December; Capital gains - June
Portfolio turnover (3 yrs): 11%, 22%, 30%
Largest holding: Enron Corporation (5.1%)
Management fee: 0.50%
Expense ratio: 0.84% (year ending 3/31/94)

RUSHMORE FUND FOR GOVERNMENT INVESTORS ◆
(See first Rushmore listing for data common to all Rushmore funds)

Portfolio manager: Richard J. Garvey (1992)
Investment objective and policies: Current income with safety of principal. Invests exclusively in short-term debt securities issued by the U.S. Government and repurchase agreements thereon.
Year organized: 1975
Ticker symbol: FUSXX
Deadline for same day wire purchase: 12 NN
Qualified for sale in: All states
Deadline for same day switch: 12 NN
Check redemptions: $250 minimum (but not enforced)
Confirmations mailed: After each purchase and each check, mail or wire redemption
Checks returned: Monthly
Periodic account statements mailed: Monthly
Dividends paid: Income - declared daily, paid monthly
Management fee: 0.50% first $500M to 0.35% over $1B
Expense ratio: 0.75% (year ending 12/31/93)

RUSHMORE FUND FOR TAX-FREE INVESTORS - MONEY MARKET PORTFOLIO ◆
(See first Rushmore listing for data common to all Rushmore funds)

Portfolio manager: T. Daniel Gillespie (1991)
Investment objective and policies: Current income exempt from federal income taxes. Invests primarily in high-quality municipal money market securities.
Year organized: 1983
Ticker symbol: FFTXX
Deadline for same day wire purchase: 12 NN
Qualified for sale in: CA, DC, FL, GA, IL, MD, NY, PA, TX, VA
Deadline for same day switch: 12 NN
Check redemptions: $250 minimum (but not enforced)
Confirmations mailed: After each purchase and each check, mail or wire redemption
Checks returned: Monthly
Periodic account statements mailed: Monthly
Dividends paid: Income - declared daily, paid monthly
Management fee: 0.50%
Expense ratio: 0.80% (year ending 12/31/93)

RUSHMORE - MARYLAND TAX-FREE PORTFOLIO ◆
(See first Rushmore listing for data common to all Rushmore funds)

Portfolio manager: An investment committee (1994)
Investment objective and policies: Current income exempt from federal and Maryland personal income taxes. Invests at least 80% of assets in high-quality long-term Maryland municipal securities with a weighted average maturity of more than 10 years.
Year organized: 1983 (objective and name change in 1991; formerly Fund for Tax-Free Investors - Long-Term Portfolio. Previous performance record may not be applicable.)
Ticker symbol: RSXLX
Deadline for same day wire purchase: 2:30 P.M.
Discount broker availability: *Schwab, *White, *Fidelity, *Siebert
Qualified for sale in: CA, DC, GA, IL, MD, NY, PA, TX, VA
Deadline for same day switch: 2:30 P.M.
Check redemptions: $250 minimum (but not enforced)
Portfolio turnover (3 yrs): 30%, 21%, 61%
Dividends paid: Income - declared daily, paid monthly; Capital gains - December
Management fee: 0.625%
Expense ratio: 0.50% (year ending 12/31/93) (0.93% without waiver)

RUSHMORE - MONEY MARKET PORTFOLIO ◆
(See first Rushmore listing for data common to all Rushmore funds)

Portfolio manager: T. Daniel Gillespie (1991)
Investment objective and policies: Maximum current income consistent with safety of principal. Invests in Government securities and other money market instruments with individual maturities of one year or less.
Year organized: 1985
Ticker symbol: RUMXX
Deadline for same day wire purchase: 12 NN
Qualified for sale in: All states except DE, HI, IA, ND, SD, VT
Deadline for same day switch: 12 NN
Check redemptions: $250 minimum (but not enforced)
Dividends paid: Income - declared daily, paid monthly
Management fee: 0.50%
Expense ratio: 0.75% (year ending 8/31/94)

RUSHMORE - U.S. GOVERNMENT SECURITIES INTERMEDIATE PORTFOLIO ◆

(See first Rushmore listing for data common to all Rushmore funds)

Newspaper listing: US Gov
Portfolio manager: Daniel O'Connor (1992)
Investment objective and policies: Maximum current income consistent with safety of principal. Invests in U.S. Government and agency securities, as well as zero coupon securities (subject to a 10% limitation) and repurchase agreements thereon, with maturities of 10 years of less.
Year organized: 1985
Ticker symbol: RSUIX
Deadline for same day wire purchase: 2:30 P.M.
Discount broker availability: *Schwab, *White, Waterhouse, *Fidelity, *Siebert
Qualified for sale in: All states except AK, AR, DE, IA, ME, NE, NH, NJ, NM, ND, OK, SC, SD, UT, VT
Deadline for same day switch: 2:30 P.M.
Dividends paid: Income - declared daily, paid monthly; Capital Gains: - December
Portfolio turnover (3 yrs): 174%, 113%, 200%
Management fee: 0.50%
Expense ratio: 0.80% (year ending 8/31/94)

RUSHMORE - U.S. GOVERNMENT SECURITIES LONG TERM PORTFOLIO ◆

(See first Rushmore listing for data common to all Rushmore funds)

Newspaper listing: USGLg
Portfolio manager: Daniel O'Connor (1992)
Investment objective and policies: Maximum current income consistent with safety of principal. Invests in U.S. Government and agency securities, as well as zero coupon securities (subject to a 10% limitation) and repurchase agreements thereon, with maturities of 10 years of more.
Year organized: 1985
Ticker symbol: RSGVX
Deadline for same day wire purchase: 2:30 P.M.
Deadline for same day switch: 2:30 P.M.
Discount broker availability: *Schwab, *White, Waterhouse, *Fidelity, *Siebert
Qualified for sale in: All states except AK, AR, DE, IA, ME, NE, NH, NJ, NM, ND, OK, SD, UT, VT
Dividends paid: Income - declared daily, paid monthly; Capital gains: Short Term - quarterly, Long Term - December
Portfolio turnover (3 yrs): 188%, 174%, 298%
Management fee: 0.50%
Expense ratio: 0.80% (year ending 8/31/94)

RUSHMORE - VIRGINIA TAX-FREE PORTFOLIO ◆

(See first Rushmore listing for data common to all Rushmore funds)

Newspaper listing: Under Rushmore Group; TxFInt
Portfolio manager: Team managed (1994)
Investment objective and policies: Current income exempt from federal and Virginia personal income taxes. Invests at least 80% of assets in high-quality long-term Virginia municipal securities with a weighted average maturity of more than 10 years.
Year organized: 1983 (objective and name change in 1991; formerly Fund for Tax-Free Investors - Intermediate Term Portfolio)
Ticker symbol: RSXIX
Deadline for same day wire purchase: 2:30 P.M.
Discount broker availability: *Schwab, *White
Qualified for sale in: CA, DC, FL, GA, IL, MD, NY, PA, TX, VA
Deadline for same day switch: 2:30 P.M.
Check redemptions: $250 minimum (but not enforced)
Portfolio turnover (3 yrs): 43%, 50%, 74%

Dividends paid: Income - declared daily, paid monthly; Capital gains - December
Management fee: 0.625%
Expense ratio: 0.50% (year ending 12/31/93) (0.93% without waiver)

RYDEX SERIES TRUST FUNDS ◆

(Data common to all Rydex funds are shown below. See subsequent listings for data specific to individual Rydex funds.)

4641 Montgomery Avenue, Suite 400
Bethesda, MD 20814
301-652-4402, 800-820-0888
prices/yields 800-717-7776
fax 301-652-7541

Shareholder service hours: M-F 8:30 A.M.-5:30 P.M. EST; After hours service: prices
Adviser: PADCO Advisors, Inc.
Custodian: Star Bank, N.A., Cincinnati
Transfer agent: PADCO Service Company, Inc.
Minimum purchase: Initial: $10,000, Subsequent: None
Telephone orders accepted: No
Wire orders accepted: Yes
Telephone redemptions: Yes
Letter redemptions: Signature guarantee not required
Telephone switching: With other Rydex funds
Number of switches permitted: Unlimited
Shareholder services: Keogh, IRA, 403(b), & corporate retirement plans, automatic investment plan—minimum $50/month, electronic funds transfer
IRA/Keogh fees: Annual $15, Closing $15

RYDEX JUNO FUND ◆

(See first Rydex listing for data common to all Rydex funds)

Portfolio manager: Michael P. Byrum (1995)
Investment objective and policies: Investment results that inversely correlate to the performance to the price movements of a benchmark U.S. Treasury debt instrument or futures contract on a specified debt instrument - currently the 30-year U.S. Treasury Bond. Fund is designed for investors speculating on anticipated decreases in the price of the long bond. Does not invest in traditional fixed-income securities but engages in short sales and options and futures transactions designed to benefit from declines in bond prices. Up to 15% of assets may be in illiquid securities. Fund is non-diversified and designed for investors using it as part of a market-timing investment strategy and who seek growth of capital rather than current income.
Year organized: 1995
Deadline for same day wire purchase:: 3 P.M.
Qualified for sale in: All states
Deadline for same day switch: 3:45 P.M.
Dividends paid: Income - December; Capital gains - December
Management fee: 0.90%

RYDEX NOVA FUND ◆

(See first Rydex listing for data common to all Rydex funds)

Portfolio manager: Thomas Michael (1994)
Investment objective and policies: Total return that exceeds the performance of the S&P 500 Index. Invests in stocks selected according to technical rather than fundamental factors. Up to 15% of assets may be in illiquid securities. Fund may margin up to 1/3 of assets and use index options, stock index futures contracts and options to enhance total return and hedge. Fund is non-diversified and designed for investors using it as part of a market-timing investment strategy and who seek growth of capital rather than current income.
Year organized: 1993 (formerly Rushmore Nova Portfolio. Current ownership acquired all assets of Rushmore Nova Portfolio on 5/20/93)
Ticker symbol: RYNVX
Deadline for same day wire purchase:: 3:45 P.M.

Discount broker availability: Schwab, White, Waterhouse, Fidelity, Siebert
Qualified for sale in: All states except DE, IA, MS, NE, NM, ND, RI, SD
Deadline for same day switch: 3:45 P.M.
Dividends paid: Income - December; Capital gains - December
Portfolio turnover (1 yr): 0%
Management fee: 0.75%
Expense ratio: 1.73% (year ending 6/30/94)

RYDEX OTC FUND ◆

(See first Rydex listing for data common to all Rydex funds)

Portfolio manager: Terry Apple (1994)
Investment objective and policies: Total return that approximates the performance of the NASDAQ Index. Invests in a representative mix of securities included in the NASDAQ composite index but is not an index fund. Up to 15% of assets may be in illiquid securities. Fund may use index options, stock index futures contracts and options to enhance total return and hedge. Fund is non-diversified and designed for investors using it as part of a market-timing investment strategy and who seek growth of capital rather than current income.
Year organized: 1994
Ticker symbol: RYOCX
Deadline for same day wire purchase:: 3:45 P.M.
Discount broker availability: White
Qualified for sale in: All states except AK, CT, DE, IA, KY, LA, ME, MA, MS, MT, NE, NV, NH, NM, ND, RI, SD, UT, VT, WV, WI
Deadline for same day switch: 3:45 P.M.
Dividends paid: Income - December; Capital gains - December
Portfolio turnover (1 yr): 1%
Management fee: 0.75%
Expense ratio: 1.97% (7 months ending 6/30/94)

RYDEX PRECIOUS METALS FUND ◆

(See first Rydex listing for data common to all Rydex funds)

Portfolio manager: Michael Byrum (1993)
Investment objective and policies: Capital appreciation. Normally invests at least 65% of assets in metals-related investments with remainder of assets in other minerals-related investments. Fund generally invests in common stocks, preferred stocks, convertible securities and warrants of companies engaged in metals/minerals activities in the U.S. and Canada. May purchase ADRs of issuers located outside the U.S. and Canada. Up to 20% of assets may be in bullion and coins. Fund may use index options, stock index futures contracts and options to enhance total return and hedge. Fund is non-diversified and designed for investors using it as part of a market-timing investment strategy and who seek growth of capital rather than current income.
Year organized: 1993
Ticker symbol: RYPMX
Deadline for same day wire purchase:: 3:30 P.M.
Discount broker availability: White
Qualified for sale in: All states except AL, AK, AR, DE, IA, KY, ME, MS, MT, NE, NH, NM, ND, OK, RI, SD, UT, VT, WV, WI
Deadline for same day switch: 3:30 P.M.
Dividends paid: Income - December; Capital gains - December
Portfolio turnover (1 yr): 3%
Largest holding: American Barrick Resources, Inc. (16.8%)
Management fee: 0.75%
Expense ratio: 2.06% (6 months ending 6/30/94)

RYDEX URSA FUND ◆

(See first Rydex listing for data common to all Rydex funds)

Portfolio manager: Albert P. Viragh, Jr. (1994)
Investment objective and policies: Investment results that inversely correlate to the performance to the total return of the S&P 500 Index. Fund is designed for investors speculating on anticipated

decreases in the S&P 500 Index. Does not invest in traditional equity securities but engages in short sales and options and futures transactions designed to benefit from bear (hence the name Ursa) market declines in stock prices. Up to 15% of assets may be in illiquid securities. Fund is non-diversified and designed for investors using it as part of a market-timing investment strategy and who seek growth of capital rather than current income.
Year organized: 1994
Ticker symbol RYURX
Deadline for same day wire purchase:: 3:30 P.M.
Discount broker availability: White, Waterhouse, Fidelity, Siebert
Qualified for sale in: All states
Deadline for same day switch: 3:45 P.M.
Dividends paid: Income - December; Capital gains - December
Portfolio turnover (1 yr): 0%
Management fee: 0.90%
Expense ratio: 1.67% (6 months ending 6/30/94)

RYDEX U.S. GOVERNMENT BOND FUND ◆
(See first Rydex listing for data common to all Rydex funds)

Portfolio managers: Michael Byrum (1994)
Investment objective and policies: High current income consistent with security of principal and liquidity. Invests primarily in debt obligations issued or guaranteed as to principal and interest by the U.S. Government, its agencies or instrumentalities. May use futures contracts and options thereon.
Year organized: 1994
Ticker symbol: RYGBX
Deadline for same day wire purchase:: 2:45 P.M.
Discount broker availability: White
Qualified for sale in: All states except AL, AK, AR, DE, ID, IA, KY, LA, ME, MS, MT, NE, NV, NH, NM, ND, OR, RI, SD, UT, VT, WV
Deadline for same day switch: 2:45 P.M.
Dividends paid: Income - declared daily, paid monthly; Capital gains - December
Portfolio turnover (1 yr): 1%
Management fee: 0.50%
Expense ratio: 3.05% (6 months ending 6/30/94)

RYDEX U.S. GOVERNMENT MONEY MARKET FUND ◆
(See first Rydex listing for data common to all Rydex funds)

Portfolio managers: Michael Byrum (1993)
Investment objective and policies: High current income consistent with security of principal and liquidity. Invests primarily in money market instruments issued or guaranteed as to principal and interest by the U.S. Government, its agencies or instrumentalities.
Year organized: 1993
Ticker symbol RYMXX
Deadline for same day wire purchase:: 1 P.M.
Qualified for sale in: All states except DE, LA, MS, NE, ND, RI, SD
Deadline for same day switch: 1 P.M.
Check redemptions: $250 minimum
Confirmations mailed: After each purchase and each check, mail or wire redemption
Checks returned: Monthly
Periodic account statements mailed: Monthly
Dividends paid: Income - declared daily, paid monthly
Management fee: 0.50%
Expense ratio: 1.16% (7 months ending 6/30/94)

SAFECO FUNDS
(Data common to all SAFECO funds are shown below. See subsequent listings for data specific to individual SAFECO funds.)

P.O. Box 34890
Seattle, WA 98124-1890
206-545-7319, 800-624-5711
prices/yields 800-835-4391
fax 206-545-5783, TDD 800-438-8718

Shareholder service hours: Full service: M-F 5:30 A.M.-7 P.M. PST; After hours service: prices, yields,

total returns, prospectuses, DJIA
Adviser: SAFECO Asset Management Co.
Custodian: U.S. Bank of Washington, N.A.
Transfer agent: Safeco Services Corp.
Minimum purchase: Initial: $1,000, Subsequent: $100; IRA: Initial: $250, Subsequent: $100; Keogh: Initial & Subsequent: $25
Telephone orders accepted: No
Wire orders accepted: Yes
Deadline for same day wire purchase: 4 P.M.
Qualified for sale in: All states (exceptions noted)
Telephone redemptions: Yes
Wire redemptions: Yes, $10 fee
Letter redemptions: Signature guarantee not required
Telephone switching: With other SAFECO funds, $1,000 minimum
Number of switches permitted: Unlimited
Shareholder services: Keogh, IRA, SEP-IRA, 401(k), 403(b), corporate retirement plans, automatic investment plan (waives initial minimum), electronic funds transfer, withdrawal plan min. req. $5,000
IRA fees: Annual $5
Keogh fees: None

SAFECO CALIFORNIA TAX-FREE INCOME FUND ◆
(See first SAFECO listing for data common to all SAFECO funds)

Portfolio manager: Stephen C. Bauer (1983)
Investment objective and policies: High level of current income exempt from federal and California income taxes, consistent with relative stability of capital. Normally invests at least 80% of assets in investment-grade securities exempt from federal and California taxes.
Year organized: 1983
Ticker symbol: SFCAX
Discount broker availability: Schwab, White, Waterhouse
Qualified for sale in: AZ, CA, NV
Dividends paid: Income - declared daily, paid monthly; Capital gains - March, December
Portfolio turnover (3 yrs): 33%, 23%, 39%
Management fee: 0.55% first $100M to 0.25% over $500M
Expense ratio: 0.68% (year ending 3/31/94)

SAFECO EQUITY FUND. INC. ◆
(See first SAFECO listing for data common to all SAFECO funds)

Portfolio manager: Richard Meagley (1995)
Investment objective and policies: Long-term growth of capital and reasonable current income. Invests primarily in common stocks, and securities convertible to common stock, taking a long-range investment viewpoint. May invest in ADRs of foreign issuers. Up to 35% of assets may be in convertible securities all of which may be below investment grade.
Year organized: 1932
Ticker symbol: SAFQX
Discount broker availability: Schwab, White, Waterhouse, Fidelity, Siebert
Dividends paid: Income - March, June, September, December; Capital gains - September, December
Portfolio turnover (3 yrs): 33%, 38%, 40%
Largest holding: Callaway Golf Co, (5.2%)
Management fee: 0.75% first $100M to 0.45% over $500M
Expense ratio: 0.85% (year ending 9/30/94)

SAFECO GNMA FUND ◆
(See first SAFECO listing for data common to all SAFECO funds)

Portfolio manager: Paul Stevenson (1988)
Investment objective and policies: High level of current income consistent with the preservation of capital. Invests at least 65% of assets in U.S. Government securities, primarily GNMAs, guaran-

teed at to timely payment of principal and interest by the full faith and credit of the U.S. Government. Up to 35% of assets may be in other investment-grade government and corporate debt securities.
Year organized: 1986 (name changed from SAFE-CO U.S. Government Securities on 2/1/94)
Ticker symbol: SFUSX
Discount broker availability: Waterhouse
Dividends paid: Income - declared daily, paid monthly; Capital Gains - September, December
Portfolio turnover (3 yrs): 55%, 71%, 25%
Management fee: 0.65% first $250M to 0.35% over $750M
Expense ratio: 0.95% (year ending 9/30/94)

SAFECO GROWTH FUND. INC. ◆
(See first SAFECO listing for data common to all SAFECO funds)

Portfolio manager: Thomas M. Maguire (1989)
Investment objective and policies: Growth of capital with income secondary. Invests primarily in common stocks selected for appreciation potential. May invest in ADRs of foreign issuers, securities convertible into common stock and investment-grade debt securities.
Year organized: 1967
Ticker symbol: SAFGX
Discount broker availability: Schwab, White, Waterhouse, Fidelity, Siebert
Dividends paid: Income - March, June, September, December; Capital gains - September, December
Portfolio turnover (3 yrs): 71%, 57%, 85%
Largest holding: Callaway Golf Co. (12.1%)
Management fee: 0.75% first $100M to 0.45% over $500M
Expense ratio: 0.95% (year ending 9/30/94)

SAFECO HIGH-YIELD BOND FUND ◆
(See first SAFECO listing for data common to all SAFECO funds)

Portfolio manager: Ronald L. Spaulding (1988)
Investment objective and policies: High current income. Invests in high-yield, fixed-income securities with maturities of 1 to 30 years with majority in the 5 to 15 year range. To increase yield, fund invests in junk bonds and in unrated securities or those in default.
Year organized: 1988
Ticker symbol: SAFHX
Discount broker availability: Schwab, White, Waterhouse
Dividends paid: Income - declared daily, paid monthly; Capital Gains - September, December
Portfolio turnover (3 yrs): 63%, 50%, 41%
Management fee: 0.65% first $250M to 0.35% over $750M
Expense ratio: 1.03% (year ending 9/30/94)

SAFECO INCOME FUND ◆
(See first SAFECO listing for data common to all SAFECO funds)

Portfolio manager: Arley N. Hudson (1978)
Investment objective and policies: Current income with long-term capital growth secondary. Invests in common stocks, convertible and non-convertible preferred stock, bonds and debentures with emphasis on common stock. Fund may invest up to 35% of assets in junk bonds and 10% in Eurodollar bonds of U.S. issuers.
Year organized: 1969
Ticker symbol: SAFIX
Discount broker availability: Schwab, White, Waterhouse, Fidelity, Siebert
Dividends paid: Income - March, June, September, December; Capital gains - September, December
Portfolio turnover (3 yrs): 19%, 21%, 20%
Largest holding: GTE Corp. (4.0%)
Management fee: 0.75% first $100M to 0.45% over $500M
Expense ratio: 0.86% (year ending 9/30/94)

SAFECO INSURED MUNICIPAL BOND FUND ◆

(See first SAFECO listing for data common to all SAFECO funds)

Portfolio manager: Stephen C. Bauer (1993)
Investment objective and policies: Current income exempt from federal income tax consistent with relative stability of capital. Invests at least 95% of assets in municipal bonds whose interest is exempt from federal income tax that are covered by insurance guaranteeing the timely payment of both principal and interest.
Year organized: 1993
Discount broker availability: Fidelity, Siebert
Dividends paid: Income - declared daily, paid monthly; Capital Gains - April, October
Portfolio turnover (1 yr): 21%
Management fee: 0.65% first $250M to 0.35% over $750M
Expense ratio: 1.41% (year ending 3/31/94)

SAFECO INTERMEDIATE-TERM MUNICIPAL BOND FUND ◆

(See first SAFECO listing for data common to all SAFECO funds)

Portfolio manager: Stephen C. Bauer (1993)
Investment objective and policies: Current income exempt from federal income tax consistent with relative stability of capital. Invests at least 80% of assets in securities exempt from federal income tax and at least 65% in municipal bonds of the 4 highest grades with an average weighted maturity of 3 to 10 years.
Year organized: 1993
Discount broker availability: Schwab, Fidelity, Siebert
Dividends paid: Income - declared daily, paid monthly; Capital Gains - April, October
Portfolio turnover (1 yr): 1%
Management fee: 0.55% first $250M to 0.25% over $750M
Expense ratio: 0.99% (year ending 3/31/94)

SAFECO INTERMEDIATE-TERM U.S. TREASURY FUND ◆

(See first SAFECO listing for data common to all SAFECO funds)

Portfolio manager: Ronald L. Spaulding (1988)
Investment objective and policies: High current income consistent with preservation of capital. Invests at least 65% of assets in U.S. treasury securities with remainder in other investment-grade, fixed-income securities. Funs maintains a weighted average maturity of 3 to 10 years.
Year organized: 1988 (name changed from Intermediate-Term Bond Fund on 1/31/93.)
Discount broker availability: White
Dividends paid: Income - declared daily, paid monthly; Capital Gains - September, December
Portfolio turnover (3 yrs): 75%, 105%, 37%
Management fee: 0.55% first $250M to 0.25% over $750M
Expense ratio: 0.90% (year ending 9/30/94)

SAFECO MONEY MARKET FUND ◆

(See first SAFECO listing for data common to all SAFECO funds)

Portfolio manager: Naomi Urata (1994)
Investment objective and policies: Current income consistent with preservation of capital and liquidity. Invests in high quality money market instruments.
Year organized: 1981
Ticker symbol: SAFXX
Dividends paid: Income - declared daily, paid monthly
Check redemptions: $500 minimum
Confirmations mailed: After each purchase and each check, mail or wire redemption
Checks returned: On request
Periodic account statements mailed: Quarterly (monthly if dividends not reinvested)
Management fee: 0.5% first $250M to 0.25% over $750M
Expense ratio: 0.79% (year ending 3/31/94)

SAFECO MUNICIPAL BOND FUND ◆

(See first SAFECO listing for data common to all SAFECO funds)

Portfolio manager: Stephen C. Bauer (1981)
Investment objective and policies: Current income exempt from federal income tax consistent with relative stability of capital. Invests at least 80% of assets in tax-exempt securities and at least 65% in municipal bonds of the 4 highest grades.
Year organized: 1981
Ticker symbol: SFCOX
Discount broker availability: Schwab, White, Waterhouse, Fidelity, Siebert
Dividends paid: Income - declared daily, paid monthly; Capital Gains - March, December
Portfolio turnover (3 yrs): 22%, 32%, 25%
Management fee: 0.55% first $100M to 0.25% over $500M
Expense ratio: 0.52% (year ending 3/31/94)

SAFECO NORTHWEST FUND ◆

(See first SAFECO listing for data common to all SAFECO funds)

Portfolio manager: Charles Driggs (1992)
Investment objective and policies: Long-term growth of capital. Invests at least 65% of assets in securities issued by companies with principal executive offices in the Northwest (Washington, Alaska, Idaho, Oregon and Montana). Fund may use common stocks and securities convertible into common stock (rated Baa or better).
Year organized: 1991
Ticker symbol: SFNWX
Discount broker availability: Schwab, White, Fidelity, Siebert
Dividends paid: Income - March, June, September, December; Capital Gains - September, December
Portfolio turnover (3 yrs): 18%, 14%, 33%
Largest holding: Expeditors International of Washington, Inc. (6.3%)
Management fee: 0.75% first $250M to 0.45% over $750M
Expense ratio: 1.06% (year ending 9/30/94)

SAFECO TAX-FREE MONEY MARKET FUND ◆

(See first SAFECO listing for data common to all SAFECO funds)

Portfolio manager: Mary V. Metastasio (1987)
Investment objective and policies: Current income exempt from federal income tax consistent with a portfolio of high-quality, municipal money market obligations selected on the basis of liquidity and preservation of capital.
Year organized: 1984
Ticker symbol: SFTXX
Dividends paid: Income - declared daily, paid monthly
Check redemptions: $500 minimum
Confirmations mailed: After each purchase and each check, mail or wire redemption
Checks returned: On request
Periodic account statements mailed: Quarterly (monthly if dividends not reinvested)
Management fee: 0.5% first $100M to 0.2% over $500
Expense ratio: 0.64% (year ending 3/31/94)

SAFECO WASHINGTON STATE MUNICIPAL BOND FUND ◆

(See first SAFECO listing for data common to all SAFECO funds)

Portfolio manager: Stephen C. Bauer (1993)
Investment objective and policies: Current income exempt from federal income tax consistent with relative stability of capital. Invests at least 80% of assets in securities exempt from federal income tax and at least 65% in municipal bonds of the 4 highest grades. Fund will normally invest at least 65% of assets in municipal bonds issued by the state of Washington or one of its political subdivisions, municipalities, agencies, instrumentalities or public authorities.
Year organized: 1993

Qualified for sale in: AZ, CA, WA
Dividends paid: Income - declared daily, paid monthly; Capital Gains - March, December
Portfolio turnover (1 yr): 17%
Management fee: 0.65% first $250M to 0.35% over $750M
Expense ratio: 1.44% (year ending 3/31/94)

SALOMON BROTHERS FUNDS ◆

(Data common to all Salomon Brothers funds are shown below. See subsequent listings for data specific to individual Salomon Brothers funds.

7 World Trade Center, 38th Floor
New York, NY 10048
212-783-1301, 800-725-6666
fax 212-783-4334

Shareholder service hours: Full service: M-F 9 A.M.-5 P.M. EST; After hours service: prices, yields, prospectuses, messages, news
Adviser: Salomon Brothers Asset Management, Inc.
Custodian: Boston Safe Deposit & Trust Co.
Transfer agent: The Shareholder Services Group, Inc.
Telephone orders accepted: No
Wire orders accepted: Yes
Deadline for same day wire purchase: 4 P.M. (12 NN for money market funds)
Qualified for sale in: All states
Letter redemptions: Signature guarantee required over $10,000
Telephone switching: With other Salomon Brothers funds
Number of switches permitted: Unlimited
Shareholder services: Keogh, IRA, withdrawal plan min. req. $7,500
IRA/Keogh fees: Annual $10, Initial $5, Closing $10

SALOMON BROTHERS CAPITAL FUND ◆

(See first Salomon Brothers listing for data common to all Salomon Brothers funds)

Portfolio manager: Ross R. Margolies (1995)
Investment objective and policies: Long-term capital appreciation. Invests primarily in common stocks and convertible securities. Fund seeks companies believed undervalued, undergoing management and/or structural changes or likely to benefit from new technological, marketing or production methods or new or unique products or services. May use foreign securities, restricted securities, futures and options. Fund is non-diversified.
Year organized: 1976
Ticker symbol: SACPX
Minimum purchase: Initial: $1,000, Subsequent: $100; IRA/Keogh: Initial: $250
Discount broker availability: Schwab, White
Dividends paid: Income - January, December; Capital gains - January, December
Portfolio turnover (3 yrs): 104%, 41%, 94%
Largest holding: General Motors Corp. (3.8%)
Management fee: 1.0% first $100M to 0.5% over $400M
Expense ratio: 1.31% (year ending 12/31/93)

SALOMON BROTHERS CASH MANAGEMENT FUND ◆

(See first Salomon Brothers listing for data common to all Salomon Brothers funds)

Portfolio manager: Michael Bouscaren (1990)
Investment objective and policies: High current income consistent with stability of principal and liquidity. Invests in high-quality U.S. dollar-denominated money market instruments.
Year organized: 1990
Minimum purchase: Initial: $5,000, Subsequent: $500; IRA/Keogh: Initial: $500
Wire redemption: Yes, $500 minimum
Check redemption: $500 minimum
Confirmations mailed: Not mailed
Checks returned: As clear
Periodic account statements mailed: Monthly

Dividends paid: Income - declared daily, paid monthly
Management fee: 0.2%
Expense ratio: 0.65% (year ending 12/31/93) (0.85% without waiver)

SALOMON BROTHERS INVESTORS FUND ◆
(See first Salomon Brothers listing for data common to all Salomon Brothers funds)

Portfolio managers: Allen R. White III (1992), Ross S. Margolies (1994)
Investment objective and policies: Long-term capital appreciation with current income secondary, Invests primarily in common and preferred stocks of well-known companies. May invest up to 20% of assets in securities of foreign issuers, invest in other mutual funds, leverage, use restricted securities and use futures and options to hedge.
Year organized: 1958
Ticker symbol: SAIFX
Minimum purchase: Initial: $500, Subsequent: $50; IRA/Keogh: Initial: $250
Discount broker availability: Schwab
Dividends paid: Income - January, April, July, October, December; Capital gains - January, December
Portfolio turnover (3 yrs): 79%, 48%, 44%
Largest holding: Motorola, Inc. (2.3%)
Management fee: 0.5% first $350M to 0.3% over $1B
Expense ratio: 0.68% (year ending 12/31/93)

SALOMON BROTHERS NEW YORK MUNICIPAL BOND FUND ◆
(See first Salomon Brothers listing for data common to all Salomon Brothers funds)

Portfolio manager: Michael Bouscaren (1993)
Investment objective and policies: High current income exempt from federal and New York state and New York City income taxes. Invests primarily in investment-grade New York municipal obligations with a weighted average duration of 20 to 30 years. May use futures to hedge.
Year organized: 1993
Minimum purchase: Initial: $5,000, Subsequent: $500
Wire redemption: Yes, $500 minimum
Dividends paid: Income - declared daily, paid monthly; Capital gains - December
Portfolio turnover (1 yr): 24%
Management fee: 0.5%
Expense ratio: 0.50% (8 months ending 12/31/93) (1.24% without waiver)

SALOMON BROTHERS NEW YORK MUNICIPAL MONEY MARKET FUND ◆
(See first Salomon Brothers listing for data common to all Salomon Brothers funds)

Portfolio manager: Michael Bouscaren (1990)
Investment objective and policies: High current income exempt from federal and New York state and New York City income taxes consistent with liquidity and stability of principal. Invests in high-quality New York municipal money market instruments.
Year organized: 1990
Minimum purchase: Initial: $5,000, Subsequent: $500
Wire redemption: Yes, $500 minimum
Check redemption: $500 minimum
Confirmations mailed: Not mailed
Checks returned: As clear
Periodic account statements mailed: Monthly
Dividends paid: Income - declared daily, paid monthly
Management fee: 0.2%
Expense ratio: 0.41% (year ending 12/31/93)

SALOMON BROTHERS OPPORTUNITY FUND ◆
(See first Salomon Brothers listing for data common to all Salomon Brothers funds)

Portfolio manager: Irving Brilliant (1979)
Investment objective and policies: Long-term capital appreciation with current income secondary. Non-diversified investments in common stocks and convertible securities believed undervalued. May use foreign securities and restricted securities and leverage.
Year organized: 1978 (formerly Lehman Opportunity)
Ticker symbol: SAOPX
Minimum purchase: Initial: $1,000, Subsequent: $100; IRA/Keogh: Initial: $250
Discount broker availability: Schwab, White
Dividends paid: Income - December; Capital gains - December
Portfolio turnover (3 yrs): 13%, 10%, 11%
Largest holding: Chubb (10.1%)
Management fee: 1.0%
Expense ratio: 1.22% (year ending 8/31/94)

SALOMON BROTHERS U.S. TREASURY SECURITIES MONEY MARKET FUND ◆
(See first Salomon Brothers listing for data common to all Salomon Brothers funds)

Portfolio manager: Michael Bouscaren (1990)
Investment objective and policies: High current income consistent with stability of principal and liquidity. Invests exclusively in high-quality U.S. government or government agency money market instruments guaranteed as to principal and interest by the United States.
Year organized: 1990
Minimum purchase: Initial: $5,000, Subsequent: $500; IRA/Keogh: Initial: $500
Wire redemption: Yes, $500 minimum
Check redemption: $500 minimum
Confirmations mailed: Not mailed
Checks returned: As clear
Periodic account statements mailed: Monthly
Dividends paid: Income - declared daily, paid monthly
Management fee: 0.1%
Expense ratio: 0.35% (year ending 12/31/93)

SBSF FUNDS ◆
(Data common to all SBSF funds are shown below. See subsequent listings for data specific to individual SBSF funds.)

45 Rockefeller Plaza - 33rd Floor
New York, NY 10111
212-903-1200, 800-422-7273
800-446-4799, fax 212-586-6102

Adviser: Spears, Benzak, Salomon & Farrell, Inc.
Custodian and transfer agent: U.S. Trust Co. of New York
Minimum purchase: Initial: $5,000 Subsequent: $100; IRA/Keogh: Initial: $500
Telephone orders accepted: No
Wire orders accepted: Yes
Deadline for same day wire purchase: 4 P.M. (12 NN for Money Market Fund)
Qualified for sale in: All states except ID, MO, NM, ND, SD
Telephone redemption: Yes, $500 minimum
Wire redemptions: Yes, $500 minimum
Letter redemptions: Signature guarantee required
Telephone switching: With other SBSF funds, $1,000 minimum
Number of switches permitted: 60 day hold
Shareholder services: Keogh, IRA, corporate retirement plans, automatic investment plan, withdrawal plan min. req. $25,000
Administrative fee: 0.25% first $50M to 0.05% over $100M
12b-1 distribution fee: Yes (not currently imposed)
IRA/Keogh fees: Annual: $10

SBSF CAPITAL GROWTH FUND ◆
(See first SBSF listing for data common to all SBSF funds)

Portfolio manager: Charles G. Crain (1993)
Investment objective and policies: Capital appreciation. Invests primarily in growth oriented common stocks of small to medium capitalized companies ($500M to $1.5B). May have up to 10% of assets in securities of foreign issuers and 10% in illiquid securities and use options.
Year organized: 1993
Ticker symbol: SFCGX
Discount broker availability: *Schwab (only through financial advisers), White
Dividends paid: Income - June, December; Capital Gains - December
Portfolio turnover (1 yr): 80%
Largest holding: System Software Associates (3.9%)
Management fee: 0.75%
Expense ratio: 1.22% (year ending 11/30/94) (2.22% without waiver)

SBSF CONVERTIBLE SECURITIES FUND ◆
(See first SBSF listing for data common to all SBSF funds)

Portfolio manager: Louis R. Benzak (1988)
Investment objective and policies: High level of current income together with long-term capital appreciation. Invests at least 65% of assets in bonds, corporate notes, preferred stocks and other securities convertible into common stock. May use options.
Year organized: 1988
Ticker symbol: SBFCX
Discount broker availability: *Schwab (only through financial advisers), White
Dividends paid: Income - March, June, September, December; Capital Gains - December
Portfolio turnover (3 yrs): 49%, 30%, 42%
Largest holding: Unocal Corp. 7.00% convertible (4.4%)
Management fee: 0.75%
Expense ratio: 1.30% (year ending 11/30/94)

SBSF FUND ◆
(See first SBSF listing for data common to all SBSF funds)

Portfolio manager: Louis R. Benzak (1983)
Investment objective and policies: High total return over the longer term consistent with reasonable risk. Invests primarily in common stocks, but may also invest in preferred stocks, convertibles, and investment-grade fixed-income securities. May have up to 10% of assets in securities of foreign issuers and 10% in illiquid securities and use options.
Year organized: 1983 (Originally SBSF Fund. Name changed to SBSF Growth Fund and back to SBSF Fund in 1993)
Ticker symbol: SBFFX
Discount broker availability: *Schwab (only through financial advisers), White
Dividends paid: Income - June, December; Capital Gains - December
Portfolio turnover (3 yrs): 83%, 70%, 45%
Largest holding: American International Group, Inc. (6.3%)
Management fee: 0.75%
Expense ratio: 1.23% (year ending 11/30/94)

SBSF MONEY MARKET FUND ◆
(See first SBSF listing for data common to all SBSF funds)

Portfolio manager: Louis Benzak (1988)
Investment objective and policies: High current income consistent with preservation of capital. Invests in bank CDs, bankers acceptances, high

grade commercial paper and other money market securities issued or guaranteed by the U.S. Government or its agencies and instrumentalities.
Year organized: 1988
Ticker symbol: SBFXX
Check redemptions: Yes, $500 minimum
Confirmations mailed: After each purchase and each check, mail or wire redemption
Checks returned: Not returned
Periodic account statements mailed: Monthly
Dividends paid: Income - declared daily, paid monthly
Management fee: 0.25%
Expense ratio: 0.59% (year ending 11/30/94) (0.84% without waiver)

SCHAFER VALUE FUND ◆
645 Fifth Avenue, 7th floor
New York, NY 10022
212-644-1800, 800-343-0481
fax 212-593-4275

Adviser: Schafer Capital Management, Inc.
Portfolio manager: David K. Schafer (1985)
Custodian and transfer agent: Firstar Trust Co.
Investment objective and policies: Long-term capital appreciation with current income secondary. Invests primarily in securities of strong established companies with capitalization of $250M or more and low stock market valuation at time of purchase. May invest up to 20% of assets in securities of foreign issuers.
Year organized: 1985
Ticker symbol: SCHVX
Minimum purchase: Initial: $2,000, Subsequent: $1,000
Telephone orders accepted: No
Wire orders accepted: Yes
Deadline for same day wire purchase: 2 P.M.
Discount broker availability: *Schwab
Qualified for sale in: All states
Letter redemptions: Signature guarantee required over $25,000
Dividends paid: Income - December; Capital gains - December
Portfolio turnover (3 yrs): 28%, 33%, 53%
Largest holding: National Health Laboratories, Inc. (3.1%)
Shareholder services: IRA, automatic investment plan—minimum $100/mo. ($500 initial minimum)
Management fee: 1.0%
Expense Ratio: 1.48% (year ending 9/30/94)
IRA fees: Annual $12.50

SCHOONER FUND ◆
9601 Wilshire Blvd., Suite 800
Beverly Hills, CA 90210
310-247-3962, 800-420-7556
prices 800-434-1983, fax 310-273-0514

Adviser: Pacific Financial Research
Portfolio managers: James H. Gipson (1993), Douglas W. Gray (1994)
Custodian: State Street Bank & Trust Co.
Transfer agent: National Financial Data Services
Investment objective and policies: Long-term growth of capital. Invests primarily in equity and equity-related securities of small capitalization companies ($50M to $1B) believed undervalued. Normally invests at least 50% of assets in common stocks, convertible long-term corporate debt, and convertible preferred stocks and warrants. Remainder of assets may be in debt obligations with at least 50% of debt securities rated A or better. Fund may invest up to 25% of assets in junk bonds, 25% in securities of foreign issuers and/or 15% in illiquid securities. Fund is non-diversified.
Year organized: 1993
Minimum purchase: Initial: $5,000, Subsequent: $1,000; IRA: Initial: $2,000, Subsequent: $200
Telephone orders accepted: Yes
Wire orders accepted: Yes
Deadline for same day wire purchase: 4 P.M.
Discount broker availability: White
Qualified for sale in: AZ, CA, CA, CO, CT, DC, DE, FL, GA, HI, IL, IN, MA, MD, MI, MN, NE, NY, NC, OR, PA, RI, SC, TX, VA, WA, WI

Telephone redemptions: Yes
Wire redemptions: Yes
Letter redemptions: Signature guarantee required
Dividends paid: Income - December; Capital gains - December
Shareholder services: IRA, automatic investment plan—minimum $150/month
Portfolio turnover rate (1 yr): 1%
Largest holding: Boston Acoustics, Inc. (4.0%)
Management fee: 1.0%
Expense ratio: 1.50% (6 months ending 12/31/93) (8.35% without waiver)
IRA fees: Annual $10

SCHRODER FUNDS
(Data common to all Schroder funds are shown below. See subsequent listings for data specific to individual Schroder funds.)

787 Seventh Avenue - 29th Floor
New York, NY 10019
212-841-3848, 800-344-8332
fax 816-292-6790

Adviser: Schroder Capital Management International Inc.
Custodian: Chase Manhattan Bank, N.A.
Transfer agent: Forum Financial Corp.
Telephone orders accepted: No
Wire orders accepted: Yes
Deadline for same day wire purchase: 4 P.M.
Telephone redemptions: Yes
Wire redemptions: Yes
Letter redemptions: Signature guarantee required
Shareholder services: IRA, withdrawal plan min. req. $10,000
IRA fees: Annual: $10, Initial: $10

SCHRODER INTERNATIONAL EQUITY FUND
(See first Schroder listing for data common to all Schroder funds)

Newspaper listing: InEq
Portfolio manager: Mark J. Smith (1989)
Investment objective and policies: Long-term capital appreciation. Invests primarily in equity securities of companies domiciled outside the U.S. Fund may also invest in the securities of closed-end investment companies investing primarily in foreign securities and in debt obligations of foreign governments, international organizations and foreign corporations. May use forward currency contracts.
Year organized: 1985 (formerly a portfolio of Fund Source)
Ticker symbol: SCIEX
Minimum purchase: Initial: $2,500, Subsequent: $100; IRA: Initial: $250
Qualified for sale in: CA, CO, FL, DC, IL, IN,, IA, KS, KY, MD, MI, MN, MS, MO, MT, NE, NJ, NY, OH, OK, PA, VA, WA
Dividends paid: Income - January; Capital gains - November
Portfolio turnover (3 yrs): 25%, 56%, 49%
Largest holding: Veba (2.7%)
Management fee: 0.50% first $100M to 0.35% in excess of $250M
Administration fee: 0.25% of first $100M to 0.175% over $250M
12b-1 distribution fee: Maximum of 0.50%
Expense ratio: 0.90% (year ending 10/31/94)

SCHRODER U.S. EQUITY FUND ◆
(See first Schroder listing for data common to all Schroder funds)

Newspaper listing: Schrodr
Portfolio manager: Fariba Talebi (1991)
Investment objective and policies: Growth of capital with income secondary. Invests primarily in common stock and securities convertible into common stock including securities with common stock purchase warrants attached, in such warrants themselves or in other rights to purchase common stock. Debt securities and non-convertible preferred stocks are normally limited to 15% of assets.

Year organized: 1970 (formerly Cheapside Dollar Fund)
Ticker symbol: SUSEX
Minimum purchase: Initial: $500, Subsequent: $100
Qualified for sale in: CA, CO, DC, FL, IL, IN, KS, KY, MN, MO, NJ, NY, PA, VA
Dividends paid: Income - January, July; Capital gains - January
Portfolio turnover (3 yrs): 27%, 58%, 31%
Largest holding: TRW, Inc. (3.1%)
Management fee: 0.75% first $100M, 0.5% over $100M
Expense ratio: 1.31% (year ending 10/31/94)

SCHRODER U.S. SMALLER COMPANIES FUND
(See first Schroder listing for data common to all Schroder funds)

Portfolio managers: Ira Unschuld (1993), Fariba Talebi (1993)
Investment objective and policies: Growth of capital. Invests at least 65% of assets in equity securities of companies with market capitalizations under $1B with prospects for above average earnings growth. May invest up to 20% of assets in securities of unseasoned companies and 15% in illiquid securities. May hedge and sell short against the box.
Year organized: 1993
Minimum purchase: Initial: $2,500, Subsequent: $100; IRA: Initial: $250
Qualified for sale in: CA, CO, DC, FL, IL, IN, MN, NJ, NY, PA, VA
Dividends paid: Income - January, July; Capital gains - January
Management fee: 0.50% first $100M to 0.35% over $250M
Portfolio turnover (1 yr): 71%
Largest holding: ABC Rail Products (1.7%)
Administration fee: 0.25% of first $100M to 0.175% in excess of $250M
Expense ratio: 1.45% (year ending 10/31/94)

SCHWAB FUNDS ◆
(Data common to all Schwab funds are shown below. See subsequent listings for data specific to individual Schwab funds.)

101 Montgomery Street
San Francisco, CA 94104
415-627-7000, 800-266-5623
800-435-4000

Shareholder service hours: Full service: Sun-Sat 24 hours
Adviser: Charles Schwab Investment Management, Inc.
Custodian: PNC Bank (exceptions noted)
Transfer agent: Charles Schwab & Co., Inc.
Minimum purchase: Initial: $1,000, Subsequent: $100; IRA/Keogh: Initial: $500 (except Retirement Money Fund and Value Advantage Money Fund)
Wire orders accepted: Yes
Deadline for same day wire purchase: 4 P.M.
Discount broker availability: *Schwab
Qualified for sale in: All states (except California tax-free funds)
Telephone redemptions: Yes
Wire redemptions: Yes, $15 fee
Letter redemptions: Signature guarantee not required
Telephone switching: With other Schwab funds and any mutual fund offered in the Schwab Mutual Fund Marketplace. No charge to other Schwab funds, regular Schwab transaction fees to non-Schwab funds.
Number of switches permitted: Unlimited
Shareholder services: Keogh, IRA, SEP-IRA, 401(k), 403(b), corporate retirement plans, automatic investment plan
Shareholder service fee: 0.45% of assets
IRA fees: Annual $22 (one fee regardless of number of funds held) (waived for IRA accounts with assets of $10,000 or more)
Keogh fees: Annual $30 (one fee regardless of number of funds held)

SCHWAB CALIFORNIA LONG-TERM TAX-FREE BOND FUND ◆
(See first Schwab listing for data common to all Schwab funds)

Portfolio managers: Joanne Keighley (1992), Stephen B. Ward (1993)
Investment objective and policies: Current income exempt from federal and California personal income taxes, consistent with preservation of capital. Invests primarily in debt securities issued by or on behalf of the State of California, its political subdivisions, agencies or authorities with a weighted average maturity of ten years or longer.
Year organized: 1992 (name changed from Schwab California Tax-Free Bond Fund on 4/21/93)
Ticker symbol: SWCAX
Qualified for sale in: CA, IL
Dividends paid: Income - declared daily, paid monthly; Capital gains - December
Portfolio turnover (3 yrs): 48%, 47%, 124%
Management fee: 0.41%
Expense ratio: 0.60% (year ending 8/31/94) (0.80% without waiver)

SCHWAB CALIFORNIA SHORT/INTERMEDIATE TAX-FREE BOND FUND ◆
(See first Schwab listing for data common to all Schwab funds)

Portfolio managers: Joanne Keighley (1993), Stephen B. Ward (1993)
Investment objective and policies: Current income exempt from federal and California personal income taxes, consistent with preservation of capital. Invests primarily in debt securities issued by or on behalf of the state of California, its political subdivisions, agencies and instrumentalities with a weighted average maturity of 2 to 5 years.
Year organized: 1993
Ticker symbol: SWCSX
Qualified for sale in: CA, IL
Dividends paid: Income - declared daily, paid monthly; Capital gains - December
Portfolio turnover (1 yr): 35%
Management fee: 0.41%
Expense ratio: 0.48% (year ending 8/31/94) (0.86% without waiver)

SCHWAB CALIFORNIA TAX-EXEMPT MONEY FUND ◆
(See first Schwab listing for data common to all Schwab funds)

Portfolio managers: Walter Beveridge (1992), Stephen B. Ward (1992)
Investment objective and policies: Maximum current income exempt from federal and California personal income taxes to the extent consistent with stability of capital. Invests in a diversified portfolio of short-term California municipal securities.
Year organized: 1990 (name changed from Schwab California Tax-Free Money Fund on 4/21/93)
Ticker symbol: SWCXX
Qualified for sale in: CA, IL
Dividends paid: Income - declared daily, paid monthly
Management fee: 0.46% first $1B to 0.40% over $2B
Expense ratio: 0.63% (year ending 12/31/93) (0.96% without waiver)

SCHWAB GOVERNMENT MONEY FUND ◆
(See first Schwab listing for data common to all Schwab funds)

Portfolio managers: Andrea Regan (1990), Stephen B. Ward (1990)
Investment objective and policies: Maximum current income consistent with stability of capital. Invests exclusively in U.S. Government obligations which mature in 12 months or less.

Year organized: 1990 (name changed from Schwab Government Securities Fund in 1993)
Ticker symbol: SWGXX
Dividends paid: Income - declared daily, paid monthly
Management fee: 0.46% first $1B to 0.40% over $2B
Expense ratio: 0.73% (year ending 12/31/93) (0.93% without waiver)

SCHWAB INSTITUTIONAL ADVANTAGE MONEY FUND ◆
(See first Schwab listing for data common to all Schwab funds)

Portfolio managers: Linda Klingman (1994), Stephen B. Ward (1994)
Investment objective and policies: Maximum current income consistent with stability of capital and liquidity. Invests in money market instruments.
Special sales restrictions: Designed for retirement plans, plan participants and other institutional investors for investment of their own funds or funds for which they act in a fiduciary, agency or custodial capacity but open to all investors.
Year organized: 1994
Ticker symbol: SWRXX
Minimum purchase: Initial: $25,000, Subsequent: $1
Dividends paid: Income - declared daily, paid monthly
Management fee: 0.46% first $2B to 0.40% over $3B

SCHWAB INTERNATIONAL INDEX FUND ◆
(See first Schwab listing for data common to all Schwab funds)

Sub-adviser: Dimensional Fund Advisors, Inc.
Custodian: State Street Bank & Trust Co.
Investment objective and policies: To match the total return of the Schwab International Index, a new index created by Schwab to represent the performance of equity securities issued by large, publicly traded companies from countries around the world with major developed securities markets, excluding the U.S. and South Africa. Fund invests substantially all its assets in the roughly 350 stocks comprising the Index in approximately the same proportion as they are represented in the Index. Fund will not be periodically rebalanced. May use stock and index futures and options thereon and engage in foreign currency exchange transactions for hedging purposes.
Year organized: 1993
Ticker symbol: SWINX
Redemption fee: 0.75% for shares held less than 6 months, payable to the fund (waived for accounts with assets of more than $10,000)
Dividends paid: Income - December; Capital gains - December
Portfolio turnover (1 yr): 6%
Largest holding: Nippon Telegraph & Telephone Co. (2.0%)
Management fee: 0.70% first $300M, 0.60% over $300M
Account maintenance fee: $10 per year, waived indefinitely
Expense ratio: 0.90% (year ending 10/31/94) (1.30% without waiver)

SCHWAB LONG-TERM GOVERNMENT BOND FUND ◆
(See first Schwab listing for data common to all Schwab funds)

Portfolio managers: Andrea Regan (1993), Stephen B. Ward (1993)
Investment objective and policies: High level of current income consistent with preservation of capital. Invests in securities issued by the U.S. Government, its agencies or instrumentalities, and repurchase agreements covering these securities with a weighted average maturity of 10 years or more.

Year organized: 1993
Ticker symbol: SWLBX
Dividends paid: Income - declared daily, paid monthly; Capital gains - December
Portfolio turnover (1 yr): 42%
Management fee: 0.41%
Expense ratio: 0.10% (year ending 8/31/94) (2.19% without waiver)

SCHWAB LONG-TERM TAX-FREE BOND FUND ◆
(See first Schwab listing for data common to all Schwab funds)

Investment objective and policies: Current income exempt from federal income tax, consistent with preservation of capital. Invests in debt securities issued by or on behalf of states, territories and possessions of the U.S. and their political subdivisions, agencies and instrumentalities with a weighted average maturity of more than 10 years.
Year organized: 1992 (name changed from Schwab National Tax-Free Bond Fund on 4/21/93)
Ticker symbol: SWNTX
Dividends paid: Income - declared daily, paid monthly; Capital gains - December
Portfolio turnover (2 yrs): 62%, 91%
Management fee: 0.41%
Expense ratio: 0.51% (year ending 8/31/94) (0.99% without waiver)

SCHWAB MONEY MARKET FUND ◆
(See first Schwab listing for data common to all Schwab funds)

Portfolio managers: Linda Klingman (1990), Stephen B. Ward (1990)
Investment objective and policies: Maximum current income consistent with stability of capital and liquidity. Invests in money market instruments.
Year organized: 1990
Ticker symbol: SWMXX
Dividends paid: Income - declared daily, paid monthly
Management fee: 0.46% first $2B to 0.40% over $3B
Expense ratio: 0.73% (year ending 12/31/93) (0.91% without waiver)

SCHWAB 1000 FUND ◆
(See first Schwab listing for data common to all Schwab funds)

Sub-adviser: Dimensional Fund Advisors, Inc.
Investment objective and policies: To match the total return of the Schwab 1000 index, which represents about 90% of U.S. stocks. Fund will not be periodically rebalanced. Fund may purchase shares of other mutual funds and use stock and index futures and options thereon.
Year organized: 1991
Ticker symbol: SNXFX
Redemption fee: 0.5% for shares held less than 6 months, payable to the fund (waived for accounts with assets of $10,000 or more)
Dividends paid: Income - June, December; Capital gains - December
Portfolio turnover (3 yr): 3%, 1%, 1%
Largest holding: AT&T Corp. (1.8%)
Management fee: 0.30% of first $500M, 0.22% over $500M
Account maintenance fee: $10 per year, waived indefinitely
Expense ratio: 0.51% (year ending 8/31/94) (0.56% without waiver)

SCHWAB RETIREMENT MONEY FUND ◆
(See first Schwab listing for data common to all Schwab funds)

Portfolio managers: Linda Klingman (1994), Stephen B. Ward (1994)
Investment objective and policies: Maximum current income consistent with stability of capital and

liquidity. Invests in money market instruments.
Special sales restrictions: Designed for retirement plans, plan participants and other institutional investors for investment of their own funds or funds for which they act in a fiduciary, agency or custodial capacity but open to all investors.
Year organized: 1994
Ticker symbol: SWRXX
Minimum purchase: Initial: $1, Subsequent: $1
Dividends paid: Income - declared daily, paid monthly
Management fee: 0.46% first $2B to 0.40% over $3B

SCHWAB SHORT/INTERMEDIATE GOVERNMENT BOND FUND ◆
(See first Schwab listing for data common to all Schwab funds)

Portfolio managers: Andrea Regan (1991), Stephen B. Ward (1993)
Investment objective and policies: High level of current income consistent with preservation of capital. Invests in securities issued by the U.S. Government, its agencies or instrumentalities, and repurchase agreements covering these securities with a weighted average maturity of 5 years or less.
Year organized: 1991 (name changed from U.S. Government Bond Fund (Short/Intermediate Term) in 1993)
Ticker symbol: SWBDX
Dividends paid: Income - declared daily, paid monthly; Capital gains - December
Portfolio turnover (3 yrs): 91%, 107%, 185%
Management fee: 0.41%
Expense ratio: 0.60% (year ending 8/31/94) (0.81% without waiver)

SCHWAB SHORT/INTERMEDIATE TAX-FREE BOND FUND ◆
(See first Schwab listing for data common to all Schwab funds)

Portfolio managers: Joanne Keighley (1993), Stephen B. Ward (1993)
Investment objective and policies: Current income exempt from federal income tax, consistent with preservation of capital. Invests primarily in debt securities issued by or on behalf of states, territories and possessions of the U.S. and their political subdivisions, agencies and instrumentalities with average weighted maturity of 2 to 5 years.
Year organized: 1993
Ticker symbol: SWITX
Dividends paid: Income - declared daily, paid monthly; Capital gains - December
Portfolio turnover (2 yrs): 19%, 11%
Management fee: 0.41%
Expense ratio: 0.48% (year ending 8/31/94) (0.91% without waiver)

SCHWAB SMALL-CAP INDEX FUND ◆
(See first Schwab listing for data common to all Schwab funds)

Sub-adviser: Dimensional Fund Advisors, Inc.
Custodian: State Street Bank & Trust Co.
Investment objective and policies: To match the total return of the Schwab Small-Cap Index, a new index created by Schwab to represent the performance of equity securities of small capitalization ($75M to $1B) domestic companies. Fund invests substantially all its assets in the roughly 1,000 stocks comprising the Index in approximately the same proportion as they are represented in the Index. May use stock and index futures and options thereon and engage in foreign currency exchange transactions for hedging purposes.
Year organized: 1993
Ticker symbol: SWSMX
Redemption fee: 0.5% for shares held less than 6 months, payable to the fund (waived for accounts with assets of $10,000 or more)
Dividends paid: Income - December; Capital gains - December

Portfolio turnover (1 yr): 16%
Management fee: 0.50% first $300M, 0.45% over $300M
Expense ratio: 0.67% (year ending 10/31/94) (1.19% without waiver)

SCHWAB TAX-EXEMPT FUND ◆
(See first Schwab listing for data common to all Schwab funds)

Portfolio managers: Walter Beveridge (1992), Stephen B. Ward (1992)
Investment objective and policies: Maximum current income exempt from federal income taxes to the extent consistent with stability of capital. Invests in a diversified portfolio of short-term municipal money market securities.
Year organized: 1990
Ticker symbol: SWXXX
Dividends paid: Income - declared daily, paid monthly
Management fee: 0.46% first $1B to 0.40% over $2B
Expense ratio: 0.63% (year ending 12/31/93) (0.93% without waiver)

SCHWAB U.S. TREASURY MONEY FUND ◆
(See first Schwab listing for data common to all Schwab funds)

Portfolio managers: Andrea Regan (1991), Stephen B. Ward (1991)
Investment objective and policies: High current income consistent with liquidity and stability of capital. Invests exclusively in U.S. Treasury notes, bills, and other direct obligations of the U.S. Treasury which mature in 13 months or less.
Year organized: 1991
Ticker symbol: SWUXX
Dividends paid: Income - declared daily, paid monthly
Management fee: 0.46% first $1B to 0.40% over $2B
Expense ratio: 0.65% (year ending 12/31/93) (1.05% without waiver)

SCHWAB VALUE ADVANTAGE MONEY FUND ◆
(See first Schwab listing for data common to all Schwab funds)

Portfolio managers: Linda Klingman (1992), Stephen B. Ward (1992)
Investment objective and policies: Maximum current income consistent with liquidity and stability of capital. Invests in money market instruments maturing in 12 months or less. Designed to deliver extra high yields for long-term buy and hold investors by maintaining a lower than average expense ratio.
Year organized: 1992
Ticker symbol: SWVXX
Minimum purchase: Initial: $25,000, Subsequent: $5,000; IRA/Keogh: Initial: $15,000, Subsequent $2,000
Administrative fee: $5 for redemptions or telephone switches in an amount less than $5,000
Dividends paid: Income - declared daily, paid monthly
Management fee: 0.46% first $2B to 0.40% over $3B
Expense ratio: 0.39% (year ending 12/31/93) (0.82% without waiver)

SCHWARTZ VALUE FUND ◆
3707 W. Maple Road
Bloomfield Hills, MI 48301
810-644-8500

Adviser: Schwartz Investment Counsel, Inc.
Portfolio manager: George P. Schwartz (1993)
Custodian: Fifth Third Bank, Cincinnati
Transfer agent: MGF Service Corp.
Investment objective and policies: Long-term capi-

tal growth. Invests primarily in basic value common stocks chosen through fundamental analysis. May have substantial holdings in small capitalization companies.
Year organized: 1993 (name changed from The RCM Fund on 9/2/94)
Ticker symbol: RCMFX
Minimum purchase: Initial: $25,000, Subsequent: None
Telephone orders accepted: No
Wire orders accepted: Yes
Deadline for same day wire purchase: 4 P.M.
Qualified for sale in: FL, IL, MI, NY, OH
Wire redemptions: Yes
Letter redemptions: Signature guarantee required over $5,000
Dividends paid: Income - December; Capital gains - December
Largest holding: The Horsham Corp. (3.2%)
Management fee: 1.50% first $75M to 1.00% over $100M

SCM PORTFOLIO FUND ◆
123 Ole Hickory Trail
P.O. Box 947
Carrollton, GA 30117
404-834-5839

Adviser: SCM Associates, Inc.
Portfolio manager: Stephen C. McCutcheon (1988)
Custodian: Nationsbank Trust, Atlanta
Transfer agent: SCM Associates, Inc.
Investment objective and policies: Total return consisting of growth, income, and preservation of principal. Invests in common stocks, bonds, money market funds, U.S. Government securities, CDs, and shares of other mutual funds. Fund allocates assets to generate real growth during favorable investment periods and emphasizes income and capital preservation during uncertain investment periods.
Year organized: 1988
Minimum purchase: Initial: $2,500, Subsequent: $250
Telephone orders accepted: No
Wire orders accepted: Yes
Deadline for same day wire purchase: 4 P.M.
Qualified for sale in: GA
Letter redemptions: Signature guarantee required
Redemption fee: 1% for shares held less than 6 months
Dividends paid: Income - July, December; Capital gains - December
Portfolio turnover (3 yrs): 21%, 28%, 35%
Management fee: 0.74%
Expense Ratio: 1.58% (year ending 12/31/93) (2.32% without waiver)

SCUDDER FUNDS ◆
(Data common to all Scudder funds, except Scudder Fund, Inc. funds, are shown below. See subsequent listings for data specific to individual Scudder funds.)

P.O. Box 2291
Boston, MA 02107-2291
617-295-1000, 800-225-2470
shareholders 800-225-5163
prices/yields 800-343-2890
TDD 800-543-7916, fax 617-261-4420

Shareholder service hours: Full service: M-F 8 A.M.-6 P.M. EST; After hours service: prices, yields, balances, last transaction
Adviser: Scudder, Stevens & Clark
Custodian: State Street Bank & Trust Co. (exceptions noted)
Transfer agent: Scudder Service Corp.
Minimum purchase: Initial: $1,000, Subsequent: $100; IRA/Keogh: Initial: $500, Subsequent: $50
Telephone orders accepted: No, exceptions noted
Wire orders accepted: Yes
Deadline for same day wire purchase: 4 P.M. (12 NN for money market funds)
Qualified for sale in: All states (exceptions noted)
Telephone redemptions: Yes

Wire redemptions: Yes, $5 fee
Letter redemptions: Signature guarantee required over $50,000
Telephone switching: With all Scudder funds
Number of switches permitted: 4 round trips per year
Shareholder services: Keogh, IRA, SEP-IRA, 401(k), 403(b), corporate retirement plans, automatic investment plan—minimum $50/month, withdrawal plan min. req. $10,000
IRA fees: None
Keogh fees: Annual $10, Initial $10

SCUDDER BALANCED FUND ◆
(See first Scudder listing for data common to all Scudder funds)

Lead portfolio manager: Howard F. Ward (1993)
Investment objective and policies: Balance of growth and income and long-term preservation of capital. Invests in common stocks and other equity securities (50-75% of assets) with remaining assets in investment-grade bonds and other fixed-income securities (25-50%) including cash. Invests primarily in domestic companies with annual revenues or market capitalization of at least $600M and above-average potential for price appreciation. Allocation of assets adjusted to changing market conditions. Fund may use foreign securities, write covered calls, and use futures contracts and options thereon.
Year organized: 1993
Ticker symbol: SCBAX
Telephone orders accepted: Subsequent only, $10,000 minimum
Discount broker availability: Fidelity, Siebert
Dividends paid: Income - April, July, October, December; Capital gains - November, December
Portfolio turnover (1 yr): 99%
Largest holding: U.S. Treasury Note 5.875% due 2/15/04 (4.6%)
Management fee: 0.70%
Expense ratio: 1.00% (year ending 12/31/93) (1.53% without waiver)

SCUDDER CALIFORNIA
TAX FREE FUND ◆
(See first Scudder listing for data common to all Scudder funds)

Lead portfolio manager: Jeremy L. Ragus (1990)
Investment objective and policies: Income exempt from both federal and California state income taxes. Invests primarily in investment-grade California state, municipal and local government obligations, but primarily AA and A. Up to 25% of assets may be in junk bonds and 20% in AMT securities. May use options, futures and options thereon.
Year organized: 1983
Ticker symbol: SCTFX
Qualified for sale in: AZ, CA, CO, DC, FL, GA, HI, ID, IL, IN, KS, MD, MA, MN, MO, NV, NJ, NY, NC, OH, OR, SC ,TX, VA, WA, WV, WI, WY
Discount broker availability: Schwab, White, Waterhouse, Fidelity, Siebert
Dividends paid: Income - declared daily, paid monthly; Capital gains - May, November, December
Portfolio turnover (3 yrs): 127%, 209%, 143%
Management fee: 0.625% first $200M, 0.60% over $200M
Expense ratio: 0.78% (year ending 3/31/94)

SCUDDER CALIFORNIA TAX FREE
MONEY FUND ◆
(See first Scudder listing for data common to all Scudder funds)

Lead portfolio manager: Rebecca L. Wilson (1987)
Investment objective and policies: High current income exempt from both federal and California state income taxes. Invests primarily in California state, municipal and local government money market instruments.
Year organized: 1987

Ticker symbol: SCAXX
Qualified for sale in: AZ, CA, CO, DC, FL, GA, HI, ID, IL, IN, KS, MD, MA, MN, MO, NV, NJ, NY, NC, OH, OR, SC ,TX, VA, WA, WV, WI, WY
Check redemptions: $100 minimum
Confirmations mailed: After each purchase and each check, mail or wire redemption.
Checks returned: Monthly
Periodic account statements mailed: Monthly
Dividends paid: Income - declared daily, paid monthly
Management fee: 0.5%
Expense ratio: 0.60% (year ending 3/31/94) (0.90% without waiver)

SCUDDER CAPITAL GROWTH FUND ◆
(See first Scudder listing for data common to all Scudder funds)

Lead portfolio manager: Steven P. Aronoff (1989)
Investment objective and policies: Long-term growth of capital. Invests primarily in common stocks, but also may use preferred stocks and investment-grade debt securities. May invest in securities of foreign issuers and use futures and options and hedge.
Year organized: 1956 (as Scudder Special Fund; in 1982 Scudder Duo-Vest open-ended, changed name to Capital Growth, and merged with Special.)
Ticker symbol: SCDUX
Telephone orders accepted: Subsequent only, $10,000 minimum
Discount broker availability: Schwab, White, Waterhouse, Fidelity, Siebert
Dividends paid: Income - December; Capital gains - December
Portfolio turnover (3 yrs): 76%, 92%, 92%
Largest holding: Time Warner, Inc. (5.1%)
Management fee: 0.75% first $500M to 0.6% over $1B
Expense ratio: 0.97% (year ending 9/30/94)

SCUDDER CASH INVESTMENT
TRUST ◆
(See first Scudder listing for data common to all Scudder funds)

Lead portfolio manager: Robert T. Neff (1976)
Investment objective and policies: Stability of capital, liquidity and income. Invests in short-term money market instruments.
Year organized: 1975
Ticker symbol: SCTXX
Check redemptions: $100 minimum
Confirmations mailed: After each purchase and each check, mail or wire redemption
Checks returned: Monthly
Periodic account statements mailed: Monthly
Dividends paid: Income - declared daily, paid monthly
Management fee: 0.5% first $250M to 0.35% over $1B
Expense ratio: 0.82% (year ending 6/30/94)

SCUDDER DEVELOPMENT FUND ◆
(See first Scudder listing for data common to all Scudder funds)

Lead portfolio manager: Roy C. McKay (1988)
Custodian: Brown Brothers Harriman & Co.
Investment objective and policies: Above-average long-term capital growth. Invests in equity securities of relatively small or little-known emerging growth companies with above-average growth potential. Up to 20% of assets may be in securities of foreign issuers. Fund may write covered calls, use stock index options and for hedging purposes use futures contracts and options thereon.
Year organized: 1970
Ticker symbol: SCDVX
Telephone orders accepted: Subsequent only, $10,000 minimum
Discount broker availability: Schwab, White, Waterhouse, Fidelity, Siebert
Dividends paid: Income - July, December; Capital gains - July, December

Portfolio turnover (3 yrs): 48%, 49%, 54%
Largest holding: Cabletron Systems, Inc. (4.6%)
Management fee: 1.0% first $500M to 0.9% over $1B
Expense ratio: 1.27% (year ending 6/30/94)

SCUDDER EMERGING MARKETS
INCOME FUND ◆
(See first Scudder listing for data common to all Scudder funds)

Lead portfolio manager: Lincoln Y. Rathnam (1993)
Custodian: Brown Brothers Harriman & Co.
Investment objective and policies: High current income with long-term capital appreciation secondary. Invests primarily in high-yielding debt securities issued by governments and corporations in emerging markets. Initial investments will be weighted toward countries in Latin America - Argentina, Brazil, Mexico, and Venezuela - but may also invest in Asia, Africa, The Middle East and Eastern Europe. Normally invests in securities from at least 3 countries with no more than 40% of assets from issuers of any single country. Fund may use futures and options to increase returns and hedge.
Year organized: 1993
Ticker symbol: SCEMX
Telephone orders accepted: Subsequent only, $10,000 minimum
Discount broker availability: Schwab, White, Waterhouse, Fidelity, Siebert
Dividends paid: Income - April, July, October, December; Capital gains - December
Portfolio turnover (1 yr): 181%
Management fee: 1.0%
Expense ratio: 1.50% (10 months ending 10/31/94) (2.23% without waiver)

SCUDDER GLOBAL FUND INC. ◆
(See first Scudder listing for data common to all Scudder funds)

Lead portfolio manager: William E. Holzer (1986)
Investment objective and policies: Long-term growth of capital. Invests in equity securities - including common stocks, preferred stocks and debt securities convertible into common stocks - of companies from at least 3 countries around the world. Seeks companies which will benefit from global economic trends, technologies, and currency changes. May also invest in investment-grade debt securities of U.S. and foreign issuers. Fund may use closed-end investment companies, stock and bond options, currency exchange contracts, and financial futures and options.
Year organized: 1986
Ticker symbol: SCOBX
Telephone orders accepted: Subsequent only, $10,000 minimum
Discount broker availability: Schwab, White, Waterhouse, Fidelity, Siebert
Dividends paid: Income - August, December; Capital gains - August, December
Portfolio turnover (3 yrs): 60%, 65%, 45%
Largest holding: Samsung Electronics (1.8%)
Management fee: 1.0% first $500M, 0.95% over $500M
Expense ratio: 1.45% (year ending 6/30/94)

SCUDDER GLOBAL SMALL COMPANY
FUND INC. ◆
(See first Scudder listing for data common to all Scudder funds)

Lead portfolio manager: Gerald J. Moran (1991)
Custodian: Brown Brothers Harriman & Co.
Investment objective and policies: Long-term growth of capital. Invests in equity securities - including common stocks, preferred stocks and securities convertible into common stocks - of small companies located throughout the world. At least 50% of assets will be in companies with market capitalization of less than $550M. Fund may use closed-end investment companies, stock and bond options, currency exchange contracts, and

financial futures and options.
Year organized: 1991
Ticker symbol SGSCX
Telephone orders accepted: Subsequent only, $10,000 minimum
Discount broker availability: Schwab, White, Waterhouse, Fidelity, Siebert
Dividends paid: Income - December; Capital gains - December
Portfolio turnover (3 yrs): 46%, 55%, 23%
Largest holding: SAP AG Preferred (4.9%)
Management fee: 1.10%
Expense ratio: 1.70% (year ending 10/31/94) (1.78% without waiver)

SCUDDER GNMA FUND ◆
(See first Scudder listing for data common to all Scudder funds)

Lead portfolio manager: David H. Glen (1985)
Investment objective and policies: High current income. Normally invests at least 65% of assets in U.S. Government mortgage-backed securities (GNMAs) with remainder in other U.S. Government securities and cash equivalents. Fund may use zero coupon securities, options, futures and options on futures.
Year organized: 1985
Ticker symbol: SGMSX
Discount broker availability: Schwab, White, Waterhouse, Fidelity, Siebert
Dividends paid: Income - declared daily, paid monthly, Capital gains - December
Portfolio turnover (3 yrs): 272%, 87%, 87%
Management fee: 0.65% first $200M to 0.55% over $500M
Expense ratio: 0.87% (year ending 3/31/94)

SCUDDER GOLD FUND ◆
(See first Scudder listing for data common to all Scudder funds)

Lead portfolio manager: Douglas D. Donald (1988)
Investment objective and policies: Maximum total return. Invests at least 65% of assets in equity securities of companies engaged in the exploration, mining, fabrication, processing or distribution of gold as well as gold bullion and coins. Remaining assets may be in other precious metals and related equities and in debt securities. Fund may use zero coupon securities, options, futures and options on futures.
Year organized: 1988
Ticker symbol: SCGDX
Telephone orders accepted: Subsequent only, $10,000 minimum
Discount broker availability: Schwab, White, Waterhouse, Fidelity, Siebert
Dividends paid: Income - August, December; Capital gains - December
Portfolio turnover (3 yrs): 51%, 59%, 58%
Largest holding: Pioneer Group, Inc. (4.2%)
Management fee: 1.0%
Expense ratio: 1.69% (year ending 6/30/94)

SCUDDER GREATER EUROPE GROWTH FUND ◆
(See first Scudder listing for data common to all Scudder funds)

Lead portfolio manager: Carol L. Franklin (1994)
Custodian: Brown Brothers Harriman & Co.
Investment objective and policies: Long-term growth of capital. Invests at least 80% of assets in equity securities of issuers from at least 3 European countries - primarily from Western and Southern Europe. May invest up to 20% of assets in European junk bonds. May use options on securities, currencies and indexes and currency futures and exchange contracts.
Year organized: 1994
Ticker symbol: SCGEX
Telephone orders accepted: Subsequent only,

$10,000 minimum
Discount broker availability: Schwab, Fidelity, Siebert
Dividends paid: Income - December; Capital gains - December
Management fee: 1.00%

SCUDDER GROWTH AND INCOME FUND ◆
(See first Scudder listing for data common to all Scudder funds)

Newspaper listing: GrwIn
Lead portfolio manager: Robert T. Hoffman (1990)
Investment objective and policies: Long-term growth of capital, current income, and growth of income. Invests primarily in common stocks, preferred stocks and convertible securities which offer prospect of growth of earnings while paying current dividends. May use foreign securities, write covered calls, and use futures contracts and options thereon.
Year organized: 1929 (formerly Scudder Common Stock Fund; name and objectives changed 11/13/84)
Ticker symbol: SCDGX
Telephone orders accepted: Subsequent only, $10,000 minimum
Discount broker availability: Schwab, White, Waterhouse, Fidelity, Siebert
Dividends paid: Income - April, July, October, December; Capital gains - December
Portfolio turnover (3 yrs): 36%, 28%, 45%
Largest holding: United Technologies Corp. (2.6%)
Management fee: 0.65% first $200M to 0.50% over $900M
Expense ratio: 0.86% (year ending 12/31/93)

SCUDDER HIGH YIELD TAX FREE FUND ◆
(See first Scudder listing for data common to all Scudder funds)

Newspaper listing: TxFHi
Lead Portfolio manager: Philip G. Condon (1987)
Investment objective and policies: High current income exempt from federal income tax. Invests primarily in investment-grade municipal bonds, Baa rated or higher. Up to 35% of assets may be in junk bonds and 20% in AMT securities. For hedging purposes fund may use financial futures and options thereon.
Year organized: 1987
Ticker symbol: SHYTX
Discount broker availability: White, Waterhouse, Fidelity, Siebert
Portfolio turnover (3 yrs): 56%, 57%, 45%
Dividends paid: Income - declared daily, paid monthly; Capital gains - March, November
Management fee: 0.70% first $200M, 0.65% over $200M
Expense ratio: 0.92% (year ending 12/31/93) (0.98% without waiver)

SCUDDER INCOME FUND ◆
(See first Scudder listing for data common to all Scudder funds)

Lead portfolio manager: William M. Hutchinson (1986)
Investment objective and policies: Current income. Invests primarily in fixed-income securities of all types as well as dividend-paying common stocks. Bonds will normally be A or better but up to 25% of assets can be in Baa rated securities, but not lower. Fund may use foreign securities, zero coupon securities, write covered calls and use financial futures and options thereon.
Year organized: 1928
Ticker symbol: SCSBX
Telephone orders accepted: Subsequent only, $10,000 minimum
Discount broker availability: Schwab, White,

Waterhouse, Fidelity, Siebert
Dividends paid: Income - April, July, October, December; Capital gains - December
Portfolio turnover (3 yrs): 131%, 121%, 110%
Management fee: 0.65% first $200M to 0.55% over $500M
Expense ratio: 0.92% (year ending 12/31/93)

SCUDDER INTERNATIONAL BOND FUND ◆
(See first Scudder listing for data common to all Scudder funds)

Lead portfolio manager: Adam Greshin (1992)
Custodian: Brown Brothers Harriman & Co.
Investment objective and policies: Current income with protection and possible enhancement of principal value secondary. Invests in high-grade debt securities rated A or better denominated in foreign currencies. Up to 35% of assets may be in U.S. debt securities. May use futures and options on futures; options on securities, currencies and indexes; and currency exchange contracts.
Year organized: 1988
Ticker symbol: SCIBX
Discount broker availability: Schwab, White, Waterhouse, Fidelity, Siebert
Dividends paid: Income - declared daily, paid monthly, Capital gains - September, December
Portfolio turnover (3 yrs): 233%, 250%, 148%
Management fee: 0.85%
Expense ratio: 1.27% (year ending 6/30/94) (1.29% without waiver)

SCUDDER INTERNATIONAL FUND ◆
(See first Scudder listing for data common to all Scudder funds)

Lead portfolio manager: Carol L. Franklin (1989)
Custodian: Brown Brothers Harriman & Co.
Investment objective and policies: Long-term growth of capital. Invests primarily in equity securities of established foreign companies and economies with growth prospects. May invest up to 20% of assets in fixed-income securities of foreign governments and companies, generally of investment-grade quality although 5% can be rated B or lower. May use options on securities, currencies and indexes and currency futures and exchange contracts.
Year organized: 1953
Ticker symbol: SCINX
Telephone orders accepted: Subsequent only, $10,000 minimum
Discount broker availability: Schwab, White, Waterhouse, Fidelity, Siebert
Telephone orders accepted: Subsequent only, $10,000 minimum
Dividends paid: Income - May, December; Capital gains - May, December
Portfolio turnover (3 yrs): 40%, 29%, 50%
Largest holding: SAP AG Preferred (1.5%)
Management fee: 0.90% first $500M to 0.75% over $2B
Expense ratio: 1.21% (year ending 3/31/94)

SCUDDER LATIN AMERICA FUND ◆
(See first Scudder listing for data common to all Scudder funds)

Lead portfolio manager: Edmund B. Games, Jr. (1992)
Custodian: Brown Brothers Harriman & Co.
Investment objective and policies: Long-term growth of capital. Invests at least 65% of assets in securities of Latin American issuers with at least 50% of assets in Latin American equity securities. May invest up to 35% of assets in equity securities of U.S. and other non-Latin American issuers. Fund may invest up to 10% of assets in closed-end mutual funds and use options on securities, currencies and indexes and currency futures and exchange contracts.
Year organized: 1992
Ticker symbol: SLAFX
Telephone orders accepted: Subsequent only, $10,000 minimum

Discount broker availability: Waterhouse
Redemption fee: 2.0% for shares held less than 1 year, payable to the fund
Dividends paid: Income - December; Capital gains - December
Portfolio turnover (2 yrs): 22%, 5%
Management fee: 1.25%
Expense ratio: 2.01% (year ending 10/31/94) (2.05% without waiver)

SCUDDER LIMITED TERM TAX FREE FUND ◆

(See first Scudder listing for data common to all Scudder portfolios)

Lead portfolio manager: M. Ashton Patton (1994)
Investment objective and policies: High income exempt from federal income tax consistent with stability of principal. Invests in high grade (at least 80% rated A or better, none less than Baa) shorter-term municipal bonds with a weighted average maturity of 1 to 5 years. May use futures and options thereon and options on portfolio securities.
Year organized: 1994
Ticker symbol: SCLTX
Check redemptions: $100 minimum
Dividends paid: Income - declared daily, paid monthly; Capital gains - December
Portfolio turnover (1 yr): 36%
Management fee: 0.60%
Expense ratio: 0.00% (8 months ending 10/31/94) (1.29% without waiver)

SCUDDER MANAGED MUNICIPAL BONDS ◆

(See first Scudder listing for data common to all Scudder funds)

Newspaper listing: MMB
Lead portfolio manager: Donald C. Carleton (1986)
Investment objective and policies: Income exempt from federal income tax. Invests in investment-grade municipal bonds (100% A or better, 50% AA or better). May invest up to 20% of assets in taxable securities. Fund may use financial futures and options thereon for hedging purposes.
Year organized: 1976
Ticker symbol: SCMBX
Discount broker availability: Schwab, White, Waterhouse, Fidelity, Siebert
Dividends paid: Income - declared daily, paid monthly; Capital gains - December
Portfolio turnover (3 yrs): 53%, 60%, 32%
Management fee: 0.55% first $200M to 0.475% over $700M
Expense ratio: 0.63% (year ending 12/31/93)

SCUDDER MASSACHUSETTS LIMITED TERM TAX FREE FUND ◆

(See first Scudder listing for data common to all Scudder portfolios)

Lead portfolio manager: Philip G. Condon (1994)
Investment objective and policies: High income exempt from federal and Massachusetts state income tax consistent with stability of principal. Invests in high grade (at least 80% rated A or better, none less than Baa) shorter-term Massachusetts municipal bonds with a weighted average maturity of 1 to 5 years. Up to 20% of assets may be in AMT securities. May use financial futures and options thereon and options on portfolio securities.
Year organized: 1994
Ticker symbol: SMLFX
Qualified for sale in: AZ, CA, CO, CT, DC, FL, GA, HI, IL, IN, ME, MD, MA, MN, NH, NJ, NY, NC, PA, RI, TX, VT, VA, WV
Check redemptions: $100 minimum
Dividends paid: Income - declared daily, paid monthly; Capital gains - December
Portfolio turnover (1 yr): 26%
Management fee: 0.60%
Expense ratio: 0.00% (8 months ending 10/31/94) (1.44% without waiver)

SCUDDER MASSACHUSETTS TAX FREE FUND ◆

(See first Scudder listing for data common to all Scudder funds)

Lead portfolio manager: Philip G. Condon (1989)
Investment objective and policies: Income exempt from federal and Massachusetts state income taxes. Invests primarily in long-term (more than 10 years) investment-grade Massachusetts state, municipal and local government obligations. May invest up to 25% of assets in junk bonds and 20% in AMT securities. Fund may use options, futures and option thereon.
Year organized: 1987
Ticker symbol: SCMAX
Qualified for sale in: AZ, CA, CO, CT, DC, FL, GA, HI, IL, IN, ME, MD, MA, MN, NH, NJ, NY, NC, PA, RI, TX, VT, VA, WV
Discount broker availability: White, Waterhouse, Fidelity, Siebert
Portfolio turnover (3 yrs): 17%, 30%, 23%
Dividends paid: Income - declared daily, paid monthly; Capital gains - May, November
Management fee: 0.6%
Expense ratio: 0.07% (year ending 3/31/94) (0.77% without waiver)

SCUDDER MEDIUM TERM TAX FREE FUND ◆

(See first Scudder listing for data common to all Scudder portfolios)

Lead portfolio manager: Donald C. Carleton (1986)
Investment objective and policies: High income exempt from federal income tax. Invests in high grade (at least 80% rated A or better, none less than Baa) intermediate-term municipal bonds with a weighted average maturity of 5 to 8 years. May use financial futures and options thereon and options on portfolio securities.
Year organized: 1990 (formerly Tax Free Target Fund - 1990 Portfolio; performance data before 1990 may not be relevant. On 5/15/92 Tax Free Target Fund 1993 Portfolio and 1996 Portfolio were merged into the fund.)
Ticker symbol: SCMTX
Discount broker availability: Schwab, White, Waterhouse, Fidelity, Siebert
Dividends paid: Income - declared daily, paid monthly; Capital gains - December
Portfolio turnover (3 yrs): 37%, 22%, 14%
Management fee: 0.60%
Expense ratio: 0.14% (year ending 12/31/93) (0.75% without waiver)

SCUDDER NEW YORK TAX FREE FUND ◆

(See first Scudder listing for data common to all Scudder funds)

Lead portfolio manager: Jeremy L. Ragus (1990)
Investment objective and policies: Income exempt from federal and New York State and City income taxes. Invests primarily in investment-grade New York state, municipal and local government obligations. May invest up to 25% of assets in junk bonds and 20% in AMT securities. Fund may use financial futures and options thereon for hedging purposes.
Year organized: 1983
Ticker symbol: SCYTX
Discount broker availability: Schwab, White, Waterhouse, Fidelity, Siebert
Qualified for sale in: AZ, CA, CO, CT, DC, FL, GA, HI, IL, IN, MD, MA, MN, MS, NH, NJ, NY, NC, OH, PA, RI, SC, TX, VT, VA, WV, WI
Dividends paid: Income - declared daily, paid monthly; Capital gains - May, December
Portfolio turnover (3 yrs): 207%, 201%, 159%
Management fee: 0.625% first $200M, 0.60% over $200M
Expense ratio: 0.82% (year ending 3/31/94)

SCUDDER NEW YORK TAX FREE MONEY FUND ◆

(See first Scudder listing for data common to all Scudder funds)

Lead portfolio manager: Rebecca L. Wilson (1987)
Investment objective and policies: High current income exempt from federal and New York State and City income taxes. Invests primarily in New York state, municipal and local government money market obligations rated Aaa or Aa.
Year organized: 1987
Ticker symbol: SCNXX
Qualified for sale in: AZ, CA, CO, CT, DC, FL, GA, HI, IL, IN, MD, MA, MN, MS, NH, NJ, NY, NC, OH, PA, RI, SC, TX, VT, VA, WV, WI
Check redemptions: $100 minimum
Confirmations mailed: After each purchase and each check, mail or wire redemption
Checks returned: Monthly
Periodic account statements mailed: Monthly
Dividends paid: Income - declared daily, paid monthly
Management fee: 0.5%
Expense ratio: 0.60% (year ending 3/31/94) (0.90% without waiver)

SCUDDER OHIO TAX FREE FUND ◆

(See first Scudder listing for data common to all Scudder funds)

Lead portfolio manager: Kimberly R. Manning (1987)
Investment objective and policies: Income exempt from federal and Ohio state income taxes. Invests primarily in long-term Ohio state, municipal and local government obligations of investment-grade quality. May invest up to 25% of assets in junk bonds and 20% in AMT securities. Fund may use financial futures and options thereon for hedging purposes.
Year organized: 1987
Ticker symbol: SCOHX
Discount broker availability: White, Waterhouse, Fidelity, Siebert
Qualified for sale in: AZ, CA, CO, DC, FL, GA, HI, IL, IN, KY, MD, MA, MN, MI, MN, NJ, NY, NC, OH, PA, TX, VA, WV
Dividends paid: Income - declared daily, paid monthly; Capital gains - May, November
Portfolio turnover (3 yrs): 12%. 35%, 13%
Management fee: 0.6%
Expense ratio: 0.50% (year ending 3/31/94) (0.90% without waiver)

SCUDDER PACIFIC OPPORTUNITIES FUND ◆

(See first Scudder listing for data common to all Scudder funds)

Lead portfolio manager: Elizabeth J. Allan (1994)
Custodian: Brown Brothers Harriman & Co.
Investment objective and policies: Long-term growth of capital. Invests at least 65% of assets in equity securities of Pacific Basin companies, excluding Japan. May invest up to 35% of assets in foreign and domestic investment-grade debt securities and 35% in U.S. and non-Pacific Basin equity securities. Fund may use options on securities, currencies and indexes and currency futures and exchange contracts.
Year organized: 1992
Ticker symbol: SCOPX
Telephone orders accepted: Subsequent only, $10,000 minimum
Discount broker availability: Schwab, White, Waterhouse, Fidelity, Siebert
Dividends paid: Income - December; Capital gains - December
Portfolio turnover (2 yrs): 39%, 10%
Largest holding: PTT Exploration and Production Co., Ltd. (2.4%)
Management fee: 1.10%
Expense ratio: 1.81% (year ending 10/31/94)

SCUDDER PENNSYLVANIA TAX FREE FUND ◆
(See first Scudder listing for data common to all Scudder funds)

Lead portfolio manager: Kimberly R. Manning (1987)
Investment objective and policies: Income exempt from federal and Pennsylvania state income taxes and property taxes. Invests primarily in investment-grade long-term Pennsylvania state, municipal and local government obligations. May invest up to 25% of assets in junk bonds and 20% in AMT securities. Fund may use financial futures and options thereon for hedging purposes.
Year organized: 1987
Ticker symbol: SCPAX
Discount broker availability: Waterhouse, Fidelity, Siebert
Qualified for sale in: AZ, CA, CO, DC, FL, GA, HI, IL, IN, KY, MD, MA, MN, NJ, NY, NC, OH, PA, TX, VA, WV
Dividends paid: Income - declared daily, paid monthly; Capital gains - May, November
Portfolio turnover (3 yrs): 17%, 29%, 11%
Management fee: 0.6%
Expense ratio: 0.50% (year ending 3/31/94) (0.95% without waiver)

SCUDDER QUALITY GROWTH FUND ◆
(See first Scudder listing for data common to all Scudder funds)

Lead portfolio manager: Howard F. Ward (1991)
Investment objective and policies: Long-term growth of capital. Invests primarily in common stocks, preferred stocks and convertible securities of seasoned, financially-strong U.S. growth companies with annual revenues of at least $200M and capitalizations of at least $300M. Fund may use foreign securities, write covered calls, and use futures contracts and options thereon.
Year organized: 1991
Ticker symbol: SCQGX
Telephone orders accepted: Subsequent only, $10,000 minimum
Discount broker availability: Schwab, White, Waterhouse, Fidelity, Siebert
Dividends paid: Income - December; Capital gains - December
Portfolio turnover (3 yrs): 120%, 111%, 27%
Largest holding: American Telephone & Telegraph Co. (3.6%)
Management fee: 0.70%
Expense ratio: 1.25% (year ending 10/31/94)

SCUDDER SHORT TERM BOND FUND ◆
(See first Scudder listing for data common to all Scudder funds)

Lead portfolio manager: Thomas M. Poor (1989)
Investment objective and policies: Current income consistent with stability of principal. Invests in high quality debt instruments, including mortgage-backed securities, with a weighted average maturity of three years or less. At least 65% of assets will be in Aaa or Aa rated securities with no securities below Baa. May use foreign securities and currency exchange contracts. Fund may use options on portfolio securities and, for hedging purposes, financial futures contracts and options thereon.
Year organized: 1982 (formerly the 3 portfolios of the Scudder Target Fund; name and objectives changed on 7/3/89)
Ticker symbol: SCSTX
Discount broker availability: Schwab, White, Waterhouse, Fidelity, Siebert
Dividends paid: Income - declared daily, paid monthly; Capital gains - December
Check redemptions: $100 minimum
Portfolio turnover (3 yrs): 66%, 87%, 41%
Management fee: 0.6% first $500M to 0.35% over $3B
Expense ratio: 0.68% (year ending 12/31/93)

SCUDDER SHORT TERM GLOBAL INCOME FUND ◆
(See first Scudder listing for data common to all Scudder funds)

Lead portfolio manager: Margaret Craddock (1991)
Custodian: Brown Brothers Harriman & Co.
Investment objective and policies: High current income. Invests in high grade money market instruments and short-term bonds, from issuers around the world, denominated in foreign currencies as well as the U.S. dollar with a weighted average maturity of 3 years or less. May use foreign currency exchange contracts, options on portfolio securities and, for hedging purposes, financial futures contracts and options thereon.
Year organized: 1991
Ticker symbol: SSTGX
Discount broker availability: Schwab, White, Waterhouse, Fidelity, Siebert
Dividends paid: Income - declared daily, paid monthly; Capital gains - December
Portfolio turnover (3 yrs): 272%, 260%, 274%
Management fee: 0.75% first $1B, 0.70% over $1B
Expense ratio: 1.00% (year ending 10/31/94) (1.15% without waiver)

SCUDDER TAX FREE MONEY FUND ◆
(See first Scudder listing for data common to all Scudder funds)

Lead portfolio manager: K. Sue Cote (1984)
Investment objective and policies: Tax-free income while seeking relative stability of principal. Invests in a high-grade (Aaa or Aa) portfolio of short-term municipal money market securities.
Year organized: 1979
Ticker symbol: STFXX
Check redemptions: $100 minimum
Confirmations mailed: After each purchase and each check, mail or wire redemption
Checks returned: Monthly
Periodic account statements mailed: Monthly
Dividends paid: Income - declared daily, paid monthly
Management fee: 0.5% first $500M, 0.48% over $500M
Expense ratio: 0.75% (year ending 12/31/93)

SCUDDER U.S. TREASURY MONEY FUND ◆
(See first Scudder listing for data common to all Scudder funds)

Lead portfolio manager: Robert T. Neff (1981)
Investment objective and policies: Safety, liquidity and stability of capital, consistent with current income. Invests in U.S. Government and government guaranteed money market obligations.
Year organized: 1981 (name changed from Government Money Fund in March 1991)
Ticker symbol: SCGXX
Check redemptions: $100 minimum
Confirmations mailed: After each purchase and each check, mail or wire redemption
Checks returned: Monthly
Periodic account statements mailed: Monthly
Dividends paid: Income - declared daily, paid monthly
Management fee: 0.5%
Expense ratio: 0.65% (year ending 6/30/94) (0.90% without waiver)

SCUDDER VALUE FUND ◆
(See first Scudder listing for data common to all Scudder funds)

Lead portfolio manager: Donald E. Hall (1992)
Investment objective and policies: Long-term growth of capital. Invests at least 80% of assets in equity securities of undervalued medium-to-large sized companies with annual revenues or market capitalizations of at least $600M and above-average potential for price appreciation. Fund may use foreign securities, write covered calls, and use futures contracts and options thereon.
Year organized: 1992

Ticker symbol: SCVAX
Telephone orders accepted: Subsequent only, $10,000 minimum
Discount broker availability: Fidelity, Siebert
Dividends paid: Income - December; Capital gains - December
Portfolio turnover (2 yrs): 75%, 61%
Largest holding: Intel Corp. (3.3%)
Management fee: 0.70%
Expense ratio: 1.25% (year ending 9/30/94) (1.61% without waiver)

SCUDDER ZERO COUPON 2000 FUND ◆
(See first Scudder listing for data common to all Scudder funds)

Lead portfolio manager: Ruth Heisler (1988)
Investment objective and policies: High investment return over selected period consistent with investment in U.S. Government securities and with the minimization of reinvestment risk. Invests in U.S. Government zero coupon securities and matures on the third Friday of December of the year 2000.
Year organized: 1986
Ticker symbol: SGZTX
Telephone orders accepted: Subsequent only, $10,000 minimum
Discount broker availability: Schwab, White, Waterhouse, Fidelity, Siebert
Dividends paid: Income - December; Capital gains - December
Portfolio turnover (3 yrs): 102%, 119%, 91%
Management fee: 0.60%
Expense ratio: 1.00% (year ending 12/31/93) (1.28% without waiver)

SEAFIRST RETIREMENT PORTFOLIO FUNDS ◆
(Data common to all Seafirst funds are shown below. See subsequent listings for data specific to individual Seafirst funds.)

Seafirst Bank Retail Retirement Services
P.O. Box 84248
Seattle, WA 98124
206-358-6234, 800-323-9919
TDD 206-358-6299, 800-232-6299
In ID 800-441-8379

Shareholder service hours: Full service: M-F 8 A.M.-6 P.M. PST, Sat 9 A.M.-1 P.M.
Adviser: Bank of America National Trust and Savings Association
Administrator: Concord Holding Corporation
Custodian: PNC Bank, N.A.
Transfer agent: PFPC
Special sales restrictions: Exclusively for investment of retirement funds held in Seafirst Retirement Accounts - including individual retirement trust accounts and single or commingled pension or profit sharing trusts for individuals (Keogh) and corporations. Seafirst must be a trustee on any such account.
Minimum purchase: IRA, SEP/QRP only: Initial: $500, Subsequent: None
Telephone orders accepted: No
Wire orders accepted: Yes
Deadline for same day wire purchase: 4 P.M.
Qualified for sale in: AK, AZ, CA, CO, GA, HI, ID, KS, MT, NM, NV, OR, SD, UT, WA
Letter redemptions: Signature guarantee not required
Telephone switching: With other Seafirst funds and Pacific Horizon Prime Fund
Number of switches permitted: Unlimited
Shareholder services: IRA, SEP-QRP, 401(k), corporate retirement plans, electronic funds transfer
IRA fees: Annual $15, Closing $15
SEP-QRP fees: Annual $15; Initial plan set-up SEP $75, QRP $125; Closing $15/participant

SEAFIRST RETIREMENT PORTFOLIO - ASSET ALLOCATION FUND ◆
(See first Seafirst listing for data common to all Seafirst funds)

Portfolio manager: E. Keith Wirtz (1993)
Investment objective and policies: Long-term

growth of capital and dividend income. Invests in a balanced portfolio of bonds, stocks, and cash equivalents using an asset allocation computer model and adjusting the mix to reflect changes in economic and market conditions. May have up to 25% of assets in securities of foreign issuers and use futures and options to hedge.
Year organized: 1988
Ticker symbol: SIAAX
Dividends paid: Income - monthly; Capital Gains - not distributed
Portfolio turnover (3 yrs): 79%, 171%, 124%
Largest holding: U.S. Treasury Note 7.875% due 4/15/98 (7.0%)
Management fee: 0.55%
Expense ratio: 0.95% (year ending 12/31/93) (includes waiver)

SEAFIRST RETIREMENT PORTFOLIO - BLUE CHIP FUND ◆
(See first Seafirst listing for data common to all Seafirst funds)

Portfolio manager: Christopher R. Helton (1993)
Investment objective and policies: Long-term growth of capital. Invests primarily in 35 blue chip stocks in approximately equal share weightings which are included in either the DJIA, the Major Market Index, or the top 200 of the S&P 500. May have up to 25% of assets in securities of foreign issuers, 20% in money market instruments, and use futures and options to hedge.
Year organized: 1988
Ticker symbol: SIBCX
Dividends paid: Income - quarterly Capital Gains - not distributed
Portfolio turnover (3 yrs): 4%, 27%, 16%
Largest holding: General Electric Co. (2.7%)
Management fee: 0.75%
Expense ratio: 0.95% (year ending 12/31/93) (includes waiver)

SEAFIRST RETIREMENT PORTFOLIO - BOND FUND ◆
(See first Seafirst listing for data common to all Seafirst funds)

Portfolio manager: Steven L. Vielhaber (1994)
Investment objective and policies: Interest income and capital appreciation. Invests in investment-grade intermediate and longer term bonds, including corporate and government fixed-income obligations and mortgage backed securities. May have up to 35% of assets in GNMA securities, 25% in securities of foreign issuers and use futures and options to hedge.
Year organized: 1988
Ticker symbol: SIBDX
Dividends paid: Income - monthly Capital Gains - not distributed
Portfolio turnover (3 yrs): 95%, 154%, 197%
Management fee: 0.45%
Expense ratio: 0.95% (year ending 12/31/93) (includes waiver)

THE SELECTED FUNDS
(Data common to all Selected funds are shown below. See subsequent listings for data specific to individual Selected funds.)

124 East Marcy Street
Santa Fe, NM 87501
505-983-4335, 800-243-1575
fax 505-983-6019

Shareholder service hours: Full service: M-F 8 A.M.-4 P.M. MST; After hours service: prices, yields, balances, total returns, last transaction
Adviser: Selected/Venture Advisors, LP (since 1993)
Custodian and transfer agent: Investors Fiduciary Trust Co.
Minimum purchase: Initial: $1,000, Subsequent: $100
Telephone orders accepted: No
Wire orders accepted: Yes

Deadline for same day wire purchase: 4 P.M.
Qualified for sale in: All states
Telephone redemptions: Yes, $25,000 maximum
Wire redemptions: Yes, $10,000 minimum ($1,000 for Daily Government Fund), $5 fee
Letter redemptions: Signature guarantee required over $25,000
Telephone switching: With other Selected funds
Number of switches permitted: 4 per year
Shareholder services: Keogh, IRA, SEP-IRA, 401(k), 403(b), 457, corporate retirement plans, automatic investment plan, electronic funds transfer ($1,000 minimum), withdrawal plan min. req. $5,000
12b-1 distribution fee: 0.25%
IRA/Keogh fees: Annual $12

SELECTED AMERICAN SHARES
(See first Selected listing for data common to all Selected funds)

Portfolio manager: Shelby M.C. Davis (1993)
Investment objective and policies: Growth of capital and income. Invests primarily in common stocks and other equity securities of U.S. companies, generally with market capitalizations of more than $1B. May invest in fixed-income securities with up to 30% of assets in junk bonds. Up to 35% of assets may be in securities of foreign issuers and 15% in illiquid securities. Fund follows a conservative approach in selecting common stocks and fixed-income securities, some of which may be convertible into common stocks.
Year organized: 1933
Ticker symbol: SLASX
Discount broker availability: Schwab, *White, *Waterhouse
Dividends paid: Income - March, June, September, December; Capital gains - September
Portfolio turnover (3 yrs): 79%, 50%, 21%
Largest holding: Wells Fargo & Co. (4.2%)
Management fee: 0.65% first $500M to 0.55% over $1B
Expense ratio: 1.01% (year ending 12/31/93) (1.22% without waiver)

SELECTED DAILY GOVERNMENT FUND
(See first Selected listing for data common to all Selected funds)

Portfolio manager: Carolyn Spolidoro (1993)
Investment objective and policies: Current income consistent with preservation of capital and liquidity. Invests exclusively in short-term U.S. Government money market obligations.
Year organized: 1988
Ticker symbol: SDGXX
Check redemptions: $250 minimum
Confirmations mailed: After each purchase and each check, mail or wire redemption
Checks returned: As clear
Periodic account statements mailed: Monthly
Dividends paid: Income - declared daily, paid monthly
Management fee: 0.3%
Expense ratio: 0.75% (year ending 12/31/93) (2.29% without waiver)

SELECTED DAILY INCOME FUND
(Fund merged into Selected Daily Government Fund on 4/29/94)

SELECTED SPECIAL SHARES
(See first Selected listing for data common to all Selected funds)

Sub-adviser: Bramwell Capital Management
Portfolio manager: Elizabeth R. Bramwell (1994)
Investment objective and policies: Capital growth. Invests primarily in common stocks and securities convertible into common stocks emphasizing companies with market capitalizations under $1B. Fund seeks companies with growth potential because of rapid growth of demand within their existing mar-

kets, expansion into new markets, new products, reduced competition, cost reduction programs and other favorable indicators. Up to 25% of assets may be in securities of foreign issuers and 15% in illiquid securities.
Year organized: 1968 (split 2 for 1 on 1/6/94)
Ticker symbol: SLSSX
Discount broker availability: Schwab, *White, *Waterhouse
Dividends paid: Income - December; Capital gains - December
Portfolio turnover (3 yrs): 100%, 41%, 74%
Largest holding: Caldor, Inc. (5.4%)
Management fee: 0.7% first $50M to 0.6% over $250M
Expense ratio: 1.24% (year ending 12/31/93) (1.51% without waiver)

SELECTED U.S. GOVERNMENT INCOME FUND
(See first Selected listing for data common to all Selected funds)

Portfolio manager: B. Clark Stamper (1993)
Investment objective and policies: Current income and short term capital gains consistent with preservation of capital. Invests primarily in debt obligations of varying maturities issued or guaranteed by the U.S. Government, its agencies and instrumentalities.
Year organized: 1987 (formerly Government Total Return)
Ticker symbol: SSGTX
Discount broker availability: *White
Dividends paid: Income - monthly; Capital gains - September
Portfolio turnover (3 yrs): 29%, 53%, 36%
Management fee: 0.5%
Expense ratio: 1.34% (year ending 12/31/93) (1.88% without waiver)

SENTRY FUND ◆
1800 North Point Drive
Stevens Point, WI 54481
715-346-7048, 800-533-7827
fax 715-346-7516

Adviser: Sentry Investment Management Inc. (a wholly owned subsidiary of Sentry Insurance)
Portfolio manager: Keith Ringberg (1977)
Custodian: Citibank, N.A.
Transfer agent: Sentry Equity Services, Inc.
Investment objective and policies: Long-term growth of capital with income secondary. Invests in common stocks and securities convertible into common stocks believed to offer favorable long-term growth prospects.
Year organized: 1969 (fund had an 8.0% load prior to 3/1/91)
Ticker symbol: SNTRX
Minimum purchase: Initial: $500, Subsequent: $50
Telephone orders accepted: Yes, $1,000 minimum
Wire orders accepted: No
Qualified for sale in: All states except HI
Letter redemptions: Signature guarantee required over $5,000
Dividends paid: Income - June, December; Capital gains - December
Portfolio turnover (3 yrs): 16%, 22%, 13%
Largest holding: Walgreen Co. (5.2%)
Shareholder services: IRA, automatic investment plan—minimum $20/month ($200 initial minimum), withdrawal plan min. req. $5,000
Management fee: 0.75%
Expense ratio: 0.86% (year ending 10/31/94)
IRA fees: Annual $5, Initial $5, Closing $5

SEQUOIA FUND ◆
767 Fifth Avenue, Suite 4701
New York, NY 10153
212-832-5280, fax 212-832-5298

Adviser: Ruane, Cunniff & Co., Inc.
Portfolio manager: William J. Ruane (1970)
Custodian: Morgan Guaranty Trust Company of New York

Transfer agent: DST Systems, Inc.
Investment objective and policies: Growth of capital. Invests in common stocks and securities convertible into common stocks believed undervalued using classic Graham and Dodd analysis which emphasizes balance sheet strength and earnings power. May invest up to 15% of assets in foreign securities, and 10% in restricted securities and special situations. Fund gives no weight to technical stock market studies.
Special sales restrictions: Fund has been closed to new shareholders since 12/23/82
Year organized: 1970
Ticker symbol: SEQUX
Minimum purchase: Subsequent: $50
Telephone orders accepted: Yes
Wire orders accepted: No
Qualified for sale in: All states except ID
Telephone redemptions: Yes
Letter redemptions: Signature guarantee required
Dividends paid: Income - February, June, December; Capital gains - February, December
Portfolio turnover (3 yrs): 32%, 24%, 28%
Largest holding: Berkshire Hathaway, Inc. (25.5%)
Shareholder services: IRA, withdrawal plan min. req. $10,000
Management fee: 1.0%
Expense ratio: 1.0% (year ending 12/31/94)
IRA fees: Annual $12

THE SEVEN SEAS SERIES FUNDS

(Data common to all Seven Seas Series funds are shown below. See subsequent listings for data specific to individual Seven Seas Series funds.)

2 International Place, 35th Floor
Boston, MA 02110
617-654-6089, 800-647-7327
fax 617-654-6011

Adviser: State Street Bank & Trust Co.
Administrator: Frank Russell Investment Management Co.
Custodian and transfer agent: State Street Bank & Trust Co.
Minimum purchase: Initial: $1,000, Subsequent: None
Telephone orders accepted: No
Wire orders accepted: Yes
Deadline for same day wire purchase: 4 P.M. (12 NN for money market funds)
Qualified for sale in: All states
Telephone redemptions: Yes
Wire redemptions: Yes, $10 fee under $1,000
Letter redemptions: Signature guarantee required
Telephone switching: With other Seven Seas Series funds
Number of switches permitted: Unlimited
Shareholder services: IRA, automatic investment plan, electronic funds transfer (redemption only)
Administration fee: $0 first $500M, 0.07% $500M-$1B to 0.03% over $1.5B (for combined assets of all funds)
IRA fees: Annual $10

THE SEVEN SEAS SERIES EMERGING MARKETS FUND

(See first Seven Seas Series listing for data common to all Seven Seas Series funds)

Portfolio manager: Rob Furdak (1994)
Investment objective and policies: Maximum total return, primarily capital growth. Invests primarily in equity securities of companies domiciled, or doing a substantial portion of their business, in at least 10 developing or emerging markets. Up to 15% of assets may be in illiquid securities. May use ADRs and EDRs and futures contracts and options on futures to hedge.
Year organized: 1994
Ticker symbol: SSEMX
Discount broker availability: Schwab, Fidelity, Siebert
Dividends paid: Income - October; Capital gains - October
Portfolio turnover (1 yr): 0%
Largest holding: Electrobras (centr) Series B NPV, Brazil (5.9%)

Management fee: 0.75%
12b-1 distribution fee: 0.25%
Expense ratio: 1.50% (6 months ending 8/31/94) (2.45% without waiver)

THE SEVEN SEAS SERIES GROWTH AND INCOME FUND

(See first Seven Seas Series listing for data common to all Seven Seas Series funds)

Portfolio manager: Brent Dixon (1993)
Investment objective and policies: Long-term capital growth, current income and growth of income. Invests primarily in common and preferred stock and securities convertible into common stock of well established companies. May also invest in ADRs, fixed-income securities of domestic issuers and U.S. dollar-denominated debt securities of foreign issuers. May use futures and options and hedge up to 25% of total assets.
Year organized: 1993
Ticker symbol: SSGWX
Discount broker availability: Fidelity, Siebert
Dividends paid: Income - February, May, August, November; Capital gains - October
Portfolio turnover: 36%
Largest holding: Vodafone Group PLC - Sponsored ADR (3.2%)
Management fee: 0.85%
12b-1 distribution fee: 0.08%
Expense ratio: 0.95% (year ending 8/31/94) (1.44% without waiver)

THE SEVEN SEAS SERIES INTERMEDIATE FUND

(See first Seven Seas Series listing for data common to all Seven Seas Series funds)

Portfolio manager: Dudley Hall (1993)
Investment objective and policies: High current income consistent with preservation of capital. Invests primarily in investment-grade debt securities with a weighted average maturity of 3 to 10 years. May invest in U.S. government securities, corporate debt securities of domestic and foreign issuers, mortgage- and asset-backed securities and instruments of U.S. and foreign banks. May use futures and options and hedge up to 25% of total assets.
Year organized: 1993
Discount broker availability: Fidelity, Siebert
Dividends paid: Income - February, May, August, November; Capital gains - October
Portfolio turnover: 16%
Management fee: 0.80%
12b-1 distribution fee: 0.09%
Expense ratio: 0.60% (year ending 8/31/94) (1.51% without waiver)

THE SEVEN SEAS SERIES MATRIX EQUITY FUND

(See first Seven Seas Series listing for data common to all Seven Seas Series funds)

Portfolio manager: Douglas Holmes (1992)
Investment objective and policies: Total returns that exceed the return of the S&P 500 Index. Invests primarily in common stocks selected on the basis of a proprietary analytical model. The model measures value and Wall Street sentiment to rank stocks on overall attractiveness. Up to 15% of assets may be in illiquid securities. May use futures and options and hedge up to 25% of total assets.
Year organized: 1992
Ticker symbol: SSMTX
Discount broker availability: Fidelity, Siebert
Dividends paid: Income - February, May, August, November; Capital gains - October
Portfolio turnover (2 yrs): 127%, 58%
Largest holding: Exxon Corp. (3.9%)
Management fee: 0.75%
12b-1 distribution fee: 0.06%
Expense ratio: 0.58% (year ending 8/31/94) (0.96% without waiver)

THE SEVEN SEAS SERIES MONEY MARKET FUND

(See first Seven Seas Series listing for data common to all Seven Seas Series funds)

Portfolio manager: Steve Boxer (1992)
Investment objective and policies: Maximum current income consistent with preservation of capital and liquidity. Invests in high-quality money market instruments.
Year organized: 1988
Ticker symbol: SSMXX
Dividends paid: Income - declared daily, paid monthly
Management fee: 0.25%
12b-1 distribution fee: 0.04%
Expense ratio: 0.36% (year ending 8/31/94)

THE SEVEN SEAS SERIES S&P 500 INDEX FUND

(See first Seven Seas Series listing for data common to all Seven Seas Series funds)

Portfolio manager: Ann Eisenberg (1992)
Investment objective and policies: Total returns that replicate the return of the S&P 500 Index. Invests in the stocks comprising the S&P 500 Index in proportion to their weighting in the Index (will purchase a representative sampling of the S&P 500 Index stocks if assets are too low to purchase all 500 stocks).
Year organized: 1992
Ticker symbol: SVSPX
Discount broker availability: Fidelity, Siebert
Dividends paid: Income - February, May, August, November; Capital gains - October
Portfolio turnover (2 yrs): 8%, 48%
Largest holding: General Electric Co. (2.4%)
Management fee: 0.10%
12b-1 distribution fee: 0.05%
Expense ratio: 0.15% (year ending 8/31/94) (0.25% without waiver)

THE SEVEN SEAS SERIES SHORT TERM GOVERNMENT SECURITIES FUND

(See first Seven Seas Series listing for data common to all Seven Seas Series funds)

Portfolio manager: Steve Boxer (1993)
Investment objective and policies: High current income consistent with preservation of capital and liquidity. Invests in securities issued or guaranteed by the U.S. Government or its agencies and instrumentalities with a weighted average maturity of less than 3 years.
Year organized: 1992
Ticker symbol: SVSGX
Discount broker availability: Fidelity, Siebert
Dividends paid: Income - declared daily, paid monthly; Capital gains - October
Portfolio turnover (3 yrs): 279%, 69%, 97%
Management fee: 0.50%
12b-1 distribution fee: 0.10%
Expense ratio: 0.70% (year ending 8/31/94) (0.96% without waiver)

THE SEVEN SEAS SERIES SMALL CAP FUND

(See first Seven Seas Series listing for data common to all Seven Seas Series funds)

Portfolio manager: Bob May (1994)
Investment objective and policies: Maximum total returns. Invests primarily in the stocks of domestic companies with market capitalizations of $100M to $1.5B selected using a proprietary analytical model. Up to 15% of assets may be in illiquid securities. May use ADRs of foreign issuers and futures and options and hedge up to 25% of total assets.
Year organized: 1992 (Formerly S&P Midcap Index Fund. Name and objective changed on 11/22/94. Prior performance may be misleading.)
Ticker symbol: SSMCX
Dividends paid: Income - February, May, August, November; Capital gains - October

Portfolio turnover (2 yrs): 45%, 81%
Largest holding: General Motors Class E preferred (1.9%)
Management fee: 0.75%
12b-1 distribution fee: 0.04%
Expense ratio: 0.30% (year ending 8/31/94) (0.81% without waiver)

THE SEVEN SEAS SERIES TAX FREE MONEY MARKET FUND
(See first Seven Seas Series listing for data common to all Seven Seas Series funds)

Investment objective and policies: Maximum current income exempt from federal income taxes consistent with preservation of capital and liquidity. Invests primarily in high-quality municipal money market instruments.
Year organized: 1991
Dividends paid: Income - declared daily, paid monthly
Management fee: 0.25%
12b-1 distribution fee: 0.03%

THE SEVEN SEAS SERIES U.S. GOVERNMENT MONEY MARKET FUND
(See first Seven Seas Series listing for data common to all Seven Seas Series funds)

Portfolio manager: Steve Boxer (1992)
Investment objective and policies: Maximum current income consistent with preservation of capital and liquidity. Invests exclusively in high-quality money market instruments issued by the U.S. Government, its agencies and instrumentalities.
Year organized: 1991
Ticker symbol: SSGXX
Dividends paid: Income - declared daily, paid monthly
Management fee: 0.25%
12b-1 distribution fee: 0.04%
Expense ratio: 0.38% (year ending 8/31/94) (0.39% without waiver)

THE SEVEN SEAS SERIES YIELD PLUS FUND
(See first Seven Seas Series listing for data common to all Seven Seas Series funds)

Portfolio manager: David Hertan (1994)
Investment objective and policies: Maximum current income consistent with preservation of liquidity. Invests in high-quality debt securities with a weighted average maturity of less than 3 years. May invest in U.S. Government securities, instruments of U.S. and foreign banks, debt instruments issued by U.S. and foreign corporations, securities of foreign governments and supranational organizations, asset- and mortgage-backed securities and interest rate swaps. May use futures and options and hedge up to 25% of total assets.
Year organized: 1992
Ticker symbol: SSYPX
Discount broker availability: Fidelity, Siebert
Dividends paid: Income - declared daily, paid monthly; Capital gains - October
Portfolio turnover (2 yrs): 143%, 138%
Management fee: 0.25%
12b-1 distribution fee: 0.04%
Expense ratio: 0.35% (year ending 8/31/94)

1784 FUNDS ◆
(Data common to all 1784 funds are shown below. See subsequent listings for data specific to individual 1784 funds.)

P.O. Box 1784
Wayne, PA 19087
800-252-1784, 800-355-2673

Adviser: The First National Bank of Boston
Administrator: SEI Financial Management Corp.
Custodian: The First National Bank of Boston
Transfer agent: SEI Financial Management Corp.

Minimum purchase: Initial: $1,000, Subsequent: $250; IRA/Keogh: Initial: $250
Telephone orders accepted: Yes
Wire orders accepted: Yes
Deadline for same day wire purchase: 4 P.M. (12 NN for money market funds)
Telephone redemptions: Yes
Wire redemptions: Yes, $12 fee
Letter redemptions: Signature guarantee required over $25,000
Telephone switching: With other 1784 funds
Number of switches permitted: Unlimited
Shareholder services: Keogh, IRA, 401(k), automatic investment plan—minimum $50/month (waives initial minimum), electronic funds transfer, withdrawal plan
Administration fee: 0.15% first $300M to 0.10% over $600M (for aggregate assets of all 1784 funds)
IRA/Keogh fees: Annual $15

1784 ASSET ALLOCATION FUND ◆
(See first 1784 listing for data common to all 1784 funds)

Portfolio managers: Ronald J. Clausen (1993), Jack A. Ablin (1993)
Investment objective and policies: Favorable total return - current income and capital appreciation - consistent with preservation of capital. Invests in equity securities (normally 30-70% of assets), fixed-income securities (30-60%), and money market instruments (0-40%) with allocation of assets adjusted to reflect changes in economic and market conditions. May invest up to 25% of assets in securities of foreign issuers and 15% in illiquid securities. May use futures and options to increase return and hedge.
Year organized: 1993
Qualified for sale in: CA, CO, CT, DC, FL, GA, IL, IN, KY, ME, MD, MA, MI, MN, NH, NJ, NY, NC, PA, RI, VT, VA
Dividends paid: Income - March, June, September, December; Capital gains - December
Portfolio turnover (1 yr): 28%
Largest holding: U.S. Treasury Note 6.250% due 2/15/03 (5.5%)
Management fee: 0.74%
12b-1 distribution fee: Maximum of 0.25% (not currently imposed)
Expense ratio: 1.25% (year ending 5/31/94) (3.61% without waiver)

1784 CONNECTICUT TAX-EXEMPT INCOME FUND ◆
(See first 1784 listing for data common to all 1784 funds)

Portfolio manager: James L. Rosland (1994)
Investment objective and policies: Current income exempt from federal and Connecticut state income taxes consistent with preservation of capital. Invests primarily in investment-grade Connecticut municipal securities with a weighted average maturity of 15 years or more. May invest up to 20% of assets in AMT securities and 15% in illiquid securities.
Year organized: 1994
Ticker symbol: SCTEX
Qualified for sale in: CA, CT, FL, ME, MA, NH, NY, RI, VT
Dividends paid: Income - declared daily, paid monthly; Capital gains - December
Management fee: 0.74%
12b-1 distribution fee: Maximum of 0.25% (not currently imposed)

1784 GROWTH AND INCOME FUND ◆
(See first 1784 listing for data common to all 1784 funds)

Portfolio managers: Eugene D. Takach (1993), Theodore E. Ober (1993)
Investment objective and policies: Long-term growth of capital with income secondary. Normally invests at least 65% of assets in common stocks of U.S. and foreign issuers with emphasis on sound

companies with records of growth in both earnings and dividends. May invest up to 25% of assets in securities of foreign issuers and 15% in illiquid securities. Fund may use futures and options to generate additional income and hedge.
Year organized: 1993
Ticker symbol: SEGWX
Discount broker availability: Fidelity, Siebert
Qualified for sale in: AL, AZ, CA, CO, CT, DC, FL, GA, IL, IN, KY, ME, MD, MA, MI, MN, NH, NJ, NY, NC, PA, RI, SC, TX, VT, VA
Dividends paid: Income - March, June, September, December; Capital gains - December
Portfolio turnover (1 yr): 32%
Largest holding: Home Depot (5.6%)
Management fee: 0.74%
12b-1 distribution fee: Maximum of 0.25% (not currently imposed)
Expense ratio: 0.35% (year ending 5/31/94) (1.36% without waiver)

1784 INCOME FUND ◆
(See first 1784 listing for data common to all 1784 funds)

Portfolio manager: Jack A. Ablin (1994)
Investment objective and policies: Maximum current income with preservation of capital secondary. Invests primarily in investment-grade debt securities with a weighted average maturity of 7 to 30 years. May invest up to 30% of assets in securities of foreign issuers and 15% in illiquid securities. May use futures and options to increase income and hedge.
Year organized: 1994
Ticker symbol: SEINX
Discount broker availability: Fidelity, Siebert
Qualified for sale in: CA, CT, FL, ME, MA, NH, NY, RI, VT
Dividends paid: Income - declared daily, paid monthly; Capital gains - December
Management fee: 0.74%
12b-1 distribution fee: Maximum of 0.25% (not currently imposed)

1784 MASSACHUSETTS TAX-EXEMPT INCOME FUND ◆
(See first 1784 listing for data common to all 1784 funds)

Portfolio manager: Susan A. Sanderson (1993)
Investment objective and policies: Current income exempt from federal and Massachusetts state income taxes consistent with preservation of capital. Invests primarily in investment-grade Massachusetts municipal securities with a weighted average maturity of 15 years or more. May invest up to 20% of assets in AMT securities and 15% in illiquid securities.
Year organized: 1993
Ticker symbol: SEMAX
Discount broker availability: Fidelity, Siebert
Qualified for sale in: CA, CO, CT, DC, FL, GA, IL, IN, KY, ME, MA, MN, NH, NJ, NY, NC, PA, RI, VT
Dividends paid: Income - declared daily, paid monthly; Capital gains - December
Portfolio turnover (1 yr): 14%
Management fee: 0.74%
12b-1 distribution fee: Maximum of 0.25% (not currently imposed)
Expense ratio: 0.33% (year ending 5/31/94) (1.41% without waiver)

1784 RHODE ISLAND TAX-EXEMPT INCOME FUND ◆
(See first 1784 listing for data common to all 1784 funds)

Portfolio manager: James L. Rosland (1994)
Investment objective and policies: Current income exempt from federal and Rhode Island state income taxes consistent with preservation of capital. Invests primarily in investment-grade Rhode Island municipal securities with a weighted average maturity of 15 years or more. May invest up to 20% of assets in AMT securities and 15% in illiquid securities.

Year organized: 1994
Qualified for sale in: CA, CT, FL, ME, MA, NH, NY, RI, VT
Dividends paid: Income - declared daily, paid monthly; Capital gains - December
Management fee: 0.74%
12b-1 distribution fee: Maximum of 0.25% (not currently imposed)

1784 SHORT-TERM INCOME FUND ◆
(See first 1784 listing for data common to all 1784 funds)

Portfolio manager: Mary K. Werler (1994)
Investment objective and policies: Maximum current income with preservation of capital secondary. Invests primarily in investment-grade debt securities with a weighted average maturity of 3 years or less. May invest up to 30% of assets in securities of foreign issuers and 15% in illiquid securities. May use futures and options to increase income and hedge.
Year organized: 1994
Ticker symbol: SESTX
Discount broker availability: Fidelity, Siebert
Qualified for sale in: CA, CT, FL, ME, MA, NH, NY, RI, VT
Dividends paid: Income - declared daily, paid monthly; Capital gains - December
Management fee: 0.50%
12b-1 distribution fee: Maximum of 0.25% (not currently imposed)

1784 TAX-EXEMPT MEDIUM-TERM INCOME FUND ◆
(See first 1784 listing for data common to all 1784 funds)

Portfolio manager: David H. Thompson (1993)
Investment objective and policies: Current income exempt from federal income taxes consistent with preservation of capital. Invests primarily in investment-grade municipal securities with a weighted average maturity of 3 to 10 years. May invest up to 20% of assets in AMT securities and 15% in illiquid securities and use futures and options to hedge.
Year organized: 1993
Ticker symbol: SETMX
Discount broker availability: Fidelity, Siebert
Qualified for sale in: CA, CO, CT, DC, FL, GA, IL, IN, KY, ME, MD, MA, MN, NH, NJ, NY, NC, PA, RI, TX, VT, VA
Dividends paid: Income - declared daily, paid monthly; Capital gains - December
Portfolio turnover (1 yr): 99%
Management fee: 0.74%
12b-1 distribution fee: Maximum of 0.25% (not currently imposed)
Expense ratio: 0.32% (year ending 5/31/94) (1.61% without waiver)

1784 TAX-FREE MONEY MARKET FUND ◆
(See first 1784 listing for data common to all 1784 funds)

Portfolio manager: James L. Bosland (1993)
Investment objective and policies: Current income exempt from federal income taxes consistent with preservation of principal and liquidity. Invests primarily in investment-grade municipal money market securities.
Year organized: 1993
Ticker symbol: SETXX
Qualified for sale in: AZ, CA, CO, CT, DE, DC, FL, GA, IL, IN, ME, MD, MA, MN, MO, NH, NJ, NY, NC, OH, PA, RI, TX, VT, VA
Check redemptions: $250 minimum
Confirmations mailed: After each purchase and each check, mail or wire redemption
Checks returned: Monthly
Periodic account statements mailed: Monthly
Dividends paid: Income - declared daily, paid monthly

Management fee: 0.40%
Expense ratio: 0.27% (year ending 5/31/94) (0.71% without waiver)

1784 U.S. GOVERNMENT MEDIUM-TERM INCOME FUND ◆
(See first 1784 listing for data common to all 1784 funds)

Portfolio manager: Jack A. Ablin (1993)
Investment objective and policies: Current income consistent with preservation of capital. Invests primarily in obligations issued or guaranteed as to payment of principal and interest by the U.S. Government or its agencies or instrumentalities with a weighted average maturity of 3 to 10 years. May invest substantially in mortgage-backed securities and have up to 15% of assets in illiquid securities. May use futures and options to hedge.
Year organized: 1993
Ticker symbol: SEGTX
Discount broker availability: Fidelity, Siebert
Qualified for sale in: AL, CA, CO, CT, DC, FL, GA, IL, IN, KY, ME, MD, MA, MN, NH, NJ, NY, NC, PA, RI, SC, VT, VA
Dividends paid: Income - declared daily, paid monthly; Capital gains - December
Portfolio turnover (1 yr): 145%
Management fee: 0.74%
12b-1 distribution fee: Maximum of 0.25% (not currently imposed)
Expense ratio: 0.31% (year ending 5/31/94) (1.35% without waiver)

1784 U.S. TREASURY MONEY MARKET FUND ◆
(See first 1784 listing for data common to all 1784 funds)

Portfolio manager: Mary K. Werler (1993)
Investment objective and policies: Current income consistent with preservation of principal and liquidity. Invests primarily in money market securities issued by the U.S. Treasury.
Year organized: 1993
Qualified for sale in: AL, CA, CO, CT, DC, FL, GA, IL, IN, KY, ME, MD, MA, MN, MO, NH, NJ, NY, NC, OH, PA, RI, VT, VA
Check redemptions: $250 minimum
Confirmations mailed: After each purchase and each check, mail or wire redemption
Checks returned: Monthly
Periodic account statements mailed: Monthly
Dividends paid: Income - declared daily, paid monthly
Management fee: 0.40%
Expense ratio: 0.65% (year ending 5/31/94) (6.42% without waiver)

SHORT TERM INCOME FUND - MONEY MARKET PORTFOLIO ◆
600 Fifth Avenue - 8th Floor
New York, NY 10020
212-676-5200, 800-676-6779
prices/yields 212-830-5225
fax 212-830-5476

Adviser: Reich & Tang, Inc.
Portfolio manager: Molly Flewharty (1980)
Custodian and transfer agent: Investors Fiduciary Trust Co.
Investment objective and policies: High current income, preservation of capital and maintenance of liquidity. Invests in money market obligations with maturities of one year or less.
Year organized: 1980
Ticker symbol: STIXX
Minimum purchase: Initial: $5,000, Subsequent: $100; IRA: Initial $250, Subsequent: None
Wire orders accepted: Yes
Deadline for same day wire purchase: 12 NN
Qualified for sale in: All states
Telephone redemptions: Yes
Wire redemptions: Yes, $1,000 minimum
Letter redemptions: Signature guarantee required

Telephone switching: With other Reich & Tang funds, $1,000 minimum
Number of switches permitted: Unlimited
Check redemptions: $250 minimum
Confirmations mailed: After each purchase and each check, mail or wire redemption
Checks returned: As clear
Periodic account statements mailed: Monthly
Dividends paid: Income - declared daily, paid monthly
Shareholder services: IRA, withdrawal plan, electronic funds transfer
Management fee: 0.5% first $750M to 0.45% over $1.5B
Expense ratio: 0.67% (year ending 8/31/94)
IRA fees: None

SHORT TERM INCOME FUND - U.S. GOVERNMENT PORTFOLIO ◆
600 Fifth Avenue - 8th Floor
New York, NY 10020
212-676-5200, 800-676-6779
prices/yields 212-830-5225
fax 212-830-5476

Adviser: Reich & Tang L. P.
Portfolio manager: Molly Flewharty (1982)
Custodian and transfer agent: Investors Fiduciary Trust Co.
Investment objective and policies: High current income, preservation of capital and maintenance of liquidity. Invests in obligations issued or guaranteed by the U.S. Government with maturities of one year or less or subject to repurchase within one year.
Year organized: 1982
Ticker symbol: SGVXX
Minimum purchase: Initial: $5,000, Subsequent: $100; IRA: Initial $250, Subsequent: None
Wire orders accepted: Yes
Deadline for same day wire purchase: 12 NN
Qualified for sale in: All states
Telephone redemptions: Yes
Wire redemptions: Yes, $1,000 minimum
Letter redemptions: Signature guarantee required
Telephone switching: With other Reich & Tang funds, $1,000 minimum
Number of switches permitted: Unlimited
Check redemptions: $250 minimum
Confirmations mailed: After each purchase and each check, mail or wire redemption
Checks returned: As clear
Periodic account statements mailed: Monthly
Dividends paid: Income - declared daily, paid monthly
Shareholder services: IRA, withdrawal plan, electronic funds transfer
Management fee: 0.475% first $250M to 0.43% over $1.5B
Expense ratio: 0.60% (year ending 8/31/94)
IRA fees: None

SIT FUNDS ◆
(Data common to all Sit funds are shown below. See subsequent listings for data specific to individual Sit funds.)

4600 Norwest Center
90 South 7th Street, Suite 4000
Minneapolis, MN 55402
612-334-5888, 800-332-5580
fax 612-342-2111

Shareholder service hours: Full service: M-F 8 A.M.-5 P.M. CST; After hours service: prices, prospectuses
Adviser: Sit Investment Associates, Inc.
Custodian and transfer agent: Norwest Bank Minnesota, N.A.
Minimum purchase: Initial: $2,000, Subsequent: $100; IRA/Keogh: None
Telephone orders accepted: No
Wire orders accepted: Yes
Deadline for same day wire purchase: 4 P.M.
Qualified for sale in: All states except NE (except Minnesota Tax-Free Income Fund)
Telephone redemptions: Yes
Wire redemptions: Yes, $8 fee

Letter redemptions: Signature guarantee not required
Telephone switching: With other Sit funds
Number of switches permitted: 4 per year for stock funds, unlimited for bond & money market funds
Shareholder services: Keogh, IRA, SEP-IRA, 401(k), corporate retirement plans, automatic investment plan, withdrawal plan, electronic funds transfer
IRA fees: Annual $15, Initial $5
Keogh fees: None

SIT BALANCED FUND ◆
(See first Sit listing for data common to all Sit funds)

Portfolio managers: Eugene C. Sit (1993), Douglas B. Rogers (1993)
Investment objective and policies: Long-term capital growth and current income consistent with preservation of principal. Invests in a mix of equity securities (40-60% of assets), fixed-income securities (40-60%) and money market instruments (0-20%). At least 25% of assets will be in fixed-income senior securities. Up to 25% of assets may be in junk bonds, 20% in ADRs of foreign issuers and 20% in foreign debt securities. May use futures and options to increase return and to hedge up to 15% of total assets.
Year organized: 1993
Discount broker availability: Schwab
Dividends paid: Income - March, June, September, December; Capital gains - December
Portfolio turnover (1 yr): 53%
Largest holding: GMNA due 9/15/01 (12.9%)
Management fee: 1.0%
Expense ratio: 1.00% (6 months ending 6/30/94) (includes waiver)

SIT BOND FUND ◆
(See first Sit listing for data common to all Sit funds)

Portfolio managers: Michael C. Brilley (1993), Douglas B. Rogers (1993)
Investment objective and policies: Maximum total return - income and capital growth - consistent with preservation of capital. Invests in a diverse mix of government and corporate debt securities, mortgage and other asset-backed securities and other debt instruments with a weighted average maturity of 2 to 30 years. Up to 25% of assets may be in junk bonds, 20% in non-dollar denominated securities of foreign issuers and 15% in illiquid securities. Up to 10% of assets may be in futures and options. Fund may hedge.
Year organized: 1993
Discount broker availability: Schwab
Check redemptions: $250 minimum
Dividends paid: Income - declared daily, paid monthly; Capital gains - December
Management fee: 0.8%
Expense ratio: 0.80% (4 months ending 3/31/94) (includes waiver)

SIT DEVELOPING MARKETS GROWTH FUND ◆
(See first Sit listing for data common to all Sit funds)

Sub-adviser: Sit/Kim International Investment Associates, Inc.
Portfolio manager: Andrew B. Kim (1994)
Investment objective and policies: Long term capital appreciation. Invests at least 65% of assets in equity securities - common and preferred stock, warrants and convertible securities - of companies in developing markets. May invest directly and in ADRs, EDRs and GDRs and use options on foreign securities and indices to hedge. Up to 15% of assets may be in illiquid securities.
Year organized: 1994

Dividends paid: Income - December; Capital gains - December
Management fee: 2.0%

SIT GROWTH FUND ◆
(See first Sit listing for data common to all Sit funds)

Portfolio managers: Eugene C. Sit (1981), Erik S. Anderson (1985)
Investment objective and policies: Long term capital appreciation. Invests primarily in common stocks of small and medium-size emerging-growth companies. May also invest in larger companies offering improved growth possibilities. Up to 20% of assets may be in ADRs of foreign issuers and 15% in illiquid securities.
Year organized: 1981
Ticker symbol: NBNGX
Discount broker availability: Schwab, White, Waterhouse, Fidelity, Siebert
Dividends paid: Income - December; Capital gains - December
Portfolio turnover (3 yrs): 47%, 45%, 25%
Largest holding: Oracle Systems Corp. (2.6%)
Management fee: 1.0% first $30M to 0.5% over $100M
Expense ratio: 0.82% (year ending 6/30/94)

SIT GROWTH & INCOME FUND ◆
(See first Sit listing for data common to all Sit funds)

Portfolio manager: Peter L. Mitchelson (1981)
Investment objective and policies: Long-term capital appreciation with current income secondary. Invests in equity (up to 100% of assets) and debt (up to 50%) securities, primarily dividend paying "blue chip" common stocks, convertible securities, corporate bonds, debentures and government securities. Up to 20% of assets may be in equity and debt securities of foreign issuers and 15% in illiquid securities.
Year organized: 1981 (formerly "New Beginning" Income and Growth Fund. Name changed 11/1/93)
Ticker symbol: SNIGX
Discount broker availability: Schwab, White, Waterhouse, Fidelity, Siebert
Dividends paid: Income - March, June, September, December; Capital gains - December
Portfolio turnover (3 yrs): 74%, 48%, 73%
Largest holding: United HealthCare Corp. (3.4%)
Management fee: 1.0% first $30M to 0.5% over $100M
Expense ratio: 1.10% (year ending 6/30/94) (1.40% without waiver)

SIT INTERNATIONAL GROWTH FUND ◆
(See first Sit listing for data common to all Sit funds)

Sub-adviser: Sit/Kim International Investment Associates, Inc.
Portfolio manager: Andrew B. Kim (1991)
Investment objective and policies: Long term capital appreciation. Normally invests at least 90% of assets in equity securities of issuers domiciled outside the U.S. May invest up to 50% of assets in smaller to medium sized growth companies with market capitalization of less than $2B. May have more than 25% of assets concentrated in Japan, the United Kingdom and/or Germany. May invest directly and use ADRs and EDRs. Up to 15% of assets may be in illiquid securities.
Year organized: 1991
Ticker symbol: SNGRX
Discount broker availability: Schwab, White, Fidelity, Siebert
Dividends paid: Income - December; Capital gains - December
Portfolio turnover (3 yrs): 42%, 53%, 19%
Management fee: 1.85% (manager pays all other fund expense)
Expense ratio: 1.65% (year ending 6/30/94) (1.85% without waiver)

SIT MINNESOTA TAX-FREE INCOME FUND ◆
(See first Sit listing for data common to all Sit funds)

Portfolio managers: Michael C. Brilley (1993), Debra A. Sit (1993)
Investment objective and policies: High level of current income exempt from federal and Minnesota personal income taxes, consistent with preservation of capital. Invests primarily in investment-grade Minnesota municipal bonds with weighted average maturity of 4 to 28 years. Up to 30% of assets may be in junk bonds and 20% in AMT securities
Year organized: 1993
Ticker symbol: SMTFX
Discount broker availability: Schwab
Qualified for sale in: MN
Dividends paid: Income - declared daily, paid monthly; Capital gains - December
Check redemption: $250 minimum
Management fee: 0.80%
Expense ratio: 0.80% (4 months ending 3/31/94) (includes waiver)

SIT MONEY MARKET FUND ◆
(See first Sit listing for data common to all Sit funds)

Portfolio managers: Michael C. Brilley (1985), Douglas S. Rogers (1993)
Investment objective and policies: Maximum current income consistent with preservation of capital and maintenance of liquidity. Invests in money market instruments.
Year organized: 1985 (formerly "New Beginning" Investment Reserve, a short-term bond fund. Name and objective changed 11/1/93)
Dividends paid: Income - declared daily, paid monthly
Check redemption: $250 minimum
Confirmations mailed: After each purchase and each check, mail or wire redemption
Checks returned: Monthly
Periodic account statements mailed: Monthly
Management fee: 0.80% first $50M, 0.60% over $50M
Expense ratio: 0.50% (5 months ending 6/30/94) (0.80% without waiver)

SIT SMALL CAP GROWTH FUND ◆
(See first Sit listing for data common to all Sit funds)

Portfolio manager: Eugene C. Sit (1994)
Investment objective and policies: Long term capital appreciation. Invests primarily in common stocks of small companies with market capitalizations under $500M. May invest in preferred stocks, convertible securities and warrants. Up to 20% of assets may be in ADRs of foreign issuers and 15% in illiquid securities.
Year organized: 1994
Dividends paid: Income - December; Capital gains - December
Management fee: 1.5%

SIT TAX-FREE INCOME FUND ◆
(See first Sit listing for data common to all Sit funds)

Portfolio managers: Michael C. Brilley (1985), Debra A. Sit (1988)
Investment objective and policies: High level of current income exempt from federal income tax consistent with preservation of capital. Invests primarily in investment-grade municipal bonds with weighted average maturity of 5 to 22 years. Fund may trade up to 5% of assets in options on debt securities for hedging purposes and may use financial futures contracts and options thereon to hedge against interest rate fluctuations (up to 5% of assets in margin). Up to 20% of assets may be in AMT securities.

Year organized: 1985 (formerly Sit "New Beginning" Yield Fund. Name and objective changed on September 15, 1988)
Ticker symbol: SNTIX
Discount broker availability: Schwab, White, Waterhouse, Fidelity, Siebert
Dividends paid: Income - declared daily, paid monthly; Capital gains - December
Portfolio turnover (3 yrs): 48%, 58%, 80%
Check redemption: $250 minimum
Management fee: 0.80%
Expense ratio: 0.77% (year ending 6/30/94) (includes waiver)

SIT U.S. GOVERNMENT SECURITIES FUND ◆
(See first Sit listing for data common to all Sit funds)

Portfolio managers: Michael C. Brilley (1987), Douglas S. Rogers (1991)
Investment objective and policies: High current income and safety of principal. Invests solely in debt obligations issued, guaranteed or insured by the U.S. Government, its agencies or instrumentalities with a weighted average maturity of 2 to 20 years.
Year organized: 1987
Ticker symbol: SNGVX
Discount broker availability: Schwab, White, Waterhouse, Fidelity, Siebert
Check redemptions: $250 minimum
Dividends paid: Income - declared daily, paid monthly; Capital gains - December
Portfolio turnover (3 yrs): 74%, 77%, 134%
Management fee: 1.00% first $50M, 0.80% over $50M
Expense ratio: 0.86% (year ending 6/30/94) (1.00% without waiver)

SKYLINE FUND PORTFOLIOS ◆
(Data common to all Skyline Fund portfolios are shown below. See subsequent listings for data specific to individual Skyline Fund Portfolios.)

350 North Clark Street
Chicago, IL 60610
312-670-6023, 800-458-5222

Shareholder service hours: Full service: M-F 8:45 A.M.-4:45 P.M. CST; After hours service: prices, yields
Adviser: Mesirow Asset Management, Inc.
Custodian and transfer agent: Firstar Trust Co.
Minimum purchase: Initial: $1,000, Subsequent: $100
Telephone orders accepted: No
Wire orders accepted: No
Qualified for sale in: All states
Telephone redemptions: Yes
Wire redemptions: Yes, $250 minimum, $7.50 fee
Letter redemptions: Signature guarantee required over $10,000
Telephone switching: With other Skyline Fund portfolios and Reserve Fund Primary and Government portfolios
Number of switches permitted: 5 per year, 15 day hold
Shareholder services: IRA
IRA fees: Annual $12.50, Closing $15.00

SKYLINE FUND - EUROPE PORTFOLIO ◆
(Merged into Skyline Fund Special Equities II on 12/23/94)

SKYLINE FUND - MONTHLY INCOME PORTFOLIO ◆
(Merged into Van Kampen Merritt High Yield Fund Class A Shares, a load fund, on 6/3/94)

SKYLINE FUND - SPECIAL EQUITIES PORTFOLIO ◆
(See first Skyline listing for data common to all Skyline Fund portfolios)
Portfolio manager: William M. Dutton (1987)
Investment objective and policies: Maximum capi-

tal appreciation. Invests in common stocks believed undervalued with emphasis on small companies with market capitalizations under $400M.
Year organized: 1987
Ticker symbol: SKSEX
Special sales restrictions: Fund closed to new shareholders on 12/11/92 and to additional investments by existing shareholders on 3/22/93.
Dividends paid: Income - December; Capital gains - July, December
Portfolio turnover (3 yrs): 104%, 87%, 104%
Largest holding: American Income Holdings, Inc. (2.5%)
Management fee: 1.5% first $200M to 1.35% over $600M (covers all normal operating expenses)
Expense ratio: 1.48% (year ending 12/31/93)

SKYLINE FUND - SPECIAL EQUITIES II ◆
(See first Skyline listing for data common to all Skyline Fund portfolios)

Portfolio manager: Kenneth S. Kailin (1993)
Investment objective and policies: Maximum capital appreciation. Invests in common stocks believed undervalued with emphasis on small and medium-sized companies with market capitalizations of $400 to $2B.
Year organized: 1993
Ticker symbol: SPEQX
Discount broker availability: *Schwab, *White, *Waterhouse, *Fidelity, *Siebert
Dividends paid: Income - December; Capital gains - July, December
Portfolio turnover (1 yr): 111%
Largest holding: HealthTrust, Inc. (3.1%)
Management fee: 1.5% first $200M to 1.35% over $600M (covers all normal operating expenses)
Expense ratio: 1.51% (11 months ending 12/31/93)

SMITH BARNEY MONEY FUNDS
(Data common to all Smith Barney Money Fund portfolios are shown below. See subsequent listing for data specific to individual Smith Barney portfolios.)

388 Greenwich Street
New York, NY 10013
212-723-9218, 800-223-7078

Adviser: Mutual Management Corp., a subsidiary of Smith Barney, Harris, Upham & Co.
Portfolio manager: Tom Rivoir (1991)
Custodian: PNC Bank, N.A.
Transfer agent: TSSG, Inc.
Wire orders accepted: Yes
Deadline for same day wire purchase: 12 NN
Qualified for sale in: All states
Telephone redemptions: Yes
Wire redemptions: Yes
Letter redemptions: Signature guarantee required
Dividends paid: Income: declared daily, paid monthly
Shareholder services: Keogh, IRA, SEP-IRA, corporate retirement plans, 403(b), withdrawal plan min. req. $5,000
12b-1 distribution fee: 0.10%
IRA fees: Annual $2.50, Initial $5, Closing $5 before 59 1/2
Keogh fees: Annual $10 or $5, Closing $5 before 59 1/2

SMITH BARNEY MONEY FUNDS - CASH PORTFOLIO
(See first Smith Barney listing for data common to all Smith Barney portfolios)

Investment objective and policies: Maximum current income and preservation of capital from a portfolio of various high quality, short-term money market instruments.
Year organized: 1974 (name changed from National Liquid Reserves - Cash Portfolio on 6/6/91)
Ticker symbol: SBCXX
Minimum purchase: Initial: $1,000, Subsequent: $50; IRA/Keogh: Initial: $250, Subsequent: $100

Check redemptions: $500 minimum
Checks returned: As clear
Periodic account statements mailed: Monthly
Management fee: 0.45% first $6B to 0.35% over $18B
Expense ratio: 0.64% (year ending 12/31/93)

SMITH BARNEY MONEY FUNDS - GOVERNMENT PORTFOLIO
(See first Smith Barney listing for data common to all Smith Barney portfolios)

Investment objective and policies: Maximum current income and preservation of capital from a portfolio of U.S. Government money market obligations and related repurchase and reverse repurchase agreements.
Year organized: 1984 (name changed from National Liquid Reserves - Government Portfolio on 6/6/91)
Ticker symbol: SBGXX
Minimum purchase: Initial: $1,000, Subsequent: $50; IRA/Keogh: Initial: $250, Subsequent: $100
Check redemptions: $500 minimum
Checks returned: As clear
Periodic account statements mailed: Monthly
Management fee: 0.45% first $2.5B to 0.35% over $5B
Expense ratio: 0.61% (year ending 12/31/93)

SMITH BARNEY MONEY FUNDS - RETIREMENT PORTFOLIO
(See first Smith Barney listing for data common to all Smith Barney portfolios)

Investment objective and policies: Maximum current income and preservation of capital from a portfolio of various high quality, short-term money market instruments.
Year organized: 1984 (name changed from National Liquid Reserves - Retirement Portfolio on 6/6/91)
Special sales restrictions: Offered exclusively to retirement plans administered through Smith Barney brokerage accounts
Minimum purchase: Initial: $200, Subsequent: $1
Management fee: 0.45% first $1B to 0.35% over $2B
Expense ratio: 0.70% (year ending 12/31/93)

SMITH BARNEY MUNICIPAL MONEY MARKET FUND
(See first Smith Barney listing for data common to all Smith Barney portfolios)

Investment objective and policies: Income exempt from federal income tax from a portfolio of high quality short-term municipal obligations selected for liquidity and stability of principal.
Year organized: 1981 (name changed from The Tax Free Money Fund to Smith Barney Tax Free Money Fund in 1991 and to current in 1994)
Ticker symbol: SBTXX
Minimum purchase: Initial: $1,000, Subsequent: $50
Check redemptions: $500 minimum
Checks returned: As clear
Periodic account statements mailed: monthly
Management fee: 0.50% first $2B to 0.45% over $5B
Expense ratio: 0.62% (year ending 3/31/93)

SMITH BREEDEN FUNDS ◆
(Data common to all Smith Breeden funds are shown below. See subsequent listings for data specific to individual Smith Breeden funds.

100 Europa Drive, Suite 200
Chapel Hill, NC 27514
919-967-7221, 800-221-3138
fax 919-933-3157

Adviser: Smith Breeden Associates, Inc.
Custodian: National Westminster Bank, NJ
Transfer agent: Fund/Plan Services, Inc.

Minimum purchase: Initial: $1,000, Subsequent: $50
Telephone orders accepted: Yes, subsequent only
Wire orders accepted: Yes
Deadline for same day wire purchase: 4 P.M.
Qualified for sale in: All states
Telephone redemptions: Yes
Wire redemptions: Yes, $1,000 minimum, $9 fee
Letter redemptions: Signature guarantee required over $25,000
Telephone switching: With other Smith Breeden funds
Number of switches permitted: Unlimited, $8 fee
Deadline for same day switch: 4 P.M.
Shareholder services: Keogh, IRA, automatic investment plan—minimum $50 per month (waives initial minimum), electronic funds transfer (purchase only), withdrawal plan min. req. $10,000
Management fee: 0.70%
IRA fees: Annual $12

SMITH BREEDEN INTERMEDIATE DURATION U.S. GOVERNMENT SERIES ◆
(See first Smith Breeden listing for data common to all Smith Breeden funds)

Portfolio manager: Daniel C. Dektar (1992)
Investment objective and policies: Total return in excess of the major market indices for mortgage-backed securities. Invests at least 70% of assets in fixed-income securities issued or guaranteed by the U.S. Government or its agencies and instrumentalities. Fund hedges.
Year organized: 1992
Ticker symbol: SBIDX
Dividends paid: Income - Monthly; Capital gains - June, December
Portfolio turnover (2 yrs): 84%, 42%
Expense ratio: 0.00% (year ending 3/31/94) (1.30% without waiver)

SMITH BREEDEN MARKET TRACKING FUND ◆
(See first Smith Breeden listing for data common to all Smith Breeden funds)

Portfolio manager: John B. Sprow (1992)
Investment objective and policies: Total return approximating the performance of the S&P 500. Invests primarily in equity swap contracts with major commercial banks and S&P futures contracts. May also invest in fixed-income securities issued or guaranteed by the U.S. Government, its agencies or instrumentalities, and mortgage-backed securities. Fund hedges.
Year organized: 1992
Dividends paid: Income - March, June, September, December; Capital gains - March, December
Portfolio turnover (2 yrs): 119%, 271%
Expense ratio: 0.90% (year ending 3/31/94) (7.08% without waiver)

SMITH BREEDEN SHORT DURATION U.S. GOVERNMENT SERIES ◆
(See first Smith Breeden listing for data common to all Smith Breeden funds)

Portfolio manager: Daniel C. Dektar (1992)
Investment objective and policies: High current income excess of the major market indices for mortgage-backed securities. Invests at least 70% of assets in fixed-income securities issued or guaranteed by the U.S. Government or its agencies and instrumentalities with volatility and NAV similar to a portfolio that invest exclusively in six-month Treasury securities on a constant maturity basis. Fund hedges.
Year organized: 1992
Ticker symbol: SBSHX
Dividends paid: Income - Monthly; Capital gains - June, December
Portfolio turnover (2 yrs): 112%, 3%
Expense ratio: 0.29% (year ending 3/31/94) (0.45% without waiver)

SMITH HAYES TRUST
(Data common to all Smith Hayes portfolios are shown below. See subsequent listings for data specific to individual Smith Hayes portfolios.)

500 Centre Terrace
1225 L Street
Lincoln, NE 68508
402-476-3000, 800-279-7437
fax 402-476-6909

Shareholder service hours: Full service: M-F 8 A.M.-5 P.M. CST
Adviser: Smith Hayes Portfolio Management, Inc.
Custodian: Union Bank & Trust Co., Lincoln, NE
Transfer agent: Smith Hayes Portfolio Management, Inc.
Minimum purchase: Initial: $500 per portfolio, Subsequent: None (Minimum total initial investment in combined Trust portfolios $1,000)
Telephone orders accepted: No
Wire orders accepted: Yes
Deadline for same day wire purchase: 11:30 A.M. (12 NN for money market funds)
Letter redemptions: Signature guarantee required
Telephone switching: With other Smith Hayes Trust portfolios
Number of switches permitted: Unlimited
Deadline for same day switch: 4 P.M.
Shareholder services: Withdrawal plan min. req. $5,000

SMITH HAYES ASSET ALLOCATION PORTFOLIO
(See first Smith Hayes listing for data common to all Smith Hayes portfolios)

Sub-adviser: Renaissance Investment Management, Inc.
Portfolio manager: Don Kennedy (1988)
Investment objective and policies: Total return and preservation of capital. Invests in undervalued stocks, bonds, and money market instruments with allocations among those investments based on the proprietary Capital Return Time formula.
Year organized: 1988
Qualified for sale in: CO, MN, NE, TX
Dividends paid: Income: June, December; Capital gains: December
Portfolio turnover (3 yrs): 118%, 41%, 19%
Largest holding: U.S. Treasury Note due 2/15/04 (16.8%)
Management and administration fee: 1.1875%
12b-1 distribution fee: 0.5%
Expense ratio: 1.96% (year ending 6/30/94)

SMITH HAYES BALANCED PORTFOLIO
(See first Smith Hayes listing for data common to all Smith Hayes portfolios)

Sub-adviser: Swanson Capital Management, Inc.
Portfolio manager: Stephen A. Swanson (1988)
Investment objective and policies: Current income and capital appreciation consistent with conservation of principal. Invests in equity and fixed-income securities and cash or money market instruments. The mix will be determined on the basis of existing and anticipated market conditions, using a combination of fundamental and technical factors. No more than 65% of assets will be in equity securities
Year organized: 1988
Qualified for sale in: CO, MN, NE, TX
Dividends paid: Income: June, December; Capital gains: December
Portfolio turnover (3 yrs): 24%, 25%, 41%
Largest holding: U.S. Treasury Note due 11/15/99 (18.8%)
Management and administration fee: 1.1875%
12b-1 distribution fee: 0.5%
Expense ratio: 1.91% (year ending 6/30/94)

SMITH HAYES CONVERTIBLE PORTFOLIO
(See first Smith Hayes listing for data common to all Smith Hayes portfolios)

Sub-adviser: Calamos Asset Management, Inc.
Portfolio manager: John P. Calamos (1988)

Investment objective and policies: Preservation of capital while maximizing total return. Invests in convertible corporate debt securities and/or convertible preferred stock (normally at least 65%). Up to 20% of assets may be in non-convertible income-producing securities and up to 15% in warrants. Fund may hedge with put and call options on underlying stocks, index options, and limited offsetting short sales.
Year organized: 1988
Qualified for sale in: CO, MN, NE
Dividends paid: Income: June, December; Capital gains: December
Portfolio turnover (3 yrs): 66%, 70%, 96%
Largest holding: Ford Motor Company preferred stock (3.8%)
Management and administration fee: 1.1875%
12b-1 distribution fee: 0.5%
Expense ratio: 2.06% (year ending 6/30/94)

SMITH HAYES GOVERNMENT/QUALITY BOND PORTFOLIO
(See first Smith Hayes listing for data common to all Smith Hayes portfolios)

Sub-adviser: Bear Stearns Asset Management, Inc.
Portfolio manager: Richard Rosen (1988)
Investment objective and policies: Income and capital appreciation consistent with preservation of capital. Invests solely in U.S. Government securities, repurchases agreements on U.S. Government securities, and corporate bonds rated Aa or better by Moody or AA or better by S&P. Normally at least 65% of assets will be invested in Government securities. Weighted average maturity will not exceed 10 years.
Year organized: 1988
Qualified for sale in: CO, MN, NE
Dividends paid: Income: June, December; Capital gains: December
Portfolio turnover (3 yrs): 218%, 176%, 508%
Management and administration fee: 0.7875%
12b-1 distribution fee: 0.4%
Expense ratio: 1.37% (year ending 6/30/94)

SMITH HAYES MONEY MARKET PORTFOLIO
(See first Smith Hayes listing for data common to all Smith Hayes portfolios)

Investment objective and policies: Maximum current income consistent with preservation of capital and liquidity. Invests in high quality money market instruments with a weighted average maturity of 90 days or less.
Year organized: 1992
Qualified for sale in: CO, MN, NE
Wire redemptions: Yes, $5,000 minimum
Dividends paid: Income: declared daily, paid monthly
Management and administration fee: 0.22%
12b-1 distribution fee: 0.7%
Expense ratio: 1.17% (year ending 6/30/94)

SMITH HAYES SMALL CAP PORTFOLIO
(See first Smith Hayes listing for data common to all Smith Hayes portfolios)

Sub-adviser: Crestone Capital Management, Inc.
Portfolio manager: Kirk, McCown (1992)
Investment objective and policies: Long-term capital appreciation. Invests primarily in stocks of companies with market capitalizations between $50M and $2B (majority of companies in the $350M-$600M range) showing above average growth, trading at low price/earnings ratios compared to the S&P 500, and exhibiting financial strength.
Year organized: 1992
Qualified for sale in: CO, MN, NE
Largest holding: TCF Financial Corp. (4.3%)
Dividends paid: Income: June, December; Capital gains: December
Portfolio turnover (2 yrs): 75%, 48%
Management and administration fee: 1.1875%
12b-1 distribution fee: 0.5%
Expense ratio: 1.91% (year ending 6/30/94)

SMITH HAYES VALUE PORTFOLIO
(See first Smith Hayes listing for data common to all Smith Hayes portfolios)

Sub-adviser: Cashman, Farrell & Associates
Portfolio manager: John Thompson (1989)
Investment objective and policies: Maximum total return - capital gains and current income. Invests primarily in securities with low price/earnings ratios relative to S&P 500 following extended price declines and/or under performance. Holding periods are expected to range from one to three years with turnover rate less than 100%.
Year organized: 1989 (name changed from Opportunity Portfolio in 1993)
Qualified for sale in: CO, MN, NE
Dividends paid: Income: June, December; Capital gains: December
Portfolio turnover (3 yrs): 68%, 62%, 114%
Largest holding: Ingersoll-Rand Co. (2.7%)
Management and administration fee: 1.1875%
12b-1 distribution fee: 0.5%
Expense ratio: 1.98% (year ending 6/30/94)

SOUND SHORE FUND ◆
61 Broadway, Suite 2770
New York, NY 10006
207-879-0001, 800-551-1980
fax 207-879-6206

Adviser: Sound Shore Management, Inc.
Administrator: Forum Financial Services, Inc.
Portfolio managers: Henry Burn III (1985), T. Gibbs Kane, Jr. (1985)
Custodian: First National Bank of Boston
Transfer agent: Forum Financial Corp.
Investment objective and policies: Growth of capital with current income secondary. Invests primarily in common stocks of companies believed undervalued. Up to 10% of assets may be in securities of other investment companies.
Year organized: 1985
Ticker symbol: SSHFX
Minimum purchase: Initial: $10,000, Subsequent: None; IRA: Initial: $250
Telephone orders accepted: No
Wire orders accepted: Yes
Deadline for same day wire purchase: 4 P.M.
Discount broker availability: Schwab, *White
Qualified for sale in: All states
Letter redemptions: Signature guarantee required
Telephone switching: With Forum Daily Assets Treasury Fund and Forum bond funds which have loads
Number of switches permitted: Unlimited
Dividends paid: Income: June, December; Capital gains: December
Portfolio turnover (3 yrs): 76%, 91%, 88%
Largest holding: Mellon Bank Corp. (3.7%)
Shareholder services: IRA, withdrawal plan min. req. $20,000
Management fee: 0.75%
Administration fee: 0.25%
12b-1 distribution fee: Yes (not currently imposed)
Expense ratio: 1.22% (year ending 12/31/94)
IRA fees: Annual $10

SOUTHEASTERN ASSET MANAGEMENT FUNDS ◆
(See Longleaf Partners funds)

SPECIAL PORTFOLIOS - CASH PORTFOLIO ◆
P.O. Box 64284
St. Paul, MN 55164
612-738-4000, 800-800-2638
fax 612-738-0996

Adviser: Fortis Advisers, Inc.
Portfolio manager: Dennis Ott (1989)
Custodian: Norwest Bank of Minnesota, N.A.
Transfer agent: Fortis Advisers, Inc.
Investment objective and policies: High level of current income consistent with stability and liquidity. Invests primarily in debt securities rated Baa or higher by Moody's or BBB or higher by S&P with

remaining maturities of 25 months or less. May invest up to 25% of assets in Canadian debt securities and up to 10% in other foreign debt securities.
Special sales restrictions: Available to employees or others associated with the St. Paul Companies and affiliates, and to employees of Jostens Inc.
Year organized: 1989
Ticker symbol: SPCSX
Minimum purchase: Initial: $500, Subsequent: $50
Telephone orders accepted: By broker-dealer only, $500 minimum
Wire orders accepted: Yes, $500 minimum
Deadline for same day wire purchase: 4 P.M.
Qualified for sale in: All states
Telephone redemptions: Yes, $10,000 maximum
Wire redemptions: Yes, $1,000 minimum
Letter redemptions: Signature guarantee not required
Telephone switching: With Stock Portfolio and Fortis funds, some of which are load
Number of switches permitted: 4 round trips per year
Dividends paid: Income - March, June, September, December; Capital gains - December
Portfolio turnover (3 yrs): 58%, 29%, 69%
Shareholder services: Keogh, IRA, SEP-IRA, 401(k), 403(b), corporate retirement plans, automatic investment plan (waives initial minimum), electronic funds transfer (purchase only), withdrawal plan min. req. $4,000
Management fee: 0.3% first $500M, 0.25% over $500M
Expense ratio: 0.42% (year ending 10/31/94) (0.52% without waiver)
IRA fees: Annual $10, Closing $7, Distributions $1 to $7
Keogh fees: Annual $30, Initial $15, Closing $10, Distributions $1 to $10

SPECIAL PORTFOLIOS - STOCK PORTFOLIO ◆
P.O. Box 64284
St. Paul, MN 55164
612-738-4000, 800-800-2638
fax 612-738-0996

Adviser: Fortis Advisers, Inc.
Portfolio manager: Stephen M. Poling (1985)
Custodian: Norwest Bank of Minnesota, N.A.
Transfer agent: Fortis Advisers, Inc.
Investment objective and policies: Appreciation of capital and capital gains. Invests in common stocks and securities convertible into common stocks, primarily of growth companies. May invest in listed and unlisted securities and in foreign as well as domestic securities. Fund is normally fully invested.
Special sales restrictions: Available to employees or others associated with the St. Paul Companies and affiliates, and to employees of Jostens Inc.
Year organized: 1965 (formerly AMEV Special Fund, Inc.)
Ticker symbol: AMSLX
Minimum purchase: Initial: $500, Subsequent: $50
Telephone orders accepted: By broker-dealer only, $500 minimum
Wire orders accepted: Yes, $500 minimum
Deadline for same day wire purchase: 1 P.M.
Qualified for sale in: All states
Telephone redemptions: Yes, $10,000 maximum
Wire redemptions: Yes, $1,000 minimum
Letter redemptions: Signature guarantee not required
Telephone switching: With Cash Portfolio and Fortis funds, some of which are load
Number of switches permitted: 4 round trips per year
Dividends paid: Income - December; Capital gains - December
Portfolio turnover (3 yrs): 26%, 37%, 38%
Largest holding: Oracle Systems Corp. (4.7%)
Shareholder services: Keogh, IRA, SEP-IRA, 401(k), 403(b), corporate retirement plans, automatic investment plan (waives initial minimum), electronic funds transfer (purchase only), withdrawal plan min. req. $4,000
Management fee: 1.00% first $100M to 0.75% over $250M
Expense ratio: 1.15% (year ending 10/31/94)

IRA fees: Annual $10, Closing $7, Distributions $1 to $7
Keogh fees: Annual $30, Initial $15, Closing $10, Distributions $1 to $10

STAGECOACH FUNDS
(Data common to all Stagecoach funds are shown below. See subsequent listings for data specific to individual Stagecoach funds.)

c/o Stagecoach Shareholder Services
Wells Fargo Bank, N.A.
P.O. Box 7033
San Francisco, CA 94120
800-222-8222

Adviser: Wells Fargo Bank, N.A.
Administrator: Stephens Inc.
Custodian and transfer agent: Wells Fargo Bank, N.A.
Minimum purchase: Initial: $1,000, Subsequent $100; Keogh: Initial $250
Telephone orders accepted: No
Wire orders accepted: Yes, $1,000 minimum
Deadline for same day wire purchase: 4 P.M. (12 NN for money market funds)
Qualified for sale in: All states
Telephone redemptions: Yes
Wire redemptions: Yes, $5,000 minimum
Letter redemptions: Signature guarantee required over $5,000
Telephone switching: With other Stagecoach funds (all except those listed in the directory have loads)
Number of switches permitted: Unlimited
Shareholder services: Keogh, IRA, automatic investment plan, withdrawal plan min. req. $10,000
IRA fees: None
Keogh fees: Annual $50, Initial $75

STAGECOACH CALIFORNIA TAX-FREE MONEY MARKET FUND
(See first Stagecoach listing for data common to all Stagecoach funds)

Portfolio managers: Laura Milner (1992), Jill Levy (1992)
Investment objective and policies: High income exempt from federal income taxes and California personal income taxes consistent with preservation of capital and liquidity. Invests primarily in California municipal money market instruments. May invest up to 20% of assets in taxable money market instruments.
Year organized: 1992
Ticker symbol: SGCXX
Dividends paid: Income - declared daily, paid monthly
Management fee: 0.50%
Administration fee: 0.03%
12b-1 distribution fee: 0.05%
Expense ratio: 0.55% (year ending 12/31/93) (1.06% without waiver)

STAGECOACH CORPORATE STOCK FUND
(See first Stagecoach listing for data common to all Stagecoach funds)

Investment objective and policies: To approximate to the extent practicable the total rate of return of the S&P 500 Composite Price Index. Invests in the same stocks in substantially the same percentages as the Index.
Year organized: 1984
Ticker symbol: SFCSX
Dividends paid: Income - March, June, September, December; Capital gains - December
Portfolio turnover (3 yrs): 5%, 4%, 4%
Management fee: 0.50% first $250M to 0.30% over $500M
Administration fee: 0.03%
12b-1 distribution fee: 0.05%
Expense ratio: 0.97% (year ending 12/31/93) (0.99% without waiver)

STAGECOACH LIFEPATH FUNDS
(See first Stagecoach listing for data common to all Stagecoach funds)

Investment objective and policies: To provide long-term investors with an asset allocation strategy designed to maximize assets for retirement, or substantial initial withdrawals, in a specific year. Fund invest in equity securities, debt securities and money market instruments with allocation dependent on anticipated initial withdrawal year. Within each category of investment each fund invests in a representative sample of securities contained in major indices (stock or bond) to achieve returns similar to the indices. Over time the composition of each LifePath fund will become more conservative as it gets closer to the target year for initial withdrawal by shareholders.
Portfolios: There are currently five LifePath funds. The normal allocation for the LifePath 2000 Fund is equities (20%), debt securities (70%) and cash equivalents (10%). For each of the other funds the comparable distribution is as follows: LifePath 2010 (30%, 60%, 10%), LifePath 2020 (40%, 50%, 10%), LifePath 2030 (70%, 30%, 0%), LifePath 2040 (100%, 0%, 0%)
Year organized: 1994
Ticker symbols: STWRX (2000), STNRX (2010), STTRX (2020), STHRX (2030), STFRX (2040)
Discount broker availability: *Schwab (only though financial advisers)
Dividends paid: Income - March, June, September, December; Capital gains - December
Management fee: 0.55%
Administration fee: 0.10%
12b-1 distribution fee: 0.25%

STAGECOACH MONEY MARKET FUND
(See first Stagecoach listing for data common to all Stagecoach funds)

Portfolio managers: Ray Wong (1992), Scott Smith (1992)
Investment objective and policies: High current income consistent with preservation of capital and liquidity. Invests in high-quality money market instruments.
Year organized: 1992
Ticker symbol: STGXX
Dividends paid: Income - declared daily, paid monthly
Management fee: 0.40%
Administration fee: 0.10%
12b-1 distribution fee: 0.05%
Expense ratio: 0.58% (year ending 12/31/93) (1.00% without waiver)

STATE FARM FUNDS ◆
(Data common to all State Farm funds are shown below. See subsequent listings for data specific to individual State Farm funds.)

One State Farm Plaza
Bloomington, IL 61710
309-766-2029, prices 800-447-0740

Shareholder service hours: Full service: M-F 8 A.M.-4:15 P.M. CST; After hours service: prices
Adviser: State Farm Investment Mngt. Corp.
Custodian: Peoples Bank of Bloomington
Transfer agent: State Farm Investment Mngt. Corp.
Special sales restrictions: Offered only to agents and employees of State Farm Insurance Companies and their families.
Minimum purchase: Initial: $50, Subsequent: $50 (except Municipal Bond)
Telephone orders accepted: No
Wire orders accepted: No
Qualified for sale in: All states
Telephone redemptions: Yes
Wire redemptions: Yes, $2,500 minimum, $7.50 fee
Letter redemptions: Signature guarantee required over $50,000
Telephone switching: With other State Farm funds
Number of switches permitted: Unlimited

Shareholder services: IRA, Keogh, withdrawal plan min. req. $5,000
IRA fees: Annual $1
Keogh fees: None

STATE FARM BALANCED FUND ◆
(See first State Farm listing for data common to all State Farm funds)

Portfolio manager: Kurt G. Moser (1991)
Investment objective and policies: Long-term growth of principal and income. Invests in common stocks (up to 75% of assets), preferred stocks and bonds with proportions varying according to market conditions. May invest up to 25% of assets in securities of foreign issuers.
Year organized: 1967
Ticker symbol: STFBX
Dividends paid: Income - June, December; Capital gains - December
Portfolio turnover (3 yrs): 4%, 4%, 4%
Largest holding: Archer Daniels Midland (3.3%)
Management fee: 0.2% first $100M to 0.1% over $200M
Expense ratio: 0.17% (year ending 11/30/94)

STATE FARM GROWTH FUND ◆
(See first State Farm listing for data common to all State Farm funds)

Portfolio manager: Kurt G. Moser (1991)
Investment objective and policies: Long-term growth of capital and income. Invests primarily in income producing equity-type securities. Remainder of assets may be in fixed-income securities such as U.S. Government obligations, investment-grade bonds and debentures, preferred stocks and in foreign securities not traded in the U.S.
Year organized: 1967
Ticker symbol: STFGX
Dividends paid: Income - June, December; Capital gains - December
Portfolio turnover (3 yrs): 3%, 2%, 2%
Largest holding: Archer Daniels Midland (5.9%)
Management fee: 0.2% first $100M to 0.1% over $200M
Expense ratio: 0.14% (year ending 11/30/94)

STATE FARM INTERIM FUND ◆
(See first State Farm listing for data common to all State Farm funds)

Portfolio manager: Kurt G. Moser (1991)
Investment objective and policies: High yield with relative price stability. Invests in high quality debt securities, government and corporate, with short (less than 5 years) and intermediate term (5 to 15 years) maturities.
Year organized: 1977
Ticker symbol: SFITX
Dividends paid: Income - declared daily, paid March, June, September, December; Capital gains - December
Portfolio turnover (3 yrs): 15%, 15%, 15%
Management fee: 0.2% first $50M to 0.1% over $100M
Expense ratio: 0.22% (year ending 11/30/94)

STATE FARM MUNICIPAL BOND FUND ◆
(See first State Farm listing for data common to all State Farm funds)

Portfolio manager: Kurt G. Moser (1991)
Investment objective and policies: Income exempt from federal income tax consistent with prudent investment management. Invests primarily in long term municipal bonds including revenue bonds with individual maturities of 1 to 15 years. Majority of investments will have maturities longer than 5 years. Up to 30% of assets may be in lower-rated or non-rated municipal securities.
Year organized: 1977
Ticker symbol: SFBDX
Minimum purchase: Initial: $1,000, Subsequent: $500

Dividends paid: Income - declared daily, paid March, June, September, December; Capital gains - December
Portfolio turnover (3 yrs): 8%, 5%, 4%
Management fee: 0.2% first $50M to 0.1% over $100M
Expense ratio: 0.16% (year ending 11/30/94)

STEADMAN FUNDS
(Data common to all Steadman funds are shown below. See subsequent listing for data specific to individual Steadman funds.)

1730 K Street, NW, Suite 904
Washington, DC 20006
202-223-1000, 800-424-8570

Adviser: Steadman Security Corp.
Portfolio manager: Charles Steadman (1991)
Custodian: National Bank of Washington
Transfer agent: Steadman Security Corp.
Special sales restrictions: At press time only the Steadman Associated fund was open to new shareholders. The other funds were seeking SEC approval to re-register and reopen for sale.
Minimum purchase: Initial: $500, Subsequent: $25
Telephone orders accepted: No
Wire orders accepted: No
Deadline for same day wire purchase: 4 P.M.
Qualified for sale in: All states
Telephone redemptions: Yes
Wire redemption: Yes, $10,000 minimum
Letter redemptions: Signature guarantee required over $10,000
Telephone switching: With other Steadman funds
Number of switches permitted: Unlimited
Shareholder services: Keogh, IRA, 401(k), withdrawal plan min. req. $10,000
Management fee: 1% first $35M to 0.75% over $70M
12b-1 distribution plan: Up to 0.25%
IRA/Keogh fees: Annual $5, Initial $5, Closing $3.50

STEADMAN AMERICAN INDUSTRY FUND
(See first Steadman listing for data common to all Steadman funds)

Investment objective and policies: Long-term capital growth through investment in common stocks. Income is secondary. Fund buys call options and leverages.
Year organized: 1959
Ticker symbol: SAMRX
Dividends paid: Income - April; Capital gains - annually
Portfolio turnover (3 yrs): 134%, 460%, 239%
Expense ratio: 12.66% (year ending 1/31/94)

STEADMAN ASSOCIATED FUND
(See first Steadman listing for data common to all Steadman funds)

Investment objective and policies: Income commensurate with reasonable risk, long-term capital growth is secondary consideration. Fund leverages. Invests in bonds and stocks.
Year organized: 1939
Ticker symbol: SASSX
Dividends paid: Income - March, June, September, December; Capital gains - annually
Portfolio turnover (3 yrs): 300%, 268%, 87%
Expense ratio: 7.76% (year ending 9/30/94)

STEADMAN INVESTMENT FUND
(See first Steadman listing for data common to all Steadman funds)

Investment objective and policies: Long-term capital appreciation, income is secondary consideration. Invests primarily in common stocks, leverages.
Year organized: 1956
Ticker symbol: SINVX
Dividends paid: Income - March; Capital gains - annually

Portfolio turnover (3 yrs): 179%, 245%, 144%
Expense ratio: 6.48% (year ending 12/31/93)

STEADMAN TECHNOLOGY & GROWTH FUND
(See first Steadman listing for data common to all Steadman funds)

Investment objective and policies: Capital appreciation. Invests at least 80% of assets in common stocks of companies which are primarily engaged in matters related to the ocean environment and companies expected to benefit from technological advances in scientifically related fields. Fund leverages.
Year organized: 1968 (name changed from Steadman Oceanographic, Technology & Growth Fund in 1993)
Ticker symbol: SOCNX
Dividends paid: Income - March; Capital gains - annually
Portfolio turnover (3 yrs): 128%, 318%, 184%
Expense ratio: 11.94% (year ending 12/31/93)

STEINROE FUNDS ◆
(Data common to all SteinRoe funds are shown below. See subsequent listings for data specific to individual SteinRoe funds.)

P.O. Box 804058
Chicago, IL 60680
312-368-7800, 800-338-2550
fax 312-368-5631

Shareholder service hours: Full service: M-F 7 A.M.-7 P.M. CST; After hours service: prices, yields, balances, orders, last transaction, news, DJIA, total returns
Adviser: Stein Roe & Farnham
Custodian: State Street Bank & Trust Co.
Transfer agent: SteinRoe Services, Inc.
Minimum purchase: Initial: $2,500, Subsequent: $100; IRA/Keogh: Initial: $500, Subsequent: $50 (except Limited Maturity Income)
Telephone orders accepted: No
Wire orders accepted: Yes
Deadline for same day wire purchase: 4 P.M.
Qualified for sale in: All states
Telephone redemptions: Yes, $1,000 minimum
Wire redemptions: Yes, $1,000 minimum, $3.50 fee
Letter redemptions: Signature guarantee required over $50,000
Telephone switching: With other Stein Roe funds
Number of switches permitted: 4 round trips per year
Shareholder services: Keogh, IRA, SEP-IRA, corporate retirement plans, automatic investment plan—minimum $50/month (reduced initial minimum to $1,000), directed dividends, withdrawal plan min. req. $10,000; electronic funds transfer
IRA fees: Annual $12, Closing $5
IRA/Keogh fees: Annual $12, $50 set-up fee

STEINROE CAPITAL OPPORTUNITIES FUND ◆
(See first SteinRoe listing for data common to all SteinRoe funds)

Portfolio managers: Gloria J. Santella (1989)
Investment objective and policies: Long-term capital appreciation. Invests in stocks of both seasoned and smaller companies with above-average earnings growth rates that may benefit from new products or services, technological developments or changes in management. May invest in ADRs without limit and have up to 25% of assets in foreign securities and 35% in debt securities, including junk bonds. May use futures and options to increase revenue and/or hedge.
Year organized: 1963
Ticker symbol: SRFCX
Discount broker availability: *Schwab, *White, *Waterhouse, *Fidelity, *Siebert
Dividends paid: Income - December; Capital gains - December

Portfolio turnover (3 yrs): 46%, 55%, 46%
Largest holding: Gartner Group, Inc. (3.6%)
Management fee: 0.75%
Expense ratio: 0.97% (year ending 9/30/94)

STEINROE CASH RESERVES ◆
(See first SteinRoe listing for data common to all SteinRoe funds)

Portfolio manager: Jane M. Naeseth (1980)
Investment objective and policies: Maximum current income consistent with preservation of capital and liquidity. Invests in high quality dollar denominated money market instruments.
Year organized: 1976
Ticker symbol: STCXX
Check redemptions: $50 minimum
Confirmations mailed: After each purchase and each check, mail or wire redemption
Checks returned: Monthly
Periodic account statements mailed: Quarterly
Dividends paid: Income - declared daily, paid monthly
Management fee: 0.5% first $1B to 0.45% over $1.5B
Expense ratio: 0.79% (year ending 6/30/94)

STEINROE GOVERNMENT INCOME FUND ◆
(See first SteinRoe listing for data common to all SteinRoe funds)

Portfolio manager: Michael T. Kennedy (1988)
Investment objective and policies: High current income. Normally invests at least 80% of assets in securities issued or guaranteed by the U.S. Government or its agencies and instrumentalities, including Treasury bills, notes and bonds. Remainder of assets may be in other types of debt securities, including collateralized mortgage obligations. May use futures and options to increase revenue and/or hedge.
Year organized: 1986 (formerly Steinroe Governments Plus before April 1990)
Ticker symbol: SRGPX
Discount broker availability: *Schwab, *White, *Waterhouse, *Fidelity, *Siebert
Dividends paid: Income - declared daily, paid monthly; Capital gains - December
Portfolio turnover (3 yrs): 167%, 170%, 139%
Management fee: 0.60% first $100M, 0.55% over $100M
Expense ratio: 0.98% (year ending 6/30/94)

STEINROE GOVERNMENT RESERVES ◆
(See first SteinRoe listing for data common to all SteinRoe funds)

Portfolio manager: Jane M. Naeseth (1982)
Investment objective and policies: Maximum current income consistent with safety of capital and liquidity. Invests in money market securities issued or guaranteed by the U.S. Government, and repurchase agreements thereon.
Year organized: 1982
Ticker symbol: SGRXX
Check redemptions: $50 minimum
Confirmations mailed: After each purchase and each check, mail or wire redemption
Checks returned: Monthly
Periodic account statements mailed: Quarterly
Dividends paid: Income - declared daily, paid monthly
Management fee: 0.5%
Expense ratio: 0.70% (year ending 6/30/94) (0.75% without waiver)

STEINROE GROWTH STOCK FUND ◆
(See first SteinRoe listing for data common to all SteinRoe funds)

Sub-adviser: Adviser's Capital Management Group
Portfolio managers: Kenneth W. Corba (1984), Eric P. Gustafson (1992)
Investment objective and policies: Long-term capi-

tal appreciation. Invests primarily in common stocks and other equity type securities. May invest in ADRs without limit and have up to 25% of assets in foreign securities and 35% in investment-grade debt securities. May use futures and options to increase revenue and/or hedge.
Year organized: 1958 (formerly SteinRoe Stock, name changed 2/1/95)
Ticker symbol: SRFSX
Discount broker availability: *Schwab, *White, *Waterhouse, *Fidelity, *Siebert
Dividends paid: Income - December; Capital gains - December
Portfolio turnover (3 yrs): 27%, 29%, 23%
Largest holding: The Gillette Co. (4.4%)
Management fee: 0.75% first $250M to 0.60% over $500M
Expense ratio: 0.94% (year ending 9/30/94)

STEINROE HIGH-YIELD MUNICIPALS ◆
(See first SteinRoe listing for data common to all SteinRoe funds)

Portfolio manager: Jane McCart (1995)
Investment objective and policies: High current income exempt from federal income tax. Invests primarily in long-term medium- or lower-quality municipal securities bearing a high rate of interest income. May invest 100% of assets in AMT securities. May use futures and options to increase revenue and/or hedge.
Year organized: 1984
Ticker symbol: SRMFX
Discount broker availability: *Schwab, *White, *Waterhouse, *Fidelity, *Siebert
Dividends paid: Income - declared daily, paid monthly; Capital gains - December
Portfolio turnover (3 yrs): 36%, 75%, 88%
Management fee: 0.6% first $100M to 0.5% over $200M
Expense ratio: 0.76% (year ending 6/30/94)

STEINROE INCOME FUND ◆
(See first SteinRoe listing for data common to all SteinRoe funds)

Portfolio manager: Ann H. Benjamin (1990)
Investment objective and policies: High current income. Invests primarily in medium-quality debt securities. May also invest in higher-quality securities and have up to 40% of assets in junk bonds. May invest in preferred and common stocks and foreign and municipal securities. May invest in ADRs without limit and have 25% of assets in foreign securities. May use futures and options to increase revenue and/or hedge.
Year organized: 1986 (formerly SteinRoe High-Yield Bond Fund)
Ticker symbol: SRHBX
Discount broker availability: *Schwab, *White, *Waterhouse, *Fidelity, *Siebert
Portfolio turnover (3 yrs): 53%, 39%, 76%
Dividends paid: Income - declared daily, paid monthly; Capital gains - December
Management fee: 0.65% first $100M, 0.60% over $100M
Expense ratio: 0.82% (year ending 6/30/94) (0.83% without waiver)

STEINROE INTERMEDIATE BOND FUND ◆
(See first SteinRoe listing for data common to all SteinRoe funds)

Portfolio manager: Michael T. Kennedy (1988)
Investment objective and policies: High current income consistent with preservation of capital. Invests at least 60% of assets in corporate debt securities with the three highest ratings of Moody's or S&P including securities issued or guaranteed by the U.S. Government or its agencies and instrumentalities, commercial paper and bank obligations. May invest in ADRs without limit and have 25% of assets in foreign securities. Up to 35% of assets may be in junk bonds. May use futures and options

to increase revenue and/or hedge. Fund maintains a weighted average maturity of 3 to 10 years.
Year organized: 1978 (formerly SteinRoe Managed Bonds)
Ticker symbol: SRBFX
Discount broker availability: *Schwab, *White, *Waterhouse, *Fidelity, *Siebert
Dividends paid: Income - declared daily, paid monthly; Capital gains - December
Portfolio turnover (3 yrs): 206%, 214%, 202%
Management fee: 0.5%
Expense ratio: 0.70% (year ending 6/30/94)

STEINROE INTERMEDIATE MUNICIPAL BOND FUND ◆
(See first SteinRoe listing for data common to all SteinRoe funds)

Portfolio manager: Joanne T. Costopoulas (1991)
Investment objective and policies: High current income exempt from federal income tax consistent with preservation of capital. Invests primarily in intermediate-term municipal bonds with a weighted average maturity of 3 to 10 years. At least 75% of assets will be in municipal securities within the 3 highest ratings. Up to 100% of assets may be in AMT securities. May use futures and options to increase revenue and/or hedge.
Year organized: 1985
Ticker symbol: SRIMX
Discount broker availability: *Schwab, *White, *Waterhouse, *Fidelity, *Siebert
Dividends paid: Income - declared daily, paid monthly; Capital gains - December
Portfolio turnover (3 yrs): 55%, 96%, 109%
Management fee: 0.6% first $100M to 0.5% over $200M
Expense ratio: 0.71% (year ending 6/30/94)

STEINROE INTERNATIONAL FUND ◆
(See first SteinRoe listing for data common to all SteinRoe funds)

Sub-adviser: Rockefeller & Co.
Portfolio managers: Bruno Bertocci (1994), David Harris (1994)
Investment objective and policies: Long-term capital growth. Invests primarily in stocks and other equity securities of both seasoned and smaller companies from at least three countries outside the U.S. Up to 35% of assets may be in investment-grade debt securities. May use futures and options to increase revenue and/or hedge.
Year organized: 1994
Ticker symbol: SRITX
Discount broker availability: *Schwab, *White, *Fidelity, *Siebert
Dividends paid: Income - December; Capital gains - December
Portfolio turnover (1 yr): 48%
Largest holding: Yizheng Chemical Fibre Co. (3.1%)
Management fee: 1.0%
Expense ratio: 1.61% (7 months ending 9/30/94)

STEINROE LIMITED MATURITY INCOME FUND ◆
(See first SteinRoe listing for data common to all SteinRoe funds)

Portfolio manager: Lisa N. Wilhelm (1993)
Investment objective and policies: High current income consistent with preservation of capital. Invests primarily in securities issued or guaranteed by the U.S. Government or its agencies and instrumentalities, including Treasury bills, notes and bonds and other high-quality fixed-income securities with a weighted average maturity of 3 years or less. May use futures and options to increase revenue and/or hedge.
Year organized: 1993
Ticker symbol: SRLIX
Minimum purchase: Initial: $10,000, Subsequent: $100; IRA/Keogh: Subsequent: $50
Discount broker availability: *Schwab, *White, *Fidelity, *Siebert

Dividends paid: Income - declared daily, paid monthly; Capital gains - December
Portfolio turnover (1 yr): 122%
Management fee: 0.60% first $100M to 0.50% over $200M
Expense ratio: 0.45% (year ending 6/30/94) (1.14% without waiver)

STEINROE MANAGED MUNICIPALS ◆
(See first SteinRoe listing for data common to all SteinRoe funds)

Portfolio manager: M. Jane McCart (1991)
Investment objective and policies: High income exempt from federal income tax consistent with preservation of capital. Invests primarily in long-term municipal securities with maturities generally longer than 10 years. At least 75% of assets will be in municipal securities within the 3 highest ratings. Up to 100% of assets may be in AMT securities. May use futures and options to increase revenue and/or hedge.
Year organized: 1976 (formerly Tax-Exempt Bond Fund)
Ticker symbol: SRMMX
Discount broker availability: *Schwab, *White, *Waterhouse, *Fidelity, *Siebert
Dividends paid: Income - declared daily, paid monthly; Capital gains - December
Portfolio turnover (3 yrs): 36%, 63%, 94%
Management fee: 0.6% first $100M to 0.45% over $1B
Expense ratio: 0.65% (year ending 6/30/94)

STEINROE MUNICIPAL MONEY FUND ◆
(See first SteinRoe listing for data common to all SteinRoe funds)

Portfolio manager: Jill K. Netzel (1994)
Investment objective and policies: Maximum current income exempt from federal income tax consistent with stability of principal and liquidity. Invests primarily in short-term municipal money market securities.
Year organized: 1983 (name changed from Tax-Exempt Money Fund in October 1992)
Ticker symbol: STEXX
Check redemptions: $50 minimum
Confirmations mailed: After each purchase and each check, mail or wire redemption
Checks returned: Monthly
Periodic account statements mailed: Quarterly
Dividends paid: Income - declared daily, paid monthly
Management fee: 0.5%
Expense ratio: 0.70% (year ending 6/30/94)

STEINROE PRIME EQUITIES ◆
(See first SteinRoe listing for data common to all SteinRoe funds)

Portfolio managers: Robert A. Christensen (1994), Millie Hurwitz (1994)
Investment objective and policies: Growth of capital. Invests primarily in common stocks, convertible securities and other equity-type investments of companies with market capitalizations of $1B or more. May invest in ADRs without limit and have up to 25% of assets in foreign securities and 35% in investment-grade debt securities. May use futures and options to increase revenue and/or hedge.
Year organized: 1987
Ticker symbol: SRPEX
Discount broker availability: *Schwab, *White, *Waterhouse, *Fidelity, *Siebert
Dividends paid: Income - February, May, August, December; Capital gains - December
Portfolio turnover (3 yrs): 85%, 50%, 40%
Largest holding: Microsoft Corp. (2.2%)
Management fee: 0.6% first $100M to 0.5% over $200M
Expense ratio: 0.90% (year ending 9/30/94)

STEINROE SPECIAL FUND ◆
(See first SteinRoe listing for data common to all SteinRoe funds)

Portfolio managers: E. Bruce Dunn (1991), Richard B. Peterson (1991)
Investment objective and policies: Capital appreciation. Invests in stocks of seasoned and new companies, securities with limited marketability and securities of companies which will benefit from management change, new product or service development, or change in demand. Seeks above-average growth stocks with limited downside risk due to being seasoned, under-followed or out of favor. May invest in ADRs without limit and have up to 25% of assets in foreign securities and up to 35% in debt securities including junk bonds. May use futures and options to increase revenue and/or hedge.
Year organized: 1968
Ticker symbol: SRSPX
Discount broker availability: *Schwab, *White, *Waterhouse, *Fidelity, *Siebert
Dividends paid: Income - December; Capital gains - December
Portfolio turnover (3 yrs): 58%, 42%, 40%
Largest holding: The Olsten Corp. (3.1%)
Management fee: 0.75%
Expense ratio: 0.96% (year ending 9/30/94)

STEINROE SPECIAL VENTURE FUND ◆
(See first SteinRoe listing for data common to all SteinRoe funds)

Portfolio managers: E. Bruce Dunn (1994), Richard B. Peterson (1994)
Investment objective and policies: Capital appreciation. Invests primarily in stocks of entrepreneurally managed companies that represent special opportunities and have market capitalizations under $3B. May invest in ADRs without limit and have up to 25% of assets in foreign securities. May use futures and options to increase revenue and/or hedge.
Year organized: 1994
Discount broker availability: *Schwab, *Fidelity, *Siebert
Dividends paid: Income - December; Capital gains - December
Management fee: 0.90%

STEINROE TOTAL RETURN FUND ◆
(See first SteinRoe listing for data common to all SteinRoe funds)

Portfolio manager: Robert A. Christensen (1981)
Investment objective and policies: Current income and capital appreciation to achieve maximum total return consistent with reasonable risk. Invests in a combination of equity, convertible and fixed-income securities. Ordinarily will maintain no more than 75% of assets in common stocks. May invest in ADRs without limit and have up to 25% of assets in foreign securities. May use futures and options to increase revenue and/or hedge.
Year organized: 1949 (formerly Stein Roe & Farnham Balanced Fund)
Ticker symbol: SRFBX
Discount broker availability: *Schwab, *White, *Waterhouse, *Fidelity, *Siebert
Dividends paid: Income - February, May, August, December; Capital gains - December
Portfolio turnover (3 yrs): 29%, 53%, 59%
Management fee: 0.625% first $100M, 0.5% over $100M
Expense ratio: 0.83% (year ending 9/30/94)

STEINROE YOUNG INVESTOR FUND ◆
(See first SteinRoe listing for data common to all SteinRoe funds)

Portfolio managers: Lawson E. Whitesides, Jr. (1994), Kenneth W. Corba (1994), Daniel K. Cantor (1994)
Investment objective and policies: Long-term capital appreciation. Invests primarily in common stocks and other equity type securities with long-term appreciation potential. May invest in ADRs without limit and have up to 25% of assets in for-

eign securities and 35% in investment-grade debt securities. May use futures and options to increase revenue and/or hedge. Fund also seeks to educate its shareholders by providing materials regarding personal finance and investing as well as materials on the fund and its portfolio holdings.
Year organized: 1994
Ticker symbol: SRYIX
Discount broker availability: *Schwab, *White
Dividends paid: Income - December; Capital gains - December
Management fee: 0.75% first $250M to 0.60% over $500M

STRATTON FUNDS ◆
(Data common to all Stratton funds are shown below. See subsequent listings for data specific to individual Stratton funds.)

Plymouth Meeting Executive Campus
610 W. Germantown Pike, Suite 300
Plymouth Meeting, PA 19462
610-941-0255, 800-634-5726

Shareholder service hours: Full service: M-F 9 A.M.-7 P.M. EST; After hours service: prices
Adviser: Stratton Management Co.
Custodian: Bank of New York
Transfer agent: Fund/Plan Services, Inc.
Telephone orders accepted: No
Wire orders accepted: Yes
Deadline for same day wire purchase: 4 P.M.
Letter redemptions: Signature guarantee required over $5,000
Telephone switching: With other Stratton funds and Investors Cash Reserve Fund
Number of switches permitted: Unlimited (fund monitors)
Shareholder services: Keogh, IRA, 403(b), corporate retirement plans, automatic investment plan, electronic funds transfer, withdrawal plan min. req. $10,000
IRA/Keogh fees: Annual $12

STRATTON GROWTH FUND ◆
(See first Stratton listing for data common to all Stratton funds)

Portfolio managers: James W. Stratton (1972), John Affleck (1979)
Investment objective and policies: Growth of capital with current income secondary. Invests primarily in quality, value-oriented, domestic common stocks and securities convertible into common stock, and other equity securities. May invest in REITs.
Year organized: 1972
Ticker symbol: STRGX
Minimum purchase: Initial: $2,000, Subsequent: $100; IRA/Keogh: None
Discount broker availability: Schwab, White
Qualified for sale in: All states except AL, AK, AR, ID, IA, LA, MO, MT, NH, NM, ND, OK, SD, UT, VT
Dividends paid: Income - July, December; Capital gains - July, December
Portfolio turnover (3 yrs): 50%, 35%, 60%
Largest holding: Sturm, Ruger & Co., Inc. (4.7%)
Management fee: 0.75%
Expense ratio: 1.34% (year ending 5/31/94)

STRATTON MONTHLY DIVIDEND SHARES ◆
(See first Stratton listing for data common to all Stratton funds)

Newspaper listing: StratDv
Portfolio managers: James W. Stratton (1980), Gerard E. Heffernan (1980)
Investment objective and policies: High dividend and interest income. Invests primarily in common stock and securities convertible into common stock. Invests at least 25% of assets in public utility companies in electric, gas, energy, water and telephone

fields. May invest in REITs.
Year organized: 1971 (formerly Energy & Utility Shares, a fund that was closed-end until 1981)
Ticker symbol: STMDX
Minimum purchase: Initial: $2,000, Subsequent: $100; IRA/Keogh: None
Discount broker availability: Schwab, White, Waterhouse, Fidelity, Siebert
Qualified for sale in: All states
Dividends paid: Income - monthly, Capital gains - March, December
Portfolio turnover (3 yrs): 19%, 36%, 44%
Largest holding: Northeast Utilities (5.5%)
Management fee: 0.625%
Expense ratio: 0.99% (year ending 1/31/94)

STRATTON SMALL-CAP YIELD FUND ◆
(See first Stratton listing for data common to all Stratton funds)

Portfolio managers: James W. Stratton (1993), Frank H. Reichel (1993)
Investment objective and policies: Dividend income and capital appreciation. Invests primarily in common stock and securities convertible into common stock of companies with market capitalizations under $500M that pay quarterly dividends at an above-average rate. May invest in REITs.
Year organized: 1993
Ticker symbol: STSCX
Minimum purchase: Initial: $5,000 ($500 until fund has 2,000 shareholders), Subsequent: $100; IRA/Keogh: None
Discount broker availability: Schwab
Qualified for sale in: All states except AK, AR, ID, MT, NH, ND, OK, SD, VT
Dividends paid: Income - March, June, September, December, Capital gains - December
Portfolio turnover (1 yr): 29%
Largest holding: The Vigoro Corp. (2.4%)
Management fee: 0.75% plus performance fee of +/- 0.50% relative to Russell 2000 Index over 24 months
Expense ratio: 2.28% (year ending 3/31/94)

STRATUS FUND PORTFOLIOS ◆
(Data common to all Stratus portfolios are shown below. See subsequent listings for data specific to individual Stratus portfolios.)

500 Centre Terrace
1225 L Street
Lincoln, NE 68508
402-476-3000, 800-279-7437
fax 402-476-6909

Adviser: Union Bank and Trust Co.
Custodian: Union Bank & Trust Co., Lincoln, NE
Transfer agent: Smith Hayes Portfolio Management, Inc.
Minimum purchase: Initial: $1,000, Subsequent: None; IRA/Keogh: Initial: None
Telephone orders accepted: No
Wire orders accepted: Yes
Deadline for same day wire purchase: 4 P.M.
Qualified for sale in: NE
Letter redemptions: Signature guarantee required
Telephone switching: With other Stratus portfolios
Number of switches permitted: Unlimited
Deadline for same day switch: 4 P.M.
Shareholder services: Withdrawal plan min. req. $5,000

STRATUS FUND - CAPITAL APPRECIATION PORTFOLIO ◆
(See first Stratus listing for data common to all Stratus portfolios)

Investment objective and policies: Capital appreciation. Invests at least 65% of assets in common stocks and securities convertible into common stock of companies believed to have above average growth potential. May also invest in U.S. Government securities, repurchase agreements,

options for hedging purposes and money market instruments.
Year organized: 1993
Dividends paid: Income - June, December; Capital gains - December
Portfolio turnover (2 yrs): 9%, 4%
Largest holding: Intel Corp. (3.6%)
Management fee: 1.40% +/- up to 1.40% based on performance relative to the S&P 500
Expense ratio: 2.13% (year ending 6/30/94) (2.28% without waiver)

STRATUS FUND - EQUITY INCOME PORTFOLIO ◆
(See first Stratus listing for data common to all Stratus portfolios)

Investment objective and policies: Capital appreciation and income. Invests at least 65% of assets in common stock or securities convertible to common stock and at least 65% of assets in equity securities yielding dividends and/or interest bearing securities convertible into common stock. Invests primarily in companies with market capitalization of $500M or more with debt to capital ratios of 60% or lower. Fund hedges.
Year organized: 1993
Dividends paid: Income - June, December; Capital gains - December
Portfolio turnover (1 yr): 10%
Largest holding: General Electric Co. (5.1%)
Management fee: 0.50%
Expense ratio: 0.76% (9 months ending 6/30/94) (0.91% without waiver)

STRATUS FUND - GOVERNMENT SECURITIES PORTFOLIO ◆
(See first Stratus listing for data common to all Stratus portfolios)

Investment objective and policies: Current income consistent with the preservation of capital. Invests at least 80% of assets in securities issued or guaranteed by the U.S. Government, its agencies or instrumentalities and the remainder in debt obligations rated A or better by Moody's or S&P. Fund maintains a weighted average maturity of 3 to 7 years.
Year organized: 1993
Portfolio turnover (1 yr): 17%
Dividends paid: Income - monthly; Capital gains - December
Management fee: 0.50%
Expense ratio: 0.74% (9 months ending 6/30/94) (0.89% without waiver)

STRATUS FUND - GROWTH/INCOME PORTFOLIO ◆
(Fund liquidated on 4/29/94)

STRATUS FUND - INTERMEDIATE GOVERNMENT BOND PORTFOLIO ◆
(See first Stratus listing for data common to all Stratus portfolios)

Investment objective and policies: Current income, some or all of which is exempt from state income tax, consistent with the preservation of capital. Invests at least 80% of assets in securities issued or guaranteed by the U.S. Government, its agencies and instrumentalities with remainder in debt obligations rated A or better by Moody's or S&P. Fund maintains a weighted average maturity of 3 to 10 years.
Year organized: 1991
Dividends paid: Income - monthly; Capital gains - December
Portfolio turnover (3 yrs): 21%, 32%, 206%
Management fee: 0.75%
Expense ratio: 1.05% (year ending 6/30/94) (1.20% without waiver)

STRONG FUNDS ◆
(Data common to all Strong funds are shown below. See subsequent listings for data specific to individual Strong funds.)

One Hundred Heritage Reserve
P.O. Box 2936
Milwaukee, WI 53201
414-359-1400, 800-368-1030
800-368-1030
Prices/yields 800-234-3863
TDD 800-999-2780, fax 414-359-0802

Shareholder service hours: Full service: Sun-Sat 24 hours
Adviser: Strong Capital Management, Inc.
Custodian: Firstar Trust Co. (exceptions noted)
Transfer agent: Strong Capital Management, Inc.
Telephone orders accepted: No
Wire orders accepted: Yes
Deadline for same day wire purchase: 4 P.M.
Qualified for sale in: All states
Telephone redemptions: Yes, $500 minimum
Wire redemptions: Yes, $500 minimum, $10 fee
Letter redemptions: Signature guarantee required over $25,000
Telephone switching: With other Strong funds
Number of switches permitted: 5 per year, 3 per quarter
Shareholder services: Keogh, IRA, SEP-IRA, 401(k), 403(b), automatic investment plan—minimum $50/month (waives initial minimum), withdrawal plan min. req. $5,000; electronic funds transfer
IRA/Keogh fees: Annual $10 (waived for retirement accounts with assets exceeding $25,000 among all Strong funds)

STRONG ADVANTAGE FUND ◆
(See first Strong listing for data common to all Strong funds)

Portfolio manager: Jeffrey A. Koch (1991)
Investment objective and policies: High current income consistent with minimum fluctuation of principal. Invests in high-quality money market instruments and longer-term fixed-income securities with a weighted averaged maturity of 90 days to 1 year. May invest up to 25% of assets in securities of foreign issuers and use futures and options to hedge.
Year organized: 1988
Ticker symbol: STADX
Minimum purchase: Initial: $1,000, Subsequent: $50; IRA/Keogh: Initial: $250
Discount broker availability: *Schwab, White, *Waterhouse, *Fidelity, *Siebert
Check redemptions: $500 minimum
Dividends paid: Income - declared daily, paid monthly; Capital gains - December
Portfolio turnover (3 yrs): 305%, 316%, 503%
Management fee: 0.6%
Expense ratio: 0.9% (year ending 12/31/93)

STRONG AMERICAN UTILITIES FUND ◆
(See first Strong listing for data common to all Strong funds)

Sub-adviser: W. H. Reaves & Co.
Portfolio manager: William H. Reaves (1993)
Investment objective and policies: Current income and capital appreciation. Invests primarily in equity securities of domestic "public utility companies" (companies that engage in the manufacture, production, generation, transmission, sale and/or distribution of water, gas and electric energy), and companies engaged in the communications field excluding public broadcasting companies. Up to 25% of assets may be in equity securities of energy companies and 35% in securities of foreign issuers. May use futures and options to increase return and hedge. Fund is non-diversified.
Year organized: 1993
Ticker symbol: SAMUX
Minimum purchase: Initial: $1,000, Subsequent: $50; IRA/Keogh: Initial: $250

Discount broker availability: *Schwab, White, *Waterhouse, *Fidelity, *Siebert
Dividends paid: Income - March, June, September, December; Capital gains - December
Portfolio turnover (2 yrs): 105%, 179%
Largest holding: Ameritech Corp. (11.2%)
Management fee: 0.75%
Expense ratio: 0.5% (year ending 12/31/94) (1.6% without waiver)

STRONG ASIA PACIFIC FUND ◆
(See first Strong listing for data common to all Strong funds)

Portfolio manager: Anthony L.T. Cragg (1994)
Custodian: Brown Brothers Harriman & Co.
Investment objective and policies: Capital appreciation. Invests primarily in equity securities of issuers located in Asia or the Pacific Basin. Up to 35% of assets may be in equity and investment-grade debt securities of issuers located elsewhere around the world, including the U.S. and 15% in illiquid securities. May use foreign currency transactions, futures and options and hedge up to 25% of total assets.
Year organized: 1994
Ticker symbol: SASPX
Minimum purchase: Initial: $1,000, Subsequent: $50; IRA/Keogh: Initial: $250
Discount broker availability: *Schwab, White, *Fidelity, *Siebert
Dividends paid: Income - March, June, September, December; Capital gains - December
Largest holding: Lend Lease Corporation, Ltd. (2.4%)
Management fee: 1.0%

STRONG ASSET ALLOCATION FUND ◆
(See first Strong listing for data common to all Strong funds)

Portfolio managers: Bradley C. Tank (1993), Jay N. Mueller (1992), Andrew C. Stephens (1993)
Investment objective and policies: Income and capital appreciation which produces highest total return consistent with preservation of capital. Invests in common stocks, preferred stocks and debt securities. Fund is balanced, with investments in equity type securities not exceeding 65% of total assets. Normal distribution of assets is 40% equity securities, 40% bonds, and 20% short-term fixed-income securities. Allocation will vary depending on market and economic conditions. Up to 25% of assets may be in securities of foreign issuers.
Year organized: 1981 (name changed from Strong Investment Fund in 1994)
Ticker symbol: STIFX
Minimum purchase: Initial: $250, Subsequent: $50
Discount broker availability: *Schwab, White, *Waterhouse, *Fidelity, *Siebert
Dividends paid: Income - March, June, September, December; Capital gains - December
Portfolio turnover (3 yrs): 360%, 348%, 320%
Largest holding: Citicorp Floating Rate Notes 6.500% due 5/1/04 (2.2%)
Management fee: 0.85% first $35M, 0.80% over $35M
Expense ratio: 1.2% (year ending 12/31/94)

STRONG COMMON STOCK FUND ◆
(See first Strong listing for data common to all Strong funds)

Portfolio managers: Richard T. Weiss (1991), Marina T. Carlson (1993)
Investment objective and policies: Capital appreciation. Designed for employee benefit plan investment needs, including a "fully-invested" position at all times. Invests in the common stocks of small and medium-sized companies and other equity-type securities. Normally invests at least 80% of assets in common stocks. May invest up to 25% in securities of foreign issuers.

Year organized: 1989
Ticker symbol: STCSX
Special sales restrictions: Closed to new shareholders on 3/19/93
Minimum purchase: Initial: $1,000, Subsequent: $50; IRA/Keogh: Initial: $250
Discount broker availability: Schwab, White, Waterhouse
Dividends paid: Income - March, June, September, December; Capital gains - December
Portfolio turnover (3 yrs): 83%, 81%, 292%
Largest holding: The United States Shoe Corp. (1.6%)
Management fee: 1.0%
Expense ratio: 1.3% (year ending 12/31/94)

STRONG DISCOVERY FUND ◆
(See first Strong listing for data common to all Strong funds)

Portfolio manager: Richard S. Strong (1987)
Investment objective and policies: Capital appreciation. Invests primarily in equity securities of smaller capitalization emerging growth companies. May invest up to 100% of assets in debt securities when they offer potential for capital appreciation. Fund will, to a substantial degree, engage in trading operations based upon short-term market considerations. May invest up to 25% of assets in securities of foreign issuers. May use futures and options to increase return and hedge and sell short against the box.
Year organized: 1987
Ticker symbol: STDIX
Minimum purchase: Initial: $1,000, Subsequent: $50; IRA/Keogh: Initial: $250
Discount broker availability: *Schwab, White, *Waterhouse, *Fidelity, *Siebert
Dividends paid: Income - March, June, September, December; Capital gains - December
Portfolio turnover (3 yrs): 606%, 668%, 1259%
Largest holding: Metallgesellschaft AG (3.1%)
Management fee: 1.0%
Expense ratio: 1.5% (year ending 12/31/94)

STRONG GOVERNMENT SECURITIES FUND ◆
(See first Strong listing for data common to all Strong funds)

Portfolio manager: Bradley C. Tank (1990)
Investment objective and policies: High current income . Invests at least 80% of assets in U.S. Government securities with remainder in other investment-grade fixed-income securities. May use futures and options to increase return and hedge.
Year organized: 1986
Ticker symbol: STVSX
Minimum purchase: Initial: $1,000, Subsequent: $50; IRA/Keogh: Initial: $250
Discount broker availability: *Schwab, White, *Waterhouse, *Fidelity, *Siebert
Check redemptions: $500 minimum
Dividends paid: Income - declared daily, paid monthly; Capital gains - December
Portfolio turnover (3 yrs): 521%, 629%, 293%
Management fee: 0.6%
Expense ratio: 0.8% (year ending 12/31/93) (1.0% without waiver)

STRONG GROWTH FUND ◆
(See first Strong listing for data common to all Strong funds)

Portfolio manager: Ronald C. Ognar (1994)
Investment objective and policies: Capital appreciation. Normally invests at least 65% of assets in equity securities believed to have above-average growth prospects. Up to 25% of assets may be in securities of foreign issuers and 35% in investment-grade debt securities. May use forward currency contracts, futures and options to increase total return and hedge and sell short against the box.
Year organized: 1994

Ticker symbol: SGROX
Minimum purchase: Initial: $1,000, Subsequent: $50; IRA/Keogh: Initial: $250
Discount broker availability: *Schwab, White, *Waterhouse, *Fidelity, *Siebert
Dividends paid: Income - March, June, September, December; Capital gains - December
Largest holding: Alco Standard Corp. (2.4%)
Management fee: 1.0%
Portfolio turnover: (1 yr.) 385%
Expense ratio: 1.6% (year ending 12/31/94)

STRONG HIGH-YIELD MUNICIPAL BOND FUND ◆
(See first Strong listing for data common to all Strong funds

Portfolio managers: Thomas J. Conlin (1993), Mary Kay H. Bourbulas (1993)
Investment objective and policies: High current income exempt from federal income taxes. Invests primarily in medium and lower ("junk bond") quality long-term municipal securities with a weighted average maturity of 10 years or more. May invest in AMT securities without limit and use futures and options to increase return and hedge.
Year organized: 1993
Ticker symbol: SHYLX
Minimum purchase: Initial: $2,500, Subsequent: $50
Discount broker availability: *Schwab, *Waterhouse, *Fidelity, *Siebert
Check redemptions: $500 minimum
Dividends paid: Income - declared daily, paid monthly; Capital gains - December
Management fee: 0.60%

STRONG INCOME FUND ◆
(See first Strong listing for data common to all Strong funds)

Portfolio manager: Jeffrey A. Koch (1992)
Investment objective and policies: High current income. Invests primarily in investment-grade fixed-income securities. Up to 35% of assets may be in dividend-paying common stocks, 25% in securities of foreign issuers and 25% in junk bonds. Common stocks will be primarily utilities. May use futures and options to increase return and hedge.
Year organized: 1985
Ticker symbol: SRNCX
Discount broker availability: *Schwab, White, *Waterhouse, *Fidelity, *Siebert
Minimum purchase: Initial: $1,000, Subsequent: $50; IRA/Keogh: Initial: $250
Check redemptions: $500 minimum
Dividends paid: Income - declared daily, paid monthly; Capital gains - December
Portfolio turnover (3 yrs): 666%, 557%, 392%
Management fee: 0.625%
Expense ratio: 1.1% (year ending 12/31/93)

STRONG INSURED MUNICIPAL BOND FUND ◆
(See first Strong listing for data common to all Strong funds

Portfolio manager: Thomas J. Conlin (1991), Mary Kay H. Bourbulas (1991)
Investment objective and policies: High current income exempt from federal income taxes consistent with preservation of capital. Invests primarily in high-quality municipal securities with at least 65% of assets insured as to payment of principal and interest. Fund maintains a weighted average maturity of 15 to 25 years. May invest in AMT securities without limit and use futures and options to increase return and hedge.
Year organized: 1991
Ticker symbol: STIMX
Minimum purchase: Initial: $2,500, Subsequent: $50
Discount broker availability: *Schwab, White, *Waterhouse, *Fidelity, *Siebert

Check redemptions: $500 minimum
Dividends paid: Income - declared daily, paid monthly; Capital gains - December
Portfolio turnover (2 yrs): 111%, 290%
Management fee: 0.50%
Expense ration: 0.6% (year ending 12/31/93)

STRONG INTERNATIONAL BOND FUND ◆
(See first Strong listing for data common to all Strong funds)

Portfolio manager: Shirish Malekar (1994)
Custodian: Brown Brothers Harriman & Co.
Investment objective and policies: High total return - capital appreciation and income. Invests primarily in investment-grade corporate and government debt securities of foreign issuers from at least three countries other than the U.S. with a weighted average maturity of 4 to 9 years. Up to 20% of assets may be in junk bonds.
Year organized: 1994
Minimum purchase: Initial: $1,000, Subsequent: $50; IRA/Keogh: Initial: $250
Discount broker availability: *Schwab, *Waterhouse, *Fidelity, *Siebert
Check redemptions: $500 minimum
Dividends paid: Income - declared daily, paid monthly; Capital gains - December
Management fee: 0.70%

STRONG INTERNATIONAL STOCK FUND ◆
(See first Strong listing for data common to all Strong funds)

Portfolio manager: Anthony L.T. Cragg (1992)
Custodian: Brown Brothers Harriman & Co.
Investment objective and policies: Long-term capital appreciation. Normally invests up to 90% (always at least 65%) of assets in equity securities - common stocks, preferred stocks, convertible securities, warrants and rights - of issuers located outside the U.S. May invest in ADRs and EDRs without limit and invest up to 35% of assets in equity and other securities of U.S. issuers and in non-convertible bonds and other debt securities issued by foreign government entities. Fund may use currency contracts, futures and options to increase return and hedge.
Year organized: 1992
Ticker symbol: STISX
Minimum purchase: Initial: $1,000, Subsequent: $50; IRA/Keogh: Initial: $250
Discount broker availability: *Schwab, White, *Waterhouse, *Fidelity, *Siebert
Dividends paid: Income - March, June, September, December; Capital gains - December
Portfolio turnover (2 yrs): 140%, 25%
Largest holding: Lend Lease Corporation, Ltd. (2.4%)
Management fee: 1.0%
Expense ratio: 1.9% (year ending 12/31/93)

STRONG INVESTMENT FUND ◆
(See Strong Asset Allocation Fund)

STRONG MONEY MARKET FUND ◆
(See first Strong listing for data common to all Strong funds)

Portfolio manager: Jay N. Mueller (1991)
Investment objective and policies: Maximum current income consistent with preservation of capital and liquidity. Invests in short-term money market instruments.
Year organized: 1985
Ticker symbol: SMNXX
Minimum purchase: Initial: $1,000, Subsequent: $50; IRA/Keogh: Initial: $250

Check redemptions: $500 minimum
Confirmations mailed: Not mailed
Periodic account statements mailed: Quarterly
Checks returned: On request
Dividends paid: Income - declared daily, paid monthly
Management fee: 0.5%
Expense ratio: 0.7% (year ending 12/31/93) (1.0% without waiver)

STRONG MUNICIPAL BOND FUND ◆
(See first Strong listing for data common to all Strong funds

Portfolio managers: Thomas J. Conlin (1991), Mary Kay H. Bourbulas (1991)
Investment objective and policies: High current income exempt from federal income taxes. Invests primarily in high-quality municipal securities with no maturity restrictions. May invest in AMT securities without limit.
Year organized: 1986 (formerly Strong Tax-Free Income Fund)
Ticker symbol: SXFIX
Minimum purchase: Initial: $2,500, Subsequent: $50
Discount broker availability: *Schwab, White, *Waterhouse, *Fidelity, *Siebert
Check redemptions: $500 minimum
Dividends paid: Income - declared daily, paid monthly; Capital gains - December
Portfolio turnover (3 yrs): 157%, 324%, 465%
Management fee: 0.60%
Expense ratio: 0.7% (year ending 12/31/93)

STRONG MUNICIPAL MONEY MARKET FUND ◆
(See first Strong listing for data common to all Strong funds)

Portfolio manager: Steven D. Harrop (1991)
Investment objective and policies: Maximum current income exempt from federal income taxes consistent with preservation of capital and liquidity. Invests in short-term municipal money market instruments. May invest in AMT securities without limit.
Year organized: 1986 (formerly Strong Tax-Free Money Market Fund)
Ticker symbol: SXFXX
Minimum purchase: Initial: $2,500, Subsequent: $50
Check redemptions: $500 minimum
Confirmations mailed: Not mailed
Periodic account statements mailed: Quarterly
Checks returned: On request
Dividends paid: Income - declared daily, paid monthly
Management fee: 0.5%
Expense ratio: 0.7% (year ending 12/31/93)

STRONG OPPORTUNITY FUND ◆
(See first Strong listing for data common to all Strong funds)

Portfolio managers: Richard T. Weiss (1991), Marina T. Carlson (1993)
Investment objective and policies: Capital appreciation. Invests at least 70% of assets in common stocks and other equity-type securities without regard to any objective investment criteria such as size, earnings history, book value or other factors. Up to 25% of assets may be in securities of foreign issuers. Fund will, to a substantial degree, engage in trading operations based upon short-term market considerations. May use futures and options to increase return and hedge and sell short against the box.
Year organized: 1985
Ticker symbol: SOPFX
Minimum purchase: Initial: $1,000, Subsequent: $50; IRA/Keogh: Initial: $250

Discount broker availability: *Schwab, White, *Waterhouse, *Fidelity, *Siebert
Dividends paid: Income - March, June, September, December; Capital gains - December
Portfolio turnover (3 yrs): 59%, 109%, 139%
Largest holding: Newmont Mining Co. (1.5%)
Management fee: 1.0%
Expense ratio: 1.4% (year ending 12/31/94)

STRONG SHORT TERM BOND FUND ◆
(See first Strong listing for data common to all Strong funds)

Portfolio manager: Bradley C. Tank (1990)
Investment objective and policies: High income consistent with minimum fluctuation of principal value and current liquidity. Invests primarily in short- and intermediate-term investment-grade debt securities with a weighted average maturity of 1 to 3 years. May have up to 25% of assets in securities of foreign issuers and use futures and options to increase return and hedge.
Year organized: 1985
Ticker symbol: SSTBX
Minimum purchase: Initial: $1,000, Subsequent: $50; IRA/Keogh: Initial: $250
Discount broker availability: *Schwab, White, *Waterhouse, *Fidelity, *Siebert
Check redemption: $500 minimum
Dividends paid: Income - declared daily, paid monthly; Capital gains - December
Portfolio turnover (3 yrs): 445%, 353%, 398%
Management fee: 0.625%
Expense ratio: 0.8% (year ending 12/31/93) (0.9% without waiver)

STRONG SHORT-TERM GLOBAL BOND FUND ◆
(See first Strong listing for data common to all Strong funds)

Portfolio manager: Shirish Malekar (1994)
Custodian: Brown Brothers Harriman & Co.
Investment objective and policies: High income consistent with capital preservation. Invests primarily in investment-grade corporate and government debt securities of issuers from at least three countries including the U.S. with a weighted average maturity of 3 years or less. Up to 20% of assets may be in junk bonds. May use foreign forward currency contracts, futures and options to increase return and hedge.
Year organized: 1994
Minimum purchase: Initial: $1,000, Subsequent: $50; IRA/Keogh: Initial: $250
Discount broker availability: *Schwab, *Waterhouse, *Fidelity, *Siebert
Check redemptions: $500 minimum
Dividends paid: Income - declared daily, paid monthly; Capital gains - December
Management fee: 0.625%

STRONG SHORT-TERM MUNICIPAL BOND FUND ◆
(See first Strong listing for data common to all Strong funds)

Portfolio managers: Thomas J. Conlin (1994), Gregory Winston (1994)
Investment objective and policies: Highest level of income exempt from federal income tax consistent with preservation of capital. Invests primarily in investment-grade municipal securities issued by or on behalf of states, territories, and possessions of the U.S. and their political subdivisions, agencies and instrumentalities with a weighted average maturity of 3 years or less. May invest in AMT securities without limit and use futures and options to increase return and hedge.
Year organized: 1991
Ticker symbol: STSMX
Minimum purchase: Initial: $2,500, Subsequent: $50
Discount broker availability: *Schwab, White, *Waterhouse, *Fidelity, *Siebert

Check redemption: $500 minimum
Dividends paid: Income - declared daily, paid monthly; Capital gains - December
Portfolio turnover (2 yrs): 142%, 290%
Management fee: 0.5%
Expense ratio: 0.6% (year ending 12/31/93)

STRONG TOTAL RETURN FUND ◆
(See first Strong listing for data common to all Strong funds)

Portfolio managers: Ronald C. Ognar (1993), Ian J. Rodgers (1994)
Investment objective and policies: Income and capital appreciation which will result in the highest total return with reasonable risks. Invests in equity and fixed-income securities and may have up to 100% of assets in either category depending on market and economic conditions. Up to 25% of assets may be in securities of foreign issuers. Fund may assume short-term trading posture when management perceives economic uncertainty. May use futures and options to increase return and hedge and sell short against the box.
Year organized: 1981
Ticker symbol: STRFX
Minimum purchase: Initial: $250, Subsequent: $50
Discount broker availability: *Schwab, White, *Waterhouse, *Fidelity, *Siebert
Dividends paid: Income - March, June, September, December; Capital gains - December
Portfolio turnover (3 yrs): 290%, 271%, 372%
Largest holding: Xerox Corp. (2.3%)
Management fee: 0.85% first $35M, 0.80% over $35M
Expense ratio: 1.2% (year ending 12/31/94)

STRONG U.S. TREASURY MONEY FUND ◆
(See first Strong listing for data common to all Strong funds)

Portfolio manager: Jay N. Mueller (1991)
Investment objective and policies: High current income consistent with capital preservation and liquidity. Invests only in securities issued directly by the U.S. Government (bills, notes, bonds), maturing within one year. Dividends will be exempt from state and local taxes in most states.
Year organized: 1991
Ticker symbol: SUSXX
Minimum purchase: Initial: $1,000, Subsequent: $50; IRA/Keogh: Initial: $250
Check redemption: $500 minimum
Confirmations mailed: Not mailed
Periodic account statements mailed: Quarterly
Checks returned: On request
Dividends paid: Income - declared daily, paid monthly
Management fee: 0.40%
Expense ratio: 0.2% (year ending 12/31/93) (1.0% without waiver)

THE TCW/DW FUNDS
(Data common to all TCW/DW funds are shown below. See subsequent listings for data specific to individual TCW/DW funds.)

Two World Trade Center
New York, NY 10048
212-392-2550, 800-869-3863

Manager: InterCapital Division of Dean Witter Reynolds, Inc.
Adviser: TCW Funds Management, Inc.
Custodian: The Bank of New York
Transfer agent: Dean Witter Trust Co.
Minimum purchase: Initial: $1,000, Subsequent: $100
Telephone orders accepted: No
Wire orders accepted: No
Qualified for sale in: All states
Letter redemptions: Signature guarantee not required
Telephone switching: With other TCW/DW funds

(some of which have back-end loads) and Dean Witter money market funds
Number of switches permitted: Unlimited
Shareholder services: Keogh, IRA, 403(b), automatic investment plan, withdrawal plan min. req. $10,000

THE TCW/DW BALANCED FUND
(See first TCW/DW listing for data common to all TCW/DW funds)

Portfolio managers: James A. Tilton (1993), James M. Goldberg (1993)
Investment objective and policies: High total return - current income and capital appreciation. Invests in common stocks and investment-grade fixed-income securities with allocation adjusted to reflect changes in market or economic conditions. Normally common stocks will represent 60-70% of assets. Up to 25% of assets may be in non-dollar denominated foreign securities and 15% in illiquid securities. May use futures and options to increase return and hedge.
Year organized: 1993
Ticker symbol: TCBLX
Dividends paid: Income - March, June, September, December; Capital gains - December
Portfolio turnover (1 yr): 113%
Largest holding: Unisys Corp. (3.4%)
Management fee: 0.75%
12b-1 distribution fee: 0.99%
Expense ratio: 2.06% (11 months ending 9/30/94)

THE TCW/DW INCOME AND GROWTH FUND
(See first TCW/DW listing for data common to all TCW/DW funds)

Portfolio manager: Howard S. Marks (1993)
Investment objective and policies: High total return - current income with potential for capital appreciation. Invests primarily in securities convertible into common stock (at least 50% of assets), other fixed-income securities, common stocks and U.S. Government securities. Up to 25% of assets may be in non-dollar denominated foreign securities and 15% in illiquid securities. May use futures and options to increase return and hedge.
Year organized: 1993
Ticker symbol: TCIGX
Dividends paid: Income - March, June, September, December; Capital gains - December
Portfolio turnover (1 yr): 84%
Management fee: 0.75% first $500M, 0.72% over $500M
12b-1 distribution fee: 0.75%
Expense ratio: 1.57% (10 months ending 1/31/94) (2.00% without waiver)

THE TCW/DW NORTH AMERICAN GOVERNMENT INCOME TRUST
(See first TCW/DW listing for data common to all TCW/DW funds)

Portfolio manager: Philip A. Barach (1992)
Investment objective and policies: High current income with relatively low volatility of principal. Invests primarily in investment-grade fixed-income securities issued or guaranteed by the U.S., Canadian or Mexican governments, or their subdivisions, or agencies or instrumentalities with a weighted average maturity of 3 years or less. Up to 25% of assets may be in Canadian securities and up to 25% in Mexican securities. Fund is non-diversified. May use futures and options to increase return and hedge.
Year organized: 1992
Ticker symbol: TCGIX
Dividends paid: Income - monthly; Capital gains - December
Portfolio turnover (2 yrs): 27%, 77%
Management fee: 0.65%
12b-1 distribution fee: 0.75%
Expense ratio: 1.52% (year ending 10/31/94)

THE TCW/DW NORTH AMERICAN INTERMEDIATE INCOME TRUST
(See first TCW/DW listing for data common to all TCW/DW funds)

Portfolio managers: James M. Goldberg (1994), Douglas R. Metcalf (1994)
Investment objective and policies: High current income. Invests primarily in investment-grade fixed-income securities issued or guaranteed by the U.S., Canadian or Mexican corporate or government issuers with a weighted average maturity of 3 to 10 years. Up to 25% of assets may be in Canadian securities and up to 25% in Mexican securities. Fund is non-diversified. May use futures and options to increase return and hedge.
Year organized: 1994
Dividends paid: Income - monthly; Capital gains - December
Management fee: 0.65%
12b-1 distribution fee: 0.75%

THIRD AVENUE VALUE FUND
(See additional fund listings on page 406)

THOMPSON, UNGER & PLUMB FUNDS ◆
(Data common to all Thompson, Unger & Plumb funds are shown below. See subsequent listings for data specific to individual Thompson, Unger & Plumb funds.)

8201 Excelsior Drive, Suite 200
Madison, WI 53717
608-831-1300, 800-999-0887
prices 800-338-1579, fax 608-831-3455

Adviser: Thompson, Plumb & Associates, Inc.
Custodian and transfer agent: Firstar Trust Co.
Minimum purchase: Initial: $1,000, Subsequent: $100; IRA/Keogh: Initial: $250
Telephone orders accepted: No
Wire orders accepted: Yes
Deadline for same day wire purchase: 4 P.M.
Qualified for sale in: CA, CO, FL, IL, IN, KS, LA, MI, MN, MT, OH, TX, WI
Wire redemptions: Yes
Letter redemptions: Signature guarantee required over $25,000
Telephone switching: With other Thompson, Unger & Plumb funds and Portico Money Market Fund, $1,000 minimum
Number of switches permitted: 15 day hold, fund reserves right to limit number, $5 fee
Shareholder services: IRA, SEP-IRA, 403(b), corporate retirement plans, automatic investment plan—minimum $50/month
IRA/Keogh fees: Annual $12.50
Note: Thompson, Unger & Plumb funds are listed in the statistical section as TU&P funds.

THOMPSON, UNGER & PLUMB BALANCED FUND ◆
(See first Thompson, Unger & Plumb listing for data common to all Thompson, Unger & Plumb funds)

Portfolio manager: Thomas G. Plumb (1987)
Investment objective and policies: Income and capital appreciation yielding the highest total return with reasonable risk. Invests primarily in blue chip stocks, mid-size growth stocks, fixed-income securities, and money market instruments. Up to 75% of assets will be in common stocks, with one third or less in companies with capitalizations under $200M.
Year organized: 1987 (name changed from Thompson, Unger & Plumb Fund in 1992)
Dividends paid: Income - December; Capital gains - December
Portfolio turnover (3 yrs): 110%, 92%, 53%
Largest holding: U.S. Treasury Note 7.500% due 10/31/99 (4.3%)
Management fee: 0.85% first $50M, 0.80% over $50M
Expense ratio: 1.42% (year ending 11/30/94)

THOMPSON, UNGER & PLUMB BOND FUND ◆
(See first Thompson, Unger & Plumb listing for data common to all Thompson, Unger & Plumb funds)

Portfolio manager: John W. Thompson (1992)
Investment objective and policies: High current income consistent with preservation of capital. Invests primarily in investment-grade debt securities of U.S. and foreign issuers (payable in U.S. dollars) and securities issued or guaranteed by the U.S. government, its agencies or instrumentalities with a weighted average maturity of 10 years or less.
Year organized: 1992
Dividends paid: Income - March, June, September, December; Capital gains - December
Portfolio turnover (3 yrs): 165%, 111%, 227%
Management fee: 0.65% first $50M, 0.60% over $50M
Expense ratio: 1.00% (year ending 11/30/94) (1.48% without waiver)

THOMPSON, UNGER & PLUMB GROWTH FUND ◆
(See first Thompson, Unger & Plumb listing for data common to all Thompson, Unger & Plumb funds)

Portfolio manager: John W. Thompson (1992)
Investment objective and policies: Long-term capital appreciation with income secondary. Invests primarily in common stocks and securities convertible into common stocks of companies believed to have above average potential for earnings and dividend growth. Up to 1/3 of assets may be in companies with capitalizations under $200M.
Year organized: 1992
Dividends paid: Income - December; Capital gains - December
Portfolio turnover (3 yrs): 117%, 99%, 43%
Largest holding: Merck & Company (4.0%)
Management fee: 1.00% first $50M, 0.90% over $50M
Expense ratio: 2.00% (year ending 11/30/94) (2.31% without waiver)

TNE MONEY MARKET FUNDS ◆
(See New England Money Market funds.)

THE TOCQUEVILLE FUND
1675 Broadway - 16th Floor
New York, NY 10019
212-698-0800, 800-697-3863
fax 212-262-0154

Adviser: Tocqueville Asset Management L.P.
Portfolio managers: Francois Sicart (1987), Robert Kleinschmidt (1991)
Custodian and transfer agent: State Street Bank & Trust Co.
Investment objective and policies: Long term capital appreciation. Invests in common stocks of U.S. companies considered to be out of favor and undervalued in relation to their potential growth & earning power. May invest 100% of assets in U.S. Government securities as defensive position. May invest up to 10% in dollar-denominated securities of foreign issuers and 10% in gold bullion.
Year organized: 1987
Ticker symbol: TOCQX
Minimum purchase: Initial: $5,000, Subsequent: $1,000; IRA/Keogh: Initial: $2,000
Telephone orders accepted: No
Wire orders accepted: Yes
Deadline for same day wire purchase: 4 P.M.
Discount broker availability: *White
Qualified for sale in: All states except AL, AK, GA, ID, IA, IL, KS, KY, MS, MT, NE, NV, ND, OK, SC, SD, UT, WA, WV
Letter redemptions: Signature guarantee required
Telephone switching: With other Tocqueville funds which have loads
Number of switches permitted: Unlimited

Dividends paid: Income - December; Capital gains - December
Portfolio turnover (3 yrs): 52%, 54%, 89%
Largest holding: International Business Machines Corp. (6.4%)
Shareholder services: Keogh, IRA, automatic investment plan—minimum $100/month, electronic funds transfer, withdrawal plan min. req. $10,000
Management fee: 0.75% first $100M, to 0.65% over $500M
12b-1 distribution fee: maximum of 0.25%
Expense ratio: 1.54% (year ending 10/31/94)
IRA/Keogh fees: Annual $10, Initial $5

THE TOCQUEVILLE EURO-PACIFIC FUND
(Fund changed name to Tocqueville Asia-Pacific Fund in 1994 and imposed a 4.0% load)

TORCHMARK GOVERNMENT SECURITIES FUND ◆
6300 Lamar Avenue
P.O. Box 2995
Shawnee Mission, KS 66201
913-236-2050, 800-733-3863

Adviser: Waddell & Reed Investment Management Co.
Portfolio manager: John E. Sundeen, Jr. (1993)
Custodian: United Missouri Bank, N.A.
Transfer agent: Torchmark Services
Investment objective and policies: Current income. Invests primarily in securities issued or guaranteed as to timely payment of principal and interest by the U.S. Government with a weighted average maturity of 10 years or less. May use futures and options to increase income and hedge.
Year organized: 1993
Minimum purchase: Initial: $1,000, Subsequent: $100; IRA/Keogh: Initial: $250
Telephone orders accepted: No
Wire orders accepted: Yes, subsequent only
Deadline for same day wire purchase: 4 P.M.
Qualified for sale in: All states
Telephone redemptions: Yes
Wire redemptions: Yes
Letter redemptions: Signature guarantee required over $50,000
Check redemptions: $250 minimum
Telephone switching: With Torchmark Insured Tax-Free Fund
Number of switches permitted: Unlimited
Dividends paid: Income - declared daily, paid monthly; Capital gains - December
Portfolio turnover (1 yr): 80%
Shareholder services: Keogh, IRA, SEP-IRA, automatic investment plan—minimum $25/month, withdrawal plan min. req. $10,000
Management fee: 0.40%
12b-1 distribution fee: Maximum of 0.25% (not currently imposed)
Expense ratio: 1.00% (10 months ending 12/31/93) (4.07% without waiver)

TORCHMARK INSURED TAX-FREE FUND ◆
6300 Lamar Avenue
P.O. Box 2995
Shawnee Mission, KS 66201
913-236-2050, 800-733-3863

Adviser: Waddell & Reed Investment Management Co.
Portfolio manager: John M. Holliday (1993)
Custodian: United Missouri Bank, N.A.
Transfer agent: Torchmark Services
Investment objective and policies: Current income exempt from federal income tax. Invests primarily in investment-grade municipal securities insured as to timely payment of principal and interest with remaining individual maturities of less than 10 years. Up to 20% of assets may be in AMT securities. May use futures and options to increase income and hedge.
Year organized: 1993

Minimum purchase: Initial: $1,000, Subsequent: $100
Telephone orders accepted: No
Wire orders accepted: Yes, subsequent only
Deadline for same day wire purchase: 4 P.M.
Qualified for sale in: All states
Telephone redemptions: Yes
Wire redemptions: Yes
Letter redemptions: Signature guarantee required over $50,000
Check redemptions: $250 minimum
Telephone switching: With Torchmark Government Securities Fund
Number of switches permitted: Unlimited
Dividends paid: Income - declared daily, paid monthly; Capital gains - December
Portfolio turnover: 79%
Shareholder services: Automatic investment plan—minimum $25/month, withdrawal plan min. req. $10,000
Management fee: 0.50%
12b-1 distribution fee: Maximum of 0.25% (not currently imposed)
Expense ratio: 1.00% (10 months ending 12/31/93) (2.74% without waiver)

THE TORRAY FUND ◆
6610 Rockledge Drive - Suite 450
Bethesda, MD 20817
301-493-4600, 800-443-4600
fax 301-530-0642

Adviser: The Torray Corporation
Portfolio manager: Robert E. Torray (1990)
Custodian: Rushmore Trust & Savings, FSB
Transfer agent: The Torray Corporation
Investment objective and policies: Long term total return consistent with prudent investment management. Invests in common stocks, convertible securities, corporate bonds, U.S. Government securities and other fixed-income instruments believed undervalued. Allocation of assets will vary depending on market conditions.
Year organized: 1990
Minimum purchase: Initial: $10,000, Subsequent: $2,500
Telephone orders accepted: No
Wire orders accepted: No
Discount broker availability: Schwab
Qualified for sale in: All states except AK, AR, IA, KY, MN, MO, MT, NE, NV, ND, RI, SD, WI
Telephone redemptions: Yes
Wire redemptions: Yes, $10 fee
Letter redemptions: Signature guarantee not required
Dividends paid: Income - March, June, September, December; Capital gains - December
Portfolio turnover (3 yrs): 37%, 29%, 37%
Largest holding: Salomon, Inc. (5.7%)
Management fee: 1.0%
Expense ratio: 1.25% (year ending 12/31/94) (1.82% without waiver)

TREASURY CASH SERIES
Federated Investors Tower
Pittsburgh, PA 15222-3779
412-288-1900, 800-245-0242
fax 412-288-1982

Adviser: Federated Advisers
Portfolio manager: Susan M. Nason (1991)
Custodian: State Street Bank & Trust Co.
Transfer agent: Federated Securities Corp.
Investment objective and policies: Income consistent with stability of principal and liquidity. Invests in short-term U.S. Treasury money market obligations.
Year organized: 1990
Minimum purchase: Initial: $10,000, Subsequent: $500; IRA: Initial: $1,000
Wire orders accepted: Yes
Deadline for same day wire purchase: 12 NN
Qualified for sale in: All states
Telephone redemptions: Yes
Wire redemptions: Yes, $10,000 minimum
Letter redemptions: Signature guarantee required over $50,000

Check redemptions: $100 minimum
Telephone switching: With Dremen Fund portfolios
Management fee: 0.5%
12b-1 distribution fee: 0.10%
Expense ratio: 0.99% (year ending 5/31/94) (1.09% without waiver)

TRENT EQUITY FUND ◆
2002 Pisgah Church Road - Suite 140
Greensboro, NC 27455
910-282-9302, 800-328-7368
fax 910-282-8272

Adviser: Trent Capital Management, Inc.
Portfolio managers: Richard T. Holderness (1992), Robert V. May (1992)
Custodian: Provident Bank of Cincinnati
Transfer agent: Wadsworth & Associates
Investment objective and policies: Capital appreciation with income secondary. Invests primarily in common stocks, preferred stocks and convertible securities. May invest in sponsored ADRs of foreign issuers traded on U.S. exchanges and use covered call options to hedge.
Year organized: 1992
Minimum purchase: Initial: $1,000, Subsequent: $100; IRA/Keogh: Initial: $500
Telephone orders accepted: No
Wire orders accepted: Yes
Deadline for same day wire purchase: 11 A.M.
Qualified for sale in: FL, KY, LA, MD, NJ, NY, NC
Telephone redemptions: Yes
Wire redemptions: Yes, $5,000 minimum, $10 fee
Letter redemptions: Signature guarantee required
Dividends paid: Income - December; Capital gains - December
Portfolio turnover (2 yrs): 149%, 315%
Largest holding: Natural Wonders, Inc. (7.4%)
Shareholder services: IRA, automatic investment plan, withdrawal plan min. req. $10,000
Management fee: 1.25%
Expense ratio: 1.85% (year ending 8/31/94) (3.16% without waiver)
IRA fees: Annual $10, Initial $5

TRUST COMPANY OF THE SOUTH GROWTH FUND ◆
(Fund liquidated on 11/30/94)

TWEEDY BROWNE AMERICAN VALUE FUND ◆
52 Vanderbilt Avenue
New York, NY 10017
212-916-0600, 800-432-4789
prices 800-873-8242, fax 317-266-0756

Shareholder service hours: Full service: M-F 9 A.M.-5 P.M. EST; After hours service: prices, prospectuses
Adviser: Tweedy Browne Company L.P.
Administrator: The Boston Company Advisors, Inc.
Custodian: Boston Safe Deposit & Trust Co.
Transfer agent: Unified Advisers, Inc.
Investment objective and policies: Long-term capital growth. Invests primarily in common stocks, preferred stocks and convertible securities of domestic companies believed undervalued. Up to 20% of assets may be in foreign securities. May use futures, options, and currency transactions to hedge and, to a limited extent, to enhance performance.
Year organized: 1993 (name changed from Value Fund on 10/1/94)
Ticker symbol: TWEBX
Minimum purchase: Initial: $2,500, Subsequent: $500; IRA/Keogh: Initial: $500
Telephone orders accepted: Yes, subsequent only, maximum 4 times value of account
Wire orders accepted: Yes, $10 fee
Deadline for same day wire purchase: 4 P.M.
Discount broker availability: Schwab, White, Waterhouse, Fidelity, Siebert
Qualified for sale in: All states
Telephone redemptions: Yes

Wire redemptions: Yes, $10 fee
Letter redemptions: Signature guarantee required over $5,000
Telephone switching: With Tweedy Browne Global Value Fund
Number of switches permitted: Unlimited
Dividends paid: Income - December; Capital gains - December
Portfolio turnover (1 yr): 0%
Largest holding: Great Atlantic and Pacific Tea Co. (3.6%)
Shareholder services: IRA, automatic investment plan, electronic funds transfer
Management fee: 1.25%
IRA fees: Annual $10
Expense ratio: 2.26% (4 months ending 3/31/94) (3.51% without waiver)

TWEEDY BROWNE GLOBAL VALUE FUND ◆
52 Vanderbilt Avenue
New York, NY 10017
212-916-0600, 800-432-4789
prices 800-873-8242, fax 317-266-0756

Shareholder service hours: Full service: M-F 9 A.M.-5 P.M. EST; After hours service: prices, prospectuses
Adviser: Tweedy Browne Company L.P.
Administrator: The Boston Company Advisors, Inc.
Custodian: Boston Safe Deposit & Trust Co.
Transfer agent: Unified Advisers, Inc.
Investment objective and policies: Long-term capital growth. Invests primarily in common stocks, preferred stocks and convertible securities of established companies believed undervalued, wherever they may be in the developed world. May use futures, options, and currency transactions to hedge and, to a limited extent, to enhance performance.
Year organized: 1993
Ticker symbol: TBGVX
Minimum purchase: Initial: $2,500, Subsequent: $500; IRA/Keogh: Initial: $500
Telephone orders accepted: Yes, subsequent only, maximum 4 times value of account
Wire orders accepted: Yes, $10 fee
Deadline for same day wire purchase: 4 P.M.
Discount broker availability: Schwab, White, Waterhouse, Fidelity, Siebert
Qualified for sale in: All states
Telephone redemptions: Yes
Wire redemptions: Yes, $10 fee
Letter redemptions: Signature guarantee required over $5,000
Telephone switching: With Tweedy Browne American Value Fund
Number of switches permitted: Unlimited
Dividends paid: Income - December; Capital gains - December
Portfolio turnover (1 yr): 14%
Largest holding: Nestle SA, Registered (3.4%)
Shareholder services: IRA, automatic investment plan, electronic funds transfer
Management fee: 1.25%
IRA/Keogh fees: None
Expense ratio: 1.73% (9 months ending 3/31/94)

TWENTIETH CENTURY FUNDS ◆
(Data common to all Twentieth Century funds are shown below. See subsequent listings for data specific to individual Twentieth Century funds.)

4500 Main Street
P.O. Box 419200
Kansas City, MO 64141-6200
816-531-5575, 800-345-2021

Shareholder service hours: Full service: M-F 8 A.M.-4:30 P.M. CST; After hours service: prices, yields, balances, orders, last transaction, prospectuses, total returns
Adviser: Investors Research Corp.
Custodian: U.S. Trust Company of New York
Transfer agent: Twentieth Century Services, Inc.
Minimum purchase: Initial: $2,500, Subsequent: $50; IRA/Keogh: Initial: None, Subsequent: None (exceptions noted)

Telephone orders accepted: No
Wire orders accepted: Yes
Deadline for same day wire purchase: 4 P.M.
Qualified for sale in: All states
Telephone redemptions: Yes
Wire redemptions: Yes, $10 fee
Letter redemptions: Signature guarantee not required
Telephone switching: With other 20th Century Funds except Giftrust
Number of switches permitted: 4 per year
Shareholder services: Keogh, IRA, 401(k), 403(b), corporate retirement plans, automatic investment plan—minimum $50/month (waives initial minimum for equity funds), withdrawal plan min. req. $5,000, electronic funds transfer (except Giftrust)
IRA fees: Annual $10 (maximum of $30, regardless of number of fund accounts, waived if total IRA assets exceed $10,000)
Keogh fees: None

TWENTIETH CENTURY BALANCED INVESTORS ◆

(See first Twentieth Century listing for data common to all Twentieth Century funds)

Portfolio managers: Equity - Robert C. Puff, Charles M. Duboc, Nancy Prial; Fixed income - Bud Hoops
Investment objective and policies: Capital growth and current income. Fund maintains a fully invested posture with approximately 60% of assets in common stocks having appreciation potential; the remaining 40% is in fixed-income securities (minimum 25% in fixed-income senior securities) with a weighted average maturity of 3-10 years. At least 80% of debt obligations will be A rated or better with the remainder Baa or equivalent. May invest in securities of foreign issuers without limit and use forward currency exchange contracts to hedge.
Year organized: 1988
Ticker symbol: TWBIX
Discount broker availability: *Schwab, *White, Waterhouse, Fidelity, Siebert
Dividends paid: Income - March, June, September, December; Capital gains - December
Portfolio turnover (3 yrs): 94%, 95%, 100%
Largest holding: U.S. Treasury Notes 8.00% due 1/15/97 (2.9%)
Management fee: 1%
Expense ratio: 1.00% (year ending 10/31/94)

TWENTIETH CENTURY CASH RESERVE ◆

(See first Twentieth Century listing for data common to all Twentieth Century funds)

Portfolio managers: Bud Hoops, Robert Gahagan
Investment objective and policies: Maximum current income consistent with preservation of principal and maintenance of liquidity. Invests in money market instruments.
Year organized: 1985 (split 100 for 1 on 11/13/93)
Ticker symbol: TWCXX
Minimum purchase: Initial: $1,000
Dividends paid: Income - declared daily, paid monthly
Check redemptions: $500 minimum
Confirmations mailed: After each purchase and each check, mail or wire redemption
Checks returned: On request
Periodic account statements mailed: Quarterly
Management fee: 0.70%
Expense ratio: 0.80% (year ending 10/31/94)

TWENTIETH CENTURY EQUITY INCOME ◆

(See first Twentieth Century listing for data common to all Twentieth Century funds)

Portfolio managers: Peter Zuger (1994), Phil Davidson (1994)
Investment objective and policies: Current income with capital growth secondary. Invests primarily in dividend-paying common stocks of companies with

favorable dividend-paying history. May have up to 25% of assets in securities of foreign issuers, including foreign debt securities. May use forward currency exchange contracts to hedge and may sell short.
Year organized: 1994
Ticker symbol: TWEIX
Discount broker availability: *Schwab, *White, Fidelity, Siebert
Dividends paid: Income - March, June, September, December; Capital gains - December
Management fee: 1%

TWENTIETH CENTURY GIFTRUST INVESTORS ◆

(See first Twentieth Century listing for data common to all Twentieth Century funds)

Portfolio managers: James E. Stowers III, Glenn Fogle
Investment objective and policies: Capital growth. Invests at least 90% of assets in securities of domestic and foreign issuers believed to have above-average appreciation potential. May invest in securities of foreign issuers without limit and use forward currency exchange contracts to hedge. Designed for persons wishing to make gifts to children, charities or others.
Year organized: 1983
Ticker symbol: TWGTX
Special sales restriction: Available only to persons executing the Twentieth Century Giftrust in which a grantor makes a gift in trust for the benefit of a child or charity. Trust is irrevocable and shares cannot be distributed before 10 years.
Minimum purchase: Initial: $250
Portfolio turnover (3 yrs): 115%, 143%, 134%
Largest holding: Microchip Technology, Inc. (6.9%)
Dividends paid: Income - December; Capital gains - December
Management fee: 1.0%
Expense ratio: 1.00% (year ending 10/31/94)

TWENTIETH CENTURY GROWTH INVESTORS ◆

(See first Twentieth Century listing for data common to all Twentieth Century funds)

Portfolio managers: James E. Stowers III, Derek Felske, Christopher Boyd
Investment objective and policies: Capital growth through investment in securities of domestic and foreign issuers believed to have above-average appreciation potential. Growth, Ultra, and Vista all have the same objective, differing only in size and trading volume of companies in portfolio. The largest companies are typically allocated to Growth, and the smallest to Vista, with fund price volatility expected to increase as the average capitalization size decreases. May use forward currency exchange contracts to hedge.
Year organized: 1957
Ticker symbol: TWCGX
Discount broker availability: *Schwab, *White, Waterhouse, Fidelity, Siebert
Dividends paid: Income - December; Capital gains - December
Portfolio turnover (3 yrs): 100%, 94%, 53%
Largest holding: International Business Machines Corp. (5.0%)
Management fee: 1%
Expense ratio: 1.00% (year ending 10/31/94)

TWENTIETH CENTURY HERITAGE INVESTORS ◆

(See first Twentieth Century listing for data common to all Twentieth Century funds)

Portfolio managers: Robert C. Puff, Charles M. Duboc, Nancy Prial
Investment objective and policies: Capital growth. Invests in common stocks of domestic and foreign issuers believed to have above-average appreciation potential. Stocks must have a record of paying cash dividends, but growth is the primary consideration

and the dividends may not be significant. Select and Heritage have the same objective, differing only in size and trading volume of companies in portfolio. The larger companies are typically allocated to Select, and the smaller to Heritage.
Year organized: 1987
Ticker symbol: TWHIX
Discount broker availability: *Schwab, *White, Waterhouse, Fidelity, Siebert
Dividends paid: Income - December; Capital gains - December
Portfolio turnover (3 yrs): 136%, 116%, 119%
Largest holding: Brunswick Corp. (3.1%)
Management fee: 1%
Expense ratio: 1.00% (year ending 10/31/94)

TWENTIETH CENTURY INTERMEDIATE-TERM BOND FUND ◆

(See first Twentieth Century listing for data common to all Twentieth Century funds)

Portfolio manager: Bud Hoops (1994)
Investment objective and policies: High current income. Invests primarily in investment-grade corporate securities and other debt obligations of domestic and foreign issuers with a weighted average maturity of 3 to 10 years. May use futures and options to hedge.
Year organized: 1994
Discount broker availability: *Schwab, *White
Dividends paid: Income - declared daily, paid monthly; Capital gains - December
Portfolio turnover (1 yr): 48%
Management fee: 0.75%
Expense ratio: 0.75% (8 months ending 10/31/94)

TWENTIETH CENTURY INTERNATIONAL EMERGING GROWTH FUND ◆

(See first Twentieth Century listing for data common to all Twentieth Century funds)

Portfolio managers: Theodore Tyson (1994), Mark Kopinski (1994), Henrik Strabo (1994)
Investment objective and policies: Capital growth. Invests primarily in equity securities of foreign companies with market capitalizations under $800M in developed markets believed to have above-average appreciation potential and companies in emerging market countries without regard to market capitalization. Normally invests at least 65% of assets in common stocks of issuers from at least three foreign countries without regard to geographic region. May use forward currency exchange contracts to hedge.
Year organized: 1994
Ticker symbol: TWEGX
Minimum purchase: Initial: $10,000
Redemption fee: 2% for shares held less than 180 days, payable to the fund
Dividends paid: Income - December; Capital gains - December
Portfolio turnover (1 yr): 56%
Largest holding: Cementos Paz Del Rio GDR (1.6%)
Management fee: 2.0%
Expense ratio: 2.00% (7 months ending 11/30/94)

TWENTIETH CENTURY INTERNATIONAL EQUITY FUND ◆

(See first Twentieth Century listing for data common to all Twentieth Century funds)

Portfolio managers: Ted Tyson (1991), Mark Kopinski (1991), Henrik Strabo (1994)
Investment objective and policies: Capital growth. Invests in securities of foreign companies believed to have above-average appreciation potential. Invests primarily in common stocks but may also hold convertible securities, preferred stocks, bonds, notes and other debt securities of companies or obligations of domestic or foreign governments and their agencies. Normally invests at least 65% of assets in common stocks of issuers from at least three foreign countries without regard to geographic region. May use forward currency exchange contracts to hedge.

Year organized: 1991
Ticker symbol: TWIEX
Discount broker availability: *Schwab, *White, Waterhouse, Fidelity, Siebert
Dividends paid: Income - December; Capital gains - December
Portfolio turnover (3 yrs): 242%, 255%, 180%
Largest holding: Lyonnaise Des Euax-Dumee (3.9%)
Management fee: 1.9%
Expense ratio: 1.84% (year ending 11/30/94)

TWENTIETH CENTURY LIMITED-TERM BOND FUND ◆
(See first Twentieth Century listing for data common to all Twentieth Century funds)

Portfolio manager: Bud Hoops (1994)
Investment objective and policies: High current income. Invests primarily in investment-grade corporate securities and other debt obligations of domestic and foreign issuers with a weighted average maturity of less than 5 years. May use futures and options to hedge.
Year organized: 1994
Discount broker availability: *Schwab, *White
Dividends paid: Income - declared daily, paid monthly; Capital gains - December
Portfolio turnover (1 yr): 48%
Management fee: 0.70%
Expense ratio: 0.70% (8 months ending 10/31/94)

TWENTIETH CENTURY LONG-TERM BOND FUND ◆
(See first Twentieth Century listing for data common to all Twentieth Century funds)

Portfolio managers: Charles M. Duboc (1987), Bud Hoops
Investment objective and policies: High current income. Invests primarily in investment-grade bonds and other debt obligations of domestic and foreign issuers with a weighted average maturity of more than 10 years. May use futures and options to hedge.
Year organized: 1987 (split 10 for 1 on 11/13/93)
Ticker symbol: TWLBX
Discount broker availability: *Schwab, *White, Waterhouse, Fidelity, Siebert
Dividends paid: Income - declared daily, paid monthly; Capital gains - December
Portfolio turnover (3 yrs): 78%, 113%, 186%
Management fee: 0.80%
Expense ratio: 0.88% (year ending 10/31/94)

TWENTIETH CENTURY SELECT INVESTORS ◆
(See first Twentieth Century listing for data common to all Twentieth Century funds)

Portfolio managers: Robert C. Puff, Charles M. Duboc, Nancy Prial
Investment objective and policies: Capital growth. Invests in common stocks of domestic and foreign issuers believed to have above-average appreciation potential. Stocks must have a record of paying cash dividends, but growth is the primary consideration and the dividends may not be significant. Select and Heritage have the same objective, differing only in size and trading volume of companies in portfolio. The larger companies are typically allocated to Select, and the smaller to Heritage.
Year organized: 1957
Ticker symbol: TWCIX
Discount broker availability: *Schwab, *White, Waterhouse, Fidelity, Siebert
Dividends paid: Income - December; Capital gains - December
Portfolio turnover (3 yrs): 126%, 82%, 95%
Largest holding: International Business Machines Corp. (4.3%)
Management fee: 1%
Expense ratio: 1.00% (year ending 10/31/94)

TWENTIETH CENTURY TAX-EXEMPT INTERMEDIATE TERM ◆
(See first Twentieth Century listing for data common to all Twentieth Century funds)

Newspaper listing: TxEIn
Portfolio managers: Bud Hoops, Laurie S. Kirby, Jeffrey Houston
Investment objective and policies: Income exempt from federal income taxes. Invests primarily in short- and intermediate-term tax-exempt bonds with a weighted average maturity of 3 to 10 years. May have up to 15% of assets in illiquid securities and use futures and options to hedge.
Year organized: 1987 (split 10 for 1 on 11/13/93)
Ticker symbol: TWTIX
Minimum purchase: Initial: $10,000
Discount broker availability: *White, Waterhouse, Fidelity, Siebert
Dividends paid: Income - declared daily, paid monthly; Capital gains - December
Portfolio turnover (3 yrs): 74%, 38%, 36%
Management fee: 0.6%
Expense ratio: 0.60% (year ending 10/31/94)

TWENTIETH CENTURY TAX-EXEMPT LONG TERM ◆
(See first Twentieth Century listing for data common to all Twentieth Century funds)

Newspaper listing: TxELT
Portfolio managers: Bud Hoops, Laurie S. Kirby, Jeffrey Houston
Investment objective and policies: High level of income exempt from federal income taxes. Invests in longer-term tax-exempt bonds with a weighted average maturity of more than 10 years. May have up to 15% of assets in illiquid securities and use futures and options to hedge.
Year organized: 1987 (split 10 for 1 on 11/13/93)
Ticker symbol: TWTLX
Minimum purchase: Initial: $10,000
Discount broker availability: *White, Waterhouse, Fidelity, Siebert
Dividends paid: Income - declared daily, paid monthly; Capital gains - December
Portfolio turnover (3 yrs): 60%, 81%, 88%
Management fee: 0.6%
Expense ratio: 0.60% (year ending 10/31/94)

TWENTIETH CENTURY TAX-EXEMPT SHORT TERM ◆
(See first Twentieth Century listing for data common to all Twentieth Century funds)

Portfolio managers: Bud Hoops, Laurie S. Kirby, Jeffrey Houston
Investment objective and policies: High income exempt from federal income taxes. Invests in short-term municipal bonds and other tax-exempt debt instruments with a weighted average maturity of 3 years or less. May have up to 15% of assets in illiquid securities and use futures and options to hedge.
Year organized: 1993
Ticker symbol: TWTSX
Minimum purchase: Initial: $10,000
Discount broker availability: *White, Fidelity, Siebert
Dividends paid: Income - declared daily, paid monthly; Capital gains - December
Portfolio turnover (2 yrs): 42%, 3%
Management fee: 0.60% (waived through 12/31/95)
Expense ratio: 0.00% (year ending 10/31/94) (0.60% without waiver)

TWENTIETH CENTURY ULTRA INVESTORS ◆
(See first Twentieth Century listing for data common to all Twentieth Century funds)

Portfolio managers: James E. Stowers III, Derek Felske, Christopher Boyd
Investment objective and policies: Capital growth through investment in securities of domestic and foreign issuers believed to have above-average

appreciation potential. Growth, Ultra, and Vista all have the same objective, differing only in size and trading volume of companies in portfolio. The largest companies are typically allocated to Growth, and the smallest to Vista. May use forward currency exchange contracts to hedge.
Year organized: 1981
Ticker symbol: TWCUX
Discount broker availability: *Schwab, *White, Waterhouse, Fidelity, Siebert
Dividends paid: Income - December; Capital gains - December
Portfolio turnover (3 yrs): 78%, 53%, 59%
Largest holding: Oracle Systems Corp. (4.1%)
Management fee: 1%
Expense ratio: 1.00% (year ending 10/31/94)

TWENTIETH CENTURY U.S. GOVERNMENTS INTERMEDIATE-TERM ◆
(See first Twentieth Century listing for data common to all Twentieth Century funds)

Portfolio managers: Bud Hoops (1994), Robert Gahagan (1994)
Investment objective and policies: High current income consistent with limited price volatility. Invests in debt securities of the U.S. Government and its agencies, with a weighted average maturity of 3 to 10 years. May invest in mortgage-related securities and have up to 15% of assets in illiquid securities.
Year organized: 1994
Discount broker availability: *Schwab, *White
Dividends paid: Income - declared daily, paid monthly; Capital gains - December
Portfolio turnover (1 yr): 205%
Management fee: 0.75%
Expense ratio: 0.75% (8 months ending 10/31/94)

TWENTIETH CENTURY U.S. GOVERNMENTS SHORT-TERM ◆
(See first Twentieth Century listing for data common to all Twentieth Century funds)

Portfolio managers: Bud Hoops, Robert Gahagan
Investment objective and policies: High current income consistent with limited price volatility. Invest in debt securities of the U.S. Government and its agencies, with a weighted average maturity of 3 years or less. May invest in mortgage-related securities and have up to 15% of assets in illiquid securities.
Year organized: 1982 (split 10 for 1 on 11/13/93) (name changed from U.S. Governments on 3/1/94)
Ticker symbol: TWUSX
Discount broker availability: *Schwab, *White, Waterhouse, Fidelity, Siebert
Dividends paid: Income - declared daily, paid monthly; Capital gains - December
Portfolio turnover (3 yrs): 470%, 413%, 391%
Management fee: 0.70%
Expense ratio: 0.81% (year ending 10/31/94)

TWENTIETH CENTURY VALUE INVESTORS ◆
(See first Twentieth Century listing for data common to all Twentieth Century funds)

Portfolio managers: Peter A. Zuger (1993), Philip Davidson (1993)
Investment objective and policies: Long-term capital growth with income secondary. Invests at least 80% of assets in equity securities of well-established companies with intermediate to large market capitalizations believed undervalued. Up to 25% of assets may be in securities of foreign issuers, via ADRs and direct investment in foreign securities, and 15% in securities convertible into common stock. May use forward currency exchange contracts to hedge and may sell short
Year organized: 1993
Ticker symbol: TUVLX
Discount broker availability: *Schwab, *White, Waterhouse, Fidelity, Siebert
Dividends paid: Income - March, June, September, December; Capital gains - December

Portfolio turnover (1 yr): 79%
Largest holding: Sears Roebuck & Co. $3.75 preferred (4.2%)
Management fee: 1%
Expense ratio: 1.00% (6 months ending 3/31/94)

TWENTIETH CENTURY VISTA INVESTORS ◆
(See first Twentieth Century listing for data common to all Twentieth Century funds)

Portfolio managers: James E. Stowers III, Glenn Fogle
Investment objective and policies: Capital growth through investment in securities of domestic and foreign issuers believed to have above-average appreciation potential. Growth, Ultra, and Vista all have the same objective, differing only in size and trading volume of companies in portfolio. The largest companies are typically allocated to Growth, and the smallest to Vista. May use forward currency exchange contracts to hedge.
Year organized: 1983
Ticker symbol: TWCVX
Discount broker availability: *Schwab, *White, Waterhouse, Fidelity, Siebert
Dividends paid: Income - December; Capital gains - December
Portfolio turnover (3 yrs): 111%, 133%, 87%
Largest holding: KLA Instruments Corp. (6.0%)
Management fee: 1%
Expense ratio: 1.00% (year ending 10/31/94)

UMB FUNDS ◆
(See Babson-UMB funds)

UNITED SERVICES FUNDS ◆
(Data common to all United Services funds are shown below. See subsequent listings for data specific to individual United Services funds.)

P.O. Box 781234
San Antonio, TX 78278-1234
210-308-1234, 800-873-8637
TDD 210-558-7249, 800-677-1212
fax 210-308-1217

Shareholder service hours: Full service: M-F 7:30 A.M.-5 P.M. CST; After hours service: prices, yields, balances, last transaction, prospectuses, news, messages, DJIA, total returns
Adviser: United Services Advisors, Inc.
Custodian: Bankers Trust Company
Transfer agent: United Shareholder Services, Inc.
Minimum purchase: Initial: $1,000, Subsequent: $50; IRA/Keogh: None
Telephone orders accepted: Subsequent only, up to 10 times account balance (except money market funds)
Wire orders accepted: Yes
Deadline for same day wire purchase: 4 P.M. (3 P.M. for Gold Shares)
Qualified for sale in: All states
Wire redemptions: Yes, $10 fee
Letter redemptions: Signature guarantee required over $15,000
Redemption fee: 0.10% for stock fund shares held less than 14 days (except China Region Opportunity Fund)
Account closing fee: $10
Telephone switching: With other United Services funds, Bonnel Growth Fund and Pauze/Swanson U.S. Government Total Return Fund
Number of switches permitted: Unlimited, $5 fee
Shareholder services: Keogh, IRA, SEP-IRA, 403(b), 401(k), corporate retirement plans, automatic investment plan—minimum $30/mo. ($100 initial minimum), withdrawal plan min. req. $5,000, electronic funds transfer (purchase only)
IRA fees: Annual $10, Closing $10
Keogh fees: Closing $10

UNITED SERVICES ALL AMERICAN EQUITY FUND ◆
(See first United Services listing for data common to all U.S. funds)

Sub-adviser: Batterymarch Financial Management
Portfolio manager: Frank E. Holmes (1993)
Investment objective and policies: Capital appreciation. Invests at least 75% of assets in domestic common stocks with goal of exceeding the total return of the S&P 500 Stock Price index. May use index options and futures contracts on up to 35% of assets and hedge up to 25% of assets.
Year organized: 1981 (name changed from Good & Bad Times Fund on 11/1/90)
Ticker symbol: GBTFX
Discount broker availability: Schwab, White, Waterhouse
Dividends paid: Income - March, June, September, December; Capital gains - December
Portfolio turnover (3 yrs): 116%, 12%, 35%
Largest holding: PPG Industries, Inc. (2.7%)
Management fee: 0.75% first $250M, 0.5% over $250M
Maintenance fee: $3 per quarter
Expense ratio: 0.61% (year ending 6/30/94) (2.08% without waiver)

UNITED SERVICES CHINA REGION OPPORTUNITY FUND ◆
(See first United Services listing for data common to all U.S. funds)

Sub-adviser: Batterymarch Financial Management
Portfolio manager: Virginie Maisonneuve (1994)
Investment objective and policies: Growth of capital by pursuing investment opportunities directly in or related to the People's Republic of China. Invests primarily in securities of Chinese enterprises through the Shenzhen, Shanghai and Hong Kong stock exchanges. May also use securities of companies that have business associations in China and are listed on other China Region stock exchanges. May use ADRs and GDRs. Up to 15% of assets may be in unlisted securities.
Year organized: 1994
Ticker symbol: USCOX
Discount broker availability: *Schwab
Redemption fee: 1% for shares held less than 180 days
Dividends paid: Income - March, June, September, December, Capital gains - December
Portfolio turnover (1 yr): 12%
Largest holding: Citic Pacific Ltd. (2.8%)
Management fee: 1.25%
Maintenance fee: $3 per quarter
Expense ratio: 1.88% (5 months ending 6/30/94) (3.26% without waiver)

UNITED SERVICES EUROPEAN INCOME FUND ◆
(Fund liquidated on 12/30/94)

UNITED SERVICES GLOBAL RESOURCES FUND ◆
(See first United Services listing for data common to all U.S. funds)

Portfolio manager: Ralph P. Aldis (1992)
Investment objective and policies: Long term growth of capital with protection against inflation and monetary instability. Invests in common stocks of companies all over the world engaged in exploration, mining, processing, fabrication and distribution of natural resources of any kind—metals, timber, minerals and hydrocarbons. No investments will be made in South African stocks.
Year organized: 1983 (formerly U.S. Prospector Fund. Name and policies changed on 1/26/90. 10 for 1 reverse split 10/1/90)
Ticker symbol: PSPFX
Discount broker availability: *Schwab, *White, Waterhouse, *Fidelity, *Siebert

Dividends paid: Income - December; Capital gains - December
Portfolio turnover (3 yrs): 58%, 120%, 55%
Largest holding: American Barrick Resources Corp. (6.6%)
Management fee: 1.00% first $250M, 0.5% over $250M
Expense ratio: 2.43% (year ending 6/30/94) (2.44% without waiver)

UNITED SERVICES GOLD SHARES FUND ◆
(See first United Services listing for data common to all U.S. funds)

Portfolio manager: Victor Flores (1992)
Investment objective and policies: Growth of capital with protection against inflation and monetary instability with current income secondary. Invests primarily in common stocks of companies involved in the exploration for, mining and processing of, or dealing in gold. Fund will invest a substantial portion of assets in South Africa. Fund may hold bullion.
Year organized: 1970 (present objective since July 1974)
Ticker symbol: USERX
Discount broker availability: Schwab, White, Waterhouse
Dividends paid: Income - June, December; Capital gains - December
Portfolio turnover (3 yrs): 29%, 20%, 25%
Largest holding: Free State Consolidated Gold Mines, Ltd., ADR (11.8%)
Management fee: 0.75% first $250M, 0.5% over $250M
Expense ratio: 1.46% (year ending 6/30/94) (1.52% without waiver)

UNITED SERVICES GOVERNMENT SECURITIES SAVINGS FUND ◆
(See first United Services listing for data common to all U.S. funds)

Portfolio manager: Victor Flores (1994)
Investment objective and policies: Highest yield consistent with safety of principal and liquidity. Invests exclusively in short-term money market obligations of the U.S. Government and its agencies and instrumentalities.
Year organized: 1986 (formerly GNMA Fund; name and objective change as of 11/1/90)
Ticker symbol: UGSXX
Dividends paid: Income - declared daily, paid monthly
Check redemptions: $500 minimum
Confirmations mailed: After each mail or wire redemption
Checks returned: On request
Periodic account statements mailed: Monthly
Account fee: $5 per month if balance is less than $1,000
Management fee: 0.50% of first $250M, 0.375% over $250M
Expense ratio: 0.16% (year ending 6/30/94) (0.71% without waiver)

UNITED SERVICES GROWTH FUND ◆
(Fund liquidated on 12/30/94)

UNITED SERVICES INCOME FUND ◆
(See first United Services listing for data common to all U.S. funds)

Portfolio manager: Frank E. Holmes (1993)
Investment objective and policies: Preservation of capital and current income with long-term capital appreciation secondary. Invests at least 80% of assets in income-producing securities - dividend-paying common stocks, securities convertible into common stocks, REITs, corporate debt securities, U.S. government obligations and securities of for-

eign issuers traded in the U.S. Fund may use options and hedge up to 25% of total assets.
Year organized: 1983
Ticker symbol: USINX
Discount broker availability: *Schwab, *White, Waterhouse
Dividends paid: Income - March, June, September, December; Capital gains - December
Portfolio turnover (3 yrs): 7%, 44%, 76%
Largest holding: Empresa Nacional de Electricidad, SA, ADR (3.7%)
Management fee: 0.75% first $250M, 0.5% over $250M
Expense ratio: 1.74% (year ending 6/30/94) (1.79% without waiver)

UNITED SERVICES INTERMEDIATE TREASURY FUND ◆
(See first United Services listing for data common to all U.S. funds)

Portfolio manager: Allen A. Parker (1992)
Investment objective and policies: High current income and preservation of capital. Invests exclusively in U.S. Treasury securities with a weighted average maturity of 3 to 10 years.
Year organized: 1992
Dividends paid: Income - monthly; Capital gains - December
Portfolio turnover (2 yrs): 93%, 207%
Management fee: 0.50%
Expense ratio: 0.00% (year ending 6/30/94) (2.18% without waiver)

UNITED SERVICES NEAR-TERM TAX FREE FUND ◆
(See first United Services listing for data common to all U.S. funds)

Portfolio manager: Allen A. Parker (1992)
Investment objective and policies: High level of current income exempt from federal income tax consistent with preservation of capital. Invests primarily in investment-grade municipal securities rated Baa or better by Moody's or BBB or better by S&P with weighted average maturity of five years or less.
Year organized: 1990 (name and objective changed from United Services California Double Tax Free Fund in 1993; previous data may be misleading)
Dividends paid: Income - monthly; Capital gains - December
Portfolio turnover (3 yrs): 140%, 45%, 42%
Management fee: 0.50%
Expense ratio: 0.00 (year ending 6/30/94) (1.80% without waiver)

UNITED SERVICES REAL ESTATE FUND ◆
(See first United Services listing for data common to all U.S. funds)

Portfolio manager: Allen A. Parker (1987)
Investment objective and policies: Long-term capital appreciation with current income secondary. Invests primarily in common and preferred stock of companies having at least 50% of their assets in or deriving at least 50% of their revenues from the ownership, construction, management or sale of residential, commercial or industrial real estate. Up to 35% of assets may be in securities of foreign issuers. Fund may use options and hedge up to 25% of total assets.
Year organized: 1987
Ticker symbol: USREX
Discount broker availability: *Schwab, *White, Waterhouse, *Fidelity, *Siebert.
Dividends paid: Income - June, December; Capital gains - December
Portfolio turnover (3 yrs): 145%, 187%, 103%
Largest holding: United Dominion Realty Trust, Inc. (4.7%)
Management fee: 0.75% first $250M, 0.5% over $250M
Expense ratio: 1.59% (year ending 6/30/94) (1.62% without waiver)

UNITED SERVICES SPECIAL-TERM GOVERNMENT FUND ◆
(See first United Services listing for data common to all United Services funds)

Portfolio managers: Ralph P. Aldis (1994), Creston King (1994)
Investment objective and policies: High current income consistent with low volatility of principal. Invests at least 65% of assets in U.S. Government agency floating rate securities whose interest rates are adjustable and reset weekly, monthly, quarterly, semi-annually or annually. May also invest in other U.S. Government obligations - U.S. Treasury securities and securities issued by the Federal Home Loan Banks, Federal Farm Credit Banks and Student Loan Marketing Association.
Year organized: 1993
Ticker symbol: USTGX
Discount broker availability: White
Dividends paid: Income - declared daily, paid monthly, Capital gains - December
Portfolio turnover (2 yrs): 73%, 20%
Management fee: 0.50%
Expense ratio: 0.05% (year ending 6/30/94) (0.88% without waiver)

UNITED SERVICES TAX FREE FUND ◆
(See first United Services listing for data common to all U.S. funds)

Portfolio manager: Allen A. Parker (1990)
Investment objective and policies: High level of current income exempt from federal income tax consistent with preservation of capital. Invests primarily in investment-grade municipal securities rated Baa or better by Moody's or BBB or better by S&P. In periods of accelerating inflation maturities will be 4-10 years, in periods when inflation is subsiding maturities will be 20-30 years.
Year organized: 1984
Ticker symbol: USUTX
Discount broker availability: Schwab, White, Waterhouse
Dividends paid: Income - monthly; Capital gains - December
Portfolio turnover (3 yrs): 51%, 94%, 70%
Management fee: 0.75% first $250M, 0.5% over $250M
Expense ratio: 0.00% (year ending 6/30/94) (1.46% without waiver)

UNITED SERVICES U.S. TREASURY SECURITIES CASH FUND ◆
(See first United Services listing for data common to all U.S. funds)

Portfolio manager: Allen A. Parker (1986)
Investment objective and policies: High current income consistent with safety and liquidity. Invests in U.S. Treasury money market securities and in repurchase agreements.
Year organized: 1982 (formerly U.S. Treasury Securities Fund. Name change 10/1/90.)
Ticker symbol: USTXX
Check redemptions: No minimum
Confirmations mailed: After each mail or wire redemption
Checks returned: On request
Periodic account statements mailed: Monthly
Dividends paid: Income - declared daily, paid monthly
Management fee: 0.50% first $250M, 0.375% over $250M
Expense ratio: 0.93% (year ending 6/30/94) (0.96% without waiver)

UNITED SERVICES WORLD GOLD FUND ◆
(See first United Services listing for data common to all U.S. funds)

Portfolio manager: Victor Flores (1988)
Investment objective and policies: Long-term growth of capital with protection against inflation and mone-

tary instability. Invests at least 65% of assets in the securities of companies involved in the exploration for, mining and processing of, or dealing in gold. At least 25% will be invested in companies engaged in natural resource operations. Fund will not invest in South Africa. Fund may hold bullion.
Year organized: 1985 (formerly New Prospector Fund. Name and investment policy changes, 10 for 1 reverse split, effected 10/1/90)
Ticker symbol: UNWPX
Discount broker availability: *Schwab, *White, Waterhouse, *Fidelity, *Siebert
Dividends paid: Income - December; Capital gains - December
Portfolio turnover (3 yrs): 20%, 26%, 47%
Largest holding: Delta Gold N.L. (10.1%)
Management fee: 1.00% first $250M, 0.5% over $250M
Expense ratio: 0.66% (year ending 6/30/94) (1.57% without waiver)

USAA FUNDS ◆
(Data common to all USAA funds are shown below. See subsequent listings for data specific to individual USAA funds.)

USAA Building
9800 Fredericksburg Rd.
San Antonio, TX 78288
210-498-6505, 800-382-8722
800-531-8181, TDD 800-531-4327
prices/yields 800-531-8066

Shareholder service hours: Full service: M-F 8 A.M.-8 P.M. CST; After hours service: prices, yields, balances, last transaction
Adviser: USAA Investment Management Co.
Custodian: State Street Bank & Trust Co.
Transfer agent: USAA Transfer Agency Co.
Telephone orders accepted: No
Wire orders accepted: Subsequent only
Deadline for same day wire purchase: 4 P.M.
Qualified for sale in: All states (except single state tax-exempt funds)
Telephone redemptions: Yes
Wire redemptions: Yes $1,000 minimum, $10 fee
Letter redemptions: Signature guarantee not required
Telephone switching: With other USAA funds
Number of switches permitted: 6 per year (unlimited for short-term bond and money market funds)
Shareholder services: IRA, SEP-IRA, 403(b), automatic investment plan, electronic funds transfer, directed dividends, withdrawal plan min. req. $10,000
IRA fees: Closing $20

USAA AGGRESSIVE GROWTH FUND ◆
(See first USAA listing for data common to all USAA funds)

Portfolio manager: William V. Fries (1994)
Investment objective and policies: Capital appreciation. Invests in common stocks and other securities convertible into common stocks of smaller, emerging growth companies with market capitalizations of less than $500M. Up to 30% of assets may be in securities of foreign issuers.
Year organized: 1981 (a portfolio of USAA Mutual Fund, Inc., formerly USAA Sunbelt Era. Prior to name change in February 1989, fund concentrated its investments in the Sunbelt region.)
Ticker symbol: USAUX
Minimum purchase: Initial: $1,000, Subsequent: $50
Discount broker availability: White
Dividends paid: Income - November; Capital gains - November
Portfolio turnover (3 yrs): 99%, 113%, 74%
Largest holding: Clear Channel Communications, Inc. (2.9%)
Management fee: 0.5% first $200M to 0.33% over $300M
Expense ratio: 0.83% (10 months ending 7/31/94)

USAA BALANCED PORTFOLIO FUND ◆

(See first USAA listing for data common to all USAA funds)

Portfolio managers: John W. Saunders, Jr. (asset allocation) (1989), Mark W. Johnson, Steve Klaffke, Kenneth E. Willmann
Investment objective and policies: Conservative balance between income (at least 50% exempt from federal income tax) and long term capital growth. Fund normally invests 30% in short-term tax-exempt securities, 30% in long-term tax exempt securities and 40% in basic value stocks. Up to 15% of assets may be in illiquid securities. Fund may hedge in forward currency markets.
Year organized: 1989 (a portfolio of USAA Investment Trust)
Ticker symbol: USBLX
Minimum purchase: Initial: $1,000, Subsequent: $50
Discount broker availability: White
Dividends paid: Income - March, June, September, December; Capital gains - November
Portfolio turnover (3 yrs): 171%, 99%, 107%
Largest holding: Georgia Municipal Electric Authority Bond (4.6%)
Management fee: 0.50%
Expense ratio: 0.84% (8 months ending 5/31/94)

USAA CALIFORNIA BOND FUND ◆

(See first USAA listing for data common to all USAA funds)

Portfolio manager: David G. Miller (1989)
Investment objective and policies: High level of interest income exempt from federal and California state income taxes. Invests in California municipal securities having maturities with no upper limit with a weighted average maturity greater than 10 years.
Year organized: 1989 (a portfolio of USAA Tax-Exempt Fund)
Ticker symbol: USCBX
Minimum purchase: Initial: $3,000, Subsequent: $50
Qualified for sale in: CA
Dividends paid: Income - declared daily, paid monthly; Capital gains - May, November
Portfolio turnover (3 yrs): 103%, 87%, 51%
Management fee: 0.5% first $50M to 0.3% over $100M (for assets of California Bond and Money Market funds combined)
Expense ratio: 0.44% (year ending 3/31/94)

USAA CALIFORNIA MONEY MARKET FUND ◆

(See first USAA listing for data common to all USAA funds)

Portfolio manager: Robert R. Pariseau (1993)
Investment objective and policies: High level of interest income exempt from federal and California state income taxes. Invests in California municipal money market securities.
Year organized: 1989 (a portfolio of USAA Tax-Exempt Fund)
Ticker symbol: UCAXX
Minimum purchase: Initial: $3,000, Subsequent: $50
Qualified for sale in: CA
Check redemptions: $250 minimum ($5 setup fee)
Confirmations mailed: After each purchase and each check, mail or wire redemption
Checks returned: As clear
Periodic account statements mailed: Quarterly
Dividends paid: Income - declared daily, paid monthly
Management fee: 0.5% first $50M to 0.3% over $100M (for assets of California Bond and Money Market funds combined)
Expense ratio: 0.49% (year ending 3/31/94)

USAA CORNERSTONE FUND ◆

(See first USAA listing for data common to all USAA funds)

Portfolio managers: Harry W. Miller (asset allocation) (1989), Steve Klaffke, John W. Saunders, Jr., Mark W. Johnson, Travis Selmier
Investment objective and policies: Preserve purchasing power of capital against inflation and achieve a "real" (inflation adjusted) rate of return by investing in gold stocks, foreign stocks, real estate stocks, U.S. Government securities, and domestic stocks believed undervalued. Percentage in each category can range from 20% to 25% (8% to 12% for gold stocks).
Year organized: 1984 (a portfolio of USAA Investment Trust)
Ticker symbol: USCRX
Minimum purchase: Initial: $1,000, Subsequent: $50
Discount broker availability: White
Dividends paid: Income - November; Capital gains - November
Portfolio turnover (3 yrs): 31%, 45%, 33%
Largest holding: GNMA 7.0% due 8/15/23 (2.8%)
Management fee: 0.75%
Expense ratio: 1.11% (8 months ending 5/31/94)

USAA EMERGING MARKETS FUND ◆

(See first USAA listing for data common to all USAA funds)

Portfolio manager: W. Travis Selmier II (1994)
Investment objective and policies: Capital appreciation. Invests at least 65% of assets in common stocks and other securities convertible into common stocks of emerging market companies. May use ADRs and GDRs and invest directly on foreign stock exchanges. May use forward foreign currency contracts to hedge.
Year organized: 1994 (a portfolio of USAA Investment Trust)
Ticker symbol: USEMX
Minimum purchase: Initial: $1,000, Subsequent: $50
Dividends paid: Income - November; Capital gains - November
Management fee: 1.0%

USAA FLORIDA TAX-FREE INCOME FUND ◆

(See first USAA listing for data common to all USAA funds)

Portfolio manager: David G. Miller (1994)
Investment objective and policies: High level of interest income exempt from federal income and Florida intangible personal property taxes. Invests in Florida municipal securities having maturities with no upper limit with a weighted average maturity greater than 10 years. Up to 20% of assets may be in AMT securities.
Year organized: 1993 (a portfolio of USAA Tax-Exempt Fund)
Ticker symbol: UFLTX
Minimum purchase: Initial: $3,000, Subsequent: $50
Qualified for sale in: FL
Dividends paid: Income - declared daily, paid monthly; Capital gains - May, November
Portfolio turnover (1 yr): 284%
Management fee: 0.5% first $50M to 0.3% over $100M (for assets of Florida Tax-Free Income and Money Market funds combined)
Expense ratio: 0.50% (6 months ending 3/31/94) (1.33% without waiver)

USAA FLORIDA TAX-FREE MONEY MARKET FUND ◆

(See first USAA listing for data common to all USAA funds)

Portfolio manager: Robert R. Pariseau (1993)
Investment objective and policies: High level of

interest income exempt from federal income and Florida intangible personal property taxes. Invests in Florida municipal money market securities.
Year organized: 1993 (a portfolio of USAA Tax-Exempt Fund)
Ticker symbol: UFLXX
Minimum purchase: Initial: $3,000, Subsequent: $50
Qualified for sale in: FL
Check redemptions: $250 minimum ($5 setup fee)
Confirmations mailed: After each purchase and each check, mail or wire redemption
Checks returned: As clear
Periodic account statements mailed: Quarterly
Dividends paid: Income - declared daily, paid monthly
Management fee: 0.5% first $50M to 0.3% over $100M (for assets of Florida Tax-Free Income and Money Market funds combined)
Expense ratio: 0.50% (6 months ending 3/31/94) (1.11% without waiver)

USAA GNMA TRUST ◆

(See first USAA listing for data common to all USAA funds)

Portfolio manager: Carl Wilson Shirley (1991)
Investment objective and policies: High level of current income consistent with preservation of principal. Invests in securities backed by the full faith and credit of the U.S. Government. At least 65% invested in GNMA pass-through certificates; remaining 35% or less in obligations back by the full faith and credit of the U.S. Government.
Year organized: 1991 (a portfolio of USAA Investment Trust)
Ticker symbol: USGNX
Minimum purchase: Initial: $3,000, Subsequent: $50; IRA: Initial $1,000
Discount broker availability: White
Dividends paid: Income - declared daily, paid monthly; Capital gains - September
Portfolio turnover (3 yrs): 90%, 81%, 36%
Management fee: 0.125%
Expense ratio: 0.31% (8 months ending 5/31/94)

USAA GOLD FUND ◆

(See first USAA listing for data common to all USAA funds)

Portfolio manager: Mark W. Johnson (1994)
Investment objective and policies: Long-term capital appreciation while protecting purchasing power of capital against inflation with current income secondary. Invests at least 80% of assets in equity securities of companies engaged in gold exploration, mining, or processing; remainder of assets in companies similarly engaged in silver, platinum, diamonds, and other precious metals and minerals.
Year organized: 1984 (a portfolio of USAA Investment Trust)
Ticker symbol: USAGX
Minimum purchase: Initial: $1,000, Subsequent: $50
Discount broker availability: White
Dividends paid: Income - November; Capital gains - November
Portfolio turnover (3 yrs): 35%, 81%, 19%
Largest holding: American Barrick Resources Corp. (8.0%)
Management fee: 0.75%
Expense ratio: 1.26% (8 months ending 5/31/94)

USAA GROWTH FUND ◆

(See first USAA listing for data common to all USAA funds)

Portfolio manager: David Parsons (1994)
Investment objective and policies: Long-term growth of capital with income and conservation of principal secondary. Invests primarily in common stocks and securities convertible into common stocks of established companies believed to have growth potential. May invest 10% of assets in foreign securities.
Year organized: 1970 (a portfolio of USAA Mutual Fund, Inc.)

Ticker symbol: USAAX
Minimum purchase: Initial: $1,000, Subsequent: $50
Discount broker availability: White
Dividends paid: Income - November; Capital gains - November
Portfolio turnover (3 yrs): 118%, 96%, 39%
Largest holding: Philip Morris Companies, Inc. (5.3%)
Management fee: 0.75%
Expense ratio: 1.04% (10 months ending 7/31/94)

USAA GROWTH & INCOME FUND ◆
(See first USAA listing for data common to all USAA funds)

Portfolio manager: David R. Ullom (1993)
Investment objective and policies: Capital growth and current income. Invests primarily in dividend-paying common stocks and securities convertible into common stocks. May also invest in non-convertible debt securities and non-convertible preferred stocks. Up to 10% of assets in may be in securities of foreign issuers traded in the U.S.
Year organized: 1993 (a portfolio of USAA Mutual Fund, Inc.)
Ticker symbol: USGRX
Minimum purchase: Initial: $1,000, Subsequent: $50
Dividends paid: Income - March, June, September, December; Capital gains - November
Portfolio turnover (2 yrs): 14%, 11%
Largest holding: Xerox Corp. (2.3%)
Management fee: 0.60%
Expense ratio: 1.12% (10 months ending 9/30/94)

USAA INCOME FUND ◆
(See first USAA listing for data common to all USAA funds)

Portfolio manager: John W. Saunders, Jr. (1985)
Investment objective and policies: Maximum current income without undue risk to principal. Invests in U.S. dollar-denominated securities selected for their high yields relative to the risk involved and interest rates. May invest in bonds, preferred and common stock or up to 100% in short term securities.
Year organized: 1973 (a portfolio of USAA Mutual Fund, Inc.)
Ticker symbol: USAIX
Discount broker availability: White
Dividends paid: Income - monthly, Capital gains - November
Portfolio turnover (3 yrs): 25%, 45%, 22%
Management fee: 0.24%
Expense ratio: 0.41% (10 months ending 9/30/94)

USAA INCOME STOCK FUND ◆
(See first USAA listing for data common to all USAA funds)

Portfolio manager: Harry W. Miller (1989)
Investment objective and policies: Current income with prospect of increasing dividend income and the potential for capital appreciation. Invests primarily in higher than average dividend-paying common stocks of well established, large companies. May also invest in convertible securities and hedge on 5% of assets.
Year organized: 1987 (a portfolio of USAA Mutual Fund, Inc.)
Ticker symbol: USISX
Minimum purchase: Initial: $1,000, Subsequent: $50
Discount broker availability: White
Dividends paid: Income - March, June, September, December; Capital gains - November
Portfolio turnover (3 yrs): 25%, 27%, 16%
Largest holding: Dow Chemical Corp. (5.2%)
Management fee: 0.5%
Expense ratio: 0.73% (year ending 7/31/94)

USAA INTERNATIONAL FUND ◆
(See first USAA listing for data common to all USAA funds)

Portfolio manager: David G. Peebles (1988)
Investment objective and policies: Capital appreciation with current income secondary. Invests at least 80% of assets in equity securities, and securities convertible into equity securities, of companies organized and operating principally outside the U.S. Fund will invest in at least four different countries. May use forward currency contracts to hedge.
Year organized: 1988 (a portfolio of USAA Investment Trust)
Ticker symbol: USIFX
Minimum purchase: Initial: $1,000, Subsequent: $50
Discount broker availability: White
Dividends paid: Income - November; Capital gains - November
Portfolio turnover (3 yrs): 44%, 53%, 34%
Largest holding: Minebea Co., Ltd. (1.8%)
Management fee: 0.75%
Expense ratio: 1.31% (8 months ending 5/31/94)

USAA MONEY MARKET FUND ◆
(See first USAA listing for data common to all USAA funds)

Portfolio manager: Eric Thorderson (1994)
Investment objective and policies: High income consistent with preservation of capital and liquidity. Invests in short-term money market instruments.
Year organized: 1981 (a portfolio of USAA Mutual Fund, Inc.)
Ticker symbol: USAXX
Minimum purchase: Initial: $1,000, Subsequent: $50
Check redemptions: $250 minimum ($5 setup fee)
Confirmations mailed: After each purchase and each check, mail or wire redemption
Checks returned: As clear
Periodic account statements mailed: Quarterly
Dividends paid: Income - declared daily, paid monthly
Management fee: 0.24%
Expense ratio: 0.46% (10 months ending 7/31/94)

USAA NEW YORK BOND FUND ◆
(See first USAA listing for data common to all USAA funds)

Portfolio manager: Kenneth E. Willmann (1990)
Investment objective and policies: High level of current interest income exempt from federal and New York State and City income taxes. Invests primarily in New York municipal securities, at least 75% of which must be investment grade. Weighted average maturity is expected to be over 10 years.
Year organized: 1990 (a portfolio of USAA Tax-Exempt Fund)
Ticker symbol: USNYX
Qualified for sale in: NY
Minimum purchase: Initial: $3,000, Subsequent: $50
Dividends paid: Income - declared daily, paid monthly; Capital gains - May, November
Portfolio turnover (3 yrs): 124%, 107%, 111%
Management fee: 0.5% of first $50M to 0.3% over $100M (combined assets of New York Bond and Money Market funds)
Expense ratio: 0.50% (year ending 3/31/94) (0.69% without waiver)

USAA NEW YORK MONEY MARKET FUND ◆
(See first USAA listing for data common to all USAA funds)

Portfolio manager: Robert R. Pariseau (1994)
Investment objective and policies: High level of current interest income exempt from federal and New York State and City income taxes. Invests primarily in New York municipal money market securities.

Year organized: 1982 (a portfolio of USAA Tax-Exempt Fund)
Qualified for sale in: NY
Minimum purchase: Initial: $3,000, Subsequent: $50
Check redemptions: $250 minimum ($5 setup fee)
Confirmations mailed: After each purchase and each check, mail or wire redemption
Checks returned: As clear
Periodic account statements mailed: Quarterly
Dividends paid: Income - declared daily, paid monthly
Management fee: 0.5% of first $50M to 0.3% over $100M (combined assets of New York Bond and Money Market funds)
Expense ratio: 0.50% (year ending 3/31/94) (0.98% without waiver)

USAA SHORT-TERM BOND FUND ◆
(See first USAA listing for data common to all USAA funds)

Portfolio manager: Paul Lundmark (1993)
Investment objective and policies: Current income consistent with preservation of capital. Invests primarily in U.S. dollar-denominated investment-grade debt securities with a weighted average maturity of 3 years or less. May invest in U.S. Government and government agency and instrumentality obligations, mortgage-backed securities, U.S. and foreign corporate debt securities, U.S. & foreign bank obligations, obligations of state and local governments and their agencies and instrumentalities, and asset-backed securities.
Year organized: 1993 (a portfolio of USAA Mutual Fund, Inc.)
Ticker symbol: USSBX
Minimum purchase: Initial: $1,000, Subsequent: $50
Dividends paid: Income - declared daily, paid monthly; Capital gains - November
Portfolio turnover (2 yrs): 142%, 32%
Management fee: 0.24%
Expense ratio: 0.50% (10 months ending 7/31/94) (0.87% without waiver)

USAA TAX EXEMPT INTERMEDIATE-TERM FUND ◆
(See first USAA listing for data common to all USAA funds)

Newspaper listing: TxEIt
Portfolio manager: Clifford A. Gladson (1993)
Investment objective and policies: High level of interest income exempt from federal income tax. Invests in investment-grade tax-exempt securities having maturities of no more than 12 years with a weighted average maturity of 3 to 10 years.
Year organized: 1982 (a portfolio of USAA Tax-Exempt Fund)
Ticker symbol: USATX
Minimum purchase: Initial: $3,000, Subsequent: $50
Discount broker availability: White
Dividends paid: Income - declared daily, paid monthly; Capital gains - May, November
Portfolio turnover (3 yrs): 69%, 74%, 67%
Management fee: 0.28%
Expense ratio: 0.40% (year ending 3/31/94)

USAA TAX-EXEMPT LONG-TERM FUND ◆
(See first USAA listing for data common to all USAA funds)

Newspaper listing: TxELT
Portfolio manager: Kenneth E. Willmann (1982)
Investment objective and policies: High level of interest income exempt from federal income tax. Invests in investment-grade tax-exempt securities with a weighted average maturity of 10 years or more.
Year organized: 1982 (a portfolio of USAA Tax-Exempt Fund) (formerly Tax-Exempt High Yield Fund. Name and objective changed on 8/7/92)
Ticker symbol: USTEX

Minimum purchase: Initial: $3,000, Subsequent: $50
Discount broker availability: White
Dividends paid: Income - declared daily, paid monthly; Capital gains - May, November
Portfolio turnover (3 yrs): 109%, 88%, 76%
Management fee: 0.28%
Expense ratio: 0.38% (year ending 3/31/94)

USAA TAX EXEMPT MONEY MARKET FUND ◆
(See first USAA listing for data common to all USAA funds)

Portfolio manager: Thomas Ramos (1994)
Investment objective and policies: High level of interest income exempt from federal income tax. Invests in investment-grade municipal money market securities having individual maturities of one year or less.
Year organized: 1984 (a portfolio of USAA Tax-Exempt Fund)
Ticker symbol: USEXX
Minimum purchase: Initial: $3,000, Subsequent: $50
Number of switches permitted: Unlimited, $5 fee
Check redemptions: $250 minimum ($5 setup fee)
Confirmations mailed: After each purchase and each check, mail or wire redemption
Checks returned: As clear
Periodic account statements mailed: Quarterly
Dividends paid: Income - declared daily, paid monthly
Management fee: 0.28%
Expense ratio: 0.40% (year ending 3/31/94)

USAA TAX EXEMPT SHORT-TERM FUND ◆
(See first USAA listing for data common to all USAA funds)

Newspaper listing: TxEST
Portfolio manager: Clifford A. Gladson (1994)
Investment objective and policies: High level of interest income exempt from federal income tax. Invests in investment-grade tax-exempt securities having maturities of no more than 5 years with a weighted average maturity of less than 3 years.
Year organized: 1982 (a portfolio of USAA Tax-Exempt Fund)
Ticker symbol: USSTX
Minimum purchase: Initial: $3,000, Subsequent: $50
Discount broker availability: White
Check redemptions: $250 minimum ($5 setup fee)
Confirmations mailed: After each purchase and each check, mail or wire redemption
Dividends paid: Income - declared daily, paid monthly; Capital gains - May
Portfolio turnover (3 yrs): 102%, 138%, 107%
Management fee: 0.28%
Expense ratio: 0.43% (year ending 3/31/94)

USAA TEXAS TAX-FREE INCOME FUND ◆
(See first USAA listing for data common to all USAA funds)

Portfolio manager: David G. Miller (1994)
Investment objective and policies: High level of current interest income exempt from federal income taxes. Invests primarily in Texas municipal securities, at least 75% of which must be investment grade. Weighted average maturity is expected to be over 10 years.
Year organized: 1994 (a portfolio of USAA State Tax-Free Trust)
Qualified for sale in: TX
Minimum purchase: Initial: $3,000, Subsequent: $50
Dividends paid: Income - declared daily, paid monthly; Capital gains - May, November
Management fee: 0.5% of first $50M to 0.3% over $100M (combined assets of Texas Tax-Free Income and Money Market funds)

USAA TEXAS TAX-FREE MONEY MARKET FUND ◆
(See first USAA listing for data common to all USAA funds)

Portfolio manager: Robert R. Pariseau (1994)
Investment objective and policies: High level of current interest income exempt from federal income taxes. Invests primarily in Texas municipal money market securities with individual maturities of less than 1 year.
Year organized: 1994 (a portfolio of USAA State Tax-Free Trust)
Qualified for sale in: VA
Minimum purchase: Initial: $3,000, Subsequent: $50
Check redemptions: $250 minimum ($5 setup fee)
Confirmations mailed: After each purchase and each check, mail or wire redemption
Checks returned: As clear
Periodic account statements mailed: Quarterly
Dividends paid: Income - declared daily, paid monthly
Management fee: 0.5% of first $50M to 0.3% over $100M (combined assets of Texas Tax-Free Income and Money Market funds)

USAA TREASURY MONEY MARKET TRUST ◆
(See first USAA listing for data common to all USAA funds)

Portfolio manager: Eric Thorderson (1994)
Investment objective and policies: Maximum current income while maintaining the highest degree of safety and liquidity. Invests exclusively in short-term money market securities backed by the full faith and credit of the U.S. Government. At least 65% in Treasury bills, notes and bonds and repurchase agreements thereon.
Year organized: 1991 (a portfolio of USAA Investment Trust)
Ticker symbol: UATXX
Minimum purchase: Initial: $3,000, Subsequent: $50; IRA: Initial: $1,000
Check redemptions: $250 minimum ($5 setup fee)
Confirmations mailed: After each purchase and each check, mail or wire redemption
Checks returned: As clear
Periodic account statements mailed: Quarterly
Dividends paid: Income - declared daily, paid monthly
Management fee: 0.125%
Expense ratio: 0.375% (8 months ending 5/31/94) (0.62% without waiver)

USAA VIRGINIA BOND FUND ◆
(See first USAA listing for data common to all USAA funds)

Portfolio manager: David G. Miller (1994)
Investment objective and policies: High level of current interest income exempt from federal and Virginia income taxes. Invests primarily in Virginia municipal securities, at least 75% of which must be investment grade. Weighted average maturity is expected to be over 10 years.
Year organized: 1990 (a portfolio of USAA Tax-Exempt Fund)
Ticker symbol: USVAX
Qualified for sale in: VA
Minimum purchase: Initial: $3,000, Subsequent: $50
Dividends paid: Income - declared daily, paid monthly; Capital gains - May, November
Portfolio turnover (3 yrs): 92%, 91%, 87%
Management fee: 0.5% of first $50M to 0.3% over $100M (combined assets of Virginia Bond and Money Market funds)
Expense ratio: 0.49% (year ending 3/31/94)

USAA VIRGINIA MONEY MARKET FUND ◆
(See first USAA listing for data common to all USAA funds)

Portfolio manager: Robert R. Pariseau (1993)
Investment objective and policies: High level of current interest income exempt from federal and Virginia income taxes. Invests primarily in Virginia municipal money market securities with individual maturities of less than 1 year.
Year organized: 1990 (a portfolio of USAA Tax-Exempt Trust)
Ticker symbol: UVAXX
Qualified for sale in: VA
Minimum purchase: Initial: $3,000, Subsequent: $50
Check redemptions: $250 minimum ($5 setup fee)
Confirmations mailed: After each purchase and each check, mail or wire redemption
Checks returned: As clear
Periodic account statements mailed: Quarterly
Dividends paid: Income - declared daily, paid monthly
Management fee: 0.5% of first $50M to 0.3% over $100M (combined assets of Virginia Bond and Money Market funds)
Expense ratio: 0.50% (year ending 3/31/94) (0.61% without waiver)

USAA WORLD GROWTH FUND ◆
(See first USAA listing for data common to all USAA funds)

Portfolio managers: David G. Peebles (1992), Harry W. Miller (1992)
Investment objective and policies: Capital appreciation. Invests in common stocks and other equity securities of both foreign and domestic issuers, including securities convertible into common stocks. Normally invests in at least three countries, one of which may be the U.S. May use forward foreign currency contracts to hedge.
Year organized: 1992 (a portfolio of USAA Investment Trust)
Ticker symbol: USAWX
Minimum purchase: Initial: $1,000, Subsequent: $50
Dividends paid: Income - November; Capital gains - November
Portfolio turnover (2 yrs): 38%, 46%
Largest holding: Minebea Co., Ltd. (1.3%)
Management fee: 0.75%
Expense ratio: 1.28% (8 months ending 5/31/94)

UST MASTER GOVERNMENT MONEY FUND ◆

73 Tremont Street
Boston, MA 02108
617-956-9744, 800-233-1136
800-446-1012, yields 800-233-9180

Adviser: United States Trust Company of New York
Portfolio manager: Christine Rugino (1985)
Custodian and transfer agent: United States Trust Company of New York
Investment objective and policies: Current income consistent with preservation of capital and liquidity. Invests in money market instruments, issued or guaranteed by the U.S. Government, its agencies or instrumentalities.
Year organized: 1985 (a portfolio of UST Master Funds, Inc.)
Ticker symbol: UTGXX
Special sales restrictions: Sold to customers of the United States Trust Co. of NY and its affiliated and correspondent banks as well as to the general public.
Minimum purchase: Initial: $500, Subsequent: $50
Telephone orders accepted: No
Wire orders accepted: Yes
Deadline for same day wire purchase: 12 NN
Qualified for sale in: All states
Telephone redemptions: Yes
Wire redemptions: Yes, $1,000 minimum, $8 fee
Letter redemptions: Signature guarantee required over $50,000
Telephone switching: With other UST funds (UST equity funds have loads) and Gintel funds
Number of switches permitted: Unlimited
Check redemptions: $500 minimum
Checks returned: Monthly
Dividends paid: Income - declared daily, paid monthly

Shareholder services: Keogh, IRA, 401(k), & corporate retirement plans, automatic investment plan, withdrawal plan min. req. $10,000
Management fee: 0.25%
Administration fee: 0.2% first $200M to 0.15% over $400M combined UST assets
Expense ratio: 0.50% (year ending 3/31/94)
IRA/Keogh fees: Annual $10, Initial $5

UST MASTER: MONEY FUND ◆
73 Tremont Street
Boston, MA 02108
617-956-9744, 800-233-1136
800-446-1012, yields 800-233-9180

Adviser: United States Trust Company of New York
Portfolio manager: Christine Rugino (1985)
Custodian and transfer agent: United States Trust Company of New York
Investment objective and policies: Current income. Invests in money market instruments.
Year organized: 1985 (a portfolio of UST Master Funds, Inc.)
Ticker symbol: UTMXX
Special sales restrictions: Sold to customers of the United States Trust Co. of NY and its affiliated and correspondent banks as well as to the general public.
Minimum purchase: Initial: $500, Subsequent: $50
Telephone orders accepted: No
Wire orders accepted: Yes
Deadline for same day wire purchase: 12 NN
Qualified for sale in: All states
Telephone redemptions: Yes
Wire redemptions: Yes, $1,000 minimum, $8 fee
Letter redemptions: Signature guarantee required over $50,000
Telephone switching: With other UST funds (UST equity funds have loads) and Gintel funds
Number of switches permitted: Unlimited
Check redemptions: $500 minimum
Checks returned: Monthly
Dividends paid: Income - declared daily, paid monthly
Shareholder services: Keogh, IRA, 401(k), & corporate retirement plans, automatic investment plan, withdrawal plan min. req. $10,000
Management fee: 0.25%
Administration fee: 0.2% first $200M to 0.15% over $400M combined UST assets
Expense ratio: 0.51% (year ending 3/31/94)
IRA/Keogh fees: Annual $10, Initial $5

VALLEY FORGE FUND, INC. ◆
P.O. Box 262
Valley Forge, PA 19087
610-688-6839, 800-548-1942
fax 610-429-0214

Adviser: Valley Forge Management Corp.
Portfolio manager: Bernard B. Klawans (1971)
Custodian and transfer agent: Valley Forge Fund, Inc.
Investment objective and policies: Capital appreciation. Invests in common stocks and convertible securities, but will invest temporarily in short term debt securities to defend capital in periods of falling stock prices. Fund is non-diversified.
Year organized: 1971
Ticker symbol: VAFGX
Minimum purchase: Initial: $1,000, Subsequent: $100; IRA: Initial: $250
Telephone orders accepted: Yes
Wire orders accepted: Yes
Deadline for same day wire purchases: 2 P.M.
Qualified for sale in: All states
Letter redemptions: Signature guarantee required
Dividends paid: Income - December; Capital gains - December
Portfolio turnover (3 yrs): 22%, 22%, 46%
Largest holding: Dun & Bradstreet Corp. (6.0%)
Shareholder services: IRA, regular investment plan—minimum $100/month (waives initial minimum)

Management fee: 1.0%
Expense ratio: 1.4% (year ending 12/31/93)
IRA fees: None

VALUE LINE FUNDS
(Data common to all Value Line funds are shown below. See subsequent listings for data specific to individual Value Line funds.)

220 East 42nd Street
New York, NY 10017
212-907-1500, 800-223-0818
prices/yields 800-243-2739
fax 816-435-1739

Shareholder service hours: Full service: M-F 8 A.M.-6 P.M. EST; After hours service: prices, yields, balances, orders, last transaction, total returns, exchanges
Adviser: Value Line, Inc.
Custodian & transfer agent: State Street Bank & Trust Co.
Telephone orders accepted: Subsequent only, $250 minimum, maximum twice shareholders existing balance
Wire orders accepted: Yes, $1,000 minimum
Deadline for same day wire purchase: 4 P.M.
Qualified for sale in: All states (except NY Tax Exempt Trust)
Telephone redemptions: Yes, $1,000 minimum
Wire redemptions: Yes, $1,000 minimum
Letter redemptions: Signature guarantee required
Telephone switching: With other Value Line Funds, $1,000 minimum
Number of switches permitted: 8 per year, 5 day hold
Shareholder services: Keogh, IRA, SEP-IRA, 403(b), automatic investment plan—minimum $40/month (waives initial minimum), withdrawal plan min. req. $5,000, electronic funds transfer
IRA/Keogh fees: Annual $10, Closing: $5

THE VALUE LINE ADJUSTABLE RATE U.S. GOVERNMENT SECURITIES FUND ◆
(See first Value Line listing for data common to all Value Line funds)

Investment objective and policies: High current income consistent with low volatility of principal. Invests at least 65% of assets in adjustable rate securities issued or guaranteed by the U.S. Government, its agencies and instrumentalities. Fund Hedges.
Year organized: 1992
Ticker symbol: VLUGX
Minimum purchase: Initial: $1,000, Subsequent: $250
Discount broker availability: Fidelity, Siebert
Check redemptions: $500 minimum
Dividends paid: Income - declared daily, paid monthly; Capital gains - December
Portfolio turnover (3 yrs): 175%, 126%, 85%
Management fee: 0.5%
Expense ratio: 0.98% (year ending 10/31/94)

VALUE LINE AGGRESSIVE INCOME TRUST ◆
(See first Value Line listing for data common to all Value Line funds)

Portfolio manager: Howard Udis (1990)
Investment objective and policies: Maximum current income with capital appreciation secondary. Invests at least 80% of assets in high-yielding junk bonds issued by companies that are rated B++ or lower for relative financial strength in The Value Line Investment Survey. May hedge up to 25% of assets and sell short.
Year organized: 1986
Ticker symbol: VAGIX
Minimum purchase: Initial: $1,000, Subsequent: $250

Discount broker availability: Schwab, *White, Waterhouse, Fidelity, Siebert
Check redemptions: $500 minimum
Dividends paid: Income - declared daily, paid monthly; Capital gains - December
Portfolio turnover (3 yrs): 320%, 148%, 59%
Management fee: 0.75% first $100M, 0.5% over $100M
Expense ratio: 1.20% (year ending 1/31/94)

THE VALUE LINE ASSET ALLOCATION FUND ◆
(See first Value Line listing for data common to all Value Line funds)

Investment objective and policies: High total return consistent with reasonable risk. Invests primarily in common stocks, bonds and money market instruments. Fund uses computer model to allocate assets among equity, debt and money market securities as economic and market conditions change. May use futures contracts and options and hedge and sell short. Neutral mix is 55% equity, 35% debt and 10% money market.
Year organized: 1993
Minimum purchase: Initial: $1,000, Subsequent: $100
Discount broker availability: *White, *Waterhouse, Fidelity, Siebert
Dividends paid: Income - December; Capital gains - December
Portfolio turnover (1 yr): 108%
Largest holding: U.S. Treasury Bond due 8/15/22 (7.9%)
Management fee: 0.65%
12b-1 distribution fee: 0.25% (not currently imposed)
Expense ratio: 0.47% (7 months ending 3/31/94) (2.24% without waiver)

THE VALUE LINE CASH FUND ◆
(See first Value Line listing for data common to all Value Line funds)

Portfolio manager: Charles Heebner (1989)
Investment objective and policies: Current income with liquidity and preservation of capital. Invests in short-term money market instruments.
Year organized: 1979
Ticker symbol: VLCXX
Minimum purchase: Initial: $1,000, Subsequent: $100
Check redemptions: $500 minimum
Confirmations mailed: After each purchase and each check, mail or wire redemption
Checks returned: Monthly
Periodic account statements mailed: Quarterly
Dividends paid: Income - declared and paid daily
Management fee: 0.40%
Expense ratio: 0.60% (year ending 12/31/93)

THE VALUE LINE CONVERTIBLE FUND ◆
(See first Value Line listing for data common to all Value Line funds)

Portfolio manager: Allan S. Lyons (1985)
Investment objective and policies: High current income with capital appreciation. Invests at least 70% of assets in convertible securities, i.e. bonds, debentures, corporate notes which are convertible into common stock. May hedge up to 25% of total assets and sell short.
Year organized: 1985
Ticker symbol: VALCX
Minimum purchase: Initial: $1,000, Subsequent: $250
Discount broker availability: Schwab, *White, Waterhouse, Fidelity, Siebert
Check redemptions: $500 minimum
Dividends paid: Income - March, June, September, December; Capital gains - December
Portfolio turnover (3 yrs): 142%, 146%, 140%
Management fee: 0.75%
Expense ratio: 1.07% (year ending 4/30/94)

THE VALUE LINE FUND ◆
(See first Value Line listing for data common to all Value Line funds)

Portfolio manager: Michael Carty (1990)
Investment objective and policies: Long-term capital growth with current income secondary. Invests primarily in common stocks or securities convertible into common stock selected, where feasible, on the basis of the Value Line rankings of normal value. May use stock index futures contracts and options and hedge up to 25% of total assets.
Year organized: 1949
Ticker symbol: VLIFX
Minimum purchase: Initial: $1,000, Subsequent: $100
Discount broker availability: Schwab, *White, Waterhouse, Fidelity, Siebert
Dividends paid: Income - March, June, September, December; Capital gains - December
Portfolio turnover (3 yrs): 120%, 129%, 109%
Largest holding: Dollar General Corp. (2.0%)
Management fee: 0.70% first $100M, 0.65% over $100M
Expense ratio: 0.80% (year ending 12/31/93)

THE VALUE LINE INCOME FUND ◆
(See first Value Line listing for data common to all Value Line funds)

Portfolio manager: Lydia Miller (1988)
Investment objective and policies: High income consistent with reasonable risk with capital growth secondary. Invests substantially all its assets in common stocks or securities convertible into common stock selected, where feasible, on the basis of the Value Line rankings of normal value. Fund may use restricted securities, foreign currency-denominated debt securities of domestic issuers, stock index futures contracts and options, and hedge up to 25% of total assets.
Year organized: 1952
Ticker symbol: VALIX
Minimum purchase: Initial: $1,000, Subsequent: $100
Discount broker availability: Schwab, *White, Waterhouse, Fidelity, Siebert
Dividends paid: Income - March, June, September, December; Capital gains - December
Portfolio turnover (3 yrs): 165%, 85%, 67%
Largest holding: McDonnell Douglas Finance Corp. Bond (3.3%)
Management fee: 0.70% first $100M, 0.65% over $100M
Expense ratio: 0.88% (year ending 12/31/93)

VALUE LINE LEVERAGED GROWTH INVESTORS ◆
(See first Value Line listing for data common to all Value Line funds)

Portfolio manager: Stewart Zobian (1990)
Investment objective and policies: Capital growth. Invests in common stocks or securities convertible into common stock selected, where feasible, on the basis of the Value Line rankings of normal value. Fund leverages up to 50% of assets and may use stock index futures contracts and options, and hedge up to 25% of total assets.
Year organized: 1972
Ticker symbol: VALLX
Minimum purchase: Initial: $1,000, Subsequent: $100
Discount broker availability: Schwab, *White, Waterhouse, Fidelity, Siebert
Dividends paid: Income - December; Capital gains - December
Portfolio turnover (3 yrs): 80%, 208%, 250%
Largest holding: U.S. Treasury Bond due 8/15/22 (3.7%)
Management fee: 0.75%
Expense ratio: 0.90% (year ending 12/31/93)

VALUE LINE NEW YORK TAX EXEMPT TRUST ◆
(See first Value Line listing for data common to all Value Line funds)

Portfolio manager: Raymond S. Cowen (1987)
Investment objective and policies: Maximum income exempt from federal, NY State and City income taxes while avoiding undue risk to principle. Invests primarily in New York State municipal and public authority debt obligations with a maturity of more than one year and rated within the 4 highest grades. Up to 20% of assets may be in taxable securities.
Year organized: 1987
Ticker symbol: VLNYX
Minimum purchase: Initial: $1,000, Subsequent: $250
Qualified for sale in: CT, FL, NJ, NY
Discount broker availability: Waterhouse
Check redemptions: $500 minimum
Dividends paid: Income - declared daily, paid monthly; Capital gains - December
Portfolio turnover (3 yrs): 54%, 137%, 124%
Management fee: 0.6%
Expense ratio: 0.87% (year ending 2/28/94)

THE VALUE LINE SMALL-CAP GROWTH FUND ◆
(See first Value Line listing for data common to all Value Line funds)

Investment objective and policies: Long-term capital growth. Invests primarily in common stocks or securities convertible into common stock of companies with market capitalizations under $1B selected, where feasible, on the basis of the Value Line rankings of normal value. May use stock index futures contracts and options and hedge up to 25% of total assets.
Year organized: 1993
Minimum purchase: Initial: $1,000, Subsequent: $100
Discount broker availability: *White, *Waterhouse, Fidelity, Siebert
Dividends paid: Income - December; Capital gains - December
Portfolio turnover (1 yr): 74%
Largest holding: Park Ohio Industries, Inc. (3.9%)
Management fee: 0.75%
12b-1 distribution fee: 0.25% (not currently imposed)
Expense ratio: 0.61% (9 months ending 3/31/94) (2.45% without waiver)

THE VALUE LINE SPECIAL SITUATIONS FUND ◆
(See first Value Line listing for data common to all Value Line funds)

Portfolio manager: Peter Shraga (1987)
Investment objective and policies: Long-term growth of capital. Invests in common stocks or securities convertible into common stocks with at least 80% of portfolio invested in "special situations" in which adviser feels unusual, and potentially non-recurring, factors will have positive impact on value of securities. May hedge up to 25% of total assets.
Year organized: 1956
Ticker symbol: VALSX
Minimum purchase: Initial: $1,000, Subsequent: $100
Discount broker availability: Schwab, *White, Waterhouse, Fidelity, Siebert
Dividends paid: Income - December; Capital gains - December
Portfolio turnover (3 yrs): 39%, 43%, 37%
Largest holding: Vencor, Inc. (2.3%)
Management fee: 0.75%
Expense ratio: 1.06% (year ending 12/31/93)

THE VALUE LINE TAX EXEMPT FUND - HIGH-YIELD PORTFOLIO ◆
(See first Value Line listing for data common to all Value Line funds)

Portfolio manager: Jim Flood (1989)
Investment objective and policies: Maximum income exempt from federal income taxes while avoiding undue risk to principle. Invests primarily in investment-grade municipal bonds with a weighted average maturity of 10 to 40 years.
Year organized: 1984
Ticker symbol: VLHYX
Minimum purchase: Initial: $1,000, Subsequent: $250
Discount broker availability: Schwab, White, Waterhouse, Fidelity, Siebert
Dividends paid: Income - declared daily, paid monthly; Capital gains - December
Portfolio turnover (3 yrs): 55%, 101%, 122%
Management fee: 0.5%
Expense ratio: 0.58% (year ending 2/28/94)

THE VALUE LINE TAX EXEMPT FUND - MONEY MARKET PORTFOLIO ◆
(See first Value Line listing for data common to all Value Line funds)

Portfolio manager: Jim Flood (1989)
Investment objective and policies: Maximum income exempt from federal income taxes while avoiding undue risk to principle. Invests primarily in investment-grade municipal money market securities.
Year organized: 1984
Ticker symbol: VLTXX
Minimum purchase: Initial: $1,000, Subsequent: $250
Check redemptions: $500 minimum
Confirmations mailed: After each purchase and each check, mail or wire redemption
Checks returned: Monthly
Periodic account statements mailed: Quarterly
Dividends paid: Income - declared and paid daily
Management fee: 0.5%
Expense ratio: 0.80% (year ending 2/28/94)

THE VALUE LINE U.S. GOVERNMENT SECURITIES FUND ◆
(See first Value Line listing for data common to all Value Line funds)

Portfolio manager: Pat Sheehan (1990)
Investment objective and policies: Maximum income without undue risk to principal with capital preservation and possible capital appreciation secondary. Normally invests at least 80% of assets in issues of U.S. Government and its agencies and instrumentalities.
Year organized: 1981 (formerly Value Line Bond Fund, Name changed 4/86)
Ticker symbol: VALBX
Minimum purchase: Initial: $1,000, Subsequent: $250
Discount broker availability: Schwab, White, Waterhouse, Fidelity, Siebert
Check redemptions: $500 minimum
Dividends paid: Income - March, June, September, December; Capital gains - December
Portfolio turnover (3 yrs): 100%, 169%, 130%
Management fee: 0.5%
Expense ratio: 0.63% (year ending 8/31/94)

VANGUARD FUNDS ◆
(Data common to all Vanguard funds are shown below. See subsequent listing for data specific to individual Vanguard funds.)

P.O. Box 2600
Valley Forge, PA 19482
610-669-1000, 800-662-2739
800-662-7447

Shareholder service hours: Full service: M-F 8 A.M.-9 P.M., Sat 9 A.M.-4 P.M. EST; After hours service: prices, yields, balances, orders, last transaction, total returns
Adviser: Vanguard Group, Inc. (exceptions noted)
Custodian: CoreStates Bank, N.A., Philadelphia (exceptions noted)
Transfer agent: The Vanguard Group, Inc.
Minimum purchase: Initial: $3,000, Subsequent: $100; IRA/Keogh: Initial: $500, (exceptions noted)
Telephone orders accepted: No
Wire orders accepted: Yes, $1,000 minimum

Deadline for same day wire purchase: 4 P.M. (12 NN for money market funds)
Qualified for sale in: All states (exceptions noted)
Telephone redemptions: Yes
Wire redemptions: Yes, $1,000 minimum, $5 fee under $5,000
Letter redemptions: Signature guarantee required over $25,000 (exceptions noted)
Telephone switching: With other open Vanguard funds except Balanced Index, Index Trust, International Equity Index, Quantitative, Small Cap Stock & Tax-Managed funds (exceptions noted)
Number of switches permitted: 2 per year (exceptions noted)
Shareholder services: Keogh, IRA, SEP-IRA, 401(k), 403(b), corporate retirement plans, automatic investment plan, directed dividends, withdrawal plan min. req. $10,000, electronic funds transfer
IRA/Keogh fees: Annual $10 (waived for IRA planholders with $50,000 or more in total Vanguard IRA assets or for any fund holding worth $5,000 or more), Initial $10

VANGUARD ADMIRAL INTERMEDIATE-TERM U.S. TREASURY PORTFOLIO ◆
(See first Vanguard listing for data common to all Vanguard funds)

Portfolio manager: Robert Auwaerter (1992)
Custodian: State Street Bank & Trust Co.
Investment objective and policies: Current income consistent with preservation of capital and liquidity. Invests at least 85% of assets in U.S. Treasury notes and bonds and other "full faith and credit" obligations of the U.S. Government with a weighted average maturity of 5 to 10 years. May use futures contracts and options and hedge up to 20% of assets. Designed to deliver extra high yields by maintaining a lower than average expense ratio.
Year organized: 1992
Ticker symbol: VAITX
Group fund code: 19
Minimum purchase: Initial: $50,000, Subsequent: $100
Minimum account balance: $25,000
Discount broker availability: Schwab (only through financial advisers)
Check redemptions: $250 minimum
Dividends paid: Income - declared daily, paid monthly; Capital gains - annually
Portfolio turnover (1 yr): 102%
Management fee: At cost
Expense ratio: 0.15% (year ending 1/31/94)

VANGUARD ADMIRAL LONG-TERM U.S. TREASURY PORTFOLIO ◆
(See first Vanguard listing for data common to all Vanguard funds)

Portfolio manager: Robert Auwaerter (1992)
Custodian: State Street Bank & Trust Co.
Investment objective and policies: Current income consistent with preservation of capital and liquidity. Invests at least 85% of assets in U.S. Treasury notes and bonds and other "full faith and credit" obligations of the U.S. Government with a weighted average maturity of 15 to 30 years. May use futures contracts and options and hedge up to 20% of assets. Designed to deliver extra high yields by maintaining a lower than average expense ratio.
Year organized: 1992
Ticker symbol: VALGX
Group fund code: 20
Minimum purchase: Initial: $50,000, Subsequent: $100
Minimum account balance: $25,000
Discount broker availability: Schwab (only through financial advisers)
Check redemptions: $250 minimum
Dividends paid: Income - declared daily, paid monthly; Capital gains - annually
Portfolio turnover (1 yr): 51%
Management fee: At cost
Expense ratio: 0.15% (year ending 1/31/94)

VANGUARD ADMIRAL SHORT-TERM U.S. TREASURY PORTFOLIO ◆
(See first Vanguard listing for data common to all Vanguard funds)

Portfolio manager: John Hollyer (1993)
Custodian: State Street Bank & Trust Co.
Investment objective and policies: Current income consistent with preservation of capital and liquidity. Invests at least 85% of assets in U.S. Treasury notes and bonds and other "full faith and credit" obligations of the U.S. Government with a weighted average maturity of 1 to 3 years. May use futures contracts and options and hedge up to 20% of assets. Designed to deliver extra high yields by maintaining a lower than average expense ratio.
Year organized: 1992
Ticker symbol: VASTX
Group fund code: 12
Minimum purchase: Initial: $50,000, Subsequent: $100
Minimum account balance: $25,000
Discount broker availability: Schwab (only through financial advisers)
Check redemptions: $250 minimum
Dividends paid: Income - declared daily, paid monthly; Capital gains - annually
Portfolio turnover (1 yr): 90%
Management fee: At cost
Expense ratio: 0.15% (year ending 1/31/94)

VANGUARD ADMIRAL U.S. TREASURY MONEY MARKET PORTFOLIO ◆
(See first Vanguard listing for data common to all Vanguard funds)

Portfolio manager: John Hollyer (1993)
Investment objective and policies: Current income consistent with preservation of capital and liquidity. Invests at least 85% of assets in U.S. Treasury notes and other "full faith and credit" obligations of the U.S. Government with a weighted average maturity of 90 days or less. Designed to deliver extra high yields by maintaining a lower than average expense ratio.
Year organized: 1992
Ticker symbol: VUSXX
Group fund code: 11
Minimum purchase: Initial: $50,000, Subsequent: $100
Minimum account balance: $25,000
Check redemptions: $250 minimum
Confirmations mailed: After each purchase and each check, mail or wire redemption
Checks returned: Monthly
Periodic account statements mailed: Monthly
Number of switches permitted: Unlimited
Dividends paid: Income - declared daily, paid monthly
Management fee: At cost
Expense ratio: 0.15% (year ending 10/31/94)

VANGUARD ASSET ALLOCATION FUND ◆
(See first Vanguard listing for data common to all Vanguard funds)

Adviser: Mellon Capital Management Corporation
Portfolio manager: Thomas Hazuka (1988)
Custodian: State Street Bank & Trust Co.
Investment objective and policies: Maximum total return. Invests in common stocks, bonds, and money market instruments in proportions consistent with their expected returns and risks as evaluated by the adviser. Allocation of asset types will vary with changing economic and market conditions. Fund may use stock and bond futures (initial margin limited to 5% of assets) and options and hedge up to 50% of assets.
Year organized: 1988
Ticker symbol: VAAPX
Group fund code: 78
Discount broker availability: Schwab, White, Waterhouse, Fidelity, Siebert

Dividends paid: Income - April, December; Capital gains - December
Portfolio turnover (3 yrs): 51%, 31%, 18%
Largest holding: U.S. Treasury Bonds 7.625% due 11/15/22 (5.8%)
Management fee: 0.20% first $100M, 0.15% over $100M plus performance fee of +/- 0.05% relative to the S&P 500 over 36 months
Expense ratio: 0.50% (year ending 9/30/94)

VANGUARD BALANCED INDEX FUND ◆
(See first Vanguard listing for data common to all Vanguard funds)

Portfolio manager: George U. Sauter (1992)
Investment objective and policies: To replicate, with respect to 60% of its assets, the investment performance of the Wilshire 5000 Index of common stocks and, with respect to 40% of its assets, the investment performance of the Lehman Brothers Index of fixed-income securities. Management is quantitatively organized and not active. May invest up to 30% of assets in stock/bond/interest rate futures contracts and options.
Year organized: 1992
Ticker symbol: VBINX
Group fund code: 2
Telephone switching: None
Dividends paid: Income - March, June, September, December; Capital gains - December
Portfolio turnover (1 yr): 25%
Largest holding: Treasury Bond due 11/15/11 (1.6%)
Management fee: At cost
Maintenance fee: Annual $10 (paid $2.50/quarter, waived for accounts with balances of $10,000 or more)
Expense ratio: 0.20% (year ending 12/31/93)

VANGUARD BOND INDEX FUND - INTERMEDIATE-TERM BOND PORTFOLIO ◆
(See first Vanguard listing for data common to all Vanguard funds)

Portfolio manager: Kenneth E. Volpert (1994)
Custodian: State Street Bank & Trust Co.
Investment objective and policies: To duplicate the total return of the Lehman Brothers Mutual Fund Intermediate (5-10) Government/Corporate Index. The Index is a market weighted index of U.S. Treasury and agency securities and investment-grade corporate bonds with a weighted average maturity of 5 to 10 years. Management is quantitatively organized and not active. Fund invests at least 80% of assets in a representative sample of the securities included in the Index. Fund may use bond/interest rate futures and options and hedge up to 20% of assets.
Year organized: 1994
Ticker symbol: VBIIX
Group fund code: 314
Check redemptions: $250 minimum
Dividends paid: Income - declared daily, paid monthly; Capital gains - January
Management fee: At cost
Maintenance fee: Annual $10 (paid $2.50/quarter, waived for accounts with balances of $10,000 or more)

VANGUARD BOND INDEX FUND - LONG-TERM BOND PORTFOLIO ◆
(See first Vanguard listing for data common to all Vanguard funds)

Portfolio manager: Kenneth E. Volpert (1994)
Custodian: State Street Bank & Trust Co.
Investment objective and policies: To duplicate the total return of the Lehman Brothers Mutual Fund Long (10+) Government/Corporate Index. The

Index is a market weighted index of U.S. Treasury and agency securities and investment-grade corporate bonds with a weighted average maturity of more than 10 years. Management is quantitatively organized and not active. Fund invests at least 80% of assets in a representative sample of the securities included in the Index. Fund may use bond/interest rate futures and options and hedge up to 20% of assets.
Year organized: 1994
Group fund code: 522
Check redemptions: $250 minimum
Dividends paid: Income - declared daily, paid monthly; Capital gains - December
Management fee: At cost
Maintenance fee: Annual $10 (paid $2.50/quarter, waived for accounts with balances of $10,000 or more)

VANGUARD BOND INDEX FUND - SHORT-TERM BOND PORTFOLIO ◆
(See first Vanguard listing for data common to all Vanguard funds)

Portfolio manager: Kenneth E. Volpert (1994)
Custodian: State Street Bank & Trust Co.
Investment objective and policies: To duplicate the total return of the Lehman Brothers Mutual Fund Short (1-5) Government/Corporate Index. The Index is a market weighted index of U.S. Treasury and agency securities and investment-grade corporate bonds with a weighted average maturity of 1 to 5 years. Management is quantitatively organized and not active. Fund invests at least 80% of assets in a representative sample of the securities included in the Index. Fund may use bond/interest rate futures and options and hedge up to 20% of assets.
Year organized: 1994
Ticker symbol: VBISX
Group fund code: 132
Check redemptions: $250 minimum
Dividends paid: Income - declared daily, paid monthly; Capital gains - December
Management fee: At cost
Maintenance fee: Annual $10 (paid $2.50/quarter, waived for accounts with balances of $10,000 or more)

VANGUARD BOND INDEX FUND - TOTAL BOND MARKET PORTFOLIO ◆
(See first Vanguard listing for data common to all Vanguard funds)

Portfolio manager: Kenneth E. Volpert (1992)
Custodian: Morgan Guaranty Trust Co.
Investment objective and policies: To duplicate the total return of the Lehman Brothers Aggregate Bond Index. Management is quantitatively organized and not active. The index consists of over 6,000 issues that have not less than one year to maturity, over $25 million in outstanding market value, and a rating of BBB or better for corporate debt. Fund invests at least 80% of assets in a representative sample of the securities included in the Index. Unlike the other portfolios of the Bond Index Fund, the Total Bond Market Portfolio may invest in GNMAs and other mortgage-backed securities. Fund may use bond/interest rate futures and options and hedge up to 20% of assets.
Year organized: 1986 (name changed from Vanguard Bond Market Fund on 5/3/93)
Ticker symbol: VBMFX
Group fund code: 84
Discount broker availability: Schwab (only through financial advisers), White, Waterhouse, Fidelity, Siebert
Check redemptions: $250 minimum
Dividends paid: Income - declared daily, paid monthly; Capital gains - December
Portfolio turnover (3 yrs): 49%, 49%, 31%
Management fee: At cost
Maintenance fee: Annual $10 (paid $2.50/quarter, waived for accounts with balances of $10,000 or more)
Expense ratio: 0.18% (year ending 12/31/93)

VANGUARD CALIFORNIA INSURED TAX-FREE INTERMEDIATE-TERM PORTFOLIO ◆
(See first Vanguard listing for data common to all Vanguard funds)

Portfolio manager: Reid O. Smith (1994)
Investment objective and policies: High level of income exempt from federal and California personal income taxes. Normally invests at least 80% of assets in long-term California municipal bonds, insured as to interest and principal payments, rated AA or better with a weighted average maturity of 7 to 12 years. Fund may invest up to 20% of assets in AMT bonds, use bond futures and options, and taxable securities in unusual circumstances. May hedge up to 20% of assets.
Year organized: 1994
Ticker symbol: VCAIX
Group fund code: 100
Discount broker availability: Schwab
Qualified for sale in: CA
Check redemptions: $250 minimum
Dividends paid: Income - declared daily, paid monthly; Capital gains - December
Portfolio turnover (1 yr): 6%
Management fee: At cost
Expense ratio: 0.19% (8 months ending 11/30/94)

VANGUARD CALIFORNIA INSURED TAX-FREE LONG-TERM PORTFOLIO ◆
(See first Vanguard listing for data common to all Vanguard funds)

Newspaper listing: Cal Ins
Portfolio manager: Reid O. Smith (1992)
Investment objective and policies: High level of income exempt from federal and California personal income taxes. Normally invests at least 80% of assets in long-term California municipal bonds, insured as to interest and principal payments, rated AA or better with a weighted average maturity of 15 to 25 years. Fund may invest up to 20% of assets in AMT bonds, use bond futures and options, and taxable securities in unusual circumstances. May hedge up to 20% of assets.
Year organized: 1986 (formerly Vanguard California Insured Tax-Free Fund)
Ticker symbol: VCITX
Group fund code: 75
Discount broker availability: Schwab, White, Fidelity, Siebert
Qualified for sale in: CA
Check redemptions: $250 minimum
Dividends paid: Income - declared daily, paid monthly; Capital gains - December
Portfolio turnover (3 yrs): 28%, 27%, 54%
Management fee: At cost
Expense ratio: 0.19% (year ending 11/30/94)

VANGUARD CALIFORNIA TAX-FREE MONEY MARKET PORTFOLIO ◆
(See first Vanguard listing for data common to all Vanguard funds)

Portfolio manager: Pamela E. Wisehaupt (1987)
Investment objective and policies: Current income exempt from federal and California personal income taxes. Invests in high quality California municipal money market securities.
Year organized: 1987
Ticker symbol: VCTXX
Group fund code: 62
Qualified for sale in: CA
Number of switches permitted: Unlimited
Check redemptions: $250 minimum
Confirmations mailed: After each purchase and each check, mail or wire redemption
Checks returned: Monthly
Periodic account statements mailed: Monthly
Dividends paid: Income - declared daily, paid monthly
Management fee: At cost
Expense ratio: 0.19% (year ending 11/30/94)

VANGUARD CONVERTIBLE SECURITIES FUND ◆
(See first Vanguard listing for data common to all Vanguard funds)

Adviser: Desai Capital Management Inc.
Portfolio manager: Rohit M. Desai (1986)
Investment objective and policies: High level of current income and capital growth. Invests at least 80% of assets in convertible securities - corporate bonds and preferred stocks convertible into common stock, as well as debt instruments with warrants or common stock attached. Up to 15% of assets may be in dollar-denominated foreign securities. Fund may write covered call options on equity securities held.
Year organized: 1986
Ticker symbol: VCVSX
Group fund code: 82
Discount broker availability: Schwab, White, Waterhouse, Fidelity, Siebert
Dividends paid: Income - March, June, September, December; Capital gains - December
Portfolio turnover (3 yrs): 52%, 81%, 55%
Management fee: 0.45% first $50M to 0.30% over $200M
Expense ratio: 0.73% (year ending 11/30/94)

VANGUARD EQUITY INCOME FUND ◆
(See first Vanguard listing for data common to all Vanguard funds)

Advisers: Newell Associates; Spare, Kaplan, Bischel & Associates; John A. Levin & Co., Inc.
Portfolio managers: Roger D. Newell (1988), Anthony E. Spare (1994), Melody P. Sarnell (1994), Jeffrey A. Kigner (1994)
Custodian: State Street Bank & Trust Co.
Investment objective and policies: High level of current income. Invests at least 80% of assets in dividend paying equity securities. Income yield is expected to exceed S&P 500 by at least 50% with price volatility less than that of the S&P. Potential for capital appreciation will also be considered in security selection. Fund may use equity futures and options and hedge up to 20% of assets.
Year organized: 1988
Ticker symbol: VEIPX
Group fund code: 65
Discount broker availability: Schwab, White, Waterhouse, Fidelity, Siebert
Dividends paid: Income - March, June, September, December; Capital gains - December
Portfolio turnover (3 yrs): 18%, 15%, 13%
Largest holding: Bristol Myers-Squibb Co. (3.1%)
Management fee: 0.20% first $250M to 0.08% over $1B
Expense ratio: 0.43% (year ending 9/30/94)

VANGUARD EXPLORER FUND ◆
(See first Vanguard listing for data common to all Vanguard funds)

Advisers: Wellington Management Co., Granahan Investment Management, Inc.
Portfolio managers: Kenneth L. Abrams (1994), John J. Granahan (1990)
Custodian: State Street Bank & Trust Co.
Investment objective and policies: Long-term growth of capital. Invests primarily in equity securities of relatively small, emerging or embryonic companies, with market capitalizations ranging from $75M to $200M. Fund may use equity futures and options and hedge up to 20% of total assets. May invest in foreign securities (up to 10% of assets) and restricted securities (15%).
Year organized: 1967 (Explorer II merged into fund in February 1990)
Ticker symbol: VEXPX
Group fund code: 24
Discount broker availability: Schwab, White, Waterhouse, Fidelity, Siebert
Dividends paid: Income - December; Capital gains - December
Portfolio turnover (3 yrs): 82%, 51%, 43%

Largest holding: Dallas Semiconductor Corp. (1.6%)
Management fee: 0.35% first $100M to 0.25% over $350M (for WMC, 47% of assets under management), 0.45% first $50M to 0.25% over $200M (for Granahan, 47% of assets), subject to an incentive adjustment depending on the fund's performance relative to the Russell 2000 Small Company Index.
Expense ratio: 0.70% (year ending 10/31/94)

VANGUARD FIXED INCOME - GNMA PORTFOLIO ◆
(See first Vanguard listing for data common to all Vanguard funds)

Adviser: Wellington Management Co.
Portfolio manager: Paul D. Kaplan (1994)
Custodian: Morgan Guarantee Trust Co.
Investment objective and policies: High current income, consistent with safety of principal and liquidity. Invests at least 80% of assets in GNMA mortgage-backed securities of the modified pass-through type. Remainder may be in other U.S. Treasury or U.S. Government agency securities as well as repurchase agreements collateralized by such securities. May have up to 15% of assets in restricted securities, use bond futures contracts and options and hedge up to 20% of assets.
Year organized: 1980
Ticker symbol: VFIIX
Group fund code: 36
Discount broker availability: Schwab, White, Waterhouse, Fidelity, Siebert
Check redemptions: $250 minimum
Dividends paid: Income - declared daily, paid monthly; Capital gains - December
Portfolio turnover (3 yrs): 2%, 7%, 1%
Management fee: pro-rata share of 0.125% first $2.5B to 0.05% over $7.5B (for GNMA, High Yield Corporate and Long-Term Corporate portfolios)
Expense ratio: 0.28% (year ending 1/31/94)

VANGUARD FIXED INCOME - HIGH YIELD CORPORATE PORTFOLIO ◆
(See first Vanguard listing for data common to all Vanguard funds)

Adviser: Wellington Management Co.
Portfolio manager: Earl E. McEvoy (1984)
Custodian: Morgan Guaranty Trust Co.
Investment objective and policies: Highest level of current income. Invests in high yielding medium and lower quality bonds ("junk" bonds). At least 80% of assets must be B or higher grade securities. May invest up to 20% of assets in restricted securities and in dollar-denominated foreign securities. May use bond futures and options and hedge up to 20% of assets.
Year organized: 1978 (name changed from High Yield Bond Portfolio in Oct. 1991)
Ticker symbol: VWEHX
Group fund code: 29
Discount broker availability: Schwab, White, Waterhouse
Redemption fee: 1.0% on shares held less than 1 year, payable to the fund
Dividends paid: Income - declared daily, paid monthly; Capital gains - December
Portfolio turnover (3 yrs): 51%, 83%, 44%
Management fee: pro-rata share of 0.125% first $2.5B to 0.05% over $7.5B (for GNMA, High Yield Corporate and Long-Term Corporate portfolios)
Expense ratio: 0.32% (year ending 1/31/94)

VANGUARD FIXED INCOME - INTERMEDIATE-TERM CORPORATE PORTFOLIO ◆
(See first Vanguard listing for data common to all Vanguard funds)

Portfolio manager: Robert Auwaerter (1993)
Custodian: State Street Bank & Trust Co.
Investment objective and policies: High current income consistent with minimum fluctuation in

principal value and current liquidity. Invests primarily in short-term investment-grade bonds with a weighted average maturity of 5 to 10 years. May invest up to 15% of assets in restricted securities and in dollar-denominated foreign securities, use bond futures contracts and options and hedge up to 20% of assets.
Year organized: 1993
Ticker symbol: VFICX
Group fund code: 71
Discount broker availability: Schwab
Check redemptions: $250 minimum
Dividends paid: Income - declared daily, paid monthly; Capital gains - December
Portfolio turnover (1 yr): 74%
Management fee: At cost
Expense ratio: 0.25% (3 months ending 1/31/94)

VANGUARD FIXED INCOME - INTERMEDIATE-TERM U.S. TREASURY PORTFOLIO ◆
(See first Vanguard listing for data common to all Vanguard funds)

Portfolio manager: Robert Auwaerter (1992)
Custodian: State Street Bank & Trust Co.
Investment objective and policies: High current income consistent with safety of principal and maintenance of liquidity. Invests at least 85% of assets in U.S. Treasury notes and bonds and other "full faith and credit" obligations of the U.S. Government with a weighted average maturity of 5 to 10 years. Remainder may be in other U.S. Treasury or U.S. Government agency securities as well as repurchase agreements collateralized by such securities. May invest up to 15% of assets in restricted securities, use bond futures contracts and options and hedge up to 20% of assets.
Year organized: 1991
Ticker symbol: VFITX
Group fund code: 35
Discount broker availability: Schwab, White, Waterhouse, Fidelity, Siebert
Check redemptions: $250 minimum
Dividends paid: Income - declared daily, paid monthly; Capital gains - December
Portfolio turnover (3 yrs): 118%, 123%, 32%
Management fee: At cost
Expense ratio: 0.26% (year ending 1/31/94)

VANGUARD FIXED INCOME - LONG-TERM CORPORATE PORTFOLIO ◆
(See first Vanguard listing for data common to all Vanguard funds)

Adviser: Wellington Management Co.
Portfolio manager: Earl E. McEvoy (1994)
Custodian: Morgan Guaranty Trust Co.
Investment objective and policies: High level of current income consistent with conservation of capital. Invests at least 80% of assets in bonds and other fixed-income securities of the 4 highest grades with weighted average maturity of 15 to 25 years. May invest up to 15% of assets in restricted securities and in dollar-denominated foreign securities. May use bond futures and options and hedge up to 20% of assets.
Year organized: 1973 (name changed from Investment Grade Corporate Portfolio on 11/1/93 and from Investment Grade Bond Portfolio, in October 1991)
Ticker symbol: VWESX
Group fund code: 28
Discount broker availability: Schwab, White, Waterhouse, Fidelity, Siebert
Check redemptions: $250 minimum
Dividends paid: Income - declared daily, paid monthly; Capital gains - December
Portfolio turnover (3 yrs): 77%, 50%. 72%
Management fee: pro-rata share of 0.125% first $2.5B to 0.05% over $7.5B (for GNMA, High Yield Corporate and Long-Term Corporate portfolios)
Expense ratio: 0.30% (year ending 1/31/94)

VANGUARD FIXED INCOME - LONG-TERM U.S. TREASURY PORTFOLIO ◆
(See first Vanguard listing for data common to all Vanguard funds)

Portfolio manager: Robert Auwaerter (1994)
Investment objective and policies: High current income consistent with safety of principal and maintenance of liquidity. Invests at least 85% of assets in long term U.S. Treasury bonds and other "full faith and credit" obligations of the U.S. Government with a weighted average maturity of 15 to 30 years. Fund may use zero coupon bonds. Remainder may be in other U.S. Treasury or U.S. Government agency securities as well as repurchase agreements collateralized by such securities. May invest up to 15% of assets in restricted securities, use bond futures contracts and options and hedge up to 20% of assets.
Year organized: 1982 (name changed from U.S. Treasury Bond in Oct. 1991)
Ticker symbol: VUSTX
Group fund code: 83
Discount broker availability: Schwab, White, Waterhouse, Fidelity, Siebert
Check redemptions: $250 minimum
Dividends paid: Income - declared daily, paid monthly; Capital gains - December
Portfolio turnover (3 yrs): 7%, 170%, 89%
Management fee: At cost
Expense ratio: 0.26% (year ending 1/31/94)

VANGUARD FIXED INCOME - SHORT-TERM CORPORATE PORTFOLIO ◆
(See first Vanguard listing for data common to all Vanguard funds)

Portfolio manager: Robert Auwaerter (1983)
Investment objective and policies: High current income consistent with minimum fluctuation in principal value and current liquidity. Invests primarily in short-term investment-grade bonds with a weighted average maturity of 1 to 3 years. Fund may invest up to 15% of assets in restricted securities and in dollar-denominated foreign securities, use bond futures contracts and options and hedge up to 20% of assets.
Year organized: 1982 (name changed from Short Term Bond Portfolio in Oct. 1991)
Ticker symbol: VFSTX
Group fund code: 39
Discount broker availability: Schwab, White, Waterhouse, Fidelity, Siebert
Check redemptions: $250 minimum
Dividends paid: Income - declared daily, paid monthly; Capital gains - December
Portfolio turnover (3 yrs): 61%, 71%, 99%
Management fee: At cost
Expense ratio: 0.26% (year ending 1/31/94)

VANGUARD FIXED INCOME - SHORT-TERM FEDERAL PORTFOLIO ◆
(See first Vanguard listing for data common to all Vanguard funds)

Portfolio manager: Robert Auwaerter (1987)
Investment objective and policies: High current income consistent with safety of principal and maintenance of liquidity. Invests primarily in U.S. Treasury bonds and other "full faith and credit" obligations of the United States Government with a weighted average maturity of 1 to 3 years. May invest up to 15% of assets in restricted securities, use bond futures contracts and options and hedge up to 20% of assets.
Year organized: 1987 (name changed from Short Term Government Bond in Oct. 1991)
Ticker symbol: VSGBX
Group fund code: 49
Discount broker availability: Schwab, White, Waterhouse, Fidelity, Siebert
Check redemptions: $250 minimum
Dividends paid: Income - declared daily, paid monthly; Capital gains - December

Portfolio turnover (3 yrs): 49%, 70%, 111%
Management fee: At cost
Expense ratio: 0.26% (year ending 1/31/94)

VANGUARD FIXED INCOME - SHORT-TERM U.S. TREASURY PORTFOLIO ◆
(See first Vanguard listing for data common to all Vanguard funds)

Portfolio manager: John Hollyer (1993)
Custodian: State Street Bank & Trust Co.
Investment objective and policies: High current income consistent with safety of principal and maintenance of liquidity. Invests at least 85% of assets in U.S. Treasury bills, notes and bonds and other "full faith and credit" obligations of the U.S. Government with a weighted average maturity of 1 to 3 years. Remainder may be in other U.S. Treasury or U.S. Government agency securities as well as repurchase agreements collateralized by such securities. Fund may invest up to 15% of assets in restricted securities, use bond futures contracts and options and hedge up to 20% of assets.
Year organized: 1991
Ticker symbol: VFISX
Group fund code: 32
Discount broker availability: Schwab, White, Waterhouse, Fidelity, Siebert
Check redemptions: $250 minimum
Dividends paid: Income - declared daily, paid monthly; Capital gains - December
Portfolio turnover (3 yrs): 86%, 71%, 40%
Management fee: At cost
Expense ratio: 0.26% (year ending 1/31/94)

VANGUARD FLORIDA INSURED TAX-FREE FUND ◆
(See first Vanguard listing for data common to all Vanguard funds)

Portfolio manager: Reid O. Smith (1992)
Investment objective and policies: High level of income exempt from federal personal income taxes and Florida intangible personal property tax. Invests at least 80% of assets in insured Florida municipal securities with a weighted average maturity of 15 to 25 years. Fund may invest up to 20% of assets in AMT bonds, use bond futures and options, and taxable securities in unusual circumstances. May hedge up to 20% of assets.
Year organized: 1992
Ticker symbol: VFLTX
Group fund code: 18
Qualified for sale in: FL
Check redemptions: $250 minimum
Dividends paid: Income - declared daily, paid monthly; Capital gains - December
Portfolio turnover (2 yrs): 43%, 34%
Management fee: At cost
Expense ratio: 0.22% (year ending 11/30/94)

VANGUARD INDEX TRUST - EXTENDED MARKET PORTFOLIO ◆
(See first Vanguard listing for data common to all Vanguard funds)

Newspaper listing: IdxExt
Portfolio manager: George U. Sauter (1987)
Custodian: State Street Bank & Trust Co.
Investment objective and policies: Investment results that correspond to the price and yield performance of the Wilshire 4500 Index of over 5,000 small and medium size companies traded on the NYSE, AMEX, or NASDAQ exchanges not included in the S&P 500. Fund may use futures and options to maintain fully invested strategy and hedge up to 20% of assets.
Year organized: 1987
Ticker symbol: VEXMX
Group fund code: 98
Sales charge: 1.0% payable to fund

Discount broker availability: Schwab (only through financial advisers), White
Dividends paid: Income - March; Capital gains - December
Portfolio turnover (3 yrs): 13%, 9%, 11%
Management fee: At cost
Maintenance fee: $10 per year (paid $2.50/quarter, waived for accounts with balances of $10,000 or more)
Expense ratio: 0.20% (year ending 12/31/93)

VANGUARD INDEX TRUST - 500 PORTFOLIO ◆
(See first Vanguard listing for data common to all Vanguard funds)

Newspaper listing: Idx500
Portfolio manager: George U. Sauter (1987)
Custodian: State Street Bank & Trust Co.
Investment objective and policies: Investment results that correspond to the price and yield performance of the S&P 500 Index, by owning all the stocks in the S&P Index. Fund may use futures and options to maintain fully invested strategy and hedge up to 20% of assets.
Year organized: 1976 (formerly Vanguard Index Trust)
Ticker symbol: VFINX
Group fund code: 40
Discount broker availability: Schwab, White, Waterhouse, Fidelity, Siebert
Dividends paid: Income - March, June, September, December; Capital gains - December
Portfolio turnover (3 yrs): 6%, 4%, 5%
Management fee: At cost
Maintenance fee: $10 per year*
Expense ratio: 0.20% (year ending 12/31/93)

VANGUARD INDEX TRUST - GROWTH PORTFOLIO ◆
(See first Vanguard listing for data common to all Vanguard funds)

Newspaper listing: IdxGro
Portfolio manager: George U. Sauter (1987)
Investment objective and policies: Investment results that correspond to the price and yield performance of the S&P/BARRA Growth Index of stocks selected from the S&P 500 Index with higher than average ratios of market price to book value. Fund may use futures and options to maintain fully invested strategy and hedge up to 20% of assets.
Year organized: 1992
Ticker symbol: VIGRX
Group fund code: 9
Dividends paid: Income - March, June, September, December; Capital gains - December
Portfolio turnover (1 yr): 36%
Management fee: At cost
Maintenance fee: $10 per year*
Expense ratio: 0.20% (year ending 12/31/93)

VANGUARD INDEX TRUST - SMALL CAPITALIZATION STOCK PORTFOLIO ◆
(See first Vanguard listing for data common to all Vanguard funds)

Portfolio manager: George U. Sauter (1989)
Investment objective and policies: Investment results that correspond to the price and yield performance of the Russell 2000 Small Stock Index, a widely followed unmanaged index of small company common stocks with an average market capitalization of $200M. Fund may use futures and options to maintain fully invested strategy and hedge up to 20% of assets.
Year organized: 1960 (formerly Naess & Thomas Special Fund, Inc. Name and objective changed to Vanguard Small Capitalization Stock Fund in September 1989. Prior performance record may not be relevant.) (3 for 1 split on 2/23/90. Became part of Index Trust in 1994)

Ticker symbol: NAESX
Group fund code: 48
Discount broker availability: Schwab (only through financial advisers), White
Dividends paid: Income - December; Capital gains - December
Portfolio turnover (3 yrs): 26%, 26%, 33%
Management fee: At cost
Maintenance fee: $10 per year (paid $2.50/quarter, waived for accounts with balances of $10,000 or more)
Expense ratio: 0.18% (year ending 9/30/94)

VANGUARD INDEX TRUST - TOTAL STOCK MARKET PORTFOLIO ◆
(See first Vanguard listing for data common to all Vanguard funds)

Newspaper listing: IdxTot
Portfolio manager: George U. Sauter (1992)
Custodian: State Street Bank & Trust Co.
Investment objective and policies: Investment results that correspond to the price and yield performance of the unmanaged Wilshire 5000 Index, the broadest stock index in the U.S. This portfolio is essentially a composite of the S&P 500 Portfolio and the Extended Market Portfolio with a dollar allocation of 75% in S&P 500 stocks and 25% in Extended Market stocks. Fund may use futures and options to maintain fully invested strategy and hedge up to 20% of assets.
Year organized: 1992
Ticker symbol: VTSMX
Group fund code: 85
Sales charge: 0.25% payable to fund
Discount broker availability: White
Dividends paid: Income - March, June, September, December; Capital gains - December
Portfolio turnover (2 yrs): 1%, 3%
Management fee: At cost
Maintenance fee: $10 per year (paid $2.50/quarter, waived for accounts with balances of $10,000 or more)
Expense ratio: 0.20% (year ending 12/31/93)

VANGUARD INDEX TRUST - VALUE PORTFOLIO ◆
(See first Vanguard listing for data common to all Vanguard funds)

Newspaper listing: IdxVal
Portfolio manager: George U. Sauter (1987)
Investment objective and policies: Investment results that correspond to the price and yield performance of the S&P/BARRA Value Index of stocks selected from the S&P 500 Index with lower than average ratios of market price to book value. Fund may use futures and options to maintain fully invested strategy and hedge up to 20% of assets.
Year organized: 1992
Ticker symbol: VIVAX
Group fund code: 6
Discount broker availability: Schwab (only through financial advisers)
Dividends paid: Income - March, June, September, December; Capital gains - December
Portfolio turnover (1 yr): 30%
Management fee: At cost
Maintenance fee: $10 per year (paid $2.50/quarter, waived for accounts with balances of $10,000 or more)
Expense ratio: 0.20% (year ending 12/31/93)

VANGUARD INTERNATIONAL EQUITY INDEX FUND - EMERGING MARKETS PORTFOLIO ◆
(See first Vanguard listing for data common to all Vanguard funds)

Portfolio manager: George U. Sauter (1994)
Custodian: Morgan Stanley International
Investment objective and policies: Investment results that correspond to the price and yield performance of the Morgan Stanley Capital

International Select Emerging Markets Free Index of companies located in 12 countries in Southeast Asia, Latin America and Europe. Invests in a statistically selected sample of the more than 460 securities which comprise the Index. Fund may use futures, options, warrants and forward currency contracts. Up to 15% of assets may be in illiquid securities.
Year organized: 1994
Ticker symbol: VEIEX
Group fund code: 533
Sales charge: 2%, payable to fund
Redemption charge: 1%, payable to the fund
Telephone switching: None (mail only)
Dividends paid: Income - December; Capital gains - December
Portfolio turnover (1 yr.): 6%
Management fee: At cost
Maintenance fee: $10 per year (paid $2.50/quarter, waived for accounts with balances of $10,000 or more)
Expense ratio: 0.60% (year ending 12/31/94)

VANGUARD INTERNATIONAL EQUITY INDEX FUND - EUROPEAN PORTFOLIO ◆
(See first Vanguard listing for data common to all Vanguard funds)

Newspaper listing: IdxEur
Portfolio manager: George U. Sauter (1990)
Custodian: Morgan Stanley International
Investment objective and policies: Investment results that correspond to the price and yield performance of the Morgan Stanley Capital International Europe (FREE) Index of companies located in 13 European countries. Invests in a statistically selected sample of the more than 600 securities which comprise the Index. Fund may use futures, options, warrants and forward currency contracts. Up to 15% of assets may be in illiquid securities.
Year organized: 1990
Ticker symbol: VEURX
Group fund code: 79
Sales charge: 1% payable to fund
Discount broker availability: Schwab (only through financial advisers), White
Telephone switching: None (mail only)
Dividends paid: Income - December; Capital gains - December
Portfolio turnover (3 years): 6%, 4%, 1%
Management fee: At cost
Maintenance fee: $10 per year (paid $2.50/quarter, waived for accounts with balances of $10,000 or more)
Expense ratio: 0.32% (year ending 12/31/94)

VANGUARD INTERNATIONAL EQUITY INDEX FUND - PACIFIC PORTFOLIO ◆
(See first Vanguard listing for data common to all Vanguard funds)

Newspaper listing: IdxPac
Portfolio manager: George U. Sauter (1990)
Custodian: Morgan Stanley International
Investment objective and policies: Investment results that correspond to the price and yield performance of the Morgan Stanley Capital International Pacific Index of companies located in Australia, Japan, Hong Kong, New Zealand and Singapore. Invests in a statistically selected sample of the more than 425 securities which comprise the Index. Fund may use futures, options, warrants and forward currency contracts. Up to 15% of assets may be in illiquid securities.
Year organized: 1990
Ticker symbol: VPACX
Group fund code: 72
Sales charge: 1% payable to fund
Discount broker availability: Schwab (only through financial advisers), White
Telephone switching: None (mail only)
Dividends paid: Income - December; Capital gains - December

Portfolio turnover (3 yrs): 4%, 7%, 3%
Management fee: At cost
Maintenance fee: $10 per year (paid $2.50/quarter, waived for accounts with balances of $10,000 or more)
Expense ratio: 0.32% (year ending 12/31/94)

VANGUARD INTERNATIONAL GROWTH PORTFOLIO ◆
(See first Vanguard listing for data common to all Vanguard funds)

Adviser: Schroder Capital Management, Inc.
Portfolio manager: Richard R. Foulkes (1981)
Custodian: Morgan Guaranty Trust Co.
Investment objective and policies: Long-term capital appreciation. Maintains a fully invested posture in equity securities of companies based outside the U.S., traded in as many as 30 foreign markets. Adviser focuses on companies with consistent above average earnings prospects not yet recognized by the market. Fund may use stock index futures and options and forward currency contracts. May hedge up to 20% of assets.
Year organized: 1961 (as Ivest Fund, primarily U.S. securities; fund changed to international securities investing in 1981; renamed Vanguard World and subdivided into two portfolios at 9/30/85; World was dropped from name 5/3/93; long-term performance history may be misleading)
Ticker symbol: VWIGX
Group fund code: 81
Discount broker availability: Schwab, White, Waterhouse, Fidelity, Siebert
Dividends paid: Income - December; Capital gains - December
Portfolio turnover (3 yrs): 28%, 51%, 58%
Largest holding: International Nederlanden Groep (2.7%)
Management fee: 0.35% first $50M to 0.125% over $1B subject to incentive adjustment depending on the funds's performance relative to the Morgan Stanley Capital International Europe, Australia, Far East Index over 36 months.
Expense ratio: 0.46% (year ending 8/31/94)

VANGUARD MONEY MARKET RESERVES - FEDERAL PORTFOLIO ◆
(See first Vanguard listing for data common to all Vanguard funds)

Portfolio manager: John Hollyer (1989)
Investment objective and policies: Current income consistent with preservation of capital and liquidity. Invests in short-term securities issued by the U.S. Treasury and agencies of the U.S. Government and repurchase agreements on these obligations with weighted average maturity of 90 days or less.
Year organized: 1981
Ticker symbol: VMFXX
Group fund code: 33
Number of switches permitted: Unlimited
Check redemptions: $250 minimum
Confirmations mailed: After each purchase and each check, mail or wire redemption
Checks returned: Monthly
Periodic account statements mailed: Monthly
Dividends paid: Income - declared daily, paid monthly
Management fee: At cost
Expense ratio: 0.32% (year ending 11/30/94)

VANGUARD MONEY MARKET RESERVES - PRIME PORTFOLIO ◆
(See first Vanguard listing for data common to all Vanguard funds)

Portfolio manager: John Hollyer (1991)
Investment objective and policies: Current income consistent with preservation of capital and liquidity; invests in high quality money market instruments with weighted average maturity of 90 days or less.
Year organized: 1975

Ticker symbol: VMMXX
Group fund code: 30
Number of switches permitted: Unlimited
Check redemptions: $250 minimum
Confirmations mailed: After each purchase and each check, mail or wire redemption
Checks returned: Monthly
Periodic account statements mailed: Monthly
Dividends paid: Income - declared daily, paid monthly
Management fee: At cost
Expense ratio: 0.32% (year ending 11/30/94)

VANGUARD MONEY MARKET RESERVES - U.S. TREASURY PORTFOLIO ◆
(See first Vanguard listing for data common to all Vanguard funds)

Portfolio manager: John Hollyer (1990)
Investment objective and policies: Maximum current income consistent with preservation of capital and liquidity. Invests primarily in direct U.S. obligations as well as repurchase agreements backed by Treasury securities, and other obligations backed by the full faith and credit of the U.S. Government with weighted average maturity of 90 days or less.
Year organized: 1983 (formerly Insured Portfolio. Name and objective changed in March 1989)
Ticker symbol: VMPXX
Group fund code: 50
Number of switches permitted: Unlimited
Check redemptions: $250 minimum
Confirmations mailed: After each purchase and each check, mail or wire redemption
Checks returned: Monthly
Periodic account statements mailed: Monthly
Dividends paid: Income - declared daily, paid monthly
Management fee: At cost
Expense ratio: 0.32% (year ending 11/30/94)

VANGUARD/MORGAN GROWTH FUND ◆
(See first Vanguard listing for data common to all Vanguard funds)

Advisers: Wellington Management Company, Franklin Portfolio Associates, Husic Capital Management, Vanguard Core Management Group
Portfolio managers: Robert D. Rands (1994), Frank J. Husic (1993), George U. Sauter (1993), John J. Nagorniak (1990)
Custodian: State Street Bank & Trust Co.
Investment objective and policies: Long term growth of capital. Invests primarily in common stocks of established growth companies, emerging growth companies and cyclical growth companies. Wellington and Vanguard Core (50% of assets) use traditional (fundamental and relative valuation) methods of stock selection; Franklin (33%) and Husic (13%) use quantitative techniques for stock selection designed to produce results which outperform Morningstar's Growth Fund Stock Index. Fund may use index futures and options to a limited extent and hedge up to 20% of assets.
Year organized: 1968 (formerly W.L. Morgan Growth Fund)
Ticker symbol: VMRGX
Group fund code: 26
Discount broker availability: Schwab, White, Waterhouse, Fidelity, Siebert
Dividends paid: Income - December; Capital gains - December
Portfolio turnover (3 yrs): 72%, 64%, 52%
Largest holding: Motorola, Inc. (2.0%)
Management fee: Varies by manager; from 0.40% first $25M to 0.15% over $1B, subject to incentive adjustment depending on the fund's performance relative to the S&P 500
Expense ratio: 0.49% (year ending 12/31/93)

VANGUARD MUNICIPAL BOND FUND - HIGH YIELD PORTFOLIO ◆

(See first Vanguard listing for data common to all Vanguard funds)

Portfolio manager: Jerome J. Jacobs (1988)
Investment objective and policies: Income exempt from federal income tax consistent with preservation of capital. Invests in lower average credit quality than Long-Term Portfolio: at least 80% rated Baa or better, up to 20% in unrated with a weighted average maturity of 15 to 25 years. Fund may invest up to 20% in AMT bonds, use bond futures and options (initial margin limited to 5% of assets) and hedge up to 20% of assets.
Year organized: 1978
Ticker symbol: VWAHX
Group fund code: 44
Discount broker availability: Schwab, White, Waterhouse, Fidelity, Siebert
Check redemptions: $250 minimum
Dividends paid: Income - declared daily, paid monthly; Capital gains - December
Portfolio turnover (3 yrs): 50%, 34%, 64%
Management fee: At cost
Expense ratio: 0.20% (year ending 8/31/94)

VANGUARD MUNICIPAL BOND FUND - INSURED LONG-TERM PORTFOLIO ◆

(See first Vanguard listing for data common to all Vanguard funds)

Newspaper listing: MInLg
Portfolio manager: David E. Hamlin (1986)
Investment objective and policies: Income exempt from federal income tax consistent with preservation of capital. Invests at least 80% of assets in investment-grade municipal bonds covered by insurance guaranteeing payment of principal and interest with a weighted average maturity of 15 to 25 years. Up to 20% may be in uninsured municipals with ratings of A or better. Fund may use bond futures and options (initial margin limited to 5% of assets) and hedge up to 20% of assets.
Year organized: 1984
Ticker symbol: VILPX
Group fund code: 58
Discount broker availability: Schwab, White, Waterhouse, Fidelity, Siebert
Check redemptions: $250 minimum
Dividends paid: Income - declared daily, paid monthly; Capital gains - December
Portfolio turnover (3 yrs): 16%, 30%, 42%
Management fee: At cost
Expense ratio: 0.20% (year ending 8/31/94)

VANGUARD MUNICIPAL BOND FUND - INTERMEDIATE-TERM PORTFOLIO ◆

(See first Vanguard listing for data common to all Vanguard funds)

Portfolio manager: Christopher M. Ryon (1991)
Investment objective and policies: Income exempt from federal income tax consistent with preservation of capital. Invests in investment-grade municipal securities, at least 95% of which must be rated A or better, with a weighted average maturity of 7 to 12 years. Fund may use bond futures and options (initial margin limited to 5% of assets) and hedge up to 20% of assets.
Year organized: 1977
Ticker symbol: VWITX
Group fund code: 42
Discount broker availability: Schwab, White, Waterhouse, Fidelity, Siebert
Check redemptions: $250 minimum
Dividends paid: Income - declared daily, paid monthly; Capital gains - December
Portfolio turnover (3 yrs): 18%, 15%, 32%
Management fee: At cost
Expense ratio: 0.20% (year ending 8/31/94)

VANGUARD MUNICIPAL BOND FUND - LIMITED-TERM PORTFOLIO ◆

(See first Vanguard listing for data common to all Vanguard funds)

Newspaper listing: MuLtd
Portfolio manager: Christopher M. Ryon (1988)
Investment objective and policies: High level of interest income exempt from federal income tax consistent with conservation of capital. Invests primarily in investment-grade municipal bonds with maturities of 10 years or less and a weighted average maturity of 2 to 5 years. At least 95% of must be rated A or better. Fund may use bond futures and options (initial margin limited to 5% of assets) and hedge up to 20% of assets.
Year organized: 1987
Ticker symbol: VMLTX
Group fund code: 31
Discount broker availability: Schwab, White, Waterhouse, Fidelity, Siebert
Check redemptions: $250 minimum
Dividends paid: Income - declared daily, paid monthly; Capital gains - December
Portfolio turnover (3 yrs): 21%, 20%, 37%
Management fee: At cost
Expense ratio: 0.20% (year ending 8/31/94)

VANGUARD MUNICIPAL BOND FUND - LONG-TERM PORTFOLIO ◆

(See first Vanguard listing for data common to all Vanguard funds)

Portfolio manager: Jerome J. Jacobs (1988)
Investment objective and policies: Income exempt from federal income tax consistent with preservation of capital. Invests in investment-grade municipal securities, at least 95% of which must be rated A or better, with a weighted average maturity of 15 to 25 years. Fund may use bond futures and options (initial margin limited to 5% of assets) and hedge up to 20% of assets.
Year organized: 1977
Ticker symbol: VWLTX
Group fund code: 43
Discount broker availability: Schwab, White, Waterhouse, Fidelity, Siebert
Check redemptions: $250 minimum
Dividends paid: Income - declared daily, paid monthly; Capital gains - December
Portfolio turnover (3 yrs): 45%, 36%, 63%
Management fee: At cost
Expense ratio: 0.20% (year ending 8/31/94)

VANGUARD MUNICIPAL BOND FUND - MONEY MARKET PORTFOLIO ◆

(See first Vanguard listing for data common to all Vanguard funds)

Portfolio manager: Pamela E. Wisehaupt (1987)
Investment objective and policies: Income exempt from federal income tax consistent with preservation of capital and liquidity. Invests in high-quality municipal money market securities.
Year organized: 1980
Ticker symbol: VMSXX
Group fund code: 45
Check redemptions: $250 minimum
Confirmations mailed: After each purchase and each check, mail or wire redemption
Checks returned: Monthly
Periodic account statements mailed: Monthly
Dividends paid: Income - declared daily, paid monthly
Management fee: At cost
Expense ratio: 0.20% (year ending 8/31/94)

VANGUARD MUNICIPAL BOND FUND - SHORT-TERM PORTFOLIO ◆

(See first Vanguard listing for data common to all Vanguard funds)

Portfolio manager: Christopher M. Ryon (1988)
Investment objective and policies: Income exempt from federal income tax consistent with preservation of capital. Invests in investment-grade munici-

pal securities with maturities of less than 5 years, at least 95% rated A or better, with a weighted average maturity of 1 to 2 years. Fund may use bond futures and options (initial margin limited to 5% of assets) and hedge up to 20% of assets.
Year organized: 1977
Ticker symbol: VWSTX
Group fund code: 41
Discount broker availability: Schwab, White, Waterhouse, Fidelity, Siebert
Check redemptions: $250 minimum
Dividends paid: Income - declared daily, paid monthly; Capital gains - December
Portfolio turnover (3 yrs): 27%, 46%, 60%
Management fee: At cost
Expense ratio: 0.20% (year ending 8/31/94)

VANGUARD NEW JERSEY INSURED TAX-FREE LONG-TERM PORTFOLIO ◆

(See first Vanguard listing for data common to all Vanguard funds)

Portfolio manager: David E. Hamlin (1988)
Investment objective and policies: High current income exempt from federal and New Jersey state income taxes. Invests at least 80% of assets in long-term municipal bonds issued by New Jersey state and local governments and covered by insurance guaranteeing payment of principal and interest, with a weighted average maturity of 15 to 25 years. Fund may invest up to 20% in AMT bonds, use bond futures and options, and taxable securities in unusual circumstances. May hedge up to 20% of assets.
Year organized: 1988
Ticker symbol: VNJTX
Group fund code: 14
Discount broker availability: Schwab, White, Waterhouse, Fidelity, Siebert
Qualified for sale in: NJ
Check redemptions: $250 minimum
Dividends paid: Income - declared daily, paid monthly; Capital gains - December
Portfolio turnover (3 yrs): 13%, 12%, 34%
Management fee: At cost
Expense ratio: 0.21% (year ending 11/30/94)

VANGUARD NEW JERSEY TAX-FREE MONEY MARKET PORTFOLIO ◆

(See first Vanguard listing for data common to all Vanguard funds)

Portfolio manager: Danine A. Mueller (1992)
Investment objective and policies: Current income exempt from federal and New Jersey state income taxes. Invests in high quality short-term New Jersey municipal securities.
Year organized: 1987
Ticker symbol: VNJXX
Group fund code: 95
Qualified for sale in: NJ
Check redemptions: $250 minimum
Confirmations mailed: After each purchase and each check, mail, or wire redemption
Checks returned: Monthly
Periodic account statements mailed: Monthly
Dividends paid: Income - declared daily, paid monthly
Management fee: At cost
Expense ratio: 0.21% (year ending 11/30/94)

VANGUARD NEW YORK INSURED TAX-FREE FUND ◆

(See first Vanguard listing for data common to all Vanguard funds)

Portfolio manager: David E. Hamlin (1986)
Investment objective and policies: High current income exempt from federal and New York state and New York City personal income taxes. Invests primarily in long-term municipal bonds issued by New York state and local municipalities which are covered by insurance guaranteeing payment of principal and interest, with a weighted average maturity of 15 to 25 years. Fund may invest up to 20% in AMT bonds, use bond futures and options,

and taxable securities in unusual circumstances. May hedge up to 20% of assets.
Year organized: 1986
Ticker symbol: VNYTX
Group fund code: 76
Discount broker availability: Schwab, White, Waterhouse, Fidelity, Siebert
Qualified for sale in: NY
Check redemptions: $250 minimum
Dividends paid: Income - declared daily, paid monthly; Capital gains - December
Portfolio turnover (3 yrs): 20%, 10%, 17%
Management fee: At cost
Expense ratio: 0.22% (year ending 11/30/94)

VANGUARD OHIO INSURED TAX-FREE LONG-TERM PORTFOLIO ◆
(See first Vanguard listing for data common to all Vanguard funds)

Portfolio manager: David E. Hamlin (1990)
Investment objective and policies: High current income exempt from federal and Ohio state income taxes. Invests at least 80% of assets in long-term municipal bonds issued by Ohio and its local municipalities covered by insurance guaranteeing payment of principal and interest, with a weighted average maturity of 15 to 25 years. Fund may invest up to 20% in AMT bonds, use bond futures and options, and taxable securities in unusual circumstances. May hedge up to 20% of assets.
Year organized: 1990
Ticker symbol: VOHIX
Group fund code: 97
Discount broker availability: Fidelity, Siebert
Qualified for sale in: OH
Check redemptions: $250 minimum
Dividends paid: Income - declared daily, paid monthly; Capital gains - December
Portfolio turnover (3 yrs): 16%, 10%, 27%
Management fee: At cost
Expense ratio: 0.23% (year ending 11/30/94)

VANGUARD OHIO TAX-FREE MONEY MARKET PORTFOLIO ◆
(See first Vanguard listing for data common to all Vanguard funds)

Portfolio manager: Pamela E. Wisehaupt (1990)
Investment objective and policies: Highest level of interest income exempt from federal and Ohio state income taxes. Invests in high quality short-term Ohio municipal securities.
Year organized: 1990
Ticker symbol: VOHXX
Group fund code: 96
Qualified for sale in: OH
Check redemptions: $250 minimum
Confirmations mailed: After each purchase and each check, mail, or wire redemption
Checks returned: Monthly
Periodic account statements mailed: Monthly
Dividends paid: Income - declared daily, paid monthly; Capital gains - December
Management fee: At cost
Expense ratio: 0.23% (year ending 11/30/94)

VANGUARD PENNSYLVANIA INSURED TAX-FREE LONG-TERM PORTFOLIO ◆
(See first Vanguard listing for data common to all Vanguard funds)

Portfolio manager: Reid O. Smith (1992)
Investment objective and policies: High current income exempt from federal and Pennsylvania state income taxes. Invests at least 80% of assets in long-term municipal bonds issued by Pennsylvania and its local municipalities covered by insurance guaranteeing payment of principal and interest, with a weighted average maturity of 15 to 25 years. Fund may invest up to 20% in AMT bonds, use bond futures and options, and taxable securities in unusual circumstances. May hedge up to 20% of assets.
Year organized: 1986
Ticker symbol: VPAIX
Group fund code: 77

Discount broker availability: Schwab, Waterhouse, Fidelity, Siebert
Qualified for sale in: PA
Check redemptions: $250 minimum
Dividends paid: Income - declared daily, paid monthly; Capital gains - December
Portfolio turnover (3 yrs): 16%, 14%, 17%
Management fee: At cost
Expense ratio: 0.20% (year ending 11/30/94)

VANGUARD PENNSYLVANIA TAX-FREE MONEY MARKET PORTFOLIO ◆
(See first Vanguard listing for data common to all Vanguard funds)

Portfolio manager: Danine A. Mueller (1992)
Investment objective and policies: Current income exempt from federal and Pennsylvania state income taxes. Invests in high quality short-term Pennsylvania municipal securities.
Year organized: 1988
Ticker symbol: VPTXX
Group fund code: 63
Qualified for sale in: PA
Check redemptions: $250 minimum
Confirmations mailed: After each purchase and each check, mail, or wire redemption
Checks returned: Monthly
Periodic account statements mailed: Monthly
Dividends paid: Income - declared daily, paid monthly
Management fee: At cost
Expense ratio: 0.20% (year ending 11/30/94)

VANGUARD PREFERRED STOCK FUND ◆
(See first Vanguard listing for data common to all Vanguard funds)

Adviser: Wellington Management Co.
Portfolio manager: Earl E. McEvoy (1982)
Custodian: State Street Bank & Trust Co.
Investment objective and policies: Maximum dividend income qualifying for the 70% corporate dividends received deduction. Normally invests at least 75% of assets in cumulative preferred stocks rated Baa or better by Moody's or BBB or better by S&P. Remainder may be in fixed-income securities and preferred stocks with lower ratings. Suitable for corporations, tax-exempt organizations and employee benefit plans.
Year organized: 1975 (formerly Qualified Dividend Portfolio II)
Ticker symbol: VQIIX
Group fund code: 38
Discount broker availability: Schwab, White, Waterhouse, Fidelity, Siebert
Dividends paid: Income - March, June, September, December; Capital gains - December
Portfolio turnover (3 yrs): 27%, 45%, 33%
Largest holding: Ford Holdings 8.00% (3.8%)
Management fee: 0.325% first $50M to 0.15% over $250M
Expense ratio: 0.51% (year ending 10/31/94)

VANGUARD PRIMECAP FUND ◆
(See first Vanguard listing for data common to all Vanguard funds)

Adviser: Primecap Management Co.
Portfolio manager: Howard B. Schow (1984)
Custodian: State Street Bank & Trust Co.
Investment objective and policies: Long-term growth of capital. Invests at least 80% of assets in common stocks selected on the basis of several fundamental factors. May invest in convertible securities, stock index futures and options to a limited extent, and in certain short-term fixed-income securities. May hedge up to 20% of assets.
Year organized: 1984 (4 for 1 split on 2/28/90)
Ticker symbol: VPMCX
Group fund code: 59
Discount broker availability: Schwab, White, Waterhouse, Fidelity, Siebert

Dividends paid: Income - December; Capital gains - December
Portfolio turnover (3 yrs): 18%, 7%, 24%
Largest holding: Federal Express Corp. (4.6%)
Management fee: 0.75% first $25M to 0.25% over $500M
Expense ratio: 0.67% (year ending 12/31/93)

VANGUARD QUANTITATIVE PORTFOLIOS ◆
(See first Vanguard listing for data common to all Vanguard funds)

Adviser: Franklin Portfolio Assoc.
Portfolio manager: John Nagorniak (1986)
Investment objective and policies: Total return (capital gains and income) greater than that of the aggregate U.S. stock market, as measured by the S&P 500 Index. Fund selects common stocks using quantitative investment techniques such as measures of earnings changes, relative value based on p/e ratios, dividend discount calculations, and measures of sensitivity to economic changes. Fund then constructs a portfolio that resembles the S&P 500 index, with at least 65% of its assets, but is weighted toward its most attractive stocks. Fund may use futures contracts and options and hedge up to 20% of assets.
Year organized: 1986
Ticker symbol: VQNPX
Group fund code: 93
Discount broker availability: Schwab (only through financial advisers), White
Dividends paid: Income - June, December; Capital gains - December
Portfolio turnover (3 yrs): 85%, 51%, 61%
Largest holding: General Electric Co. (3.3%)
Management fee: At cost
Expense ratio: 0.50% (year ending 12/31/93)

VANGUARD SMALL CAPITALIZATION STOCK FUND ◆
(See Vanguard Index Trust - Small Capitalization Stock Portfolio)

VANGUARD SPECIALIZED PORTFOLIOS ◆
(Data common to all specialized portfolios are shown below. See subsequent listings for data specific to individual specialized portfolios.)

Custodian: Morgan Guaranty Trust for Gold & Pr. Met.; for others, State Street Bank & Trust Co.
Investment objective and policies: Long term capital appreciation, using equity securities, primarily U.S. Fund comprises a series of portfolios, each concentrated in a particular industry or related group of industries. Each fund normally invests at least 80% of assets in equity securities of its industry category (75% for Utilities Income), may use stock futures and options and hedge up to 20% of assets. Funds generally may invest up to 20% in foreign securities.
Year organized: 1984
Redemption fee: 1% for shares held less than one year, including exchanges among the Specialized Portfolios, paid to the fund (except Utilities Income)
Dividends paid: Income - March; Capital gains - March (except Utilities Income)
Management fee: 0.30% first $100M to 0.10% over $1B (except Gold & Precious Metals)

VANGUARD SPECIALIZED PORTFOLIOS - ENERGY ◆
(See first Specialized Portfolios listing for data common to all Specialized Portfolios)

Adviser: Wellington Management Co.
Portfolio manager: Ernst Von Metzsch (1984)
Investment objective and policies: Invests in companies engaged in the production, transmission, marketing, and control of energy, both conventional and alternative, as well as component products, research, conservation and pollution control related to energy. Electric utilities are specifically excluded.

Ticker symbol: VGENX
Group fund code: 51
Discount broker availability: Schwab, Waterhouse, Fidelity, Siebert
Portfolio turnover (3 yrs): 41%, 37%, 42%
Largest holding: Exxon Corp. (3.5%)
Expense ratio: 0.17% (year ending 1/31/94)

VANGUARD SPECIALIZED PORTFOLIOS - GOLD & PRECIOUS METALS ◆

(See first Specialized Portfolios listing for data common to all Specialized Portfolios)

Adviser: M & G Investment Management Ltd.
Portfolio manager: David Hutchins (1986)
Investment objective and policies: Invests in companies engaged in the exploration, mining, fabricating, processing or dealing in precious metals and minerals. Fund may use up to 20% of assets to purchase bullion and coin directly from banks and commodity exchange dealers. Fund may invest up to 100% in foreign securities.
Ticker symbol: VGPMX
Group fund code: 53
Discount broker availability: Schwab, Waterhouse, Fidelity, Siebert
Portfolio turnover (3 yrs): 14%, 2%, 3%
Largest holding: Newcrest Mining Ltd. (3.3%)
Management fee: 0.30% first $100M to 0.20% over $400M
Expense ratio: 0.26% (year ending 1/31/94)

VANGUARD SPECIALIZED PORTFOLIOS - HEALTH CARE ◆

(See first Specialized Portfolios listing for data common to all Specialized Portfolios)

Adviser: Wellington Management Co.
Portfolio manager: Edward Owens (1984)
Investment objective and policies: Invests in companies engaged in the development, production or distribution of products and services related to the treatment or prevention of diseases and other medical infirmities. This includes companies involved in products, supplies, equipment, facility management and research.
Ticker symbol: VGHCX
Group fund code: 52
Discount broker availability: Schwab, Waterhouse, Fidelity, Siebert
Portfolio turnover (3 yrs): 19%, 15%, 7%
Largest holding: Zeneca Group ADR (4.6%)
Expense ratio: 0.19% (year ending 1/31/94)

VANGUARD SPECIALIZED PORTFOLIOS - SERVICE ECONOMY ◆

(Fund merged into Vanguard/Morgan Growth Fund in 1994)

VANGUARD SPECIALIZED PORTFOLIOS - TECHNOLOGY ◆

(Fund merged into Vanguard Explorer Fund in 1994)

VANGUARD SPECIALIZED PORTFOLIOS - UTILITIES INCOME ◆

(See first Specialized Portfolios listing for data common to all Specialized Portfolios)

Adviser: Wellington Management Co.
Portfolio manager: John R. Ryan (1992)
Investment objective and policies: Invests in companies engaged in the generation, transmission, or distribution of electricity, telecommunications, gas, or water.
Ticker symbol: VGSUX
Group fund code: 57
Discount broker availability: Schwab, White, Waterhouse, Fidelity, Siebert
Redemption fee: None
Dividends paid: Income - March, June, September, December; Capital gains - March

Portfolio turnover (2 yrs): 46%, 20%
Largest holding: Southwestern Bell Corp. (3.2%)
Expense ratio: 0.42% (year ending 1/31/94)

VANGUARD STAR FUND - CONSERVATIVE GROWTH PORTFOLIO ◆

(See first Vanguard listing for data common to all Vanguard funds)

Custodian: Morgan Guarantee Trust Co.
Investment objective and policies: Current income and low to moderate growth of capital. Invests in other Vanguard common stock and fixed-income mutual funds as follows: U.S. Equity 17% (Index Trust Total Stock Market Portfolio); International Equity 5% (International Equity Index Fund European and Pacific Portfolios); Bonds 28% (Short-Term Corporate, Intermediate-Term Corporate, Long -Term Corporate and GNMA); Reserves 20% (Short-Term Corporate and cash) and Asset Allocation 30% (Asset Allocation). Fund may use short term fixed-income instruments on a temporary basis. Fund is especially suited to tax-advantaged retirement accounts.
Year organized: 1994
Group fund code: 724
Dividends paid: Income - March, June, September, December; Capital gains - December
Management fee: None. (See fees of underlying portfolio funds)
Expense ratio: None. (See expense ratios of underlying portfolio funds)

VANGUARD STAR FUND - GROWTH PORTFOLIO ◆

(See first Vanguard listing for data common to all Vanguard funds)

Custodian: Morgan Guarantee Trust Co.
Investment objective and policies: Growth of capital. Invests in other Vanguard common stock and fixed-income mutual funds as follows: U.S. Equity 45% (Index Trust Total Stock Market Portfolio); International Equity 15% (International Index Fund European and Pacific Portfolios); Bonds 10% (Short-Term Corporate, Intermediate-Term Corporate, Long -Term Corporate and GNMA); Reserves 0% (Short-Term Corporate and cash) and Asset Allocation 30% (Asset Allocation). Fund may use short term fixed-income instruments on a temporary basis. Fund is especially suited to tax-advantaged retirement accounts.
Year organized: 1994
Group fund code: 122
Dividends paid: Income - June, December; Capital gains - December
Management fee: None. (See fees of underlying portfolio funds)
Expense ratio: None. (See expense ratios of underlying portfolio funds)

VANGUARD STAR FUND - INCOME PORTFOLIO ◆

(See first Vanguard listing for data common to all Vanguard funds)

Custodian: Morgan Guarantee Trust Co.
Investment objective and policies: Current income. Invests in other Vanguard common stock and fixed-income mutual funds as follows: U.S. Equity 5% (Index Trust Total Stock Market Portfolio); International Equity 0% (International Equity Index Fund European and Pacific Portfolios); Bonds 45% (Short-Term Corporate, Intermediate-Term Corporate, Long -Term Corporate and GNMA); Reserves 20% (Short-Term Corporate and cash) and Asset Allocation 30% (Asset Allocation). Fund may use short term fixed-income instruments on a temporary basis. Fund is especially suited to tax-advantaged retirement accounts.
Year organized: 1994
Group fund code: 723
Dividends paid: Income - March, June, September, December; Capital gains - December

Management fee: None. (See fees of underlying portfolio funds)
Expense ratio: None. (See expense ratios of underlying portfolio funds)

VANGUARD STAR FUND - MODERATE GROWTH PORTFOLIO ◆

(See first Vanguard listing for data common to all Vanguard funds)

Custodian: Morgan Guarantee Trust Co.
Investment objective and policies: Growth of capital and a reasonable level of current income. Invests in other Vanguard common stock and fixed-income mutual funds as follows: U.S. Equity 35% (Index Trust Total Stock Market Portfolio); International Equity 10% (International Equity Index Fund European and Pacific Portfolios); Bonds 25% (Short-Term Corporate, Intermediate-Term Corporate, Long -Term Corporate and GNMA); Reserves 0% (Short-Term Corporate and cash) and Asset Allocation 30% (Asset Allocation). Fund may use short term fixed-income instruments on a temporary basis. Fund is especially suited to tax-advantaged retirement accounts.
Year organized: 1994
Ticker symbol: VSMGX
Group fund code: 914
Dividends paid: Income - June, December; Capital gains - December
Management fee: None. (See fees of underlying portfolio funds)
Expense ratio: None. (See expense ratios of underlying portfolio funds)

VANGUARD STAR FUND - STAR PORTFOLIO ◆

(See first Vanguard listing for data common to all Vanguard funds)

Investment objective and policies: Maximum total return (capital growth and income). Invests in other Vanguard common stock and fixed-income mutual funds as follows: common stock 60-70% (Windsor, Windsor II, Explorer, Morgan, U.S. Growth, PRIMECAP and Index Trust - 500); bond 20-30% (GNMA and Long-Term Corporate); and money market 10-20% (Money Market Prime). Since inception, fund has targeted 62.5% equities, 25% bonds, and 12.5% money market funds versus market timing. Fund may use short term fixed-income instruments on a temporary basis. Fund is especially suited to tax-advantaged retirement accounts.
Year organized: 1985
Ticker symbol: VGSTX
Group fund code: 56
Minimum purchase: Initial: $500, Subsequent: $100
Discount broker availability: Schwab, White, Waterhouse, Fidelity, Siebert
Dividends paid: Income - June, December; Capital gains - December
Portfolio turnover (3 yrs): 3%, 3%, 11%
Management fee: None. (See fees of underlying portfolio funds)
Expense ratio: None. (See expense ratios of underlying portfolio funds)

VANGUARD TAX-MANAGED FUND - BALANCED PORTFOLIO ◆

(See first Vanguard listing for data common to all Vanguard funds)

Portfolio manager: George U. Sauter (1994)
Investment objective and policies: Capital growth and reasonable current income (nominal taxable income and moderate income exempt from federal taxes). Normally invests 50-55% of assets in investment-grade intermediate-term municipal securities with a weighted average maturity of 7-12 years. Remaining 45-50% of assets are in a statistical sample of the stocks included in the Russell 1000 Index with emphasis on stocks with low dividend yields. May use futures, options, warrants and forward currency contracts. Up to 15% of assets may be in illiquid securities. Fund is designed for long-

term investors seeking to minimize the impact of taxes on their returns.
Year organized: 1994
Group fund code: 103
Minimum purchase: Initial: $10,000, Subsequent: $100
Redemption charge: 2% for shares held less than 1 year, 1% for shares held between 1 and 5 years, payable to fund
Telephone switching: None (mail only)
Dividends paid: Income - March, June, September, December; Capital gains - December
Management fee: At cost

VANGUARD TAX-MANAGED FUND - CAPITAL APPRECIATION PORTFOLIO ◆
(See first Vanguard listing for data common to all Vanguard funds)

Portfolio manager: George U. Sauter (1994)
Investment objective and policies: Capital growth and reasonable current income. Invests in a statistical sample of the stocks included in the Russell 1000 Index with emphasis on stocks with low dividend yields. May use futures, options, warrants and forward currency contracts. Up to 15% of assets may be in illiquid securities. Fund is designed for long-term investors seeking to minimize the impact of taxes on their returns.
Year organized: 1994
Ticker symbol: VMCAX
Group fund code: 102
Minimum purchase: Initial: $10,000, Subsequent: $100
Redemption charge: 2% for shares held less than 1 year, 1% for shares held between 1 and 5 years, payable to fund
Telephone switching: None (mail only)
Dividends paid: Income - December; Capital gains - December
Management fee: At cost

VANGUARD TAX-MANAGED FUND - GROWTH AND INCOME PORTFOLIO ◆
(See first Vanguard listing for data common to all Vanguard funds)

Portfolio manager: George U. Sauter (1994)
Investment objective and policies: Long-term capital growth and moderate current income. Invests in substantially all 500 stocks in the S&P 500 Index. Management techniques used to minimize the realization of capital gains may affect the proportion of assets in each stock compared to the Index and cause the Portfolios return to differ from the Index. May use futures, options, warrants and forward currency contracts. Up to 15% of assets may be in illiquid securities. Fund is designed for long-term investors seeking to minimize the impact of taxes on their returns.
Year organized: 1994
Ticker symbol: VTGIX
Group fund code: 101
Minimum purchase: Initial: $10,000, Subsequent: $100
Redemption charge: 2% for shares held less than 1 year, 1% for shares held between 1 and 5 years, payable to fund
Telephone switching: None (mail only)
Dividends paid: Income - March, June, September, December; Capital gains - December
Management fee: At cost

VANGUARD TRUSTEES' EQUITY FUND - INTERNATIONAL PORTFOLIO ◆
(See first Vanguard listing for data common to all Vanguard funds)

Adviser: Batterymarch Financial Management
Portfolio manager: Debra Miller (1994)
Custodian: Morgan Guaranty Trust Co.
Investment objective and policies: Maximum long-term total return consistent with reasonable risk. Normally invests at least 65% of assets in non-U.S.

equity securities selected on the basis of adviser's proprietary scoring system for identifying undervalued securities. Fund concentrates in five largest of more than 20 foreign markets. Fund may use stock futures, options, and forward currency contracts. May hedge up to 20% of assets.
Year organized: 1983 (formerly Vanguard Trustee's Commingled-Int'l Port., name change 5/3/93)
Ticker symbol: VTRIX
Group fund code: 46
Minimum purchase: Initial: $10,000, Subsequent: $1,000; IRA/Keogh: Initial: $500; Subsequent: $100
Discount broker availability: Schwab, White, Waterhouse, Fidelity, Siebert
Dividends paid: Income - March, June, September, December; Capital gains - December
Portfolio turnover (3 yrs): 39%, 51%, 46%
Largest holding: Onward Kashiyama Co. (1.5%)
Management fee: 0.85% first $10M to 0.12% over $500M
Expense ratio: 0.40% (year ending 12/31/93)

VANGUARD TRUSTEES' EQUITY FUND - UNITED STATES PORTFOLIO ◆
(See first Vanguard listing for data common to all Vanguard funds)

Adviser: Geewax, Terker & Company (fund receives administrative and distribution services from The Vanguard Group)
Portfolio manager: John Geewax (1992)
Custodian: State Street Bank & Trust Co.
Investment objective and policies: Maximum long-term total return consistent with reasonable risk. Invests primarily in domestic common stocks considered undervalued. Adviser uses proprietary valuation and ranking system to select companies with best relative total return potential. Selections will generally be characterized as smaller capitalization, low price to book value, and higher yield vehicles associated with value or contrarian investing. Fund may use stock futures and options. May hedge up to 20% of assets.
Year organized: 1980 (formerly Vanguard Trustee's Commingled-U.S. Port., name change 5/3/93)
Ticker symbol: VTRSX
Group fund code: 25
Minimum purchase: Initial: $10,000, Subsequent: $1,000; IRA/Keogh: Initial: $500; Subsequent: $100
Discount broker availability: Schwab, White, Waterhouse, Fidelity, Siebert
Dividends paid: Income - March, June, September, December; Capital gains - December
Portfolio turnover (3 yrs): 140%, 209%, 84%
Largest holding: Chevron Corp. (2.2%)
Management fee: Incentive/penalty fee ranging from 0.60% to 0.20% depending on performance relative to the S&P 500 over 36 months.
Expense ratio: 0.90% (year ending 12/31/93)

VANGUARD U.S. GROWTH PORTFOLIO ◆
(See first Vanguard listing for data common to all Vanguard funds)

Adviser: Lincoln Capital Management
Portfolio manager: J. Parker Hall III (1987)
Custodian: State Street Bank & Trust Co.
Investment objective and policies: Long-term capital appreciation. Invests primarily in equity securities, including common stocks and securities convertible into common stocks, of seasoned U.S. companies with above average growth prospects. Fund is normally fully invested. May use stock index futures and options to a limited extent and hedge up to 20% of assets.
Year organized: 1961 (as Ivest Fund, primarily U.S. securities; fund changed to international securities investing in 1981; renamed Vanguard World and subdivided into two portfolios at 9/30/85; World was dropped from name on 5/3/93)
Ticker symbol: VWUSX
Group fund code: 23

Discount broker availability: Schwab, White, Waterhouse, Fidelity, Siebert
Dividends paid: Income - December; Capital gains - December
Portfolio turnover (3 yrs): 47%, 37%, 24%
Largest holding: General Electric Co. (5.0%)
Management fee: 0.40% first $25M to 0.10% over $2.5B
Expense ratio: 0.52% (year ending 8/31/94)

VANGUARD WELLESLEY INCOME FUND ◆
(See first Vanguard listing for data common to all Vanguard funds)

Adviser: Wellington Management Corp.
Portfolio managers: Earl E. McEvoy (fixed-income, 1982), John Ryan (equity, 1987)
Custodian: Morgan Guaranty Trust Co.
Investment objective and policies: Current income consistent with reasonable risk with moderate growth of capital secondary. Invests in fixed-income securities (normally 60% of assets) with remainder primarily in dividend-paying common stocks. Fixed-income securities may include U.S. Government and corporate bonds and mortgage-backed securities as well as securities convertible into common stock. May use stock and bond futures contracts and options and hedge up to 20% of assets.
Year organized: 1970
Ticker symbol: VWINX
Group fund code: 27
Discount broker availability: Schwab, White, Waterhouse, Fidelity, Siebert
Dividends paid: Income - March, June, September, December; Capital gains - December
Portfolio turnover (3 yrs): Stocks: 26%, 16%, 19%; Bonds: 18%, 24%, 34%
Largest holding: Treasury Bond due 5/15/16 (3.6%)
Management fee: 0.15% first $500M to 0.05% over $4B
Expense ratio: 0.33% (year ending 12/31/93)

VANGUARD WELLINGTON FUND ◆
(See first Vanguard listing for data common to all Vanguard funds)

Adviser: Wellington Management Corp.
Portfolio managers: Vincent Bajakian (1972), Paul D. Kaplan (1994)
Custodian: Morgan Guaranty Trust Co.
Investment objective and policies: Conservation of principal, reasonable income, and profits without undue risk. Invests in a balanced portfolio of 60-70% common stocks, with remainder in investment-grade fixed-income securities. May invest up to 10% of assets in foreign securities and use stock and bond index futures and options to a limited extent and hedge up to 20% of assets.
Year organized: 1928
Ticker symbol: VWELX
Group fund code: 21
Discount broker availability: Schwab, White, Waterhouse, Fidelity, Siebert
Dividends paid: Income - March, June, September, December; Capital gains - December
Portfolio turnover (3 yrs): 32%, 34%, 24%
Largest holding: GNMA Certificate 6.50% due 6/15/24 (2.7%)
Management fee: 0.125% first $500M to 0.04% over $3B
Expense ratio: 0.35% (year ending 11/30/94)

VANGUARD WINDSOR FUND ◆
(See first Vanguard listing for data common to all Vanguard funds)

Adviser: Wellington Management Co.
Portfolio manager: John C. Neff (1964)
Custodian: State Street Bank & Trust Co.
Investment objective and policies: Long-term growth of capital and income with current income

secondary. Invests primarily in common stocks of companies based on their fundamental values, principally underlying earnings power and dividend payout ration. Stocks selected will generally fall within the characterization of undervalued or overlooked. Fund may use stock futures contracts and options to a limited extent and hedge up to 20% of assets.

Year organized: 1958 (Vanguard High Yield Stock Fund merged in February 1991)
Ticker symbol: VWNDX
Group fund code: 22
Special sales restrictions: Fund is currently closed to new shareholders. Current shareholders are limited to an additional $25,000 per year.
Minimum purchase: Subsequent: $100
Discount broker availability: Schwab, White, Waterhouse
Dividends paid: Income - June, December; Capital gains - December
Portfolio turnover (3 yrs): 34%, 25%, 32%
Largest holding: Citicorp (6.7%)
Management fee: 0.35% first $200M to 0.15% over $750M subject to incentive adjustment depending on the fund's performance relative to the S&P 500
Expense ratio: 0.45% (year ending 10/31/94)

VANGUARD WINDSOR II ◆

(See first Vanguard listing for data common to all Vanguard funds)

Advisers: Barrow, Hanley, Mewhinney & Strauss; Equinox Capital Management; Tukman Capital Management; and Core Management Group
Portfolio managers: James Barrow (1985), Ronald J. Ulrich (1991), Melvin T. Tukman (1991), George U. Sauter (1991)
Custodian: State Street Bank & Trust Co.
Investment objective and policies: Long-term growth of capital and income with current income secondary. Invests primarily in income producing common stocks of companies believed undervalued, based on relative price to earnings and price to book ratios rather than earnings expectations. Fund stays substantially fully invested. May use stock futures contracts and options to a limited extent and hedge up to 20% of assets.
Year organized: 1985
Ticker symbol: VWNFX
Group fund code: 73
Discount broker availability: Schwab, White, Waterhouse, Fidelity, Siebert
Dividends paid: Income - June, December; Capital gains - December
Portfolio turnover (3 yrs): 24%, 26%, 23%
Largest holding: Anheuser-Busch Companies, Inc. (3.5%)
Management fee: BHM&S: 0.75% first $10M to 0.125% over $1B; Equinox: 0.30% first $100M to 0.15% over $400M (+/- performance adjustment); Tukman 0.40% first $25M to 0.15% over $1B (+/- performance adjustment)
Expense ratio: 0.39% (year ending 10/31/94)

VISTA FUNDS

(Data common to all Vista funds are shown below. See subsequent listings for data specific to individual funds.)

P.O. Box 419392
Kansas City, MO 64179
800-348-4782

Adviser: Chase Manhattan Bank, N.A.
Custodian: Chase Manhattan Bank, N.A.
Transfer agent: Investors Fiduciary Trust Co.
Minimum purchase: Initial: $2,500, Subsequent: None; IRA/Keogh: Initial: $100
Telephone orders accepted: Yes
Wire orders accepted: Yes
Deadline for same day wire purchase: 4 P.M. (12 NN for money market funds)
Telephone redemptions: Yes
Wire redemptions: Yes, $1,000 minimum, $10 fee
Letter redemptions: Signature guarantee required over $25,000

Telephone switching: With other Vista funds, some of which have loads
Number of switches permitted: Unlimited
Deadline for same day switch: 4 P.M. for equity funds, 12 NN for money market funds
Shareholder services: Keogh, IRA, SEP-IRA, 401(k), 403(b), corporate retirement plans, automatic investment plan, withdrawal plan min. req. $10,000, electronic funds transfer
Administration fee: 0.10%
IRA fees: Annual $12
Keogh fees: Annual $25

VISTA BOND FUND

(See first Vista listing for data common to all Vista funds.)

Portfolio manager: Mark Buonaugurio (1991)
Investment objective and policies: High income consistent with reasonable risk. Invests primarily in government bonds, investment-grade corporate bonds and other fixed-income securities. May use futures contracts and options.
Year organized: 1990 (name changed from Trinity Bond Fund on 12/31/92)
Ticker symbol: TRBDX
Discount broker availability: *White (only through financial advisers), Fidelity, Siebert
Qualified for sale in: CA, CO, CT, DC, FL, GA, HI, IL, IN, MN, MT, NJ, NY, NC, PA, VA, WV, WY
Dividends paid: Income - declared daily, paid monthly; Capital gains - July
Portfolio turnover (3 yrs): 17%, 20%, 31%
Management fee: 0.3%
12b-1 distribution fee: 0.25%
Expense ratio: 0.31% (year ending 10/31/94) (0.92% without waiver)

VISTA CALIFORNIA TAX FREE MONEY MARKET FUND

(See first Vista listing for data common to all Vista funds)

Portfolio manager: Nicholas Robiecki (1992)
Investment objective and policies: Current income exempt from federal and state of California income taxes consistent with preservation of capital and liquidity. Invests in high quality short-term California state and local municipal securities.
Year organized: 1992
Qualified for sale in: CA, CO, DC, FL, HI, NJ, NY, VA, WY
Check redemptions: $500 minimum
Confirmations mailed: After each purchase and each check, mail, or wire redemption
Checks returned: On request
Periodic account statements mailed: Monthly
Dividends paid: Income - declared daily, paid monthly
Management fee: 0.10%
12b-1 distribution fee: 0.10%
Expense ratio: 0.46% (10 months ending 8/31/94) (0.94% without waiver)

VISTA EQUITY FUND

(See first Vista listing for data common to all Vista funds.)

Portfolio manager: Mark A. Tincher (1994)
Investment objective and policies: Long-term capital growth. Invests primarily in common stocks of well-known and established companies with market capitalizations of $200M or more whose stocks are included in the S&P 500 or the DJIA. May use futures and options.
Year organized: 1990 (name changed from Trinity Equity Fund on 12/31/92)
Ticker symbol: TREQX
Discount broker availability: *White (only through financial advisers), Fidelity, Siebert
Qualified for sale in: CA, CO, CT, DC, FL, GA, HI, IL, IN, MN, MT, NJ, NY, NC, PA, VA, WV, WY
Dividends paid: Income - January, April, July, October; Capital gains - July

Portfolio turnover (3 yrs): 53%, 33%, 14%
Largest holding: Citicorp (1.5%)
Management fee: 0.3%
12b-1 distribution fee: 0.10%
Expense ratio: 0.31% (year ending 6/30/94) (0.95% without waiver)

VISTA GLOBAL MONEY MARKET FUND ◆

(See first Vista listing for data common to all Vista funds)

Portfolio manager: Thomas Nelson (1992)
Investment objective and policies: Maximum current income consistent with preservation of capital and liquidity. Invests in U.S. dollar denominated commercial paper, obligations of foreign governments, obligations guaranteed by U.S. banks, and securities issued by the U.S. Government or its agencies with a weighted average maturity of 90 days or less. Fund normally invests in securities of at least 3 countries.
Year organized: 1983 (name changed from Trinity Money Market Fund on 12/31/92)
Ticker symbol: VRMXX
Qualified for sale in: All states
Check redemptions: $500 minimum
Confirmations mailed: After each purchase and each check, mail, or wire redemption
Checks returned: On request
Periodic account statements mailed: Monthly
Dividends paid: Income - declared daily, paid monthly
Management fee: 0.10%
Expense ratio: 0.60% (10 months ending 8/31/94) (0.74% without waiver)

VISTA NEW YORK TAX FREE MONEY MARKET FUND

(See first Vista listing for data common to all Vista funds)

Portfolio manager: Nicholas Robiecki (1988)
Investment objective and policies: Current income exempt from federal and New York State and New York City income taxes consistent with preservation of capital and liquidity. Invests in high quality short-term New York municipal money market instruments.
Year organized: 1987
Ticker symbol: VNYXX
Qualified for sale in: CA, CO, CT, DC, FL, GA, HI, IL, IN, MN, MT, NC, NJ, NY, PA, VA, WV, WY
Check redemptions: $500 minimum
Confirmations mailed: After each purchase and each check, mail, or wire redemption
Checks returned: On request
Periodic account statements mailed: Monthly
Dividends paid: Income - declared daily, paid monthly
Management fee: 0.10%
12b-1 distribution fee: 0.12%
Expense ratio: 0.85% (10 months ending 10/31/94)

VISTA SHORT-TERM BOND FUND

(See first Vista listing for data common to all Vista funds.)

Portfolio manager: Linda M. Struble (1990)
Investment objective and policies: High income consistent with preservation of capital. Invests primarily in short-term government bonds, investment-grade corporate bonds and other fixed-income securities with a weighted average maturity of 1 to 3 years. May use futures contracts and options.
Year organized: 1990 (name changed from Trinity Short-Term Bond Fund on 12/31/92)
Ticker symbol: TRSBX
Discount broker availability: *White (only through financial advisers), Fidelity, Siebert
Qualified for sale in: CA, CO, CT, DC, FL, GA, HI, IL, IN, MN, MT, NJ, NY, NC, PA, VA, WV, WY

Dividends paid: Income - declared daily, paid monthly; Capital gains - July
Portfolio turnover (3 yrs): 44%, 17%, 29%
Management fee: 0.3%
12b-1 distribution fee: 0.07%
Expense ratio: 0.31% (year ending 10/31/94) (0.86% without waiver)

VISTA TAX FREE MONEY MARKET FUND

(See first Vista listing for data common to all Vista funds)

Portfolio manager: Nicholas Robiecki (1988)
Investment objective and policies: Current income exempt from federal income taxes consistent with preservation of capital and liquidity. Invests in high quality short-term municipal money market instruments.
Year organized: 1987
Ticker symbol: VTMXX
Qualified for sale in: All states
Check redemptions: $500 minimum
Confirmations mailed: After each purchase and each check, mail, or wire redemption
Checks returned: On request
Periodic account statements mailed: Monthly
Dividends paid: Income - declared daily, paid monthly
Management fee: 0.10%
12b-1 distribution fee: 0.13%
Expense ratio: 0.85% (10 months ending 10/31/94)

VISTA U.S. GOVERNMENT MONEY MARKET FUND

(See first Vista listing for data common to all Vista funds)

Portfolio manager: Thomas Darby (1992)
Investment objective and policies: High level of current income consistent with preservation of capital and liquidity. Invests in high quality short-term obligations issued or guaranteed by the U.S. Treasury and agencies of the U.S. Government or its instrumentalities.
Year organized: 1983
Ticker symbol: VGMXX
Qualified for sale in: All states
Check redemptions: $500 minimum
Confirmations mailed: After each purchase and each check, mail, or wire redemption
Checks returned: On request
Periodic account statements mailed: Monthly
Dividends paid: Income - declared daily, paid monthly
Management fee: 0.10%
12b-1 distribution fee: 0.10%
Expense ratio: 0.80% (10 months ending 8/31/94)

VOLUMETRIC FUND ◆

87 Violet Drive
Pearl River, NY 10965
914-623-7637, 800-541-3863
fax 914-623-7732

Adviser: Volumetric Advisers, Inc.
Portfolio manager: Gabriel J. Gibs (1978)
Custodian: The Chase Manhattan Bank
Transfer agent: Volumetric Advisers, Inc.
Investment objective and policies: Capital growth. Invests in common stocks, principally those of the New York Stock Exchange. Uses proprietary methodology of technical analysis, developed by founder Gabriel Gibs, to quantitatively analyze the demand and supply for individual stocks by volume. The thesis is that volume aberrations from normal trading precede price movements. Stocks singled out are then researched on a traditional fundamental basis for inclusion in the portfolio.
Year organized: 1978
Ticker symbol: VOLMX
Minimum purchase: Initial: $500, Subsequent: $200
Telephone orders accepted: Yes, subsequent only, maximum 3 times value of account

Wire orders accepted: Yes
Deadline for same day wire purchase: 4 P.M.
Discount broker availability: *White
Qualified for sale in: CA, FL, NJ, NY, PA
Telephone redemptions: Yes
Wire redemptions: No
Letter redemptions: Signature guarantee not required
Dividends paid: Income - December; Capital gains - December
Portfolio turnover (3 yrs): 150%, 177%, 125%
Largest holding: Hudson Foods (2.6%)
Shareholder services: Keogh, IRA, SEP-IRA, corporate retirement plans
Management fee: 2.0% first $10M to 1.5% over $100M
Expense ratio: 1.99% (year ending 12/31/94)
IRA/Keogh fees: None

VONTOBEL FUNDS ◆

(Data common to all Vontobel funds are shown below. See subsequent listings for data specific to individual Vontobel funds.)

1500 Forest Avenue, Suite 223
Richmond, VA 23229
804-285-8211, 800-527-9500
fax 804-285-8251

Adviser: Vontobel USA, Inc.
Custodian: Brown Brothers Harriman & Co.
Transfer agent: Fund Services, Inc.
Minimum purchase: Initial: $1,000, Subsequent: $100
Telephone orders accepted: No
Wire orders accepted: Yes
Deadline for same day wire purchases: 2 P.M.
Qualified for sale in: All states
Telephone redemptions: Yes, $10 fee
Wire redemptions: Yes, $10 fee
Letter redemptions: Signature guarantee not required
Telephone switching: With other Vontobel funds and Newport Tiger Fund (a load fund)
Number of switches permitted: Unlimited
Shareholder services: IRA, automatic investment plan, withdrawal plan min. req. $10,000
IRA fees: Annual $20

VONTOBEL EUROPACIFIC FUND ◆

(See first Vontobel listing for data common to all Vontobel funds)

Newspaper listing: Under World Funds; VontblEP
Portfolio manager: Fabrizio Pierallini (1994)
Investment objective and policies: Capital appreciation. Invests primarily in equity securities of issuers of developed countries in Europe and the Pacific Basin. May also use ADRs, options, currency futures and options thereon, and invest up to 10% of assets in restricted securities.
Year organized: 1985 (as Nicholson Growth Fund. Name changed to Newport Global Growth Fund in January 1987 and T.V. EuroPacific Fund in July 1990. Current name and management since 3/7/91)
Ticker symbol: VNEPX
Discount broker availability: *Schwab, *White, Fidelity, Siebert
Dividends paid: Income - December; Capital gains - December
Portfolio turnover (3 yrs): 11%, 27%, 3%
Largest holding: Skis Rossignol (1.1%)
Management fee: 1.00% first $100M, 0.75% over $100M
Expense ratio: 1.77% (year ending 12/31/93)

VONTOBEL INTERNATIONAL BOND FUND ◆

(See first Vontobel listing for data common to all Vontobel funds)

Portfolio manager: Sven Rump (1994)
Investment objective and policies: Maximum total return - capital growth and income. Invests primarily in investment-grade bonds issued by foreign gov-

ernments and companies that are denominated in non-U.S. currencies, including bonds denominated in the European Currency Unit (ECU). Fund is non-diversified.
Year organized: 1994
Discount broker availability: *Schwab, *White
Dividends paid: Income - December; Capital gains - December
Portfolio turnover (1 yr): 0%
Management fee: 1.00%
Expense ratio: 1.35% (4 months ending 6/30/94)

VONTOBEL U.S. VALUE FUND ◆

(See first Vontobel listing for data common to all Vontobel funds)

Newspaper listing: Under World Funds; VontblV
Portfolio manager: Edwin Walczak (1990)
Investment objective and policies: Long-term capital appreciation in excess of the broad market. Invests primarily in equity securities - including convertible bonds, warrants, debentures and convertible preferred stock - traded on U.S. exchanges.
Year organized: 1990
Ticker symbol: VUSVX
Discount broker availability: *Schwab, *White, Fidelity, Siebert
Dividends paid: Income - December; Capital gains - December
Portfolio turnover (3 yrs): 137%, 100%, 166%
Largest holding: Torchmark (3.3%)
Management fee: 1.00% first $100M, 0.75% over $100M
Expense ratio: 1.82% (year ending 12/31/93)

WADE FUND ◆

5100 Poplar Avenue - Suite 2224
Memphis, TN 38137
901-682-4613

Adviser: Maury Wade & Co.
Portfolio manager: Maury Wade, Jr. (1973)
Custodian: First Tennessee Bank
Transfer agent: Wade Fund, Inc.
Investment objective and policies: Long-term capital gains with income secondary. Invests primarily in common stocks with appreciation potential. Will only invest in established companies doing business for at least 3 years
Year organized: 1949
Minimum purchase: Initial: $500, Subsequent: 1 share
Telephone orders accepted: No
Wire orders accepted: No
Qualified for sale in: TN
Letter redemptions: Signature guarantee required
Dividends paid: Income - December; Capital gains - December
Portfolio turnover (3 yrs): 18%, 6%, 0%
Largest holding: Texas Instruments, Inc. (9.5%)
Management fee: 0.75%
Expense ratio: 2.72% (year ending 12/31/93)

WARBURG, PINCUS FUNDS

(Data common to all Warburg, Pincus funds are shown below. See subsequent listings for data specific to individual Warburg, Pincus funds.)

466 Lexington Ave.
New York, NY 10017-3147
212-878-0600, 800-888-6878
800-257-5615, fax 212-878-9351

Shareholder service hours: Full service: M-F 9 A.M.-5 P.M. EST; After hours service: prices
Adviser: Warburg, Pincus Counsellors, Inc. Name changed from Counsellors funds 3/9/92.
Custodian: Provident National Bank (exceptions noted)
Administrator and transfer agent: Provident Financial Processing Corp.
Telephone orders accepted: No
Wire orders accepted: Yes
Deadline for same day wire purchase: 4 P.M.
Qualified for sale in: All states (except NY funds)

Additional marketing: Several Warburg, Pincus funds are available in a second series through certain service organizations which impose 12b-1 fees. Investors buying series 2 shares will obtain lower performance. The Handbook reports only the performance for investors buying directly from Counsellors.
Telephone redemptions: Yes
Wire redemptions: Yes
Letter redemptions: Signature guarantee required over $50,000
Telephone switching: With other Warburg, Pincus funds
Number of switches permitted: 3 per month
Shareholder services: IRA, SEP-IRA, automatic investment plan—minimum $50/month, directed dividends, electronic funds transfer, withdrawal plan ($1,000 per month minimum)
Administrative fee: Generally 0.10%
IRA fees: Annual $10

WARBURG, PINCUS BALANCED FUND
(See first Warburg, Pincus listing for data common to all Warburg, Pincus funds)

Portfolio managers: Dale C. Christensen (1994), Anthony G. Orphanos (1994)
Investment objective and policies: Long-term growth of capital and current income. Invests primarily in dividend-paying equity securities (minimum 25% of assets), fixed-income securities (minimum 25% of assets) and money market instruments with allocation adjusted to changing market conditions. May have up to 15% of assets in illiquid securities.
Year organized: 1988 (name changed from RBB Balanced Portfolio on 10/1/94)
Minimum purchase: Initial: $1,000, Subsequent: $100; IRA: Initial: $500, Subsequent: $500
Discount broker availability: *Waterhouse
Dividends paid: Income - March, June, September, December; Capital gains - December
Portfolio turnover (3 yrs): 32%, 30%, 93%
Management fee: 0.90%
12b-1 distribution fee: 0.25%
Expense ratio: 0.00% (year ending 8/31/94) (5.46% without waiver)

WARBURG, PINCUS CAPITAL APPRECIATION FUND ◆
(See first Warburg, Pincus listing for data common to all Warburg, Pincus funds)

Portfolio managers: George U. Wyper (1994), Susan L. Black (1994)
Investment objective and policies: Long-term capital appreciation. Invests at least 80% of assets in equity securities of financially strong domestic companies with opportunities for growth through increased earning power and improved utilization or recognition of assets. Up to 20% of assets may be in securities of foreign issuers. May use options on stocks and indices, and interest rate and index futures and options thereon.
Year organized: 1987 (name changed from Counsellors Capital Appreciation Fund on 3/9/92)
Dow Jones ticker symbol: CUCAX
Minimum purchase: Initial: $2,500, Subsequent: $500; IRA: Initial: $500
Discount broker availability: *Schwab, *White, *Waterhouse, *Fidelity, *Siebert
Dividends paid: Income - June, December; Capital gains - December
Portfolio turnover (3 yrs): 52%, 48%, 56%
Largest holding: Molex Inc. (2.9%)
Management fee: 0.70%
12b-1 distribution fee: Yes (not currently imposed)
Expense ratio: 1.05% (year ending 10/31/94) (1.06% without waiver)

WARBURG, PINCUS CASH RESERVE FUND ◆
(See first Warburg, Pincus listing for data common to all Warburg, Pincus funds)

Sub-adviser: Provident Institutional Management Corp.
Portfolio manager: Dale C. Christensen (1992)

Investment objective and policies: High current income consistent with liquidity and stability of principal. Invests in money market instruments.
Year organized: 1985 (name changed from Counsellors Cash Reserve Fund on 3/9/92)
Ticker symbol: CRFXX
Minimum purchase: Initial: $1,000, Subsequent: $500; IRA: Initial: $500
Check redemptions: $500 minimum
Confirmations mailed: Not mailed
Checks returned: Monthly
Periodic account statements mailed: Monthly
Dividends paid: Income - declared daily, paid monthly
Management fee: 0.5%
Expense ratio: 0.54% (year ending 2/28/94) (0.68% without waiver)

WARBURG, PINCUS EMERGING GROWTH FUND ◆
(See first Warburg, Pincus listing for data common to all Warburg, Pincus funds)

Portfolio managers: Elizabeth B. Dater (1988), Stephen J. Lurito (1990)
Investment objective and policies: Maximum capital appreciation. Invests at least 65% of assets in common stocks and equivalents (including convertibles and warrants) of emerging growth companies with capitalizations up to $500M. Fund also focuses on special situations - acquisitions/consolidations, reorganizations/recapitalizations, mergers, liquidations, tenders, litigation and changes in corporate control. May have up to 10% of assets in foreign securities and use options on stocks and indices, and interest rate and index futures and options thereon. Fund is non-diversified.
Year organized: 1988 (name changed from Counsellors Emerging Growth Fund on 3/9/92)
Ticker symbol: CUEGX
Minimum purchase: Initial: $2,500, Subsequent: $500; IRA: Initial: $500
Discount broker availability: *Schwab, *White, *Waterhouse, *Fidelity, *Siebert
Dividends paid: Income - June, December; Capital gains - December
Portfolio turnover (3 yrs): 60%, 68%, 63%
Largest holding: Maxim Integrated Products, Inc. (3.7%)
Management fee: 0.9%
12b-1 distribution fee: Yes (not currently imposed)
Expense ratio: 1.22% (year ending 10/31/94) (1.26% without waiver)

WARBURG, PINCUS EMERGING MARKETS FUND
(See first Warburg, Pincus listing for data common to all Warburg, Pincus funds)

Portfolio managers: Richard H. King (1994), Nicholas P.W. Horsley (1994)
Investment objective and policies: Capital growth. Invests at least 65% of assets in equity securities of issuers in emerging markets around the world. Normally invests in at least 3 countries outside the U.S. May have up to 35% of assets in junk bonds and use currency exchange contracts, futures and options and sell short.
Year organized: 1994
Minimum purchase: Initial: $2,500, Subsequent: $100; IRA: Initial: $500
Dividends paid: Income - June, December; Capital gains - December
Management fee: 1.25%
12b-1 distribution fee: 0.25%

WARBURG, PINCUS FIXED INCOME FUND ◆
(See first Warburg, Pincus listing for data common to all Warburg, Pincus funds)

Portfolio managers: Dale C. Christensen (1991), Anthony E. van Daalen
Investment objective and policies: High current income consistent with reasonable risk. Invests in corporate bonds, debentures and notes, convertible

debt securities, preferred stocks, government obligations and repurchase agreements with a weighted average maturity of less than 10 years. May invest up to 35% of assets in junk bonds, 20% in securities of foreign issuers, 10% in zero coupon bonds and 10% in restricted securities.
Year organized: 1987 (name changed from Counsellors Fixed Income Fund on 3/9/92)
Ticker symbol: CUFIX
Minimum purchase: Initial: $2,500, Subsequent: $500; IRA: Initial: $500
Discount broker availability: *Schwab, *White, *Waterhouse, *Fidelity, *Siebert
Dividends paid: Income - declared daily, paid monthly; Capital gains - December
Portfolio turnover (3 yrs): 179%, 227%, 122%
Management fee: 0.5%
12b-1 distribution fee: Yes (not currently imposed)
Expense ratio: 0.75% (year ending 10/31/94) (0.93% without waiver)

WARBURG, PINCUS GLOBAL FIXED INCOME FUND ◆
(See first Warburg, Pincus listing for data common to all Warburg, Pincus funds)

Portfolio managers: Dale C. Christensen (1990), Laxmi C. Bhandari (1993)
Custodians: Provident National Bank and Fiduciary Trust Company International
Investment objective and policies: Maximum total return consistent with prudent management. Invests primarily in investment-grade fixed-income securities of government and corporate issuers denominated in various currencies, including the U.S. dollar with a weighted average maturity of 3 to 10 years. At least 3 countries will be represented and no country, other than the U.S., may comprise more than 40% of assets. May invest up to 35% of assets in junk bonds, 20% in zero coupon securities, write covered options up to 25% of assets; sell short against the box (limited to 10% of assets); and invest in illiquid securities (up to 10% of assets).
Year organized: 1990 (name changed from Counsellors Global Fixed Income Fund on 3/9/92)
Ticker symbol: CGFIX
Minimum purchase: Initial: $2,500, Subsequent: $500; IRA: Initial: $500
Discount broker availability: *Schwab, *White, *Waterhouse, *Fidelity, *Siebert
Dividends paid: Income - March, June, September, December; Capital gains - December
Portfolio turnover (3 yrs): 178%, 110%, 93%
Management fee: 1.0%
12b-1 distribution fee: Yes (not currently imposed)
Expense ratio: 0.95% (year ending 10/31/94) (1.60% without waiver)

WARBURG, PINCUS GROWTH & INCOME FUND ◆
(See first Warburg, Pincus listing for data common to all Warburg, Pincus funds)

Portfolio manager: Anthony G. Orphanos (1992)
Investment objective and policies: Long-term growth of capital and income and reasonable current return. Invests primarily in income-producing securities - dividend-paying equity securities, fixed-income securities and money market instruments. May invest in ADRs without limit, have up to 10% of assets in foreign securities and 15% in illiquid securities and use options on stocks and indices, and interest rate and index futures and options thereon.
Year organized: 1988 (name changed from RBB Equity Growth and Income Portfolio on 9/30/93)
Dow Jones ticker symbol: RBEGX
Minimum purchase: Initial: $1,000, Subsequent: $100; IRA: Initial: $500, Subsequent: $500
Discount broker availability: *Schwab, *White, *Waterhouse, *Fidelity, *Siebert
Dividends paid: Income - March, June, September, December; Capital gains - December
Portfolio turnover (3 yrs): 150%, 344%, 175%
Largest holding: International Business Machines Corp. (3.5%)

Management fee: 0.75%
12b-1 distribution fee: Yes (not currently imposed)
Expense ratio: 1.28% (year ending 8/31/94)

WARBURG, PINCUS INTERMEDIATE MATURITY GOVERNMENT FUND ◆
(See first Warburg, Pincus listing for data common to all Warburg, Pincus funds)

Portfolio managers: Dale C. Christensen (1998), Anthony E. van Daalen (1992)
Investment objective and policies: High current income consistent with preservation of capital. Invests primarily in intermediate-term U.S. Treasury bonds and notes and other obligations issued or guaranteed by, or backed by the full faith and credit of the U.S. Government. At least 65% of investments will have maturities of 3 to 7 years, none longer than 10 years. Fund may use zero coupon bonds but is not authorized to use financial futures and options.
Year organized: 1988 (name changed from Counsellors Intermediate Maturity Government Fund on 3/9/92)
Ticker symbol: CUIGX
Minimum purchase: Initial: $2,500, Subsequent: $500; IRA: Initial: $500
Discount broker availability: *Schwab, *White, *Waterhouse, *Fidelity, *Siebert
Dividends paid: Income - declared daily, paid monthly; Capital gains - December
Portfolio turnover (3 yrs): 115%, 108%, 166%
Management fee: 0.5%
12b-1 distribution fee: Yes (not currently imposed)
Expense ratio: 0.60% (year ending 10/31/94) (1.02% without waiver)

WARBURG, PINCUS INTERNATIONAL EQUITY FUND ◆
(See first Warburg, Pincus listing for data common to all Warburg, Pincus funds)

Portfolio manager: Richard H. King (1989)
Custodians: Provident National Bank and Fiduciary Trust Company International
Investment objective and policies: Long term capital appreciation. Invests at least 65% of assets in common stocks and equivalents (including convertibles and warrants) of non-U.S. issuers. Up to 35% may be in companies with principal business activities in the U.S. Fund may use closed end investment companies, and forward currency contracts and futures and options to hedge.
Year organized: 1989 (name changed from Counsellors International Equity Fund on 3/9/92)
Ticker symbol: CUIEX
Minimum purchase: Initial: $2,500, Subsequent: $500; IRA: Initial: $500
Discount broker availability: *Schwab, *White, *Waterhouse, *Fidelity, *Siebert
Dividends paid: Income - June, December; Capital gains - December
Portfolio turnover (2 yrs): 17%, 23%, 53%
Largest holding: East Japan Railway Co. (2.2%)
Management fee: 1.0%
12b-1 distribution fee: Yes (not currently imposed)
Expense ratio: 1.44% (year ending 10/31/94)

WARBURG, PINCUS JAPAN OTC FUND
(See first Warburg, Pincus listing for data common to all Warburg, Pincus funds)

Sub-adviser: SPARX Investment & Research, USA, Inc.
Portfolio managers: Richard H. King (1994), Shuhei Abe (1994), Nicholas P.W. Horsley (1994)
Custodian: State Street Bank & Trust Co.
Investment objective and policies: Long term capital appreciation. Invests at least 65% of assets in securities traded on the Japanese over-the-counter market (JASADQ). Up to 35% of assets may be in securities of other Asian (non-Japanese) issuers. Fund may use currency exchange transactions and futures and options to hedge up to 25% of total assets.

Year organized: 1994
Minimum purchase: Initial: $2,500, Subsequent: $500; IRA: Initial: $500
Discount broker availability: *Schwab, *Waterhouse, *Fidelity, *Siebert
Dividends paid: Income - June, December; Capital gains - December
Largest holding: Hikari Furniture Co., Ltd. (3.9%)
Management fee: 1.0%
12b-1 distribution fee: 0.25%

WARBURG, PINCUS NEW YORK MUNICIPAL BOND FUND ◆
(See first Warburg, Pincus listing for data common to all Warburg, Pincus funds)

Portfolio managers: Dale C. Christensen (1992), Sharon B. Parente (1992)
Investment objective and policies: Maximum current interest income exempt from federal, New York State and New York City personal income taxes. Invests primarily in investment-grade New York municipal bonds with remaining maturities of 5 to 15 years. Up to 20% of assets may be in AMT securities.
Year organized: 1987 (name changed from Counsellors New York Municipal Bond Fund on 3/9/92)
Ticker symbol: CNMBX
Minimum purchase: Initial: $2,500, Subsequent: $500
Qualified for sale in: CO, CT, DC, FL, HI, NY, OK, PA
Discount broker availability: *Schwab, *White, *Waterhouse, *Fidelity, *Siebert
Dividends paid: Income - declared daily, paid monthly; Capital gains - December
Portfolio turnover (3 yrs): 167%, 116%, 48%
Management fee: 0.4%
12b-1 distribution fee: Yes (not currently imposed)
Expense ratio: 0.60% (year ending 10/31/94) (0.80% without waiver)

WARBURG, PINCUS NEW YORK TAX EXEMPT FUND ◆
(See first Warburg, Pincus listing for data common to all Warburg, Pincus funds)

Sub-adviser: Provident Institutional Management Corp.
Portfolio manager: Dale C. Christensen (1992)
Investment objective and policies: High current income exempt from federal, New York State, and New York City personal income taxes consistent with preservation of capital and liquidity. Invests in New York municipal money market instruments.
Year organized: 1985 (name changed from Counsellors New York Tax Exempt Fund on 3/9/92)
Ticker symbol: COEXX
Minimum purchase: Initial: $1,000, Subsequent: $500
Qualified for sale in: CO, CT, DC, FL, HI, NY, OK, PA
Check redemptions: $500 minimum
Confirmations mailed: Not mailed
Checks returned: Monthly
Periodic account statements mailed: Monthly
Dividends paid: Income - declared daily, paid monthly
Management fee: 0.5%
12b-1 distribution fee: Yes (not currently imposed)
Expense ratio: 0.54% (year ending 2/28/94) (0.73% without waiver)

WARBURG, PINCUS SHORT-TERM AFTER-TAX BOND FUND
(See first Warburg, Pincus listing for data common to all Warburg, Pincus funds)

Portfolio managers: Anthony E. van Daalen (1994), Sharon B. Parente (1994)
Investment objective and policies: Maximum income after the effect of federal income taxes with capital growth secondary. Invests primarily in taxable and tax-exempt debt securities with a weighted

average maturity of 3 years or less. May invest up to 25% in securities of foreign issuers and use futures and options to hedge. Designed for investors in high tax brackets who would otherwise invest in tax-exempt bond funds and would benefit from investments that would generate, after taxes, a net return higher than available from tax-free securities.
Year organized: 1994
Minimum purchase: Initial: $2,500, Subsequent: $500; IRA: Initial: $500
Dividends paid: Income - declared daily, paid monthly; Capital gains - December
Management fee: 0.55%
12b-1 distribution fee: 0.25%

WASATCH ADVISORS FUNDS ◆
(Data common to all Wasatch funds are shown below. See subsequent listing for data specific to individual Wasatch funds.)

68 South Main Street
Salt Lake City, UT 84101
801-533-0778, 800-551-1700
prices/yields 800-382-3616
fax 801-533-9828

Shareholder service hours: Full service: M-F 9 A.M.-5 P.M. MST
Adviser: Wasatch Advisors, Inc.
Custodian & transfer agent: Firstar Trust Co.
Minimum purchase: Initial: $2,000; Subsequent: $100; IRA/Keogh: Initial: $1,000, Subsequent: None
Telephone orders accepted: No
Wire orders accepted: Yes
Deadline for same day wire purchase: 4 P.M.
Telephone redemptions: Yes, $1,000 minimum
Wire redemptions: Yes, $1,000 minimum, $7.50 fee
Letter redemptions: Signature guarantee required over $25,000
Telephone switching: With other Wasatch Funds and Portico Money Market funds, $500 minimum, $5 fee
Number of switches permitted: 4 per year
Dividends paid: Income - December; Capital gains - December
Shareholder services: Keogh, IRA, automatic investment plan, electronic funds transfer, withdrawal plan min. req. $10,000
IRA/Keogh fees: Annual $10

WASATCH AGGRESSIVE EQUITY FUND ◆
(See first Wasatch listing for data common to all Wasatch funds)

Portfolio manager: Samuel S. Stewart (1986)
Investment objective and policies: Long-term growth of capital with income secondary. Normally invests at least 65% of assets in common stocks of companies believed to possess superior growth potential. Up to 10% of assets may be in foreign securities and 5% in companies in reorganization or buyout. The fund holds relatively few securities and is non-diversified.
Year organized: 1986
Ticker symbol: WAAEX
Discount broker availability: *Schwab, *White, *Fidelity, *Siebert
Qualified for sale in: All states except NE, NH, VT
Portfolio turnover (3 yrs): 64%, 70%, 32%
Largest holding: United Assets Management Corp. (5.9%)
Management fee: 1.0%
Expense ratio: 1.50% (year ending 9/30/94) (1.52% without waiver)

WASATCH GROWTH FUND ◆
(See first Wasatch listing for data common to all Wasatch funds)

Portfolio manager: Samuel S. Stewart (1986)
Investment objective and policies: Long-term growth of capital. Normally invests at least 65% of

assets in common stock of companies believed to possess superior growth potential. Up to 10% of assets may be in foreign securities and 5% in companies in reorganization or buyout. The fund holds more securities than the Wasatch Aggressive Growth Fund and is diversified.
Year organized: 1986
Qualified for sale in: All states except AK, IA, KS, KY, LA, MA, MS, MT, NE, NH, ND, SD, TN, VT, WV
Discount broker availability: *Schwab, *White, *Fidelity, *Siebert
Portfolio turnover (3 yrs): 163%, 104%, 40%
Largest holding: Intercel, Inc. (4.1%)
Management fee: 1.0%
Expense ratio: 1.50% (year ending 9/30/94) (1.64% without waiver)

WASATCH INCOME FUND ◆
(See first Wasatch listing for data common to all Wasatch funds)

Portfolio manager: Samuel S. Stewart (1986)
Investment objective and policies: High level of current income at low risk with capital appreciation secondary. Invests in high grade fixed-income securities, including U.S. Government, government agency and instrumentality securities, corporate bonds and notes, convertible securities, preferred stocks and short-term securities.
Year organized: 1986
Qualified for sale in: All states except AK, IA, KS, KY, LA, MA, MS, MT, NE, NH, ND, TN, VT, WV
Discount broker availability: *Schwab, *White, *Fidelity, *Siebert
Portfolio turnover (3 yrs): 45%, 46%, 95%
Management fee: 0.5%
Expense ratio: 1.00% (year ending 9/30/94) (1.39% without waiver)

WASATCH MID-CAP FUND ◆
(See first Wasatch listing for data common to all Wasatch funds)

Portfolio manager: Samuel S. Stewart (1992)
Investment objective and policies: Long-term growth of capital. Normally invests at least 65% of assets in common stock of mid-size companies with annual sales from $500M to $5B believed to possess superior growth potential. Up to 10% of assets may be in foreign securities and 5% in companies in reorganization or buyout. The fund is non-diversified.
Year organized: 1992
Qualified for sale in: All states except AK, IA, KS, KY, LA, MA, MS, MT, NE, NH, ND, RI, SC, TN, VT, WV, WI
Discount broker availability: *Schwab, *White, *Fidelity, *Siebert
Portfolio turnover (2 yrs): 213%, 113%
Largest holding: Haemonetics Corp. (10.9%)
Management fee: 1.25%
Expense ratio: 1.75% (year ending 9/30/94) (3.33% without waiver)

WAYNE HUMMER FUNDS ◆
(Data common to all Wayne Hummer funds are shown below. See subsequent listings for data specific to individual Wayne Hummer funds.)

300 South Wacker Drive
Chicago, IL 60606
312-431-1700, 800-621-4477
fax 312-431-6741

Shareholder service hours: Full service: M-F 8 A.M.-5 P.M. CST
Advisor: Wayne Hummer Management Co.
Custodian and transfer agent: State Street Bank & Trust Co.
Telephone orders accepted: No
Wire order accepted: No
Telephone redemptions: Yes
Letter redemptions: Signature guarantee not required
Telephone switching: With other Wayne Hummer funds

Number of switches permitted: Unlimited
Shareholder services: Keogh, IRA, SEP-IRA, 401(k), corporate retirement plans, automatic investment plan—minimum $100/mo., electronic funds transfer (purchase only)
IRA fees: Annual $36, Initial prorated, Closing $50
Keogh fees: Varies according to number of participants

WAYNE HUMMER GROWTH FUND ◆
(See first Wayne Hummer listing for data common to all Wayne Hummer funds.)

Newspaper listing: Hummer
Portfolio managers: Allan W. Bird (1983), Thomas J. Rowland (1987)
Investment objective and policies: Long-term capital growth with current income secondary. Invests in common stocks and other securities with potential for long-term capital growth. May also invest in preferred stocks, bonds, and convertible securities. May use options to hedge.
Year organized: 1983
Ticker symbol: WHGRX
Minimum purchase: Initial: $2,000, Subsequent: $500; IRA/Keogh: Initial: $500, Subsequent: $200
Discount broker availability: *White
Qualified for sale in: All states
Dividends paid: Income - April, July, October, December; Capital gains - December
Portfolio turnover (3 yrs): 2%, 1%, 3%
Largest holding: Avery Dennison Corp. (3.8%)
Management fee: 0.8% first $100M to 0.50% over $250M
Expense ratio: 1.07% (year ending 3/31/94)

WAYNE HUMMER INCOME FUND ◆
(See first Wayne Hummer listing for data common to all Wayne Hummer funds.)

Portfolio manager: David P. Poitras (1992)
Investment objective and policies: High current income consistent with prudent investment management. Invests primarily in investment-grade corporate and government debt securities, including dollar denominated debt securities of foreign issuers. Up to 15% of assets may be in illiquid securities, May use options, index options, financial futures contracts and convertible securities.
Year organized: 1992
Ticker symbol: WHICX
Minimum purchase: Initial: $2,500, Subsequent: $1,000; IRA/Keogh: Initial: $2,000, Subsequent: $500
Qualified for sale in: All states except MO, NH
Dividends paid: Income - monthly; Capital gains - April, December
Portfolio turnover (2 yrs): 86%, 141%
Management fee: 0.5% first $100M to 0.30% over $250M
Expense ratio: 1.13% (year ending 3/31/94)

WAYNE HUMMER MONEY FUND TRUST ◆
(See first Wayne Hummer listing for data common to all Wayne Hummer funds.)

Portfolio manager: David P. Poitras (1986)
Investment objective and policies: Maximum current income consistent with preservation of capital and liquidity. Invests in money market instruments.
Year organized: 1981
Ticker symbol: WHMXX
Minimum purchase: Initial: $500, Subsequent: $100
Qualified for sale in: All states
Check redemptions: $500 minimum
Confirmations mailed: After each purchase and mail or wire redemption
Checks returned: Monthly
Periodic account statements mailed: Monthly
Dividends paid: Income - declared daily, paid monthly
Management fee: 0.5% first $500M to 0.275% over $2.5B
Expense ratio: 0.80% (year ending 3/31/94)

WEITZ FUNDS ◆
(Data common to all Weitz funds are shown below. See subsequent listing for data specific to individual Weitz funds.)

9290 West Dodge Rd., Suite 405
Omaha, Nebraska 68114-3349
402-391-1980, 800-232-4161
fax 402-391-2125

Adviser: Wallace R. Weitz & Co.
Custodian: Norwest Bank Nebraska, N.A.
Transfer agent: Wallace R. Weitz & Co.
Minimum purchase: Initial: $25,000 (total among all portfolios), Subsequent: $5,000 (total among all portfolios); IRA/Keogh: Initial: $10,000, Subsequent: None (except Partners Value Fund)
Telephone orders accepted: No
Wire orders accepted: Yes
Deadline for same day wire purchase: 4 P.M.
Telephone redemptions: Yes
Wire redemptions: Yes
Letter redemptions: Signature guarantee required
Telephone switching: With other Weitz Series portfolios
Number of switches permitted: Unlimited, but fund monitors
Shareholder services: IRA, 403(b), automatic investment plan, electronic funds transfer, withdrawal plan
IRA fees: Annual $20

WEITZ PARTNERS, INC. - PARTNERS VALUE FUND ◆
(See first Weitz listing for data common to all Weitz funds)

Portfolio manager: Wallace R. Weitz (1993)
Investment objective and policies: Capital appreciation. Invests primarily in common stocks, convertible bonds, and preferred stocks trading at prices significantly below their estimated intrinsic, or "going concern" value. May also invest in bonds and other debt obligations of both corporate and governmental issuers. Up to 25% of assets may be in securities of foreign issuers. Fund may hedge and is non-divesified.
Year organized: 1993
Ticker symbol: WPVLX
Minimum purchase: Initial: $100,000, Subsequent: None
Qualified for sale in: AZ, CA, CO, CT, DC, FL, GA, HI, IA, LA, MD, MA, MN, NE, NJ, NM, NC, ND, SD, TN, TX, WA, WY
Dividends paid: Income - December; Capital gains - December
Portfolio turnover (1 yr): 33%
Largest holding: Comcast Corporation (4.8%)
Management fee: 1.0%
Expense ratio: 1.29% (year ending 12/31/94)

WEITZ SERIES FUND - FIXED INCOME PORTFOLIO ◆
(See first Weitz listing for data common to all Weitz funds)

Portfolio manager: Wallace R. Weitz (1988)
Investment objective and policies: High current income consistent with preservation of capital. Invests at least 65% of assets in fixed-income debt securities with a weighted average maturity of 7 years or less. Securities will be in the top 4 categories as rated by Moody's or S&P. Up to 15% of assets may be in junk bonds. May use interest rate futures, bond index futures and options to hedge.
Year organized: 1988
Qualified for sale in: All states except AL, AK, DE, ID, KS, ME, MA, MS, MT, NV, ND, RI, SC, TN, VT, WV, WI
Dividends paid: Income - April, July, October, December; Capital gains - April, July, October, December
Portfolio turnover (3 yrs): 12%, 15%, 31%
Management fee: 0.5%
Expense ratio: 0.75% (year ending 3/31/94) (0.93% without waiver)

WEITZ SERIES FUND - GOVERNMENT MONEY MARKET PORTFOLIO ◆
(See first Weitx listing for data common to all Weitz funds)

Portfolio manager: Wallace R. Weitz (1991)
Investment objective and policies: Current income consistent with preservation of capital and maintenance of liquidity. Invests at least 90% of assets in money market instruments issued or guaranteed by the U.S. Government, its agencies and instrumentalities and repurchase agreements thereon.
Year organized: 1991
Qualified for sale in: All states except AL, AK, AR, CT, DE, ID, KS, ME, MD, MA, MS, MO, MT, NV, NM, NY, ND, RI, SC, TN, TX, VT, WV, WI
Dividends paid: Income - declared daily, paid monthly
Check redemptions: $500 minimum
Confirmations mailed: After each purchase and each check, mail or wire redemption
Checks returned: Not returned
Periodic account statements mailed: Monthly
Management fee: 0.5%
Expense ratio: 0.25% (year ending 3/31/94) (3.45% without waiver)

WEITZ SERIES FUND - HICKORY PORTFOLIO ◆
(See first Weitz listing for data common to all Weitz funds)

Portfolio manager: Richard Lawson (1993)
Investment objective and policies: Capital appreciation with income secondary. Invests primarily in common stocks, convertible bonds, and preferred stocks trading at prices significantly below their estimated intrinsic, or "going concern" value. May also invest in bonds and other debt obligations of both corporate and governmental issuers. Up to 25% of assets may be in securities of foreign issuers. Fund is non-diversified and may hedge. Unlike the Value Portfolio, which has the same basic policies, the Hickory Portfolio is non-diversified.
Year organized: 1993
Qualified for sale in: AK, CA, CO, CT, DC,FL, GA, HI, IL, IN, LA, MI, NE, NH, NJ, NC,ND, OH, OK, OR, PA, SD, VA, WA, WY
Dividends paid: Income - April, December; Capital gains - April, December
Portfolio turnover (1 yr): 29%
Largest holding: Countrywide Credit, Inc. (12.5%)
Management fee: 1.0%
Expense ratio: 1.50% (year ending 3/31/94) (3.15% without waiver)

WEITZ SERIES FUND - VALUE PORTFOLIO ◆
(See first Weitz listing for data common to all Weitz funds)

Portfolio manager: Wallace R. Weitz (1986)
Investment objective and policies: Capital appreciation with income secondary. Invests primarily in common stocks, convertible bonds, and preferred stocks trading at prices significantly below their estimated intrinsic, or "going concern" value. May also invest in bonds and other debt obligations of both corporate and governmental issuers. Up to 25% of assets may be in securities of foreign issuers. Fund may hedge.
Year organized: 1986; formerly Weitz Value Fund; merged 4/1/90
Ticker symbol: WVALX
Discount broker availability: White
Qualified for sale in: All states
Dividends paid: Income - April, December; Capital gains - April, December
Portfolio turnover (3 yrs): 23%, 23%, 35%
Largest holding: Tele-Communications, Inc. (5.3%)
Management fee: 1.0%
Expense ratio: 1.41% (year ending 3/31/93)

WERTHEIM FUNDS ◆
(Data common to all Wertheim funds are shown below. See subsequent listings for data specific to individual Wertheim funds.)

P.O. Box 8507
Boston, MA 02266
800-464-3108

Adviser: Wertheim Shroder Investment Services, Inc.
Custodian: State Street Bank & Trust Co.
Transfer agent: Boston Financial Data Services, Inc.
Year organized: 1994
Minimum purchase: Initial: $25,000 (total among all funds), Subsequent: $1,000; IRA/Keogh: Subsequent: $50
Telephone orders accepted: No
Wire orders accepted: Yes
Deadline for same day wire purchase: 4 P.M.
Qualified for sale in: All states except AR, AZ, IN, MN, MO, OH, SD, TX ,WI
Telephone redemptions: Yes
Wire redemptions: Yes, $1,000 minimum
Letter redemptions: Signature guarantee required over $25,000
Telephone switching: With other Wertheim funds, $1,000 minimum
Number of switches permitted: Unlimited
Shareholder services: IRA, automatic investment plan, electronic funds transfer
IRA fees: Annual: $12 per social security number

WERTHEIM EQUITY VALUE FUND ◆
(See first Wertheim listing for data common to all Wertheim funds)

Portfolio manager: E. William Smethurst, Jr. (1994)
Investment objective and policies: Long-term capital growth. Invests primarily in common and preferred stocks of undervalued companies with above average long-term growth potential. May invest in securities of foreign issuers without limit and use futures and options to enhance return and hedge.
Ticker symbol: WEQVX
Dividends paid: Income - December; Capital gains - December
Portfolio turnover (1 yr): 103%
Largest holding: Emerson Electric Company (4.4%)
Management fee: 0.75%
Expense ratio: 1.30% (8 months ending 10/31/94) (2.17% without waiver)

WERTHEIM HIGH YIELD INCOME FUND ◆
(See first Wertheim listing for data common to all Wertheim funds)

Portfolio manager: Kenneth D. Malamed (1994)
Investment objective and policies: High current income with capital growth secondary. Invests primarily in junk bonds but may also purchase preferred stocks, common stocks or any other security with capital growth potential. May invest in securities of foreign issuers without limit and use futures and options to enhance return and hedge.
Dividends paid: Income - Monthly; Capital gains - December
Portfolio turnover (1 yr): 59%
Management fee: 0.90%
Expense ratio: 1.30% (8 months ending 10/31/94) (3.59% without waiver)

WERTHEIM INVESTMENT GRADE INCOME FUND ◆
(See first Wertheim listing for data common to all Wertheim funds)

Portfolio manager: Gary S. Zeltzer (1994)
Investment objective and policies: Current income consistent with preservation of capital with capital growth secondary. Invests primarily in investment-grade U.S. government and corporate debt securi-

ties with weighted average maturity that varies from relatively short (under 5 years) to relatively long (more than 10 years) depending on the interest rate outlook. May invest in securities of foreign issuers without limit and use futures and options to enhance return and hedge.
Dividends paid: Income - Monthly; Capital gains - December
Portfolio turnover (1 yr): 156%
Management fee: 0.50%
Expense ratio: 0.87% (8 months ending 10/31/94) (3.98% without waiver)

WERTHEIM SHORT-TERM INVESTMENT FUND ◆
(See first Wertheim listing for data common to all Wertheim funds)

Portfolio manager: Gary S. Zeltzer (1994)
Investment objective and policies: High current income consistent with preservation of capital and liquidity. Invests primarily in investment-grade U.S. government and corporate debt securities with remaining maturities of 3 years or less and a weighted average maturity of one year or less. May invest in securities of foreign issuers without limit and use futures and options to enhance return and hedge.
Ticker symbol: WSTFX
Dividends paid: Income - declared daily, paid monthly; Capital gains - December
Portfolio turnover (1 yr): 71%
Management fee: 0.40%
Expense ratio: 0.78% (10 months ending 10/31/94) (1.66% without waiver)

WERTHEIM SMALL CAPITALIZATION VALUE FUND ◆
(See first Wertheim listing for data common to all Wertheim funds)

Portfolio manager: Nancy Tooke (1994)
Investment objective and policies: Long-term capital growth. Invests primarily in common and preferred stocks of companies with market capitalizations under $1B believed to have above average long-term growth potential. May invest in securities of foreign issuers without limit and use futures and options to enhance return and hedge.
Ticker symbol: WSCVX
Dividends paid: Income - December; Capital gains - December
Portfolio turnover (1 yr): 19%
Largest holding: Teradyne, Inc. (3.7%)
Management fee: 0.95%
Expense ratio: 1.45% (8 months ending 10/31/94) (3.15% without waiver)

WESTON PORTFOLIOS - NEW CENTURY CAPITAL PORTFOLIO
20 William Street
Wellesley Office Park
Wellesley, MA 02181
617-239-0445, 617-235-7055
fax 617-239-0741

Adviser: Weston Financial Group, Inc.
Portfolio manager: Douglas A. Biggar (1989)
Custodian: National Westminster Bank NJ
Transfer agent: Fund/Plan Services, Inc.
Investment objective and policies: Capital growth with income secondary. Invests primarily in other mutual funds which emphasize investments in growth stocks. Fund maintains varying levels of cash and cash equivalents depending on market conditions.
Year organized: 1989
Ticker symbol: NCCPX
Minimum purchase: Initial: $5,000, Subsequent: $100; IRA/Keogh: Initial: $1.000
Telephone orders accepted: No
Wire orders accepted: Yes
Deadline for same day wire purchase: 4 P.M.
Qualified for sale in: CT, FL, GA, HI, KS, ME, MA, NH, NJ, NY, PA, RI, VT, WY
Telephone redemptions: Yes, $5,000 minimum

Wire redemptions: Yes, $5,000 minimum, $9 fee
Letter redemptions: Signature guarantee required over $5,000
Telephone switching: With Weston New Century I
Number of switches permitted: 10 per year
Dividends paid: Income - December; Capital gains - December
Shareholder services: Keogh, IRA, 401(k), 403(b), corporate retirement plans, withdrawal plan min. req. $10,000
Portfolio turnover (3 yrs): 107%, 133%, 224%
Management fee: 1.0% first $100M, 0.75% over $100M
12b-1 distribution fee: 0.01%
Expense ratio: 1.60% (year ending 10/31/94)
IRA/Keogh fees: Annual $10

WESTON PORTFOLIOS - NEW CENTURY I PORTFOLIO
20 William Street
Wellesley Office Park
Wellesley, MA 02181
617-239-0445, 617-235-7055
fax 617-239-0741

Adviser: Weston Financial Group
Portfolio manager: Douglas A. Biggar (1989)
Custodian: National Westminster Bank NJ
Transfer agent: Fund/Plan Services, Inc.
Investment objective and policies: Income with some capital growth secondary. Invests primarily in other mutual funds which emphasize investments in fixed-income securities, preferred stocks, and high dividend paying stocks. Fund maintains varying levels of cash and cash equivalents depending on market conditions.
Year organized: 1989
Ticker symbol: NCIPX
Minimum purchase: Initial: $5,000, Subsequent: $100; IRA/Keogh: Initial: $1,000
Telephone orders accepted: No
Wire orders accepted: Yes
Qualified for sale in: CT, FL, GA, HI, KS, ME, MA, NH, NJ, NY, PA, RI, VT, WY
Telephone redemptions: Yes, $5,000 minimum
Wire redemptions: Yes, $5,000 minimum
Letter redemptions: Signature guarantee required over $5,000
Telephone switching: With Weston New Century Capital
Number of switches permitted: 10 per year
Dividends paid: Income - March, June, September, December; Capital gains - December
Shareholder services: Keogh, IRA, 401(k), 403(b), corporate retirement plans, withdrawal plan min. req. $10,000
Portfolio turnover (3 yrs): 130%, 73%, 172%
Management fee: 1.0% first $100M, 0.75% over $100M
12b-1 distribution fee: 0.22%
Expense ratio: 1.73% (year ending 10/31/94)
IRA/Keogh fees: Annual: $10

WESTWOOD FUNDS
(Data common to all Westwood funds are shown below. See subsequent listings for data specific to individual Westwood funds.)

One Corporate Center
Rye, NY 02181
914-921-5000, 800-937-8909
fax 914-921-5118

Adviser: Teton Advisers LLC (a subsidiary of Gabelli Funds, Inc.)
Sub-adviser: Westwood Management Corp.
Custodian: Bank of New York
Transfer agent: Boston Financial Data Services, Inc.
Minimum purchase: Initial: $1,000, Subsequent: None
Telephone orders accepted: No
Wire orders accepted: Yes
Deadline for same day wire purchase: 12 NN
Telephone redemptions: Yes
Wire redemptions: Yes, $1,000 minimum
Letter redemptions: Signature guarantee required over $25,000

Telephone switching: With other Westwood funds and Gabelli funds (some of which have loads)
Number of switches permitted: Unlimited
Shareholder services: IRA, SEP-IRA, automatic investment plan (waives initial minimum), withdrawal plan min. req. $10,000
IRA fees: Annual: $10, Initial $5 (per social security number)

WESTWOOD BALANCED FUND
(See first Westwood listing for data common to all Westwood funds)

Portfolio managers: Susan M. Byrne (1991), Patricia R. Fraze (1991)
Investment objective and policies: High total return - capital growth and current income consistent with prudent investment risk. Invests in equity securities (30-70% of assets) of companies of all sizes with above average growth prospects and debt securities (30-70%) with allocation adjusted to reflect changes in market conditions. At least 25% of assets are in fixed-income senior securities and up to 25% in securities of foreign issuers. May use futures and options to enhance income and hedge.
Year organized: 1991
Ticker symbol: WEBAX
Qualified for sale in: All states except MD, MO
Dividends paid: Income - March, June, September, December; Capital gains - December
Portfolio turnover (3 yrs): 168%, 192%, 178%
Largest holding: U.S. Treasury Notes 7.875% due 8/15/01 (5.3%)
Management fee: 0.75%
12b-1 distribution fee: Maximum of 0.25%
Expense ratio: 1.68% (year ending 9/31/94) (2.36% without waiver)

WESTWOOD EQUITY FUND
(See first Westwood listing for data common to all Westwood funds)

Portfolio manager: Susan M. Byrne (1987)
Investment objective and policies: Capital growth with current income secondary. Invests primarily in common stocks and securities convertible into common stocks of companies of all sizes with above average growth prospects. May have up to 25% of assets in securities of foreign issuers and use futures and options to enhance income and hedge.
Year organized: 1987
Ticker symbol: WESWX
Qualified for sale in: All states
Dividends paid: Income - December; Capital gains - December
Portfolio turnover (3 yrs): 137%, 102%, 75%
Largest holding: U.S. Treasury Notes 7.250% due 5/15/04 (9.0%)
Management fee: 1.00%
12b-1 distribution fee: Maximum of 0.25%
Expense ratio: 0.71% (year ending 9/31/94) (1.94% without waiver)

WESTWOOD INTERMEDIATE BOND FUND
(See first Westwood listing for data common to all Westwood funds)

Portfolio manager: Patricia R. Fraze (1991)
Investment objective and policies: High total return - capital growth and current income consistent with maintenance of principal and liquidity. Invests primarily in investment-grade domestic and foreign government and corporate debt securities with a weighted average maturity of 3 to 10 years. Up to 25% of assets may be in securities of foreign issuers. May use futures and options to enhance income and hedge.
Year organized: 1991
Ticker symbol: WEIBX
Qualified for sale in: All states except MD, MO
Dividends paid: Income - declared daily, paid monthly; Capital gains - December
Portfolio turnover (3 yrs): 203%, 222%, 198%

Management fee: 0.60%
12b-1 distribution fee: Maximum of 0.25%
Expense ratio: 0.92% (year ending 9/31/94) (1.75% without waiver)

THE WEXFORD TRUST - MUHLENKAMP FUND ◆
(See The Muhlenkamp Fund)

WILLIAM BLAIR MUTUAL FUNDS ◆
(Data common to all William Blair funds are shown below. See subsequent listings for data specific to individual William Blair funds.)

222 West Adams St.
Chicago, IL 60606
312-364-8000, 800-742-7272
800-635-2840, fax 312-853-2321

Shareholder service hours: Full service: M-F 8:30 A.M.-4:30 P.M. EST; After hours service: prices, yields, messages, prospectuses
Adviser: William Blair & Co.
Custodian and transfer agent: State Street Bank & Trust Co.
Telephone orders accepted: No
Wire orders accepted: Yes
Deadline for same day wire purchase: 3 P.M.
Qualified for sale in: All states
Wire redemptions: Yes
Letter redemptions: Signature guarantee required over $5,000
Telephone switching: With other William Blair funds
Number of switches permitted: 4 per year
Shareholder services: Keogh, IRA, SEP-IRA, corporate retirement plans, automatic investment plan—minimum $25/month, electronic funds transfer (purchase only), withdrawal plan min. req. $5,000
IRA/Keogh fees: Annual $15

WILLIAM BLAIR MUTUAL FUND - GROWTH FUND ◆
(See first William Blair listing for data common to all William Blair funds)

Portfolio managers: Rocky Barber (1993), Mark Fuller (1993)
Investment objective and policies: Long-term growth of capital with income secondary. Invests primarily in equity securities of well-managed companies in growing industries - small, rapid growth companies, medium-sized companies of emerging investment quality and large well-managed companies in industries growing faster than the GNP.
Year organized: 1946 (2-1 split, 4/24/84) (name changed from Growth Industry Shares in May 1991)
Ticker symbol: WBGSX
Minimum purchase: Initial: $1,000, Subsequent: $250; IRA/Keogh: Initial: $500
Discount broker availability: Schwab, *White
Dividends paid: Income - July, December; Capital gains - December
Portfolio turnover (3 yrs): 55%, 27%, 33%
Largest holding: Alco Standard Corp. (2.6%)
Management fee: 0.625% first $75M, 0.5% over $75M
Expense ratio: 0.78% (year ending 12/31/93)

WILLIAM BLAIR MUTUAL FUND - INCOME FUND ◆
(See first William Blair listing for data common to all William Blair funds)

Portfolio manager: Bentley M. Myer (1992)
Investment objective and policies: High current income consistent with preservation of capital. Invests primarily in high grade intermediate-term debt securities - U.S. dollar denominated debt securities rated A- or better, obligations of or guaranteed by the U.S. Government, its agencies or instrumentalities, collateralized obligations and commercial paper - with a weighted average maturity of 3 to 7 years.

Year organized: 1990
Ticker symbol: WBRRX
Minimum purchase: Initial: $5,000, Subsequent: $250; IRA/Keogh: Initial: $500
Discount broker availability: Schwab, *White
Dividends paid: Income - declared daily, paid monthly; Capital gains - December
Portfolio turnover (3 yrs): 114%, 47%, 64%
Management fee: 0.25% first $100M to, 0.15% over $250M + 5.0% of the gross income earned
Expense ratio: 0.70% (year ending 12/31/93)

WILLIAM BLAIR MUTUAL FUND - INTERNATIONAL GROWTH FUND ◆
(See first William Blair listing for data common to all William Blair funds)

Sub-adviser: Framlington Overseas Investment Management Limited
Portfolio managers: Norbert W. Truderung (1992), Julian G. St. Lawrence (1992), Simon Key (1992)
Investment objective and policies: Long-term capital appreciation. Invests primarily in common stocks of companies domiciled outside the U.S. and securities convertible into, exchangeable for, or having the right to buy such common stocks. May also invest in ADRs, EDRs and GDRs. May use forward currency exchange contracts to protect against changes in foreign exchange rates and foreign currency futures to hedge. Normally invests in at least 6 countries but may have more than 25% of assets in companies from a single developed country.
Year organized: 1992
Ticker symbol: WBIGX
Minimum purchase: Initial: $5,000, Subsequent: $250; IRA/Keogh: Initial: $500
Discount broker availability: *White
Dividends paid: Income - December; Capital gains - December
Portfolio turnover (1 yr): 83%
Largest holding: Thai Farmers Bank (1.5%)
Management fee: 1.10% first $100M, 0.95% over $100M
Expense ratio: 1.71% (year ending 12/31/93)

WILLIAM BLAIR MUTUAL FUND - LIMITED TERM TAX-FREE FUND ◆
(See first William Blair listing for data common to all William Blair funds)

Portfolio manager: Bentley M. Myer (1994)
Investment objective and policies: High current income exempt from federal income tax consistent with preservation of capital. Invests primarily in high grade intermediate-term municipal debt securities with a weighted average maturity of 3 to 7 years. Up to 20% of assets may be in AMT securities.
Year organized: 1994
Ticker symbol: WBLTX
Minimum purchase: Initial: $5,000, Subsequent: $250; IRA/Keogh: Initial: $500
Dividends paid: Income - declared daily, paid monthly; Capital gains - December
Management fee: 0.25% first $250M, 0.20% over $250M + 7.0% of the gross income earned

WILLIAM BLAIR MUTUAL FUND - READY RESERVES FUND ◆
(See first William Blair listing for data common to all William Blair funds)

Portfolio manager: Bentley M. Myer (1991)
Investment objective and policies: Maximum current income consistent with preservation of capital. Invests exclusively in high quality money market instruments.
Year organized: 1988
Ticker symbol: WBRXX
Minimum purchase: Initial: $2,500, Subsequent: $250; IRA/Keogh: Initial: $500
Telephone redemptions: Yes
Check redemption: $500 minimum

Confirmations mailed: Not mailed
Checks returned: As clear
Periodic account statements mailed: Quarterly
Dividends paid: Income - declared daily, paid monthly
Management fee: 0.625% first $250M to 0.40% over $5B
Expense ratio: 0.71% (year ending 12/31/93)

WOMEN'S EQUITY MUTUAL FUND ◆
479 West 22nd Street
New York, NY 10011
800-424-2295

Adviser: Pro-Conscience Funds, Inc.
Portfolio managers: Linda C.Y. Pei (1993), Amy L. Domini (1993)
Custodian and transfer agent: Provident Bank, Cincinnati
Investment objective and policies: Long-term capital growth. Invests primarily in equity securities (common and preferred stocks) of companies that satisfy certain social responsibility criteria and are proactive towards women's social and economic equality. Considerations include high quality products or services, fair employee relations, environmental sensitivity, sensitivity to minority issues, and contributions to the community. Proactivity considerations include progress in promoting women into management positions, having an above average percentage of women in its work force, having a woman chief executive, having benefit programs that address work/family concerns, chooses women-owned businesses as vendors or service providers, provides career development and training programs for women employees and promotes positive images of women in its product advertising. May have up to 20% of assets in securities of foreign issuers and use foreign currency tranasactions to hedge. May sell short.
Year organized: 1993
Minimum purchase: Initial: $1,000, Subsequent: $100; IRA: Initial $500
Telephone orders accepted: No
Wire orders accepted: Yes
Deadline for same day wire purchase: 4 P.M.
Qualified for sale in: All states except AL, AR, DE, ID, KY, LA, MS, MT, NV, NH, ND, OK, SC, SD, TN, VT, WI
Telephone redemptions: Yes
Wire redemptions: Yes, $1,000 minimum
Letter redemptions: Signature guarantee required
Dividends paid: Income - March, December; Capital gains - March, December
Portfolio turnover (1 yr): 139%
Largest holding: Echo Bay Mines, Ltd. (4.1%)
Shareholder services: IRA, automatic investment plan (waives initial minimum), withdrawal plan min. req. $10,000
Management fee: 1.0%
Expense ratio: 1.50% (6 months ending 3/31/94) (21.93% without waiver)
IRA/Keogh fees: Annual: $10

WOOD ISLAND GROWTH FUND
Wood Island, 4th Floor
80 East Sir Francis Drake Blvd.
Larkspur, CA 94939
415-461-3850, fax 415-461-8491

Adviser: Wood Island Associates, Inc.
Portfolio manager: Gary Kirk (1984)
Custodian: First Interstate Bank of California
Transfer agent: Wood Island Associates, Inc.
Investment objective and policies: Long-term capital appreciation. Invests primarily in common and preferred stocks and convertible securities of companies believed undervalued with remaining assets in high quality fixed-income debt obligations. Companies generally have market capitalization of over $200M. Up to 25% of assets may be in other no-load mutual funds and 15% in ADRs, ADSs and domestic closed-end investment companies with investments in securities of foreign issuers.
Special sales restrictions: The individual or entity is an investor earning at least $75,000 per year, or worth at least $200,000, and assures Fund in writing that the investment is for his or its account and not with a view to or for sale in connection with any distribution of the shares. The Fund reserves the right in its sole discretion to reject any offer to purchase its shares.
Year organized: 1983 (name and objective changed from Adams Investors on 9/10/92)
Minimum purchase: Initial: $5,000, Subsequent: $1,000
Telephone orders accepted: No
Wire orders accepted: No
Qualified for sale in: CA, NY, OR, TX, WI
Letter redemptions: Signature guarantee required
Dividends paid: Income - December; Capital gains - December
Portfolio turnover (3 yrs): 28%, 31%, 40%
Largest holding: Federal National Mortgage Association (2.9%)
Management fee: 1.35%
Expense ratio: 2.15% (year ending 12/31/93)

WOOD ISLAND TOTAL RETURN FUND
(Fund liquidated on 11/18/94)

WOODWARD EQUITY INDEX FUND
P.O. Box 7058
Troy, MI 48007-7058
313-259-0729, 800-688-3350
fax 313-828-2464

Adviser: NBD Bank, N.A.
Portfolio manager: Frederick R. Neumann (1992)
Custodian and transfer agent: NBD Bank, N.A. of Troy, Michigan
Investment objective and policies: Investment return which replicates the price and yield performance of the S&P 500. Invests in a representative sample of the common stocks that comprise the Index in accordance with their relative capitalizations and sector weightings within the Index.
Year organized: 1992
Ticker symbol: WOEIX
Minimum purchase: Initial: $1,000, Subsequent: $100; IRA: Initial: $250
Telephone orders accepted: No
Wire orders accepted: Yes
Deadline for same day wire purchase: 4 P.M.
Qualified for sale in: CA, DC, FL, GA, HI, IL, IN, KY, MI, NJ, NY, OH, PA, VA, WI, WY
Telephone redemptions: Yes
Wire redemptions: Yes, $1,000 minimum, $16 fee
Letter redemptions: Signature guarantee required
Telephone switching: With other Woodward funds (other Woodward stock and bond funds are load)
Number of switches permitted: 30 day hold
Dividends paid: Income - March, June, September, December; Capital gains - December
Portfolio turnover (2 yrs): 16%, 1%
Largest holding: General Electric Co. (2.5%)
Shareholder services: IRA, 401(k), 403(b), automatic investment plan, directed dividends, electronic funds transfer, withdrawal plan min. req. $15,000
Management fee: 0.10%
12b-1 distribution fee: 0.015%
Expense ratio: 0.20% (year ending 12/31/93)
IRA fees: Initial $10

WORKING ASSETS MONEY MARKET PORTFOLIO
111 Pine Street
San Francisco, CA 94111
603-436-5152, 800-223-7010
fax 603-433-4209

Adviser: Working Assets Capital Management
Sub-adviser: GMG/Seneca Capital Management
Portfolio manager: Danita Wright (1993)
Custodian: Norwest Bank, NA, Minneapolis, MN
Transfer agent: Financial Data Services, Inc.
Investment objective and policies: High income consistent with liquidity and safety of capital, and concern with the social impact of investments. Invests in U.S. dollar denominated money market instruments. Fund favors investments that support

housing, education, farming, small business, and energy conservation. It avoids investments in firms that pollute the environment, manufacture weapons, practice discrimination or invest in nations controlled by repressive regimes.
Year organized: 1983
Ticker symbol: WKAXX
Minimum purchase: Initial: $2,500, Subsequent: $50; IRA/Keogh: Initial: $250, Subsequent: $50
Wire orders accepted: Yes
Deadline for same day wire purchase: 4 P.M.
Qualified for sale in: All states
Telephone redemptions: Yes
Wire redemptions: Yes, $10 fee under $10,000
Letter redemptions: Signature guarantee required
Check redemptions: No minimum, $0.30 fee under $250
Confirmations mailed: After each purchase and each mail or wire redemption
Telephone switch privileges: With other Working Assets funds and Muir California Tax-Free Income Fund (all of which have loads)
Checks returned: Monthly
Periodic account statements mailed: Quarterly
Dividends paid: Income - declared and paid daily
Shareholder services: Keogh, IRA, SEP-IRA, automatic investment plan, withdrawal plan min. req. $10,000, electronic funds transfer
Management fee: 0.5%
12b-1 distribution fee: 0.25%
Expense ratio: 1.16% (year ending 6/30/94)
IRA fees: Annual $10
Keogh fees: Annual $20, Initial $20

WPG FUNDS ◆
(Data common to all WPG funds are shown below. See subsequent listings for data specific to individual WPG funds.)

One New York Plaza
New York, NY 10004
212-908-9582, 800-223-3332
fax 212-908-9867

Shareholder service hours: Full service: M-F 9 A.M.-5 P.M. EST; After hours service: prices, prospectuses
Adviser: Weiss, Peck & Greer Advisers, Inc.
Custodian: Boston Safe Deposit & Trust Co.
Transfer agent: The Shareholders Services Group. Inc.
Minimum purchase: Initial: $2,500, Subsequent: $100; IRA/Keogh: Initial: $250, Subsequent: None (except Growth Fund and Quantitative Equity Fund)
Telephone orders accepted: No
Wire orders accepted: Yes, $9 fee
Deadline for same day wire purchase: 4 P.M. (12 NN for money market funds)
Qualified for sale in: All states
Letter redemptions: Signature guarantee not required
Telephone switching: With other WPG Funds
Number of switches permitted: 6 per year
Shareholder services: Keogh, IRA, SEP-IRA, 401(k), corporate retirement plans, automatic investment plan—minimum $50/month, withdrawal plan min. req. $10,000 (except Growth Fund)
IRA/Keogh fees: Annual $15, Initial $10, Closing $10

WPG DIVIDEND INCOME FUND ◆
(Fund liquidated on 12/22/94)

WPG GOVERNMENT MONEY MARKET FUND ◆
(See first WPG listing for data common to all WPG funds)

Portfolio manager: Ellen Welsh (1988)
Investment objective and policies: High current income consistent with preservation of capital and liquidity. Invests in short-term U.S. Government money market securities maturing in one year or less.
Year organized: 1988 (name changed from WPG Short-Term Income Fund on 1/2/92)

Ticker symbol: WPSXX
Check redemptions: $500 minimum
Confirmations mailed: After each purchase and each check, mail or wire redemption
Checks returned: Monthly
Periodic account statements mailed: Monthly
Dividends paid: Income - declared daily, paid monthly
Management fee: 0.50% on first $500M to 0.35% over $1.5B
Expense ratio: 0.81% (year ending 12/31/93)

WPG GOVERNMENT SECURITIES FUND ◆
(See first WPG listing for data common to all WPG funds)

Newspaper listing: Under Weiss Peck Greer; Govt
Portfolio manager: David W. Hoyle (1986)
Investment objective and policies: High current return, consistent with capital preservation. Invests at least 65% of assets in U.S. Government securities maturing in one year or more, with remainder in shorter term U.S. Government securities, other debt instruments and cash or cash equivalents. Fund may use futures and options to hedge.
Year organized: 1986
Ticker symbol: WPGVX
Discount broker availability: Schwab, *White, Fidelity, Siebert
Dividends paid: Income - declared daily, paid monthly; Capital gains - December
Portfolio turnover (3 yrs): 98%, 137%, 190%
Management fee: 0.60% on first $300M to 0.50% over $500M
12b-1 distribution fee: Yes (not currently imposed)
Expense ratio: 0.79% (year ending 12/31/93)

WPG GROWTH FUND ◆
(See first WPG listing for data common to all WPG funds)

Newspaper listing: Under Weiss Peck Greer; Gwth
Portfolio manager: John P. Callaghan (1993)
Investment objective and policies: Maximum capital growth. Invests aggressively in common stocks or securities convertible into common stocks of emerging growth companies with market capitalizations under $750M and special situations. May invest in securities of foreign issuers and use options and futures. Fund is non-diversified.
Year organized: 1985
Dow Jones ticker symbol: WPGRX
Special sales restrictions: Fund is designed especially for institutional investors but is available to all investors.
Minimum purchase: Initial: $250,000, Subsequent: $25,000
Discount broker availability: Schwab, *White, Fidelity, Siebert
Dividends paid: Income - March, June, September, December; Capital gains - December
Portfolio turnover (3 yrs): 127%, 84%, 84%
Largest holding: BMC Software, Inc. (4.0%)
Shareholder services: None
Management fee: 0.75%
Expense ratio: 0.98% (year ending 12/31/93)

WPG GROWTH AND INCOME FUND ◆
(See first WPG listing for data common to all WPG funds)

Newspaper listing: Under Weiss Peck Greer; GrInc
Portfolio manager: A. Roy Knutsen (1992)
Investment objective and policies: Long-term capital growth, current income and growth of income. Invests primarily in income producing common and preferred stocks, convertible and fixed-income securities of companies growing faster than the U.S. economy. May invest in securities of foreign issuers and write call options and purchase options in closing transactions.
Year organized: 1979 (WPG Fund prior to 1/1/91, prior to that ADV Fund, prior to that American Dualvest—dual purpose fund)

Ticker symbol: WPGFX
Discount broker availability: Schwab, *White, Fidelity, Siebert
Dividends paid: Income - March, June, September, December; Capital gains - December
Portfolio turnover (3 yrs): 86%, 76%, 89%
Largest holding: Nucor Corp. (2.9%)
Management fee: 0.75%
Expense ratio: 1.26% (year ending 12/31/93)

WPG INTERMEDIATE MUNICIPAL BOND FUND ◆
(See first WPG listing for data common to all WPG funds)

Portfolio managers: Arthur Schwartz (1993), S. Blake Miller (1993)
Investment objective and policies: High current income exempt from federal income tax consistent with stability of principal. Invests primarily in investment-grade municipal securities with a weighted average maturity of 4 to 10 years. May invest in AMT securities.
Year organized: 1993
Discount broker availability: *White, Fidelity, Siebert
Dividends paid: Income - declared daily, paid monthly; Capital gains - December
Portfolio turnover (1 yr): 17%
Management fee: 0.50%
Expense ratio: 0.85% (6 months ending 12/31/93)

WPG INTERNATIONAL FUND ◆
(See first WPG listing for data common to all WPG funds)

Sub-adviser: Lloyds Investment Management International Ltd.
Portfolio manager: Raymond Haines (1994)
Investment objective and policies: Long-term capital growth with current income secondary. Invests primarily in common stocks and equity-related securities of established larger capitalization non-U.S. companies. May use ADRs, EDRs and IDRs in addition to direct investment. May also invest in fixed-income securities of foreign governments or companies. Fund hedges.
Year organized: 1989
Discount broker availability: Schwab, *White, Fidelity, Siebert
Dividends paid: Income - March, June, September, December; Capital gains - December
Portfolio turnover (3 yrs): 110%, 97%, 77%
Largest holding: Bangkok Bank (2.1%)
Management fee: 1.0%
12b-1 distribution fee: Yes (not currently imposed)
Expense ratio: 2.12% (year ending 12/31/93)

WPG QUANTITATIVE EQUITY FUND ◆
(See first WPG listing for data common to all WPG funds)

Newspaper listing: Under Weiss Peck Greer
Portfolio manager: Joseph Pappo (1993)
Investment objective and policies: Results that exceed the performance of the S&P 500 Index. Invests in a portfolio of stocks that maximizes expected return for any risk level or minimizes risk level for any expected return. Uses a proprietary computer model for stock selection.
Year organized: 1993
Ticker symbol: WPGQX
Minimum purchase: Initial: $5,000, Subsequent: $500; IRA/Keogh: Initial: $250, Subsequent: None
Discount broker availability: *White, Fidelity, Siebert
Dividends paid: Income - June, December; Capital gains - December
Portfolio turnover (1 yr): 21%
Largest holding: Exxon Corp. (4.6%)
Management fee: 0.75%
Expense ratio: 1.32% (year ending 12/31/93)

WPG TAX FREE MONEY MARKET FUND ◆
(See first WPG listing for data common to all WPG funds)

Portfolio managers: Janet Fiorenza (1988), Arthur Schwartz (1988)
Investment objective and policies: High current income exempt from regular federal income taxes consistent with preservation of capital and liquidity. Invests in short-term tax exempt money market instruments.
Year organized: 1988
Dow Jones ticker symbol: WPTXX
Check redemptions: $500 minimum
Confirmations mailed: After each purchase and each check, mail or wire redemption
Checks returned: Monthly
Periodic account statements mailed: Monthly
Dividends paid: Income - declared daily, paid monthly
Management fee: 0.50% on first $500M to 0.35% over $1.5B
Expense ratio: 0.74% (year ending 12/31/93)

WPG TUDOR FUND ◆
(See first WPG listing for data common to all WPG funds)

Newspaper listing: Under Weiss Peck Greer
Portfolio manager: Melville Straus (1973)
Investment objective and policies: Capital appreciation. Invests in high potential common stocks and convertible securities with market capitalizations generally under $1,5B with about 50% of assets invested in "special situations." May write call options and purchase call options in closing transactions. Fund is non-diversified.
Year organized: 1969
Ticker symbol: TUDRX
Discount broker availability: Schwab, *White, Fidelity, $iebert
Dividends paid: Income - March, June, September, December; Capital gains - December
Portfolio turnover (3 yrs): 118%, 89%, 90%
Largest holding: Informix Corp. (3.1%)
Management fee: 0.90% first $300M to 0.75% over $500M
Expense ratio: 1.25% (year ending 12/31/93)

THE WRIGHT MANAGED FUNDS
(Data common to all Wright Managed funds are shown below. See subsequent listings for data specific to individual Wright Managed funds.)

24 Federal Street
Boston, MA 02110
617-482-8260, 800-225-6265

Adviser: Wright Investors' Service
Administrator: Eaton Vance Management
Custodian: Investors Bank & Trust Co.
Transfer agent: The Shareholders Services Group. Inc.
Special sales restrictions: The Wright National Fiduciary Equity Funds, Wright International Blue Chip Equities Fund and Wright U.S. Treasury Money Market Fund are available to all investors. Shares of the other Wright funds may be purchased only by participating bank trust departments, either for their own accounts or the accounts of their clients, or by clients of Wright Investors' Service.
Minimum purchase: Initial: $1,000, Subsequent: None
Telephone orders accepted: No
Wire orders accepted: Yes
Deadline for same day wire purchase: 4 P.M.
Wire redemptions: Yes
Letter redemptions: Signature guarantee required
Telephone switching: With other Wright Funds (see Special Sales Restrictions for individual fund availability)
Number of switches permitted: Unlimited
Shareholder services: Keogh, IRA, 401(k), corpo-

rate retirement plans, withdrawal plan min. req. $10,000
Management fee: 0.40% first $100M to 0.33% over $1B for Managed Income Trust, Equity Trust varies by portfolio
Administration fee: 0.10% first $100M (0.20% for equity funds) to 0.02% over $500M (all funds)
IRA/Keogh fees: Annual $10

WRIGHT CURRENT INCOME FUND
(See first Wright listing for data common to all Wright funds)

Investment objective and policies: High current income. Invests primarily in debt obligations issued or guaranteed by the U.S. Government or its agencies or instrumentalities, mortgage-related securities of governmental or federally-chartered corporate issuers, and corporate debt securities rated A or better.
Year organized: 1987 (a series of The Wright Managed Income Trust)
Ticker symbol: WCIPX
Qualified for sale in: All states except AK, AR, MS, MT, NH, NM, ND, WV
Dividends paid: Income - declared daily, paid monthly; Capital gains - December
Portfolio turnover (3 yrs): 4%, 13%, 5%
12b-1 distribution fee: 0.20%
Expense ratio: 0.78% (year ending 12/31/93)

WRIGHT GOVERNMENT OBLIGATIONS FUND
(See first Wright listing for data common to all Wright funds)

Investment objective and policies: High current income. Invests at least 65% of assets in Treasury bills, notes and bonds, and other obligations of the U.S. Government or its agencies or instrumentalities, guaranteed as to principal and interest by the full faith and credit of the U.S. Government, with a weighted average maturity of 10 to 20 years. Fund does not invest in mortgage-related securities.
Year organized: 1983 (a series of The Wright Managed Income Trust)
Ticker symbol: WGOBX
Qualified for sale in: All states except AK, AR, MS, MT, NH, NM, ND, WV
Dividends paid: Income - declared daily, paid monthly; Capital gains - December
Portfolio turnover (3 yrs): 12%, 15%, 15%
12b-1 distribution fee: 0.14%
Expense ratio: 0.90% (year ending 12/31/93) (0.96% without waiver)

WRIGHT INSURED TAX FREE BOND FUND ◆
(See first Wright listing for data common to all Wright funds)

Investment objective and policies: High current income exempt from federal income tax. Invests primarily in high-grade municipal bonds and other long-term debt securities rated A or better. At least 65% of assets will be in municipal securities insured for timely payment of principal and interest. Up to 20% of assets may be in AMT securities.
Year organized: 1985 (a series of The Wright Managed Income Trust)
Ticker symbol: WTFBX
Qualified for sale in: All states except AL, AK, AR, ID, MS, MT, NH, NM, ND, WV
Dividends paid: Income - monthly; Capital gains - December
Portfolio turnover (3 yrs): 7%, 10%, 2%
12b-1 distribution fee: Maximum of 0.20% (not currently imposed)
Expense ratio: 0.90% (year ending 12/31/93) (1.15% without waiver)

WRIGHT INTERNATIONAL BLUE CHIP EQUITIES FUND
(See first Wright listing for data common to all Wright funds)

Investment objective and policies: Long-term capital growth and reasonable current income. Invests at least 80% of assets in equity securities of well-established non-U.S. companies meeting strict quality standards. Invests in companies based in at least 3 foreign countries, but may use ADRs. May use futures and options to hedge both currencies and individual equity holdings. All companies are selected from the Approved Wright Investment List.
Year organized: 1989 (a series of The Wright Managed Equity Trust)
Ticker symbol: WIBCX
Discount broker availability: *Schwab, *White, *Waterhouse, *Fidelity, *Siebert
Qualified for sale in: All states
Dividends paid: Income - June, December; Capital gains - December
Portfolio turnover (3 yrs): 30%, 15%, 23%
Largest holding: Kurita Water Industries Ltd. (1.2%)
Management fee: 0.75% first $100M to 0.68% over $1B
12b-1 distribution fee: 0.20%
Expense ratio: 1.46% (year ending 12/31/93)

WRIGHT JUNIOR BLUE CHIP EQUITIES FUND
(See first Wright listing for data common to all Wright funds)

Investment objective and policies: Total return. Invests at least 80% of assets in equity securities of smaller companies with capitalization of $25M-$300M still experiencing their rapid growth period. All companies are selected from the Approved Wright Investment List.
Year organized: 1985 (a series of The Wright Managed Equity Trust)
Ticker symbol: WJBEX
Qualified for sale in: All states except AK, AR, MS, MT, NM, ND, WV, WI
Discount broker availability: *White
Dividends paid: Income - March, June, September, December; Capital gains - December
Portfolio turnover (3 yrs): 38%, 80%, 60%
Largest holding: Morrison Restaurants, Inc. (2.4%)
Management fee: 0.55% first $100M to 0.58% over $1B
12b-1 distribution fee: 0.20%
Expense ratio: 1.09% (year ending 12/31/93)

WRIGHT NATIONAL FIDUCIARY EQUITY FUNDS - EQUIFUND
(See first Wright listing for data common to all Wright funds)

Investment objective and policies: Total return. Invests in a broadly based portfolio of equity securities of substantially all the publicly traded companies in the National Equity Index for the nation or nations in which each fund is permitted to invest.
Portfolios: There are currently nine active funds - Dutch (since 1990), Hong Kong (1990), Italian (1990), Spanish (1990), Belgian/Luxembourg (1994), Japanese (1994), Mexico (1994), Nordic (1994) and Swiss (1994). Australasian was liquidated in 1993 and United Kingdom was liquidated on 1/31/94
Year organized: 1990
Ticker symbols: WEBEX (Belgian/Luxembourg), WENLX (Dutch), WEHKX (Hong Kong), WEJPX (Japanese), WEMEX (Mexico), WENOX (Nordic), WESPX (Spanish), WECHX (Swiss)
Discount broker availability: *Schwab, *White, *Waterhouse, *Fidelity, *Siebert
Qualified for sale in: All states
Dividends paid: Income - June, December; Capital gains - December
Portfolio turnover (3 yrs): Dutch 47%, 69%, 59%;

Hong Kong - 76%, 39%, 77%; Italian - 114%, 32%, 68%; Spanish - 88%, 44%, 70%
Management fee: 0.75% first $500M to 0.68% over $1B
12b-1 distribution fee: Maximum of 0.25% (currently only imposing 0.25% for Belgian/Luxembourg and 0.18% for Hong Kong)
Expense ratio: 2.00% (year ending 12/31/93) (expenses for all EquiFunds are capped at 2.00%)

WRIGHT NEAR TERM BOND FUND
(See first Wright listing for data common to all Wright funds)

Investment objective and policies: High current income. Invests primarily in debt obligations issued or guaranteed by the U.S. Government or its agencies or instrumentalities and FDIC-insured CDs and bankers acceptances with a weighted average maturity of less than 5 years.
Year organized: 1983 (a series of The Wright Managed Income Trust)
Ticker symbol: WNTBX
Qualified for sale in: All states except AK, MS, MT, NH, NM, ND
Dividends paid: Income - declared daily, paid monthly; Capital gains - December
Portfolio turnover (3 yrs): 22%, 6%, 18%
12b-1 distribution fee: 0.20%
Expense ratio: 0.7% (year ending 12/31/93)

WRIGHT QUALITY CORE EQUITIES FUND
(See first Wright listing for data common to all Wright funds)

Investment objective and policies: Total return. Invests at least 80% of assets in equity securities of larger-capitalization well-established companies meeting strict quality standards. All companies are selected from the Approved Wright Investment List.
Year organized: 1985 (a series of The Wright Managed Equity Trust)
Ticker symbol: WQCEX
Qualified for sale in: All states except AK, MS, MT, NM, ND, WV, WI
Dividends paid: Income - March, June, September, December; Capital gains - December
Portfolio turnover (3 yrs): 53%, 70%, 9%
Largest holding: Nike, Inc. (1.1%)
Management fee: 0.45% first $100M to 0.48% over $1B
12b-1 distribution fee: 0.20%
Expense ratio: 0.97% (year ending 12/31/93)

WRIGHT SELECTED BLUE CHIP EQUITIES FUND
(See first Wright listing for data common to all Wright funds)

Investment objective and policies: Total return. Invests in equity securities of well-established companies meeting strict quality standards. Companies are chosen for likelihood of providing superior total investment return over the intermediate term. All companies are selected from the Approved Wright Investment List.
Year organized: 1982 (a series of The Wright Managed Equity Trust)
Ticker symbol: WSBEX
Discount broker availability: *White
Qualified for sale in: All states except AK, AR, ID, MS, MT, NM, ND, WI
Dividends paid: Income - March, June, September, December; Capital gains - December
Portfolio turnover (3 yrs): 28%, 77%, 72%
Largest holding: Keycorp (1.2%)
Management fee: 0.55% first $100M to 0.58% over $1B
12b-1 distribution fee: 0.20%
Expense ratio: 1.03% (year ending 12/31/93)

WRIGHT TOTAL RETURN BOND FUND
(See first Wright listing for data common to all Wright funds)

Investment objective and policies: High current income. Invests in corporate bonds or other debt securities rated A or better with a weighted average maturity that, in the advisor's judgement, produces the best total return. May invest in both government and corporate investment-grade fixed-income securities.
Year organized: 1983
Ticker symbol: WTRBX
Year organized: 1983 (a series of The Wright Managed Bond Trust)
Qualified for sale in: All states except AK, AR, MS, MT, NH, NM, ND, WV
Dividends paid: Income - declared daily, paid monthly; Capital gains - December
Portfolio turnover (3 yrs): 36%, 13%, 56%
12b-1 distribution fee: 0.20%
Expense ratio: 0.76% (year ending 12/31/93)

WRIGHT U.S. TREASURY MONEY MARKET FUND ◆
(See first Wright listing for data common to all Wright funds)

Investment objective and policies: High current income consistent with preservation of capital and liquidity. Invests exclusively in money market instruments issued by the U.S. Government and its agencies that are backed by the full faith and credit of the U.S. Government and in repurchase agreements relating to such securities.
Year organized: 1991
Qualified for sale in: All states except AK, AR, MS, MT, NH, NM, ND, WV
Check redemptions: $500 minimum
Confirmations mailed: After each purchase and each check, mail or wire redemption
Checks returned: Quarterly
Periodic account statements mailed: Quarterly
Dividends paid: Income - declared daily, paid monthly
Management fee: 0.35% first $100M to 0.30% over $500M
Expense ratio: 0.45% (year ending 12/31/93) (0.97% without waiver)

THE YACKTMAN FUND
303 West Madison Street, Suite 1925
Chicago, IL 60606
800-525-8258, 800-457-6033

Adviser: Yacktman Asset Management Co.
Administrator: Sunstone Financial Group, Inc.
Portfolio manager: Donald A. Yacktman (1992)
Custodian & transfer agent: Firstar Trust Company
Investment objective and policies: Long-term capital growth with current income secondary. Invests primarily in common stocks and other equity securities for growth and money market instruments for income. May invest in fixed-income securities when they offer potential for capital growth. Up to 10% of assets may be in non-U.S. dollar denominated foreign securities.
Year organized: 1992
Ticker symbol: YACKX
Minimum purchase: Initial: $2,500, Subsequent: $100; IRA/Keogh: Initial: $500
Telephone orders accepted: No
Wire orders accepted: Yes
Deadline for same day wire purchase: 4 P.M.
Discount broker availability: *Schwab, *White, *Waterhouse, *Fidelity, *Siebert
Qualified for sale in: All states
Telephone redemptions: Yes, $1,000 minimum
Wire redemptions: Yes, $1,000 minimum, $7.50 fee
Letter redemptions: Signature guarantee required over $25,000
Telephone switching: With Portico money market funds, $1,000 minimum

Number of switches permitted: Unlimited, $5 fee
Dividends paid: Income - March, June, September, December; Capital gains - December
Portfolio turnover (3 yrs): 49%, 61%, 31%
Largest holding: Philip Morris Companies, Inc. (6.6%)
Shareholder services: Keogh, IRA, SEP-IRA, 401(k), 403(b), corporate retirement plans, automatic investment plan—$500 initial minimum, withdrawal plan min. req. $10,000
Management fee: 0.65% first $500M to 0.55% over $1B
Administration fee: 0.15% first $50M to 0.025% over $100M
12b-1 distribution fee: Maximum of 0.20%
Expense ratio: 1.07% (year ending 12/31/94)
IRA/Keogh fees: Annual $12.50

THE ZSA ASSET ALLOCATION FUND ◆
105 North Washington Street
P.O. Drawer 69
Rocky Mount, NC 27802
919-977-9922, 800-525-3863
fax 919-442-4226

Adviser: Zaske, Sarafa & Associates, Inc.
Administrator: The Nottingham Company
Custodian: Wachovia Bank of North Carolina N.A.
Transfer agent: The Nottingham Company
Investment objective and policies: Long-term capital growth and income. Invests in a flexible portfolio of equity securities (25-65% of assets), fixed-income securities (35-65%) and money market instruments (0-40%). Allocation among categories is adjusted to changing market and economic conditions. Fund may invest in ADRs of foreign issuers and hedge its portfolio.
Year organized: 1992 (name changed from Growth and Income Fund in 1994)
Minimum purchase: Initial: $10,000, Subsequent: $500; IRA/Keogh: Initial: $2,000
Telephone orders accepted: No
Wire orders accepted: Yes
Deadline for same day wire purchase: 4 P.M.
Qualified for sale in: All states
Telephone redemptions: Yes
Wire redemptions: Yes, $5,000 minimum
Letter redemptions: Signature guarantee required over $50,000
Dividends paid: Income - March, June, September, December; Capital gains - December
Portfolio turnover (2 yrs): 54%, 22%
Largest holding: U.S. Treasury Bond 7.500% due 11/15/16 (10.8%)
Shareholder services: Keogh, IRA, SEP-IRA, automatic investment plan—minimum $100, withdrawal plan min. req. $10,000
Management fee: 0.90%
Administration fee: 0.25% first $10M to 0.15% over $25M
12b-1 distribution fee: 0.35% (not currently imposed)
Expense ratio: 1.92% (year ending 3/31/94) (2.75% without waiver)
IRA/Keogh fees: Annual $15

THE ZSA EQUITY FUND ◆
105 North Washington Street
P.O. Drawer 69
Rocky Mount, NC 27802
919-977-9922, 800-525-3863
fax 919-442-4226

Adviser: Zaske, Sarafa & Associates, Inc.
Administrator: The Nottingham Company
Custodian: Wachovia Bank of North Carolina N.A.
Transfer agent: The Nottingham Company
Investment objective and policies: Long-term capital growth. Invests primarily (at least 80% of assets) in common stocks, preferred stocks and convertible securities. Fund may invest in ADRs of foreign issuers and hedge its portfolio.
Year organized: 1992

Minimum purchase: Initial: $10,000, Subsequent: $500; IRA/Keogh: Initial: $2,000

Telephone orders accepted: No

Wire orders accepted: Yes

Deadline for same day wire purchase: 4 P.M.

Qualified for sale in: All states

Telephone redemptions: Yes

Wire redemptions: Yes, $5,000 minimum

Letter redemptions: Signature guarantee required over $50,000

Dividends paid: Income - March, June, September, December; Capital gains - December

Portfolio turnover (2 yrs): 80%, 24%

Largest holding: Chevron Corp. (3.5%)

Shareholder services: Keogh, IRA, SEP-IRA, automatic investment plan—minimum $100, withdrawal plan nin. req. $10,000

Management fee: 0.90%

Administration fee: 0.25% first $10M to 0.15% over $25M

12b-1 distribution fee: 0.35% (not currently imposed)

Expense ratio: 1.93% (year ending 3/31/94) (5.35% without waiver)

IRA/Keogh fees: Annual $15

Late directory information

Following are Directory additions and changes received after the alphabetical directory listings were completed.

IAI DEVELOPING COUNTRIES FUND
(See first IAI listing in main directory for data common to all IAI funds)

Portfolio manager: Roy C. Gillson (1995)
Investment objective and policies: Long-term capital appreciation. Invests primarily in equity securities of companies domiciled or having substantial operations in developing foreign countries. May invest directly in foreign securities as well as in ADRs, EDRs and GDRs. May use options, futures contracts, currency exchange contracts and sell short.
Year organized: 1995
Dividends paid: Income - December; Capital gains - December
Management fee: 1.25% first $200M to 1.00% over $400M
12b-1 distribution fee: Maximum of 0.25%

INVESCO EUROPEAN SMALL COMPANY FUND
(See first INVESCO listing in main directory for data common to all INVESCO funds)

Portfolio managers: Andy Crossley (1995), Claire Griffiths (1995)
Investment objective and policies: Capital appreciation by investing in equity securities of European companies whose market caps place them in the same size range as U.S. companies in the lowest 25% of market capitalizations—typically under $1 billion.
Year organized: 1995
Dividends paid: Income - Annually; Capital gains - December
Management fee: 0.75% first $500M to 0.55% over $1B
12b-1 distribution fee: 0.25%

INVESCO LATIN AMERICA GROWTH FUND
(See first INVESCO listing in main directory for data common to all INVESCO funds)

Portfolio manager: Philip Ehrmann (1995)
Investment objective and policies: Capital appreciation by investing in common stocks, and to a lesser degree, depository receipts, preferred stocks, and convertibles of Latin American issuers. Countries include Mexico, Central and South America, and the Spanish speaking islands of the Carribean.
Year organized: 1995
Dividends paid: Income - Annually; Capital gains - December
Redemption fee: 2.00% on shares held less than 12 months
Management fee: 0.75% first $500M to 0.55% over $1B
12b-1 distribution fee: 0.25%

JANUS GOVERNMENT MONEY MARKET FUND ◆
(See first Janus listing in main directory for data common to all Janus funds)

Portfolio manager: Sharon Pichler (1995)
Investment objective and policies: Maximum current income consistent with stability of capital. Invests exclusively in obligations issued and/or guaranteed as to principal and interest by the United States government or its agencies and instrumentalities, and repurchase agreements secured by such obligatons.
Year organized: 1995
Dividends paid: Income - Declared daily, paid monthly
Management fee: 0.10%

JANUS MONEY MARKET FUND ◆
(See first Janus listing in main directory for data common to all Janus funds)

Portfolio manager: Sharon Pichler (1995)
Investment objective and policies: Maximum current income consistent with stability of capital. Invests in high quality commercial paper and obligations of financial institutions.
Year organized: 1995
Dividends paid: Income - Declared daily, paid monthly
Management fee: 0.10%

JANUS TAX-EXEMPT MONEY MARKET FUND ◆
(See first Janus listing in main directory for data common to all Janus funds)

Portfolio manager: Sharon Pichler (1995)
Investment objective and policies: Maximum current income exempt from federal income taxes consistent with stability of capital. Invests primarily in municipal securities whose interest is exempt from federal income taxes including the alternative minimum tax. Fund reserves the right to invest up to 20% of assets in taxable securities.
Year organized: 1995
Dividends paid: Income - Declared daily, paid monthly
Management fee: 0.10%

THIRD AVENUE VALUE FUND
767 Third Avenue
New York, NY 10017
212-888-6685, 800-443-1021

Adviser: EQSF Advisers, Inc.
Portfolio manager: Martin J. Whitman (1990)
Custodian: Danielson Trust Company, San Diego, CA
Transfer agent: Fund/Plan Services, Inc.
Investment objective and policies: Long-term capital appreciation. Invests primarily in common and preferred stocks and debt securities including junk bonds. Up to 33% of assets may be in securities of foreign issuers, 15% in illiquid securities and 10% in other mutual funds. Fund leverages up to 50% of net assets.
Year organized: 1990
Ticker symbol: TAVFX
Minimum purchase: Initial: $1,000, Subsequent: $1,000; IRA: Initial: $500, Subsequent: $200
Telephone orders accepted: No
Wire orders accepted: Yes
Deadline for same day wire purchase: 4 PM.
Qualified for sale in: All states except AR, WI
Telephone redemptions: Yes
Wire redemptions: Yes, $9 fee
Letter redemptions: Signature guarantee required over $5,000
Dividends paid: Income - December; Capital gains - December
Portfolio turnover (3 yrs): 5%, 17%, 31%
Largest holding: The First American Financial Corp. (5.0%)
Shareholder services: IRA, automatic investment plan—minimum $200/month
Management fee: 0.75% first $100M to 0.50% over $200M
Expense ratio: 1.16% (year ending 10/31/94)
IRA fees: Annual $12

CHAPTER 12

Additional stock and bond funds available no-load through discount brokers

This section lists funds available through discount brokerage firms that are normally not available to individual investors. They include the following:

■ Institutional funds that either have minimum initial investments of $100,000 or more, or are not available to individual investors, that can be purchased through discount brokerage firms at lower ($10,000 or less) initial minimums. Some are available to all brokerage customers and some are available only through financial advisers.

■ Load funds that are available through discount brokerage firms at NAV. Some are available to all customers and some are available only through financial advisers.

Note: All load funds purchased at NAV through financial advisers at Jack White (except no transaction fee funds) incur a $100 transaction fee. White charges no transaction fee for redemptions. Charles Schwab charges its standard fees on both purchases and redemptions.

ACCESSOR PORTFOLIOS ◆
1420 Fifth Avenue, Suite 3130
Seattle, WA 98101
206-224-7420, 800-759-3504
fax 206-224-4274

Adviser: Bennington Capital Management L.P.
Special sales restrictions: Designed for sales through financial advisers only, but individuals may invest through Charles Schwab.
Discount broker availability: Schwab
Minimum purchase through discount broker: $1,000

ACCESSOR EQUITY MARKET PORTFOLIO ◆
(Fund liquidated in 1994)

ACCESSOR GROWTH PORTFOLIO ◆
(See first Accessor listing for data common to all Accessor portfolios)

Sub-adviser: State Street Bank & Trust Co.
Investment objective and policies: Capital growth. Invests in equity securities with above-average growth characteristics selected from S&P 500 issuers with goal of total return exceeding the S&P/BARRA Growth Index. Up to 20% of assets may be in securities of foreign issuers.
Year organized: 1992

ACCESSOR INTERMEDIATE FIXED-INCOME PORTFOLIO ◆
(See first Accessor listing for data common to all Accessor portfolios)

Sub-adviser: Smith Barney Capital Management
Portfolio managers: Joshua H. Lane (1992), Xavier J. Urpi (1992)
Investment objective and policies: Current income. Invests in bonds, debentures and other fixed-income securities with a weighted average maturity of 3 to 10 years. May use U.S. dollar denominated securities of foreign issuers.
Year organized: 1992
Ticker symbol: AIFIX

ACCESSOR INTERNATIONAL EQUITY PORTFOLIO ◆
(See first Accessor listing for data common to all Accessor portfolios)

Sub-adviser: Nicholas-Applegate Capital Management
Portfolio managers: Arthur E. Nicholas (1994), Lawrence S. Speidell (1994), Loretta J. Morris (1994)

Investment objective and policies: Capital growth. Invests in equity securities of companies domiciled in countries other than the U.S. and traded on foreign stock exchanges - primarily in Western Europe and the Pacific Rim. Up to 20% of assets may be in fixed-income securities.
Year organized: 1994

ACCESSOR INTERNATIONAL FIXED-INCOME PORTFOLIO ◆
(See first Accessor listing for data common to all Accessor portfolios)

Sub-adviser: OFFITBANK
Portfolio managers: Leslie F.B. Ashburner (1994), Joseph A. Giglia (1994)
Investment objective and policies: Current income. Invests in fixed-income securities with maturities of 1 to 5 years issued by entities outside the U.S. and traded by large international banks and primary dealers in government securities.
Year organized: 1994

ACCESSOR MORTGAGE SECURITIES PORTFOLIO ◆
(See first Accessor listing for data common to all Accessor portfolios)

Sub-adviser: BlackRock Financial Management L.P.
Investment objective and policies: High current income consistent with preservation of capital. Invests in mortgage-related securities, primarily issued or guaranteed by the U.S. Government, its agencies or instrumentalities.
Year organized: 1992
Ticker symbol: AMSFX

ACCESSOR MUNICIPAL INTERMEDIATE FIXED-INCOME PORTFOLIO ◆
(See first Accessor listing for data common to all Accessor portfolios)

Sub-adviser: Lazard Freres Asset Management L.P.
Portfolio managers: James W. O'Grady (1994), James Evans (1994)
Investment objective and policies: High current income consistent with preservation of capital. Invests in municipal bonds with a weighted average maturity of 3 to 10 years.
Year organized: 1994

ACCESSOR SHORT-INTERMEDIATE FIXED-INCOME PORTFOLIO ◆
(See first Accessor listing for data common to all Accessor portfolios)

Sub-adviser: Bankers Trust Company
Investment objective and policies: Current income consistent with preservation of capital. Invests in bonds, debentures and other fixed-income securities with a weighted average maturity of 2 to 5 years. May use U.S. dollar denominated securities of foreign issuers.
Year organized: 1992
Ticker symbol: ASIFX

ACCESSOR SMALL CAP PORTFOLIO ◆
(See first Accessor listing for data common to all Accessor portfolios)

Sub-adviser: Wells Fargo Nikko Investment advisers
Portfolio managers: Nancy L. Feldkircher (1992), Blake R. Grossman (1992), John A. Ferry (1993)
Investment objective and policies: Capital growth. Invests in equity securities of companies with market capitalizations under $1B with goal of total return exceeding the BARRA Institutional Small Index. Up to 20% of assets may be in securities of foreign issuers.
Year organized: 1992

ACCESSOR VALUE AND INCOME PORTFOLIO ◆
(See first Accessor listing for data common to all Accessor portfolios)

Sub-adviser: Martingale Asset Management L.P.
Portfolio manager: William E. Jacques (1992)
Investment objective and policies: Current income. Invests in income-producing equity securities selected from S&P 500 issuers with goal of total return exceeding the S&P/BARRA Value Index. Up to 20% of assets may be in income-producing securities of foreign issuers.
Year organized: 1992

ALGER FUND PORTFOLIOS
75 Maiden Lane
New York, NY 10038
201-547-3600, 800-992-3863

Adviser: Fred Alger Management, Inc.
Sales Charge: 5.0% contingent deferred sales charge (available at NAV through discount brokers)
Discount broker availability: *Schwab (only through financial advisers), *White (only through financial advisers)
Minimum purchase through discount broker: Schwab: $1,000; White: $2,500

ALGER BALANCED PORTFOLIO
(See first Alger listing for data common to all Alger portfolios)

Portfolio manager: David Alger (1992)
Investment objective and policies: Current income and long-term capital growth. Invests in equity and investment-grade debt securities with at least 25% of assets in fixed-income senior securities.
Year organized: 1992

ALGER GROWTH PORTFOLIO
(See first Alger listing for data common to all Alger portfolios)

Portfolio manager: David Alger (1986)
Investment objective and policies: Long-term capital growth. Invests primarily in equity securities and securities convertible into equity securities of domestic companies with capitalizations over $1B.
Year organized: 1986
Ticker symbol: AFGPX

ALGER INCOME AND GROWTH PORTFOLIO
(See first Alger listing for data common to all Alger portfolios)

Portfolio manager: David Alger (1986)
Investment objective and policies: High dividend income consistent with prudent investment management with capital growth secondary. Invests primarily in dividend-paying common and preferred stocks and securities convertible into such stocks.
Year organized: 1986
Ticker symbol: AINGX

ALGER LEVERAGED ALLCAP PORTFOLIO
(See first Alger listing for data common to all Alger portfolios)

Portfolio manager: David Alger (1993)
Investment objective and policies: Long-term capital growth. Invests primarily in equity securities and securities convertible into equity securities of domestic companies. Fund hedges and leverages.
Year organized: 1993

ALGER MIDCAP GROWTH PORTFOLIO
(See first Alger listing for data common to all Alger portfolios)

Portfolio manager: David Alger (1993)
Investment objective and policies: Long-term capital growth. Invests primarily in equity securities and securities convertible into equity securities of domestic companies with capitalizations of $750M to $3.5B.
Year organized: 1993
Ticker symbol: AMCGX

ALGER SMALL CAPITALIZATION PORTFOLIO
(See first Alger listing for data common to all Alger portfolios)

Portfolio manager: David Alger (1986)
Investment objective and policies: Long-term capital growth. Invests primarily in equity securities and securities convertible into equity securities of domestic companies with capitalizations under $1B.
Year organized: 1986
Ticker symbol: ALSCX

ATLANTA GROWTH FUND
1100 Peachtree Street N.E., Suite 1661
Atlanta, GA 30309
404-875-2161, 800-989-3343

Advisers: Wedgewood Equities, Inc., Shapiro Capital Management, Astrop Advisory Corp.
Portfolio managers: Michael A. McCarthy (1992), William B. Astrop (1992)
Investment objective and policies: Capital appreciation. Invests in common stocks of the 50 most highly capitalized companies headquartered in the 18-county metropolitan statistical area of Atlanta, Georgia.
Year organized: 1992
Ticker symbol: ATGTX

Sales charge: 3.75% (available at NAV through discount brokers)
Discount broker availability: Schwab (only through financial advisers)
Minimum purchase through discount broker: $1,000

BT INVESTMENT FUNDS
6 St. James Avenue
Boston, MA 02116
800-545-1074, 800-422-6577

Adviser: Bankers Trust Company
Special sales restrictions: Designed for customers of Bankers Trust or customers of other banks or dealers or institutions with sub-servicing agreements with Bankers Trust, but individuals may invest through discount brokers.

BT INVESTMENT FUNDS - EQUITY APPRECIATION FUND
(See first BT Investment listing for data common to all BT Investment funds)

Portfolio manager: Mary Lisanti (1993)
Investment objective and policies: Long-term capital growth with income secondary. Invests in growth-oriented common stocks of companies of any size. Up to 25% of assets may be in securities of foreign issuers.
Year organized: 1993
Discount broker availability: *Schwab
Minimum purchase through discount broker: $1,000

BT INVESTMENT FUNDS - GLOBAL HIGH YIELD SECURITIES FUND
(See first BT Investment listing for data common to all BT Investment funds)

Portfolio manager: Tim Tucker (1993)
Investment objective and policies: High current income. Invests primarily in junk bonds issued in many of the world's securities markets. May invest in both governmental and corporate issues in both major industrialized markets and emerging markets.
Year organized: 1993
Discount broker availability: *Schwab (only through financial advisers)
Minimum purchase through discount broker: $2,500; IRA: $1,000

BT INVESTMENT FUNDS - INTERMEDIATE TAX FREE FUND
(See first BT Investment listing for data common to all BT Investment funds)

Portfolio manager: Gary Pollack (1992)
Investment objective and policies: High current income exempt from federal income tax consistent with moderate risk of capital. Invests in investment-grade municipal securities with a weighted average maturity of 3 to 8 years.
Year organized: 1992
Ticker symbol: BTTFX
Discount broker availability: *Schwab (only through financial advisers)
Minimum purchase through discount broker: $2,500; IRA: $1,000

BT INVESTMENT FUNDS - INTERNATIONAL EQUITY FUND
(See first BT Investment listing for data common to all BT Investment funds)

Portfolio manager: Francis J.K. Ledwidge (1992)
Investment objective and policies: Long-term capital appreciation. Invests in equity securities of issuers from at least 3 countries other than the U.S.

May invest in both developed and underdeveloped countries.
Year organized: 1992
Ticker symbol: BTEQX
Discount broker availability: *Schwab (only through financial advisers)
Minimum purchase through discount broker: $2,500; IRA: $1,000

BT INVESTMENT FUNDS - LATIN AMERICAN EQUITY FUND
(See first BT Investment listing for data common to all BT Investment funds)

Portfolio manager: Maria Carrion (1993)
Investment objective and policies: Long-term capital appreciation. Invests in equity securities of issuers from at least 3 countries domiciled in, or doing business in, Latin America - Mexico and all countries in Central America and South America.
Year organized: 1993
Ticker symbol: BTLAX
Discount broker availability: *Schwab (only through financial advisers)
Minimum purchase through discount broker: $2,500; IRA: $1,000

BT INVESTMENT FUNDS - LIFECYCLE LONG RANGE FUND
(See first BT Investment listing for data common to all BT Investment funds)

Portfolio manager: Steven Lauer (1993)
Investment objective and policies: High total return with reduced risk over the long term. Allocates assets among stocks (40-70% of assets), bonds (25-55%) and money market instruments (0-25%). Neutral balance is 55% stocks, 35% bonds and 10% money market instruments.
Year organized: 1993
Discount broker availability: *Schwab
Minimum purchase through discount broker: $1,000

BT INVESTMENT FUNDS - LIFECYCLE MID RANGE FUND
(See first BT Investment listing for data common to all BT Investment funds)

Portfolio manager: Steven Lauer (1993)
Investment objective and policies: High total return with reduced risk over the long term. Allocates assets among stocks (20-50% of assets), bonds (30-60%) and money market instruments (0-50%). Neutral balance is 35% stocks, 45% bonds and 20% money market instruments.
Year organized: 1993
Ticker symbol: BTLRX
Discount broker availability: *Schwab
Minimum purchase through discount broker: $1,000

BT INVESTMENT FUNDS - LIFECYCLE SHORT RANGE FUND
(See first BT Investment listing for data common to all BT Investment funds)

Portfolio manager: Steven Lauer (1993)
Investment objective and policies: High total return with reduced risk over the long term. Allocates assets among stocks (0-30% of assets), bonds (35-70%) and money market instruments (0-65%). Neutral balance is 15% stocks, 55% bonds and 30% money market instruments.
Year organized: 1993
Discount broker availability: *Schwab
Minimum purchase through discount broker: $1,000

BT INVESTMENT FUNDS - LIMITED TERM U.S. GOVERNMENT SECURITIES FUND
(See first BT Investment listing for data common to all BT Investment funds)

Portfolio manager: Robert M. Goodchild (1992)
Investment objective and policies: High current income consistent with preservation of capital. Invests exclusively in U.S. Government securities or repurchase agreements secured by U.S. Government securities with a weighted average maturity of 7 years or less.
Year organized: 1992
Discount broker availability: *Schwab
Minimum purchase through discount broker: $1,000

BT INVESTMENT FUNDS - PACIFIC BASIN EQUITY FUND
(See first BT Investment listing for data common to all BT Investment funds)

Portfolio manager: Paul Durham (1993)
Investment objective and policies: Long-term capital appreciation. Invests in equity securities of issuers from at least 3 countries domiciled in, or doing business in, the Pacific Basin - Hong Kong, India, Indonesia, Japan, Malaysia, New Zealand, the Philippines, China, Singapore, South Korea, Thailand, and Taiwan.
Year organized: 1993
Ticker symbol: BTBEX
Discount broker availability: *Schwab (only through financial advisers)
Minimum purchase through discount broker: $2,500; IRA: $1,000

BT INVESTMENT FUNDS - SMALL CAP FUND
(See first BT Investment listing for data common to all BT Investment funds)

Portfolio manager: Mary Lisanti (1993)
Investment objective and policies: Long-term capital appreciation with current income secondary. Invests primarily in equity securities of issuers with capitalizations under $750M. Up to 25% of assets may be in securities of foreign issuers.
Year organized: 1993
Ticker symbol: BTSCX
Discount broker availability: *Schwab (only through financial advisers)
Minimum purchase through discount broker: $2,500; IRA: $1,000

BT INVESTMENT FUNDS - UTILITY FUND
(See first BT Investment listing for data common to all BT Investment funds)

Portfolio manager: Murray Stahl (1992)
Investment objective and policies: High current income. Invests primarily in equity securities of private utility companies providing electricity, natural gas, water, sanitary services, telephone and telegraph and other public communications services.
Year organized: 1992
Ticker symbol: BTIUX
Discount broker availability: *Schwab (only through financial advisers)
Minimum purchase through discount broker: $2,500; IRA: $1,000

THE BURNHAM FUND, INC.
1325 Avenue of the Americas, 17th Floor
New York, NY 10019
212-262-3100, 800-874-3863

Adviser: Burnham Asset Management Corp.
Portfolio manager: I.W. Burnham, II (1994)
Investment objective and policies: Capital appreciation with income secondary. Invests primarily in common stock, securities convertible into common stock and options. Up to 15% of assets may be in foreign securities.

Year organized: 1961
Ticker symbol: BURHX
Sales charge: 3% (available at NAV through discount brokers)
Discount broker availability: *White (only through financial advisers)
Minimum purchase through discount broker: $2,500

CALVERT FUNDS
4550 Montgomery Avenue - Suite 1000N
Bethesda, MD 20814
301-951-4800, 800-368-2748
800-368-2745, TDD 800-541-1524

Adviser: Calvert Asset Management Company, Inc.
Discount broker availability: *Schwab (only through financial advisers), *White (only through financial advisers), Waterhouse (only Social Investment funds, only through financial advisers)
Minimum purchase through discount broker: Schwab: $1,000; White: $2,000 ($1,000 for Social Investment funds)

CALVERT ARIEL APPRECIATION FUND
(See Ariel Appreciation Fund in main directory)

CALVERT ARIZONA MUNICIPAL INTERMEDIATE FUND
(See first Calvert listing for data common to all Calvert funds)

Portfolio manager: Reno J. Martini (1993)
Investment objective and policies: High current income exempt from federal and Arizona personal income taxes consistent with preservation of capital. Invests primarily in Arizona municipal securities with a weighted average maturity of 3 to 10 years.
Year organized: 1993
Sales charge: 2.75% (available at NAV through discount brokers)

CALVERT CALIFORNIA MUNICIPAL INTERMEDIATE FUND
(See first Calvert listing for data common to all Calvert funds)

Portfolio manager: Reno J. Martini (1993)
Investment objective and policies: High current income exempt from federal and California personal income taxes consistent with preservation of capital. Invests primarily in California municipal securities with a weighted average maturity of 3 to 10 years.
Year organized: 1993
Ticker symbol: CCIMX
Sales charge: 2.75% (available at NAV through discount brokers)

CALVERT FLORIDA MUNICIPAL INTERMEDIATE FUND
(See first Calvert listing for data common to all Calvert funds)

Portfolio manager: Reno J. Martini (1993)
Investment objective and policies: High current income exempt from federal income and Florida Intangible Personal Property taxes consistent with preservation of capital. Invests primarily in Florida municipal securities with a weighted average maturity of 3 to 10 years.
Year organized: 1993
Sales charge: 2.75% (available at NAV through discount brokers)

CALVERT INCOME FUND
(See first Calvert listing for data common to all Calvert funds)

Portfolio managers: Robert C. Gilkison (1982), James H. Patterson (1982)
Investment objective and policies: High income consistent with preservation of capital. Invests primarily in investment-grade bonds and other debt securities with a weighted average maturity of 5 to 20 years.
Year organized: 1982
Ticker symbol: CFICX
Sales charge: 3.75% (available at NAV through discount brokers)

CALVERT MARYLAND MUNICIPAL INTERMEDIATE FUND
(See first Calvert listing for data common to all Calvert funds)

Portfolio manager: Reno J. Martini (1993)
Investment objective and policies: High current income exempt from federal and Maryland personal income taxes consistent with preservation of capital. Invests primarily in Maryland municipal securities with a weighted average maturity of 3 to 10 years.
Year organized: 1993
Sales charge: 2.75% (available at NAV through discount brokers)

CALVERT MICHIGAN MUNICIPAL INTERMEDIATE FUND
(See first Calvert listing for data common to all Calvert funds)

Portfolio manager: Reno J. Martini (1993)
Investment objective and policies: High current income exempt from federal and Michigan personal income taxes consistent with preservation of capital. Invests primarily in Michigan municipal securities with a weighted average maturity of 3 to 10 years.
Year organized: 1993
Sales charge: 2.75% (available at NAV through discount brokers)

CALVERT NATIONAL MUNICIPAL INTERMEDIATE FUND
(See first Calvert listing for data common to all Calvert funds)

Portfolio manager: Reno J. Martini (1992)
Investment objective and policies: High current income exempt from federal income taxes consistent with preservation of capital. Invests primarily in investment-grade municipal securities with a weighted average maturity of 3 to 10 years.
Year organized: 1992
Ticker symbol: CINMX
Sales charge: 2.75% (available at NAV through discount brokers)

CALVERT NEW YORK MUNICIPAL INTERMEDIATE FUND
(See first Calvert listing for data common to all Calvert funds)

Portfolio manager: Reno J. Martini (1993)
Investment objective and policies: High current income exempt from federal and New York state and city personal income taxes consistent with preservation of capital. Invests primarily in New York municipal securities with a weighted average maturity of 3 to 10 years.
Year organized: 1993
Sales charge: 2.75% (available at NAV through discount brokers)

CALVERT PENNSYLVANIA MUNICIPAL INTERMEDIATE FUND
(See first Calvert listing for data common to all Calvert funds)

Portfolio manager: Reno J. Martini (1993)
Investment objective and policies: High current income exempt from federal and Pennsylvania personal income taxes consistent with preservation of capital. Invests primarily in Pennsylvania municipal securities with a weighted average maturity of 3 to 10 years.

Year organized: 1993
Sales charge: 2.75% (available at NAV through discount brokers)

CALVERT SOCIAL INVESTMENT FUND - BOND PORTFOLIO
(See first Calvert listing for data common to all Calvert funds)

Sub-adviser: U.S. Trust Company, Boston
Portfolio manager: Lawrence Litvak (1987)
Investment objective and policies: High current income. Invests in investment-grade bonds and other straight debt securities, with a weighted average maturity of 5 to 20 years, that satisfy the investment and social concern criteria established by the fund.
Year organized: 1987
Ticker symbol: CSIBX
Sales charge: 3.75% (available at NAV through discount brokers)

CALVERT SOCIAL INVESTMENT FUND - EQUITY PORTFOLIO
(See first Calvert listing for data common to all Calvert funds)

Sub-adviser: Loomis Sayles & Company, L.P.
Portfolio manager: Philip J. Schettewi (1994)
Investment objective and policies: Capital growth. Invests in common and preferred stocks, and securities convertible into common stocks which offer income and capital growth and satisfy the investment and social concern criteria established by the fund.
Year organized: 1987
Ticker symbol: CSIEX
Sales charge: 4.75% (available at NAV through discount brokers)

CALVERT SOCIAL INVESTMENT FUND - MANAGED GROWTH PORTFOLIO
(See first Calvert listing for data common to all Calvert funds)

Portfolio manager: Domenic Colasacco (1984)
Investment objective and policies: Total return. Invests in common and preferred stocks, bonds and money market instruments which offer income and capital growth and satisfy the investment and social concern criteria established by the fund.
Year organized: 1983
Ticker symbol: CSIFX
Sales charge: 4.75% (available at NAV through discount brokers)

CALVERT STRATEGIC GROWTH FUND
(See first Calvert listing for data common to all Calvert funds)

Sub-adviser: Portfolio Advisory Services, Inc.
Portfolio manager: Cedd Moses (1994)
Investment objective and policies: Long-term capital growth. Invests in equity securities of companies with low debt and high relative strength and substantial management ownership. May invest in securities of foreign issuers.
Year organized: 1994
Ticker symbol: CSGFX
Sales charge: 4.75% (available at NAV through discount brokers)

CALVERT TAX-FREE RESERVES LIMITED-TERM PORTFOLIO
(See first Calvert listing for data common to all Calvert funds)

Portfolio manager: Reno J. Martini (1991)
Investment objective and policies: High current income exempt from federal income taxes consistent with preservation of capital. Invests in municipal obligations with remaining maturities of 3 years or less.

Year organized: 1983
Ticker symbol: CTFLX
Sales charge: 2.00% (available at NAV through discount brokers)

CALVERT TAX-FREE RESERVES LONG-TERM PORTFOLIO
(See first Calvert listing for data common to all Calvert funds)

Portfolio manager: Reno J. Martini (1983)
Investment objective and policies: High current income exempt from federal income taxes consistent with preservation of capital. Invests in municipal obligations with a weighted average maturity of 20 years or longer.
Year organized: 1983
Ticker symbol: CTTLX
Sales charge: 3.75% (available at NAV through discount brokers)

CALVERT TAX-FREE RESERVES VERMONT MUNICIPAL PORTFOLIO
(See first Calvert listing for data common to all Calvert funds)

Portfolio managers: David R. Rochat (1993), Reno J. Martini (1993)
Investment objective and policies: High current income exempt from federal and Vermont state income taxes consistent with preservation of capital. Invests in Vermont municipal obligations generally with a weighted average maturity of 4 to 9 years.
Year organized: 1993
Ticker symbol: CGVTX
Sales charge: 3.75% (available at NAV through discount brokers)

CALVERT U.S. GOVERNMENT FUND
(See first Calvert listing for data common to all Calvert funds)

Portfolio managers: Colleen M. Trosko (1986), Stephen N. Van Order (1993)
Investment objective and policies: High current income exempt consistent with safety of principal. Invests primarily in U.S. Government-backed obligations with a substantial portion in GNMA certificates.
Year organized: 1986
Ticker symbol: CGUSX
Sales charge: 3.75% (available at NAV through discount brokers)

CALVERT VIRGINIA MUNICIPAL INTERMEDIATE FUND
(See first Calvert listing for data common to all Calvert funds)

Portfolio manager: Reno J. Martini (1993)
Investment objective and policies: High current income exempt from federal and Virginia personal income taxes consistent with preservation of capital. Invests primarily in Virginia municipal securities with a weighted average maturity of 3 to 10 years.
Year organized: 1993
Sales charge: 2.75% (available at NAV through discount brokers)

CALVERT WORLD VALUES GLOBAL EQUITY FUND
(See first Calvert listing for data common to all Calvert funds)

Sub-adviser: Murray Johnstone International, Ltd.
Portfolio manager: Andrew Preston (1992)
Investment objective and policies: High total return with reasonable risk. Invests in a globally diversified portfolio of equity securities. Focuses on companies with strong interests in the environment, human rights and health care.
Year organized: 1992

Ticker symbol: CWVGX
Sales charge: 4.75% (available at NAV through discount brokers)

THE COWEN INCOME + GROWTH FUND
Financial Square
New York, NY 10005
212-495-6000, 800-262-7116

Adviser: Cowen Asset Management, Inc.
Portfolio manager: William Rechter (1986)
Investment objective and policies: High current income with capital growth secondary. Invests primarily in dividend-paying common stocks with the potential to increase their dividend rates.
Year organized: 1986
Ticker symbol: COIGX
Sales charge: 4.75% (available at NAV through discount brokers)
Discount broker availability: Schwab (only through financial advisers)
Minimum purchase through discount broker: $1,000

THE COWEN OPPORTUNITY FUND
Financial Square
New York, NY 10005
212-495-6000, 800-262-7116

Adviser: Cowen Asset Management, Inc.
Portfolio managers: William Church (1988), Jarrod Cohen (1993)
Investment objective and policies: Capital growth. Invests primarily in common stocks of companies with market capitalization under $1B with above average growth prospects.
Year organized: 1988
Ticker symbol: CWNOX
Sales charge: 4.75% (available at NAV through discount brokers)
Discount broker availability: Schwab (only through financial advisers)
Minimum purchase through discount broker: $1,000

DELAWARE FUNDS
1818 Market Street
Philadelphia, PA 19103
215-988-1333, 800-523-4640
800-523-1918

Adviser: Delaware Management Company, Inc.
Discount broker availability: *Schwab (only through financial advisers)

DELAWARE FUNDS - DECATUR INCOME FUND
(See first Delaware listing for data common to all Delaware funds)

Portfolio manager: John B. Fields (1993)
Investment objective and policies: High current income with capital growth secondary. Invests primarily in dividend-paying common stocks of both domestic and foreign issuers.
Year organized: 1957 (formerly Decatur Fund - Series I)
Ticker symbol: DELDX
Sales charge: 5.75% (available at NAV through discount brokers)
Minimum purchase through discount broker: $1,000, IRA: $500

DELAWARE FUNDS - DECATUR TOTAL RETURN FUND
(See first Delaware listing for data common to all Delaware funds)

Portfolio manager: John B. Fields (1992)
Investment objective and policies: High total return - current income and capital growth. Invests pri-

marily in common stocks and income-producing securities convertible into common stocks of both domestic and foreign issuers.
Year organized: 1986 (formerly Decatur Fund - Series II)
Ticker symbol: DEDTX
Sales charge: 5.75% (available at NAV through discount brokers)
Minimum purchase through discount broker: $1,000, IRA: $500

DELAWARE FUNDS - DELCAP CONCEPT I SERIES
(See first Delaware listing for data common to all Delaware funds)

Portfolio manager: Edward N. Antoian (1986)
Investment objective and policies: Long-term capital growth. Invests primarily in common stocks and securities convertible into common stocks of companies with above-average growth potential. Up to 25% of assets may be in securities of foreign issuers.
Year organized: 1986
Ticker symbol: DFCIX
Sales charge: 5.75% (available at NAV through discount brokers)
Minimum purchase through discount broker: $1,000, IRA: $500

DELAWARE FUNDS - DELCHESTER HIGH YIELD BOND FUND
(See first Delaware listing for data common to all Delaware funds)

Portfolio managers: Gerald T. Nichols (1993), Paul A. Matlack (1990), James R. Raith, Jr. (1994)
Investment objective and policies: High current income. Invests primarily in corporate bonds and government securities. May invest 100% of assets in junk bonds.
Year organized: 1970
Ticker symbol: DETIX
Sales charge: 4.75% (available at NAV through discount brokers)
Minimum purchase through discount broker: $1,000

DELAWARE FUNDS - INTERNATIONAL EQUITY FUND
(See first Delaware listing for data common to all Delaware funds)

Portfolio managers: David G. Tilles (1991), Clive A. Gilmore (1991)
Investment objective and policies: Long-term capital growth. Invests primarily in equity securities of at least 3 countries outside the U.S. denominated in the U.S. dollar or other currencies.
Year organized: 1991
Ticker symbol: DEGIX
Sales charge: 5.75% (available at NAV through discount brokers)
Minimum purchase through discount broker: $1,000

DELAWARE FUNDS - TREND FUND
(See first Delaware listing for data common to all Delaware funds)

Portfolio manager: Edward N. Antoian (1984)
Investment objective and policies: Long-term capital growth. Invests primarily in common stocks and securities convertible into common stocks of emerging and other growth-oriented companies likely to benefit from trends in the economy, the political arena and society in general.
Year organized: 1968
Ticker symbol: DELTX
Sales charge: 5.75% (available at NAV through discount brokers)
Minimum purchase through discount broker: $1,000

DELAWARE FUNDS - VALUE FUND INSTITUTIONAL SHARES
(See first Delaware listing for data common to all Delaware funds)

Portfolio manager: Edward A. Trumpbour (1987)
Investment objective and policies: Capital growth. Invests primarily in common stocks and securities convertible into common stocks undervalued in relation to their asset value or long-term earning power.
Year organized: 1987
Ticker symbol: DEVLX
Sales charge: 5.75% (available at NAV through discount brokers)
Minimum purchase through discount broker: $1,000

DFA INVESTMENT DIMENSIONS GROUP PORTFOLIOS ◆
1299 Ocean Avenue - 11th Floor
Santa Monica, CA 90401
310-395-8005, 800-342-6684

Adviser: Dimensional Fund Advisers, Inc.
Special sales restrictions: Designed for institutional investors only, but individuals may invest through fee-only financial advisers at discount brokerage firms.
Discount broker availability: Schwab (only through financial advisers), White (only through financial advisers)
Minimum purchase through discount broker: Schwab: $1,000; White: $2,500

DFA CONTINENTAL SMALL COMPANY PORTFOLIO ◆
(See first DFA listing for data common to all DFA portfolios)

Portfolio manager: Rex Sinquefield (1988)
Investment objective and policies: Capital appreciation. Invests in stocks of companies with market capitalization under $500M organized and traded on the European continent.
Year organized: 1988
Ticker symbol: DFCSX
Sales charge: 1.5% payable to the fund

DFA EMERGING MARKETS PORTFOLIO ◆
(See first DFA listing for data common to all DFA portfolios)

Portfolio manager: Rex Sinquefield (1994)
Investment objective and policies: Capital appreciation. Invests in equity securities of larger companies domiciled in, or primarily doing business in, emerging markets.
Year organized: 1994
Sales charge: 1.5% payable to the fund

DFA FIVE YEAR GOVERNMENT PORTFOLIO ◆
(See first DFA listing for data common to all DFA portfolios)

Portfolio manager: Ramakrishnan Chandrasekar (1987)
Investment objective and policies: Maximum total return - income and capital gains. Invests in U.S. Government and U.S. Government agency debt obligations which mature within 5 years from the settlement date.
Year organized: 1987
Ticker symbol: DFFGX

DFA GLOBAL FIXED INCOME PORTFOLIO ◆
(See first DFA listing for data common to all DFA portfolios)

Portfolio manager: Ramakrishnan Chandrasekar (1990)
Investment objective and policies: Market rate of return with low relative volatility. Invests in fixed-income obligations issued or guaranteed by the U.S. and foreign governments and/or agencies.
Year organized: 1990 (name changed from Global Bond Portfolio on 3/17/92)
Ticker symbol: DFGBX

DFA INTERMEDIATE GOVERNMENT FIXED INCOME PORTFOLIO ◆
(See first DFA listing for data common to all DFA portfolios)

Portfolio manager: Ramakrishnan Chandrasekar (1990)
Investment objective and policies: Current income consistent with preservation of capital. Invests in U.S. Government obligations, foreign government obligations and futures contracts on U.S. Treasuries with a weighted average maturity of 7 to 10 years.
Year organized: 1990 (name changed from Intermediate Government Bond Portfolio on 3/17/92)
Ticker symbol: DFIGX

DFA INTERNATIONAL HIGH BOOK TO MARKET PORTFOLIO ◆
(See first DFA listing for data common to all DFA portfolios)

Portfolio manager: Rex Sinquefield (1993)
Investment objective and policies: Long-term capital appreciation. Invests in stocks of large non-US companies with high book values in relation to their market values. Portfolio is market capitalization weighted.
Year organized: 1993
Ticker symbol: DFHBX

DFA INTERNATIONAL SMALL CAP VALUE PORTFOLIO ◆
(See first DFA listing for data common to all DFA portfolios)

Portfolio manager: Rex Sinquefield (1994)
Investment objective and policies: Long-term capital appreciation. Invests in stocks of small non-US companies with high book values in relation to their market values. Portfolio is market capitalization weighted.
Year organized: 1994
Ticker symbol: DFIVX

DFA JAPANESE SMALL COMPANY PORTFOLIO ◆
(See first DFA listing for data common to all DFA portfolios)

Portfolio manager: Rex Sinquefield (1986)
Investment objective and policies: Capital appreciation. Invests in stocks of small Japanese companies, with market capitalizations not greater than the bottom half of the First Section of the Tokyo Stock Exchange.
Year organized: 1986
Ticker symbol: DFJSX
Sales charge: 1.0% payable to the fund

DFA LARGE CAP INTERNATIONAL PORTFOLIO ◆

(See first DFA listing for data common to all DFA portfolios)

Portfolio manager: Rex Sinquefield (1991)
Investment objective and policies: Long-term capital appreciation. Invests in stocks of large companies in at least three different countries in Europe, Australia and the Far East. Portfolio is market capitalization weighted.
Year organized: 1991
Ticker symbol: DFALX

DFA ONE-YEAR FIXED INCOME PORTFOLIO ◆

(See first DFA listing for data common to all DFA portfolios)

Portfolio manager: Ramakrishnan Chandrasekar (1983)
Investment objective and policies: Return in excess of the rate of inflation with minimum risk. Invests in high quality U.S. Government and bank obligations and commercial paper with a weighted average maturity of 1 year or less.
Year organized: 1983 (formerly Inflation Hedge Portfolio A)
Ticker symbol: DFIHX

DFA PACIFIC RIM SMALL COMPANY PORTFOLIO ◆

(See first DFA listing for data common to all DFA portfolios)

Portfolio manager: Rex Sinquefield (1992)
Investment objective and policies: Capital appreciation. Invests in stocks of small companies located in Australia, New Zealand, Singapore, Hong Kong and Malaysia.
Year organized: 1992 name changed from Asia/Australia Portfolio in 1994)
Ticker symbol: DFRSX
Sales charge: 1.5% payable to the fund

DFA/AEW REAL ESTATE SECURITIES PORTFOLIO ◆

(See first DFA listing for data common to all DFA portfolios)

Investment objective and policies: Long-term capital appreciation. Invests primarily in readily marketable securities of companies whose principal activities include development, ownership, construction, management, or sale of residential, commercial or industrial real estate.
Year organized: 1992
Ticker symbol: DFREX

DFA U.S. LARGE CAP VALUE PORTFOLIO ◆

(See first DFA listing for data common to all DFA portfolios)

Investment objective and policies: Long-term capital appreciation. Invests in common stocks of large U.S. companies with shares that have high book values in relation to their market values.
Year organized: 1992 (name changed from U.S. Large Cap High Book to Market in 1993)
Ticker symbol: DFLVX

DFA U.S. LARGE COMPANY PORTFOLIO ◆

(See first DFA listing for data common to all DFA portfolios)

Portfolio manager: Rex Sinquefield (1990)
Investment objective and policies: To approximate the investment performance of the S&P 500 Index. Invests in all the stocks in the S&P 500 Index in approximately the same proportions as they are represented in the index.
Year organized: 1990
Ticker symbol: DFLCX

DFA U.S. 6-10 SMALL COMPANY PORTFOLIO ◆

(See first DFA listing for data common to all DFA portfolios)

Portfolio manager: Rex Sinquefield (1992)
Investment objective and policies: Long-term capital appreciation. Invests in readily marketable common stocks, as a quasi-index, of small companies making up the smallest 50% of NYSE companies.
Year organized: 1992
Ticker symbol: DFSTX

DFA U.S. 9-10 SMALL COMPANY PORTFOLIO ◆

(See first DFA listing for data common to all DFA portfolios)

Portfolio manager: Rex Sinquefield (1981)
Investment objective and policies: Long-term capital appreciation. Invests in readily marketable common stocks, as a quasi-index, of small companies making up the smallest 20% of NYSE companies.
Year organized: 1981 (formerly the Small Company Portfolio)
Ticker symbol: DFSCX

DFA U.S. SMALL CAP VALUE PORTFOLIO ◆

(See first DFA listing for data common to all DFA portfolios)

Investment objective and policies: Long-term capital appreciation. Invests in common stocks of small U.S. companies with shares that have a high book value in relation to their market value.
Year organized: 1992 (name changed from U.S. Small Cap High Book to Market Portfolio in 1993)
Ticker symbol: DFSVX

DFA UNITED KINGDOM SMALL COMPANY PORTFOLIO ◆

(See first DFA listing for data common to all DFA portfolios)

Portfolio manager: Rex Sinquefield (1986)
Investment objective and policies: Capital appreciation. Invests in readily marketable stocks of small United Kingdom companies traded on the International Stock Exchange of the U.K. and Ireland
Year organized: 1986
Ticker symbol: DFUKX
Sales charge: 1.5% payable to the fund

ENTERPRISE PORTFOLIOS
3343 Peachtree Road, Suite 450
Atlanta, GA 30326
404-396-8118, 800-432-4320
800-368-3527

Adviser: Enterprise Capital Management, Inc.
Sales charge: 4.75% (available at NAV through discount brokers)
Discount broker availability: Schwab (only through financial advisers), *White (only through financial advisers)
Minimum purchase through discount broker: Schwab: $1,000; White: $2,500

ENTERPRISE CAPITAL APPRECIATION PORTFOLIO

(See first Enterprise listing for data common to all Enterprise portfolio)

Sub-adviser: Provident Investment Counsel, Inc.
Portfolio manager: Jeffrey J. Miller (1987)
Investment objective and policies: Long-term capital appreciation. Invests in common stocks of small and large capitalization companies with accelerating earnings momentum and consistently strong financial characteristics.
Year organized: 1987
Ticker symbol: ENCAX

ENTERPRISE GOVERNMENT SECURITIES PORTFOLIO

(See first Enterprise listing for data common to all Enterprise portfolios)

Sub-adviser: TCW Funds Management, Inc.
Portfolio managers: Philip A. Barach (1992), Jeffrey E. Gundlach (1992)
Investment objective and policies: Current income consistent with safety of principal. Invests in obligations of the U.S. Government, its agencies or instrumentalities.
Year organized: 1987
Ticker symbol: ENGVX

ENTERPRISE GROWTH PORTFOLIO

(See first Enterprise listing for data common to all Enterprise portfolios)

Sub-adviser: Montag & Caldwell, Inc.
Portfolio manager: Ronald E. Canakaris (1980)
Investment objective and policies: Capital appreciation. Invests in stocks of companies having growth characteristics and others with potential for capital appreciation due to special developments or temporary price depression.
Year organized: 1967 (as the Alpha Fund. Name changed on 11/17/87)
Ticker symbol: ENGRX

ENTERPRISE GROWTH AND INCOME PORTFOLIO

(See first Enterprise listing for data common to all Enterprise portfolios)

Sub-advisers: 1740 Advisers, Inc., Carl Domino Associates, L.P.
Portfolio manager: John V. Rock (1987)
Investment objective and policies: Above-average total return. Invests in dividend-paying common stocks of companies with above-average yields and relatively low price-to-earnings ratios or price to book value ratios.
Year organized: 1987
Ticker symbol: ENGIX

ENTERPRISE HIGH-YIELD BOND PORTFOLIO

(See first Enterprise listing for data common to all Enterprise portfolios)

Sub-adviser: Caywood-Scholl Capital Management
Portfolio manager: James Caywood (1987)
Investment objective and policies: Maximum current income. Invests primarily in high-yielding, income-producing corporate bonds rated Ba or lower by Moody's or BB or lower by S&P.
Year organized: 1987
Ticker symbol: ENHYX

ENTERPRISE INTERNATIONAL GROWTH PORTFOLIO

(See first Enterprise listing for data common to all Enterprise portfolios)

Sub-adviser: Brinson Partners, Inc.
Investment objective and policies: Capital appreciation. Invests in equity securities of companies domiciled outside the U.S. Normally invests in companies based in a minimum of 8 to 12 countries in Europe and the Far East.
Year organized: 1987
Ticker symbol: ENIGX

ENTERPRISE SMALL COMPANY PORTFOLIO

(See first Enterprise listing for data common to all Enterprise portfolios)

Sub-adviser: Fisher Investments, Inc.
Portfolio manager: Kenneth L. Fisher (1993)
Investment objective and policies: Maximum capital appreciation. Invests in equity securities of com-

panies with market capitalizations of less than $1B whose value may not be reflected by current stock price.
Year organized: 1993
Ticker symbol: ENSPX

ENTERPRISE TAX-EXEMPT INCOME PORTFOLIO
(See first Enterprise listing for data common to all Enterprise portfolios)

Sub-adviser: Morgan Stanley Asset Management, Inc.
Portfolio manager: Gerald P. Barth (1992)
Investment objective and policies: High current income exempt from federal income tax. Invests in investment-grade municipal securities with weighted average maturity of 10 to 25 years.
Year organized: 1987
Ticker symbol: ETTEX

FEDERATED FUNDS ◆
Federated Investors Tower
Pittsburgh, PA 15222-3779
412-288-1900, 800-245-0242
fax 412-288-1982

Adviser: Federated Management
Special sales restrictions: Designed for institutional investors only, but individuals may invest at discount brokerage firms through financial advisers.
Minimum purchase through discount broker: Schwab: $1,000; White: $2,500

FEDERATED - FORTRESS ADJUSTABLE RATE U.S. GOVERNMENT FUND
(See first Federated listing for data common to all Federated funds)

Portfolio manager: Gary Madich (1991)
Investment objective and policies: Current income consistent with lower volatility of principal. Invests in adjustable and floating rate mortgage securities issued or guaranteed by the U.S. Government, its agencies or instrumentalities.
Year organized: 1991
Ticker symbol: FADJX
Sales charge: 1.00% (available at NAV through discount brokers)
Discount broker availability: *Schwab, *White
Minimum purchase through discount broker: Schwab: $1,500; White: $2,500

FEDERATED - FORTRESS BOND FUND
(See first Federated listing for data common to all Federated funds)

Portfolio manager: Joseph M. Balestrino (1993)
Investment objective and policies: High current income consistent with preservation of capital. Invests primarily in investment-grade corporate and government fixed-income securities.
Year organized: 1992
Ticker symbol: ISHIX
Sales charge: 1.00% (available at NAV through discount brokers)
Discount broker availability: *White

FEDERATED - FORTRESS CALIFORNIA MUNICIPAL INCOME FUND
(See first Federated listing for data common to all Federated funds)

Portfolio manager: James D. Roberge (1993)
Investment objective and policies: Current income exempt from federal and California state income taxes. Invests in California municipal securities.
Year organized: 1992
Sales charge: 1.00% (available at NAV through discount brokers)
Discount broker availability: *Schwab, *White

FEDERATED - FORTRESS GOVERNMENT INCOME SECURITIES FUND
(See first Federated listing for data common to all Federated funds)

Portfolio managers: Gary J. Madich (1987)
Investment objective and policies: High current income consistent with preservation of capital. Invests primarily in securities guaranteed as to payment of principal and interest by the U.S. Government, its agencies or its instrumentalities.
Year organized: 1981
Ticker symbol: FGOIX
Sales charge: 1.00% (available at NAV through discount brokers)
Discount broker availability: *White

FEDERATED - FORTRESS MUNICIPAL INCOME FUND
(See first Federated listing for data common to all Federated funds)

Portfolio managers: Jonathan C. Conley (1987)
Investment objective and policies: Current income exempt from federal income taxes. Invests primarily in investment-grade municipal securities. Up to 35% of assets may be in municipal junk bonds.
Year organized: 1987
Ticker symbol: FHTFX
Sales charge: 1.00% (available at NAV through discount brokers)
Discount broker availability: *White

FEDERATED - FORTRESS NEW YORK MUNICIPAL INCOME FUND
(See first Federated listing for data common to all Federated funds)

Portfolio manager: James D. Roberge (1992)
Investment objective and policies: Current income exempt from federal and New York state and municipality income taxes. Invests in New York municipal securities.
Year organized: 1992
Sales charge: 1.00% (available at NAV through discount brokers)
Discount broker availability: *Schwab, *White

FEDERATED - FORTRESS OHIO MUNICIPAL INCOME FUND
(See first Federated listing for data common to all Federated funds)

Portfolio manager: James D. Roberge (1992)
Investment objective and policies: Current income exempt from federal and Ohio state income taxes. Invests in Ohio municipal securities.
Year organized: 1990
Ticker symbol: OMIFX
Sales charge: 1.00% (available at NAV through discount brokers)
Discount broker availability: *White

FEDERATED - FORTRESS UTILITY FUND
(See first Federated listing for data common to all Federated funds)

Portfolio manager: Christopher H. Wiles (1990)
Investment objective and policies: High current income and moderate capital appreciation. Invests in equity and debt securities of utility companies.
Year organized: 1987
Ticker symbol: FEUTX
Sales charge: 1.00% (available at NAV through discount brokers)
Discount broker availability: *Schwab, *White

FEDERATED - LIBERTY AMERICAN LEADERS FUND
(See first Federated listing for data common to all Federated funds)

Portfolio managers: Peter R. Anderson (1991), Michael P. Donnelly (1993)
Investment objective and policies: Growth of capi-

tal and income. Invests primarily in common stocks chosen from the 100 companies contained in "The Leaders List" of blue-chip companies selected by the adviser on the basis of fundamental analysis.
Year organized: 1968
Ticker symbol: FALDX
Sales charge: 5.50% (available at NAV through discount brokers)
Discount broker availability: *White

FEDERATED - LIBERTY CAPITAL GROWTH FUND
(See first Federated listing for data common to all Federated funds)

Portfolio manager: Gregory M. Melvin (1992)
Investment objective and policies: Capital growth. Invests primarily in common stocks of companies with market capitalizations of $100M or more with potential for above-average growth in earnings and dividends or where significant fundamental changes are taking place that will enhance their value.
Year organized: 1992
Ticker symbol: LCGFX
Sales charge: 5.50% (available at NAV through discount brokers)
Discount broker availability: *White

FEDERATED - LIBERTY EQUITY INCOME FUND
(See first Federated listing for data common to all Federated funds)

Portfolio manager: Christopher H. Wiles (1991)
Investment objective and policies: Above-average income and capital appreciation. Invests primarily in common stocks with good value, attractive dividend yield, and dividend growth potential.
Year organized: 1986
Ticker symbol: LEIFX
Sales charge: 5.50% (available at NAV through discount brokers)
Discount broker availability: *Schwab, *White

FEDERATED - LIBERTY FUND FOR U.S. GOVERNMENT SECURITIES
(See first Federated listing for data common to all Federated funds)

Portfolio manager: Gary J. Madich (1987)
Investment objective and policies: High current income consistent with preservation of capital. Invests primarily in long-term U.S. Government securities guaranteed as to payment of principal and interest.
Year organized: 1987
Ticker symbol: FUSGX
Sales charge: 5.50% (available at NAV through discount brokers)
Discount broker availability: *White

FEDERATED - LIBERTY HIGH INCOME BOND FUND
(See first Federated listing for data common to all Federated funds)

Portfolio manager: Mark E. Durbiano (1989)
Investment objective and policies: High current income. Invests primarily in lower-rated corporate debt securities, commonly known as junk bonds.
Year organized: 1977
Ticker symbol: FHIIX
Sales charge: 5.50% (available at NAV through discount brokers)
Discount broker availability: *White

FEDERATED - LIBERTY INTERNATIONAL EQUITY FUND
(See first Federated listing for data common to all Federated funds)

Portfolio manager: Randall S. Bauer (1990)
Investment objective and policies: Long-term capital growth and income. Invests primarily in equity

securities of established non-U.S. issuers in at least 3 developed foreign countries.
Year organized: 1984
Ticker symbol: FTITX
Sales charge: 5.50% (available at NAV through discount brokers)
Discount broker availability: *Schwab, *White

FEDERATED - LIBERTY INTERNATIONAL INCOME FUND
(See first Federated listing for data common to all Federated funds)

Portfolio manager: Randall S. Bauer (1991)
Investment objective and policies: High current income in U.S. Dollars consistent with prudent investment risk and capital appreciation. Invests in high-quality debt securities denominated in the currencies of the nations that are members of the Organization for Economic Cooperation and Development.
Year organized: 1991
Ticker symbol: FTIIX
Sales charge: 5.50% (available at NAV through discount brokers)
Discount broker availability: *Schwab, *White

FEDERATED - LIBERTY MUNICIPAL SECURITIES FUND
(See first Federated listing for data common to all Federated funds)

Portfolio manager: Jonathan C. Conley (1984)
Investment objective and policies: High current income exempt from federal income tax. Invests primarily in investment-grade municipal bonds.
Year organized: 1976
Ticker symbol: LMSFX
Sales charge: 5.50% (available at NAV through discount brokers)
Discount broker availability: *Schwab, *White

FEDERATED - LIBERTY UTILITY FUND
(See first Federated listing for data common to all Federated funds)

Portfolio manager: Christopher H. Wiles (1990)
Investment objective and policies: High current income and long-term growth of income with capital growth secondary. Invests primarily in securities of companies in the utilities industry.
Year organized: 1987
Ticker symbol: LBUTX
Sales charge: 5.50% (available at NAV through discount brokers)
Discount broker availability: *White

FEDERATED MICHIGAN INTERMEDIATE MUNICIPAL TRUST
(See first Federated listing for data common to all Federated funds)

Portfolio manager: J. Scott Albrecht (1994)
Investment objective and policies: High current income exempt from federal and Michigan state and municipal personal income taxes. Invests primarily in investment-grade Michigan municipal bonds.
Year organized: 1991 (name changed from Michigan Municipal Income Fund in 1994)
Ticker symbol: MMIFX
Sales charge: 3.00% (available at NAV through discount brokers)
Discount broker availability: Schwab, *White

FEDERATED PENNSYLVANIA MUNICIPAL INCOME FUND
(See first Federated listing for data common to all Federated funds)

Portfolio manager: James D. Roberge (1993)
Investment objective and policies: High current income exempt from federal and Pennsylvania personal income taxes. Invests primarily in investment-grade Pennsylvanian municipal bonds.
Year organized: 1990
Ticker symbol: PAMFX
Sales charge: 3.00% (available at NAV through discount brokers)
Discount broker availability: Schwab, *White

FPA FUNDS
11400 West Olympic Blvd., Suite 1200
Los Angeles, CA 90064
310-473-0225, 800-982-4372

Adviser: First Pacific Advisors, Inc.
Discount broker availability: White (only through financial advisers)
Minimum purchase through discount broker: $2,500

FPA CAPITAL FUND, INC.
(See first FPA listing for data common to all FPA funds)

Portfolio manager: Robert L. Rodriguez (1984)
Investment objective and policies: Long-term capital growth with income secondary. Invests primarily in stocks of companies with above average growth prospects in areas temporarily out-of-favor.
Year organized: 1968
Ticker symbol: FPPTX
Sales charge: 6.5% (available at NAV through discount brokers)

FPA NEW INCOME, INC.
(See first FPA listing for data common to all FPA funds)

Portfolio manager: Robert L. Rodriguez (1984)
Investment objective and policies: High current income consistent with preservation of capital. Invests in debt obligations guaranteed by the U.S. Government, corporate bonds, convertible bonds and high-yield short-duration bonds.
Year organized: 1969
Ticker symbol: FPNIX
Sales charge: 4.5% (available at NAV through discount brokers)

FPA PERENNIAL FUND, INC.
(See first FPA listing for data common to all FPA funds)

Portfolio manager: Christopher Linden (1984)
Investment objective and policies: Long-term capital growth with income secondary. Invests in growth stocks believed undervalued, preferred stocks, convertible securities and corporate and government debt securities. Fund is designed for retirement plans and other entities exempt from federal taxation.
Year organized: 1984
Ticker symbol: FPPFX
Sales charge: 6.5% (available at NAV through discount brokers)

FRANKLIN/TEMPLETON FUNDS
777 Mariners Island Blvd
P.O. Box 7777
San Mateo, CA 94403-7777
415-312-3200, 800-342-5236

Adviser: Franklin Advisers, Inc.
Sub-adviser: Templeton Investment Counsel, Inc.
Sales charge: 3% (available at NAV through discount brokers)
Discount broker availability: Schwab (only through financial advisers), White (only through financial advisers)
Minimum purchase through discount broker: $2,500; IRA: $1,000

FRANKLIN/TEMPLETON GERMAN GOVERNMENT BOND FUND
(See first Franklin/Templeton listing for data common to all Franklin/Templeton funds)

Investment objective and policies: High current income with potential for capital appreciation. Invests in debt obligations issued or guaranteed by the Federal Republic of Germany, its agencies, instrumentalities and political subdivisions.
Year organized: 1992 (name changed from Huntington German Government Bond Fund in 1993)
Ticker symbol: HGGBX

FRANKLIN/TEMPLETON GLOBAL CURRENCY FUND
(See first Franklin/Templeton listing for data common to all Franklin/Templeton funds)

Investment objective and policies: Maximum total return - interest income and appreciation due to changes in currency exchange rates. Invests in money market instruments denominated in at least 3 major currencies, including the U.S. dollar.
Year organized: 1986 (name changed from Huntington Global Currency Fund in 1993)
Ticker symbol: ICPGX

FRANKLIN/TEMPLETON HARD CURRENCY FUND
(See first Franklin/Templeton listing for data common to all Franklin/Templeton funds)

Investment objective and policies: Protect against depreciation of the U.S. dollar relative to other currencies. Invests in money market instruments denominated in foreign major currencies with low rates of inflation and currency appreciation versus the U.S. dollar over the long term.
Year organized: 1989 (name changed from Huntington Hard Currency Fund in 1993)
Ticker symbol: ICPHX

FRANKLIN/TEMPLETON INCOME CURRENCY FUND
(See first Franklin/Templeton listing for data common to all Franklin/Templeton funds)

Investment objective and policies: High current income at a level significantly higher than U.S. dollar money market funds. Invests in money market instruments denominated in at least 3 high yielding foreign currencies and the U.S. dollar with maximum of 25% of assets in any currency other than the U.S. dollar.
Year organized: 1989 (name changed from Huntington Income Currency Fund in 1993)
Ticker symbol: ICHIX

GAM FUNDS
135 East 57th Street
New York, NY 10022
212-407-4700, 800-426-4685
fax 212-888-4989

Adviser: Gam International Management Limited
Sales charge: 5.0% (available at NAV through discount brokers)
Discount broker availability: *Schwab (only through financial advisers, does not offer GAM North America), White (only through financial advisers)
Minimum purchase through discount broker: Schwab: $1,000; White: $10,000 (among all GAM funds)

GAM EUROPE FUND
(See first GAM listing for data common to all GAM funds)

Portfolio managers: John Bennett (1993), David Houston (1993)
Investment objective and policies: Capital appreciation. Invests primarily in stocks of companies in

Europe including the Eastern European countries of Hungary, Yugoslavia, Poland and Czechoslovakia.
Year organized: 1990
Ticker symbol: GEURX

GAM GLOBAL FUND
(See first GAM listing for data common to all GAM funds)

Portfolio manager: John R. Horseman (1990)
Investment objective and policies: Capital appreciation. Invests in stocks of companies from around the world - primarily in the U.S., Canada, the U.K., Continental Europe and the Pacific Basin.
Year organized: 1986
Ticker symbol: GAGLX

GAM INTERNATIONAL FUND
(See first GAM listing for data common to all GAM funds)

Portfolio manager: John R. Horseman (1990)
Investment objective and policies: Capital appreciation. Invests in stocks of non-U.S. companies - primarily domiciled in Canada, the U.K., Continental Europe and the Pacific Basin.
Year organized: 1985
Ticker symbol: GAMNX

GAM JAPAN CAPITAL FUND
(See first GAM listing for data common to all GAM funds)

Portfolio manager: Paul S. Kirkby (1994)
Investment objective and policies: Capital appreciation. Invests primarily in securities of companies domiciled in Japan, or generating at least 50% of their revenues from operations in Japan.
Year organized: 1994

GAM NORTH AMERICA FUND
(See first GAM listing for data common to all GAM funds)

Co-adviser: Fayez Sarofim & Co.
Portfolio manager: Fayez Sarofim (1990)
Investment objective and policies: Capital appreciation. Invests in blue chip growth stocks of companies in the U.S. and Canada.
Year organized: 1990

GAM PACIFIC BASIN FUND
(See first GAM listing for data common to all GAM funds)

Portfolio manager: Michael S. Bunker (1987)
Investment objective and policies: Capital appreciation. Invests in stocks of companies domiciled in the Pacific Basin - including Japan, Hong Kong, Singapore, Malaysia, Indonesia, the Philippines, Korea, Taiwan, India, Australia and New Zealand.
Year organized: 1987
Ticker symbol: GAPCX

GOVETT FUNDS
P.O. Box 419439
Kansas City, MO 64141
415-393-0350, 800-634-6838
800-821-0803
fax 212-888-4989

Adviser: John Govett & Co., Limited
Sales charge: 4.95% (available at NAV through discount brokers)
Minimum purchase through discount broker: Schwab: $1,000; White: $1,000,000 (among all Govett funds)

GOVETT DEVELOPING MARKETS BOND FUND
(See first Govett listing for data common to all Govett funds)

Portfolio manager: Simon J. Osborne (1994)
Investment objective and policies: High current income and capital growth. Invests primarily in debt securities of issuers located in emerging markets with maximum of 40% of assets in issuers of a single market. Fund is non-diversified.
Year organized: 1994
Ticker symbol: GDMBX
Discount broker availability: *Schwab (only though financial advisers)

GOVETT EMERGING MARKETS FUND
(See first Govett listing for data common to all Govett funds)

Portfolio manager: Rachel Maunder (1992)
Investment objective and policies: Long-term capital growth. Invests primarily in equity securities of companies located in at least 3 different emerging market countries as classified by the World Bank.
Year organized: 1992
Ticker symbol: GIEMX
Discount broker availability: *Schwab (only though financial advisers), White (only though financial advisers)

GOVETT GLOBAL GOVERNMENT INCOME FUND
(See first Govett listing for data common to all Govett funds)

Portfolio manager: Simon J. Osborne (1992)
Investment objective and policies: High current income with capital growth secondary. Invests primarily in debt securities issued or guaranteed by the governments or government agencies of certain foreign countries as well as the U.S.
Year organized: 1992
Ticker symbol: GGGIX
Discount broker availability: *Schwab (only though financial advisers), White (only though financial advisers)

GOVETT INTERNATIONAL EQUITY FUND
(See first Govett listing for data common to all Govett funds)

Portfolio manager: Gareth L. Watts (1992)
Investment objective and policies: Long-term capital growth. Invests primarily in equity securities of companies located in at least 3 different countries other than the U.S. Fund maintains a list of acceptable countries for investment.
Year organized: 1992
Ticker symbol: GIEQX
Discount broker availability: *Schwab (only though financial advisers), White (only though financial advisers)

GOVETT LATIN AMERICA FUND
(See first Govett listing for data common to all Govett funds)

Portfolio manager: Caroline Lane (1994)
Investment objective and policies: Long-term capital growth. Invests primarily in equity and debt securities of companies located in at least 3 different countries in Latin America. Fund maintains a list of acceptable countries for investment.
Year organized: 1994
Discount broker availability: *Schwab (only though financial advisers)

GOVETT PACIFIC STRATEGY FUND
(See first Govett listing for data common to all Govett funds)

Portfolio manager: Peter Robson (1994)
Investment objective and policies: Long-term capital growth. Invests primarily in equity securities of companies located in at least 3 different countries in the Pacific Rim. Fund maintains a list of acceptable countries for investment.
Year organized: 1994
Ticker symbol: GPSQX
Discount broker availability: *Schwab (only though financial advisers)

GOVETT SMALLER COMPANIES FUND
(See first Govett listing for data common to all Govett funds)

Portfolio manager: Garett R. Van Wagoner (1993)
Investment objective and policies: Long-term capital growth. Invests primarily in common stocks of companies with market capitalizations under $1B from around the world. No more than 35% of assets may be from issuers in any one country other than the U.S.
Year organized: 1993
Ticker symbol: GSCQX
Discount broker availability: *Schwab (only though financial advisers), White (only though financial advisers)

THE HANOVER FUNDS
230 Park Avenue
New York, NY 10169
800-821-2371

Adviser: The Portfolio Group, Inc. (except Small Capitalization Growth Fund)
Sales charge: 3.00% for equity funds, 1.25% for Government funds (available at NAV through discount brokers)
Discount broker availability: Schwab (only through financial advisers)
Minimum purchase through discount broker: $1,000

THE HANOVER BLUE CHIP GROWTH FUND
(See first Hanover listing for data common to all Hanover funds)

Portfolio manager: Stephen M. Duff (1993)
Investment objective and policies: Capital appreciation. Invests primarily in equity securities of large well-established companies with substantial capitalizations. Up to 35% of assets may be invested in securities of foreign issuers.
Year organized: 1993
Ticker symbol: HBCGX

THE HANOVER SHORT-TERM U.S. GOVERNMENT FUND
(See first Hanover listing for data common to all Hanover funds)

Portfolio manager: Guy Barba (1993)
Investment objective and policies: High current income consistent with preservation of capital. Invests primarily in securities issued or guaranteed by the U.S. Government, its agencies or instrumentalities with a weighted average maturity of 3 years or less.
Year organized: 1993
Ticker symbol: HSTGX

THE HANOVER SMALL CAPITALIZATION GROWTH FUND
(See first Hanover listing for data common to all Hanover funds)

Adviser: Princeton Bank and Trust Company
Portfolio manager: Francis B. Lane (1993)
Investment objective and policies: Capital appreciation. Invests primarily in common stocks of smaller companies with market capitalizations of less

than $800M. Up to 20% of assets may be in ADRs of foreign issuers.
Year organized: 1993
Ticker symbol: HSCGX

THE HANOVER U.S. GOVERNMENT SECURITIES FUND
(See first Hanover listing for data common to all Hanover funds)

Portfolio manager: Pam Wooster (1993)
Investment objective and policies: High current income consistent with preservation of capital. Invests primarily in securities issued or guaranteed by the U.S. Government, its agencies or instrumentalities with no upper or lower limits on its weighted average maturity.
Year organized: 1993
Ticker symbol: HUSGX

ISRAEL GROWTH FUND
1800 Sherman Avenue, Suite 210
Evanston, IL 60201
708-328-1234, 800-708-7228
fax 708-328-1449

Adviser: Israel Growth Investment Adviser, Ltd.
Portfolio managers: Stewart R. Flink (1994), Merrill E. Weber (1994), Mark Meiras (1994)
Custodian and transfer agent: Thé Provident Bank, Cincinnati
Investment objective and policies: Long-term capital growth. Invests primarily in securities of issuers organized or headquartered in Israel or that otherwise conduct business with, in or from Israel. It is anticipated that at least 65% of assets will be in securities traded on U.S. stock exchanges either directly or through ADRs. May use futures and options to hedge up to 20% of total assets.
Year organized: 1994
Sales charge: 4.5% (available at NAV through discount brokers)
Discount broker availability: White
Minimum purchase through discount broker: $1,000

IVY INTERNATIONAL FUND
Via Mizner Financial Plaza
700 South Federal Highway
Boca Raton, FL 33432
800-777-6472, 800-456-5111

Adviser: Mackenzie Investment Management, Inc.
Sub-adviser: Northern Cross Investments Limited
Portfolio manager: Hakan Castegren (1986)
Investment objective and policies: Long-term capital growth with current income secondary. Invests in stocks and other equity securities of companies in at least 3 countries other than the U.S., primarily in the European, Pacific Basin, and Latin American markets
Year organized: 1985
Ticker symbol: IVINX
Sales charge: 5.75% (available at NAV through discount brokers)
Discount broker availability: *Schwab (only through financial advisers), White (only through financial advisers)
Minimum purchase through discount broker: $1,000

JPM ADVISOR FUNDS ◆
6 St. James Avenue
Boston, MA 02116
800-576-3637

Adviser: Morgan Guaranty Trust Co. of New York (a wholly-owned subsidiary of J.P. Morgan & Co.)
Special sales restrictions: Designed for financial planners only and available through financial advisers at discount brokerage firms
Discount broker availability: Schwab (only through financial advisers)
Minimum purchase through discount broker: Initial: $5,000, Subsequent: $1,000

JPM ADVISOR ASIA GROWTH FUND
(See first JPM Advisor listing for data common to all JPM Advisor funds)

Portfolio managers: Douglas Dooley (1995), Stephen Ho (1995)
Investment objective and policies: Long-term total return. Invests in equity securities of companies based in the developing countries of Asia, excluding Japan.
Year organized: 1995

JPM ADVISOR EMERGING MARKETS EQUITY FUND
(See first JPM Advisor listing for data common to all JPM Advisor funds)

Portfolio managers: Douglas Dooley (1995), Satyen Mehta (1995)
Investment objective and policies: Long-term total return. Invests in equity securities of companies based in emerging markets which include all countries except Australia, Canada, Japan and New Zealand the U.S. and Western Europe.
Year organized: 1995

JPM ADVISOR EUROPEAN EQUITY FUND
(See first JPM Advisor listing for data common to all JPM Advisor funds)

Portfolio managers: Paul Quinsee (1995), Rudolph Leuthold (1995)
Investment objective and policies: Long-term total return. Invests in equity securities of issuers from Western European countries and Turkey. Seeks to exceed the performance of the Morgan Capital International Europe Index of more than 500 companies in 14 European companies.
Year organized: 1995

JPM ADVISOR INTERNATIONAL EQUITY FUND
(See first JPM Advisor listing for data common to all JPM Advisor funds)

Portfolio manager: Paul Quinsee (1995)
Investment objective and policies: Long-term total return. Invests in equity securities of non-U.S. issuers from countries all over the world. The universe of companies is represented by the Morgan Stanley Europe, Australia and Far East (EAFE) Index.
Year organized: 1995

JPM ADVISOR INTERNATIONAL FIXED INCOME FUND
(See first JPM Advisor listing for data common to all JPM Advisor funds)

Portfolio manager: Robert Browne (1995)
Investment objective and policies: High total return consistent with moderate risk of capital. Invests in fixed-income securities of non-U.S. issuers from countries all over the world. Securities may be denominated in U.S. dollars and other foreign currencies.
Year organized: 1995

JPM ADVISOR JAPAN EQUITY FUND
(See first JPM Advisor listing for data common to all JPM Advisor funds)

Portfolio manager: Yoshihiro Takahashi (1995)
Investment objective and policies: Long-term total return. Invests in equity securities of issuers that have their principal activities in Japan or are organized under Japanese law. Fund seeks to outperform the Tokyo Stock Price Index.
Year organized: 1995

JPM ADVISOR U.S. EQUITY FUND
(See first JPM Advisor listing for data common to all JPM Advisor funds)

Portfolio manager: William Petersen (1995)
Investment objective and policies: Long-term total return. Invests in equity securities of large and medium-sized U.S. companies, as represented by the S&P 500. Up to 30% of assets may be in securities of foreign issuers.
Year organized: 1995

JPM ADVISOR U.S. FIXED INCOME FUND
(See first JPM Advisor listing for data common to all JPM Advisor funds)

Portfolio manager: William Tennille (1995)
Investment objective and policies: High total return consistent with moderate risk of capital and maintenance of liquidity. Invests primarily in investment-grade government and corporate fixed-income securities.
Year organized: 1995

JPM ADVISOR U.S. SMALL CAP EQUITY FUND
(See first JPM Advisor listing for data common to all JPM Advisor funds)

Portfolio managers: James Otness (1995), Fred Kittler (1995)
Investment objective and policies: Long-term total return. Invests in equity securities small U.S. companies, as represented by the Russell 2500 Index. Up to 30% of assets may be in securities of foreign issuers.
Year organized: 1995

JURIKA & VOYLES FUNDS ◆
2025 E. Financial Way, Suite 101
Glendora, CA 91741
818-852-1033, 800-584-6878
fax 818-852-1039

Adviser: Jurika & Voyles, Inc.
Special sales restrictions: Designed primarily for institutional investors. Funds are available at lower initial and subsequent minimums through discount brokerage firms which have established accounts with Jurika & Voyles.
Discount broker availability: Schwab, White
Minimum purchase through discount broker: Schwab: $1,000; White: $2,500

JURIKA & VOYLES BALANCED FUND ◆
(See first Jurika & Voyles listing for data common to all Jurika & Voyles funds)
Portfolio managers: William K. Jurika (1992), Glenn C. Voyles (1992)
Investment objective and policies: Total return. Invests in a combination of equity (45-75% of assets), fixed-income (at least 25% of assets) and money market securities. Fund adjusts mix in reaction to changing market and economic conditions.
Year organized: 1992
Ticker symbol: JVBAX

JURIKA & VOYLES MINI-CAP FUND ◆
(See first Jurika & Voyles listing for data common to all Jurika & Voyles funds)
Portfolio managers: William K. Jurika (1994), Glenn C. Voyles (1994)
Investment objective and policies: Long-term capital growth. Invests in common stocks of companies with market capitalizations under $500M offering current value and high growth potential. Up to 25% of assets may be in securities of foreign issuers.
Year organized: 1994

JURIKA & VOYLES VALUE + GROWTH FUND ◆

(See first Jurika & Voyles listing for data common to all Jurika & Voyles funds)
Portfolio managers: William K. Jurika (1994), Glenn C. Voyles (1994)
Investment objective and policies: Long-term capital growth. Invests in common stocks of companies with market capitalizations over $500M offering current value and high growth potential. Up to 25% of assets may be in securities of foreign issuers.
Year organized: 1994

KEELEY SMALL CAP VALUE FUND

401 South LaSalle Street, Suite 1201
Chicago, IL 60605
312-786-5050, 800-533-5344

Adviser: Keeley Asset Management Corp.
Portfolio manager: John L. Keeley, Jr. (1993)
Investment objective and policies: Long-term capital growth. Invests in stocks of undervalued companies with market capitalizations under $1B undergoing substantial changes like spin-offs and recapitalizations.
Year organized: 1993
Sales charge: 4.5% (available at NAV through discount brokers)
Discount broker availability: White (only through financial advisers)
Minimum purchase through discount broker: $50,000 (aggregate for financial adviser)

THE LAIDLAW COVENANT FUND

275 Madison Avenue
New York, NY 10016
212-949-5400, 800-652-4352

Adviser: Laidlaw Holdings Asset Management, Inc.
Portfolio manager: Godfried Hohenberg (1993)
Investment objective and policies: Long-term capital growth and income. Invests in stocks of companies which meet certain standards of corporate responsibility and ethical business behavior, as well as traditional investment standards.
Year organized: 1993
Ticker symbol: LEIFX
Sales charge: 4.5% (available at NAV through discount brokers)
Discount broker availability: White (only through financial advisers)
Minimum purchase through discount broker: $2,500

LEXINGTON FUNDS

Park 80 West Plaza Two
Saddle Brook, NJ 07663
201-845-7300, 800-526-0056
prices/yields 800-526-0052
fax 201-845-3534

Adviser: Lexington Management Corp.
Sales charge: 5.75% (available at NAV through discount brokers)
Minimum purchase through discount broker: $1,000

LEXINGTON STRATEGIC INVESTMENTS

(See first Lexington listing for data common to all Lexington funds)

Portfolio manager: Robert W. Radsch (1994)
Investment objective and policies: Capital appreciation with current income secondary. Invests in common stocks of companies engaged in exploration, mining, processing, fabrication and distribution gold and other precious metals. At least 50% of assets are in securities of foreign corporations.
Year organized: 1974
Ticker symbol: STIVX
Discount broker availability: *Schwab, *White, *Waterhouse, *Fidelity, *Siebert

LEXINGTON STRATEGIC SILVER

(See first Lexington listing for data common to all Lexington funds)

Portfolio manager: Robert W. Radsch (1994)
Investment objective and policies: Maximum total return. Invests in equity securities of established companies throughout the world engaged in exploration, mining, processing, fabrication or distribution of silver.
Year organized: 1984
Ticker symbol: STSLX
Discount broker availability: *Schwab, *White, *Waterhouse, *Fidelity, *Siebert

MAS TRUST FUND PORTFOLIOS ◆

One Tower Bridge
West Conshohocken, PA 19428
610-940-5000, 800-354-8185
prices 800-522-1525, fax 610-940-5098

Adviser: Miller, Anderson & Sherrerd
Special sales restrictions: Designed principally for the investments of tax-exempt fiduciary investors who are entrusted with the responsibility of investing assets held for the benefit of others. Funds are available at lower initial and subsequent minimums through discount brokerage firms which have established accounts with the MAS funds.
Minimum purchase through discount broker: $2,500; IRA: $1,000

MAS EMERGING GROWTH PORTFOLIO ◆

(See first MAS listing for data common to all MAS portfolios)

Portfolio managers: Arden C. Armstrong (1990), John D. Connolly (1990)
Investment objective and policies: Long-term capital growth with no emphasis on current income. Invests primarily in common stocks of smaller and medium size companies with market capitalizations from $300M to $2B and above average growth potential.
Year organized: 1990
Ticker symbol: MPEGX
Discount broker availability: White

MAS EQUITY PORTFOLIO ◆

(See first MAS listing for data common to all MAS portfolios)

Portfolio manager: Team managed
Investment objective and policies: Above-average total return consistent with reasonable risk. Invests in common stocks of companies with earnings and dividend growth potential greater than the economy in general and inflation.
Year organized: 1984
Ticker symbol: MPEQX
Discount broker availability: Schwab

MAS FIXED INCOME PORTFOLIO ◆

(See first MAS listing for data common to all MAS portfolios)

Portfolio manager: Team managed
Investment objective and policies: Maximum total return consistent with conservation of capital. Invests in corporate bonds, mortgage-backed securities and U.S. Government securities with weighted average maturity of more than 5 years.
Year organized: 1984
Ticker symbol: MPFIX
Discount broker availability: Schwab, White

MAS GLOBAL FIXED INCOME PORTFOLIO ◆

(See first MAS listing for data common to all MAS portfolios)

Portfolio managers: J. David Germany (1993), James L. Kichline (1993), Richard B. Worley (1993)

Investment objective and policies: Above average total return consistent with conservation of capital. Invests in domestic and foreign corporate and government debt securities, from at least 3 countries including the U.S., with weighted average maturity of more than 5 years.
Year organized: 1993
Ticker symbol: MAGFX
Discount broker availability: White

MAS HIGH-YIELD SECURITIES PORTFOLIO ◆

(See first MAS listing for data common to all MAS portfolios)

Portfolio managers: Stephen F. Esser (1989), Thomas L. Bennett (1989)
Investment objective and policies: Above average total return consistent with reasonable risk. Invests primarily in high-yields corporate fixed-income securities, including junk bonds, with weighted average maturity of more than 5 years.
Year organized: 1989
Ticker symbol: MPHYX
Discount broker availability: Schwab, White

MAS INTERNATIONAL EQUITY PORTFOLIO ◆

(See first MAS listing for data common to all MAS portfolios)

Portfolio managers: Dean Williams (1988), Horacio A. Valeiras (1992)
Investment objective and policies: Above-average total return consistent with reasonable risk. Invests in common stocks of companies based outside the U.S. chosen from the Morgan Stanley Capital International World ex-U.S. Index of more than 1,100 securities.
Year organized: 1988
Ticker symbol: MPIEX
Discount broker availability: Schwab, White

MAS INTERNATIONAL FIXED INCOME PORTFOLIO ◆

(See first MAS listing for data common to all MAS portfolios)

Portfolio managers: J. David Germany (1994), James L. Kichline (1994), Richard B. Worley (1994)
Investment objective and policies: Above average total return consistent with conservation of capital. Invests in high quality foreign corporate and government securities, from at least 3 countries other than the U.S. with a weighted average maturity of more than 5 years.
Year organized: 1994
Ticker symbol: MPIFX
Discount broker availability: White

MAS SMALL CAPITALIZATION VALUE PORTFOLIO ◆

(See first MAS listing for data common to all MAS portfolios)

Portfolio managers: Gary G. Schlarbaum (1986), Gary D. Haubold (1993), Bradley S. Daniels (1986)
Investment objective and policies: Above-average total return consistent with reasonable risk. Invests in common stocks of companies with market capitalizations of $50M to $800M believed undervalued.
Year organized: 1986
Ticker symbol: MPSCX
Discount broker availability: Schwab, White

MAS VALUE PORTFOLIO ◆

(See first MAS listing for data common to all MAS portfolios)

Portfolio managers: Robert J. Marcin (1990), A. Morris Williams, Jr. (1984)
Investment objective and policies: Above-average total return consistent with reasonable risk. Invests

in common stocks of companies with market capitalizations greater than $300M believed undervalued. Will generate higher income than Equity Portfolio.
Year organized: 1986
Ticker symbol: MPVLX
Discount broker availability: Schwab, White

MONITREND MUTUAL FUNDS
272 Closter Dock Road
Closter, NJ 07624
615-298-1000, 800-251-1970

Sales charge: 4.5% (available at NAV through discount brokers; exception noted)
Discount broker availability: White (only through financial advisers)
Minimum purchase through discount broker: $5,000

MONITREND GAMING AND LEISURE FUND
(See first Monitrend listing for data common to all Monitrend funds)

Adviser: Monitrend Investment Management, Inc.
Sub-adviser: Lucky Management Corp.
Investment objective and policies: Long-term growth of capital. Invests in equity securities of companies engaged in activities related to the following - sporting goods, recreational equipment, toys, games, photographic equipment, musical instruments, recordings, motion pictures, broadcasting, cable TV, air transportation, hotels and motels, sports arenas, gambling casinos, amusement or theme parks and restaurants.
Year organized: 1993

MONITREND GOLD FUND
(See first Monitrend listing for data common to all Monitrend funds)

Adviser: Kensington Asset Management, Inc.
Portfolio manager: Johann Devilliers (1991)
Investment objective and policies: Long-term growth of capital. Invests in equity securities of domestic and foreign companies engaged in exploration, refinement, development, manufacture, production or marketing of gold and other precious metals.
Year organized: 1988
Ticker symbol: MNTGX

MONITREND GOVERNMENT INCOME FUND
(See first Monitrend listing for data common to all Monitrend funds)

Adviser: Pacific Income Advisers, Inc.
Investment objective and policies: Growth of capital, income and preservation of capital. Invests in securities issued or guaranteed by the U.S. government, its agencies or instrumentalities with average maturity dependent on market conditions.
Year organized: 1986

MONITREND GROWTH FUND
(See first Monitrend listing for data common to all Monitrend funds)

Adviser: Robert L. Bender, Inc.
Sub-adviser: Monitrend Investment Management, Inc.
Portfolio manager: Robert L. Bender (1992)
Investment objective and policies: Long-term growth of capital. Invests in common stocks of companies with above average sales and earnings growth. Up to 10% of assets may be in securities of foreign issuers.
Year organized: 1992

MONITREND PIA ADJUSTABLE RATE GOVERNMENT SECURITIES FUND
(See first Monitrend listing for data common to all Monitrend funds)

Adviser: Pacific Income Advisers, Inc.
Investment objective and policies: High current income consistent with low volatility of principal. Invests in adjustable rate U.S. government securities with a maximum duration equal to a two-year U.S. Treasury security and target range equal to a six-month to one-year U.S. Treasury security.
Year organized: 1994
Sales charge: 1.25% (available at NAV through discount brokers)

MONITREND SUMMATION INDEX FUND
(See first Monitrend listing for data common to all Monitrend funds)

Adviser: Monitrend Investment Management, Inc.
Investment objective and policies: Long-term total return exceeding the S&P 100 Index. Invests in common stocks which parallel the composition of the Index and uses options and futures and other strategies to increase the portfolio's return.
Year organized: 1988
Ticker symbol: MNTIX

MONITREND TECHNOLOGY FUND
(See first Monitrend listing for data common to all Monitrend funds)

Adviser: Monitrend Investment Management, Inc.
Sub-adviser: Negative Beta Associates, Inc.
Investment objective and policies: Long-term growth of capital. Invests in equity securities of companies that can produce products or services that provide or benefit from advances in technology.
Year organized: 1993

MUIR CALIFORNIA TAX-FREE BOND FUND
111 Pine Street
San Francisco, CA 94111
415-989-3200, 800-223-7010

Adviser: Sand County Securities L.P.
Portfolio managers: Gail Seneca (1991), Mary Schiavone (1994)
Investment objective and policies: Maximum current income exempt from federal and California state income taxes consistent with preservation of capital. Invests in investment-grade California municipal securities.
Year organized: 1991
Ticker symbol: MRCAX
Sales charge: 4.5% (available at NAV through discount brokers)
Discount broker availability: Schwab (only through financial advisers), White (only through financial advisers)
Minimum purchase through discount broker: Schwab: $1,000; White: $2,500

NAVELLIER AGGRESSIVE SMALL CAP EQUITY PORTFOLIO
920 Incline Way, Building 1
Incline Village, NV 89450
800-887-8671

Adviser: Navellier Management, Inc.
Portfolio manager: Louis Navellier (1994)
Investment objective and policies: Long-term capital growth. Invests in stocks of companies with market capitalizations under $1B with growth potential. Up to 25% of assets may be in ADRs of foreign issuers.
Year organized: 1994

Ticker symbol: NASCX
Sales charge: 3.0% (available at NAV through discount brokers)
Discount broker availability: White (only through financial advisers)
Minimum purchase through discount broker: $5,000

NEW YORK LIFE INSTITUTIONAL EAFE INDEX FUND ◆
51 Madison Avenue
New York, NY 10010
800-695-2126

Adviser: Monitor Capital Advisors, Inc. (a subsidiary of New York Life)
Portfolio manager: James Mehling (1992)
Investment objective and policies: Total investment results comparable to the Morgan Stanley Capital International Europe, Australia and Far East (EAFE) Index. Invests in a representative sample of the stocks in the Index.
Year organized: 1991
Ticker symbol: NIEAX
Special sales restrictions: Designed for institutional investors only, but individuals may invest through fee-only financial advisers at Charles Schwab.
Discount broker availability: Schwab (only through financial advisers)
Minimum purchase through discount broker: $1000

NEW YORK LIFE INSTITUTIONAL VALUE EQUITY FUND ◆
51 Madison Avenue
New York, NY 10010
800-695-2126

Adviser: MacKay-Shields Financial Corp. (a subsidiary of New York Life)
Portfolio managers: Denis La Plaige (1991), Thomas Kolefas (1991)
Investment objective and policies: Maximum total return - capital growth and current income. Invests in a equity securities of domestic and foreign issuers selected according to fundamental value analysis.
Year organized: 1991
Ticker symbol: NIVEX
Special sales restrictions: Designed for institutional investors only, but individuals may invest through fee-only financial advisers at Charles Schwab.
Discount broker availability: Schwab (only through financial advisers)
Minimum purchase through discount broker: $1,000

NEWPORT TIGER FUND
1500 Forest Avenue, Suite 223
Richmond, VA 23229
804-285-8211, 800-527-9500
fax 804-285-8251

Adviser: Newport Fund Management, Inc.
Portfolio manager: John M. Mussey (1989)
Investment objective and policies: Capital appreciation. Invests in equity securities of companies in the four Tigers of Asia (Hong Kong, Singapore, South Korea and Taiwan) and the other mini Tigers of South East Asia - Malaysia, Thailand, Indonesia, China and the Phillipines.
Year organized: 1989
Ticker symbol: NWTRX
Sales charge: 5.0% (available at NAV through discount brokers)
Discount broker availability: *Schwab, *White (only through financial advisers)
Minimum purchase through discount broker: Schwab: $1,000; White: $5,000

PACIFIC ADVISORS BALANCED FUND
215 North Marengo Ave., Suite 115
Pasadena, CA 91101
818-796-6931, 800-282-6693
fax 804-285-8251

Adviser: Hamilton & Bache, Inc.
Portfolio managers: Mary N. Hamilton (1994), Stephen K. Bache (1994)
Investment objective and policies: Long-term capital growth and income consistent with reduced market risk. Invests in equity securities, fixed-income securities and money market instruments with allocation adjusted to reflect changes in market and economic conditions.
Year organized: 1993
Sales charge: 5.75% (available at NAV through discount brokers)
Discount broker availability: Schwab (only through financial advisers)
Minimum purchase through discount broker: $1,000

PACIFIC ADVISORS GOVERNMENT SECURITIES FUND
215 North Marengo Ave., Suite 115
Pasadena, CA 91101
818-796-6931, 800-282-6693
fax 804-285-8251

Adviser: Spectrum Asset Management, Inc.
Portfolio managers: R. "Kelly" Kelly (1993), Marc Kelly (1993)
Investment objective and policies: High current income, preservation of capital, and rising future income. Invests primarily in fixed-income securities issued or guaranteed by the U.S. Government or its agencies and instrumentalities.
Year organized: 1993
Sales charge: 4.75% (available at NAV through discount brokers)
Discount broker availability: Schwab (only through financial advisers)
Minimum purchase through discount broker: $1,000

PACIFIC HORIZON FUNDS
7863 Girard Avenue, Suite 306
La Jolla, CA 92037
619-456-9197, 800-332-3863

Adviser: Bank of America National Trust and Savings Association
Sales charge: 4.5% (available at NAV through discount brokers)
Discount broker availability: Schwab (only through financial advisers), White (only through financial advisers)
Minimum purchase through discount broker: Schwab: $1,000; White: $2,500

PACIFIC HORIZON AGGRESSIVE GROWTH FUND
(See first Pacific Horizon listing for data common to all Pacific Horizon funds)

Portfolio manager: Jeff Mallet (1990)
Investment objective and policies: Long-term growth. Invests in common stocks and securities convertible into common stocks of smaller-capitalization U.S. companies. Up to 20% of assets may be in securities of foreign issuers.
Year organized: 1984
Ticker symbol: PHAGX

PACIFIC HORIZON CALIFORNIA TAX-EXEMPT BOND FUND
(See first Pacific Horizon listing for data common to all Pacific Horizon funds)

Portfolio manager: Kim Michalski (1984)
Investment objective and policies: Current income exempt from federal and California state personal income taxes. Invests in California municipal securities. Up to 20% of assets may be in AMT securities.
Year organized: 1984
Ticker symbol: PHCTX

PACIFIC HORIZON CAPITAL INCOME FUND
(See first Pacific Horizon listing for data common to all Pacific Horizon funds)

Portfolio manager: William S. Hensel (1987)
Investment objective and policies: Total return consistent with prudent investment risk. Invests in convertible bonds and convertible preferred stocks of domestic issuers. 15% of assets may be in Eurodollar convertible securities.
Year organized: 1987
Ticker symbol: PACIX

PACIFIC HORIZON U.S. GOVERNMENT SECURITIES FUND
(See first Pacific Horizon listing for data common to all Pacific Horizon funds)

Portfolio manager: Michael Kagawa (1992)
Investment objective and policies: Current income consistent with preservation of capital. Invests at least 65% of assets in GNMA securities. May invest in other U.S. Government securities.
Year organized: 1988
Ticker symbol: PHGVX

PARNASSUS FUND
244 California Street
San Francisco, CA 94111
415-362-3505, 800-999-3505

Adviser: Parnassus Financial Management
Portfolio manager: Jerome L. Dodson (1984)
Investment objective and policies: Capital appreciation with current income secondary. Invests primarily in equity securities of established, mature (at least 10 years old) companies that pay regular dividends and are believed undervalued. Fund invests in companies that have a positive social impact.
Year organized: 1984
Ticker symbol: PARNX
Sales charge: 3.5% (available at NAV through discount brokers)
Discount broker availability: Schwab (only through financial advisers), White (only through financial advisers)
Minimum purchase through discount broker: Schwab: $2,000; IRA: $1,000; White: $2,500

PIMCO ADVISORS FUNDS
One Stratton Place
Stamford, CT 06902
800-426-0107

Adviser: PIMCO Advisors L.P.
Sales charge: Ranges from 5.50% to 3.00% for individual funds (available at NAV through discount brokers).
Discount broker availability: White (only through financial advisers)
Minimum purchase through discount broker: $2,500

PIMCO ADVISORS EQUITY INCOME FUND
(See first PIMCO Advisors listing for data common to all PIMCO Advisors funds)

Sub-adviser: Columbus Circle Investors
Investment objective and policies: Long-term capital growth and current income. Invests in dividend-paying common stocks, preferred stocks and securities convertible into common stocks.
Year organized: 1988
Ticker symbol: PQNAX

PIMCO ADVISORS GROWTH FUND
(See first PIMCO Advisors listing for data common to all PIMCO Advisors funds)

Sub-adviser: Columbus Circle Investors
Investment objective and policies: Long-term capital growth. Invests primarily in common stocks of medium to large capitalization companies believed undervalued.
Year organized: 1984
Ticker symbol: PGWAX

PIMCO ADVISORS HIGH INCOME FUND
(See first PIMCO Advisors listing for data common to all PIMCO Advisors funds)

Sub-adviser: Pacific Investment Management Company
Portfolio manager: Benjamin Trosky (1994)
Investment objective and policies: Maximum total return consistent with preservation of capital. Invests primarily in domestic and foreign junk bonds with a weighted average maturity of 2 to 6 years.
Year organized: 1984
Ticker symbol: PHNAX

PIMCO ADVISORS INNOVATION FUND
(See first PIMCO Advisors listing for data common to all PIMCO Advisors funds)

Sub-adviser: Columbus Circle Investors
Investment objective and policies: Capital growth. Invests primarily in common stocks of companies which use innovative technologies to gain strategic competitive advantages in their industries and companies that provide and service those technologies.
Year organized: 1994
Ticker symbol: PIVAX

PIMCO ADVISORS INTERNATIONAL FUND
(See first PIMCO Advisors listing for data common to all PIMCO Advisors funds)

Sub-adviser: Blairlogie Capital Management
Portfolio manager: James G.S. Smith
Investment objective and policies: Long-term capital growth. Invests primarily in common stocks and other equity securities of foreign issuers from at least 3 countries other than the U.S. May invest in emerging as well as developed markets.
Year organized: 1986
Ticker symbol: PILAX

PIMCO ADVISORS OPPORTUNITY FUND
(See first PIMCO Advisors listing for data common to all PIMCO Advisors funds)

Sub-adviser: Columbus Circle Investors
Investment objective and policies: Capital growth. Invests primarily in common stocks of companies with market capitalizations under $1B and above average growth prospects.
Year organized: 1984
Ticker symbol: POPAX

PIMCO ADVISORS PRECIOUS METALS FUND
(See first PIMCO Advisors listing for data common to all PIMCO Advisors funds)

Sub-adviser: Van Eck Associates Corporation
Portfolio manager: Henry J. Bingham (1988)

Investment objective and policies: Long-term capital growth. Invests in common stocks of companies from all over the world primarily engaged in precious metal-related activities.
Year organized: 1988
Ticker symbol: PPMAX

PIMCO ADVISORS
SHORT-INTERMEDIATE FUND
(See first PIMCO Advisors listing for data common to all PIMCO Advisors funds)

Sub-adviser: Pacific Investment Management Company
Portfolio manager: David H. Edington (1994)
Investment objective and policies: High current income consistent with relatively low volatility of principal. Invests primarily in domestic and foreign investment-grade fixed income securities with a weighted average maturity of 1 to 3 years.
Year organized: 1991

PIMCO ADVISORS TARGET FUND
(See first PIMCO Advisors listing for data common to all PIMCO Advisors funds)

Sub-adviser: Columbus Circle Investors
Investment objective and policies: Capital growth. Invests primarily in common stocks of companies with market capitalizations in the range of the S&P 400 MidCap Index.
Year organized: 1992
Ticker symbol: PTAAX

PIMCO ADVISORS
TAX EXEMPT FUND
(See first PIMCO Advisors listing for data common to all PIMCO Advisors funds)

Sub-adviser: Columbus Circle Investors
Portfolio manager: Norman Seltzer
Investment objective and policies: High current income exempt from federal income taxes consistent with preservation of capital. Invests primarily in investment-grade municipal securities with a weighted average maturity of 3 to 10 years.
Year organized: 1985
Ticker symbol: PTEAX

PIMCO ADVISORS
TOTAL RETURN INCOME FUND
(See first PIMCO Advisors listing for data common to all PIMCO Advisors funds)

Sub-adviser: Pacific Investment Management Company
Portfolio manager: William H. Gross (1994)
Investment objective and policies: Maximum total return consistent with preservation of capital. Invests primarily in investment-grade domestic and foreign fixed-income securities with a weighted average maturity of 3 to 6 years.
Year organized: 1994
Ticker symbol: PTNAX

PIMCO ADVISORS
U.S. GOVERNMENT FUND
(See first PIMCO Advisors listing for data common to all PIMCO Advisors funds)

Sub-adviser: Pacific Investment Management Company
Portfolio manager: Frank B. Rabinovitch (1994)
Investment objective and policies: Maximum total return consistent with preservation of capital. Invests exclusively in U.S. Government securities, related repurchase agreements and futures and options thereon with a weighted average maturity of 3 to 6 years.
Year organized: 1985
Ticker symbol: PUSAX

PIMCO ADVISORS
INSTITUTIONAL FUNDS ◆
840 Newport Center Drive
Newport Beach, CA 92660
800-800-7674, fax 714-644-4651

Adviser: Pacific Investment Management Corp.
Special sales restrictions: Designed primarily to provide pension and profit sharing plans, endowments, employee benefit trusts, foundations, other institutions, corporations, and high net worth individuals with access to the professional investment management services offered by Pacific Investment Management Corporation and its investment management affiliates. Funds are available at lower initial and subsequent minimums through discount brokerage firms which have established accounts within the PIMCO Advisors Institutional funds.
Minimum purchase through discount broker: $1,000

PIMCO ADVISORS
INSTITUTIONAL FUNDS -
BALANCED FUND ◆
(See first PIMCO Advisors Institutional listing for data common to all PIMCO Advisors Institutional funds)

Sub-advisers: Parametric Portfolio Associates (a subsidiary of PIMCO) - common stocks; PIMCO - fixed-income
Portfolio managers: William H. Gross (1992), Mark England-Markun (1992), Devin Wate (1992)
Investment objective and policies: Total return consistent with prudent investment management. Invests in common stocks (normally 40-65% of assets), fixed-income securities (normally at least 25%) and money market instruments.
Year organized: 1992 (name changed from Strategic Allocation Portfolio in 1993 and from PFAMCo Balanced Portfolio on 11/15/94)
Ticker symbol: PBLIX
Discount broker availability: *White

PIMCO ADVISORS INSTITUTIONAL
FUNDS - BLAIRLOGIE EMERGING
MARKETS FUND ◆
(See first PIMCO Advisors Institutional listing for data common to all PIMCO Advisors Institutional funds)

Sub-adviser: Blairlogie Capital Management Ltd. (an indirect subsidiary of PIMCO)
Portfolio manager: James Smith (1993)
Investment objective and policies: Long-term growth of capital. Invests primarily in common stocks of companies located in countries identified as "emerging market" countries.
Year organized: 1993 (name changed from PFAMCo Emerging Markets Portfolio on 11/15/94)
Ticker symbol: PEMIX
Discount broker availability: Schwab, *White

PIMCO ADVISORS INSTITUTIONAL
FUNDS - BLAIRLOGIE
INTERNATIONAL ACTIVE FUND ◆
(See first PIMCO Advisors Institutional listing for data common to all PIMCO Advisors Institutional funds)

Sub-adviser: Blairlogie Capital Management Ltd. (an indirect subsidiary of PIMCO)
Portfolio manager: James Smith (1993)
Investment objective and policies: Long-term growth of capital. Invests in international equity securities chosen from the Morgan Stanley Capital International Europe, Australia, Far East Stock Market Index ("EAFE Index").
Year organized: 1993 (name changed from PFAMCo International Active Portfolio on 11/15/94)
Discount broker availability: Schwab, *White

PIMCO ADVISORS INSTITUTIONAL
FUNDS - CADENCE CAPITAL
APPRECIATION FUND ◆
(See first PIMCO Advisors Institutional listing for data common to all PIMCO Advisors Institutional funds)

Sub-adviser: Cadence Capital Management (a subsidiary of PIMCO)
Portfolio managers: David B. Breed (1991), William B. Bannick (1992)
Investment objective and policies: Growth of capital. Invests stocks of companies with market capitalizations of at least $100M with improving fundamentals and stocks reasonably valued by the market.
Year organized: 1991 (name changed from PFAMCo Capital Appreciation Portfolio on 11/15/94)
Ticker symbol: PAPIX
Discount broker availability: Schwab, *White

PIMCO ADVISORS INSTITUTIONAL
FUNDS - CADENCE MICRO
CAP GROWTH FUND ◆
(See first PIMCO Advisors Institutional listing for data common to all PIMCO Advisors Institutional funds)

Sub-adviser: Cadence Capital Management (a subsidiary of PIMCO)
Portfolio managers: David B. Breed (1993), William B. Bannick (1993)
Investment objective and policies: Growth of capital. Invests in common stocks of companies with market capitalizations of under $100M with improving fundamentals stocks reasonably valued by the market.
Year organized: 1993 (name changed from PFAMCo Micro Cap Growth Portfolio on 11/15/94)
Ticker symbol: PMCIX
Redemption fee: 2% on shares held less than 1 year, payable to the fund
Discount broker availability: Schwab

PIMCO ADVISORS INSTITUTIONAL
FUNDS - CADENCE MID CAP
GROWTH FUND ◆
(See first PIMCO Advisors Institutional listing for data common to all PIMCO Advisors Institutional funds)

Sub-adviser: Cadence Capital Management (a subsidiary of PIMCO)
Portfolio managers: David B. Breed (1991), William B. Bannick (1992)
Investment objective and policies: Growth of capital. Invests in stocks of companies with market capitalizations of at least $500M, excluding the 200 largest, with improving fundamentals stocks reasonably valued by the market.
Year organized: 1991 (name changed from PFAMCo Mid Cap Growth Portfolio on 11/15/94)
Ticker symbol: PMGIX
Discount broker availability: *White

PIMCO ADVISORS INSTITUTIONAL
FUNDS - CADENCE SMALL
CAP GROWTH FUND ◆
(See first PIMCO Advisors Institutional listing for data common to all PIMCO Advisors Institutional funds)

Sub-adviser: Cadence Capital Management (a subsidiary of PIMCO)
Portfolio managers: David B. Breed (1991), William B. Bannick (1992)
Investment objective and policies: Growth of capital. Invests in stocks of companies with market capitalizations of $50M to $500M with improving fundamentals and stocks reasonably valued by the market.

Year organized: 1991 (name changed from PFAMCo Small Cap Growth Portfolio on 11/15/94)
Ticker symbol: PSCIX
Special sales restrictions: Fund closed to new shareholders on 8/19/91
Discount broker availability: *White

PIMCO ADVISORS INSTITUTIONAL FUNDS - NFJ DIVERSIFIED LOW P/E FUND ◆

(See first PIMCO Advisors Institutional listing for data common to all PIMCO Advisors Institutional funds)

Sub-adviser: NFJ Investment Group (a subsidiary of PIMCO)
Portfolio manager: Chris Najork (1991)
Investment objective and policies: Long-term growth of capital. Invests in common stocks of companies with market capitalizations of at least $200M with below average price to earnings ratios relative to their industry groups.
Year organized: 1991 (name changed from PFAMCo Diversified Low P/E Portfolio on 11/15/94)
Ticker symbol: PDLIX
Discount broker availability: Schwab, *White

PIMCO ADVISORS INSTITUTIONAL FUNDS - NFJ EQUITY INCOME FUND ◆

(See first PIMCO Advisors Institutional listing for data common to all PIMCO Advisors Institutional funds)

Sub-adviser: NFJ Investment Group (a subsidiary of PIMCO)
Portfolio manager: Chris Najork (1991)
Investment objective and policies: Current income with capital growth secondary. Invests in stocks of companies with below average price to earnings ratios and higher dividend yields relative to their industry groups.
Year organized: 1991 (name changed from PFAMCo Equity Income Portfolio on 11/15/94)
Ticker symbol: PEIIX
Discount broker availability: Schwab, *White

PIMCO ADVISORS INSTITUTIONAL FUNDS - NFJ SMALL CAP VALUE FUND ◆

(See first PIMCO Advisors Institutional listing for data common to all PIMCO Advisors Institutional funds)

Sub-adviser: NFJ Investment Group (a subsidiary of PIMCO)
Portfolio manager: Chris Najork (1991)
Investment objective and policies: Long-term growth of capital and income. Invests in common stocks of companies with market capitalizations between $50M and $500M with below average price to earnings ratios relative to their industry groups
Year organized: 1991 (name changed from PFAMCo Small Cap Value Portfolio on 11/15/94)
Ticker symbol: PSVIX
Discount broker availability: *White

PIMCO ADVISORS INSTITUTIONAL FUNDS - PARAMETRIC ENHANCED EQUITY FUND ◆

(See first PIMCO Advisors Institutional listing for data common to all PIMCO Advisors Institutional funds)

Sub-adviser: Parametric Portfolio Associates (a subsidiary of PIMCO)
Portfolio managers: Mark England-Markun (1991), Devin Wate (1991)

Investment objective and policies: Total return to equal or exceed the S&P 500 Index. Fund uses quantitative optimization techniques to select some, but not all, of the common stocks in the S&P 500 Index.
Year organized: 1991 (name changed from PFAMCo Enhanced Equity Portfolio on 11/15/94)
Ticker symbol: PEEIX
Discount broker availability: *White

PIMCO ADVISORS INSTITUTIONAL FUNDS - PARAMETRIC INTERNATIONAL EQUITY FUND ◆

(See first PIMCO Advisors Institutional listing for data common to all PIMCO Advisors Institutional funds)

Sub-adviser: Parametric Portfolio Associates (a subsidiary of PIMCO)
Portfolio managers: Mark England-Markun (1990), Devin Wate (1990)
Investment objective and policies: Total return to equal or exceed the total return performance of the Morgan Stanley Capital International Europe, Australia, Far East Stock Market Index ("EAFE Index").
Year organized: 1990 (name changed from PFAMCo International Equity Portfolio on 11/15/94)
Ticker symbol: PINIX
2
Sales charge: 1% payable to the fund
Discount broker availability: *White

PIMCO ADVISORS INSTITUTIONAL FUNDS - PIMCO MANAGED BOND AND INCOME FUND ◆

(See first PIMCO Advisors Institutional listing for data common to all PIMCO Advisors Institutional funds)

Portfolio manager: William H. Gross (1991)
Investment objective and policies: Total return consistent with prudent investment risk. Invests in high quality bonds, debentures and other fixed-income securities with weighted average maturity of 3 to 6 years.
Year organized: 1991 (name changed from PFAMCo Managed Bond and Income Portfolio on 11/15/94)
Ticker symbol: PMBIX
Discount broker availability: *White

PIMCO ADVISORS INSTITUTIONAL FUNDS - UTILITY STOCK FUND ◆

(See first PIMCO Advisors Institutional listing for data common to all PIMCO Advisors Institutional funds)

Portfolio manager: Ronald D. Minke (1994)
Investment objective and policies: Long-term growth of capital and income. Invests in common stocks of utility companies, including electric and telephone utilities, telecommunications services companies, cable television, and natural gas and water companies.
Year organized: 1994 (name changed from PFAMCo Utility Stock Portfolio on 11/15/94)
Ticker symbol: PUSIX
Discount broker availability: *White

PIMCO FUNDS ◆

840 Newport Center Drive, Suite 360
Newport Beach, CA 92660
714-760-4880, 800-927-4648
fax 714-760-4456

Adviser: Pacific Investment Management Co.
Special sales restrictions: Designed primarily to provide pension and profit sharing plans, endowments, employee benefit trusts, foundations, other institutions, corporations, and high net worth individuals with access to professional investment management. Funds are available at lower initial and

subsequent minimums through discount brokerage firms which have established accounts within the PIMCO funds.
Minimum purchase through discount broker: $1,000

PIMCO FOREIGN FUND ◆

(See first PIMCO listing for data common to all PIMCO funds)

Portfolio manager: John L. Hague (1992)
Investment objective and policies: Maximum total return. Invests in fixed-income securities of non-U.S. issuers from at least 3 foreign countries or currencies with a weighted average maturity of 3 to 6 years.
Year organized: 1992
Ticker symbol: PFORX
Discount broker availability: Schwab, *White, Waterhouse, Fidelity, Siebert

PIMCO GLOBAL FUND ◆

(See first PIMCO listing for data common to all PIMCO funds)

Portfolio manager: John Hague (1993)
Investment objective and policies: Maximum total return. Invests in fixed-income securities of U.S. and foreign issuers with a weighted average maturity of 3 to 8 years. Foreign bonds will vary from 25% to 75% of total assets.
Year organized: 1992
Ticker symbol: PIGLX
Discount broker availability: Schwab, *White

PIMCO GROWTH STOCK FUND ◆

(See first PIMCO listing for data common to all PIMCO funds)

Portfolio manager: A. Benjamin Ehlert (1987)
Investment objective and policies: Maximum capital appreciation. Invests primarily in equity securities which, in the adviser's opinion, have above average market appreciation potential.
Year organized: 1987
Ticker symbol: PTGSX
Discount broker availability: Schwab, *White, Fidelity, Siebert

PIMCO HIGH YIELD FUND ◆

(See first PIMCO listing for data common to all PIMCO funds)

Portfolio manager: Benjamin Trosky (1992)
Investment objective and policies: Maximum total return. Invests in fixed-income securities of domestic and foreign issuers rated below investment-grade but rated at least B with a weighted average maturity of 2 to 6 years.
Year organized: 1992
Ticker symbol: PHIYX
Discount broker availability: Schwab, *White, Waterhouse, Fidelity, Siebert

PIMCO LONG-TERM U.S. GOVERNMENT FUND ◆

(See first PIMCO listing for data common to all PIMCO funds)

Portfolio manager: Frank B. Rabinovitch (1991)
Investment objective and policies: Maximum total return. Invests in U.S. Government securities, rated A or better with a weighted average maturity of 8 years or more.
Year organized: 1991 (name changed from Long Duration Fund on 12/18/92)
Ticker symbol: PGOVX
Discount broker availability: Schwab, *White, Fidelity, Siebert

PIMCO LOW DURATION FUND ◆
(See first PIMCO listing for data common to all PIMCO funds)

Portfolio manager: William H. Gross (1987)
Investment objective and policies: Maximum total return consistent with preservation of capital and prudent investment risk. Invests in fixed-income securities with a weighted average maturity of 1 to 3 years. Up to 20% of assets may be in foreign securities.
Year organized: 1987
Ticker symbol: PTLDX
Discount broker availability: Schwab, *White, Waterhouse, Fidelity, Siebert

PIMCO LOW DURATION FUND II ◆
(See first PIMCO listing for data common to all PIMCO funds)

Portfolio manager: William H. Gross (1991)
Investment objective and policies: Maximum total return. Invests in domestic investment-grade fixed-income securities with a weighted average portfolio duration of 1 to 3 years.
Year organized: 1991
Ticker symbol: PLDTX
Discount broker availability: *White, Fidelity, Siebert

PIMCO SHORT-TERM FUND ◆
(See first PIMCO listing for data common to all PIMCO funds)

Portfolio manager: David H. Edington (1987)
Investment objective and policies: Maximum current income consistent with preservation of capital and daily liquidity. Invests in money market and other short-term securities with a weighted average maturity of less than 1 year.
Year organized: 1987
Ticker symbol: PTSHX
Discount broker availability: Schwab, *White, Fidelity, Siebert

PIMCO STOCKSPLUS FUND ◆
(See first PIMCO listing for data common to all PIMCO funds)

Portfolio manager: David H. Edington (1993)
Investment objective and policies: Total return exceeding that of the S&P 500. Invests in selected stocks represented on the S&P 500 and index futures, options on indexes and options on index futures based on the S&P 500.
Year organized: 1993
Discount broker availability: Schwab, *White

PIMCO TOTAL RETURN FUND ◆
(See first PIMCO listing for data common to all PIMCO funds)

Portfolio manager: William H. Gross (1987)
Investment objective and policies: Maximum total return. Invests in fixed-income securities, including corporate bonds, U.S. Government securities and mortgage-related securities with a weighted average maturity of 3 to 6 years.
Year organized: 1987
Ticker symbol: PTTRX
Discount broker availability: Schwab, *White, Waterhouse, Fidelity, Siebert

PIMCO TOTAL RETURN FUND III ◆
(See first PIMCO listing for data common to all PIMCO funds)

Portfolio manager: William H. Gross (1991)
Investment objective and policies: Maximum total return. Invests in fixed-income securities, including

corporate bonds, U.S. Government securities and mortgage-related securities with a weighted average maturity of 3 to 6 years. Will not invest in securities of companies conducting business in South Africa.
Year organized: 1991 (name changed from Total Return South Africa-Free on 8/7/92)
Ticker symbol: PTSAX
Discount broker availability: Schwab, *White, Fidelity, Siebert

RAINIER PORTFOLIOS
601 Union Street, Suite 2801
Seattle, WA 98101
206-464-0400, 800-248-6314

Adviser: Rainier Investment Management, Inc.
Special sales restrictions: Designed primarily for institutional investors. Funds are available at lower initial and subsequent minimums through discount brokerage firms which have established accounts with Rainier.
Discount broker availability: *Schwab
Minimum purchase through discount broker: $1,000

RAINIER BALANCED PORTFOLIO
(See first Rainier listing for data common to all Rainier portfolios)

Portfolio manager: James R. Margard (1994)
Investment objective and policies: Long-term capital growth and current income. Invests in a mix of U.S. common stocks (35-65% of assets), fixed-income senior securities (30-55%) and cash equivalents (0-35%) with allocation adjusted to reflect changing market and economic conditions.
Year organized: 1993

RAINIER CORE EQUITY PORTFOLIO
(See first Rainier listing for data common to all Rainier portfolios)

Portfolio managers: James R. Margard (1994), David A. Veterane (1994)
Investment objective and policies: Maximum long-term capital growth. Invests primarily in common stocks of companies within the S&P 500 Index with above average earnings and growth potential. May also invest in convertible securities and ADRs.
Year organized: 1993

RAINIER INTERMEDIATE FIXED-INCOME PORTFOLIO
(See first Rainier listing for data common to all Rainier portfolios)

Portfolio managers: Patricia L. Frost (1994), Michael E. Raney (1994)
Investment objective and policies: Current income. Invests primarily in investment-grade government and corporate debt securities of U.S. issuers and foreign issuers denominated in U.S. dollars with a weighted average maturity of 3 to 10 years.
Year organized: 1993

RAINIER SMALL/MID CAP EQUITY PORTFOLIO
(See first Rainier listing for data common to all Rainier portfolios)

Portfolio managers: James R. Margard (1994), David A. Veterane (1994)
Investment objective and policies: Maximum long-term capital growth. Invests primarily in common stocks of small capitalization ($10M to $3B) and mid capitalization ($500M to $5B) companies. May also invest in convertible securities and ADRs.
Year organized: 1993

REA-GRAHAM BALANCED FUND
10966 Chalon Road
Los Angeles, CA 90077
213-208-2282, 800-433-1998

Adviser: James Buchanan Rea, Inc.
Portfolio managers: Dr. James B. Rea (1976), James B. Rea, Jr. (1979)
Investment objective and policies: Medium-term capital growth, income and safety. Invests in common stocks, preferred stocks, U.S. Government securities and money market instruments with allocation adjusted to reflect market conditions.
Year organized: 1976
Ticker symbol: REAGX
Sales charge: 4.50% (available at NAV through discount brokers)
Discount broker availability: Schwab
Minimum purchase through discount broker: $1,000

THE REGIS FUND, INC. PORTFOLIOS
The Regis Fund Service Center
c/o Mutual Funds Service Company
P.O. Box 2798
Boston, MA 02208-2798
617-557-8000, 800-638-7983

Administrator: Mutual Funds Service Company
Special sales restrictions: Designed primarily for institutional investors. Funds are available at lower initial and subsequent minimums through discount brokerage firms which have established accounts with Regis.
Discount broker availability: *Schwab (only through financial advisers)
Minimum purchase through discount broker: $2,000; IRA: $1,000

REGIS - ACADIAN EMERGING MARKETS PORTFOLIO ◆
(See first Regis listing for data common to all Regis portfolios)

Adviser: Acadian Asset Management, Inc.
Investment objective and policies: Long-term capital growth. Invests primarily in common stocks of issuers domiciled in emerging countries. Invests in a representative sample of the securities in each country in which it has holdings.
Year organized: 1993

REGIS - ACADIAN INTERNATIONAL EQUITY PORTFOLIO ◆
(See first Regis listing for data common to all Regis portfolios)

Adviser: Acadian Asset Management, Inc.
Investment objective and policies: Long-term total return that exceeds the performance of the Morgan Stanley EAFE Index. Invests primarily in equity securities of non-U.S. issuers, through direct investment, ADRs and EDRs.
Year organized: 1993

REGIS - ICM EQUITY PORTFOLIO ◆
(See first Regis listing for data common to all Regis portfolios)

Adviser: Investment Counselors of Maryland, Inc.
Portfolio managers: David E. Nelson (1993)
Investment objective and policies: Maximum long-term total return with reasonable risk. Invests primarily in common stocks of relatively large companies, virtually all exceeding the median market capitalization of the stocks on the NYSE.
Year organized: 1993

REGIS - ICM FIXED
INCOME PORTFOLIO ◆
(See first Regis listing for data common to all Regis portfolios)

Adviser: Investment Counselors of Maryland, Inc.
Portfolio managers: Linda W. McCleary (1992), Daniel O. Shackelford (1993)
Investment objective and policies: Maximum total return with reasonable risk. Invests primarily in investment grade corporate and government bonds with weighted average maturity of 3 to 12 years.
Year organized: 1992

REGIS - SIRACH FIXED
INCOME PORTFOLIO ◆
(See first Regis listing for data common to all Regis portfolios)

Adviser: Sirach Capital Management, Inc.
Portfolio managers: Stephen J. Romano (1993), David A. Anderson (1993)
Investment objective and policies: Above-average total return with reasonable risk. Invests primarily in investment grade corporate and government bonds with weighted average maturity of 4 to 12 years.
Year organized: 1993

REGIS - SIRACH
GROWTH PORTFOLIO ◆
(See first Regis listing for data common to all Regis portfolios)

Adviser: Sirach Capital Management, Inc.
Portfolio managers: George B. Kauffman (1993), Robert L. Stephenson, Jr. (1993), David A. Anderson (1993)
Investment objective and policies: Long-term capital growth with reasonable risk. Invests primarily in common stocks with long-term growth potential. Up to 20% of assets may be in securities of foreign issuers.
Year organized: 1993
Ticker symbol: SGRWX

REGIS - SIRACH SHORT-TERM
RESERVES PORTFOLIO ◆
(See first Regis listing for data common to all Regis portfolios)

Adviser: Sirach Capital Management, Inc.
Portfolio managers: Stephen J. Romano (1993), David A. Anderson (1993)
Investment objective and policies: High current income consistent with maintenance of principal and liquidity. Invests in investment grade fixed-income securities with weighted average maturity of 3 years or less.
Year organized: 1993
Ticker symbol: SSTRX

REGIS - SIRACH STRATEGIC
BALANCED PORTFOLIO ◆
(See first Regis listing for data common to all Regis portfolios)

Adviser: Sirach Capital Management, Inc.
Portfolio managers: George B. Kauffman (1993), Robert L. Stephenson, Jr. (1993), Stephen J. Romano (1993), David A. Anderson (1993)
Investment objective and policies: Long-term capital growth with reasonable risk. Invests in common stocks and fixed-income securities with mix adjusted to reflect changing economic and market conditions.
Year organized: 1993
Ticker symbol: SSBAX

REGIS - STERLING PARTNERS
BALANCED PORTFOLIO ◆
(See first Regis listing for data common to all Regis portfolios)

Adviser: Sterling Capital Management, Inc.
Portfolio managers: Paul A. Ehrsam (1991), James R. Norris (1991), David M. Ralston (1991), Mark W. Whalen (1991)
Investment objective and policies: Long-term capital growth with reasonable risk. Invests in common stocks and fixed-income securities with mix adjusted to reflect changing economic and market conditions.
Year organized: 1991
Ticker symbol: SPBPX

REGIS - STERLING PARTNERS
EQUITY PORTFOLIO ◆
(See first Regis listing for data common to all Regis portfolios)

Adviser: Sterling Capital Management, Inc.
Portfolio managers: Paul A. Ehrsam (1991), James R. Norris (1991)
Investment objective and policies: Maximum long-term total return with reasonable risk. Invests in common stocks and other equity securities believed undervalued. Up to 20% of assets may be in securities of foreign issuers.
Year organized: 1991

REGIS - TS&W EQUITY PORTFOLIO ◆
(See first Regis listing for data common to all Regis portfolios)

Adviser: Thompson, Siegel & Walmsley, Inc.
Portfolio managers: Horace P. Whitworth II (1992), Paul A. Ferwerda (1992)
Investment objective and policies: Maximum long-term total return with reasonable risk. Invests in common stocks and other equity securities of relatively large companies believed undervalued. Up to 20% of assets may be in securities of foreign issuers.
Year organized: 1992
Ticker symbol: TSWEX

REGIS - TS&W FIXED
INCOME PORTFOLIO ◆
(See first Regis listing for data common to all Regis portfolios)

Adviser: Thompson, Siegel & Walmsley, Inc.
Portfolio manager: Charles A. Gomer III (1992)
Investment objective and policies: Maximum long-term total return with reasonable risk. Invests primarily in investment-grade fixed-income securities with weighted average maturity of 4 to 12 years. Up to 20% of assets may be in securities of foreign issuers.
Year organized: 1992
Ticker symbol: TSWFX

REGIS - TS&W INTERNATIONAL
EQUITY PORTFOLIO ◆
(See first Regis listing for data common to all Regis portfolios)

Adviser: Thompson, Siegel & Walmsley, Inc.
Portfolio manager: G. D. Rothenberg (1992)
Investment objective and policies: Maximum long-term total return with reasonable risk. Invests primarily in common stocks and other equity securities of established companies in non-U.S. markets.
Year organized: 1992
Ticker symbol: TSWIX

SEI FUNDS
680 East Swedesford Road
Wayne, PA 19087-1658
610-254-1000, 800-342-5734

Administrator: SEI Financial Management Corp.
Special sales restrictions: Designed primarily for institutional investors. Funds are available at lower initial and subsequent minimums through discount brokerage firms which have established accounts with SEI.
Minimum purchase through discount broker: Schwab: $1,000; White: $2,500

SEI BOND INDEX PORTFOLIO
(See first SEI listing for data common to all SEI portfolios)

Adviser: Woodbridge Capital Management
Portfolio manager: Paul Greff (1993)
Investment objective and policies: Investment results approximating the total return of the Salomon Brothers Broad Investment-Grade Bond Index. Invests in a representative sample of the securities which comprise the Index.
Year organized: 1986
Ticker symbol: BIPFX
Discount broker availability: Schwab (only through financial advisers)

SEI BOND PORTFOLIO
(See first SEI listing for data common to all SEI portfolios)

Adviser: Boatmen's Trust Co. (a subsidiary of Boatmen's Bancshares, Inc.)
Portfolio manager: Paul Rapponetti (1987)
Investment objective and policies: Current income consistent with preservation of capital. Invests in U.S. Government and agency securities and investment-grade corporate debt with a weighted average maturity of more than 10 years.
Year organized: 1987
Ticker symbol: SEBDX
Discount broker availability: Schwab (only through financial advisers), White

SEI CAPITAL APPRECIATION
PORTFOLIO
(See first SEI listing for data common to all SEI portfolios)

Adviser: Sun Bank Capital Management, N.A. (a wholly-owned subsidiary of Sun Trust Banks, Inc.)
Portfolio manager: Anthony Gray (1988)
Investment objective and policies: Capital growth. Invests in common stocks and securities convertible into common stocks selected on factors believed favorable for long-term growth, i.e. historical returns on equity & earnings growth rates.
Year organized: 1988
Ticker symbol: SECAX
Discount broker availability: Schwab (only through financial advisers), White

SEI CORE FIXED
INCOME PORTFOLIO
(See first SEI listing for data common to all SEI portfolios)

Adviser: Western Asset Management, Inc.
Portfolio manager: Kent S. Engel (1994)
Investment objective and policies: Current income. Invests in U.S. Government and agency securities and high-quality corporate bonds with a weighted average maturity of 3 to 10 years.
Year organized: 1987 (formerly Limited Volatility Portfolio. Name changed to Intermediate Bond Portfolio on 1/1/94 and to current on 1/1/95)
Ticker symbol: TRLVX
Discount broker availability: Schwab (only through financial advisers),

SEI EQUITY INCOME PORTFOLIO

(See first SEI listing for data common to all SEI portfolios)

Adviser: Merus Capital Management (a division of the Bank of California
Portfolio manager: Tom Arrington (1988)
Investment objective and policies: Current income and moderate capital growth. Invests in common stocks with high current yield and low level of volatility relative to the market.
Year organized: 1988
Ticker symbol: SEEIX
Discount broker availability: Schwab (only through financial advisers), White

SEI GNMA PORTFOLIO

(See first SEI listing for data common to all SEI portfolios)

Adviser: Wellington Management Co.
Portfolio manager: Paul Kaplan (1987)
Investment objective and policies: Current income consistent with preservation of capital and liquidity. Invests in U.S. Government and agency securities, primarily in GNMA instruments.
Year organized: 1987
Ticker symbol: SEGMX
Discount broker availability: White

SEI INTERMEDIATE-TERM GOVERNMENT PORTFOLIO

(See first SEI listing for data common to all SEI portfolios)

Adviser: Wellington Management Company
Portfolio manager: Paul Kaplan (1987)
Investment objective and policies: Current income consistent with preservation of capital and liquidity. Invests in high-quality fixed-income U.S. government securities with a weighted average maturity of 3 to 5 years.
Year organized: 1987
Ticker symbol: TCPGX
Discount broker availability: White

SEI INTERMEDIATE-TERM MUNICIPAL PORTFOLIO

(See first SEI listing for data common to all SEI portfolios)

Adviser: Weiss, Peck & Greer Advisers, Inc.
Portfolio manager: Janet Fiorenza (1989)
Investment objective and policies: Current income exempt from federal income taxes consistent with preservation of capital. Invests in high-quality municipal securities with a weighted average maturity of 3 to 10 years.
Year organized: 1987
Ticker symbol: SEIMX
Discount broker availability: Schwab (only through financial advisers), White

SEI INTERNATIONAL PORTFOLIO

(See first SEI listing for data common to all SEI portfolios)

Adviser: Brinson Partners, Inc.
Portfolio manager: Gary P. Brinson (1991)
Investment objective and policies: Diversification and capital growth. Invests in equity securities of foreign issuers. Fund favors large capitalization stocks with lower price/earnings and market/book ratios and above average dividend yields.
Year organized: 1989 (formerly Wealth Management Trust)
Ticker symbol: SEITX
Discount broker availability: Schwab (only through financial advisers), White

SEI LARGE CAP VALUE PORTFOLIO

(See first SEI listing for data common to all SEI portfolios)

Adviser: Duff & Phelps Investment Management Co.
Portfolio manager: Robert D. Milne (1992)
Investment objective and policies: Long-term capital growth and moderate income. Invests in common stocks of large capitalization companies with low price-to-earnings multiples and above-average dividend yields relative to the market.
Year organized: 1987 (name changed from Value Portfolio in 1994)
Ticker symbol: TRMVX
Discount broker availability: Schwab (only through financial advisers), White

SEI MID-CAP GROWTH PORTFOLIO

(See first SEI listing for data common to all SEI portfolios)

Adviser: Nicholas Applegate Capital Management, Inc.
Portfolio manager: John C. Marshall, Jr. (1994)
Investment objective and policies: Capital growth. Invests in common stocks and securities convertible into common stocks of companies with market capitalizations of $500M to $5B.
Year organized: 1993
Ticker symbol: SEMCX
Discount broker availability: Schwab (only through financial advisers), White

SEI PENNSYLVANIA MUNICIPAL PORTFOLIO

(See first SEI listing for data common to all SEI portfolios)

Adviser: Bessemer Trust Co., N.A.
Portfolio manager: Peter Pellett (1989)
Investment objective and policies: Current income exempt from federal and Pennsylvania income taxes consistent with preservation of capital. Invests in high-quality Pennsylvania municipal securities with a weighted average maturity of 5 to 7 years.
Year organized: 1987
Ticker symbol: SEIPX
Discount broker availability: Schwab (only through financial advisers), White

SEI S&P 500 INDEX PORTFOLIO

(See first SEI listing for data common to all SEI portfolios)

Adviser: Woodbridge Capital Management
Portfolio manager: Todd Johnson (1994)
Investment objective and policies: Investment results approximating the total return of the S&P 500. Invests in the common stocks of the companies in the S&P 500 in the same proportion as their representation in the Index.
Year organized: 1985
Ticker symbol: TRQIX
Discount broker availability: Schwab (only through financial advisers), White

SEI SHORT-TERM GOVERNMENT PORTFOLIO

(See first SEI listing for data common to all SEI portfolios)

Adviser: Wellington Management Company
Portfolio manager: Paul Kaplan (1987)
Investment objective and policies: Current income consistent with preservation of capital and liquidity. Invests in high-quality fixed-income U.S. government securities with a weighted average maturity of 3 years or less.
Year organized: 1987
Ticker symbol: TCSGX
Discount broker availability: White

SEI SMALL CAP GROWTH PORTFOLIO

(See first SEI listing for data common to all SEI portfolios)

Advisers: Investment Advisers, Inc.; Nicholas-Applegate Capital Management; Pilgrim Baxter Grieg & Associates)
Investment objective and policies: Capital growth. Invests in equity securities of companies with market capitalizations under $1B with potential for above average capital growth.
Year organized: 1988
Ticker symbol: SSCGX
Discount broker availability: Schwab (only through financial advisers), White

SOGEN FUNDS

1221 Avenue of the Americas
New York, NY 10020
212-399-1141, 800-334-2143

Adviser: Societe Generale Asset Management Corp. (an indirect subsidiary of Societe Generale, a major French bank)
Sales charge: 3.75% (available at NAV through discount brokers)
Minimum purchase through discount broker: Schwab: $1,000; White: $2,500; Waterhouse: $1,000

SOGEN GOLD FUND

(See first SoGen listing for data common to all SoGen funds)

Portfolio manager: Jean-Marie Eveillard (1993)
Investment objective and policies: Long-term capital appreciation. Invests primarily in securities of companies engaged in mining, processing, dealing or holding gold or other precious metals both in the U.S. and in foreign countries.
Year organized: 1993
Ticker symbol: SGGDX
Discount broker availability: *Schwab (only through financial advisers), *White (only through financial advisers)

SOGEN INTERNATIONAL FUND

(See first SoGen listing for data common to all SoGen funds)

Portfolio manager: Jean-Marie Eveillard (1979)
Investment objective and policies: Long-term capital appreciation. Invests primarily in common stocks of U.S. and foreign companies selected on a value basis. May also invest in U.S. and foreign fixed-income securities.
Year organized: 1970
Ticker symbol: SGENX
Discount broker availability: *Schwab (only through financial advisers), *White (only through financial advisers), Waterhouse

SOGEN OVERSEAS FUND

(See first SoGen listing for data common to all SoGen funds)

Portfolio manager: Jean-Marie Eveillard (1993)
Investment objective and policies: Long-term capital appreciation. Invests primarily in securities of small and medium size non-U.S. companies selected on a value basis. Up to 20% of assets may be in foreign debt securities.
Year organized: 1993
Ticker symbol: SGOVX
Discount broker availability: *Schwab (only through financial advisers), *White (only through financial advisers), Waterhouse

SOLON SHORT DURATION GOVERNMENT FUNDS - ONE YEAR PORTFOLIO ◆
1981 N. Broadway, Suite 325
Walnut Creek, CA 94596
510-988-7110, 800-223-7110

Adviser: Solon Asset Management, L.P.
Portfolio manager: James I. Midanek (1994)
Investment objective and policies: Maximum total return consistent with preservation of capital. Invests in obligations issued or guaranteed by the U.S. Government, its agencies and instrumentalities with weighted average maturity of one year or less.
Year organized: 1994
Special sales restrictions: Designed for institutional investors but available through discount brokerage firms at reduced minimum investments.
Discount broker availability: Schwab
Minimum purchase through discount broker: $1,000

SOLON SHORT DURATION GOVERNMENT FUNDS - THREE YEAR PORTFOLIO ◆
1981 N. Broadway, Suite 325
Walnut Creek, CA 94596
510-988-7110, 800-223-7110

Adviser: Solon Asset Management, L.P.
Portfolio manager: James I. Midanek (1994)
Investment objective and policies: Maximum total return consistent with preservation of capital. Invests in obligations issued or guaranteed by the U.S. Government, its agencies and instrumentalities with weighted average maturity of three years or less.
Year organized: 1994
Special sales restrictions: Designed for institutional investors but available through discount brokerage firms at reduced minimum investments.
Discount broker availability: Schwab
Minimum purchase through discount broker: $1,000

STAGECOACH ASSET ALLOCATION FUND
c/o Wells Fargo Bank, N.A. - Shareholder Services
P.O. Box 7033
San Francisco, CA 94120
800-222-8222

Adviser: Wells Fargo Bank, N.A.
Investment objective and policies: Maximum total return consistent with reasonable risk. Invests in common stocks, U.S. Treasury bonds and money market instruments with percentage of assets in each category adjusted to reflect changes in economic and market conditions.
Year organized: 1986
Ticker symbol: WFAAX
Sales charge: 4.5% (available at NAV through discount brokers)
Discount broker availability: *Schwab (only through financial advisers)
Minimum purchase through discount broker: $1,000

STAGECOACH U.S. TREASURY ALLOCATION FUND
c/o Wells Fargo Bank, N.A. - Shareholder Services
P.O. Box 7033
San Francisco, CA 94120
800-222-8222

Adviser: Wells Fargo Bank, N.A.
Investment objective and policies: Maximum total return consistent with reasonable risk. Invests in long-term U.S. Treasury bonds, intermediate-term U.S. Treasury notes and money market instruments with percentage of assets in each category adjusted to reflect changes in the interest rate environment.
Year organized: 1986
Ticker symbol: WFTRX
Sales charge: 4.5% (available at NAV through discount brokers)
Discount broker availability: *Schwab (only through financial advisers)
Minimum purchase through discount broker: $1,000

UST MASTER FUNDS
73 Tremont Street
Boston, MA 02108
617-451-1912, 800-223-1136
800-446-1012, prices/yields 800-223-9180

Adviser: United States Trust Company of New York
Sales charge: 4.5% (available at NAV through discount brokers)
Discount broker availability: *White (only through financial advisers)
Minimum purchase through discount broker: $2,500

UST MASTER FUNDS - AGING OF AMERICA FUND
(See first UST Master listing for data common to all UST Master funds)

Portfolio manager: Roger F. Schaefer (1992)
Investment objective and policies: Long-term capital growth. Invests in equity securities of companies likely to benefit from the changes occurring in the demographic structure of the U.S., particularly in the growing population of individuals over the age of 40.
Year organized: 1992

UST MASTER FUNDS - BUSINESS AND INDUSTRIAL RESTRUCTURING FUND
(See first UST Master listing for data common to all UST Master funds)

Portfolio manager: David J. Williams (1992)
Investment objective and policies: Long-term capital growth. Invests in equity securities of companies likely to benefit from their restructuring or redeployment of assets and operations in order to become more competitive or profitable.
Year organized: 1992
Ticker symbol: UMBIX

UST MASTER FUNDS - COMMUNICATIONS AND ENTERTAINMENT FUND
(See first UST Master listing for data common to all UST Master funds)

Portfolio manager: John J. Apruzzese (1992)
Investment objective and policies: Long-term capital growth. Invests in equity securities of companies likely to benefit from the technological and international transformation of the communications and entertainment industries, particularly the convergence of information, communication and entertainment media.
Year organized: 1992
Ticker symbol: UMCEX

UST MASTER FUNDS - EARLY LIFE CYCLE FUND
(See first UST Master listing for data common to all UST Master funds)

Portfolio manager: Timothy W. Evnin (1992)
Investment objective and policies: Long-term capital growth. Invests in equity securities of smaller companies in the earlier stages of their development or larger or more mature companies engaged in new and higher growth potential operations.
Year organized: 1992
Ticker symbol: UMLCX

UST MASTER FUNDS - EMERGING AMERICAS FUND
(See first UST Master listing for data common to all UST Master funds)

Sub-advisers: Foreign and Colonial Emerging Markets Limited, Foreign and Colonial Asset Management
Portfolio manager: Harry C. Rowney (1992)
Investment objective and policies: Long-term capital growth. Invests primarily in companies and securities of governments based in all countries in the Western Hemisphere, except the U.S.
Year organized: 1992
Ticker symbol: UMEAX

UST MASTER FUNDS - ENVIRONMENTALLY-RELATED PRODUCTS AND SERVICES FUND
(See first UST Master listing for data common to all UST Master funds)

Portfolio manager: Victor Sapuppo (1992)
Investment objective and policies: Long-term capital growth. Invests in equity securities of companies providing products, technologies and services related to conservation, protection and restoration of the environment.
Year organized: 1992

UST MASTER FUNDS - EQUITY FUND
(See first UST Master listing for data common to all UST Master funds)

Portfolio manager: Laird I. Grant (1989)
Investment objective and policies: Long-term capital growth. Invests in equity securities of companies believed to represent good long-term values not currently recognized in the market price of their securities.
Year organized: 1985
Ticker symbol: UMEQX

UST MASTER FUNDS - GLOBAL COMPETITORS FUND
(See first UST Master listing for data common to all UST Master funds)

Portfolio manager: Wendy S. Popowich (1992)
Investment objective and policies: Long-term capital growth. Invests primarily in equity securities of U.S.-based companies likely to benefit from their position as effective and strong competitors on a global basis.
Year organized: 1992

UST MASTER FUNDS - INCOME AND GROWTH FUND
(See first UST Master listing for data common to all UST Master funds)

Portfolio manager: Richard L. Bayles (1990)
Investment objective and policies: Moderate current income with capital growth secondary. Invests primarily in dividend-paying equity securities - common stock, preferred stock and convertible securities - of established companies.
Year organized: 1987
Ticker symbol: UMIGX

UST MASTER FUNDS - INTERMEDIATE-TERM MANAGED INCOME FUND
(See first UST Master listing for data common to all UST Master funds)

Portfolio manager: Henry M. Milwekicz (1992)
Investment objective and policies: High current income consistent with prudent risk of capital. Invests primarily in investment-grade debt obligations and money market instruments with a weighted average maturity of 3 to 10 years.
Year organized: 1992
Ticker symbol: UIMIX

UST MASTER FUNDS - INTERMEDIATE-TERM TAX-EXEMPT FUND
(See first UST Master listing for data common to all UST Master funds)

Portfolio manager: Michael G. Crofton (1991)
Investment objective and policies: High current income exempt from federal income taxes consistent with relative stability of principal. Invests primarily in investment-grade municipal debt obligations with a weighted average maturity of 3 to 10 years.
Year organized: 1985
Ticker symbol: UMITX

UST MASTER FUNDS - INTERNATIONAL FUND
(See first UST Master listing for data common to all UST Master funds)

Sub-adviser: Foreign and Colonial Asset Management
Portfolio manager: Harry C. Rowney (1987)
Investment objective and policies: Total return - long-term capital growth and current income. Invests primarily in equity securities of foreign issuers likely to benefit from global economic trends, promising technologies or products and other opportunities resulting from changing geopolitical, economic or currency relationships.
Year organized: 1987
Ticker symbol: UMINX

UST MASTER FUNDS -LONG-TERM SUPPLY OF ENERGY FUND
(See first UST Master listing for data common to all UST Master funds)

Portfolio manager: Richard L. Bayles (1992)
Investment objective and policies: Long-term capital growth. Invests in equity securities of companies likely to benefit from the availability, development and delivery of secure hydrocarbon and other energy sources.
Year organized: 1992

UST MASTER FUNDS - LONG-TERM TAX-EXEMPT FUND
(See first UST Master listing for data common to all UST Master funds)

Portfolio manager: Kenneth J. McAlley (1986)
Investment objective and policies: High current income exempt from federal income taxes. Invests primarily in investment-grade municipal bonds with a weighted average maturity of up to 30 years.
Year organized: 1986
Ticker symbol: UMLTX

UST MASTER FUNDS - MANAGED INCOME FUND
(See first UST Master listing for data common to all UST Master funds)

Portfolio manager: Henry M. Milkewicz (1986)
Investment objective and policies: High current

income consistent with prudent risk of capital. Invests primarily in investment-grade debt obligations and money market instruments with a weighted average maturity that varies with market and economic conditions, comparative yields and other factors.
Year organized: 1986
Ticker symbol: UMMGX

UST MASTER FUNDS - NEW YORK INTERMEDIATE-TERM TAX-EXEMPT FUND
(See first UST Master listing for data common to all UST Master funds)

Portfolio manager: Michael G. Crofton (1991)
Investment objective and policies: High current income exempt from federal and New York State and New York City personal income taxes consistent with relative stability of principal. Invests primarily in investment-grade New York municipal debt obligations with a weighted average maturity of 3 to 10 years.
Year organized: 1990
Ticker symbol: UMNYX

UST MASTER FUNDS - PACIFIC/ASIA FUND
(See first UST Master listing for data common to all UST Master funds)

Sub-advisers: Foreign and Colonial Emerging Markets Limited, Foreign and Colonial Asset Management
Portfolio manager: Harry C. Rowney (1992)
Investment objective and policies: Long-term capital growth. Invests primarily in companies and securities of governments based in all countries in Asia and on the Asian side of the Pacific Ocean.
Year organized: 1992
Ticker symbol: USPAX

UST MASTER FUNDS - PAN EUROPEAN FUND
(See first UST Master listing for data common to all UST Master funds)

Sub-adviser: Foreign and Colonial Asset Management
Portfolio manager: Harry C. Rowney (1992)
Investment objective and policies: Long-term capital growth. Invests primarily in companies and securities of governments based in Europe - all countries of Western Europe and Eastern European countries as they become economically viable.
Year organized: 1992
Ticker symbol: UMPNX

UST MASTER FUNDS - PRODUCTIVITY ENHANCERS FUND
(See first UST Master listing for data common to all UST Master funds)

Portfolio manager: Ronald C. Steele (1992)
Investment objective and policies: Long-term capital growth. Invests in equity securities of companies that innovate, develop and supply goods and services which enhance service and manufacturing productivity or companies that are most effective at obtaining and applying productivity enhancement developments.
Year organized: 1992

UST MASTER FUNDS - SHORT-TERM GOVERNMENT SECURITIES FUND
(See first UST Master listing for data common to all UST Master funds)

Portfolio manager: Charles E. Rabus (1992)
Investment objective and policies: High current

income consistent with stability of principal. Invests primarily in obligations issued or guaranteed by the U.S. Government, its agencies or instrumentalities with a weighted average maturity of 1 to 3 years.
Year organized: 1992
Ticker symbol: UMGVX

UST MASTER FUNDS - SHORT-TERM TAX-EXEMPT SECURITIES FUND
(See first UST Master listing for data common to all UST Master funds)

Portfolio manager: Michael G. Crofton (1992)
Investment objective and policies: High current income exempt from federal income taxes consistent with stability of principal. Invests primarily in investment-grade municipal debt obligations with a weighted average maturity of 1 to 3 years.
Year organized: 1992
Ticker symbol: USSSX

VAN ECK FUNDS
122 East 42nd Street
New York, NY 10168
212-907-1500, 800-687-5201
800-544-4653

Adviser: Van Eck Associates Corp.
Sales charge: 4.75% (5.75% for gold funds) (available at NAV through discount brokers)
Minimum purchase through discount broker: Schwab: $1,000; White: $2,500

VAN ECK ASIA DYNASTY FUND
(See first Van Eck listing for data common to all Van Eck funds)

Sub-adviser: AIG Asset Management, Inc.
Portfolio manager: Peter Soo (1993)
Investment objective and policies: Long-term capital growth. Invests in equity securities of companies expected to benefit from the development and growth of the economies of the Asian region.
Year organized: 1993
Ticker symbol: ASDYX
Discount broker availability: *Schwab (only through financial advisers), *White (only through financial advisers)

VAN ECK ASIA INFRASTRUCTURE FUND
(See first Van Eck listing for data common to all Van Eck funds)

Sub-adviser: AIG Asset Management, Inc.
Portfolio manager: Peter Soo (1993)
Investment objective and policies: Long-term capital growth. Invests in equity securities of infrastructure companies expected to benefit from the development and growth of the economies of the Asian region.
Year organized: 1993
Ticker symbol: AIFAX
Discount broker availability: *Schwab (only through financial advisers), *White (only through financial advisers)

VAN ECK GLOBAL BALANCED FUND
(See first Van Eck listing for data common to all Van Eck funds)

Sub-adviser: Fiduciary International, Inc.
Portfolio managers: Brian Hopkinson (1993), Cheng-Hock Lau (1993)
Investment objective and policies: Long-term capital growth and current income. Invests in equity securities, fixed-income securities and short-term instruments in the U.S. and other countries throughout the world adjusting mix to changing economic and market conditions.

Year organized: 1993
Ticker symbol: GBFAX
Discount broker availability: *Schwab (only through financial advisers), *White (only through financial advisers)

VAN ECK GLOBAL HARD ASSETS FUND
(See first Van Eck listing for data common to all Van Eck funds)

Portfolio manager: John C. van Eck (1994)
Investment objective and policies: Long-term capital growth with income secondary. Invests primarily in securities of companies involved in the exploration, development, production and/or distribution of precious and non-precious metals, hydrocarbons, forest products, real estate and other basic non-agricultural commodities.
Year organized: 1994
Discount broker availability: *Schwab (only through financial advisers)

VAN ECK GLOBAL INCOME FUND
(See first Van Eck listing for data common to all Van Eck funds)

Portfolio manager: Madis Senner (1994)
Investment objective and policies: Long-term capital growth and current income. Invests in equity securities, fixed-income securities and short-term instruments in the U.S. and other countries throughout the world adjusting mix to changing economic and market conditions.
Year organized: 1987 (name changed from World Income Fund in 1994)
Ticker symbol: WIFRX
Discount broker availability: *Schwab (only through financial advisers), *White (only through financial advisers)

VAN ECK GLOBAL SMALLCAP FUND
(See first Van Eck listing for data common to all Van Eck funds)

Sub-adviser: Pictet International Management Ltd.
Portfolio manager: Fabien Pictet (1994)
Investment objective and policies: Long-term capital growth. Invests in equity securities of companies with capitalizations below $500M from all over the world. Normally is invested in at least 3 countries, including the U.S.
Year organized: 1994
Ticker symbol: GSFAX
Discount broker availability: *Schwab (only through financial advisers), *White (only through financial advisers)

VAN ECK GOLD/RESOURCES FUND
(See first Van Eck listing for data common to all Van Eck funds)

Portfolio manager: Lucille Palermo (1992)
Investment objective and policies: Long-term capital growth. Invests in equity and debt securities of companies engaged in the exploration, development, production and distribution of gold and other natural resources.
Year organized: 1986
Ticker symbol: GRFRX
Discount broker availability: *Schwab (only through financial advisers), *White (only through financial advisers)

VAN ECK INTERNATIONAL INVESTORS GOLD FUND
(See first Van Eck listing for data common to all Van Eck funds)

Portfolio manager: Henry J. Bingham (1993)
Investment objective and policies: Long-term capital growth with some current income. Invests primarily in common stocks of gold mining companies

but may have up to 75% of assets in other investments for defensive purposes.
Year organized: 1956
Ticker symbol: INIVX
Discount broker availability: *Schwab (only through financial advisers), *White (only through financial advisers)

VAN ECK WORLD TRENDS FUND
(See first Van Eck listing for data common to all Van Eck funds)

Portfolio managers: Derek S. van Eck (1985), David R. Kenerson, Jr. (1986)
Investment objective and policies: Long-term capital growth with income secondary. Invests in equity securities of companies throughout the world believed to benefit from new and changing economic and business trends.
Year organized: 1985
Ticker symbol: WTFDX
Discount broker availability: *White (only through financial advisers)

VISTA FUNDS
P.O. Box 419392
Kansas City, MO 64141-6392
800-348-4782, fax 716-258-7962

Adviser: Chase Manhattan Bank, N.A.
Minimum purchase through discount broker: Schwab: $1,000; White: $2,500

VISTA BALANCED FUND
(See first Vista listing for data common to all Vista funds)

Portfolio managers: Gregory Adams (1992), Thomas Nelson (1992)
Investment objective and policies: Long-term capital growth and current income. Invests in equity and debt securities, including common stocks, convertible securities and government and fixed-income obligations. Adjusts allocation to changing economic and market conditions.
Year organized: 1993
Ticker symbol: VBALX
Sales charge: 4.50% (available at NAV through discount brokers)
Discount broker availability: *White (only through financial advisers)

VISTA CALIFORNIA INTERMEDIATE TAX FREE FUND
(See first Vista listing for data common to all Vista funds)

Portfolio manager: Pamela Hunter (1993)
Investment objective and policies: Income exempt from federal and California state income taxes consistent with preservation of capital. Invests primarily in high quality CA municipal securities with weighted average maturity of 10 years or less.
Year organized: 1993
Ticker symbol: VCATX
Sales charge: 4.50% (available at NAV through discount brokers)
Discount broker availability: *White (only through financial advisers)

VISTA CAPITAL GROWTH FUND
(See first Vista listing for data common to all Vista funds)

Portfolio managers: Mark A. Tincher (1991), David Klassen (1993)
Investment objective and policies: Long-term growth. Invests in common stocks and securities convertible into common stocks of small to medium-sized companies believed to benefit from certain social and economic trends.

Year organized: 1987
Ticker symbol: VCAGX
Sales charge: 4.75% (available at NAV through discount brokers)
Discount broker availability: *Schwab (only through financial advisers), *White (only through financial advisers)

VISTA EQUITY INCOME FUND
(See first Vista listing for data common to all Vista funds)

Portfolio manager: Mark A. Tincher (1993)
Investment objective and policies: Current income. Invests in income-producing common stocks, preferred stocks, convertible preferred stocks and corporate bonds convertible into common stocks. Up to 20% of assets may be in securities of foreign issuers.
Year organized: 1993
Sales charge: 4.50% (available at NAV through discount brokers)
Discount broker availability: *White (only through financial advisers)

VISTA GLOBAL FIXED INCOME FUND
(See first Vista listing for data common to all Vista funds)

Portfolio manager: Gordon Ross (1994)
Investment objective and policies: Current income and capital growth. Invests primarily in domestic and foreign fixed-income securities. Uses currency futures and options to enhance income and hedge.
Year organized: 1993
Sales charge: 4.50% (available at NAV through discount brokers)
Discount broker availability: *White (only through financial advisers)

VISTA GROWTH AND INCOME FUND
(See first Vista listing for data common to all Vista funds)

Portfolio manager: Mark A. Tincher (1991)
Investment objective and policies: Long-term growth and current income secondary. Invests in undervalued common stocks currently out of favor that are believed to offer significant potential for appreciation.
Year organized: 1987
Ticker symbol: VGRIX
Sales charge: 4.75% (available at NAV through discount brokers)
Discount broker availability: *Schwab (only through financial advisers), *White (only through financial advisers)

VISTA GROWTH FUND OF WASHINGTON
(See first Vista listing for data common to all Vista funds)

Adviser: Washington Investment Advisers, Inc.
Sub-adviser: The Chase Manhattan Bank, N.A.
Portfolio manager: Prabha S. Carpenter (1986)
Investment objective and policies: Long-term capital growth. Invests in securities of companies headquartered or having a major place of business in Washington, D.C., Maryland or Virginia.
Year organized: 1986
Ticker symbol: GRWAX
Sales charge: 4.75% (available at NAV through discount brokers)
Discount broker availability: *White (only through financial advisers)

VISTA INTERNATIONAL EQUITY FUND
(See first Vista listing for data common to all Vista funds)

Portfolio manager: Joseph DeSantis (1993)
Investment objective and policies: Long-term growth and income. Invests in common stocks of

companies domiciled outside the U.S. with potential for growth of capital or income or both. May use ADRs and EDRs.
Year organized: 1992
Ticker symbol: VIEAX
Sales charge: 4.75% (available at NAV through discount brokers)
Discount broker availability: *Schwab (only through financial advisers), *White (only through financial advisers)

VISTA NEW YORK TAX
FREE INCOME FUND
(See first Vista listing for data common to all Vista funds)

Portfolio manager: Pamela Hunter (1987)
Investment objective and policies: Income exempt from federal and New York State and New York City personal income taxes consistent with preservation of capital. Invests primarily in high quality NY municipal securities.
Year organized: 1987
Ticker symbol: VTNYX
Sales charge: 4.50% (available at NAV through discount brokers)
Discount broker availability: Schwab (only through financial advisers), *White (only through financial advisers)

VISTA TAX FREE INCOME FUND
(See first Vista listing for data common to all Vista funds)

Portfolio manager: Pamela Hunter (1987)
Investment objective and policies: Income exempt from federal income taxes consistent with preservation of capital. Invests primarily in high quality municipal securities.
Year organized: 1987
Ticker symbol: VTFIX
Sales charge: 4.50% (available at NAV through discount brokers)
Discount broker availability: *Schwab (only through financial advisers), *White (only through financial advisers)

VISTA U.S. GOVERNMENT
INCOME FUND
(See first Vista listing for data common to all Vista funds)

Portfolio manager: Thomas Nelson (1992)
Investment objective and policies: Maximum current income consistent with preservation of capital.

Invests primarily in securities guaranteed as to payment of principal and interest by the U.S. Government, its agencies or instrumentalities.
Year organized: 1988
Ticker symbol: VGVIX
Sales charge: 4.50% (available at NAV through discount brokers)
Discount broker availability: *Schwab (only through financial advisers), *White (only through financial advisers)

WORKING ASSETS PORTFOLIOS
111 Pine Street
San Francisco, CA 94111
415-989-3200, 800-223-7010
fax 603-433-4209

Adviser: Working Assets Capital Management
Common policies: All portfolios favor investments that support housing, education, farming, small business, and energy conservation. Avoid companies that pollute the environment, manufacture weapons, drain capital from the U.S. or support repressive regimes.
Sales charge: 4.0% (2.0% for Income) (available at NAV through discount brokers)
Minimum purchase through discount broker: Schwab: $1,000; White: $2,500
Discount broker availability: *Schwab (only through financial advisers), White (only through financial advisers)

WORKING ASSETS CITIZENS
BALANCED PORTFOLIO
(See first Working Assets listing for data common to all Working Assets portfolios)

Portfolio managers: Rick Little (1993), Gail Seneca (1993)
Investment objective and policies: Current income and capital growth. Invests in common stocks (50-70% of assets) and fixed-income securities (minimum 25% of assets).
Year organized: 1992
Ticker symbol: WABLX

WORKING ASSETS CITIZENS
EMERGING GROWTH PORTFOLIO
(See first Working Assets listing for data common to all Working Assets portfolios)

Portfolio managers: Ron K. Jacks (1994), Rick Little (1994)
Investment objective and policies: Long-term capital

growth. Invests in common stocks of small- and medium-sized companies with market capitalizations under $2B and above-average growth potential.
Year organized: 1994

WORKING ASSETS CITIZENS
GLOBAL EQUITY PORTFOLIO
(See first Working Assets listing for data common to all Working Assets portfolios)

Portfolio manager: Lilia Clemente (1993)
Investment objective and policies: Long-term capital growth. Invests in common stocks of domestic and foreign companies of all sizes with above-average growth potential on stock exchanges from around the world.
Year organized: 1993
Ticker symbol: WAGEX

WORKING ASSETS CITIZENS
GROWTH PORTFOLIO
(See first Working Assets listing for data common to all Working Assets portfolios)

Portfolio manager: Harold Janeway (1992)
Investment objective and policies: Long-term capital growth. Invests in common stocks of domestic companies of all sizes with above-average growth potential.
Year organized: 1992
Ticker symbol: WAGRX

WORKING ASSETS CITIZENS
INCOME PORTFOLIO
(See first Working Assets listing for data common to all Working Assets portfolios)

Portfolio manager: Gail Seneca (1993)
Investment objective and policies: Current income. Invests in fixed-income securities with a weighted average maturity of 5 to 15 years. Up to 35% of assets may be in junk bonds.
Year organized: 1992
Ticker symbol: WAIMX

CHAPTER 13

Directory of discount brokers trading mutual funds

CHARLES SCHWAB & CO
Mutual Fund Market Place

Phone: 800-526-8600
Trading hours: 24 hours a day; 2 P.M. EST for today's price.
No. of branch offices: 208
Reinvests dividends: Yes
IRA account fee: $29 per year under $10,000 value
Margin rules: Schwab funds must be in the account 30 days, non-Schwab funds can be margined immediately.
Shorts funds: No
No. of Handbook funds traded: 970
No. of NTF (no transaction fee) funds traded: 447
NTF Assets: $13 billion
No. of load funds available NAV & institutional w/low min: 207
NTF short-term trading rules: Shares held for at least 90 days can be sold without penalty. Standard fees will be charged on the sale if held less than 90 days. A maximum of 15 short-term redemptions (less than 90 days) per calendar year will be allowed. If this is exceeded, all transactions (i.e. both on the buy and sell side) become commissionable.
Fee schedule for commissionable funds
Overriding minimum: $39 per trade.

Transaction Size	Transaction fees
$0-14,999	0.7% of principal
$15,000-99,999	0.7% on first $15,000
	0.2% on amount over $15,000
$100,000+	0.7% on first $15,000
	0.2% on amount
	between $15,000 & $100,000
	0.08% on amount over $100,000

When placing simutaneous orders to sell one fund and purchase a new fund with the proceeds you pay the standard fee on the larger transaction and $25 on the corresponding buy or sell. Funds sales or redemption fees also apply.

FIDELITY BROKERAGE
Funds Network

Phone: 800-544-9697
Trading hours: 24 hours a day; 1:00 P.M. for today's price for non-Fidelity funds; 2:30 P.M. for exchanges in the same family.
No. of branch offices: 79
Reinvests dividends: Yes
IRA account fee: $20 per year under $5,000 value
Margin rules: Funds must be in account 30 days
Shorts funds: Yes
No. of Handbook funds traded: 676
No. of NTF funds traded: 345
NTF Assets: $10 billion
No. of load funds available NAV & institutional w/low min: 0
NTF short-term trading rules: Reserves the right to limit short-term redemptions to 5 per 12-months periods. Short-term is defined as shares held less than 6 months.
Fee schedule for commissionable funds

Transaction Size	Transaction fees
$0-5,000	$17.50 + 0.8% of principal
$5,001-10,000	$29.50 + 0.4% of principal
$10,001-25,000+	$39.50 + 0.2% of principal
$25,001-95,000	$67.50 + 0.1% of principal
$95,001 +	$157.50 + 0.08% of principal

Minimum fee on commissionable funds: $28

JACK WHITE & CO.
Mutual Fund Network

Phone: 800-323-3263
Trading hours: 24 hours per day, 7 day a week. 9 AM or 12:00 NOON PST for today's price depending on fund.
No. of branch offices: 0
Reinvests dividends: Some funds
IRA account fee: $35 per year, under $10,000.
Margin rules: Available for funds (except for T. Rowe Price's) with NAV's over $5.
Shorts funds: Yes, subject to availability; $15,000 equity required.
No. of Handbook funds traded: 1030
No. of NTF funds traded: 533
NTF Assets: $1 billion
No. of load funds available NAV & institutional w/low min: 174
NTF short-term trading rules: Positions liquidated within 60 days of purchase are charged applicable transaction fee. If a customer makes 5 short-term redemptions (defined as less than 6 months) in a calendar year, regular transaction fees apply to all transactions the balance of the year.

Fee schedule for commissionable funds

Transaction Size	Transaction fees
$0 to $5,000 including NTF funds	$27
$5,001 to $25,000	$35
$25,000 and above	$50

WATERHOUSE SECURITIES
Mutual Fund Connection

Phone: 800-934-4443
Trading hours: Monday-Friday, 8:30 AM - 5 PM EST; 2 PM for today's price.
No. of branch offices: 64
Reinvests dividends: Yes
IRA account fee: $25 per year
Margin rules: Available for funds with NAV's over $4 1/8
Shorts funds: No
No. of Handbook funds traded: 591
No. of NTF funds traded: 177
NTF Assets: $90 million
No. of load funds available NAV & institutional w/low min: 3
Fee schedule for commissionable funds

Transaction Size	Transaction fees
$0-15,000	0.6% of principal
$15,001-100,000	0.6% on first $15,000
	0.2% on amount over $15,000
$100,000+	0.6% on first $15,000
	0.2% over $15,000
	0.08% over $100,000

Minimum fee on commissionable funds: $29
Sell orders for load funds: $35

MURIAL SIEBERT
Fundsmart

Phone: 800-872-0666
Trading hours: Monday-Friday, 9:00 AM - 5:00 PM; 1:00 PM or 4:00 PM for today's price.
No. of branch offices: 2
Reinvests dividends: Yes
IRA account fee: $30 per year
Margin rules: Funds must be in account 30 days
Shorts funds: No
No. of Handbook funds traded: 676
No. of NTF funds traded: 345
NTF Assets: Over $15 million
No. of load funds available NAV & institutional w/low min: 0
NTF minimum investments: $5,000, $2,000 for IRAs
NTF short-term trading rules: Minimum holding period to qualify for NTF: $2,000-$9,999 = 9 months, $10,000-$19,999 = 6 months, $20,000-$49,999 = 3 months, $50,000+ = 1 month.
Fee schedule for commissionable funds

Transaction Size	Transaction fees
$0-5,000	$17.50 + 0.8% of principal
$5,001-10,000	$29.50 + 0.4% of principal
$10,001-25,000+	$39.50 + 0.2% of principal
$25,001-100,000	$67.50 + 0.1% of principal
$100,001 +	$157.50 + 0.08% of principal

Minimum fee on commissionable funds: $39.50

General information: All services provide consolidated monthly statements and insurance protection.

Other discount brokers offering no-load fund trading

The following brokers also offer fund services. Contact them for details:

Discount broker	800 telephone
AccuFunds	582-5534
Accutrade	228-3011
Andrew Peck	221-5873
Arnold Securities	328-4076
Aufhauser & Co.	368-3668
Barry Murphy & Co.	221-2111
Bidwell & Co.	547-6337
Broker's Exchange	922-0960
Bruno, Stolze & Co.	899-6878
Bull & Bear Sec.	262-5800
Bush Burns Sec.	821-4800
Calvert Sec. Corp	999-3699
CoreStates Sec.	222-0124
Fleet Brokerage Sec.	221-8210
Freeman Welwood & Co.	729-7585
Lombard Institutional	688-3462
Marsh Block & Co.	366-1500
Midwood Discount	643-9663
PC Financial Net	825-5732
Peremel & Co.	666-1440
Quick & Riley	221-5220
Seaport Sec.	732-7678
Securities Research	327-3156
Sherman, Ralston	221-4242
Spear Sec.	455-2211
State Discount	222-5520
Sterling Investment	782-1522
T. Rowe Price Discount	638-5660
Thomas F. White	669-4483
Tuttle Sec.	962-5489
U.J.B. Investor Services	631-1635
Unified Mngt Corp.	862-7283
Wall St. Discount	221-7990
York Sec.	221-3154

CHAPTER 14

Directory of portfolio managers
Arranged alphabetically

Portfolio Manager	Fund
Abe, Shuhei	Warburg, Pincus Japan OTC
Ablin, Jack A.	1784 Asset Alloc,Income,US Govt Med Term
Abrams, Kenneth L.	Vanguard Explorer
Adams, Gregory	Vista Balanced
Adams, Patrick S.	Founders Balanced,Blue Chip
Adibi, Catherine	Dreyfus European
Adler, Steven H.	ASM Fund
Affleck, John	Stratton Growth
Aglione, Joan	Green Century MM
Akant, Adnan	Harbor Short Duration
Albrecht, J. Scott	Federated MI Inter Muni Tr
Aldis, Ralph P.	United Services Global Resources, Special Term Govt
Alger, David	Alger Balanced,Growth,Inc & Gr, Leveraged AllCap,MidCap Gr,Sm Cap
Allan, Elizabeth J.	Japan Fund,Scudder Pacific Opportunites
Alogna, John A.	Monetta Govt MM,Inter Bond,Mid Cap Eq
Anderson, David A.	Regis Sirach FI,Sirach Gr,Sirach ST Reserves,Sirach Strat Bal
Anderson, David B.	Babson UMB Heartland,UMB Stock
Anderson, Erik S.	SIT Growth
Anderson, Peter R.	Federated Fortress High Qual Stock, Growth Tr,Liberty Am Leaders,Stock Tr
Antico, Paul	Fidelity Sel Developing Communications
Antoian, Edward N.	Delaware Delcap Concept I Series,Trend
Apple, Terry	Rydex OTC
Apruzzese, John J.	UST Master Communications & Entertainment
Armknecht, Bob	Galaxy Equity Growth
Armstrong, Arden C.	MAS Emerging Growth
Aronoff, Steven P.	Scudder Capital Growth
Arrington, Tom	SEI Equity Income
Ashburner, Leslie F.B.	Accessor Int'l Fixed Income
Askew, Peter B.	Price, Rowe Emerg Mkts Bond,Global Govt Bond,Int'l Bond,ST Global Income
Aster, Richard F. Jr.	Meridian,Meridian Value
Astrop, William B.	Atlanta Growth
Athey, Preston G.	Price, Rowe Small Cap Value
Augustin, Elizabeth A.	Pierpont TE Bond,TE MM
Auriana, Lawrence	Kaufmann Fund
Aushwitz, David R.	Primary Income,Trend
Auwaerter, Robert	Vanguard Adm Inter US Treas,Adm LT US Treas,FI Inter Corp,FI Inter US Treas,FI LT US Treas,FI ST Corp,FI ST Federal
Ayoub, Chris	Merrill Lynch Retirement Res MF
Bacarella, Robert S.	Monetta Fund
Bache, Stephen K.	Pacific Advisors Balanced
Bagnoli, Paul	Bernstein Int'l Value
Bajakian, Vincent	Vanguard Wellington
Baker, James	Invesco Inter Govt Bond
Baker, James Edward	Amtrust Value
Balco, George J.	59 Wall St Small Company
Balestrino, Joseph M.	Federated Fortress Bond,Stock and Bond
Bannick, William B	PIMCO Adv Inst Cadence Cap Appr,Cadence Micro Cap Gr,Cadence Mid Cap Gr,Cadence Sm Cap Gr
Barach, Philip	Enterprise Govt Sec,TCW/DW North Am Govt Inc Tr
Barba, Guy	Hanover Short-Term U.S. Govt
Barbaro, Steve	Galaxy Small Company Equity
Barber, Rocky	William Blair Mutual Gr Shares
Bardin, Gail	Hotchkis and Wiley Eq Inc
Baron, Ronald S.	Baron Asset,Gr & Inc

Portfolio Manager	Fund
Barone, Richard A.	Maxus Equity,Income
Barr, Dean	Quantitative Disciplined Growth
Barrett, Richard C.	National Industries
Barron, Leland	Fidelity Spartan US Govt MM,Spartan US Treas MM,US Govt Res
Barrow, James	Vanguard Windsor II
Barth, Gerald P.	Enterprise Tax-Exempt Income
Barton, Bruce R.	Galaxy Inter Bond
Barton, Philip	Fidelity Sel Environmental Svcs
Basten, David D.	API Trust Capital Inc,Growth,Special Mkts,T-1 Treas Tr,Total Return
Bauer, Randall S.	Federated Liberty Int'l Eq,Liberty Int'l Inc
Bauer, Stephen C.	SAFECO CA TF Inc,Insured Muni Bond,Inter Muni Bond,Muni Bond, WA State Muni Bond
Baxter, Christine	PBHG Emerging Gr
Baxter, Donald H.	Philadelphia Fund
Bayles, Richard L.	UST Master Inc & Gr,LT Supply of Energy
Beaty, Bruce F.	AARP Capital Growth
Beausoleil, Robert	Maxus Laureate
Beckerman, Mark D.	44 Wall St Equity
Beckwitt, Bob	Fidelity Asset Mgr, Asset Mgr Gr, Asset Mgr Inc
Bender, Robert L.	Monitrend Growth
Benito, Donaldo S.	CMA Govt Securities
Benjamin, Ann H.	SteinRoe Income
Benner, H. Dean	Brundage Story & Rose SI FI
Bennett, John	GAM Europe
Bennett, Thomas L.	MAS High Yield Sec
Benzak, Louis R.	SBSF Converible Sec,Fund,MM
Berchtenbreiter, Patrice L.	Price, Rowe CA TF MF,NY TF MF, Summit Muni MM,TE MF
Berghuis, Brian W.H.	Price, Rowe Mid Cap Growth
Bergstrom, Gary L.	Fremont Int'l Small Cap
Bernstein, Edwin R.	Prudent Speculator
Bertelson, Bob	Fidelity Sel Industrial Equipment
Berthy, Les	Forum Daily Assets Treasury
Bertocci, Bruno	SteinRoe Int'l
Besecker, Bruce	FFB Lexicon Fixed Income
Bettin, Scott A.	IAI Govt
Beveridge, Walter	Schwab CA TE MF,TE MF
Bhandari, Laxmi C.	Warburg, Pincus Global FI
Biggar, Douglas A.	Weston - New Century Capital, New Century I
Biggs, Jeremy H.	Blanchard Global Growth
Binder, Steve	Fidelity Sel Medical Delivery
Bingham, Henry J.	PIMCO Adv Precious Metals,Van Eck Int'l Investors Gold
Bird, Allan W.	Wayne Hummer Growth
Black, Susan L.	Warburg, Pincus Cap Apprec
Boeckmann, Eric	Northern Inter TE
Boesel, Stephen W.	Price, Rowe Growth & Income
Bogle, John C., Jr.	Quantitative Numeric,Numeric II
Boich, John D.	Montgomery Global Communications, Global Opportunities,Int'l Sm Cap
Bolton, Eugene	GE US Equity,General Electric S&S Program Mutual
Bonnel, Arthur J.	Bonnel Growth
Boritzke, John D.	Marshall Inter TF,ST TF
Bosland, James L.	1784 CT TE Inc,RI TE Inc,TF MM
Bourbulas, Mary-Kay H.	Strong HY Muni Bond,Insured Muni Bond,Muni Bond
Bouscaren, Michael	Salomon Brothers Cash Mgmt,NY Muni Bond,NY Muni MM,US Treas Sec MM
Bouwer, Dennis	Hotchkis and Wiley Int'l

Portfolio Manager	Fund
Bouzakis, Alex V.	CMA Treasury Fund
Bower, Bill	Fidelity Sel Construction & Housing
Boxer, Steve	Seven Seas MM,US Govt MM
Boyd, Christopher	Twentieth Century Gr,Ultra
Bradburn, Janice	Fidelity MA TF MM,NY TF MM, OH Muni MM, Spartan MA Muni MM Spartan NY Muni MM
Bramwell, Elizabeth R.	Bramwell Growth,Selected Special Shares
Bray, Catherine H.	Price, Rowe High Yield
Breazzano, David	Fidelity Capital & Income
Breed, David B.	PIMCO Adv Inst Cadence Cap Appr,Cadence Micro Cap Gr,Cadence Mid Cap Gr,Cadence Sm Cap Gr
Bridges, Edson L. II	Bridges Investment
Brilley, Michael C.	SIT Bond,MN TF, MM,TF Inc, US Govt Sec
Brilliant, Irving	Salomon Brothers Opportunity
Brinkley, Barbara A.	59 Wall St TF SI FI
Brinson, Gary P.	Brinson Global,Global Bond,Global Eq, Non-Us Eq, SEI Int'l Eq
Broadus, Thomas H. Jr.	Price, Rowe Blue Chip Gr, Eq Inc
Brofman, Lance N.	Fundamental CA Muni,NY Muni
Brown, Anthony S.	Pax World
Brown, John H.	Montgomery Equity Income
Browne, Robert	JPM Advisor Int'l Fixed Inc
Bruce, John T.	FBP Contrarian Balanced,Equity
Bruce, Robert B.	Bruce Fund
Bruno, Gregory L.	Countdown to Retirement Retire 2010, Retire 2020
Bryan, Caesar M.P.	Gabelli Gold
Bunker, Michael S.	GAM Pacific Basin
Buonaugurio, Mark	Vista Bond
Burgess, Frank	Bascom Hill Balanced,Investors
Burks, Jack D.	Blanchard Flexible Inc,ST Bond
Burn, Harry III	Sound Shore
Burnham, I.W. II	Burnham Fund
Burshtan, David	Northern Growth Equity
Byrne, Susan M.	Westwood Balanced,Equity ,Inter Bond
Byrum, Michael P.	Rydex Juno,Precious Metals,US Govt Bond,US Govt MM
Calamos, John P.	Smith Hayes Convertible
Caldwell, Roland G.	Caldwell Fund,Govt,Gr Stock,TF
Callaghan, John P.	WPG Growth
Callahan, Lawrence G.	Lindner Bulwark
Canakaris, Ronald E.	CT&T Montag & Caldwell Balanced,Montag & Caldwell Gr,Enterprise Gr
Cannell, Julie M.	America's Utility Fund
Cantor, Daniel K.	SteinRoe Young Investor
Cappelli, Robert J.	Advance Capital I Balanced,LT Inc,Retirement Inc
Cappiello, Frank A.	Cappiello-Rushmore Emerg Gr,Gold, Growth,Utility Inc
Carleton, Donald C.	AARP High Quality TF MM,Ins TF Gen Bond,Scudder Managed Munis, Ins TF Gen Bond,Medium Term TF
Carlin, Julian P.	IAI Regional
Carlson, Charles vK.	Greenspring
Carlson, David B.	Elfun Diversified Inc,Trusts,GE Strategic Investment
Carlson, Kathleen A.	PC&J Preservation
Carlson, Marina T.	Strong Common Stock,Opportunity
Carney, Richard P.	GIT Special Growth
Carpenter, Prabha S.	Vista Growth Fund of Washington
Carr, David R.	Oak Value
Carrion, Maria-Elena	BT Investment Latin Am Eq,Hercules Latin Am Value
Carroll, Laurie	Dreyfus Bond Mkt Index,Dreyfus/Laurel Prime MM,ST Govt Sec,US Treas MM
Carty, Michael	Value Line Fund
Castegren, Hakan	Harbor Int'l,Ivy Int'l
Castellini, Jerome A.	Loomis-Sayles Growth
Castro, Oscar A.	Montgomery Global Communications, Global Opportunities,Int'l Sm Cap
Cates, G. Staley	Longleaf Partners Fund,Sm Cap
Cavelti, Peter	Blanchard Precious Metals

Portfolio Manager	Fund
Caywood, James	Enterprise High-Yield Bond
Cerny, Rodney D.	KPM Equity Portfolio
Chamberlain, Steven	Invesco European
Chambers, Terry L.	Columbia Common Stock
Chandrasekar, Ramakrishman	DFA Inv Dim Five Yr Govt,Global FI, Inter Govt FI,One-Year FI
Chaney, James E.	Marshall Int'l Stock
Chapman, Dick	First Omaha FI,SI FI
Chase, Doug	Fidelity Sel Industrial Materials
Chaux, Keli Brereton	Pacifica Short Term CA TF
Cheshire, Robert	FFB Lexicon Inter Govt Securities
Chisholm, O. Beirne	Kidder Peabody Cash Reserve, Premium Acct
Chow, Bob	Fidelity Sel Insurance
Christensen, Dale C.	Warburg, Pincus Balanced,Cash Res, FI,Global FI,Inter Mat Govt,NY Muni Bond,NY TE MM
Christensen, Robert A.	SteinRoe Prime Equities,Total Return
Chuang, Carol	Matthews Pacific Tiger
Church, William	Cowen Opportunity
Clausen, Ronald J.	1784 Asset Allocation
Clemenson, Vern M.	Northwest Inv Trust Idaho TE
Clemente, Lilia	Working Assets Citizens Global Equity
Cleveland, A. Bruce	GIT Worldwide Growth
Cleworth, Montgomery C.	Founders Govt Se,MM,Opportunity Bond
Coffey, Diane M.	Dreyfus Third Century
Cohen, David L.	First Eagle Fund of America
Cohen, Jarrod	Cowen Opportunity
Cohen, Martin	Cohen & Steers Realty
Colasacco, Domenic	Calvert Social Inv Mgd Growth
Colby, James T. III	Evergreen Natl TF Bond,Tax Strat Foundation, US Govt Sec
Coleman, Stephen C.	IAI Minnesota TF
Coll, Arieh	Fidelity Export
Colton, Steven	Benham Eq Gr,Inc & Gr,Utilities Inc
Como, David P.	First Mutual Fund
Condon, Philip G.	AARP Ins TF Gen Bd,Scudder HY TF,MA Ltd-Term TF,MA TF
Conley, Jonathan C.	Federated Fortress Muni Inc,Inter Muni Inc,Liberty Muni Sec,ST Muni Tr
Conlin, Thomas J.	Strong HY Muni Bond,Insured Muni Bond,Muni Bond,ST Muni Bond
Connolly, John D.	MAS Emerging Growth
Conxicoeur, Patrice	Dreyfus Int'l Equity Allocation
Coombe, Michael A.	Matrix Emerging Growth
Corba, Kenneth W.	SteinRoe Stock,Young Investor
Corner, Robert	FFB Lexicon Cash Management
Cosby, Ingeborg	Invesco TF MM
Costanzo, Linda	Merrill Lynch USA Govt Reserves
Costopoulas, Joanne T.	SteinRoe Inter Munis
Cote, K. Sue	AARP High Quality TF Money, Scudder TF MF
Coughlin, James P.	Retirement System Funds Core Eq,RSI Ret Trust Core Eq
Coughlin, William F.	Dreman Fixed Income
Countryman, Dean C.	Amcore Vintage FI,Inter TF,US Govt Obligations
Cowen, Raymond S.	Value Line NY TE Trust
Cox, Julia	Green Century Balanced
Coxon, Terry	Permanent Portfolio Aggr Gr,Perm Portfolio,Treas Bill,Versatile Bond
Crabbe, James E.	Crabbe Huson Special
Craddock, Margaret	Scudder ST Global Income
Cragg, Anthony L.T.	Strong Asia Pacific,Int'l Stock
Craig, James P. III	Janus Balanced,Fund
Crane, Charles G.	SBSF Capital Growth
Crofton, Michael G.	UST Master Inter TENY Inter TE,ST TE
Crowley, Robert A.	Crowley Diversified Mngt, Growth, Income
Cseh, Sandor	Dreyfus/Laurel Int'l
Cunningham, Deborah A.	Federated ST Inc, Prime Cash Series
Czepiel, Robert Charles	Robertson Stephens Emerg Growth
Dagiau, Deborah	Retirement System Funds MM,RSI Ret Trust ST Invest
Daniels, Bradley S.	MAS Sm Cap Val
Danoff, Will	Fidelity Contrafund

Portfolio Manager	Fund	Portfolio Manager	Fund
Darby, Thomas	Vista US Govt MM	English, Mary	Fidelity Sel Consumer Products
Darcy, Joseph	Dreyfus Basic Inter Muni Bond, Basic Muni Bond	Esielonis, Steven M.	Quantitative Growth & Income
		Esser, Stephen F.	MAS High Yield Sec
Dater, Elizabeth B.	Warburg, Pincus Emerging Gr	Evans, G. Jay	Galaxy Equity Value
Davidson, Philip	Twentieth Century Eq Inc,Value	Evans, James	Accessor Muni Inter FI
Davidson, W. Lindsay	Invesco Int'l Growth	Eveillard, Jean-Marie	SoGen Gold,Int'l.Overseas
Davis, George	Hotchkis and Wiley Small Cap	Evnin, Timothy F.	UST Master Early Life Cycle
Davis, Lyle H.	Quantitative Foreign Frontier,Int'l Eq	Fairweather, James	Blanchard Worldwide Emerg Mkts
Davis, Shelby M.C.	Selected American Shares	Falcone, Nola Maddox	Evergreen Sm Cap Eq Inc,Tot Ret
Dean, James T. Jr.	Primary US Govt	Farrelly, Jennifer	Fidelity Market Index
DeBard, Roger	Hotchkis and Wiley Balanced Inc	Fasciano, Michael F.	Fasciano Fund
deBeer, E. John	Loomis-Sayles Global Bond	Feeney, William M.	Fremont CA Inter TF
Defour, Stephen	Fidelity Sel Multimedia	Feinberg, Jeffrey	Fidelity Sel Brokerage & Investment Mngt, Sel Retailing
Dektar, Daniel C.	Smith Breeden Inter US Govt, Short US Govt		
		Feingold, John	Managers Inter Mtge Sec
Delafield, J. Dennis	Delafield	Feldkircher, Nancy L.	Accessor Small Cap
Denison, Hugh F.	Heartland Value	Felman, David	Fidelity Sel Chemicals,Sel Telecommunications
Dennis, Robert A.	Managers Muni Bond		
Denzler, Colleen	Calvert Social Inv MM	Felske, Derek	Twentieth Century Growth,Ultra
DePrince, Gregory M.	Harbor Value	Fentin, Richard	Fidelity Puritan
Desai, Rohit M.	Vanguard Convertible Sec	Ferenback, Colin	Haven Fund
DeSantis, Joseph	Vista Int'l Equity	Ferry, John A.	Accessor Small Cap
DeVilliers, Johann	Monitrend Gold	Ferwerda, Paul A.	Regis TS&W Equity
Diamond, Terrance	CT&T Talon	Fields, John B.	Delaware Decatur Inc,Decatur Tot Ret
Dickson, Brent	Seven Seas Growth & Income	Fields, Michael W.	American AAdvantage Ltd-Term Inc,MM,Muni MM,US Treas MM
Diedrich, James	IAI Balanced		
Dillon, Mary	Prudential Govt Sec Tr MM		
Disdier, A. Paul	Dreyfus General CA Muni Bond,General Muni Bond	Fiorenza, Janet	SEI Inter Muni,WPG TF MM
		Firestone, Karen	Fidelity Sel Biotechnology
Dobkin, Penelope	Fidelity Worldwide	Fischer, Ben J.	RSI Ret Trust Value Equity
Dobson, Charles L.	Analytic Optioned Equity	Fischer, George	Fidelity Spartan Bond Strategist
Dodson, Jerome L.	Parnassus Balanced,FI,Fund	Fisher, Kenneth L.	Enterprise Small Company
Domini, Amy L.	Domini Social Equity,Women's Equity	Fitilis, Art	FFB Lexicon Cap Apprec Equity
Domolky, George	Fidelity Canada	Flahive, John F.	Neuberger & Berman NY Insured Inter
Donald, Douglas D.	Scudder Gold	Flewharty, Molly	CA Daily TF,CT Daily TF,Daily TF, FL Daily Muni,MI Daily TF,NJ Daily Muni,NY Daily TF,NV Daily Muni,PA Daily Muni,Reich & Tang Govt Sec,ST Inc MM,ST Inc US Govt
Donaldson, Gregory C.	Anthem Balanced,Eq Inc,Govt Sec,Muni Sec		
Donnelly, Michael P.	Federated Liberty American Leaders		
Donovan, Mark E.	Dreyfus Core Value		
Dooley, Douglas J.	JPM Advisor Asia Gr,Emerg Mkts Eq,Pierpont Emerg Mkts	Flink, Stewart R.	Israel Growth Fund
		Flom, John A.	Analytic Master FI,ST Govt
Dow, Paul	Hercules North Am Gr & Inc	Flood, Jim	Value Line TE HY,TE MM
Doyle, Thomas P.	Managers Short Govt Inc	Flood, Peter J.	Northern Tax Exempt
Dreman, David N.	Dreman Contrarian,High Return	Flores, Victor	United Services Gold Shares,Govt Sec,World Gold
Driggs, Charles	SAFECO Northwest		
Duboc, Charles M.	Twentieth Century Balanced, Heritage,Select	Flynn, Mary Ann	Northern MM
		Fogle, Glenn	Twentieth Century GifTrust,Vista
Duff, Stephen M.	Hanover Blue Chip Growth	Fontaine, Richard H.	Fontaine Cap Apprec,Global Gr,Global Inc
DuFour, Steve	Fidelity Sel Transportation	Foody-Malus, Kathleen M.	Federated Income Tr
Dunn, E. Bruce	SteinRoe Special,Special Venture	Foulkes, Richard R.	Vanguard Int'l Growth
Durbiano, Mark E.	Federated HY Tr,Liberty High Inc Bond	Frank, Thomas A.	Dreyfus New Leaders
Durham, Paul	BT Investment Pacific Basin Eq	Franklin, Carol L.	Scudder Greater Europe Gr,Int'l
Dutton, William M.	Skyline Special Equities	Frantzen, Henry A.	59 Wall St European Eq,Pacific Basin
Eaker, Ronald S.	Gabelli US Treas MM	Fraser, Greg	Fidelity Diversified Int'l
Ebert, Barry F.	Pinnacle Fund	Fraser, Simon	Fidelity Pacific Basin
Ebright, Thomas R.	Royce PA Mutual,Revest Gr & Inc,Eq Inc,Micro-Cap,Premiere,Value	Fraze, Patricia	Westwood Balanced,Inter Bond
		Frels, William B.	Mairs & Power Income
		French, Susan J.	Northern Small Cap Gr
Edington, David H.	PIMCO Short-Term,StocksPLUS,PIMCO Adv S-I	Friedman, Barbara	Loomis-Sayles Small Cap
		Friedman, John M.	Nottingham II Investek FI Tr
Edwards, Jonathan	GIT Govt Portfolio,Maximum Inc,Government Investors TR MM	Fries, William V.	USAA Aggressive Growth
		Friess, Foster S.	Brandywine,Brandywine Blue,RSI Ret Tr Emerg Gr Eq
Ehlert, A. Benjamin	PIMCO Growth Stock		
Ehrman, Phillip	Invesco Int'l Growth	Frost, Patricia L.	Rainier Inter Fixed Inc
Ehrsam, Paul A.	Regis Sterling Partners Bal,Sterling Partners Eq	Frucci, Richard	Retirement System Funds Emerg Gr Eq,RSI Ret Tr Emerg Gr Eq
Eichstaedt, Carl L.	Legg Mason Cash Res,US Govt Inter,US Govt MM	Fulkerson, Allan W.	Century Shares Trust
		Fuller, Mark	William Blair Mutual Growth Shares
Eisenberg, Ann	Seven Seas S&P 500 Index	Furdak, Rob	Seven Seas Emerg Mkts
Elfe, Gary	Portico TE MM	Furman, Robert M.	Rainbow Fund
Elias, Caren S.	Reserve TE Tr CA,TE TR Interstate,TE Tr MA,TE Tr NJ,TE Tr NY	Fuss, Daniel J.	Loomis-Sayles Bond,Managers Bond
		G. Robert Kincheloe	Flex-Fund Bond
Elijah, Ronald E.	Robertson Stephens Value + Growth	Gabelli, Mario J.	Gabelli - ABC,Asset.Global Inter Couch Potato
Ellison, David	Fidelity Sel Home Finance		
Engel, Kent S.	Legg Mason Invest Grade Inc	Gadsden, William F.	AARP Capital Growth
England-Markun, Mark	PIMCO Adv Inst Bal,Parametric Enhanced Eq,Parametric Int'l Eq	Gahagan, Robert	Twentieth Century Cash Res,US Govts Inter,US Govts Short

433

Portfolio Manager	Fund	Portfolio Manager	Fund
Galuska, Pat	Galaxy Govt MM,MM,TE,US Treas	Hamlin, David E.	Vanguard Muni Ins LT,NJ TF Ins LT,NY Ins TF LT,OH TF Ins LT
Games, Edmund B., Jr.	Scudder Latin America		
Gardner, Keith J.	Legg Mason Global Govt Tr	Hand, Karen M.	Dreyfus Basic Muni MM,General Muni MM,General NY Muni MM,Muni MM, NJ Muni MM,NY TE MM,OH Muni MM
Garvey, Richard J.	Rushmore Fund For Govt Investors		
Gasaway, Kent W.	Babson Buffalo Balanced		
Gee, Norman	Fremont MM		
Geewax, John	Vanguard Trustees Equity US		
Gerding, Michael W.	Founders Passport,Worldwide Gr	Hannan, James M.	Ark MM,TF MM,US Govt MM,US Treas MM
Germany, J. David	MAS Global FI,Int'l FI		
Gerry, Elbridge T., III	Pierpont TE Bond,TE MM	Hanson, Andrew M.	Lepercq-Istel Fund
Getts, Gregory B.	MIM Mutual MM	Harhai, Michael	Invesco Value Equity
Gibs, Gabriel J.	Volumetric Fund	Harris, David	SteinRoe Int'l
Giglia, Joseph A.	Accessor Int'l FI	Harrison, Joseph A.	Advsr Innr Crcl Roulston Govt Sec,Roulston Gr & Inc
Gilkison, Robert C.	Calvert Income		
Gillespie, Dan	GIT TF AZ,TF MD,TF MO,TF MM,TF National,TF VA	Harrop, Steven D.	Strong Muni MM
		Hartford, Harry	Hotchkis and Wiley Int'l
Gillespie, John D.	Price, Rowe Growth Stock	Hartman, David A.	Kidder Peabody CA TE MM,Govt MF, TE MF
Gillespie, T. Daniel	Rushmore Fund For TF Investors,MD TF,MM,VA TF		
		Harvey, Steven	Fidelity MN TF,OH TF HY,Spartan MD Muni Inc,Spartan PA HY
Gillmore, Clive A.	Delaware Int'l Equity		
Gillson, Roy C.	IAI Int'l	Hathaway, John C.	Oak Hall Equity
Gintel, Robert M.	Gintel Erisa,Gintel Fund	Haubold, Gary D.	MAS Sm Cap Val
Gipson, James H.	Clipper,Schooner	Havell, Theresa A.	Neuberger & Berman Cash Res,Govt MM,Ltd Mat Bond,Muni MM,Muni Sec,NY Ins Inter,Ultra Short
Gladson, Clifford A.	USAA TE Inter,TE Short		
Glancy, David	Fidelity Spartan High Inc		
Glen, David H.	AARP GNMA & US Treasury,Scudder GNMA		
		Hawkins, O. Mason	Longleaf Partners Fund,Sm Cap
Godman, Cecil A. III	Gintel Fund	Hayes, Helen Young	Janus Overseas,Worldwide
Goff, James P.	Janus Enterprise,Venture	Hayes, James A.	Pierpont Treasury MM
Goldberg, James M.	TCW/DW Bal,North AM Inter Inc	Hayes, Peter J.	CMA NY Muni MF,TE MM
Goldstein, Mark	Neuberger & Berman Manhattan	Hayward, Steven D.	Marshall Mid-Cap Stock
Gomer, Charles A. III	Regis TS&W Fixed Income	Hazelwood, Richard	Fidelity Emerging Markets
Goodchild, Robert M.	BT Investment Ltd Term US Govt	Hazuka, Thomas B.	Preferred Asset Alloc,Vanguard Asset Alloc
Goodwin, John R.	Northern Small Cap Gr		
Gordon, Michael	Fidelity Blue Chip Growth	Healey, Timothy S.	Government Street AL TF Bond
Gotham, Diane	Fortis Money	Heebner, Charles	Value Line Cash
Grabovac, James S.	SteinRoe High Yield Munis	Heebner, G. Kenneth	CGM Capital Development,FI,Mutual,Realty
Graham, David	Prudential Govt Sec Tr Inter		
Granahan, John J.	Vanguard Explorer	Heffernan, Gerard E.	Stratton Monthly Div Sh
Grandich, Peter	Peter Grandich Contrarian	Heine, Leonard M. Jr.	LMH Fund
Grant, Kevin	Fidelity GNMA,Mortgage Sec, Spartan GBMA	Heisler, Ruth	Scudder Zero Cpn 2000
		Helton, Christopher R.	Seafirst Blue Chip
Grant, Laird I.	UST Master Equity	Henry, D. Kirk	Dreyfus/Laurel Int'l
Gray, Anthony	SEI Cap Appreciaton	Hensel, William S.	Pacific Horizon Capital Income
Gray, Douglas W.	Schooner Fund	Herro, David G.	Oakmark Int'l
Gray, Michael	Fidelity Inter Bond,Inv Grade Bond, Spartan Inv Grade Bond	Hershey, Michael L.	Henlopen Fund
		Hertan, David	Seven Seas Yield Plus
Green, Frederick W.	Merger Fund	Heuer, Emily	Dreyfus/Laurel TE MM
Greenberg, Lawrence	Fidelity Emerging Growth	Hickling, John R.	Fidelity Overseas
Greenfield, Barry A.	Fidelity Real Estate	Hill, Larry R.	IAI Bond
Greff, Paul	SEI Bond Index	Hinderlie, Richard R.	Invesco Cash Res,ST Bond,US Govt MM,US Govt Sec
Greig, W. George	PBHG Int'l		
Griffin, David	Invesco Total Return	Hinzman, Otto G., Jr.	Managers Balanced
Griggs, William T. II	Dupree Inter Govt Bond,KY TF Inc,KY TF Sht-Med,TN TF	Hirsch, Michael D.	FundTrust Aggr Gr,Growth,Gr & Inc,Income,Managed Tot Ret,Republic US Govt MF
Gross, William H.	Fremont Bond,Harbor Bond,PIMCO Low Dur,Low Dur II,Tot Ret,Tot Ret III,PIMCO Adv Tot Ret,PIMCO Adv Inst Bal,Mgd Bond & Inc		
		Hitchman, John	Hotchkis and Wiley Sm Cap
		Ho, Stephen	JPM Advisor Asia Growth
		Hodgman, Martha F.	Loomis-Sayles Muni Bond
		Hoerle, Robert F.	Reich & Tang Equity
Grossman, Blake R.	Accessor Small Cap	Hoey, Richard B.	Dreyfus Growth & Income
Gundlach, Jeffrey E.	Enterprise Govt Securities	Hoffman, Michael	Robertson Stephens Emerg Mkts
Gupta, Rajesh K.	Dean Witter ST U.S. Treas	Hoffman, Robert T.	AARP Bal Stock & Bond,Gr & Inc, Scudder Gr & Inc
Gurun, David P.	American AAdvantage Ltd-Term Inc		
Gustafson, Eric P.	SteinRoe Stock	Hohenberg, Godfried	Laidlaw Covenant Portfolio
Haber, Robert	Fidelity Bal,Global Bal	Hohenstein, Vicki	First Omaha Equity
Haboucha, Farha-Joyce	Neuberger & Berman Socially Responsive	Holbrook, Richard	Bailard Biehl & Kaiser Int'l Eq
		Holderness, Richard T.	Trent Equity
Hague, John L.	PIMCO Foreign,Global	Holliday, John M.	Torchmark Insured TF
Haines, Michael K.	Founders Discovery,Frontier	Hollingsworth, Curt	Fidelity, S-I Govt,Spartan Ltd Mat Govt,Spartan LT Govt,Spartan S-I Govt
Haines, Raymond	WPG Int'l		
Haley, John F.	Fidelity CA TF HY,CA TF Ins,Spartan CA Muni HY	Hollyer, John	Vanguard Adm ST US Treas,Adm US Treas MM,FI ST US Treas,MM Res Federal,MM Res Prime,MM Res US Treas
Hall, Donald E.	Scudder Value		
Hall, Dudley	Seven Seas Intermediate	Holmes, Douglas T.	Quantitative Gr & Inc,Seven Seas Matrix Eq
Hall, J. Parker III	Vanguard US Growth		
Hamilton, Mary N.	Pacific Advisors Balanced	Holmes, Frank E.	United Services All Am Eq,Income
		Holzer, William E.	Managers Int'l Eq,Scudder Global

Portfolio Manager	Fund	Portfolio Manager	Fund
Honour, Roger W.	Montgomery Asset Alloc,Growth,Micro Cap	Keelan, Jane	Portico MM,US Federal MM,US Govt MM
Hooper, Charles	Founders - Special	Keeley, John L., Jr.	Keeley Small Cap Value
Hoops, Bud	Twentieth Century Bal,Cash Res,Inter Bond,Ltd Term Bond,LT Bond,TE Inter,TE LT,TE ST,US Govts Inter, US Govts ST	Keely, Edward F.	Founders Growth
		Keers, Joanne E.	Babson TF MM,UMB TF MM
		Keighley, Joanne	Schwab CA LT TF,CA S-I TF,LT TF, S-I TF
Hopkinson, Brian	Van Eck Global Balanced	Keithler, William R.	Berger Small Company Gr
Horseman, John R.	GAM Global,Int'l	Kellner, Ted D.	Fiduciary Capital Growth
Horsley, Nicholas P.W.	Warburg, Pincus Emerg Mkts,Japan OTC	Kelly, Brian F.	Invesco Balanced,Strat Utilities, Worldwide Communications
Houser, Denis N.	Rightime Fund		
Houston, David	GAM Europe	Kelly, Jeanette A.	AARP High Quality Money
Houston, Jeffrey	Twentieth Century TE Inter,TE LT,TE ST	Kelly, Jonathan	Fidelity Global Bond,New Markets Inc
Howard, Richard P.	Price, Rowe Capital Apprec	Kelly, Marc	Pacific Advisors Govt Sec
Hoyle, David W.	WPG Govt Securities	Kelly, R. "Kelly"	Pacific Advisors Govt Sec
Hudson, Arley N.	SAFECO Income	Kenerson, David R., Jr.	Van Eck World Trends
Hudson, Daryl L.	Camco 100% US Treas Inter,100% US Treas Short,100% US Treas Tot Ret	Kennedy, Don	Smith Hayes Asset Alloc
		Kennedy, Michael T.	SteinRoe Govt Inc,Inter Bond
Hunter, Pamela	Vista CA Inter TF,NY TF Inc,TF Inc	Kern, Douglas G.	Homestead ST Bond
Huntsinger, Steven N.	Analytic Enhanced Equity	Kern, Robert E.	Fremont U.S. Micro-Cap
Hurley, John	Fidelity Sel Software & Computer Services	Ketterer, Sarah	Hotchkis and Wiley Int'l
		Key, Simon	William Blair Mutual Int'l Gr
Hurwitz, Millie	SteinRoe Prime Equities	Kichline, James L.	MAS Global FI,Int'l FI
Husic, Frank J.	Vanguard Morgan Growth	Kigner, Jeffrey A.	Vanguard Equity Income
Huson, Richard S.	Crabbe Huson Asset Alloc,Equity, Real Estate	Killen, Edward	Berwyn Income Fund
		Killen, Robert E.	Berwyn Fund
Hutchins, David	Vanguard Sp Gold & Precious Mtls	Kim, Andrew B.	Fremont Int'l Gr,SIT Dev Mkts Gr,Int'l Gr
Hutchinson, William M.	AARP Bal Stock & Bond,High Qual Bond,Scudder Inc	Kincheloe, G. Robert	Flex-Fund Bond
		King, Creston	United Services Special Term Govt
Hutson, Bruce P.	Marshall Equity Inc	King, Luther	LKCM Small Cap Equity
Hyatt, William E.	Northern Income Equity	King, Richard H.	Warburg, Pincus Emerg Mkts,Int'l Eq,Japan OTC
Hyll, John	Loomis-Sayles ST Bond		
Irrgang, Terrence	Invesco Value Equity	Kirby, Laurie S.	Twentieth Century TE Inter,TE LT,TE ST,US Govts Inter,US Govts ST
Ives, Robert	Fidelity Govt Sec,Spartan Govt Inc		
Jacks, Ron K.	Working Assets Citizens Emerg Gr	Kirk, David G.	Babson Growth
Jacobs, Jerome J.	Vanguard Muni HY,Muni LT	Kirk, Gary V.	Wood Island Growth
Jacobson, Todd C.	59 Wall St TF S/I FI	Kirkby, Paul S.	GAM Japan Capital
Jacques, William E.	Accessor Value and Income	Kittler, Fred W.	JPM Advisor U.S. Sm Cap Eq,Pierpont Cap Apprec
James, Frank E.	Golden Rainbow A James Advised		
James, Lance F.	Babson Enterprise II	Klaffke, Steve	USAA Balanced,Cornerstone
Jamison, Denis P.	Lexington GNMA Inc,MM,Ramirez Global Inc,S-I Govt Sec,TF MM	Klaskin, David M.	ORI Growth Fund
		Klassen, David	Blanchard Cap Gr,Gr & Inc,Vista Cap Gr
Jeddeloh, Larry E.	Managers Global Opportunity	Klawans, Bernard B.	Valley Forge
Jedlicka, Frank E.	Loomis-Sayles Int'l Equity	Kleinschmidt, Robert	Tocqueville Fund
Jellison, David W.	Columbia Real Estate Equity	Klingman, Linda	Schwab Inst Adv MF,MM,Retirement MF, Value Adv MF
Jenkins, Ralph	Invesco Inter Govt Bond		
Jensen, Val E.	Jensen Portfolio	Klink, Patricia deBlank	Managers MM
Jermain, Robert K.	Dreyfus Strategic Growth	Klisiewicz, Edward	Galaxy Equity Income
Jimenez, Josephine S.	Montgomery Emerging Markets	Klopp, Norman F.	Advsr Innr Crcl Roulston Midwest Gr
Johnson, Abigail	Fidelity OTC	Knudsen, Charles E. III	Ark Growth & Inc
Johnson, James M.	PC&J Performance	Knutsen, A. Roy	WPG Growth & Income
Johnson, Mark W.	USAA Balanced,Cornerstone,Gold	Koch, Jeffrey A.	Strong Advantage,Income
Johnson, Robert K.	Pierpont MM	Kolefas, Thomas	New York Life Inst Value Eq
Johnson, Robert R.	Pierpont Treas MM,Preferred MM	Konecki, Joan	CT&T MM
Johnson, Todd	SEI S&P 500 Index	Kono, Garitt	Dreyfus A Bonds Plus,GNMA,Gr Opportunity,Investors GNMA
Johnston, Richard M.	Blanchard Worldwide Emerg Mkts		
Johnstone, Lynda	Guinness Flight China & Hong Kong	Kopinski, Mark	Twentieth Century Int'l Emerg Gr,Int'l Eq
Jones, Donald	Galaxy NY Muni Bond	Kozemchak, J. A.	OH Muni Cash Tr Cash II Series
Jones, Gregory M.	Northern Int'l Gr Eq,Int'l Sel Gr	Kris, Stephen	Dreyfus CT Inter Muni,FL Inter Muni, NJ Inter
Jones, Michael	Advsr Innr Crcl Clvr Cap Eq Val,Clvr Cap FI		
		Kuhl, Herbert, Jr.	Retirement System Funds Inter FI,Actively Managed Bond,Inter Bond
Jurika, William K.	Jurika & Voyles Bal,Mini-Cap, Value + Gr		
		Kuldell, Scott	Fidelity Foreign Currencies,ST World Inc
Kaelin, Robert R.	Elfun TE Income,GE TE	Kurokawa, Barry	Invesco Strat Health Sciences
Kagawa, Michael	Pacific Horizon U.S. Govt Sec	Kutler, Veena A.	Price, Rowe ST Bond,Summit Ltd Term Bond
Kailin, Kenneth S.	Skyline Special Equities II		
Kaiser, Nicholas	Amana Growth,Income, Northwest Inv Tr NW Gr	Kwak, Seung	Japan Fund
		Kyritz, Ed	Northern US Govt MM, US Govt Select MM
Kane, T. Gibbs, Jr.	Sound Shore		
Kaplan, Mark D.	Payson Value	La Plaige, Denis	New York Life Inst Value Eq
Kaplan, Paul	SEI GNMA,Inter Govt,ST Govt	LaFleur, Robert A.	Northern Gr Eq,Income Eq,Int'l Gr Eq, Int'l Select Eq
Kaplan, Paul D.	Vanguard FI GNMA,Wellington		
Kassen, Michael	Neuberger & Berman Partners	Lammert, Warren B.	Janus Mercury,Venture
Kauffman, George B.	Regis Sirach Gr,Sirach Strat Bal	Landini, Peter F.	Fremont Global
Kaye, Steven	Fidelity Growth & Income	Landmann, Laird R.	Hotchkis and Wiley Bal Inc,Low Dur,ST Investment,Tot Ret
Keblusek, Lawrence P.	Northern Select Equity		
		Lane, Caroline	Govett Latin America

Portfolio Manager	Fund		Portfolio Manager	Fund
McStay, John Dewitt	Aquinas Eq Gr		Mullins, Bert	Dreyfus Disciplined Stock,Eq Inc
Meagley, Richard	SAFECO Equity		Mulvey, Daniel B.	Pierpont MM
Meeder, Robert S. Jr.	Flex-Fund Growth,Muirfield		Muoio, Salvatore	Gabelli Glbl Telecommunications
Mehling, James	New York Life Inst EAFE Index		Muresianu, John	Fidelity Sel Utilities Gr,Utilities
Mehta, Satyen	JPM Advisor Emerg Mkts Eq,Pierpont Emerg Mkts		Murphy, David	Fidelity Ltd Term Muni,Spartan CA Inter,Spartan Inter Muni,Spartan NJ HY,Spartan NY Inter,S-I Muni
Meiras, Mark	Israel Growth Fund		Mussey, John M.	Newport Tiger
Melhouse, Charles L.	Marshall Balanced,Stock		Myer, Bentley M.	William Blair Mutual Income,Ltd Term TF,Ready Reserves
Mellon, Catharine L.	59 Small Company			
Melvin, Gregory M.	Federated Gr Tr,Liberty Cap Gr		Myers, Marcia Z.	Ark Income
Memler, Monty M.	Northern U.S. Govt		Naeseth, Jane M.	SteinRoe Cash Res,Govt Res
Mendell, James M.	MIM Mutual AFA Eq Inc		Nagorniak, John	Vanguard Morgan Gr,Quantitative
Merk, Randall	Benham Adj Rate Govt,GNMA Inc		Najork, Chris	PIMCO Adv Inst NFJ Divers Low P/E,NFJ Eq Inc,NFJ Sm Cap Value
Merkele, Edward J.	Blanchard 100% Treas MM			
Merriman, Paul A.	Merriman Asset Alloc,Cap Apprec,Flexible Bond,Gr & Inc,Leveraged Gr		Nakamura, Takeo	Nomura Pacific Basin
			Nasgovitz, William J.	Heartland NB TF,US Govt Sec,Value,Value & Inc,WI TF
Messina, Susan	RMA Money Fund MM,US Govt, Tax-Free		Nason, Susan M.	Federated ARMs,Inter Govt Tr,S-I Govt Tr,US Govt Bond,Government Cash,Treasury Cash
Metastasio, Mary V.	SAFECO Tax-Free MM			
Metcalf, Douglas R.	TCW/DW North Am Inter Inc Tr			
Meuser, John F.	Retirement System Funds MM,RSI Ret Trust ST Invest		Navellier, Louis	Navellier Aggr Sm Cap Eq
			Neff, John C.	Vanguard Windsor
Michael, Thomas	Rydex Nova		Neff, Robert T.	AARP High Quality MM,Scudder Cash Invest Tr,US Treas MM
Michalski, Kim	Pacific Horizon CA TE Bond			
Micheletti, Arthur	Bailard Biehl & Kaiser Diversa,Int'l FI		Nelson, David E.	Regis ICM Equity
Midanek, James I.	Solon Short Dur Govt Funds - 1 Yr Portfolio,3 Yr Portfolio		Nelson, John P.	59 Wall St MM,US Treas MF
			Nelson, Thomas	Vista Balanced,Global MM,US Govt Inc
Mika, Chris	CT&T Inter FI,Inter Muni		Netzel, Jill K.	SteinRoe Muni MM
Milkewicz, Henry M.	UST Master Inter Managed Inc, Managed Inc		Neumann, Frederick R.	Woodward Equity Index
			Newell, Roger D.	Vanguard Equity Income
Mill, Jerry W.	Invesco European,Worldwide Capital Goods		Newman, Maureen	Fidelity MI TF HY,Spartan Aggr Muni,Spartan AZ Muni Inc, Spartan CT Muni HY
Millard, Kathleen T.	AARP Bal Stock & Bond,Gr & Inc			
Miller, David G.	USAA CA Bond,FL TF Inc,TX TF Inc,VA Bond		Newmark, Kent P.	Loomis-Sayles US Govt Sec
			Ng, John	Merrill Lynch Ready Assets Tr
Miller, Debra	Vanguard Trustees Eq Int'l		Ngudu, Tsering	Lepercq-Istel Fund
Miller, Harry W.	USAA Cornerstone,Inc Stock,World Gr		Nicholas, Albert O.	Nicholas Eq Inc,Nicholas Fund,Income,MM
Miller, James A.	Bartlett Basic Value			
Miller, Jeffrey	Blanchard Am Equity		Nicholas, Arthur E.	Accessor Int'l Eq,Harbor Growth
Miller, Jeffrey J.	Enterprise Cap Apprec		Nicholas, David O.	Nicholas II, Ltd Edition
Miller, Lydia	Value Line Inc		Nichols, Gerald T.	Delaware Delchester Fund
Miller, Mary J.	Price, Rowe CA TF Bond,GA TF Bond,MD ST TF Bond,MD TF Bond,Summit Muni Inter,TF S-I,VA ST TF Bond,VA TF Bond		Nicholson, J. Scott	New England Cash Mgmt Tr MM, US Govt
			Nicklin, Edmund H., Jr.	Evergreen Growth & Income
			Nielsen, John A.	59 Wall St European Eq,Pacific Basin
Miller, Neal	Fidelity New Millenium		Nix, Paul D.A.	Dreyfus Global Bond,Int'l Eq
Miller, S. Blake	WPG Inter Muni Bond		Nolan, David	Arbor OVB Cap Appr,Emerg Gr
Miller, Timothy J.	Invesco Dynamics,Strat Leisure		Norris, James R.	Regis Sterling Partners Bal,Sterling Partners Eq
Miller, William H. III	Legg Mason Special Invest Tr,Tot Ret Tr,Value Tr			
			Notaro, William L.	Merriman Asset Alloc,Cap Appr,Flexible Bond,Gr & Inc,Leveraged Gr
Milman, Stephen	Neuberger & Berman Genesis			
Milne, Robert D.	SEI Large Cap Value		O'Connor, Daniel	Rushmore US Govt Inter,US Govt Long
Milner, Laura	Stagecoach CA TF MM		O'Donnell, Amy	Benham Cap Preservation II,Govt Agency,Prime MM
Miner, Patrick M.	KPM FI Portfolio			
Minke, Ronald D.	PIMCO Adv Inst Utility Stock		O'Grady, James W.	Accessor Muni Inter FI
Mitchell, Edward C.	Invesco Total Return		O'Grady, Timothy	FFB Lexicon Select Value
Mitchell, Jerry	Galaxy Int'l Equity		O'Hara, Dennis M.	American AAdvantage Bal,Gr & Inc, Int'l Eq
Mitchelson, Peter L.	SIT Growth & Income			
Moffett, James L.	Babson UMB Worldwide		O'Neill, Irene D.	Evergreen American Ret Tr
Monagle, Joseph T.	CMA Money		O'Toule, John	Dreyfus Disciplined Midcap, S&P 500 Index
Monrad, Ernest E.	Northeast Investors Trust			
Montgomery, John N.R.	Bridgeway Aggr Gr,Social Responsibility,Ultra Sm Co		Oates, William A. Jr.	Northeast Investors Growth
			Ober, Theodore E.	1784 Growth & Income
Moran, Gerald J.	Scudder Global Small Co		Oberweis, James D.	Oberweis Emerging Growth
Morris, Charles A.	Price, Rowe Science & Technology		Ochson, Mary Jo	Municipal Cash Series
Morris, Loretta J.	Accessor Int'l Equity		Oelschlager, James D.	Advsr Innr Crcl Pin Oak Aggr Stock, White Oak Gr Stock
Morrison, Charles	Fidelity St Bond,Spartan ST			
Moser, Kurt G.	State Farm Balanced, Growth, Interim,Muni Bond		Offen, Scott	Fidelity Sel Paper & Forest Products
			Offit, Andrew S.	Fidelity Convertible Sec
Moses, Cedd	Calvert Strategic Growth		Ognar, Ronald C.	Strong Growth,Total Return
Moss, Howard B.	Harbor Int'l Growth		Oliver, Michael T.	PRA: Real Estate
Moynihan, Richard	Dreyfus Muni Bond		Orkin, Michael B.	Caldwell & Orkin Aggr Growth
Mueller, Danine A.	Vanguard NJ TF MM,PA TF MM		Orphanos, Anthony G.	Warburg, Pincus Bal,Gr & Inc
Mueller, Jay N.	Strong Asset Alloc,MM,US Treas MF		Orr, Scott	Fidelity CT Muni MM,MI Muni MM,NJ TF MM,Spartan AZ Muni MM, Spartan
Muhlenkamp, Ronald H.	Muhlenkamp Fund			

Portfolio Manager	Fund	Portfolio Manager	Fund
Wade, Martin G.	Price, Rowe European Stock,Int'l Discovery,Int'l Stock,Japan,Latin Am, New Asia	Wickwire, Guy E.	Fidelity Ins TF,MA TF HY
		Wieboldt, Monica S.	Dreyfus General NY Muni Bond,Inter Muni Bond,NY TE Bond,NY TE Inter,PA Inter Muni
Wade, Maury Jr.	Wade Fund		
Wakeman, John F.	Price, Rowe Cap Opportunity	Wieder, David P.	Fundamental FI HY Muni
Walczak, Edwin	Vontobel US Value	Wiese, Edward A.	Price, Rowe Prime Res,Summit Cash Res,US Treas MF
Walden, Sally	Fidelity Europe		
Wallace, Roy L.	Liquid Capital Inc Tr	Wiggins, Ernest	Dreyfus Asset Alloc Gr,Asset Alloc Inc,Asset Alloc Tot Ret,Focus Large Co Value,Focus Sm Co Value
Wang, Lulu C.	Preferred Growth		
Wanger, Ralph L. Jr.	Acorn,Acorn Int'l		
Wapnick, Alan	Lexington Global,Gr & Inc	Wiles, Christopher H.	Federated Fortress Utility,Liberty Eq Inc,Liberty Utility
Ward, Howard F.	Scudder Bal,Quality Gr		
Ward, Howard Frank	Gabelli Growth	Wiley, George	Hotchkis and Wiley Eq Inc
Ward, Stephen B.	Schwab CA LT TF,CA S/I TF,CA TE MF,Govt MF,Inst Adv MF,LT Govt,LT TF,MM,Retirement MF,S/I Govt,S/I TF,TE MF,US Treas MF,Value Adv MF	Wilhelm, Lisa N.	SteinRoe Ltd Mat Income
		Williams, A. Morris, Jr.	MAS Value
		Williams, David J.	UST Master Business & Indust Restr
		Williams, Dean	MAS Int'l Equity
		Williams, Peter H.	Matrix Growth
Wardlow, Jeffrey W.	Loomis-Sayles Gr & Inc	Willmann, Kenneth E.	USAA Balanced,NY Bond,TE Fund LT
Wate, Devin	PIMCO Adv Inst Bal,Parametric Enhanced Eq,Parametric Int'l Eq	Willoughby, Jay L.	Crabbe Huson Inc,OR Muni Bond,Real Estate Invest,US Govt Inc,US Govt MM
Watson, Charles G.	Brundage Story & Rose Gr & Inc		
Watson, Deborah	Fidelity CA TF MM,Spartan CA Muni MM,Spartan FL Muni MM,Spartan PA Muni MM	Wilson, Donald S.	Eastcliff Tot Ret,Fiduciary Cap Gr
		Wilson, Rebecca L.	Scudder CA TF MM,NY TF MM
		Wilson, Steven M.	Reich & Tang Equity
		Windmueller, Andrew S.	Dreyfus/Laurel CA TF MM,MA TF MM,NY TF MM
Watts, Gareth L.	Govett Int'l Equity		
Watts, John H.	Harbor MM	Winmill, Bassett S.	Bull & Bear Gold Inv,Quality Gr
Wayne, N. Russell	LMH Fund	Winston, Gregory	Strong ST Muni Bond
Weber, Merrill E.	Israel Growth Fund	Wirtz, E. Keith	Seafirst Asset Allocation
Weinblatt, Margaret Didi	Neuberger & Berman Ltd Mat Bond	Wisehaupt, Pamela E.	Vanguard CA TF MM,Muni MM, OH TF MM
Weiner, Jason	Fidelity Sel Air Transport		
Weinstock, Samuel	Dreyfus NJ Muni Bond,S-I Muni Bond	Wohler, Stephen	AARP High Quality Bond
Weisberg, Martin A.	MIM Mutual Stock Appr,Stock Gr	Wolfe, C. Stephen II	Price, Rowe TF HY
Weiss, Richard T.	Strong Common Stock,Opportunity	Wong, Ray	Stagecoach MM
Weiss, William M.	59 Wall St US Equity	Wood, Gary B.	Concorde Value
Weitz, Wallace R.	Weitz FI,Govt MM,Partners Value,Value	Woodruff, Steve	Galaxy CT Muni Bond
Weller, Fred W.	Matrix Emerging Gr	Woodson, A. Hartswell III	Gabelli Global Conv Sec
Welsh, Ellen	WPG Govt MM	Wooster, Pam	Hanover US Govt Securities
Wenger, Derrick	Evergreen Limited Market	Worley, Richard B.	MAS Global FI,Int'l FI
Werler, Mary K.	1784 ST Inc,US Treas MM	Wright, Danita	Working Assets Money Fund
Wesselkamper, C. Stephan	Gradison-McDonald US Govt Res	Wright, John G. L.	Babson Stewart Ivory Int'l
Whalen, Mark W.	Regis Sterling Partners Bal	Wronskyj, Wolodymyr	Dreyfus Fund
Wheeler, Deborah	Fidelity Sel Leisure	Wyper, George U.	Warburg, Pincus Cap Appr
White, Allan R. III	Salomon Brothers Investors	Yacktman, Donald A.	Yacktman Fund
White, Stephen A.	Neuberger & Berman Govt Inc	Zak, Suzanne	IAI MidCap Growth
Whitehead, Trudie D.	Legg Mason HY Bond	Zarr, Joseph A.	Flex-Fund ST Global Inc
Whitesides, Lawson E., Jr.	SteinRoe Young Investor	Zeltzer, Gary S.	Wertheim Investment Grade Inc, ST Investment
Whitney, Richard T.	Advance Capital I Bal,Eq Gr,Price Rowe Bal,Equity Index		
		Zemsky, Paul L.	Preferred Fixed Income
Whitridge, Roland W.	Babson Shadow Stock,Value	Zenoble, Sarah	Fidelity Spartan Muni MF,TE MM Tr
Whitsides, Lawson E., Jr.	SteinRoe Stock	Zobian, Stewart	Value Line Leveraged Gr
Whitworth, Horace P. II	Regis TS&W Equity	Zuger, Peter A.	Twentieth Century Eq Inc,Value
Whyte, Mary Beth	Hercules MM		

CHAPTER 15

Geographical guide to no-load funds

State/City	Funds
Arizona	
Phoenix	Papp group
California	
Beverly Hills	Pacific Financial group
Glendora	Jurika & Voyles group
Irvine	Analytic group
La Jolla	Pacific Horizon group
Larkspur	Meridian group
"	Reynolds group
"	Wood Island Growth
Los Angeles	FPA group
"	Hotchkis & Wiley group
"	Prudent Speculator
"	Rea-Graham Balanced
Mountain View	Benham group
Newport Beach	PIMCO group
"	PIMCO Advisors Inst. group
Pasadena	Guinness Flight group
"	Pacific Advisors group
Petaluma	Permanent Portfolio group
San Francisco	Cal Inv Trust group
"	Dodge & Cox group
"	Fremont group
"	Matthews group
"	McM group
"	Montgomery group
"	Muir California TF Bond
"	Pacific Horizon group
"	Parnassus Income group
"	Robertson Stephens group
"	Schwab group
"	Stagecoach group
"	Working Assets group
San Mateo	"Bailard, Biehl & Kaiser group"
"	Franklin/Templeton group
Santa Monica	DFA group
Walnut Creek	Solon Short Dur. Govt group
Colorado	
Denver	Berger group
"	Founders group
"	INVESCO group
"	Janus group
Englewood	National Industries
Connecticut	
Greenwich	Gintel group
Hartford	Aetna group
Norwalk	Managers group
Stamford	General Electric group
"	PIMCO Advisors group
Delaware	
Greenville	Brandywine group
Wilmington	Crowley group
"	Henlopen
District of Columbia	
Washington	Homestead group
"	Steadman group
Florida	
Boca Raton	Ivy group
"	Philadelphia
St. Petersburg	Hough group
Tampa	ASM
Venice	Caldwell

State/City	Funds
Georgia	
Atlanta	Atlanta Growth
"	Caldwell & Orkin Agg Gr
"	EBI group
"	Enterprise group
Carrollton	SCM Portfolio
Peachtree City	Eclipse group
Hawaii	
Honolulu	Leahi Tax-Free Income
Illinois	
Aurora	Oberweis Emerging Growth
Bannockburn	Mathers
Bloomington	State Farm group
Chicago	Acorn
"	American Aadvantage group
"	Ariel group
"	Asset Management Financial group
"	Brinson group
"	Bruce
"	CT&T group
"	Fasciano
"	Goldman Sachs group
"	Household Personal group
"	Keeley Small Cap Value
"	Kemper group
"	Nuveen Tax-Free Reserves
"	Oakmark group
"	Omni Investment
"	O.R.I. Growth
"	Perritt Capital Growth
"	PRA Real Estate Securities
"	Skyline group
"	Stein Roe & Farnham group
"	Wayne Hummer group
"	William Blair group
"	Yacktman
Evanston	Israel Growth
Naperville	Countdown to Retirement group
Northbrook	"Grandich Contrarian, Peter"
Peoria	Preferred group
Wheaton	Monetta group
Indiana	
Indianapolis	Anthem group
"	Pinnacle
Kansas	
Shawnee Mission	Torchmark group
Kentucky	
Lexington	Dupree group
Louisville	Fairmont
Maine	
Portland	Austin Global Equity
"	Forum group
"	Oak Hall Equity
Maryland	
Baltimore	Ark group
"	Legg Mason group
"	T. Rowe Price group
Bethesda	Calvert Asset Mgt group
"	Cappiello-Rushmore group
"	Rydex group
"	Torray

State/City	Funds	State/City	Funds
Maryland		**New Jersey**	
Lutherville	Greenspring	Saddle Brook	Lexington group
Towson	Fontaine group	Short Hills	Mutual Series group
Massachusetts		**New Mexico**	
Boston	AARP group	Santa Fe	Selected/Venture group
"	Beacon Hill		
"	BT Investment group	**New York**	
"	Century Shares Trust	Cobleskill	FAM Value
"	CGM group	New York	Active Assets Money group
"	Domini Social Equity	"	Alger group
"	Eaton Vance group	"	Alliance group
"	Fidelity group	"	American Heritage
"	59 Wall Street group	"	Baron group
"	FundTrust group	"	Bernstein group
"	Galaxy group	"	Blanchard group
"	Green Century group	"	Bramwell Growth
"	JPM Advisor group	"	Bull & Bear group
"	Loomis Sayles	"	Burnham
"	New England group	"	Cohen & Steers Realty
"	Northeast group	"	Cowen group
"	Pierpont group	"	Dean Witter group
"	Regis group	"	FFTW group
"	Scudder group	"	First Eagle group
"	Seven Seas group	"	First Mutual
"	UST Group	"	44 Wall St Equity
"	Wertheim group	"	Fundamental group
"	Wright Managed group	"	GAM group
Fall River	Copley	"	Hanover group
Lincoln	Quantitative group	"	Haven
Wellesley	Weston Portfolios group	"	Kaufmann
		"	Kidder Peabody group
Michigan		"	Laidlaw Covenant
Bloomfield Hills	Schwartz Value	"	Lepercq-Istel
Southfield	Advance Capital I group	"	M.S.B.
Troy	Woodward Equity Index	"	Neuberger & Berman group
		"	New York Life Inst group
Minnesota		"	Nomura Pacific Basin
Minneapolis	Eastcliff Total Return	"	Pacifica group
"	General Securities	"	Paine Webber group
"	Hercules group	"	Prudential group
"	IAI group	"	Rainbow
"	SIT group	"	Reich & Tang group
St. Paul	Fortis group	"	Reserve group
"	Mairs & Power group	"	Retirement System (RSI) group
		"	Royce group
Missouri		"	Salomon Brothers group
Kansas City	Advisors' Inner Circle group	"	SBSF group
"	Babson group	"	Schafer Value
"	Govett group	"	Schroder Capital group
"	Longleaf Partners group	"	Sequoia
"	PBHG Group	"	Smith Barney group
"	Twentieth Century group	"	SoGen group
"	Vista group	"	Sound Shore
St. Louis	Lindner group	"	TCW/DW group
		"	Tocqueville group
Nebraska		"	Tweedy Browne group
Lincoln	Smith Hayes group	"	Value Line group
"	Stratus group	"	Warburg Pincus group
Omaha	Bridges Investment	"	Women's Equity
"	KPM group	"	"Weiss, Peck & Greer group (WPG)"
"	Weitz group	"	Van Eck group
		Pearl River	Volumetric
Nevada		Purchase	Evergreen group
Incline Village	Navellier Aggr Sm Cap Equity	Rye	Gabelli group
		"	Westwood group
New Hampshire		Uniondale	Dreyfus group
Portsmouth	Pax World	Valhalla	Merger
New Jersey		**North Carolina**	
Closter	Monitrend group	Chapel Hill	Smith Breeden group
Hackensack	LMH	Greensboro	Trent Equity
Jersey City	Dremen group	Rocky Mount	Brown Capital Mgmt group
Princeton	Merrill Lynch group	"	North Carolina Tax-Free Bond

State/City	Funds	State/City	Funds
North Carolina		**Texas**	
"	Nottingham group	Dallas	Aquinas group
"	Oak Value	"	Armstrong Assoc
"	ZSA group	"	Concorde Value
		Ft. Worth	LKCM Small Cap Equity
Ohio		Houston	Bridgeway group
Cincinnati	Analysts group	"	Capstone Govt Income
"	Bartlett group	San Antonio	Bonnel Growth
"	Brundage Story & Rose group	"	Pauze/Swanson US Govt Tot Ret
"	Crescent	"	United Services group
"	FBP Contrarian Group	"	USAA group
"	Government Street group	Victoria	Amtrust Value
"	Gradison-McDonald group	Wichita Falls	Avondale Total Return
"	Matrix group		
Cleveland	Carnegie group		
"	Maxus group	**Utah**	
"	MIM group	Salt Lake City	Wasatch group
Columbus	Amcore Vintage group		
"	First Omaha group		
"	HighMark group	**Virginia**	
Dayton	Golden Rainbow A James Adv	Alexandria	Leeb Personal Finance
"	PC&J group	Arlington	GIT group
Dublin	Flex-fund group	Lynchburg	American Pension Investors group
Milford	Gateway group	Richmond	America's Utility Fund
Toledo	Harbor group	"	Cornerstone Growth
		"	World Funds group
Oregon			
Portland	Columbia group		
"	Crabbe Huson group	**Washington**	
"	Jensen Portfolio	Bellingham	Saturna Capital group
		Seattle	Accessor group
Pennsylvania		"	Merriman group
Berwyn	Berwyn group	"	Rainier group
Conshohochen	Camco group	"	SAFECO group
Philadelphia	Delaware group	"	Seafirst Retirement group
Pittsburgh	Federated group		
Plymouth Meeting	Stratton group	**Wisconsin**	
Rosemont	Gibralter Equity Growth	Madison	Bascom Hill group
Valley Forge	Valley Forge	"	Thompson Unger & Plumb group
"	Vanguard group	Milwaukee	CharterCapital Blue Chip
Wayne	Arbor OVB group	"	Fiduciary Capital Growth
"	FFB Lexicon group	"	Heartland group
"	SEI group	"	Marshall group
"	1784 group	"	Nicholas group
West Conshohochen	MAS	"	Northern group
Wexford	Muhlenkamp	"	Portico group
Wyncote	Rightime	"	Primary group
		"	Strong group
Tennessee		Stevens Point	Sentry
Memphis	Wade		

Section IV

Appendixes

Mutual Fund Milestones

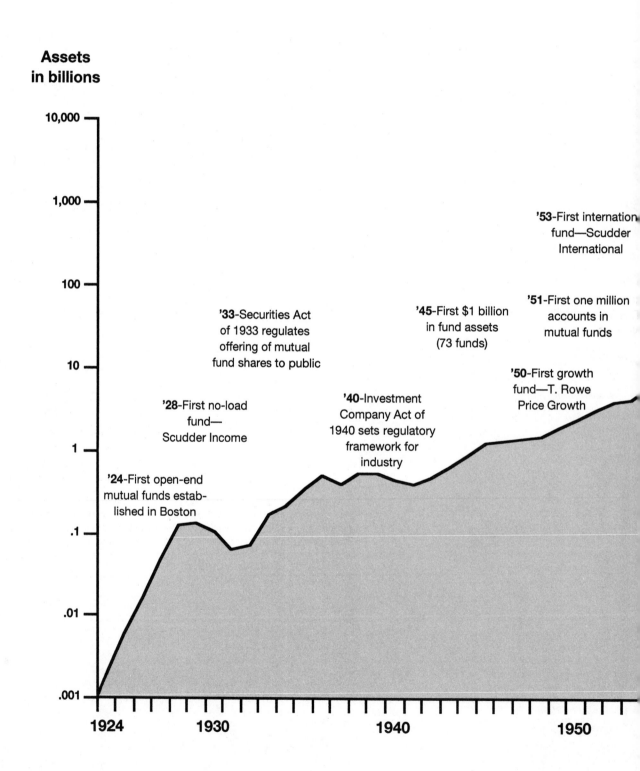

Assets in billions

10,000

1,000

'53-First internation
fund—Scudder
International

100

'33-Securities Act
of 1933 regulates
offering of mutual
fund shares to public

'45-First $1 billion
in fund assets
(73 funds)

'51-First one million
accounts in
mutual funds

10

'28-First no-load
fund—
Scudder Income

'40-Investment
Company Act of
1940 sets regulatory
framework for
industry

'50-First growth
fund—T. Rowe
Price Growth

1

'24-First open-end
mutual funds estab-
lished in Boston

.1

.01

.001

1924   1930   1940   1950

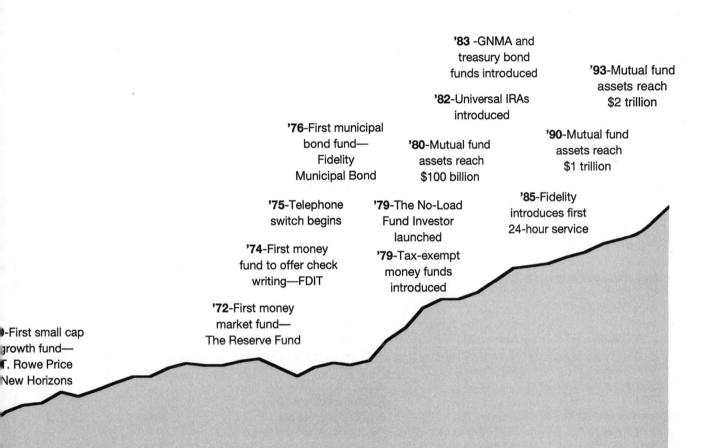

'83 -GNMA and treasury bond funds introduced

'93-Mutual fund assets reach $2 trillion

'82-Universal IRAs introduced

'76-First municipal bond fund— Fidelity Municipal Bond

'80-Mutual fund assets reach $100 billion

'90-Mutual fund assets reach $1 trillion

'75-Telephone switch begins

'79-The No-Load Fund Investor launched

'85-Fidelity introduces first 24-hour service

'74-First money fund to offer check writing—FDIT

'79-Tax-exempt money funds introduced

'72-First money market fund— The Reserve Fund

-First small cap growth fund— T. Rowe Price New Horizons

The mutual fund industry has grown astonishingly over the past seven decades. From 1924, when the first open-ended fund began and 1928 when Scudder Income fund became the first no-load, the business took 20 years to reach the $1 billion mark in assets. The next two decades, to the mid-60s, saw a succession of firsts: T. Rowe Price started the first growth fund, for example, and Scudder the first international fund. But those inventions were dwarfted by the innovations of the next quarter century. The privilege of switching among funds in a particular family by simply making a phone call—now taken for granted—was inaugurated during the 70s. Money market, municipal bond and government bond funds were introduced. And ultimately, the industry grew into a $2 trillion powerhouse!

1960   1970   1980   1990

Index and passively managed funds

Fund	Index	Comments	% return 1994	Annualized 3 yrs
S&P 500 funds				
CA Inv Tr-S&P 500 Index	S&P 500	500 large and medium size companies	1.0	—
DFA U.S. Lg Co‡	S&P 500	500 large and medium size companies	1.3	6.1
Dreyfus Peoples Index	S&P 500	500 large and medium size companies	0.7	5.9
Dreyfus S&P 500 Index	S&P 500	500 large and medium size companies	0.8	—
Federated Max-Cap	S&P 500	500 large and medium size companies	1.2	5.9
Fidelity Market Index	S&P 500	500 large and medium size companies	1.1	5.9
Galaxy Lg Co Index‡	S&P 500	500 large and medium size companies	1.0	5.8
Price, Rowe Equity Index	S&P 500	500 large and medium size companies	1.0	5.8
SEI S&P 500 Index	S&P 500	500 large and medium size companies	1.0	6.0
Seven Seas S&P 500 Index	S&P 500	500 large and medium size companies	1.3	—
Vangd Index 500	S&P 500	500 large and medium size companies	1.2	6.1
Woodward Equity Index	S&P 500	500 large and medium size companies	1.0	—
Other large company indexes				
ASM Fund	DJIA	Dow look-a-like	1.1	6.6
DFA U.S. Large Cap Value		Listed stocks with high book value relative to market value	-4.5	—
Drey-Wilsh Lg Co Gro	Wilshire 5000	Growth companies w/$725 million ‡ market caps	2.3	—
Drey-Wilsh Lg Co Value	Wilshire 5000	Value companies w/$725 million ‡ market caps	-5.2	—
Gateway Index Plus	S&P 100 OEX	100 large stocks, actively trades options	5.6	6.0
Lexington Corporate Leaders Trust		23 blue chip corporations	-0.8	8.6
Schwab 1000		1000 largest US companies	-0.1	5.9
Vangd Index Total Market†	Wilshire 5000	Broadest index available	-0.1	—
Vangd Index Growth	S&P/BARRA Growth	174 companies w/hi price/book ratios	2.9	—
Vangd Index Value	S&P/BARRA Value	326 companies w/low price/book ratios	-0.6	—
MidCap indexes				
CA Inv Tr-S&P MidCap Index	S&P MidCap 400	Medium-size stocks with medium market caps of approx $800M	-3.9	—
Dreyfus Peoples MidCap	S&P MidCap 400	Medium-size stocks with medium market caps of approx $800M	-4.0	6.9
Federated Mid-Cap	S&P MidCap 400	Medium-size stocks with medium market caps of approx $800M	-4.3	—
Gateway Mid-Cap Index	S&P MidCap 400	Medium-size stocks, may actively trade options	-5.1	—
Vangd Index Extended Mkt†	Wilshire 4500	All companies except S&P 500	-1.8	8.1
Small cap indexes				
DFA U.S. Small Cap Value		Listed stocks with high book value relataive to market value	1.2	—
DFA U.S. Small Co (6-10)‡		Bottom half of listed stocks	-1.3	—
DFA U.S. Small Co (9-10)‡		Bottom 2 deciles of listed stocks	3.1	15.4
Drey-Wilsh Sm Co Gro	Wilshire 5000	Growth companies w/$70-$725 million market caps	-1.4	—
Drey-Wilsh Sm Co Val	Wilshire 5000	Value companies w/$70-$725 million market caps	-4.5	—
Federated Mini-Cap	Russell 2000	Small companies with avg market cap of $180 million	-2.8	3.6
Galaxy Sm Co Index‡	Russell Small Co.	Russell 3000 excluding S&P 500 stocks	-3.7	6.4
Gateway Small-Cap Index	Wilshire Small Cap	250 small size companies, may actively trade options	-6.0	—
Schwab Small Cap Index		1000 companies with capitalization from $150M-$600M	-3.1	—
Vangd Sm Cap Stk† SC	Russell 2000	Small companies with avg market cap of $180 million	-0.5	11.7

Fund	Index	Comments	% return 1994	Annualized 3 yrs
Specialized indexes				
Benham Gold Eq Index		30 North American mining companies	-16.8	11.3
Benham Global Natural Resources Index	Dow Jones World Stock Index	selected companies in the energy and basic materials sectors of DJWSI		
DFA Real Estate Sec‡		REITs	-8.4	—
Domini Social Equity Fund		400 social stocks, half drawn from S&P 500	-0.4	6.1
Dreyfus Edison Electric		members of the Edison Electric Institute (electric companies)	-12.9	1.1
Galaxy Utility Index‡	Russell Utility	121 large utility companies	-8.6	—
Rushmore Amer Gas Indx		members of the American Gas Assoc.	-9.8	5.4
International indexes				
DFA Continental Sm Co‡		Small companies on European continent	11.0	3.7
DFA Japan Small Co‡		Bottom half Tokyo Stock Exchange stocks	29.5	3.0
DFA Lg Cap Int'l‡		Large companies in Europe, Australia & Far East	5.3	4.8
DFA Pacific Rim Small Co.		Small companies in Singapore, Hong Kong, Australia, Malaysia	-12.1	—
DFA U.K. Small Co‡	Financial Times Index	Bottom half of United Kingdom index	4.6	5.5
Schwab Int'l Index		350 large companies excluding U.S. & South Africa	3.8	—
Vangd Int'l Indx-Emerging Mkts†	MSCI Selected Emerg Mkts Free Index	Companies in 12 SE Asia, Latin America & European countries	—	—
Vangd Int'l Indx-Europe†	MSCI-Europe	Morgan Stanley large cap European stocks	1.9	8.3
Vangd Int'l Indx-Pacific†	MSCI-Pacific	Morgan Stanley large cap Pacific stocks	12.9	7.8
Wright Equifund - Belgian/Luxem			—	—
Wright Equifund - Dutch			11.7	7.0
Wright Equifund - Hong Kong			-37.0	10.5
Wright Equifund - Italian			5.0	-8.1
Wright Equifund - Japanese			—	—
Wright Equifund - Mexico			—	—
Wright Equifund - Nordic			—	—
Wright Equifund - Spanish			-9.5	-9.6
Wright Equifund - Swiss			—	—
Bond and balanced indexes				
Dreyfus Bond Market Index	Lehman Bros Govt/ Corp Bond		-3.4	—
Galaxy US Treas Index‡	Salomon Bros. U.S. Treasury Index	US Treasury notes and bonds with remaining maturities of 1‡ yrs	-3.7	4.3
SEI Bond Index	Salomon Bros. Broad Invest-Grade Bond	Representative sample of index	-3.2	4.3
Vangd Balanced Index	Wilshire/Salomon	60% Vanguard Total Market Fund, 40% Bond Market Fund	-1.5	—
Vangd Bond Index - Inter Bond	Lehman Bros Inter Corp/Govt Bond	5-10 year bonds	—	—
Vangd Bond Index - Long Bond	Lehman Bros Long Corp/Govt Bond	10‡ year bonds	—	—
Vangd Bond Index - Short Bond	Lehman Bros Short Corp/Govt Bond	1-5 year bonds	—	—
Vangd Bond Index - Tot Bond Mkt	Lehman Bros Aggregate Bond Index		-2.7	4.6

Summary of sector and industry funds

Agriculture: Fidelity Food and Agriculture.
Chemicals: Fidelity Chemicals.
Consumer: Fidelity Consumer Products.
Defense and Aerospace: Fidelity Defense & Aerospace.
Energy: American Gas Index, Benham Global Natural Resources Index, Fidelity Energy, Fidelity Energy Services, Fidelity Natural Gas, Invesco Energy, Vanguard Energy.
Environment: Fidelity Environmental Services, Invesco Environmental Services.
Financial Services: Century Shares Trust, Fidelity Brokerage and Investment Management, Fidelity Financial Services, Home Finance, Fidelity Insurance, Fidelity Regional Banks, Fidelity Invesco Financial.
Health/Biotechnology: Fidelity Biotechnology, Fidelity Health Care, Fidelity Medical Delivery, Invesco Health, Vanguard Health Care.
Housing: Fidelity Construction and Housing.
Industrial: Fidelity Automotive, Fidelity Industrial Equipment, Fidelity Industrial Materials, Fidelity Paper & Forest Products, Invesco Worldwide Capital Goods.
Leisure: Fidelity Multimedia, Fidelity Leisure, Invesco Leisure.
Precious Metals: Benham Gold Equity Index, Blanchard Precious Metals, Bull & Bear Gold Investors, Capiello-Rushmore Gold Fund, Fidelity American Gold, Fidelity Precious Metals and Minerals, Gabelli Gold, Invesco Gold, Lexington Goldfund, Rydex Precious Metals, Scudder Gold, United Services World Gold, Gold Shares and Global Resources, USAA Gold, Vanguard Gold & Precious Metals.
Real Estate: Cohen & Steers Realty, CGM Realty, Columbia Real Estate Equity, Crabbe Huson Real Estate Investment, DFA Real Estate Sec., Fidelity Real Estate, PRA Real Estate, U.S. Real Estate.
Service: Fidelity Retailing.
Technology: Fidelity Computers, Fidelity Developing Communications, Fidelity Electronics, Fidelity Software and Computer Services, Fidelity Technology, Fidelity Telecommunications, Invesco Technology, Invesco World Communications, Montgomery Global Communications, T. Rowe Price Science and Technology.
Transportation: Fidelity Air Transportation, Fidelity Transportation.
Utilities: America's Utility Fund, Benham Utilities Income, Capiello-Rushmore Utility Income, Dreyfus Edison Electric Index Fund, Fidelity Utilities, Fidelity Utilities Growth, Galaxy Utility Index, Invesco Utilities, Lindner Utilities, Nottingham-Harris Utilities, Stratton Monthly Dividend Shares, Strong American Utilities, U.S. Income, Vanguard Utilities Income.

Precious metals funds

Holdings by country, region, or bullion

Benham Gold Equities Index: Canada, 67%; U.S. 27%; Ghana, 3%; cash, 3%.
Blanchard Precious Metals: Canada, 39%; U.S., 33%; gold bullion, 8%; Australia, 6%; South Africa, 5%; cash, 9%.
Bull & Bear Gold Investors: South Africa, 46%; North America, 22%; Australia, 9%; bullion, 4%; platinum, 2%; convertibles, 4%; U.S. Gov. sec. 14%.
Fidelity Select American Gold: Canada, 57%; U.S., 26%; repos, 7%; bullion, 3%; indexed sec., 4%; convertibles, 2%.
Fidelity Select Precious Metals: South Africa, 48%; Canada, 20%; Australia, 10%; U.S. 8%; bullion, 1%; repos, 12%; indexed sec., 2%; convertibles, 1%.
Gabelli Gold: North America, 46%; South Africa, 26%; Australia, 13%; Europe, 3%; South America, 1%; cash, 11%.

Invesco Strategic Gold: Canada, 57%; U.S., 30%; Australia, 10%; Switzerland, 2%; Mexico, 1%.
Lexington Goldfund: North America; 41%; South Africa, 35%; Australia, 17%; gold bullion, 5%, cash, 3%.
Scudder Gold: Canada, 50%; U.S., 31%; Australia, 11%; South Africa, 1%; cash, 7%.
USAA Gold: Canada, 42%; U.S., 33%; Australia, 10%; South Africa, 8%; Ghana, 3%; cash, 4%.
US Global Resources: North America, 21%; non-precious metals stocks, 41%; repos, 10%; Australia, 5%; U.K., 5%; other metals, 16%.
US Gold Shares: South Africa, 85%; North America, 14%; repos, 14%; cash, -13%.
US World Gold: North America, 70%; Australia, 22%; Ghana, 5%; repos, 3%
Vanguard Specialized Gold & Precious Metals: South Africa, 38%; North America, 27%; Australia, 23%; bullion, 6%; U.K., 3%; Japan, 1%; cash, 2%

Top 50 no-load fund groups

Ranked by 1994 assets of funds listed in Chapter 7 of the Handbook

Rank	Group	Year-end assets in millions $ 1994	1993	Rank	Group	Year-end assets in millions $ 1994	1993
1	Fidelity Research & Management	$209,852	$181,427	26	Warburg, Pincus Counsellors	$3,369	$1,482
2	Vanguard Group	130,679	125,872	27	Columbia	3,359	3,054
3	Dreyfus Corporation	41,910	45,646	28	Lindner/Ryback Management	3,240	2,851
4	T. Rowe Price Associates	37,724	35,437	29	Goldman Sachs	2,863	1,919
5	Scudder, Stevens, & Clark	30,570	32,802	30	Berger Associates	2,773	1,838
6	Twentieth Century	24,271	23,323	31	Reich & Tang	2,354	2,616
7	Schwab Funds	23,152	15,764	32	Marshall	2,254	1,711
8	Janus Capital	17,062	17,016	33	Montgomery Asset Management	2,253	1,301
9	USAA Investment Management	13,653	13,718	34	Galaxy	2,161	3,850
10	Federated Research	9,364	13,428	35	Value Line Funds	1,813	2,212
11	Benham Management	9,222	10,847	36	Founders Asset Management	1,806	1,915
12	Invesco	9,008	9,593	37	Gabelli	1,793	1,880
13	Pacific Investment Management	8,868	6,763	38	Jones & Babson	1,710	1,801
14	Mutual Series	8,316	6,675	39	SAFECO Asset Management	1,684	1,610
15	Strong	8,149	7,088	40	State Farm Investment Management	1,544	1,457
16	General Electric-Elfun Funds	7,100	7,649	41	Capital Growth Management	1,538	1,509
17	Neuberger & Berman	6,036	5,625	42	Investment Advisors, Inc	1,501	1,543
18	Seven Seas Funds	4,908	1,723	43	Dodge & Cox	1,464	1,103
19	SteinRoe & Farnham	4,495	4,947	44	Gradison-McDonald Funds	1,347	1,332
20	Pierpont	4,191	1,259	45	1784	1,346	737
21	Sanford Bernstein & Co	4,144	3,145	46	United Services	1,341	1,349
22	Dimensional Fund Advisors	3,962	3,032	47	Asset Management Financial	1,333	1,974
23	Nicholas Company	3,837	4,346	48	Pennsylvania-Royce	1,248	1,350
24	Harbor Capital	3,795	3,301	49	Vista Funds (Chase Manhattan)	1,162	1,437
25	Legg Mason	3,621	3,332	50	Lexington Management	1,118	1,068

Top 20 fund groups — load and no-load

Rank	Fund group	December 31, 1994 Assets ($ mil)	Market share %	Rank	Fund group	December 31, 1994 Assets ($ mil)	Market share %
1	Fidelity	$275,270	12.72%	11	Smith Barney	$53,673	2.48%
2	Vanguard	135,516	6.26	12	Prudential	50,606	2.34
3	Merrill Lynch	120,629	5.57	13	IDS	46,311	2.14
4	Capital Research	110,215	5.09	14	T. Rowe Price	38,807	1.79
5	Franklin/Templeton	87,711	4.05	15	Kemper	38,285	1.77
6	Dreyfus	62,831	2.90	16	Scudder	31,716	1.47
7	Putnam	62,262	2.88	17	SEI	31,047	1.43
8	Federated	61,886	2.86	18	Oppenheimer	29,174	1.35
9	TIAA-CREFF	60,271	2.78	19	Twentieth Century	25,492	1.18
10	Dean Witter	55,999	2.59	20	AIM	25,204	1.16

Source: Investment Co. Institute

Combined effective federal and state marginal tax rates on dividends

State	Marginal federal rate 28%	31%	36%	39.6%	Highest listed rate
Alabama*	30.59	33.38	38.05	41.42	5
Alaska	28.00	31.00	36.00	39.60	0
Arizona	32.97	35.76	40.42	43.77	6.9
Arkansas	33.04	35.83	40.48	43.83	7
California	35.92	38.59	43.04	46.24	11
Colorado	31.60	34.45	39.20	42.62	5
Connecticut	31.24	34.11	38.88	42.32	4.5
Delaware	33.54	36.31	40.93	44.25	7.7
District of Columbia	34.84	37.56	42.08	45.34	9.5
Florida	28.00	31.00	36.00	39.60	0
Georgia	32.32	35.14	39.84	43.22	6
Hawaii	35.20	37.90	42.40	45.64	10
Idaho	33.90	36.66	41.25	44.55	8.2
Illinois	30.16	33.07	37.92	41.41	3
Indiana	30.45	33.35	38.18	41.65	3.4
Iowa*	33.17	35.75	40.09	43.24	9.98
Kansas	32.64	35.45	40.13	43.50	6.45
Kentucky	32.32	35.14	39.84	43.22	6
Louisana*	31.11	33.86	38.46	41.79	6
Maine	34.12	36.87	41.44	44.73	8.5
Maryland	32.32	35.14	39.84	43.22	6
Massachusetts	36.64	39.28	43.68	46.85	12
Michigan	31.17	34.04	38.82	42.26	4.4
Minnesota	34.12	36.87	41.44	44.73	8.5
Mississippi	31.60	34.45	39.20	42.62	5
Missouri*	31.11	33.86	38.46	41.79	6
Montana*	33.70	36.24	40.51	43.61	11
Nebraska	33.03	35.82	40.47	43.82	6.99
Nevada	28.00	31.00	36.00	39.60	0
New Hampshire	31.60	34.45	39.20	42.62	5
New Jersey	32.79	35.59	40.26	43.62	6.65
New Mexico	34.12	36.87	41.44	44.73	8.5
New York	33.67	36.43	41.04	44.36	7.875
New York City	36.88	39.51	43.89	47.05	12.33
North Carolina	33.58	36.31	40.96	44.28	7.75
North Dakota*	34.22	36.71	40.92	43.96	12
Ohio	33.40	36.18	40.80	44.13	7.5
Oklahoma*	31.63	34.33	38.87	41.16	7
Oregon	32.67	35.28	39.69	42.88	9
Pennsylvania	30.02	32.93	37.79	41.29	2.8
Rhode Island**	33.15	36.42	41.77	45.53	0
South Carolina	33.04	35.83	40.48	43.83	7
South Dakota	28.00	31.00	36.00	39.60	0
Tennessee	32.32	35.14	39.84	43.22	6
Texas	28.00	31.00	36.00	39.60	0
Utah*	31.73	34.43	38.95	42.23	7.2
Vermont***	32.71	35.96	41.28	45.04	0
Virginia	32.14	34.97	39.68	43.07	5.75
Washington	28.00	31.00	36.00	39.60	0
West Virginia	32.68	35.49	40.16	43.53	6.5
Wisconsin	32.99	35.78	40.44	43.79	6.93
Wyoming	28.00	31.00	36.00	39.60	0

* Takes into consideration the applicable deduction of federal taxes at the state level
** State tax is 27.5% of federal liability
*** State tax is 25% of federal liability

Source: Deloitte & Touche

Industry assets (millions)

Year	All Funds	All Funds Excluding Sht Term Funds	All No-Load Funds	Money Market Funds	No-Load Funds Excluding Sht-term funds	No-Load Percentage (Excl Sht-term)
1994	$2,168,681	$1,553,069	$1,180,708	$615,612	$565,096	36.4%
1993	2,077,767	1,510,047	1,118,929	567,720	551,209	36.5
1992	1,602,731	1,055,209	934,960	547,522	387,438	36.7
1991	1,354,280	807,001	845,240	547,279	297,961	36.9
1990	1,018,298	525,397	684,937	492,901	192,036	36.6
1989	942,793	511,130	619,671	431,663	188,008	36.8
1988	807,134	481,370	474,172	325,764	148,408	30.8
1987	763,976	463,725	438,538	300,251	138,287	29.8
1986	701,788	424,088	420,937	277,700	143,237	33.8
1985	520,310	289,071	331,698	231,239	100,459	34.8
1984	346,955	149,211	251,772	197,744	54,028	36.2
1983	278,351	119,420	199,407	158,931	40,476	33.9
1982	282,758	80,432	227,801	202,326	25,475	31.7
1981	240,786	59,356	199,606	181,430	18,176	30.6
1980	136,135	61,449	93,383	74,686	18,697	30.4
1979	96,901	51,456	60,651	45,445	15,206	29.6
1978	57,493	46,827	22,051	10,666	11,385	24.3
1977	50,605	46,744	14,545	3,861	10,684	22.9
1976	52,732	49,078	11,222	3,655	7,567	15.4
1975	46,807	43,117	9,229	3,690	5,540	12.8
1974	37,376	34,913	6,867	2,462	4,405	12.6
1973	47,639	47,626	6,006	13	5,993	12.6
1972	61,326	61,326	7,419	—	7,419	12.1
1971	56,889	56,889	5,854	—	5,854	10.3
1970	48,971	48,971	4,112	—	4,112	8.4
1969	49,041	49,041	3,799	—	3,799	7.7
1968	52,912	52,912	3,464	—	3,464	6.5
1967	44,827	44,827	2,489	—	2,489	5.6
1966	35,076	35,076	1,975	—	1,975	5.6
1965	34,991	34,991	1,512	—	1,512	4.3
1964	28,963	28,963	1,257	—	1,257	4.3
1963	24,485	24,485	1,116	—	1,116	4.6
1962	20,651	20,651	959	—	959	4.6

No-load mutual fund sales

As a percent of total mutual fund sales
(Excluding short-term funds)

Year	Total Fund Sales* ($ Mil.)	Total No-Load Sales (Mil.)	No-Load As A Percent	Year	Total Fund Sales* ($ Mil.)	Total No-Load Sales (Mil.)	No-Load As A Percent
1994	$474,336	$192,342	40.6%	1981	$11,926	$5,483	46.0%
1993	510,686	200,362	39.2	1980	11,208	5,301	47.3
1992	362,478	160,419	44.3	1979	8,039	4,247	52.8
1991	234,454	103,767	44.3	1978	7,818	3,917	50.1
1990	149,513	62,414	41.7	1977	6,962	3,360	48.3
1989	135,488	55,224	40.1	1976	4,724	1,401	29.7
1988	87,234	33,363	38.2	1975	3,506	816	23.3
1987	183,639	75,450	41.1	1974	3,269	734	22.5
1986	217,382	81,698	37.6	1973	4,642	1,091	23.5
1985	116,543	45,820	39.3	1972	5,080	1,021	20.1
1984	49,946	20,077	40.2	1971	5,564	1,015	18.2
1983	50,112	24,708	49.3	1970	4,974	848	17.1
1982	17,849	7,498	42.0				

Source: ICI, Donoghue's Money Fund Report, The No-Load Fund Association, The No-Load Fund Investor

The power of compound growth

■ The tables in this chapter illustrate the power of compound growth. Table 1 shows how an initial investment will multiply into thousands of dollars in your lifetime. The table is set up to show how much $10,000 will grow to in a given number of years at various rates of return with annual compounding. To use it, first estimate the rate of growth your investment will achieve and the number of years it will be invested. Figures in the body of the table will tell you the how much wealth will accumulate. In addition, you can determine the rate of growth needed for $10,000 to grow to a target sum over a given period of time. For example, if you need $31,000 ten years from now for college expenses, then run your finger down the first column of the table to the line showing total value after ten years. Then look across till you find the number closest to $31,000—in this case, $31,058. Then note the percentage at the top of the column. In this example, it is 12%, the annual compounded rate you need to achieve your goal.

Similarly, table 1 can be used to determine how much money you will need at retirement. First assume an inflation rate and note the number of years you have before retirement. Then divide the applicable number in the table by 10,000. For example, if you assume a 5% inflation rate, and you will be retiring in 10 years, divide 16,289 (10th figure in the first column) by 10,000 to get 1.6289. If you will need $2,000 per month in today's dollars to live on, multiply $2,000 by 1.6289 to get $3,258. That's what you will need in the inflated dollars of a decade from now.

It is important to understand that past growth rates should be used for forecasting only after careful consideration of the basic reasons for the observed growth patterns as well as for any new factors that may change the growth rates.

Table 2 illustrates the far greater growth when $1,000 is deposited at the beginning of every year and compounded annually at various growth rates. The base in this table is $1,000 (not $10,000 as in the first table) since this amount can be multiplied by two to easily obtain the size nest egg that can be accumulated with maximum IRA contributions. Multiply by other factors if you are contributing less. If the sum is deposited at the end of the year rather than at the beginning, then the resulting growth can be obtained by taking the year earlier figure and adding $1,000. For frequent periodic deposits via a payroll deduction plan, growth will fall in between the two methods described.

Tables 3 and 4 provide the flip side of tables 1 and 2. Where the first two tables show future value, the last two show present value. Table 3 calculates the present value of $1,000 at various rates of interest. Use table 3 when you want to determine the amount of one initial investment needed in order to accumulate $1,000 over various periods of times at various interest rates. For example, if you will need $1,000 in ten years and expect a 10% growth rate, you can realize this growth objective by investing $386 and letting it grow for ten years. Other growth targets can by obtained by multiplying the annual amounts by the ratio of your target sum over $1,000.

Table 4 calculates the present value of annual investments made over a period of one or more years. Use table 4 when you want to determine the size of annual investments needed in order to accumulate $1,000 at a target date at various interest rates. For example, if you will need $1,000 in ten years and expect a 10% growth rate, you can realize this growth objective by investing $57.04 at the beginning of each year for ten years. Other growth targets can by obtained by multiplying the annual amounts by the ratio of your target sum over $1,000. Table 4 is known as a table of sinking fund payments. Tables 3 and 4 are simply the reciprocals of tables 1 and 2.

Table 1

What $10,000 will be worth in a given number of years

% increase compounded annually

Year	5%	6%	7%	8%	9%	10%	11%	12%	13%	14%	15%	16%	17%	18%	19%	20%
1	10,500	10,600	10,700	10,800	10,900	11,000	11,100	11,200	11,300	11,400	11,500	11,600	11,700	11,800	11,900	12,000
2	11,025	11,236	11,449	11,664	11,881	12,100	12,321	12,544	12,769	12,996	13,225	13,456	13,689	13,924	14,161	14,400
3	11,576	11,910	12,250	12,597	12,950	13,310	13,676	14,049	14,429	14,815	15,209	15,609	16,016	16,430	16,852	17,280
4	12,155	12,625	13,108	13,605	14,116	14,641	15,181	15,735	16,305	16,890	17,490	18,106	18,739	19,388	20,053	20,736
5	12,763	13,382	14,026	14,693	15,386	16,105	16,851	17,623	18,424	19,254	20,114	21,003	21,924	22,878	23,864	24,883
6	13,401	14,185	15,007	15,869	16,771	17,716	18,704	19,738	20,820	21,950	23,131	24,364	25,652	26,996	28,398	29,860
7	14,071	15,036	16,058	17,138	18,280	19,487	20,762	22,107	23,526	25,023	26,600	28,262	30,012	31,855	33,793	35,832
8	14,775	15,938	17,182	18,509	19,926	21,436	23,045	24,760	26,584	28,526	30,590	32,784	35,115	37,589	40,214	42,998
9	15,513	16,895	18,385	19,990	21,719	23,579	25,580	27,731	30,040	32,519	35,179	38,030	41,084	44,355	47,854	51,598
10	16,289	17,908	19,672	21,589	23,674	25,937	28,394	31,058	33,946	37,072	40,456	44,114	48,068	52,338	56,947	61,917
11	17,103	18,983	21,049	23,316	25,804	28,531	31,518	34,785	38,359	42,262	46,524	51,173	56,240	61,759	67,767	74,301
12	17,959	20,122	22,522	25,182	28,127	31,384	34,985	38,960	43,345	48,179	53,503	59,360	65,801	72,876	80,642	89,161
13	18,856	21,329	24,098	27,196	30,658	34,523	38,833	43,635	48,980	54,924	61,528	68,858	76,987	85,994	95,964	106,993
14	19,799	22,609	25,785	29,372	33,417	37,975	43,104	48,871	55,348	62,613	70,757	79,875	90,075	101,472	114,198	128,392
15	20,789	23,966	27,590	31,722	36,425	41,772	47,846	54,736	62,543	71,379	81,371	92,655	105,387	119,737	135,895	154,070
16	21,829	25,404	29,522	34,259	39,703	45,950	53,109	61,304	70,673	81,372	93,576	107,480	123,303	141,290	161,715	184,884
17	22,920	26,928	31,588	37,000	43,276	50,545	58,951	68,660	79,861	92,765	107,613	124,677	144,265	166,722	192,441	221,861
18	24,066	28,543	33,799	39,960	47,171	55,599	65,436	76,900	90,243	105,752	123,755	144,625	168,790	196,733	229,005	266,233
19	25,270	30,256	36,165	43,157	51,417	61,159	72,633	86,128	101,974	120,557	142,318	167,765	197,484	232,144	272,516	319,480
20	26,533	32,071	38,697	46,610	56,044	67,275	80,623	96,463	115,231	137,435	163,665	194,608	231,056	273,930	324,294	383,376
21	27,860	33,996	41,406	50,338	61,088	74,002	89,492	108,038	130,211	156,676	188,215	225,745	270,336	323,238	385,910	460,051
22	29,253	36,035	44,304	54,365	66,586	81,403	99,336	121,003	147,138	178,610	216,447	261,864	316,293	381,421	459,233	552,061
23	30,715	38,197	47,405	58,715	72,579	89,543	110,263	135,523	166,266	203,616	248,915	303,762	370,062	450,076	546,487	662,474
24	32,251	40,489	50,724	63,412	79,111	98,497	122,392	151,786	187,881	232,122	286,252	352,364	432,973	531,090	650,320	794,968
25	33,864	42,919	54,274	68,485	86,231	108,347	135,855	170,001	212,305	264,619	329,190	408,742	506,578	626,686	773,881	953,962

Table 2

What $1,000 deposited annually will grow to in a given number of years

% increase compounded annually

Year	5%	6%	7%	8%	9%	10%	11%	12%	13%	14%	15%	16%	17%	18%	19%	20%
1	1,050	1,060	1,070	1,080	1,090	1,100	1,110	1,120	1,130	1,140	1,150	1,160	1,170	1,180	1,190	1,200
2	2,153	2,184	2,215	2,246	2,278	2,310	2,342	2,374	2,407	2,440	2,473	2,506	2,539	2,572	2,606	2,640
3	3,310	3,375	3,440	3,506	3,573	3,641	3,710	3,779	3,850	3,921	3,993	4,066	4,141	4,215	4,291	4,368
4	4,526	4,637	4,751	4,867	4,985	5,105	5,228	5,353	5,480	5,610	5,742	5,877	6,014	6,154	6,297	6,442
5	5,802	5,975	6,153	6,336	6,523	6,716	6,913	7,115	7,323	7,536	7,754	7,977	8,207	8,442	8,683	8,930
6	7,142	7,394	7,654	7,923	8,200	8,487	8,783	9,089	9,405	9,730	10,067	10,414	10,772	11,142	11,523	11,916
7	8,549	8,897	9,260	9,637	10,028	10,436	10,859	11,300	11,757	12,233	12,727	13,240	13,773	14,327	14,902	15,499
8	10,027	10,491	10,978	11,488	12,021	12,579	13,164	13,776	14,416	15,085	15,786	16,519	17,285	18,086	18,923	19,799
9	11,578	12,181	12,816	13,487	14,193	14,937	15,722	16,549	17,420	18,337	19,304	20,321	21,393	22,521	23,709	24,959
10	13,207	13,972	14,784	15,645	16,560	17,531	18,561	19,655	20,814	22,045	23,349	24,733	26,200	27,755	29,404	31,150
11	14,917	15,870	16,888	17,977	19,141	20,384	21,713	23,133	24,650	26,271	28,002	29,850	31,824	33,931	36,180	38,581
12	16,713	17,882	19,141	20,495	21,953	23,523	25,212	27,029	28,985	31,089	33,352	35,786	38,404	41,219	44,244	47,497
13	18,599	20,015	21,550	23,215	25,019	26,975	29,095	31,393	33,883	36,581	39,505	42,672	46,103	49,818	53,841	58,196
14	20,579	22,276	24,129	26,152	28,361	30,772	33,405	36,280	39,417	42,842	46,580	50,660	55,110	59,965	65,261	71,035
15	22,657	24,673	26,888	29,324	32,003	34,950	38,190	41,753	45,672	49,980	54,717	59,925	65,649	71,939	78,850	86,442
16	24,840	27,213	29,840	32,750	35,974	39,545	43,501	47,884	52,739	58,118	64,075	70,673	77,979	86,068	95,022	104,931
17	27,132	29,906	32,999	36,450	40,301	44,599	49,396	54,750	60,725	67,394	74,836	83,141	92,406	102,740	114,266	127,117
18	29,539	32,760	36,379	40,446	45,018	50,159	55,939	62,440	69,749	77,969	87,212	97,603	109,285	122,414	137,166	153,740
19	32,066	35,786	39,995	44,762	50,160	56,275	63,203	71,052	79,947	90,025	101,444	114,380	129,033	145,628	164,418	185,688
20	34,719	38,993	43,865	49,423	55,765	63,002	71,265	80,699	91,470	103,768	117,810	133,841	152,139	173,021	196,847	224,026
21	37,505	42,392	48,006	54,457	61,873	70,403	80,214	91,503	104,491	119,436	136,632	156,415	179,172	205,345	235,438	270,031
22	40,430	45,996	52,436	59,893	68,532	78,543	90,148	103,603	119,205	137,297	158,276	182,601	210,801	243,487	281,362	325,237
23	43,502	49,816	57,177	65,765	75,790	87,497	101,174	117,155	135,831	157,659	183,168	212,978	247,808	288,494	336,010	391,484
24	46,727	53,865	62,249	72,106	83,701	97,347	113,413	132,334	154,620	180,871	211,793	248,214	291,105	341,603	401,042	470,981
25	50,113	58,156	67,676	78,954	92,324	108,182	126,999	149,334	175,850	207,333	244,712	289,088	341,763	404,272	478,431	566,377

Table 3

What $1,000 in the future is worth today (present value)

Year	5%	6%	7%	8%	9%	10%	11%	12%	13%	14%	15%	16%	17%	18%	19%	20%
1	952	943	935	926	917	909	901	893	885	877	870	862	855	847	840	833
2	907	890	873	857	842	826	812	797	783	769	756	743	731	718	706	694
3	864	840	816	794	772	751	731	712	693	765	658	641	624	609	593	579
4	823	792	763	735	708	683	659	636	613	592	572	552	534	516	499	482
5	784	747	713	681	650	621	593	567	543	519	497	476	456	437	419	402
6	746	705	666	630	596	564	535	507	480	456	432	410	390	370	352	335
7	711	665	623	583	547	513	482	452	425	400	376	354	333	314	296	279
8	677	627	582	540	502	467	434	404	376	351	327	305	285	266	249	233
9	645	592	544	500	460	424	391	361	333	308	284	263	243	225	209	194
10	614	558	508	463	422	386	352	322	295	270	247	227	208	191	176	162
11	585	527	475	429	388	350	317	287	261	237	215	195	178	162	148	135
12	557	497	444	397	356	319	286	257	231	208	187	168	152	137	124	112
13	530	469	415	368	326	290	258	229	204	182	163	145	130	116	104	93
14	505	442	388	340	299	263	232	205	181	160	141	125	111	99	88	78
15	481	417	362	315	275	239	209	183	160	140	123	108	95	84	74	65
16	458	394	339	292	252	218	188	163	141	123	107	93	81	71	62	54
17	436	371	317	270	231	198	170	146	125	108	93	80	69	60	52	45
18	416	350	296	250	212	180	153	130	111	95	81	69	59	51	44	38
19	396	331	277	232	194	164	138	116	98	83	70	60	51	43	37	31
20	377	312	258	215	178	149	124	104	87	73	61	51	43	37	31	26
21	359	294	242	199	164	135	112	93	77	64	53	44	37	31	26	22
22	342	278	226	184	150	123	101	83	68	56	46	38	32	26	22	18
23	326	262	211	170	138	112	91	74	60	49	40	33	27	22	18	15
24	310	247	197	158	126	102	82	66	53	43	35	28	23	19	15	13
25	295	233	184	146	116	92	74	59	47	38	30	24	20	16	13	10

Table 4

Periodic investments that will grow to $1,000 at a future date

Year	5%	6%	7%	8%	9%	10%	11%	12%	13%	14%	15%	16%	17%	18%	19%	20%
1	952.38	943.40	934.58	925.93	917.43	909.09	900.90	892.86	884.96	877.19	869.57	862.07	854.70	847.46	840.34	833.33
2	464.58	457.96	451.49	445.16	438.96	432.90	426.97	421.16	415.47	409.90	404.45	399.11	393.87	388.74	383.72	378.79
3	302.10	296.33	290.70	285.22	279.87	274.65	269.56	264.60	259.75	255.03	250.41	245.91	241.52	237.22	233.03	228.94
4	220.96	215.65	210.49	205.48	200.61	195.88	191.29	186.82	182.47	178.25	174.14	170.15	166.27	162.49	158.82	155.24
5	172.36	167.36	162.51	157.83	153.30	148.91	144.66	140.54	136.56	132.70	128.97	125.35	121.85	118.46	115.17	111.98
6	140.02	135.25	130.65	126.22	121.94	117.82	113.85	110.02	106.33	102.77	99.34	96.03	92.83	89.75	86.79	83.92
7	116.97	112.39	107.99	103.77	99.72	95.82	92.09	88.50	85.05	81.75	78.57	75.53	72.60	69.80	67.10	64.52
8	99.74	95.32	91.09	87.05	83.19	79.49	75.96	72.59	69.37	66.29	63.35	60.54	57.85	55.29	52.84	50.51
9	86.37	82.10	78.02	74.15	70.46	66.95	63.61	60.43	57.41	54.53	51.80	49.21	46.74	44.40	42.18	40.07
10	75.72	71.57	67.64	63.92	60.39	57.04	53.88	50.88	48.04	45.36	42.83	40.43	38.17	36.03	34.01	32.10
11	67.04	63.01	59.21	55.63	52.24	49.06	46.05	43.23	40.57	38.07	35.71	33.50	31.42	29.47	27.64	25.92
12	59.83	55.92	52.24	48.79	45.55	42.51	39.66	37.00	34.50	32.17	29.98	27.94	26.04	24.26	22.60	21.05
13	53.77	49.96	46.40	43.08	39.97	37.07	34.37	31.85	29.51	27.34	25.31	23.43	21.69	20.07	18.57	17.18
14	48.59	44.89	41.44	38.24	35.26	32.50	29.94	27.56	25.37	23.34	21.47	19.74	18.15	16.68	15.32	14.08
15	44.14	40.53	37.19	34.10	31.25	28.61	26.18	23.95	21.90	20.01	18.28	16.69	15.23	13.90	12.68	11.57
16	40.26	36.75	33.51	30.53	27.80	25.29	22.99	20.88	18.96	17.21	15.61	14.15	12.82	11.62	10.52	9.53
17	36.86	33.44	30.30	27.43	24.81	22.42	20.24	18.26	16.47	14.84	13.36	12.03	10.82	9.73	8.75	7.87
18	33.85	30.53	27.49	24.72	22.21	19.94	17.88	16.02	14.34	12.83	11.47	10.25	9.15	8.17	7.29	6.50
19	31.19	27.94	25.00	22.34	19.94	17.77	15.82	14.07	12.51	11.11	9.86	8.74	7.75	6.87	6.08	5.39
20	28.80	25.65	22.80	20.23	17.93	15.87	14.03	12.39	10.93	9.64	8.49	7.47	6.57	5.78	5.08	4.46
21	26.66	23.59	20.83	18.36	16.16	14.20	12.47	10.93	9.57	8.37	7.32	6.39	5.58	4.87	4.25	3.70
22	24.73	21.74	19.07	16.70	14.59	12.73	11.09	9.65	8.39	7.28	6.32	5.48	4.74	4.11	3.55	3.07
23	22.99	20.07	17.49	15.21	13.19	11.43	9.88	8.54	7.36	6.34	5.46	4.70	4.04	3.47	2.98	2.55
24	21.40	18.57	16.06	13.87	11.95	10.27	8.82	7.56	6.47	5.53	4.72	4.03	3.44	2.93	2.49	2.12
25	19.95	17.20	14.78	12.67	10.83	9.24	7.87	6.70	5.69	4.82	4.09	3.46	2.93	2.47	2.09	1.77

THE **NO-LOAD** FUND INVESTOR, INC.

PO Box 318
Irvington-on-Hudson, NY 10533-0318

FOR A FREE UPDATE OF THE PERFORMANCE DATA IN THIS HANDBOOK, SEE OTHER SIDE.

THE **NO-LOAD** FUND INVESTOR, INC.

PO Box 318
Irvington-on-Hudson, NY 10533-0318